my Pearson . com
corirnea @ yahoo.com
flowergirl3

D1543441

How this Text Can Help You Succeed

Your Sullivan/Struve text helps you *Do the Math* with innovative features designed to provide help when you need it most—when you are away from the classroom and your instructor.

Sullivan/Struve Examples

Our Examples place the annotations to the left of the algebra, rather than to the right, as is the practice in other math texts.

Placing the annotations on the left makes more sense because you are used to reading from left-to-right.

The left-to-right annotations explain what you are about to do in solving the problem. Think of these annotations as your "teacher in the book."

EXAMPLE 3 Solving a Linear Equation by Combining Like Terms

Solve the linear equation: $3y - 2 + 5y = 2y + 5 + 4y + 3$

Solution

$$3y - 2 + 5y = 2y + 5 + 4y + 3$$

Combine like terms: $\qquad 8y - 2 = 6y + 8$

Subtract $6y$ from both sides: $\quad 8y - 2 - 6y = 6y + 8 - 6y$

$$2y - 2 = 8$$

Add 2 to both sides: $\quad 2y - 2 + 2 = 8 + 2$

$$2y = 10$$

Divide both sides by 2: $\quad \dfrac{2y}{2} = \dfrac{10}{2}$

$$y = 5$$

Check $\qquad 3y - 2 + 5y = 2y + 5 + 4y + 3$

Let $y = 5$ in the original equation: $3(5) - 2 + 5(5) \overset{?}{=} 2(5) + 5 + 4(5) + 3$

$$15 - 2 + 25 \overset{?}{=} 10 + 5 + 20 + 3$$

$$38 = 38 \quad \text{True}$$

Because $y = 5$ satisfies the equation, the solution of the equation is 5, or the solution set is $\{5\}$. ∎

Quick ✔ *In Problems 12–14, solve each linear equation. Be sure to verify your solution.*

12. $2x + 3 + 5x + 1 = 4x + 10$
13. $4b + 3 - b - 8 - 5b = 2b - 1 - b - 1$
14. $2w + 8 - 7w + 1 = 3w - 1 + 2w - 5$

Quick Check Exercises

Each group of Quick Check exercises is preceded by an Example that teaches you how to work the problems. Your instructor may assign Quick Check exercises as part of your homework.

The Quick Checks are visually linked to the exercise sets by the tan background so they are easy to find.

Answers to all of the Quick Checks and the odd-numbered exercises are found in the Answer Section at the back of the text.

1.1 EXERCISES

PRACTICE WATCH DOWNLOAD READ REVIEW

1–30. *are the* Quick ✔*s that follow each* EXAMPLE

Building Skills

In Problems 31–36, determine which of the numbers are solutions to the given equation. See Objective 1.

31. $8x - 10 = 6; x = -2, x = 1, x = 2$

32. $-4x - 3 = -15; x = -2, x = 1, x = 3$

33. $5m - 3 = -3m + 5; m = -2, m = 1, m = 3$

34. $6x + 1 = -2x + 9; x = -2, x = 1, x = 4$

35. $4(x - 1) = 3x + 1; x = -1, x = 2, x = 5$

36. $3(t + 1) - t = 4t + 9; t = -3, t = -1, t = 2$

In Problems 37–58, solve each linear equation. Be sure to verify your solution. See Objective 2.

37. $3x + 1 = 7$

38. $8x - 6 = 18$

39. $5x + 4 = 14$

40. $-6x - 5 = 13$

41. $4z + 3 = 2$

42. $8y + 3 = 5$

43. $-3w + 2w + 5 = -4$

44. $-7t - 3 + 5t = 11$

45. $3m + 4 = 2m - 5$

46. $-5z + 3 = -3z + 1$

47. $5x + 2 - 2x + 3 = 7x + 2 - x + 5$

48. $-6x + 2 + 2x + 9 + x = 5x + 10 - 6x + 11$

49. $3(x + 2) = -6$

50. $4(z - 2) = 12$

51. $\dfrac{4y}{5} - \dfrac{14}{15} = \dfrac{y}{3}$

52. $\dfrac{3x}{2} + \dfrac{x}{6} = -\dfrac{5}{3}$

53. $\dfrac{4x + 3}{9} - \dfrac{2x + 1}{2} = \dfrac{1}{6}$

54. $\dfrac{2x + 1}{3} - \dfrac{6x - 1}{4} = -\dfrac{5}{12}$

STUDY SMARTER

CHAPTER
Test Prep
VIDEO CD

Step-by-step solutions on video for all chapter test exercises from the text

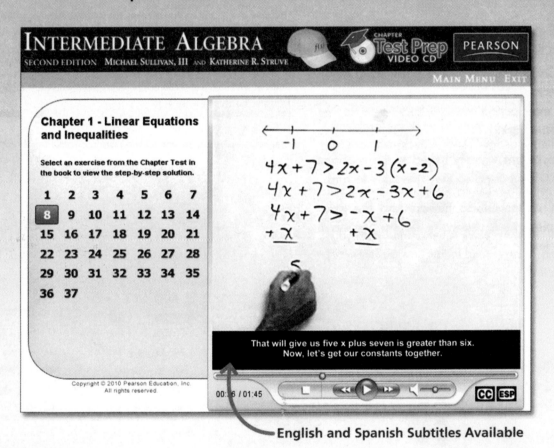

INTERMEDIATE ALGEBRA

SECOND EDITION MICHAEL SULLIVAN, III AND KATHERINE R. STRUVE

Test Prep VIDEO CD

PEARSON

MAIN MENU EXIT

Chapter 1 - Linear Equations and Inequalities

Select an exercise from the Chapter Test in the book to view the step-by-step solution.

1	2	3	4	5	6	7
8	9	10	11	12	13	14
15	16	17	18	19	20	21
22	23	24	25	26	27	28
29	30	31	32	33	34	35
36	37

$$4x + 7 > 2x - 3(x-2)$$
$$4x + 7 > 2x - 3x + 6$$
$$4x + 7 > -x + 6$$
$$+x \qquad\qquad +x$$

That will give us five x plus seven is greater than six.
Now, let's get our constants together.

00:36 / 01:45

Copyright © 2010 Pearson Education, Inc. All rights reserved.

English and Spanish Subtitles Available

INCLUDED WITH EVERY NEW COPY OF THIS TEXTBOOK!

Intermediate Algebra

Michael Sullivan, III
Katherine R. Struve

Math 102
Custom Edition for Trident Technical College

Taken from:
Intermediate Algebra, Second Edition
by Michael Sullivan, III and Katherine R. Struve

Custom Publishing

New York   Boston   San Francisco
London   Toronto   Sydney   Tokyo   Singapore   Madrid
Mexico City   Munich   Paris   Cape Town   Hong Kong   Montreal

Cover Art: Courtesy of PhotoDisc/Getty Images

Taken from:
Intermediate Algebra, Second Edition
by Michael Sullivan, III, and Katherine R. Struve
Copyright © 2010, 2007 by Pearson Education, Inc.
Published by Prentice Hall
Upper Saddle River, New Jersey 07458

All rights reserved. No part of this book may be reproduced, in any form or by any means, without permission in writing from the publisher.

This special edition published in cooperation with Pearson Custom Publishing.

All trademarks, service marks, registered trademarks, and registered service marks are the property of their respective owners and are used herein for identification purposes only.

Printed in the United States of America

10 9 8 7 6 5 4 3 2 1

2009360151

MT

Pearson
Custom Publishing
is a division of

PEARSON

www.pearsonhighered.com

ISBN 10: 0-558-23159-4
ISBN 13: 978-0-558-23159-0

To Michael, Kevin, and Marissa, who patiently waited until Dad could come out to play.

—Michael Sullivan

To Ruth and Ed Struve, for loving hospitality.

—Katherine R. Struve

About the Authors

With training in mathematics, statistics, and economics, Michael Sullivan, III has a varied teaching background that includes 18 years of instruction in both high school and college-level mathematics. He is currently a full-time professor of mathematics at Joliet Junior College. Michael has numerous textbooks in publication, including an Introductory Statistics series and a Precalculus series, which he writes with his father, Michael Sullivan.

Michael believes that his experiences writing texts for college-level math and statistics courses give him a unique perspective as to where students are headed once they leave the developmental mathematics tract. This experience is reflected in the philosophy and presentation of his developmental text series. When not in the classroom or writing, Michael enjoys spending time with his three children, Michael, Kevin, and Marissa, and playing golf. Now that his two sons are getting older, he has the opportunity to do both at the same time!

Kathy Struve has been a classroom teacher for nearly 30 years, first at the high school level and, for the past 16 years, at Columbus State Community College. Kathy emphasizes classroom diversity: diversity of age, learning styles, and previous learning success. She is aware of the challenges of teaching mathematics at a large, urban community college, where students have varied mathematics backgrounds and may enter college with a high level of mathematics anxiety.

Kathy served as Lead Instructor of the Developmental Algebra sequence at Columbus State where she developed curriculum and provided leadership to adjunct faculty in implementing graphing calculator technology in the classroom. She has authored classroom activities at the Elementary Algebra, Intermediate Algebra, and College Algebra levels and conducted workshops at local, state, and national conferences. In her spare time Kathy enjoys spending time with her two adult daughters and biking, hiking, and traveling with her husband.

Contents

CHAPTER 7   Quadratic Equations and Functions   547

Preface

We would like to thank the reviewers, class testers, and users of the first edition of *Intermediate Algebra* who helped to make the book an overwhelming success. Their thoughtful comments and suggestions provided strong guidance for improvements to the second edition that we believe will enhance this solid, student-friendly text.

Intermediate Algebra is a gateway course to other college-level mathematics courses. The goal of the course is to provide students with the mathematical skills that are prerequisites for courses such as College Algebra, Elementary Statistics, Liberal-Arts Math, and Mathematics for Teachers. In addition, Intermediate Algebra must expose students to a variety of mathematical concepts that build on one another and that range from the basics such as linear equations to sophisticated concepts such as exponential functions.

Of particular importance in this course are rigor and mathematical thinking. It is imperative that the coverage be sufficiently rigorous to teach students how to study math successfully. At the same time, the course must develop students' ability to think mathematically. The rigor in the course exists both in the material presented (such as a more thorough development of functions) as well as in the array of problems and examples. As a result, it should be clear to students that this course is not simply a rehash of Elementary Algebra.

Most students have seen the content of this course at some point in their high school careers or in other college coursework. For some students, success at studying and facility with math concepts did not develop during their previous contact with the material, and they need a fresh start. In addition, the number of nontraditional students who have lost some of their math skills over the course of time continues to grow, especially at community colleges. Nontraditional students often are highly motivated to succeed because of their life experiences, yet they may be rusty at the business of "going to school." For nontraditional students, this course refreshes and reinforces their study skills as well as their mathematical skills.

To address the many needs and the diversity of today's Intermediate Algebra students, we have been guided by the following ideas as broad goals for this text:

- Provide the student with a strong conceptual foundation in mathematics through a clear, comprehensive presentation of topics with a special emphasis on functions.

- Present a variety of innovative pedagogical features, tools, study tips, and easy-to-use aids to help students see the value of the text as an important resource and guide that will increase their success in the course.

- Provide comprehensive exercise sets with paired exercises that build problem-solving skills, show a variety of applications of mathematics, and reinforce mathematical concepts for students.

- Streamline the Intermediate Algebra course through the strategic placement of topics that will provide instructors with the flexibility to review material, as needed, instead of reteaching it.

Build a Strong Foundation through a Functions Approach

The approach that we take in Intermediate Algebra is that the function is the overriding theme of the text. The reason for this stress on functions is twofold. First, Intermediate Algebra is not a terminal course but rather a gateway to the future, and functions form the basis for much study in mathematics. The introduction of functions helps make the "jump" from Intermediate Algebra to College Algebra less severe because students feel more comfortable with functions and function notation. Second, today's students like to learn in context so that they can see the relevancy of the material. The function provides a great way to present the usefulness of the material we are teaching.

Develop an Effective Text for Use In and Out of the Classroom

Given the hectic lives led by most students, coupled with the anxiety and trepidation with which they approach this course, an outstanding developmental mathematics text must provide pedagogical support that makes the text valuable to students as they study and do assignments. Pedagogy must be presented within a framework that teaches students how to study math; pedagogical devices must also address what students see as the "mystery" of mathematics—and solve that mystery.

To encourage students and to clarify the material, we developed a set of pedagogical features that help students develop good study skills, garner an understanding of the connections between topics, and work smarter in the process. The pedagogy used is based upon the more than 45 years of classroom teaching experience that the authors bring to this text.

Examples are often the determining factor in how valuable a textbook is to a student. Students look to examples to provide them with guidance and instruction when they need it most—the times when they are away from the instructor and the classroom. We have developed several example formats in an attempt to provide superior guidance and instruction for students. The formats include:

Innovative Sullivan/Struve Examples

The innovative *Sullivan/Struve Example* has a two-column format in which annotations are provided to the **left** of the algebra, rather than the right, as is the practice in most texts. Because we read from **left to right,** placing the annotation on the left will make more sense to the student. It becomes clear that the annotation describes what we are about to do instead of what was just done. The annotations may be thought of as the teacher's voice offering clarification immediately before writing the next step in the solution on the board. Consider the following:

⌜**EXAMPLE 6** Solving Linear Inequalities

Solve the inequality: $x - 4 \geq 5x + 12$

Solution

$$x - 4 \geq 5x + 12$$

Add 4 to both sides: $\quad x - 4 + 4 \geq 5x + 12 + 4$

$$x \geq 5x + 16$$

Subtract $5x$ from both sides: $\quad x - 5x \geq 5x + 16 - 5x$

$$-4x \geq 16$$

Divide both sides by -4. Don't forget to change the direction of the inequality: $\quad \dfrac{-4x}{-4} \leq \dfrac{16}{-4}$

$$x \leq -4$$

The solution using set-builder notation is $\{x \mid x \leq -4\}$. The solution using interval notation is $(-\infty, -4]$. See Figure 20 for the graph of the solution set. ▪

Quick ✔ *In Problems 20–22, solve each linear inequality. Express your solution using set-builder notation and interval notation. Graph the solution set.*

20. $3x + 1 > x - 5$ **21.** $-2x + 1 \leq 3x + 11$

22. $-5x + 12 < x - 3$

Showcase Examples

Showcase Examples are used strategically to introduce key topics or important problem-solving techniques. These examples provide "how-to" instruction by offering a guided, step-by-step approach to solving a problem. Students can then immediately see how each of the steps is employed. We remind students that the *Showcase Example* is meant to provide "how-to" instruction by including the words "how to" in the example title. The *Showcase Example* has a three-column format in which the left column describes a step, the middle column provides a brief annotation, as needed, to explain the step, and the right column presents the algebra. With this format, students can see each step in the problem-solving process in context so that the steps make more sense. This approach is more effective than simply stating each step in the text.

EXAMPLE 5 How to Solve a Linear Inequality

Solve the inequality $3x - 2 > 13$. Graph the solution set.

Step-by-Step Solution

The goal in solving any linear inequality is to get the variable by itself with a coefficient of 1.

Step 1: Isolate the term containing the variable.	Add 2 to both sides (Addition Property):	$3x - 2 > 13$ $3x - 2 + 2 > 13 + 2$ $3x > 15$
Step 2: Get a coefficient of 1 on the variable.	Divide both sides by 3 (Multiplication Property):	$\dfrac{3x}{3} > \dfrac{15}{3}$ $x > 5$

Figure 19

The solution using set-builder notation is $\{x \mid x > 5\}$. The solution using interval notation is $(5, \infty)$. Figure 19 shows the graph of the solution set. ∎

> **Quick ✔** *In Problems 16–19, solve each linear inequality. Express your solution using set-builder notation and interval notation. Graph the solution set.*
>
> **16.** $x + 3 > 5$
>
> **17.** $\dfrac{1}{3}x \le 2$
>
> **18.** $4x - 3 < 13$
>
> **19.** $-2x + 1 \le 13$

Quick Check Exercises

Placed at the conclusion of most examples, the *Quick Check* exercises provide students with an opportunity for immediate reinforcement. By working the problems that mirror the example just presented, students get instant feedback and gain confidence in their understanding of the concept. All *Quick Check* exercises answers are provided in the back of the text. We think that the *Quick Check* exercises will make the text more accessible and encourage students to read, consult, and use the text regularly.

Superior Exercise Sets: Paired with Purpose

Students learn algebra by doing algebra. The superior end-of-section exercise sets in this text provide students with ample practice of both procedures and concepts. The exercises are paired and present problem types with every possible derivative. The exercises also present a gradual increase in difficulty level. The early, basic exercises keep the student's focus on as few "levels of understanding" as possible. The later or higher-numbered exercises are "multi-task" (or Mixed Practice) exercises where students are required to utilize multiple skills, concepts, or problem-solving techniques.

Throughout the textbook, the exercise sets are grouped into nine categories—some of which appear only as needed:

1. **Preparing for...** problems are located at the opening of the section. They are problems that deal with prerequisite material for the section along with page references so students may remediate, if necessary. Answers to the Preparing for... problems appear as a footnote on the page.

2. **Quick Check** exercises, which provide the impetus to get students into the text, follow most examples and are numbered sequentially as the first problems in each section exercise set. By doing these problems as homework and the first exercises attempted, the student is directed into the material in the section. If a student gets stuck, he or she will learn that the example immediately preceding the Quick Check exercise illustrates the concepts needed to solve the problem.

3. **Building Skills** exercises are drill problems that develop the student's understanding of the procedures and skills in working with the methods presented in the section. These exercises can be linked back to a single objective in the section. Notice that the Building Skills problems begin the numbering scheme where the Quick Checks leave off. For example, if the last Quick Check exercise is Problem 20, then we begin the Building Skills exercises with Problem 21. This serves as a reminder that Quick Check exercises should be assigned as homework.

4. **Mixed Practice** exercises are also drill problems, but they offer a comprehensive assessment of the skills learned in the section by asking problems that relate to more than one concept or objective. In addition, we may present problems from previous sections so students must first recognize the type of problem and then employ the appropriate technique to solve the problem.

5. **Applying the Concepts** exercises are problems that allow students to see the relevance of the material learned within the section. Problems in this category either are situational problems that use material learned in the section to solve "real-world" problems or are problems that ask a series of questions to enhance a student's conceptual understanding of the mathematics presented in the section.

6. **Extending the Concepts** exercises can be thought of as problems that go beyond the basics. Within this block of exercises an instructor will find a variety of problems to sharpen students' critical-thinking skills.

7. **Explaining the Concepts** problems require students to think about the big picture concepts of the section and express these ideas in their own words. It is our belief that students need to improve their ability to communicate complicated ideas both orally and in writing. When they are able to explain mathematical methods or concepts to another individual, they have truly mastered the ideas. These problems can serve as a basis for classroom discussion or can be used as writing assignments.

8. Starting with Chapter 5, we provide **Synthesis Review** exercises to help students grasp the "big picture" of algebra—once they have a sufficient conceptual foundation to build upon from their work in Chapters R through 4. Synthesis Review exercises ask students to perform a single operation (adding, solving, and so on) on several objects (polynomials, rational expressions, and so on). The student is then asked to discuss the similarities and differences in performing the same operation on the different objects.

9. Finally, we include coverage of the **graphing calculator.** Instructors' philosophies about the use of graphing devices vary considerably. Because instructors disagree about the value of this tool, we have made an effort to make graphing technology entirely optional. When appropriate, technology exercises are included at the close of a section's exercise set.

Problem Icons In addition to the carefully structured categories of exercises, selected problems are flagged with icons to denote that:

- ⦿ Complete worked-out solutions to these problems are found on the CD Lecture Series.

- △ These problems focus on geometry concepts.

What's New to the Second Edition

Quick Check Exercises: Encourage Study Skills that Lead to Independent Learning

What is one of the overarching goals of an education? We believe it is to learn to solve problems independently. In particular, we would like to see students develop the ability to pick up a text or manual and teach themselves the skills they need. In our mathematics classes, however, we are often frustrated because students rarely read the text and often struggle to understand the concepts independently.

To encourage students to use the text more effectively and to help them achieve greater success in the course, we have structured the exercises in the second edition of our text differently from other mathematics textbooks. The aim of this new structure is to get students "into the text" in order to increase their ability and confidence to work any math problem—particularly when they are away from the classroom and an instructor who can help.

With the second edition of *Intermediate Algebra,* each section's exercise set begins with *Quick Check* exercises. The *Quick Checks* are consecutively numbered. The end-of-section exercises begin their numbering scheme based on where the *Quick Checks* end. For example:

- Section 1.1: *Quick Checks* end at Problem 30, so the end-of-section exercise set starts with Problem 31 (see page 56).

- Section 1.2: *Quick Checks* end at Problem 26, so the end-of-section exercise set starts with Problem 27 (see pages 69 and 70).

You'll recall that the *Quick Checks* follow most examples and provide the platform for students to get "into the text." By integrating these exercises into the exercise set, we direct students to the instructional material in that section. Our hope is that students will then become more aware of the instructional value of the text and will be more likely to succeed when studying away from the classroom and the instructor.

To facilitate this change in numbering of the Quick Checks and end-of-section exercise sets, the following changes have also been made:

- Answer annotations to Quick Checks and exercises have been placed directly next to each problem in the Annotated Instructor's Edition to make it easier for instructors to create assignments.

- We have used the same tan background color for the Quick Checks and the exercise sets to reinforce the connection between them visually. The colored background will also make the Quick Checks easier to find on the page.

- Answers to Selected Exercises at the back of the text now integrate the answers to every Quick Check exercise with the answers to every odd problem from the section exercise sets.

Organizational Changes

Two major changes to the organization of the content have been made from the first edition of *Intermediate Algebra.*

- The first is a consolidation of Chapters 1 and 3 into a new Chapter 1. Chapter 1, "Linear Equations and Inequalities," is divided into two parts. The first part is a review of solving linear equations and inequalities in one variable. Part II is a review of linear equations and inequalities in two variables. The motivation for combining this content into a single chapter is to alert students to the fact that this material may be review and therefore may be skipped by the instructor. It is our experience that when instructor's re-teach too much material students are either lulled into a false sense of security about the course and content before they become seriously challenged when the level ratchets up, or students "tune out instructors" because they believe they already know the content.

- The second significant organizational change is that the sections on Compound Inequalities (formerly 1.5) and Absolute Value Equations and Inequalities (formerly 1.6) have been moved to Chapter 2 as Sections 2.5 and 2.6. Moving these topics later in the book allows us to provide students with visual evidence for the solutions after presenting the power of the graph of a function at the beginning of Chapter 2. Further, these topics are not necessarily review topics from Elementary Algebra.

Hallmark Features of Sullivan/Struve

Streamlining Intermediate Algebra: *Getting Ready for Chapter ... Review Sections*

To maintain the pace of the course, we created several *Getting Ready* sections that review material taught in Elementary Algebra courses. The *Getting Ready* sections are designed to allow students to brush up on topics and skills as needed before beginning the chapters in the Intermediate Algebra text where the skills will be used or further developed. These optional, yet integrated, sections provide the student with timely review. They also streamline the Intermediate Algebra course by providing the instructors with the flexibility to decide if the *Getting Ready* sections should be covered in their entirety, briefly reviewed, or skipped, depending upon the needs of their students. *Getting Ready* review sections have been placed before Chapters 4, 5, and 6 in the text.

Study Skills and Student Success

We have included study skills and student success as regular themes throughout this text starting with *Section R.1, Success in Mathematics*. In addition to this dedicated section that covers many of the basics that are essential to success in any math course, we have included several recurring study aids that appear in the margin. These features were designed to anticipate the student's needs and to provide immediate help—as if the teacher were looking over his or her shoulder. These margin features include *In Words; Work Smart;* and *Work Smart: Study Skills*.

Section R.1: *Success in Mathematics* focuses the student on basic study skills, including what to do during the first week of the semester; what to do before, during, and after class; how to use the text effectively; and how to prepare for an exam.

In Words helps to address the difficulty that students have in reading mathematically precise definitions and theorems by explaining them in plain English.

Work Smart provides "tricks of the trade" hints, tips, reminders, and alerts. It also identifies some common errors to avoid and helps students work more efficiently.

Work Smart: Study Skills reminds students of study skills that will help them to succeed at various points in the course. Attention to these practices will help them to become better, more proficient learners.

Test Preparation and Student Success

The Chapter Tests in this text and the companion Chapter Test Prep Video CD have been designed to help students make the most of their valuable study time.

Chapter Test In preparation for their classroom test, students should take the practice test to make sure they understand the key topics in the chapter. The exercises in the Chapter Tests have been crafted to reflect the level and types of exercises a student is likely to see on a classroom test.

Chapter Test Prep Video CD Packaged with each new copy of the text, the Chapter Test Prep Video CD provides students with help at the critical juncture when they are studying for a test. The Video CD presents step-by-step solutions to the exact exercises found in each of the book's Chapter Tests. Easy video navigation allows students instant access to the worked-out solutions to the exercises they want to study or review.

How It All Fits Together: The Big Picture

Another important role of the pedagogy in this text is to help students see and understand the connection between the mathematical topics being presented. Several section-opening and margin features help to reinforce connections:

The Big Picture: Putting It Together (**Chapter Opener**) This feature is based on how we start each chapter in the classroom—with a quick sketch of what we plan to cover. Before tackling a chapter, we tie concepts and techniques together by summarizing material covered previously and then relate these ideas to material we are about to discuss. It is important for students to understand that content truly builds from one chapter to the next. We find that students need to be reminded that the familiar operations of addition, subtraction, multiplication, and division are being applied to different or more complex objects.

Preparing for This Section As part of this building process, we think it is important to remind students of specific material that they will need from earlier in the course to be successful within a given section. The *Preparing for ...* feature that begins each section not only provides a list of prerequisite skills that a student should understand before tackling the content of a new section but also offers a short quiz to test students' preparedness. Answers to the quiz are provided in a footnote on the same page, and a cross-reference to the material in the text is provided so that the student can remediate when necessary.

Putting the Concepts Together (**Mid-Chapter Review**) Each chapter has a group of exercises at the appropriate point in the chapter, entitled *Putting the Concepts Together*. These exercises serve as a review—synthesizing material introduced up to that point in the chapter. The exercises in these mid-chapter reviews are carefully chosen to assist students in seeing the "big picture."

Synthesis Review Exercises Starting with Chapter 5, we provide Synthesis Review exercises to help students grasp the "big picture" of algebra—once they have a sufficient conceptual foundation to build upon from their work in Chapters R through 4.

Cumulative Review Learning algebra is a building process, and building involves considerable reinforcement. The Cumulative Review exercises at the end of each odd-numbered chapter, starting with Chapter 1, help students reinforce and solidify their knowledge by revisiting concepts and using them in context. This way, studying for the final exam should be fairly easy. Cumulative Reviews for each even-numbered chapter can be found on the Instructor's Resource Center.

In Closing

When we started writing this textbook, we discussed what improvement we could make in coverage; in staples such as examples and problems; and in any pedagogical features that we found truly useful. After writing and rewriting, and reading many thoughtful reviews from instructors, we focused on the following features of the text to set it apart.

- **Functions** are introduced early and revisited often throughout the course. This integration helps prepare students for the quantitative courses that they will take after Intermediate Algebra.

- The **innovative *Sullivan/Struve Examples*** and ***Showcase Examples*** provide students with superior guidance and instruction when they need it most—when they are away from the instructor and the classroom. Each of the margin features *In Words, Work Smart,* and *Work Smart: Study Skills* are designed to improve study skills, make the textbook easier to navigate, and increase student success.

- **Exercise Sets: Paired with Purpose**—The exercise sets are structured to assess student understanding of vocabulary, concepts, drill, problem solving, and applications. The exercise sets are graded in difficulty level to build confidence and to enhance students' mathematical thinking. The *Quick Check* exercises provide students with immediate reinforcement and instant feedback to determine their understanding of the concepts presented in the examples. *Putting the Concepts Together* and *Synthesis Review* help students see the big picture and provide a structure for learning each new concept and skill in the course.

- The text is written to streamline Intermediate Algebra (and distinguish it from Elementary Algebra) through a single-chapter presentation of linear equations and inequalities along with the strategic placement of *Getting Ready* review sections that provide instructors with the flexibility to review material instead of reteaching it.

Student and Instructor Resources

STUDENT RESOURCES

Available for purchase at MyPearsonStore.com

Student's Solutions Manual
(ISBN: 0321589297/9780321589293)

Complete worked solutions to the odd-numbered problems in the end-of-section exercises and all of the Quick Checks and end-of-chapter exercises.

***Do the Math* Workbook**
(ISBN: 0321593057/9780321593054)

A collection of 5-minute Warm-Up exercises, Guided Practice exercises, and *Do the Math* exercises for each section in the text. These exercises are designed for students to show their work in homework, during class, or in a lab setting.

Videos on DVD for *Intermediate Algebra,* 2/e
(ISBN: 0321593480/9780321593481)

Keyed to each section in the text, mini-lectures provide a 15–20 minute review of the key concepts and step through the solution to the exercises identified with a ● symbol. Videos include optional subtitles in English and Spanish.

MathXL® Tutorial on CD
(ISBN: 0321593278/9780321593276)

Algorithmically generated practice exercises that correlate to exercises at the end of sections with correlated examples and guided solutions. Selected exercises include a video clip.

Chapter Test Prep Video CD (packaged with each new copy of the text)

Includes fully worked-out solutions to each problem in the Chapter Tests.

INSTRUCTOR RESOURCES

Available through your Pearson representative

Annotated Instructor's Edition
(ISBN: 0321570642/9780321570642)

Instructor's Solutions Manual
(ISBN: 0321589556/9780321589552)

Instructor's Resource Manual
(ISBN: 0321589483/9780321589484)

Includes Mini-Lectures (one-page lesson plans at-a-glance) for each section in the text feature, key examples and Teaching Tips on how students respond to the material. Printed Test Forms (free response and multiple choice), Additional Exercises, and Chapter Activitities.

PowerPoint Lecture Slides

TestGen for® *Intermediate Algebra,* 2/e
(Available for download from the IRC)

ONLINE RESOURCES

MyMathLab® (access code required)

MathXL® (access code required)

Acknowledgments

Textbooks are written by authors but evolve through the efforts of many people. We would like to extend our thanks to the following individuals for their important contributions to the project. From Pearson: Paul Murphy, who saw the vision of this text from its inception and made it happen; Michelle Renda for her innovative marketing ideas; Ann Heath for her dedication, enthusiasm, and attention to detail (quite honestly, Ann was the cement of the project); Chris Hoag for her support and encouragement; Heather Scott and the design team for the attractive and functional design; Karin Kipp and Linda Behrens for keeping a watchful eye and managing countless production details; Tom Benfatti for managing the art program; Ilene Kahn, our operations specialist; and finally, the Pearson Arts & Sciences sales team for their confidence and support of our books.

We would also like to thank Sarah Streett, Brad Davis, and Cindy Trimble for their attention to details and consistency in accuracy checking the text and answer sections. A huge thanks goes out to Janet Mazzarella, who provided valuable insight and created the outstanding classroom worksheets that accompany the text. We offer many thanks to all the instructors from across the country who participated in reviewer conferences and focus groups, reviewed or class-tested some aspect of the manuscript, and taught from the first edition. Their insights and ideas form the backbone of this text. Hundreds of instructors contributed their time, energy, and ideas to help us shape this text. We will attempt to thank them all here. We apologize for any omissions.

The following individuals, many of whom reviewed or class-tested the first edition, provided direction and guidance in shaping the second edition.

Marwan Abu–Sawwa, *Florida Community College—Jacksonville*

MaryAnne Anthony, *Santa Ana College*

Darla Aguilar, *Pima State University*

Grant Alexander, *Joliet Junior College*

Philip Anderson, *South Plains College*

Mary Lou Baker, *Columbia State Community College*

Bill Bales, *Rogers State*

Tony Barcellos, *American River College*

John Beachy, *Northern Illinois University*

Donna Beatty, *Ventura College*

David Bell, *Florida Community College—Jacksonville*

Sandy Berry, *Hinds Community College*

Linda Blanco, *Joliet Junior College*

Kevin Bodden, *Lewis and Clark College*

Cherie Bowers, *Santa Ana College*

Becky Bradshaw, *Lake Superior College*

Lori Braselton, *Georgia Southern University*

Tim Britt, *Jackson State Community College*

Beverly Broomell, *Suffolk Community College*

Joanne Brunner, *Joliet Junior College*

Hien Bui, *Hillsborough Community College—Dale Mabry*

Connie Buller, *Metropolitan Community College*

Annette Burden, *Youngstown State University*

James Butterbach, *Joliet Junior College*

Marc Campbell, *Daytona Beach Community College*

Elena Catoiu, *Joliet Junior College*

Nancy Chell, *Anne Arundel Community College*

John F. Close, *Salt Lake Community College*

Bobbi Cook, *Indian River Community College*

Carlos Corona, *San Antonio College*

Faye Dang, *Joliet Junior College*

Shirley Davis, *South Plains College*

Vivian Dennis-Monzingo, *Eastfield College*

Alvio Dominguez, *Miami Dade Community College—Wolfson*

Karen Driskell, *South Plains College*

Thomas Drucker, *University of Wisconsin—Whitewater*

Brenda Dugas, *McNeese State University*

Doug Dunbar, *Okaloosa-Walton Junior College*

Laura Dyer, *Southwestern Illinois State University*

Bill Echols, *Houston Community College—Northwest*

Erica Egizio, *Joliet Junior College*

Laura Egner, *Joliet Junior College*

Jason Eltrevoog, *Joliet Junior College*

Nancy Eschen, *Florida Community College—Jacksonville*

Mike Everett, *Santa Ana College*

Phil Everett, *Ohio State University*

Scott Fallstrom, *Shoreline Community College*

Betsy Farber, *Bucks County Community College*

Fitzroy Farqharson, *Valencia Community College—West*

Jacqueline Fowler, *South Plains College*

Dorothy French, *Community College of Philadelphia*

Randy Gallaher, *Lewis and Clark College*

Sanford Geraci, *Broward Community College*

Donna Gerken, *Miami Dade Community College—Kendall*

Adrienne Goldstein, *Miami Dade Community College—Kendall*

Marion Graziano, *Montgomery County Community College*

Susan Grody, *Broward Community College*

Tom Grogan, *Cincinnati State University*

Barbara Grover, *Salt Lake Community College*

Shawna Haider, *Salt Lake Community College*

Margaret Harris, *Milwaukee Area Technical College*

Teresa Hasenauer, *Indian River Community College*

Mary Henderson, *Okaloosa-Walton Junior College*

Celeste Hernandez, *Richland College*

Paul Hernandez, *Palo Alto College*

Pete Herrera, *Southwestern College*

Bob Hervey, *Hillsborough Community College—Dale Mabry*

Teresa Hodge, *Broward Community College*

Sandee House, *Georgia Perimeter College*

Becky Hubiak, *Tidewater Community College—Virginia Beach*

Sally Jackman, *Richland College*

John Jarvis, *Utah Valley State College*

Nancy Johnson, *Broward Community College*

Steven Kahn, *Anne Arundel Community College*

Linda Kass, *Bergen Community College*

Donna Katula, *Joliet Junior College*

Mohammed Kazemi, *University of North Carolina—Charlotte*

Doreen Kelly, *Mesa Community College*

Mike Kirby, *Tidewater Community College—Virginia Beach*

Keith Kuchar, *College of Dupage*

Carla Kulinsky, *Salt Lake Community College*

Julie Labbiento, *Leigh Carbon Community College*

Kathy Lavelle, *Westchester Community College*

Deanna Li, *North Seattle Community College*

Brian Macon, *Valencia Community College—West*

Lynn Marecek, *Santa Ana College*

Jim Matovina, *Community College of Southern Nevada*

Jean McArthur, *Joliet Junior College*

Michael McComas, *Marshall University*

Mikal McDowell, *Cedar Valley College*

Lee McEwen, *Ohio State University*

David McGuire, *Joliet Junior College*

Angela McNulty, *Joliet Junior College*

Debbie McQueen, *Fullerton College*

Judy Meckley, *Joliet Junior College*

Lynette Meslinsky, *Erie Community College—City Campus*

Kausha Miller, *Lexington Community College*

Chris Mizell, *Okaloosa Walton Junior College*

Jim Moore, *Madison Area Technical College*

Ronald Moore, *Florida Community College—Jacksonville*

Elizabeth Morrison, *Valencia Community College—West*

Roya Namavar, *Rogers State*

Hossein Navid-Tabrizi, *Houston Community College*

Carol Nessmith, *Georgia Southern University*

Kim Neuburger, *Portland Community College*

Larry Newberry, *Glendale Community College*

Elsie Newman, *Owens Community College*

Charlotte Newsome, *Tidewater Community College*

Charles Odion, *Houston Community College*

Viann Olson, *Rochester Community and Technical College*

Linda Padilla, *Joliet Junior College*

Carol Perry, *Marshall Community and Technical College*

Faith Peters, *Miami Dade Community College—Wolfson*

Dr. Eugenia Peterson, *Richard J. Daley College*

Jean Pierre Victor, *Richard J. Daley College*

Philip Pina, *Florida Atlantic University*

Carol Poos, *Southwestern Illinois University*

Elise Price, *Tarrant County Community College*

R.B. Pruitt, *South Plains College*

William Radulovich, *Florida Community College—Jacksonville*

Pavlov Rameau, *Miami Dade Community College—Wolfson*

David Ray, *University of Tennessee—Martin*

Nancy Ressler, *Oakton Community College*

Michael Reynolds, *Valencia Community College—West*

George Rhys, *College of the Canyons*

Jorge Romero, *Hillsborough Community College—Dale Mabry*

David Ruffato, *Joliet Junior College*

Carol Rychly, *Augusta State University*

David Santos, *Community College of Philadelphia*

Togba Sapolucia, *Houston Community College*

Doug Smith, *Tarrant Community College*

Catherine J. W. Snyder, *Alfred State College*

Gisela Spieler-Persad, *Rio Hondo College*

Raju Sriram, *Okaloosa-Walton Junior College*

Patrick Stevens, *Joliet Junior College*

Bryan Stewart, *Tarrant Community College*

Jennifer Strehler, *Oakton Community College*

Elizabeth Suco, *Miami Dade Community College—Wolfson*

Katalin Szucs, *East Carolina University*

KD Taylor, *Utah Valley State College*

Mary Ann Teel, *University of North Texas*

Suzanne Topp, *Salt Lake Community College*

Suzanne Trabucco, *Nassau Community College*

Jo Tucker, *Tarrant Community College*

Bob Tuskey, *Joliet Junior College*

Mary Vachon, *San Joaquin Delta College*

Carol Walker, *Hinds Community College*

Kim Ward, *Eastern Connecticut State University*

Richard Watkins, *Tidewater Community College*

Natalie Weaver, *Daytona Beach Community College*

Darren Wiberg, *Utah Valley State College*

Rachel Wieland, *Bergen Community College*

Christine Wilson, *Western Virginia University*

Brad Wind, *Miami Dade Community College—North*

Roberta Yellott, *McNeese State University*

Steve Zuro, *Joliet Junior College*

Additional Acknowledgments

We also would like to extend thanks to our colleagues at Joliet Junior College and Columbus State Community College, who provided encouragement, support, and the teaching environment where the ideas and teaching philosophies in this text were developed.

Michael Sullivan, III

Katherine R. Struve

R Real Numbers and Algebraic Expressions

The image to the right of a sunburst carrier shell fossil (*stellaria solaris*) demonstrates how a specific sequence of numbers, called the Fibonacci sequence, occurs frequently in nature. Problem 128 in Section R.3 explores the Fibonacci sequence further.

OUTLINE

The Big Picture: Putting It Together

As the "R" in the title implies, this chapter is a review. The purpose of the chapter is to help you recall mathematical concepts that you learned in earlier courses. The topics chosen for inclusion here are important building blocks that will help you succeed in this course.

Your instructor may or may not decide to cover this chapter, depending on the course syllabus. Regardless, as you proceed through the book, references will be made to Chapter R so that you can use it as a "just-in-time" review.

R.1 Success in Mathematics

Let's start by having a frank discussion about the "big picture" goals of the course and how this book can help you to be successful at mathematics. Our first "big picture" goal is to develop algebraic skills and gain an appreciation for the power of algebra and mathematics. But there is also a second "big picture" goal. By studying mathematics, we develop a sense of logic and exercise the part of our brains that deals with logical thinking. The examples and problems that appear throughout the text are like the crunches that we do in a gym to exercise our body. The goal of running or walking is to get from point A to point B, so doing fifty crunches on a mat does not accomplish that goal, but crunches do make our upper bodies, backs, and heart stronger when we need to run or walk.

Logical thinking can assist us in solving difficult everyday problems, so solving algebra problems "builds the muscles" in the part of our brain that performs logical thinking. So, when you are studying algebra and getting frustrated with the amount of work that needs to be done, and you say, "My brain hurts," remember the phrase that we all use in the gym, "No pain, no gain."

Another phrase to keep in mind is "Success Breeds Success." Mathematics is everywhere. You already are successful at doing some everyday mathematics. With practice, you can take your initial successes and become even more successful. Have you ever done any of the following everyday activities?

- Compare the price per ounce of different sizes of jars of peanut butter or jam.
- Leave a tip at a restaurant.
- Figure out how many calories your bowl of breakfast cereal provides.
- Take an opinion survey along with many other people.
- Measure the distances between cities as you plan your summer vacation.
- Order the appropriate number of gallons of paint to cover the walls of a room that you are renovating.
- Buy a car and take out a car loan with interest.
- Double a cookie recipe.
- Change American dollars for Canadian dollars.
- Fill up a basketball or soccer ball with air (balls are spheres, after all).
- Coach a Little League team (scores, statistics, catching, and throwing all involve math).
- Check the percentages of saturated and unsaturated fats in a chocolate bar.

We just listed twelve of many everyday mathematical activities, and you may do five or ten in a single day! The everyday mathematics that you already know is the foundation for your success in this course.

1   What to Do the First Week of the Semester

You have enrolled in an intermediate algebra course. The first week of the semester gives you the opportunity to prepare your road to success. Here are the things that you should do:

1. **Pick a good seat.**   As you enter the classroom for the first time, choose a seat that gives you a good view of the room. Sit close enough to the front so that you can easily see the board and hear the professor.

2. **Read the syllabus to learn about your instructor and the course.**   Be sure to take note of your instructor's name, office location, e-mail address, telephone number, and office hours. Also, pay attention to any additional help that can be found on campus such as tutoring centers, videos in the library, software, online tutorials, and so on. Make sure that you fully understand all of the instructor's policies for the

class. This includes the policy on absences, missed exams or quizzes, and homework. Ask questions.

3. **Learn the names of some of your classmates and exchange contact information.** One of the best ways to learn math is through group study sessions. Try to create time each week to study with your classmates. Knowing how to get in contact with classmates is also useful if you ever miss class because you can obtain the assignment for the day.

4. **Budget your time.** Most students have a tendency to "bite off more than they can chew." To help with time management, consider the following general rule for studying mathematics: You should plan on studying *at least* two hours outside of class for each hour in class. So, if you enrolled in a four-hour math class, you should set aside at least eight hours each week to study for the course. If this is not your only course, you will have to set aside time for other courses as well. Consider your work schedule and personal life when creating your time budget as well.

2 What to Do Before, During, and After Class

Now that the semester is under way, we present the following ideas for what to do before, during, and after each class meeting. While these suggestions may sound overwhelming, we guarantee that by following them, you will be successful in mathematics (and other courses). Also, you will find that studying for exams becomes much easier by following this plan.

Before Class Begins

1. Make sure you are mentally prepared for class. This means that your mind should be alert and ready to concentrate for the entire class period. (Invest in a cup of coffee at breakfast and eat lots of protein!)

2. Read the section or sections that will be covered in the upcoming class meeting.

3. Based upon your reading, prepare a list of questions. Jot them down. In many cases, your questions will be answered through the lecture. You can then ask any that are not answered completely.

During Class

1. Arrive early enough to prepare your mind and material for the lecture.

2. Stay alert. Do not doze off or daydream during class. It will be very difficult to understand the lecture when you "return to class."

3. Take thorough notes. It is normal not to get certain topics the first time that you hear them through the lecture. However, this does not mean that you throw your hands up in despair. Rather, continue to take class notes.

4. You can ask questions when appropriate. Do not be afraid to ask questions. In fact, instructors love when students ask questions, for two reasons. First, we know as teachers that if one student has a question that there are many more in class with the same question. Second, by asking questions, you are teaching the teacher what topics cause difficulty.

After Class

1. Reread (and possibly rewrite) your class notes. In our experience as students, we were amazed how often confusion that existed during class went away after studying our in-class notes later when we had more time to absorb the material.

2. Reread the section. This is an especially important step. Once you have heard the lecture, the section will make more sense and you will understand much more.

3. Do your homework. **Homework is not optional.** There is an old Chinese proverb that says,

I hear ... and I forget

I see ... and I remember

I do ... and I understand

Work Smart: Study Skills

Plan on studying two hours outside of class for each hour in class every week. Take a few minutes to plan out the upcoming academic term.

Work Smart: Study Skills

Be sure to ask questions during class.

Work Smart: Study Skills

The reason for doing homework is to build your skill and confidence. Don't skip assignments.

This proverb applies to any situation in life in which you want to succeed. Would a pianist expect to be the best if she didn't practice? The only way you are going to learn algebra is by doing algebra. Remember: Success breeds success.

4. And don't forget, when you get a problem wrong, try to figure out why you got the problem wrong. If you can't discover your error, be sure to ask for help.

5. If you have questions, visit your professor during office hours. You can also ask someone in your study group or go to the tutoring center on campus, if available.

Math Courses: No Brain Freezes Here!

Learning algebra is a building process. Learning is the art of making connections between thousands of neurons (specialized cells) in the brain. Memory is the ability to reactivate these neural networks—it is a conversation among neurons.

Math isn't a mystery. You already know some math. But you do have to practice what you know and expand your knowledge. Why? The brain contains thousands of neurons. Through repeated practice, a special coating forms that allows the signals to travel faster and reduces interference. The cells "fire" more quickly and connections are made faster and with less effort. Practice forms the pathways that allow us to retrieve concepts and facts at test time. Remember those crunches, which are a way of making your body more robust and nimble—learning does the same to your brain.

Have We Mentioned Asking Questions?

To move information from short-term memory to long-term memory, we need to think about the information, comprehend its meaning, and ask questions about it.

⌈3⌉ How to Use the Text Effectively

When we sat down to write this text, we knew based upon experience from teaching our own students that students typically do not read their mathematics text. Rather than saying to you, "Ah, but our book is different—it can be read!," we decided to accept how students study math.

Students usually go through the following steps:

1. Attend the lecture and watch the instructor do some problems on the board. Perhaps work some problems in class.

2. Go home and work on the homework assignment.

3. After each problem, check the answer in the back of the text. If right, move on, but if wrong, go back and see where the solution went wrong.

4. Maybe the mistake can be identified, but if not, go to the class notes or try to find a similar example in the text. With a little luck, a similar example can be found and you can determine where the solution went wrong in the problem.

5. If not, mark the problem and ask about it in the next class meeting, which leads us back to step 1.

So with this model in mind, we started to develop this text so that there is more than one way to extract the information you need from it.

All of the features have been included in the text to help you succeed. These features are based on time-tested techniques we use in class. We list the features in the order they appear and briefly explain the purpose of each feature and how it can be used to help you succeed in this course:

Preparing for This Section: Warming Up

Immediately after the title of the section, each section (after Chapter R) begins with a short "readiness quiz." The readiness quiz presents questions about material that was presented earlier in the course and is needed for the upcoming section. You should take the readiness quiz to be sure that you understand the material that the new

Work Smart: Study Skills

Learn what the different features of this book are designed to do. Decide which ones you may need the most.

section will be based on. Answers to the readiness quiz appear as footnotes on the page of the quiz. Check your answers. If you get a problem wrong, or don't know how to do a problem, go back to the section listed and review the material.

Objectives: A "Road Map" through the Course

To the left of the readiness quiz, we present a list of objectives to be covered in the section. If you follow the objectives, you will get a good idea of the section's "big picture"—the important concepts, techniques, and procedures.

The objectives are numbered. When we begin discussing a particular objective within the section, the objective number appears along with the stated objective.

Examples: Where to Look for Information

You look to examples to provide you with guidance and instruction when you need it most—when you are away from the instructor and the classroom. With this in mind, we have developed two special example formats.

Step-by-Step Examples have a three-column format where the left column describes a step, the middle column provides a brief explanation of the step, and the right column presents the algebra. With this format, the left and middle columns can be thought of as your instructor's voice during a lecture. *Step-by-Step Examples* are used to introduce key topics or important problem-solving strategies. They are meant to provide easy-to-understand, practical instructions by including the words "how to" in the examples' headline.

Annotated Examples have a two-column format in which explanations are provided to the left of the algebra. Because we read from left to right, placing the explanation on the left clearly describes what we are about to do. Again, the annotations can be thought of as your instructor's voice right before he or she writes the solution on the board.

In Words: Math in Everyday Language

Have you ever been given a math definition in class and said, "What in the world does that mean?" As teachers, we have heard that from our students. So we added the "In Words" feature, which takes definitions that are in their mathematical form and restates them in everyday language. This margin feature will help you understand the language of mathematics better.

Work Smart

These are "tricks of the trade" that can be used to help you solve problems and appear in the margin. They also show alternative approaches to solving problems. Yes, there is more than one way to solve a math problem!

Work Smart: Study Skills

Working smart also means studying smart. We provide study skill tips in the margin throughout the text to help you understand the study skills required for success in this and other mathematics courses.

Exercises: A Unique Numbering Scheme

We know from our own experiences as teachers that students typically jump right to the exercises after attending a lecture. So, all of the examples and explanation of concepts that are contained within the section are glossed over, or skipped entirely. In the interest of helping you use the book most effectively to learn the math, we have structured the exercises differently from textbooks you have experienced thus far in your mathematics career. Our structure is designed to increase your confidence and ability to work any mathematical problem while decreasing your dependence on the bad

Work Smart: Study Skills
Selected problems in the exercise sets are identified by a ⊙ symbol. For extra help, view the worked solutions to these problems on the book's CD Lecture Series.

habit of looking back in the book for an example that mimics the exact problem you are currently working. Consequently, the exercises in each section are broken into as many as eight parts. Each exercise set will have some, or all, of the following exercise types.

1. Quick Checks
2. Building Skills
3. Mixed Practice
4. Applying the Concepts

5. Extending the Concepts
6. Explaining the Concepts
7. Synthesis Review
8. The Graphing Calculator

1. **Quick Checks: Learning to Ride a Bicycle with Training Wheels** Do you remember when you were first learning to ride a bicycle? Training wheels were placed on the bicycle to assist you in learning balance. The Quick Checks can be thought of as exercises with training wheels. What are the training wheels? Well, Quick Check exercises appear right after the example or examples that illustrate the concept being taught. So, if you get stuck on a Quick Check problem, you simply need to consult the example immediately preceding the Quick Check problems. You don't have to search back through the text. The Quick Check exercises also verify your understanding of the vocabulary introduced in the section. See page 20 in Section R.3.

2. **Building Skills: Learning to Ride a Bicycle with Assistance** Let's continue with the bicycle analogy. Once you felt ready to ride without training wheels, you likely had an adult follow closely behind you holding the bicycle for balance and helping build your confidence in your ability. The Building Skills problems serve a similar purpose. They are keyed to the objectives within the section, so the directions for the problem indicate which objective is being developed. As a result, you know exactly what part of the text to consult if you get stuck. (But you won't necessarily know exactly which example to read.) See page 30 in Section R.3.

3. **Mixed Practice: Now You Are Ready to Ride!** You have mastered training wheels and have learned to balance with assistance. Now you are ready to go off on your own. This stage is the Mixed Practice portion of the exercises. These exercises are composed of a potpourri of problems from the section. They may also include problems that develop your ability to see the big picture of mathematics. They are not keyed to a particular objective and require you to determine the appropriate approach to solving a problem on your own. See page 31 in Section R.3.

4. **Applying the Concepts: Where Will I Ever Use This Stuff?** The Applying the Concepts part not only presents problems that illustrate the application of mathematics in your life, but also provides some problems that test your conceptual understanding of the mathematics. See page 31 in Section R.3.

5. **Extending the Concepts: Stretching Your Mind** Sometimes we need to be challenged. These exercises extend your skills to a new level and provide further insight into where mathematics can be used. See page 31 in Section R.3.

6. **Explaining the Concepts: Verbalize Your Understanding** These problems require you to think about the big-picture concepts of the section and express these concepts in your own words. It is our belief that students need to improve their ability to communicate complicated ideas (both orally and in writing). These problems can serve as a basis for classroom discussion or can be used as writing assignments. If you truly understand the material in the section, you should be able to clearly articulate the concepts. See page 32 in Section R.3.

7. **Synthesis Review: Seeing the Forest for the Trees** Starting with Chapter 5, we provide Synthesis Review exercises to help you grasp the "big picture" of algebra. Synthesis review exercises ask you to perform a single operation (adding, solving, and so on) on several objects (polynomials, rational expressions, and so on). You are then asked to discuss the similarities and differences in performing the same operation on the different objects. See page 422 in Section 5.1.

8. **The Graphing Calculator** The graphing calculator is a great tool for verifying answers, but it is also very useful in helping us to visualize results. These exercises illustrate how the graphing calculator can be incorporated into the material of the section. See page 32 in Section R.3.

Chapter Review

The chapter review is arranged section by section. For each section, we list key concepts, key terms, and objectives. For each objective, we provide the examples from the text that illustrate the objective, along with page references. Also, for each objective, we list the problems in the review exercises that test your understanding. If you get a problem wrong, use this feature to determine where to look in the book to help you to work the problem. Cumulative Review exercises are also provided at the end of every odd-numbered chapter to refresh your memory on important skills and concepts.

Chapter Test

We have included a chapter test. Once you think that you are prepared for the exam, take the chapter test. If you do well on the chapter test, chances are you will do well on your in-class exam. Be sure to take the chapter test under the conditions that you will face in class.

Chapter Test Prep Video CD

Packaged with each new copy of the text, the Chapter Test Prep Video CD provides students with help at the critical juncture when they are studying for a test. The CD video presents step-by-step solutions to the exercises found in each of the book's Chapter Tests. Easy video navigation allows students to access instantly the worked-out solutions to the exercises they want to study or review.

☐4 How to Prepare for an Exam

The following steps are time-tested suggestions to help you prepare for an exam.

Step 1: Revisit your homework and the chapter review problems Beginning about one week before your exam, start to redo your homework assignments. If you don't understand a topic, be sure to seek out help. You should also work the problems given in the chapter review. The problems are keyed to the objectives in the course. If you get a problem wrong, identify the objective and examples that illustrate the objective. Then review this material and try the problem in the chapter review again. If you get the problem wrong again, seek out help.

Step 2: Test yourself A day or two before the exam, take the chapter test under test conditions. Be sure to check your answers. If you got any problems wrong, determine why you got them wrong and remedy the situation.

Step 3: View the Chapter Test Prep Video CD These videos provide you with step-by-step solutions to the exact exercises found in each of the book's Chapter Tests. To get the most from this valuable resource, follow the worked-out solutions to any of the exercises on the Chapter Test that you want to study or review.

Step 4: Follow these rules as you train Be sure to arrive early at the location of the exam. Prepare your mind for the exam. Also, be sure that you are well rested. Don't try to pull "all-nighters." If you need to study all night long for an exam, then your time management is poor and you should rethink how you are using your time or whether you have enough time set aside for the course.

Work Smart: Study Skills

Do not "cram" for an exam by pulling an "all-nighter."

R.1 EXERCISES

PRACTICE   WATCH   DOWNLOAD   READ   REVIEW

1. Why do you want to be successful in mathematics? Are your goals positive or negative? If you stated your goal negatively ("Just get me out of this course!), can you restate it positively?

2. Name three activities in your daily life that involve the use of math (for instance, playing cards, operating your computer, or reading a credit-card bill).

3. What is your instructor's name?

4. What are your instructor's office hours? Where is your instructor's office?

5. Does your instructor have an e-mail address? If so, what is it?

6. Does your class have a website? Do you know how to access it? What information is located on the website?

7. Are there tutors available for this course? If so, where are they located? When are they available?

8. Name two other students in your class. What is their contact information? When can you meet with them to study?

9. List some of the things that you should do before class begins.

10. List some of the things that you should do during class.

11. List some of the things that you should do after class.

12. What is the point of the Chinese proverb on page 3?

13. What is the "readiness quiz"? How should it be used?

14. Name three features that appear in the margins. What is the purpose of each of them?

15. Name the categories of exercises that appear in this book.

16. How should the chapter review material be used?

17. How should the chapter test be used?

18. What is the Chapter Test Prep Video CD?

19. List the four steps that should be followed when preparing for an exam. Can you think of other methods of preparing for an exam that have worked for you?

20. How is mathematics like doing crunches at the gym?

---

21. Use the chart to help manage your time. Be sure to fill in time allocated to various activities in your life including school, work, and leisure.

	Monday	Tuesday	Wednesday	Thursday	Friday	Saturday	Sunday
7 am							
8 am							
9 am							
10 am							
11 am							
Noon							
1 pm							
2 pm							
3 pm							
4 pm							
5 pm							
6 pm							
7 pm							
8 pm							
9 pm							

1 Linear Equations and Inequalities

Did you know that the amount of income tax that we pay to the federal government can be found by solving a linear equation? See Problems 103 and 104 in Section 1.1.

OUTLINE

The Big Picture: Putting It Together

In Chapter R, we reviewed skills learned in earlier courses. These skills will be used throughout the text and should always be kept fresh in your mind.

We now begin our discussion of *algebra* in earnest. The word "algebra" is derived from the Arabic word *al-jabr*. The word is part of the title of a ninth-century work, "Hisâb al-jabr w'al-muqâbalah," written during the golden age of Islamic science and mathematics by Muhammad ibn Mûqâ al-Khowârizmî.

The word *al-jabr* means "restoration," a reference to the fact that, if a number is added to one side of an equation, then it must also be added to the other side in order to "restore" the equality. The title of the work "Hisâb al-jabr w'al-muqâbalah" means "the science of restoring and canceling." Today, algebra has come to mean a great deal more.

The material in Chapter 1 is presented in two parts. Part I reviews linear equations and inequalities in one variable, and Part II reviews linear equations and inequalities in two variables.

PART I: LINEAR EQUATIONS AND INEQUALITIES IN ONE VARIABLE

1.1 Linear Equations in One Variable

OBJECTIVES

1. Determine Whether a Number Is a Solution to an Equation
2. Solve Linear Equations
3. Determine Whether an Equation Is a Conditional Equation, Identity, or Contradiction

Preparing for Linear Equations

Before getting started, take this readiness quiz. If you get a problem wrong, go back to the section cited and review the material.

P1. Determine the additive inverse of 5.   [Section R.3, p. 21]

P2. Determine the multiplicative inverse of -3.   [Section R.3, pp. 23–24]

P3. Use the Reduction Property to simplify $\frac{1}{5} \cdot 5x$.   [Section R.3, pp. 25–26]

P4. Find the Least Common Denominator of $\frac{3}{8}$ and $\frac{5}{12}$.   [Section R.3, pp. 27–28]

P5. Use the Distributive Property to remove the parentheses: $6(z - 2)$ [Section R.3, pp. 29–30]

P6. What is the coefficient of $-4x$?   [Section R.5, p. 41]

P7. Simplify by combining like terms: $4(y - 2) - y + 5$ [Section R.5, pp. 41–43]

P8. Evaluate the expression $-5(x + 3) - 8$ when $x = -2$ [Section R.5, pp. 40–41]

P9. Is $x = 3$ in the domain of $\frac{2}{x + 3}$? Is $x = -3$ in the domain?   [Section R.5, pp. 43–44]

1 Determine Whether a Number Is a Solution to an Equation

An **equation in one variable** is a statement made up of two expressions that are equal, and in the statement, at least one of the expressions contains the variable. The expressions are called the **sides** of the equation. Examples of equations in one variable are

$$2y + 5 = 0 \qquad 4x + 5 = -2x + 10 \qquad \frac{3}{z + 2} = 9$$

In this section, we will concentrate on solving *linear equations in one variable*.

> **In Words**
>
> In the equation $2y + 5 = 0$, the expression $2y + 5$ is the *left side* of the equation and 0 is the *right side*. In this equation only the left side contains the variable, y. In the equation $4x + 5 = -2x + 10$, the expression $4x + 5$ is the *left side* of the equation and $-2x + 10$ is the right side. In this equation both sides have expressions that contain the variable, x.

DEFINITION

A **linear equation in one variable** is an equation that has one unknown and the unknown is written to the first power. Linear equations in one variable can be written in the form

$$ax + b = 0$$

where a and b are real numbers and $a \neq 0$.

The following are all examples of linear equations in one variable because they can be written in the form $ax + b = 0$ with a little algebraic manipulation.

$$4x - 3 = 12 \qquad \frac{2}{3}y + \frac{1}{5} = \frac{2}{15} \qquad -0.73p + 1.23 = 1.34p + 8.05$$

Because an equation is a statement, it can be either true or false, depending upon the value of the variable. Any value of the variable that results in a true statement is called a **solution** of the equation. When a value of the variable results in a true statement, we say that the value **satisfies** the equation. To determine whether a number satisfies an equation, we replace the variable with the number and determine whether the left side of the equation equals the right side of the equation—if it does, then we have a true statement and the number substituted is a solution.

Preparing for...Answers   **P1.** -5

P2. $-\frac{1}{3}$ **P3.** x **P4.** 24   **P5.** $6z - 12$

P6. -4 **P7.** $3y - 3$ **P8.** -13

P9. Yes; No

EXAMPLE 1 **Determining Whether a Number Is a Solution to a Linear Equation**

Determine if the following numbers are solutions to the equation

$$3(x - 1) = -2x + 12$$

(a) $x = 5$ **(b)** $x = 3$

Solution

(a) Let $x = 5$ in the equation and simplify.

$$3(x - 1) = -2x + 12$$
$$3(5 - 1) \stackrel{?}{=} -2(5) + 12$$
Simplify: $3(4) \stackrel{?}{=} -10 + 12$
$$12 \neq 2$$

Because the left side of the equation does not equal the right side of the equation, we do not have a true statement. Therefore, $x = 5$ is not a solution.

(b) Let $x = 3$ in the equation and simplify.

$$3(x - 1) = -2x + 12$$
$$3(3 - 1) \stackrel{?}{=} -2(3) + 12$$
Simplify: $3(2) \stackrel{?}{=} -6 + 12$
$$6 = 6 \quad \text{True}$$

Because the left side of the equation equals the right side of the equation, we have a true statement. Therefore, $x = 3$ is a solution to the equation. ∎

In Words

The symbol $\stackrel{?}{=}$ is used to indicate that we are unsure whether the left side of the equation equals the right side of the equation.

Quick ✔

1. The equation $3x + 5 = 2x - 3$ is a _____ equation in one variable. The expressions $3x + 5$ and $2x - 3$ are called _____ of the equation.

2. The values of the variable that result in a true statement are called _____ .

In Problems 3–5, determine which of the given numbers are solutions to the equation.

3. $-5x + 3 = -2; x = -2, x = 1, x = 3$

4. $3x + 2 = 2x - 5; x = 0, x = 6, x = -7$

5. $-3(z + 2) = 4z + 1; z = -3, z = -1, z = 2$

Work Smart

The directions solve, simplify, and evaluate are different! We *solve* equations. We *simplify* algebraic expressions to form equivalent algebraic expressions. We *evaluate* algebraic expressions to find the value of the expression for a specific value of the variable.

▏2▕ Solve Linear Equations

To **solve an equation** means to find ALL the solutions of the equation. The set of all solutions to the equation is called the **solution set** of the equation.

One method for solving equations algebraically requires that a series of *equivalent equations* be developed from the original equation until a solution results.

DEFINITION

Two or more equations that have precisely the same solutions are called **equivalent equations.**

But how do we obtain equivalent equations? The first method we introduce for obtaining an equivalent equation is called the *Addition Property of Equality.*

In Words

The Addition Property says that whatever you add to one side of an equation, you must also add to the other side.

ADDITION PROPERTY OF EQUALITY

The **Addition Property of Equality** states that for real numbers a, b, and c,

$$\text{if } a = b, \quad \text{then} \quad a + c = b + c$$

For example, if $x = 3$, then $x + 2 = 3 + 2$ (we added 2 to both sides of the equation). Because $a - b$ is equivalent to $a + (-b)$, the Addition Property can be used to add a real number to each side of an equation or subtract a real number from each side of an equation. You will use this handy property a great deal in algebra.

A second method that results in an equivalent equation is called the *Multiplication Property of Equality*.

In Words

The Multiplication Property says that whenever you multiply one side of an equation by a nonzero expression, you must also multiply the other side by the same nonzero expression.

MULTIPLICATION PROPERTY OF EQUALITY

The **Multiplication Property of Equality** states that for real numbers a, b, and c where $c \neq 0$,

$$\text{if } a = b, \quad \text{then} \quad ac = bc$$

For example, if $5x = 30$, then $\frac{1}{5} \cdot 5x = \frac{1}{5} \cdot 30$. Remember, the quotient $\frac{a}{b}$ is equivalent to the product $a \cdot \frac{1}{b}$, so dividing by some number b is really multiplying by the multiplicative inverse of b, $\frac{1}{b}$. So, the Multiplication Property can be used to multiply or divide each side of the equation by some nonzero quantity.

EXAMPLE 2 Using the Addition and Multiplication Properties to Solve a Linear Equation

Solve the linear equation: $\frac{1}{3}x - 2 = 4$

Solution

The goal in solving any linear equation is to get the variable by itself with a coefficient of 1, that is, to isolate the variable.

Work Smart

The number in front of the variable expression is the coefficient. For example, the coefficient in the expression 2x is 2.

$$\frac{1}{3}x - 2 = 4$$

Addition Property of Equality; add 2 to both sides: $\left(\frac{1}{3}x - 2\right) + 2 = 4 + 2$

Simplify: $\frac{1}{3}x = 6$

Multiplication Property of Equality; multiply both sides by 3: $3\left(\frac{1}{3}x\right) = 3 \cdot 6$

Simplify: $x = 18$

Check $\frac{1}{3}x - 2 = 4$

Let $x = 18$ in the original equation: $\frac{1}{3}(18) - 2 \overset{?}{=} 4$

$$6 - 2 \overset{?}{=} 4$$

$$4 = 4 \quad \text{True}$$

Because $x = 18$ satisfies the equation, the solution of the equation is 18, or the solution set is $\{18\}$.

Quick ✔

6. What does it mean to solve an equation?

7. State the Addition Property of Equality.

8. State the Multiplication Property of Equality.

In Problems 9–11, solve each equation and verify your solution.

9. $3x + 8 = 17$ **10.** $-4a - 7 = 1$ **11.** $5y + 1 = 2$

Often, we must combine like terms or use the Distributive Property to eliminate parentheses before we can use the Addition or Multiplication Properties. Remember, when solving linear equations, our goal is to get all terms involving the variable on one side of the equation and all constants on the other side.

EXAMPLE 3 Solving a Linear Equation by Combining Like Terms

Solve the linear equation: $3y - 2 + 5y = 2y + 5 + 4y + 3$

Solution

$$3y - 2 + 5y = 2y + 5 + 4y + 3$$

Combine like terms: $8y - 2 = 6y + 8$

Subtract 6y from both sides: $8y - 2 - 6y = 6y + 8 - 6y$

$$2y - 2 = 8$$

Add 2 to both sides: $2y - 2 + 2 = 8 + 2$

$$2y = 10$$

Divide both sides by 2: $\dfrac{2y}{2} = \dfrac{10}{2}$

$$y = 5$$

Check $3y - 2 + 5y = 2y + 5 + 4y + 3$

Let $y = 5$ in the original equation: $3(5) - 2 + 5(5) \overset{?}{=} 2(5) + 5 + 4(5) + 3$

$$15 - 2 + 25 \overset{?}{=} 10 + 5 + 20 + 3$$

$$38 = 38 \quad \text{True}$$

Because $y = 5$ satisfies the equation, the solution of the equation is 5, or the solution set is $\{5\}$. ∎

Quick ✔ *In Problems 12–14, solve each linear equation. Be sure to verify your solution.*

12. $2x + 3 + 5x + 1 = 4x + 10$

13. $4b + 3 - b - 8 - 5b = 2b - 1 - b - 1$

14. $2w + 8 - 7w + 1 = 3w - 1 + 2w - 5$

EXAMPLE 4 Solving a Linear Equation Using the Distributive Property

Solve the linear equation: $4(x + 3) = x - 3(x - 2)$

Solution

Use the Distributive Property $4(x + 3) = x - 3(x - 2)$
to remove parentheses:

$$4x + 12 = x - 3x + 6$$

Combine like terms: $4x + 12 = -2x + 6$

Add 2x to both sides: $4x + 12 + 2x = -2x + 6 + 2x$

$$6x + 12 = 6$$

Subtract 12 from both sides: $6x + 12 - 12 = 6 - 12$

$$6x = -6$$

Divide both sides by 6: $\dfrac{6x}{6} = \dfrac{-6}{6}$

$$x = -1$$

Check $\qquad\qquad\qquad\qquad\qquad\qquad 4(x + 3) = x - 3(x - 2)$

Let $x = -1$ in the original equation: $\quad 4(-1 + 3) \overset{?}{=} -1 - 3(-1 - 2)$

$$4(2) \overset{?}{=} -1 - 3(-3)$$

$$8 \overset{?}{=} -1 + 9$$

$$8 = 8 \quad \text{True}$$

Because $x = -1$ satisfies the equation, the solution of the equation is -1, or the solution set is $\{-1\}$. ∎

Quick ✔ *In Problems 15–18, solve each linear equation. Be sure to verify your solution.*

15. $4(x - 1) = 12$

16. $-2(x - 4) - 6 = 3(x + 6) + 4$

17. $4(x + 3) - 8x = 3(x + 2) + x$

18. $5(x - 3) + 3(x + 3) = 2x - 3$

We now summarize the steps for solving a linear equation. Bear in mind that it is possible that one or more of these steps may not be necessary when solving a linear equation.

> **SUMMARY** STEPS FOR SOLVING A LINEAR EQUATION
>
> **Step 1:** Remove any parentheses using the Distributive Property.
>
> **Step 2:** Combine like terms on each side of the equation.
>
> **Step 3:** Use the Addition Property of Equality to get all variables on one side of the equation and all constants on the other side.
>
> **Step 4:** Use the Multiplication Property of Equality to get the coefficient of the variable to equal 1.
>
> **Step 5:** Check your answer to be sure that it satisfies the original equation.

Linear Equations with Fractions or Decimals

A linear equation that contains fractions can be rewritten (transformed) into an equivalent equation without fractions by multiplying both sides of the equation by the Least Common Denominator (LCD) of all the fractions in the equation.

EXAMPLE 5 **How to Solve a Linear Equation That Contains Fractions**

Solve the linear equation: $\dfrac{y + 1}{4} + \dfrac{y - 2}{10} = \dfrac{y + 7}{20}$

Step-by-Step Solution

Before we follow the summary steps, we rewrite the equation without fractions by multiplying both sides of the equation by the Least Common Denominator (LCD). The LCD is 20, so we multiply both sides of the equation by 20 and obtain

$$20 \cdot \left(\dfrac{y + 1}{4} + \dfrac{y - 2}{10} \right) = 20 \cdot \left(\dfrac{y + 7}{20} \right)$$

Now we can follow Steps 1–5 for solving a linear equation.

Step 1: Remove all parentheses using the Distributive Property.	$20 \cdot \left(\dfrac{y+1}{4} + \dfrac{y-2}{10} \right) = 20 \cdot \left(\dfrac{y+7}{20} \right)$
Use the Distributive Property:	$20 \cdot \dfrac{y+1}{4} + 20 \cdot \dfrac{y-2}{10} = 20 \cdot \dfrac{y+7}{20}$
Divide out common factors:	$5(y+1) + 2(y-2) = y+7$
Use the Distributive Property:	$5y + 5 + 2y - 4 = y + 7$

Step 2: Combine like terms on each side of the equation.	$7y + 1 = y + 7$

Step 3: Use the Addition Property of Equality to get all variables on one side of the equation and all constants on the other side.	
Subtract y from both sides:	$7y + 1 - y = y + 7 - y$
	$6y + 1 = 7$
Subtract 1 from both sides:	$6y + 1 - 1 = 7 - 1$
	$6y = 6$

Step 4: Use the Multiplication Property of Equality to get the coefficient on the variable to equal 1.	
Divide both sides by 6:	$\dfrac{6y}{6} = \dfrac{6}{6}$
	$y = 1$

Step 5: Check: Verify the solution.	$\dfrac{y+1}{4} + \dfrac{y-2}{10} = \dfrac{y+7}{20}$
Let $y = 1$ in the original equation:	$\dfrac{1+1}{4} + \dfrac{1-2}{10} \overset{?}{=} \dfrac{1+7}{20}$
	$\dfrac{2}{4} + \dfrac{-1}{10} \overset{?}{=} \dfrac{8}{20}$
Rewrite each rational number with LCD = 20:	$\dfrac{2}{4} \cdot \dfrac{5}{5} + \dfrac{-1}{10} \cdot \dfrac{2}{2} \overset{?}{=} \dfrac{8}{20}$
	$\dfrac{10}{20} + \dfrac{-2}{20} \overset{?}{=} \dfrac{8}{20}$
	$\dfrac{8}{20} = \dfrac{8}{20}$ True

Because $y = 1$ satisfies the equation, the solution of the equation is 1, or the solution set is $\{1\}$.   ■

Quick ✔ *In Problems 19–22, solve each linear equation. Be sure to verify your solution.*

19. $\dfrac{3y}{2} + \dfrac{y}{6} = \dfrac{10}{3}$

20. $\dfrac{3x}{4} - \dfrac{5}{12} = \dfrac{5x}{6}$

21. $\dfrac{x+2}{6} + 2 = \dfrac{5}{3}$

22. $\dfrac{4x+3}{9} - \dfrac{2x+1}{2} = \dfrac{1}{6}$

When decimals occur in a linear equation, we can rewrite (transform) the equation into an equivalent equation that does not have a decimal. We use the same technique that we used in equations with fractions. The idea behind the procedure is to multiply both sides of the equation by a power of 10 so that the decimals are removed. For example, because $0.7 = \dfrac{7}{10}$, multiplying 0.7 by 10 "eliminates" the decimal since $10(0.7) = 10 \cdot \dfrac{7}{10} = 7$. Because $0.03 = \dfrac{3}{100}$, multiplying 0.03 by 100 "eliminates" the decimal.

EXAMPLE 6 Solving a Linear Equation That Contains Decimals

Solve the linear equation: $0.5x - 0.4 = 0.3x + 0.2$

Solution

We want to rewrite the equation so that the equivalent equation does not contain a decimal. This is done by multiplying both sides of the equation by 10. Do you see why? Each of the decimals is written to the tenths position, so multiplying by 10 will "eliminate" the decimal.

$$10(0.5x - 0.4) = 10(0.3x + 0.2)$$

Use the Distributive Property: $\quad 10(0.5x) - 10(0.4) = 10(0.3x) + 10(0.2)$

$$5x - 4 = 3x + 2$$

Subtract $3x$ from both sides: $\quad 5x - 4 - 3x = 3x + 2 - 3x$

$$2x - 4 = 2$$

Add 4 to both sides: $\quad 2x - 4 + 4 = 2 + 4$

$$2x = 6$$

Divide both sides by 2: $\quad \dfrac{2x}{2} = \dfrac{6}{2}$

$$x = 3$$

Check $\qquad\qquad\qquad\qquad 0.5x - 0.4 = 0.3x + 0.2$

Let $x = 3$ in the original equation: $\quad 0.5(3) - 0.4 \overset{?}{=} 0.3(3) + 0.2$

$$1.5 - 0.4 \overset{?}{=} 0.9 + 0.2$$

$$1.1 = 1.1 \quad \text{True}$$

Because $x = 3$ satisfies the equation, the solution of the equation is 3, or the solution set is $\{3\}$. ∎

Quick ✔ *In Problems 23–25, solve each linear equation. Be sure to verify your solution.*

23. $0.2t + 1.4 = 0.8$ $\qquad\qquad$ **24.** $0.07x - 1.3 = 0.05x - 1.1$

25. $0.4(y + 3) = 0.5(y - 4)$

⌐3⌐ Determine Whether an Equation Is a Conditional Equation, Identity, or Contradiction

All of the linear equations that we have studied thus far have had one solution. While it is tempting to say that all linear equations must have one solution, this statement is not true in general. In fact, linear equations may have either one solution, no solution, or infinitely many solutions. We give names to the type of equation depending upon the number of solutions that the linear equation has.

The equations that we have solved thus far are called *conditional equations*.

DEFINITION

A **conditional equation** is an equation that is true for some values of the variable and false for other values of the variable.

For example, the equation

$$x + 7 = 10$$

is a conditional equation because it is true when $x = 3$ and false for every other real number x.

> **DEFINITION**
>
> An equation that is false for every value of the variable is called a **contradiction.**

For example, the equation

$$3x + 8 = 3x + 6$$

is a contradiction because it is false for any value of x. Contradictions are identified through the process of creating equivalent equations. For example, if we subtract $3x$ from both sides of $3x + 8 = 3x + 6$, we obtain $8 = 6$, which is clearly false. Contradictions have no solution and therefore the solution set is empty. We express the solution set of contradictions as either $\varnothing$ or $\{\ \}$.

> **DEFINITION**
>
> An equation that is satisfied for every choice of the variable for which both sides of the equation are defined is called an **identity.**

In Words

Conditional equations are true for some values of the variable and false for others. Contradictions are false for all values of the variable. Identities are true for all allowed values of the variable.

For example,

$$2x + 3 + x + 8 = 3x + 11$$

is an identity because any real number x satisfies the equation. Just as with contradictions, identities are recognized through the process of creating equivalent equations. For example, if we combine like terms in the equation $2x + 3 + x + 8 = 3x + 11$ we obtain $3x + 11 = 3x + 11$, which is true no matter what value of x we choose. Therefore, the solution set of linear identities is the set of all real numbers. We express the solution of linear identities as either $\{x \mid x \text{ is any real number}\}$ or $\mathbb{R}$.

EXAMPLE 7 Classifying a Linear Equation

Solve the linear equation $3(x + 3) - 6x = 5(x + 1) - 8x$. State whether the equation is an identity, contradiction, or conditional equation.

Solution

As with any linear equation, our goal is to get the variable by itself with a coefficient of 1.

$$3(x + 3) - 6x = 5(x + 1) - 8x$$

Use the Distributive Property: $\quad 3x + 9 - 6x = 5x + 5 - 8x$

Combine like terms: $\quad -3x + 9 = -3x + 5$

Add $3x$ to both sides: $\quad -3x + 9 + 3x = -3x + 5 + 3x$

$$9 = 5$$

Work Smart

In the solution to Example 7 we obtained the equation

$$-3x + 9 = -3x + 5$$

You may recognize at this point that the equation is a contradiction and state the solution set as $\varnothing$ or $\{\ \}$.

The last statement states that $9 = 5$. This is a false statement, so the equation is a contradiction. The original equation is a contradiction and has no solution. The solution set is $\varnothing$ or $\{\ \}$. ∎

EXAMPLE 8 Classify a Linear Equation

Solve the linear equation $-4(x - 2) + 3(4x + 2) = 2(4x + 7)$. State whether the equation is an identity, contradiction, or conditional equation.

Solution

$$-4(x - 2) + 3(4x + 2) = 2(4x + 7)$$

Use the Distributive Property: $\qquad -4x + 8 + 12x + 6 = 8x + 14$

Combine like terms: $\qquad\qquad\qquad 8x + 14 = 8x + 14$

At this point it should be clear that the equation $8x + 14 = 8x + 14$ is true for all real numbers x. So, the original equation is an identity and its solution set is all real numbers or $\{x \,|\, x$ is any real number$\}$ or $\mathbb{R}$. ∎

Had we continued to solve the equation in Example 8 by subtracting $8x$ from both sides of the equation, we would obtain

$$8x + 14 - 8x = 8x + 14 - 8x$$
$$14 = 14$$

The statement $14 = 14$ is true for all real numbers x, so the solution set of the original equation is all real numbers.

Quick ✔

26. Identify the three classifications of equations. Explain what each classification means.

In Problems 27–30, solve the equation and state whether it is an identity, contradiction, or conditional equation.

27. $4(x + 2) = 4x + 2$

28. $3(x - 2) - 2x - 6 + x$

29. $-4x + 2 + x + 1 = -4(x + 2) + 11$

30. $-3(z + 1) + 2(z - 3) = z + 6 - 2z - 15$

Work Smart: Study Skills

Selected problems in the exercise sets are identified by a ⊚ symbol. For extra help, view the worked solutions to these problems on the book's CD Lecture Series.

1.1 EXERCISES

MyMathLab
Powered by CourseCompass™ and MathXL™

 Math XL
PRACTICE

WATCH

DOWNLOAD

READ

REVIEW

1–30. are the **Quick ✔**s *that follow each* **EXAMPLE**

Building Skills

In Problems 31–36, determine which of the numbers are solutions to the given equation. See Objective 1.

31. $8x - 10 = 6$; $x = -2, x = 1, x = 2$

32. $-4x - 3 = -15$; $x = -2, x = 1, x = 3$

33. $5m - 3 = -3m + 5$; $m = -2, m = 1, m = 3$

34. $6x + 1 = -2x + 9$; $x = -2, x = 1, x = 4$

⊚**35.** $4(x - 1) = 3x + 1$; $x = -1, x = 2, x = 5$

36. $3(t + 1) - t = 4t + 9$; $t = -3, t = -1, t = 2$

In Problems 37–58, solve each linear equation. Be sure to verify your solution. See Objective 2.

37. $3x + 1 = 7$

38. $8x - 6 = 18$

39. $5x + 4 = 14$

40. $-6x - 5 = 13$

41. $4z + 3 = 2$

42. $8y + 3 = 5$

43. $-3w + 2w + 5 = -4$

44. $-7t - 3 + 5t = 11$

45. $3m + 4 = 2m - 5$

46. $-5z + 3 = -3z + 1$

⊚**47.** $5x + 2 - 2x + 3 = 7x + 2 - x + 5$

48. $-6x + 2 + 2x + 9 + x = 5x + 10 - 6x + 11$

49. $3(x + 2) = -6$

50. $4(z - 2) = 12$

51. $\dfrac{4y}{5} - \dfrac{14}{15} = \dfrac{y}{3}$

52. $\dfrac{3x}{2} + \dfrac{x}{6} = -\dfrac{5}{3}$

53. $\dfrac{4x + 3}{9} - \dfrac{2x + 1}{2} = \dfrac{1}{6}$

54. $\dfrac{2x + 1}{3} - \dfrac{6x - 1}{4} = -\dfrac{5}{12}$

55. $0.5x - 3.2 = -1.7$

56. $0.3z + 0.8 = -0.1$

57. $0.14x + 2.23 = 0.09x + 1.98$

58. $0.12y - 5.26 = 0.05y + 1.25$

In Problems 59–74, solve the equation. Identify each equation as an identity, contradiction, or conditional equation. Be sure to verify your solution. See Objective 3.

59. $4(x + 1) = 4x$

60. $5(s + 3) = 3s + 2s$

61. $4m + 1 - 6m = 2(m + 3) - 4m$

62. $10(x - 1) - 4x = 2x - 1 + 4(x + 1)$

63. $2(y + 1) - 3(y - 2) = 5y + 8 - 6y$

64. $8(w + 2) - 3w = 7(w + 2) + 2(1 - w)$

65. $\dfrac{x}{4} + \dfrac{3x}{10} = -\dfrac{33}{20}$

66. $\dfrac{z - 2}{4} + \dfrac{2z - 3}{6} = 7$

67. $3p - \dfrac{p}{4} = \dfrac{11p}{4} + 1$

68. $\dfrac{r}{2} + 2(r - 1) = \dfrac{5r}{2} + 4$

69. $\dfrac{2x + 1}{2} - \dfrac{x + 1}{5} = \dfrac{23}{10}$

70. $\dfrac{3x + 1}{4} - \dfrac{7x - 4}{2} = \dfrac{26}{3}$

71. $0.4(z + 1) - 0.7z = -0.1z + 0.7 - 0.2z - 0.3$

72. $0.9(z - 3) - 0.2(z - 5) = 0.4(z + 1) + 0.3z - 2.1$

73. $\dfrac{1}{3}(2x - 3) + 2 = \dfrac{5}{6}(x + 3) - \dfrac{11}{12}$

74. $\dfrac{4}{5}(y - 4) + 3 = \dfrac{2}{3}(y + 1) + \dfrac{4}{15}$

Mixed Practice

In Problems 75–90, solve each linear equation and verify the solution. State whether the equation is an identity, contradiction, or a conditional equation.

75. $7y - 8 = -7$ **76.** $4y + 5 = 7$

77. $4a + 3 - 2a + 4 = 5a - 7 + a$

78. $-5x + 5 + 3x + 7 = 5x - 6 + x + 12$

79. $4(p + 3) = 3(p + 2) + p + 18$

80. $7(x + 2) = 5(x - 2) + 2(x + 12)$

81. $4b - 3(b + 1) - b = 5(b - 1) - 5b$

82. $13z - 8(z + 1) = 2(z - 3) + 3z$

83. $\dfrac{m + 1}{4} + \dfrac{5}{6} = \dfrac{2m - 1}{12}$

84. $\dfrac{z - 4}{6} - \dfrac{2z + 1}{9} = \dfrac{1}{3}$

85. $0.3x - 1.3 = 0.5x - 0.7$

86. $-0.8y + 0.3 = 0.2y - 3.7$

87. $-0.8(x + 1) = 0.2(x + 4)$

88. $0.5(x + 3) = 0.2(x - 6)$

89. $\dfrac{1}{4}(x - 4) + 3 = \dfrac{1}{3}(2x + 6) - \dfrac{5}{6}$

90. $\dfrac{1}{5}(2a - 5) - 4 = \dfrac{1}{2}(a + 4) - \dfrac{7}{10}$

Applying the Concepts

91. Find a such that the solution set of $ax + 3 = 15$ is $\{-3\}$.

92. Find a such that the solution set of $ax + 6 = 20$ is $\{7\}$.

93. Find a such that the solution set of $a(x - 1) = 3(x - 1)$ is the set of all real numbers.

94. Find a such that the solution set of $ax + 3 = 2x + 3(x + 1)$ is the set of all real numbers.

In Section R.5 we introduced the domain of a variable. The domain of a variable is the set of all values that a variable may assume. Recall that division by zero is not defined, so any value of the variable that results in division by zero must be excluded from the domain. In Problems 95–100, determine which values of the variable must be excluded from the domain.

95. $\dfrac{5}{2x + 1}$ **96.** $\dfrac{-3}{5x + 8}$

97. $\dfrac{3x + 7}{4x - 3}$ **98.** $\dfrac{2x}{3x + 1}$

99. $\dfrac{6x - 2}{3(x + 1) - 6}$ **100.** $\dfrac{-2x + 7}{4(x - 3) + 2}$

101. Interest Suppose you have a credit card debt of $2000. Last month, the bank charged you $25 interest on the debt. The solution to the equation $25 = \dfrac{2000}{12} \cdot r$ represents the annual interest rate on the credit card, r. Find the annual interest rate on the credit card.

102. How Much Do I Make? Last week, before taxes, you earned $539 after working 26 hours at your regular hourly rate and 6 hours at time-and-a-half. The solution to the equation $26x + 9x = 539$ represents your regular hourly rate, x. Determine your regular hourly rate.

103. Paying Your Taxes You are single and just determined that you paid $3727.50 in federal income taxes in 2008. The solution to the equation $3727.50 = 0.15(x - 8025) + 802.50$ represents the amount x that you earned in 2008. Determine how much you earned in 2008. (SOURCE: *Internal Revenue Service*)

104. Paying Your Taxes You are married and just determined that you paid $10,187.50 in federal income taxes in 2008. The solution to the equation $10,187.50 = 0.25(x - 65,100) + 8962.50$ represents the amount x that you and your spouse earned in 2008. Determine how much you and your spouse earned in 2008. (SOURCE: *Internal Revenue Service*)

Explaining the Concepts

105. Explain the difference between $4(x + 1) - 2$ and $4(x + 1) = 2$. In general, what is the difference between an algebraic expression and an equation?

106. Explain the difference between the directions "solve" and "simplify."

107. Make up a linear equation that has one solution. Make up a linear equation that has no solution. Make up a linear equation that is an identity. Comment on the differences and similarities in making up each equation.

1.4 Linear Inequalities in One Variable

OBJECTIVES

1. Represent Inequalities Using the Real Number Line and Interval Notation
2. Understand the Properties of Inequalities
3. Solve Linear Inequalities
4. Solve Problems Involving Linear Inequalities

Preparing for Linear Inequalities in One Variable

Before getting started, take the following readiness quiz. If you get a problem wrong, go back to the section cited and review the material.

In Problems P1–P4, replace the question mark by $<$, $>$, or $=$ to make the statement true. [Section R.2, pp. 16–17]

P1. $3 ? 6$ **P2.** $-3 ? -6$ **P3.** $\dfrac{1}{2} ? 0.5$ **P4.** $\dfrac{2}{3} ? \dfrac{3}{5}$

P5. *True or False:* The inequality $\geq$ is called a strict inequality. [Section R.2, p. 17]

P6. Use set-builder notation to represent the set of all digits that are divisible by 3. [Section R.2, pp. 8–9]

An **inequality in one variable** is a statement involving two expressions, at least one containing the variable, separated by one of the inequality symbols $<$, $\leq$, $>$, or $\geq$. To **solve an inequality** means to find all values of the variable for which the statement is true. These values are called **solutions** of the inequality. The set of all solutions is called the **solution set.**

> **DEFINITION**
>
> A **linear inequality in one variable** is an inequality that can be written in the form
>
> $$ax + b < c \quad \text{or} \quad ax + b \leq c \quad \text{or} \quad ax + b > c \quad \text{or} \quad ax + b \geq c$$
>
> where a, b, and c are real numbers and $a \neq 0$.

For example, the following are all linear incqualities involving one variable:

$$x - 4 > 9 \qquad 5x - 1 \leq 14 \qquad 8z < 0 \qquad 5x - 1 \geq 3x + 8$$

Before we discuss methods for solving linear inequalities, we will present three ways of representing the solution set. One of the methods for representing the solution set is through set-builder notation—something we are already familiar with. However, set-builder notation can be somewhat cumbersome, so we introduce a more streamlined way to represent a solution set to an inequality using *interval notation*. Finally, because we often like to visualize solution sets, we present a method for graphing the solution set on a real number line.

1 Represent Inequalities Using the Real Number Line and Interval Notation

Suppose that a and b are two real numbers and $a < b$. We shall use the notation

$$a < x < b$$

Work Smart

Remember that the inequalities $<$ and $>$ are called strict inequalities, while $\leq$ and $\geq$ are called nonstrict inequalities.

to mean that x is a number *between* a and b. So, the expression $a < x < b$ is equivalent to the two inequalities $a < x$ and $x < b$. Similarly, the expression $a \leq x \leq b$ is equivalent to the two inequalities $a \leq x$ and $x \leq b$. We define $a \leq x < b$ and $a < x \leq b$ similarly. Expressions such as $-2 < x < 5$ or $x \geq 5$ are said to be in **inequality notation.**

While the expression $3 \geq x \geq 2$ is technically correct, it is not the preferred way to write an inequality. For ease of reading, we prefer that the numbers in the inequality go from smaller values to larger values. So, we would write $3 \geq x \geq 2$ as $2 \leq x \leq 3$.

A statement such as $3 \leq x \leq 1$ is false because there is no number x for which $3 \leq x$ and $x \leq 1$. We also never mix inequalities as in $2 \leq x \geq 3$.

In addition to representing inequalities using inequality notation, we can use *interval notation*.

Preparing for...Answers P1. $<$ **P2.** $>$
P3. $=$ **P4.** $>$ **P5.** False **P6.** $\{x \mid x$ is a digit that is divisible by 3$\}$

DEFINITION INTERVAL NOTATION

Let a and b represent two real numbers with $a < b$.

A **closed interval,** denoted by $[a, b]$, consists of all real numbers x for which $a \leq x \leq b$.

An **open interval,** denoted by (a, b), consists of all real numbers x for which $a < x < b$.

The **half-open,** or **half-closed, intervals** are $(a, b]$, consisting of all real numbers x for which $a < x \leq b$, and $[a, b)$, consisting of all real numbers x for which $a \leq x < b$.

In each of these definitions, a is called the **left endpoint** and b is called the **right endpoint** of the interval.

The symbol ∞ (read as "infinity") is not a real number, but a notational device used to indicate unboundedness in the positive direction. In other words, the symbol ∞ means that there is no right endpoint on the inequality. The symbol $-\infty$ (read as "minus infinity" or "negative infinity") also is not a real number, but a notational device used to indicate unboundedness in the negative direction. The symbol $-\infty$ means that there is no left endpoint on the inequality. Using the symbols ∞ and $-\infty$, we can define five other kinds of intervals.

Work Smart

The symbols ∞ and $-\infty$ are never included as endpoints because they are not real numbers. So, we use parentheses when $-\infty$ or ∞ are endpoints.

INTERVALS INCLUDING ∞

$[a, \infty)$	consists of all real numbers x for which $x \geq a$
(a, ∞)	consists of all real numbers x for which $x > a$
$(-\infty, a]$	consists of all real numbers x for which $x \leq a$
$(-\infty, a)$	consists of all real numbers x for which $x < a$
$(-\infty, \infty)$	consists of all real numbers x (or $-\infty < x < \infty$)

Figure 9
$x > 3$

Figure 10
$x \geq 3$

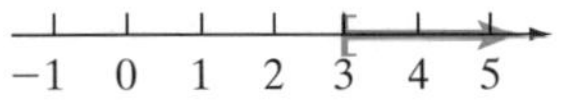

In addition to representing inequalities using interval notation, we can represent inequalities using a graph on the real number line. The inequality $x > 3$ or the interval $(3, \infty)$ consists of all numbers x that lie to the right of 3 on the real number line. We can represent these values by shading the real number line to the right of 3. To indicate that 3 is not included in the set, we will agree to use a parenthesis on the endpoint. See Figure 9.

To represent the inequality $x \geq 3$ or the interval $[3, \infty)$ graphically, we also shade to the right of 3, but this time we use a bracket on the endpoint to indicate that 3 is included in the set. See Figure 10.

Table 7 summarizes interval notation, inequality notation, and their graphs.

Table 7		
Interval Notation	Inequality Notation	Graph
The open interval (a, b)	$\{x \mid a < x < b\}$	
The closed interval $[a, b]$	$\{x \mid a \leq x \leq b\}$	
The half-open interval $[a, b)$	$\{x \mid a \leq x < b\}$	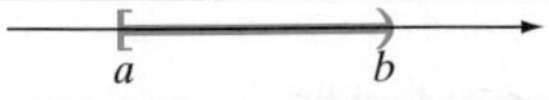
The half-open interval $(a, b]$	$\{x \mid a < x \leq b\}$	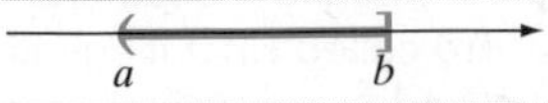
The interval $[a, \infty)$	$\{x \mid x \geq a\}$	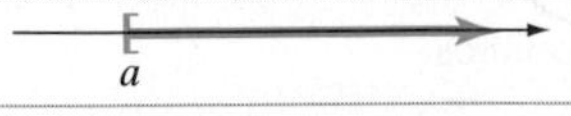
The interval (a, ∞)	$\{x \mid x > a\}$	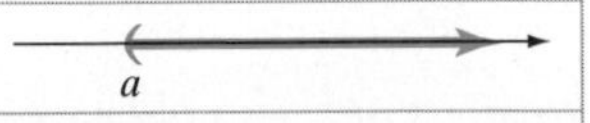
The interval $(-\infty, a]$	$\{x \mid x \leq a\}$	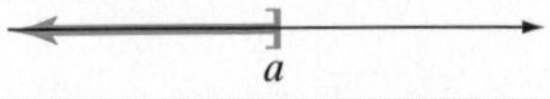
The interval $(-\infty, a)$	$\{x \mid x < a\}$	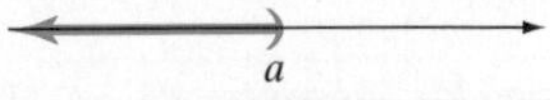
The interval $(-\infty, \infty)$	$\{x \mid x \text{ is a real number}\}$	

EXAMPLE 1 Using Interval Notation and Graphing Inequalities

Write each inequality using interval notation. Graph the inequality.

(a) $-2 \le x \le 4$ **(b)** $1 < x \le 5$

Solution

(a) $-2 \le x \le 4$ describes all numbers x between -2 and 4, inclusive. In interval notation, we write $[-2, 4]$. To graph $-2 \le x \le 4$, we place brackets at -2 and 4 and shade in between. See Figure 11.

Figure 11

(b) $1 < x \le 5$ describes all numbers x greater than 1 and less than or equal to 5. In interval notation, we write $(1, 5]$. To graph $1 < x \le 5$, we place a parenthesis at 1 and a bracket at 5 and shade in between. See Figure 12.

Figure 12

EXAMPLE 2 Using Interval Notation and Graphing Inequalities

Write each inequality using interval notation. Graph the inequality.

(a) $x < 2$ **(b)** $x \ge -3$

Solution

(a) $x < 2$ describes all numbers x less than 2. In interval notation, we write $(-\infty, 2)$. To graph $x < 2$, we place a parenthesis at 2 and then shade to the left. See Figure 13.

Figure 13

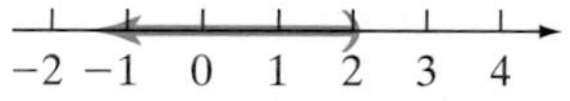

(b) $x \ge -3$ describes all numbers x greater than or equal to -3. In interval notation, we write $[-3, \infty)$. To graph $x \ge -3$, we place a bracket at -3 and then shade to the right. See Figure 14.

Figure 14

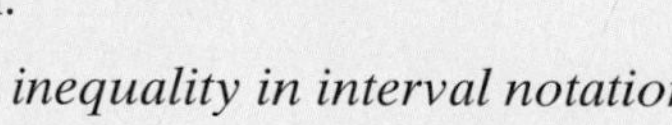

Quick ✔

1. A(n) _____ _____, denoted $[a, b]$, consists of all real numbers x for which $a \le x \le b$.

2. In the interval (a, b), a is called the ___ _____ and b is called the _____ _____ of the interval.

In Problems 3–6, write each inequality in interval notation. Graph the inequality.

3. $-3 \le x \le 2$ **4.** $3 \le x < 6$

5. $x \le 3$ **6.** $\dfrac{1}{2} < x < \dfrac{7}{2}$

EXAMPLE 3 Using Inequality Notation and Graphing Inequalities

Write each interval in inequality notation involving x. Graph the inequality.

    (a) $[-2, 4)$ **(b)** $(1, 5)$

Solution

    (a) The interval $[-2, 4)$ consists of all numbers x for which $-2 \leq x < 4$. See Figure 15 for the graph.

    (b) The interval $(1, 5)$ consists of all numbers x for which $1 < x < 5$. See Figure 16 for the graph.

Figure 15   **Figure 16**

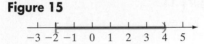

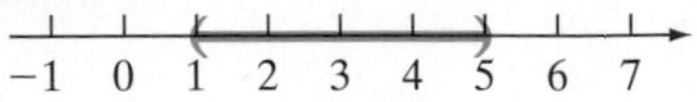

EXAMPLE 4 Using Inequality Notation and Graphing Inequalities

Write each interval in inequality notation involving x. Graph the inequality.

    (a) $\left[\dfrac{3}{2}, \infty \right)$ **(b)** $(-\infty, 1)$

Solution

    (a) The interval $\left[\dfrac{3}{2}, \infty \right)$ consists of all numbers x for which $x \geq \dfrac{3}{2}$.

        See Figure 17 for the graph.

    (b) The interval $(-\infty, 1)$ consists of all numbers x for which $x < 1$. See Figure 18 for the graph.

Figure 17   **Figure 18**

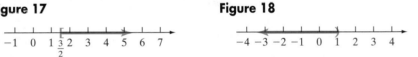

> **Quick** ✔ *In Problems 7–10, write each interval as an inequality. Graph the inequality.*
>
> **7.** $(0, 5]$ **8.** $(-6, 0)$
>
> **9.** $(5, \infty)$ **10.** $\left(-\infty, \dfrac{8}{3} \right]$

2 Understand the Properties of Inequalities

Consider the inequality $2 < 5$. If we add 3 to both sides of the inequality, the expression on the left becomes 5 and the expression on the right becomes 8. Since $5 < 8$, we can see that adding the same quantity to both sides of an inequality does not change the sense, or direction, of the inequality. This result is called the *Addition Property of Inequalities*.

In Words

The Addition Property states that the direction of the inequality does not change when the same quantity is added to each side of the inequality.

ADDITION PROPERTY OF INEQUALITIES

For real numbers a, b, and c,

$$\text{If} \quad a < b, \quad \text{then} \quad a + c < b + c$$
$$\text{If} \quad a > b, \quad \text{then} \quad a + c > b + c$$

For example, since $2 < 5$, we have that $2 + 4 < 5 + 4$ or $6 < 9$. In addition, since $3 > -1$, we have that $3 + (-2) > -1 + (-2)$ or $1 > -3$.

Because $a - b$ is equivalent to $a + (-b)$, the Addition Property of Inequalities can also be used to subtract a real number from each side of an inequality without changing the direction of the inequality.

We've seen what happens when we add a real number to both sides of an inequality. What happens when we multiply both sides by a nonzero constant? Let's see.

Consider the inequality $3 < 5$. Multiply both sides of the inequality by 2. The expression on the left side of the inequality becomes $2(3) = 6$ and the expression on the right becomes $2(5) = 10$. Certainly $6 < 10$, so the direction of the inequality did not change.

Again consider the inequality $3 < 5$. Now multiply both sides of the inequality by -2. The expression on the left side of the inequality becomes $-2(3) = -6$ and the expression on the right becomes $-2(5) = -10$. Because $-6 > -10$ we see that the direction of the inequality is reversed.

These results are true in general and lead us to the *Multiplication Properties of Inequalities*.

In Words

The Multiplication Property states that if both sides of an inequality are multiplied by a positive real number, the direction of the inequality is unchanged. If both sides of an inequality are multiplied by a negative real number, the direction of the inequality is reversed.

MULTIPLICATION PROPERTIES OF INEQUALITIES

Let a, b, and c be real numbers.

$$\text{If } a < b \text{ and if } c > 0, \text{ then } ac < bc$$
$$\text{If } a > b \text{ and if } c > 0, \text{ then } ac > bc$$

$$\text{If } a < b \text{ and if } c < 0, \text{ then } ac > bc$$
$$\text{If } a > b \text{ and if } c < 0, \text{ then } ac < bc$$

Because the quotient $\dfrac{a}{b}$ is equivalent to $a \cdot \dfrac{1}{b}$, the Multiplication Properties of Inequalities can also be used to divide both sides of an inequality by a nonzero real number.

Quick ✔

11. Write the inequality that results by adding 5 to each side of the inequality $4 < 7$. What property of inequalities does this illustrate?

12. Write the inequality that results by subtracting 3 from each side of the inequality $x + 3 > -6$. What property of inequalities does this illustrate?

13. Write the inequality that results by multiplying both sides of the inequality $2 < 8$ by $\dfrac{1}{2}$. What property of inequalities does this illustrate?

14. Write the inequality that results by dividing both sides of the inequality $-6 < 9$ by -3. What property of inequalities does this illustrate?

15. Write the inequality that results by dividing both sides of the inequality $5x < 30$ by 5. What property of inequalities does this illustrate?

⌐3 Solve Linear Inequalities

Two inequalities that have exactly the same solution set are called **equivalent inequalities.** As with equations, one method for solving a linear inequality is to replace it by a series of equivalent inequalities until an inequality with an obvious solution, such as $x > 2$, is obtained. We obtain equivalent inequalities by applying some of the same operations as those used to find equivalent equations. The Addition Property and Multiplication Properties form the basis for the procedures.

Although not essential, it is easier to read an inequality if the variable is placed on the left side and the constant on the right. If the variable does end up on the right side of the inequality, we can rewrite it with the variable on the left side using the fact that

In Words

If the sides of an inequality are interchanged, the direction of the inequality reverses.

$$a < x \qquad \text{is equivalent to} \qquad x > a$$
$$\text{and}$$
$$a > x \qquad \text{is equivalent to} \qquad x < a$$

EXAMPLE 5 How to Solve a Linear Inequality

Solve the inequality $3x - 2 > 13$. Graph the solution set.

Step-by-Step Solution

The goal in solving any linear inequality is to get the variable by itself with a coefficient of 1.

Step 1: Isolate the term containing the variable.	Add 2 to both sides (Addition Property):	$3x - 2 > 13$ $3x - 2 + 2 > 13 + 2$ $3x > 15$
Step 2: Get a coefficient of 1 on the variable.	Divide both sides by 3 (Multiplication Property):	$\dfrac{3x}{3} > \dfrac{15}{3}$ $x > 5$

Figure 19

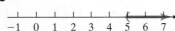

The solution using set-builder notation is $\{x \mid x > 5\}$. The solution using interval notation is $(5, \infty)$. Figure 19 shows the graph of the solution set. ∎

> **Quick** ✔ *In Problems 16–19, solve each linear inequality. Express your solution using set-builder notation and interval notation. Graph the solution set.*
>
> **16.** $x + 3 > 5$
>
> **17.** $\dfrac{1}{3}x \leq 2$
>
> **18.** $4x - 3 < 13$
>
> **19.** $-2x + 1 \leq 13$

EXAMPLE 6 Solving Linear Inequalities

Solve the inequality: $x - 4 \geq 5x + 12$

Solution

$$x - 4 \geq 5x + 12$$

$$\text{Add 4 to both sides:} \quad x - 4 + 4 \geq 5x + 12 + 4$$

$$x \geq 5x + 16$$

$$\text{Subtract } 5x \text{ from both sides:} \quad x - 5x \geq 5x + 16 - 5x$$

$$-4x \geq 16$$

$$\text{Divide both sides by } -4. \text{ Don't forget to} \atop \text{change the direction of the inequality:} \quad \dfrac{-4x}{-4} \leq \dfrac{16}{-4}$$

$$x \leq -4$$

Figure 20

The solution using set-builder notation is $\{x \mid x \leq -4\}$. The solution using interval notation is $(-\infty, -4]$. See Figure 20 for the graph of the solution set. ∎

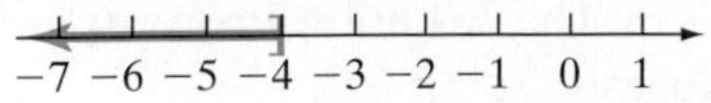

> **Quick** ✔ *In Problems 20–22, solve each linear inequality. Express your solution using set-builder notation and interval notation. Graph the solution set.*
>
> **20.** $3x + 1 > x - 5$
>
> **21.** $-2x + 1 \leq 3x + 11$
>
> **22.** $-5x + 12 < x - 3$

EXAMPLE 7 Solving Linear Inequalities

Solve the inequality: $3(x - 1) + 2x < 6x + 3$

Solution

$$3(x - 1) + 2x < 6x + 3$$

Distribute the 3: $3x - 3 + 2x < 6x + 3$

Combine like terms: $5x - 3 < 6x + 3$

Add 3 to both sides: $5x - 3 + 3 < 6x + 3 + 3$

$$5x < 6x + 6$$

Subtract 6x from both sides: $5x - 6x < 6x + 6 - 6x$

$$-x < 6$$

Multiply both sides of the inequality by -1: $(-1)(-x) > (-1)6$

$$x > -6$$

The solution using set-builder notation is $\{x \mid x > -6\}$. The solution using interval notation is $(-6, \infty)$. See Figure 21 for the graph of the solution set.

Figure 21

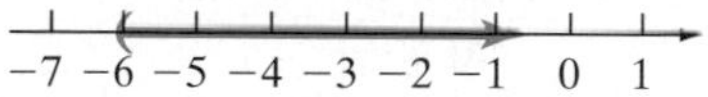

$$\begin{array}{ccccccccc} -7 & -6 & -5 & -4 & -3 & -2 & -1 & 0 & 1 \end{array}$$

Quick ✔ *In Problems 23–25, solve each linear inequality. Express your solution using set-builder notation and interval notation. Graph the solution set.*

23. $4(x - 2) < 3x - 4$

24. $-2(x + 1) \geq 4(x + 3)$

25. $7 - 2(x + 1) \leq 3(x - 5)$

EXAMPLE 8 Solving Linear Inequalities Involving Fractions

Solve the inequality: $\dfrac{2x + 1}{3} > \dfrac{x - 2}{2}$

Solution

We begin by rewriting the linear inequality without fractions by multiplying both sides of the inequality by 6, the Least Common Denominator.

$$6 \cdot \left(\frac{2x + 1}{3} \right) > 6 \cdot \left(\frac{x - 2}{2} \right)$$

$$2(2x + 1) > 3(x - 2)$$

Distribute: $4x + 2 > 3x - 6$

Subtract 2 from both sides: $4x + 2 - 2 > 3x - 6 - 2$

$$4x > 3x - 8$$

Subtract 3x from both sides: $4x - 3x > 3x - 8 - 3x$

$$x > -8$$

The solution using set-builder notation is $\{x \mid x > -8\}$. The solution using interval notation is $(-8, \infty)$. See Figure 22 for the graph of the solution set.

Figure 22

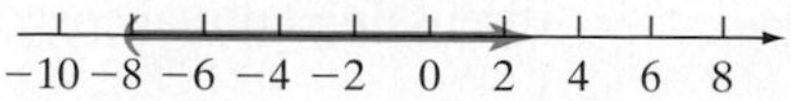

$$\begin{array}{cccccccc} -10 & -8 & -6 & -4 & -2 & 0 & 2 & 4 & 6 & 8 \end{array}$$

Quick ✔ *In Problems 26–28, solve each linear inequality. Express your solution using set-builder notation and interval notation. Graph the solution set.*

26. $\dfrac{3x + 1}{5} \geq 2$

27. $\dfrac{2}{5} x + \dfrac{3}{10} < \dfrac{1}{2}$

28. $\dfrac{1}{2}(x + 3) > \dfrac{1}{3}(x - 4)$

4 Solve Problems Involving Linear Inequalities

When you are confronted with a word problem, one of the first things that you need to do is look for key words that tip you off as to the type of word problem that it is. There are certain phrases that frequently occur in problems that lead to linear inequalities. We list some of these phrases for you in Table 8.

<table>
<tr><td colspan="4" align="center">Table 8</td></tr>
<tr><td>Phrase</td><td>Inequality</td><td>Phrase</td><td>Inequality</td></tr>
<tr><td>At least</td><td>$\geq$</td><td>No more than</td><td>$\leq$</td></tr>
<tr><td>No less than</td><td>$\geq$</td><td>At most</td><td>$\leq$</td></tr>
<tr><td>More than</td><td>$>$</td><td>Fewer than</td><td>$<$</td></tr>
<tr><td>Greater than</td><td>$>$</td><td>Less than</td><td>$<$</td></tr>
</table>

When solving applications involving linear inequalities, we use the same steps for setting up applied problems that we introduced in Section 1.2 on page 61.

EXAMPLE 9 Comparing Credit Cards

Chase Bank has offered you two different credit card options. The Southwest rewards card charges an annual fee of $39 plus 12.90% simple interest on all outstanding balances. The Marriott rewards card charges an annual fee of $30 plus 14.15% simple interest on all outstanding balances. What annual balance results in the Southwest card costing less than the Marriott card? (SOURCE: *chase.com*)

Solution

Step 1: Identify We want to know the credit card balance for which the Southwest credit card costs less than the Marriott rewards card. The phrase "costs less" implies that this is an inequality problem.

Step 2: Name Let b represent the credit card balance on each card.

Step 3: Translate Each card charges an annual fee plus simple interest. So, for each card the cost will be "annual fee + interest."

Recall from Section 1.2 that simple interest is found using the formula

$$I = Prt$$

where I is the interest charged, P is the balance on the credit card, r is the annual interest rate, and t is time.

In this problem, we let b represent the credit card balance. The annual interest rate r will either be 0.129 (for Southwest) or 0.1415 (for Marriott). Because we are discussing annual cost, we have that $t = 1$.

Since we want to know what balance results in Southwest costing less than Marriott, we have the following inequality:

Southwest Credit Card Cost $<$ Marriott Credit Card Cost

Annual Fee for Southwest		Interest Charged for Southwest		Annual Fee for Marriott		Interest Charged for Marriott	
39	$+$	$0.129b$	$<$	30	$+$	$0.1415b$	The Model

Step 4: Solve Solve the inequality for b.

$$39 + 0.129b < 30 + 0.1415b$$

Subtract 39 from both sides: $\qquad 0.129b < -9 + 0.1415b$

Subtract $0.1415b$ from both sides: $\qquad -0.0125b < -9$

Divide both sides by -0.0125.
Don't forget to reverse the
inequality symbol: $\qquad\qquad b > 720$

Step 5: Check If the balance is $720, then the annual cost for Southwest is $39 + 0.129(720) = \$131.88$. The annual cost for Marriott is $30 + 0.1415(720) = \$131.88$. For a balance greater than \$720, say \$750, the annual cost for Southwest is $39 + 0.129(750) = \$135.75$. The annual cost for Marriott is $30 + 0.1415(750) = \$136.13$.

Step 6: Answer the Question If the annual balance is greater than \$720, then the Southwest card offers a better deal than the Marriott card. ∎

Quick ✔

29. You have just received two credit card applications in the mail. The card from Bank A has an annual fee of $25 and charges 9.9% simple interest. The card from Bank B has no annual fee, but charges 14.9% simple interest. For what annual balance will the card from Bank A cost less than the card from Bank B?

30. Suppose the daily revenue from selling x boxes of candy is given by the equation $R = 12x$. The daily cost of operating the store and making the candy is given by the equation $C = 8x + 96$. For how many boxes of candy will revenue exceed costs? That is, solve $R > C$.

1.4 EXERCISES

PRACTICE   WATCH   DOWNLOAD   READ   REVIEW

1–30. are the Quick ✔*s that follow each* EXAMPLE

Building Skills

In Problems 31–38, write each inequality using interval notation. Graph the inequality. See Objective 1.

31. $2 \le x \le 10$ **32.** $1 < x < 7$

33. $-4 \le x < 0$ **34.** $-8 < x \le 1$

35. $x \ge 6$ **36.** $x < 0$

37. $x < \dfrac{3}{2}$ **38.** $x \ge -\dfrac{5}{2}$

In Problems 39–46, write each interval as an inequality involving x. Graph each inequality. See Objective 1.

39. $(1, 8)$ **40.** $[-2, 3]$

41. $(-5, 1]$ **42.** $[1, 4)$

43. $(-\infty, 5)$ **44.** $(2, \infty)$

45. $[3, \infty)$ **46.** $(-\infty, 8]$

In Problems 47–54, fill in the blank with the correct inequality symbol. State which property of inequalities is being utilized. See Objective 2.

47. If $x - 3 < 7$, then x ___ 10.

48. If $2x - 5 > 6$, then $2x$ ___ 11.

49. If $\frac{1}{3}x > 5$, then x ___ 15.

50. If $4x > 36$, then x ___ 9.

51. If $2x + 5 \le 9$, then $2x$ ___ 4.

52. If $\frac{2}{5}x + 6 \le 8$, then $\frac{2}{5}x$ ___ 2.

53. If $-2x \ge 10$, then x ___ -5.

54. If $-6x < 30$, then x ___ -5.

In Problems 55–92, solve each linear inequality. Express your solution using set-builder notation and interval notation. Graph the solution set. See Objective 3.

55. $x - 4 \le 2$

56. $x + 6 < 9$

57. $6x < 24$

58. $4x \ge 20$

59. $-7x < 21$

60. $-8x > 32$

61. $\frac{4}{15}x > \frac{8}{5}$

62. $\frac{3}{8}x < \frac{9}{16}$

63. $3x + 2 > 11$

64. $5x - 4 \le 16$

65. $-3x + 1 > 13$

66. $-6x - 5 < 13$

67. $6x + 5 \le 3x + 2$

68. $8x + 3 \ge 5x - 9$

69. $-3x + 1 < 2x + 11$

70. $3x + 4 \ge 5x - 8$

71. $3(x - 3) < 2(x + 4)$

72. $3(x - 2) + 5 > 4(x + 1) + x$

73. $4(x + 1) - 2x \ge 5(x - 2) + 2$

74. $-3(x + 4) + 5x < 4(x + 3) - 14$

75. $0.5x + 4 \le 0.2x - 5$

76. $2.3x - 1.2 > 1.8x + 0.4$

77. $\frac{3x + 1}{4} < \frac{1}{2}$

78. $\frac{2x - 3}{3} > \frac{4}{3}$

79. $\frac{1}{2}(x - 4) > \frac{3}{4}(2x + 1)$

80. $\frac{1}{3}(3x + 5) < \frac{1}{6}(x + 4)$

81. $\frac{3}{5} - x > \frac{5}{3}$

82. $\frac{2}{3} - \frac{5}{6}x > 2$

83. $-5(x - 3) \ge 3[4 - (x + 4)]$

84. $-3(2x + 1) \le 2[3x - 2(x - 5)]$

85. $4(3x - 1) - 5(x + 4) \ge 3[2 - (x + 3)] - 6x$

86. $7(x + 2) - 4(2x + 3) < -2[5x - 2(x + 3)] + 7x$

87. $\frac{2}{3}(4x - 1) - \frac{4}{9}(x - 4) > \frac{5}{12}(2x + 3)$

88. $\frac{5}{6}(3x - 2) - \frac{2}{3}(4x - 1) < -\frac{2}{9}(2x + 5)$

89. $\frac{4x - 3}{3} < 3$

90. $\frac{2}{5}x + \frac{3}{10} < \frac{1}{2}$

91. $\frac{2}{3}x < \frac{1}{4}(2x + 3)$

92. $\frac{x}{12} \ge \frac{x}{2} - \frac{2x + 1}{4}$

Mixed Practice

In Problems 93–106, solve each linear inequality. Express your solution using set-builder notation and interval notation. Graph the solution set.

93. $y + 8 > -7$

94. $y - 5 \ge 7$

95. $-3a \le -21$

96. $-5x < 30$

97. $13x - 5 > 10x - 6$

98. $4x + 3 \ge -6x - 2$

99. $4(x + 2) \le 3(x - 2)$

100. $5(y + 7) < 6(y + 4)$

101. $3(4 - 3x) > 6 - 5x$

102. $2(5 - x) - 3 \le 4 - 5x$

103. $2[4 - 3(x + 1)] \le -4x + 8$

104. $3[1 + 2(x - 4)] \ge 3x + 3$

105. $\dfrac{x}{2} + \dfrac{3}{4} \ge \dfrac{3}{8}$

106. $\dfrac{b}{3} + \dfrac{5}{6} < \dfrac{11}{12}$

Applying the Concepts

107. Find the set of all x such that the sum of twice x and 5 is at least 13.

108. Find the set of all x such that the difference between 3 times x and 2 is less than 7.

109. Find the set of all z such that the product of 4 and z minus 3 is no more than 9.

110. Find the set of all y such that the sum of twice y and 3 is greater than 13.

111. Computing Grades In order to earn an A in Mr. Ruffatto's Intermediate Algebra course, Jackie must earn at least 540 points. Thus far, Jackie has earned 90, 83, 95, and 90 points on her four exams. The final exam, which counts as 200 points, is rapidly approaching. How many points does Jackie need to earn on the final to earn an A in Mr. Ruffatto's class?

112. Computing Grades In order to earn an A in Mrs. Padilla's Intermediate Algebra course, Mark must obtain an average score of at least 90. On his first four exams Mark scored 94, 83, 88, and 92. The final exam counts as two test scores. What score does Mark need on the final to earn an A in Mrs. Padilla's class?

113. McDonald's Suppose that you have ordered one medium order of French Fries and one 16-ounce triple-thick chocolate shake from McDonald's. The fries have 22 grams of fat and the shake has 17 grams of fat. Each McDonald's hamburger has 10 grams of fat. How many hamburgers can you order and still keep the total fat content of the meal to no more than 69 grams? (SOURCE: *McDonald's Corporation*)

114. Burger King Suppose that you have ordered one medium onion ring and one 16-ounce chocolate shake from Burger King. The onion rings have 16 grams of fat and the shake has 8 grams of fat. Each cheeseburger has 21 grams of fat. How many cheeseburgers can you order and still keep the total fat content of the meal to no more than 87 grams? (SOURCE: *Burger King*)

115. Payload Restrictions An Airbus A320 has a maximum payload of 45,686 pounds. Suppose that on a flight from Chicago to New Orleans, United Airlines sold out the flight at 179 seats. Assuming that the average passenger weighs 150 pounds, determine the weight of the luggage and other cargo that the plane can carry. (SOURCE: *Airbus*)

116. Moving Trucks A 15-foot moving truck from Budget costs $39.95 per day plus $0.65 per mile. If your budget only allows for you to spend at most $125.75, what is the number of miles you can drive? (SOURCE: *Budget*)

117. Health Benefits The average monthly benefit B, in dollars, for individuals on disability is given by the equation $B = 19.25t + 585.72$, where t is the number of years since 1990. In what year will the monthly benefit B exceed $1000? That is, solve $B > 1000$.

118. Health Expenditures Total private health expenditures H, in billions of dollars, are given by the equation $H = 26t + 411$, where t is the number of years since 1990. In what year will total private health expenditures exceed $1 trillion ($1000 billion)? That is, solve $26t + 411 > 1000$.

119. Commissions Susan sells computer systems. Her annual base salary is $34,000. She also earns a commission of 1.2% on the sale price of all computer systems that she sells. For what value of the computer systems sold will Susan's annual salary be at least $100,000?

120. Commissions Al sells used cars for a Chevy dealer. His annual base salary is $24,300. He also earns a commission of 3% on the sale price of the cars that he sells. For what value of the cars sold will Al's annual salary be more than $60,000? If used cars at this particular dealership sell for an average of $15,000, how many cars does Al have to sell to meet his salary goal?

121. Supply and Demand The quantity demanded of custom monogrammed shirts is given by the equation $D = 1000 - 20p$. The quantity supplied of custom monogrammed shirts is given by the equation $S = -200 + 10p$, where p is the price of a shirt. For what prices will quantity supplied exceed quantity demanded, thereby resulting in a surplus of shirts? That is, solve $S > D$.

122. Supply and Demand The quantity supplied of digital cameras is given by the equation $S = -2800 + 13p$. The quantity demanded of digital cameras is given by the equation $D = 1800 - 12p$, where p is the price of a camera. For what prices will quantity demanded exceed quantity supplied, thereby resulting in a shortage of cameras? That is, solve $D > S$.

Extending the Concepts

123. Solve the linear inequality
$3(x + 2) + 2x > 5(x + 1)$.

124. Solve the linear inequality
$-3(x - 2) + 7x > 2(2x + 5)$.

Explaining the Concepts

125. Write a brief paragraph that explains the circumstances under which the direction, or sense, of an inequality changes.

126. Explain why the inequality $5 < x < 1$ is false.

127. Explain why we never mix inequalities as in $4 < x > 7$.

PUTTING THE CONCEPTS TOGETHER (Sections 1.1–1.4)

These problems cover important concepts from Sections 1.1 through 1.4. We designed these problems so that you can review the chapter so far and show your mastery of the concepts. Take time to work these problems before proceeding with the next section. The answers to these problems are located at the back of the text on page AN-4.

1. Determine which, if any, of the following are solutions to
$$5(2x - 3) + 1 = 2x - 6$$
   (a) $x = -3$ **(b)** $x = 1$

In Problems 2 and 3, solve the equation.

2. $3(2x - 1) + 6 = 5x - 2$

3. $\dfrac{7}{3}x + \dfrac{4}{5} = \dfrac{5x + 12}{15}$

Determine if the equation is an identity, a contradiction, or a conditional equation.

4. $5 - 2(x + 1) + 4x = 6(x + 1) - (3 + 4x)$

In Problems 5 and 6, translate the English statement into a mathematical statement. Do not solve the equation.

5. The difference of a number and 3 is two more than half the number.

6. The quotient of a number and 2 is less than the number increased by 5.

7. Mixture Two acid solutions are available to a chemist. One is a 20% nitric acid solution and the other is a 40% nitric acid solution. How much of each type of solution should be mixed together to form 16 liters of a 35% nitric acid solution?

8. Travel Two cars leave from the same location and travel in opposite directions along a straight road. One car travels 30 miles per hour while the other travels at 45 miles per hour. How long will it take the two cars to be 255 miles apart?

9. Solve $3x - 2y = 4$ for y.

10. Solve the formula $A = P + Prt$ for r.

11. The volume of a right circular cylinder is given by the formula $V = \pi r^2 h$, where r is the radius of the cylinder and h is the height of the cylinder.

   (a) Solve the formula for h.
   (b) Use the result from part (a) to find the height of a right circular cylinder with volume $V = 294\pi$ inches^3 and radius $r = 7$ inches.

12. Write the following inequalities in interval notation. Graph the inequality.

   (a) $x > -3$
   (b) $2 < x \le 5$

13. Write the interval in inequality notation involving x. Graph the inequality.

   (a) $(-\infty, -1.5]$
   (b) $(-3, 1]$

In Problems 14–16, solve the inequality and graph the solution set on a real number line.

14. $2x + 3 \le 4x - 9$

15. $-3 > 3x - (x + 5)$

16. $x - 9 \le x + 3(2 - x)$

17. Birthday Party A recreational center offers a children's birthday party for $75 plus $5 for each child. How many children can Logan invite to his birthday party if the budget for the party is no more than $125?

PART II: LINEAR EQUATIONS AND INEQUALITIES IN TWO VARIABLES

1.5 Rectangular Coordinates and Graphs of Equations

OBJECTIVES

1. Plot Points in the Rectangular Coordinate System
2. Determine Whether an Ordered Pair Is a Point on the Graph of an Equation
3. Graph an Equation Using the Point-Plotting Method
4. Identify the Intercepts from the Graph of an Equation
5. Interpret Graphs

Preparing for Rectangular Coordinates and Graphs of Equations

Before getting started, take this readiness quiz. If you get a problem wrong, go back to the section cited and review the material.

P1. Plot the following points on the real number line: $-2, 4, 0, \frac{1}{2}$. [Section R.2, pp. 15–16]

P2. Determine which of the following are solutions to the equation $3x - 5(x + 2) = 4$.
 (a) $x = 0$ **(b)** $x = -3$ **(c)** $x = -7$ [Section 1.1, pp. 48–49]

P3. Evaluate the expression $2x^2 - 3x + 1$ for the given values of the variable.
 (a) $x = 0$ **(b)** $x = 2$ **(c)** $x = -3$ [Section R.5, pp. 40–41]

P4. Solve the equation $3x + 2y = 8$ for y. [Section 1.3, pp. 73–76]

P5. Evaluate $|-4|$. [Section R.3, pp. 19–20]

⌐1 Plot Points in the Rectangular Coordinate System

Recall from Section R.2 that we locate a point on the real number line by assigning it a single real number, called the *coordinate of the point*. See *Preparing for* Problem P1. When we graph a point on the real number line, we are working in one dimension. When we wish to work in two dimensions, we locate a point using two real numbers.

We begin by drawing two real number lines that intersect at right (90°) angles. One of the real number lines is drawn horizontal, while the other is drawn vertical. We call the horizontal real number line the **x-axis,** and the vertical real number line is the **y-axis.** The point where the x-axis and y-axis intersect is called the **origin, O.** See Figure 23.

Figure 23

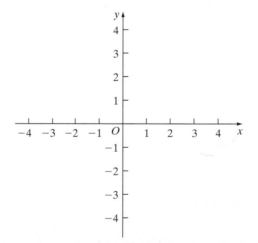

The origin O has a value of 0 on the x-axis and the y-axis. Points on the x-axis to the right of O are positive real numbers; points on the x-axis to the left of O are negative real numbers. Points on the y-axis that are above O are positive real numbers; points on the y-axis that are below O are negative real numbers. In Figure 23 we label the x-axis "x" and the y-axis "y." Notice that an arrow is used at the end of each axis to denote the positive direction. We do not use an arrow to denote the negative direction.

The coordinate system presented in Figure 23 is called a **rectangular** or **Cartesian coordinate system,** named after René Descartes (1596–1650), a French mathematician, philosopher, and theologian. The plane formed by the x-axis and y-axis is often referred to as the **xy-plane,** and the x-axis and y-axis are called the **coordinate axes.**

We can represent any point P in the rectangular coordinate system by using an **ordered pair (x, y)** of real numbers. If $x > 0$, we travel x units to the right of the y-axis;

Preparing for...Answers

P1.

-3 -2 -1 0 $\frac{1}{2}$ 1 2 3 4 5 6

P2. (a) No **(b)** No **(c)** Yes **P3. (a)** 1
(b) 3 **(c)** 28 **P4.** $y = -\frac{3}{2}x + 4$ **P5.** 4

if $x < 0$, we travel $|x|$ units to the left of the y-axis. If $y > 0$, we travel y units above the x-axis; if $y < 0$, we travel $|y|$ units below the x-axis. The ordered pair (x, y) is also called the **coordinates** of P.

The origin O has coordinates $(0, 0)$. Any point on the x-axis has coordinates of the form $(x, 0)$, and any point on the y-axis has coordinates of the form $(0, y)$.

If (x, y) are the coordinates of a point P, then x is called the **x-coordinate,** or **abscissa,** of P and y is called the **y-coordinate** or **ordinate,** of P.

If you look back at Figure 23, you should notice that the x- and y-axes divide the plane into four separate regions or **quadrants.** In quadrant I, both the x- and y-coordinate are positive; in quadrant II, x is negative and y is positive; in quadrant III, both x and y are negative; and in quadrant IV, x is positive and y is negative. Points on the coordinate axes do not belong to a quadrant. See Figure 24.

Figure 24

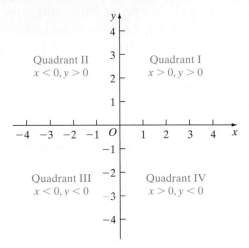

EXAMPLE 1 **Plotting Points in the Rectangular Coordinate System and Determining the Quadrant in which the Point Lies**

Plot the points in the xy-plane. Tell which quadrant each point is in.

(a) $A(3, 2)$ (b) $B(-2, 4)$ (c) $C(-1, -3)$

(d) $D(3, -4)$ (e) $E(-2, 0)$

Solution

Before we plot the points, we draw a rectangular or Cartesian coordinate system. See Figure 25(a). We now plot the points.

(a) To plot point $A(3, 2)$, from the origin O, we travel 3 units to the right and then 2 units up. Label the point A. See Figure 25(b). Point A is in quadrant I because both x and y are positive.

Figure 25

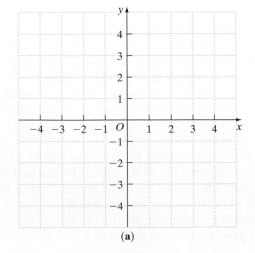

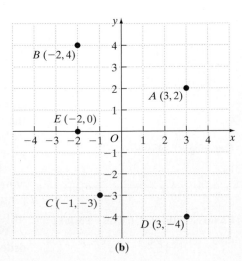

(a)   (b)

(b) To plot point $B(-2, 4)$, from the origin O, we travel 2 units to the left and then 4 units up. Label the point B. See Figure 25(b). Point B is in quadrant II.

(c) See Figure 25(b). Point C is in quadrant III.

(d) See Figure 25(b). Point D is in quadrant IV.

(e) See Figure 25(b). Point E is not in a quadrant because it lies on the x-axis.   ■

Quick ✔

1. The point where the x-axis and y-axis intersect in the Cartesian coordinate system is called the _____ .

2. *True or False:* If a point lies in quadrant III of the Cartesian coordinate system, then both x and y are negative.

In Problems 3 and 4, plot each point in the xy-plane. Tell in which quadrant or on which coordinate axis each point lies.

3. **(a)** $A(5, 2)$
   (b) $B(4, -2)$
   (c) $C(0, -3)$
   (d) $D(-4, -3)$

4. **(a)** $A(-3, 2)$
   (b) $B(-4, 0)$
   (c) $C(3, -2)$
   (d) $D(6, 1)$

2 Determine Whether an Ordered Pair Is a Point on the Graph of an Equation

In Section 1.1, we solved linear equations in one variable. The solution was either a single value of the variable, the empty set, or all real numbers. We will now look at equations in two variables. Our goal is to learn a method for representing the solution to an equation in two variables.

DEFINITION

An **equation in two variables,** say x and y, is a statement in which the algebraic expressions involving x and y are equal. The expressions are called **sides** of the equation.

Since an equation is a statement, it may be true or false, depending upon the values of the variables. Any values of the variable that make the equation a true statement are said to **satisfy** the equation.

For example, the following are all equations in two variables.

$$x^2 = y + 2 \qquad 3x + 2y = 6 \qquad y = -4x + 5$$

The first equation $x^2 = y + 2$ is satisfied when $x = 3$ and $y = 7$ since $3^2 = 7 + 2$. It is also satisfied when $x = -2$ and $y = 2$. In fact, there are infinitely many choices of x and y that satisfy the equation $x^2 = y + 2$. However, there are some choices of x and y that do not satisfy the equation $x^2 = y + 2$. For example, $x = 3$ and $y = 4$ does not satisfy the equation because $3^2 \neq 4 + 2$ (that is, $9 \neq 6$).

When we find a value of x and y that satisfies an equation, it means that the ordered pair (x, y) represents a point on the graph of the equation.

In Words

The graph of an equation is a geometric way of representing the set of all points that make the equation a true statement.

DEFINITION

The **graph of an equation in two variables** x and y is the set of all points whose coordinates, (x, y), in the xy-plane satisfy the equation.

EXAMPLE 2 Determining Whether a Point Is on the Graph of an Equation

Determine if the following coordinates represent points that are on the graph of $3x - y = 6$.

(a) $(2, 0)$ **(b)** $(1, -2)$ **(c)** $\left(\frac{1}{2}, -\frac{9}{2}\right)$

Solution

(a) For $(2, 0)$, we check to see if $x = 2$, $y = 0$ satisfies the equation $3x - y = 6$.

$$3x - y = 6$$
$$\text{Let } x = 2, y = 0: \quad 3(2) - 0 \overset{?}{=} 6$$
$$6 = 6 \quad \text{True}$$

The statement is true when $x = 2$ and $y = 0$, so the point whose coordinates are $(2, 0)$ is on the graph.

(b) For $(1, -2)$, we have

$$3x - y = 6$$
$$\text{Let } x = 1, y = -2: \quad 3(1) - (-2) \overset{?}{=} 6$$
$$3 + 2 \overset{?}{=} 6$$
$$5 = 6 \quad \text{False}$$

The statement $5 = 6$ is false, so the point whose coordinates are $(1, -2)$ is not on the graph.

(c) For $\left(\frac{1}{2}, -\frac{9}{2}\right)$, we have

$$3x - y = 6$$
$$\text{Let } x = \frac{1}{2}, y = -\frac{9}{2}: \quad 3\left(\frac{1}{2}\right) - \left(-\frac{9}{2}\right) \overset{?}{=} 6$$
$$\frac{3}{2} + \frac{9}{2} \overset{?}{=} 6$$
$$\frac{12}{2} \overset{?}{=} 6$$
$$6 = 6 \quad \text{True}$$

The statement is true when $x = \frac{1}{2}$ and $y = -\frac{9}{2}$, so the point whose coordinates are $\left(\frac{1}{2}, -\frac{9}{2}\right)$ is on the graph. ■

Quick ✔

5. *True or False:* The graph of an equation in two variables x and y is the set of all points whose coordinates, (x, y), in the Cartesian plane satisfy the equation.

6. Determine if the following coordinates represent points that are on the graph of $2x - 4y = 12$.

   (a) $(2, -3)$ **(b)** $(2, -2)$ **(c)** $\left(\frac{3}{2}, -\frac{9}{4}\right)$

7. Determine if the following coordinates represent points that are on the graph of $y = x^2 + 3$.

   (a) $(1, 4)$ **(b)** $(-2, -1)$ **(c)** $(-3, 12)$

For the remainder of the course we will say "the point (x, y)" rather than "the point whose coordinates are (x, y)" for the sake of brevity.

3 Graph an Equation Using the Point-Plotting Method

One of the most elementary methods for graphing an equation is the **point-plotting method.** With this method, we choose values for one of the variables and use the equation to determine the corresponding values of the remaining variable. If x and y are the variables in the equation, it does not matter whether we choose values of x and use the equation to find the corresponding y or choose y and find x. Convenience will determine which way we go.

EXAMPLE 3 How to Graph an Equation by Plotting Points

Graph the equation $y = -2x + 4$ by plotting points.

Step-by-Step Solution

Step 1: We want to find all points (x, y) that satisfy the equation. To determine these points we choose values of x (do you see why?) and use the equation to determine the corresponding values of y. See Table 9.

Table 9		
x	$y = -2x + 4$	(x, y)
-3	$-2(-3) + 4 = 10$	$(-3, 10)$
-2	$-2(-2) + 4 = 8$	$(-2, 8)$
-1	$-2(-1) + 4 = 6$	$(-1, 6)$
0	$-2(0) + 4 = 4$	$(0, 4)$
1	$-2(1) + 4 = 2$	$(1, 2)$
2	$-2(2) + 4 = 0$	$(2, 0)$
3	$-2(3) + 4 = -2$	$(3, -2)$

Step 2: We plot the ordered pairs listed in the third column of Table 9 as shown in Figure 26(a). Now connect the points to obtain the graph of the equation (a line) as shown in Figure 26(b).

Figure 26

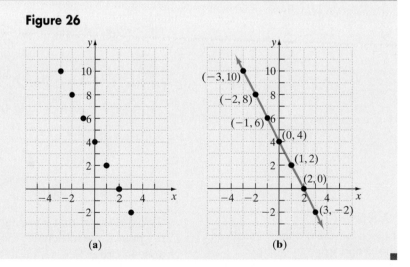

(a)   (b)

The graph of the equation shown in Figure 26(b) does not show all the points that satisfy $y = -2x + 4$. For example, in Figure 26(b) the point $(8, -12)$ is part of the graph of $y = -2x + 4$, but it is not shown. Since the graph of $y = -2x + 4$ can be extended as far as we please, we use arrows on the ends of the graph to indicate that the pattern shown continues. It is important to show enough of the graph so that anyone who is looking at it will "see" the rest of it as an obvious continuation of what is there. This is called a **complete graph.**

EXAMPLE 4 Graphing an Equation by Plotting Points

Graph the equation $y = x^2$ by plotting points.

Solution

Table 10 shows several points on the graph.

	Table 10	
x	$y = x^2$	(x, y)
-4	$y = (-4)^2 = 16$	$(-4, 16)$
-3	$y = (-3)^2 = 9$	$(-3, 9)$
-2	$y = (-2)^2 = 4$	$(-2, 4)$
-1	$y = (-1)^2 = 1$	$(-1, 1)$
0	$y = (0)^2 = 0$	$(0, 0)$
1	$y = (1)^2 = 1$	$(1, 1)$
2	$y = (2)^2 = 4$	$(2, 4)$
3	$y = (3)^2 = 9$	$(3, 9)$
4	$y = (4)^2 = 16$	$(4, 16)$

In Figure 27(a), we plot the ordered pairs listed in Table 10. In Figure 27(b), we connect the points in a smooth curve.

Figure 27

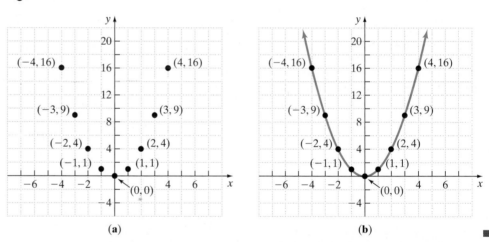

(a)   (b)

Work Smart

Notice we use a different scale on the x- and y-axis in Figure 27.

Work Smart

Experience will play a huge role in determining which x-values to choose in creating a table of values. For the time being, start by choosing values of x around $x = 0$ as in Table 10.

Two questions that you might be asking yourself right now are "How do I know how many points are sufficient?" and "How do I know which x-values (or y-values) I should choose in order to obtain points on the graph?" Often, the type of equation we wish to graph indicates the number of points that are necessary. For example, we will learn in the next section that if the equation is of the form $y = mx + b$, then its graph is a line and only two points are required to obtain the graph (as in Example 3). Other times, more points are required. At this stage in your math career, you will need to plot quite a few points to obtain a complete graph. However, as your experience and knowledge grow, you will learn to be more efficient in obtaining complete graphs.

Quick ✔ *In Problems 8–10, graph each equation using the point-plotting method.*

8. $y = 3x + 1$ **9.** $2x + 3y = 8$ **10.** $y = x^2 + 3$

EXAMPLE 5 Graphing the Equation $x = y^2$

Graph the equation $x = y^2$ by plotting points.

Solution

Because the equation is solved for x, we will choose values of y and use the equation to find the corresponding values of x. See Table 11. We plot the ordered pairs listed in Table 11 and connect the points in a smooth curve. See Figure 28.

Table 11		
y	$x = y^2$	(x, y)
-3	$(-3)^2 = 9$	$(9, -3)$
-2	$(-2)^2 = 4$	$(4, -2)$
-1	$(-1)^2 = 1$	$(1, -1)$
0	$0^2 = 0$	$(0, 0)$
1	$1^2 = 1$	$(1, 1)$
2	$2^2 = 4$	$(4, 2)$
3	$3^2 = 9$	$(9, 3)$

Figure 28

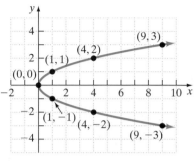

Quick ✔ *In Problems 11 and 12, graph each equation using the point-plotting method.*

11. $x = y^2 + 2$ **12.** $x = (y - 1)^2$

Work Smart

In order for a graph to be complete, all of its intercepts must be displayed.

Figure 29

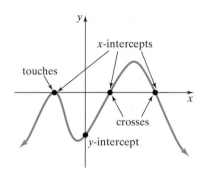

4 Identify the Intercepts from the Graph of an Equation

One of the key components that should be displayed in a complete graph is the *intercepts* of the graph.

> **DEFINITION**
>
> The **intercepts** are the coordinates of the points, if any, where a graph crosses or touches the coordinate axes. The x-coordinate of a point at which the graph crosses or touches the x-axis is an **x-intercept,** and the y-coordinate of a point at which the graph crosses or touches the y-axis is a **y-intercept.**

See Figure 29 for an illustration. Notice that an x-intercept exists when $y = 0$ and a y-intercept exists when $x = 0$.

EXAMPLE 6 Finding Intercepts from a Graph

Find the intercepts of the graph shown in Figure 30. What are the x-intercepts? What are the y-intercepts?

Figure 30

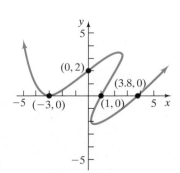

Solution

The intercepts of the graph are the points

$$(-3, 0), \quad (0, 2), \quad (1, 0), \quad \text{and} \quad (3.8, 0)$$

The x-intercepts are -3, 1, and 3.8. The y-intercept is 2. ∎

In Example 6, you should notice the following: If we do not specify the type of intercept (x- versus y-), then we report the intercept as an ordered pair. However, if we specify the type of intercept, then we only need to report the coordinate of the intercept. For x-intercepts, we report the x-coordinate of the intercept (since it is understood that the y-coordinate is 0); for y-intercepts, we report the y-coordinate of the intercept (since the x-coordinate is understood to be 0).

Quick ✔

13. The points, if any, at which a graph crosses or touches a coordinate axis are called _____.

14. *True or False*: The graph of an equation must have at least one x-intercept.

15. Find the intercepts of the graph shown in the figure. What are the x-intercepts? What are the y-intercepts?

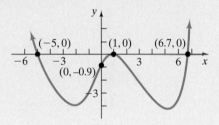

5 Interpret Graphs

Graphs play an important role in helping us to visualize relationships that exist between two variables or quantities. We have all heard the expression "A picture is worth a thousand words." A graph is a "picture" that illustrates the relationship between two variables. By visualizing this relationship, we are able to see important information and draw conclusions regarding the relationship between the two variables.

EXAMPLE 7 Interpret a Graph

The graph in Figure 31 shows the profit P for selling x gallons of gasoline in an hour at a gas station. The vertical axis represents the profit and the horizontal axis represents the number of gallons of gasoline sold.

Figure 31

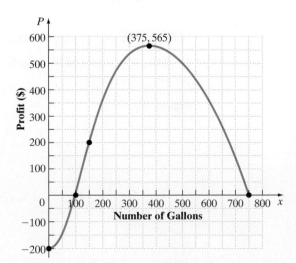

(a) What is the profit if 150 gallons of gasoline are sold?

(b) How many gallons of gasoline are sold when profit is highest? What is the highest profit?

(c) Identify and interpret the intercepts.

Solution

(a) Draw a vertical line up from 150 on the horizontal axis until we reach the point on the graph. Then draw a horizontal line from this point to the vertical axis. The point where the horizontal line intersects the vertical axis is the profit when 150 gallons of gasoline are sold. The profit from selling 150 gallons of gasoline is $200.

(b) The profit is highest when 375 gallons of gasoline are sold. The highest profit is $565.

(c) The intercepts are $(0, -200)$, $(100, 0)$, and $(750, 0)$. For $(0, -200)$: If the price of gasoline is too high, demand for gasoline (in theory) will be 0 gallons. This is the explanation for selling 0 gallons of gasoline. The negative profit is due to the fact that the company has $0 in revenue (since it didn't sell any gas), but had hourly expenses of $200. For $(100, 0)$: The company sells just enough gas to pay its bills. This can be thought of as the break-even point. For $(750, 0)$: The 750 gallons sold represents the maximum number of gallons that the station can pump and still break even.

Quick ✔

16. The graph shown represents the cost C (in thousands of dollars) of refining x gallons of gasoline per hour (in thousands). The vertical axis represents the cost and the horizontal axis represents the number of gallons of gasoline refined.

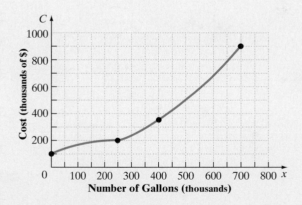

(a) What is the cost of refining 250 thousand gallons of gasoline per hour?

(b) What is the cost of refining 400 thousand gallons of gasoline per hour?

(c) In the context of the problem, explain the meaning of the graph ending at 700 thousand gallons of gasoline.

(d) Identify and interpret the intercept.

1.5 EXERCISES

PRACTICE   WATCH   DOWNLOAD   READ   REVIEW

1–16. are the **Quick ✔s** *that follow each* **EXAMPLE**

Building Skills

17. Determine the coordinates of each of the points plotted. Tell in which quadrant or on what coordinate axis each point lies. See Objective 1.

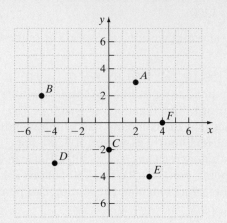

18. Determine the coordinates of each of the points plotted. Tell in which quadrant or on what coordinate axis each point lies. See Objective 1.

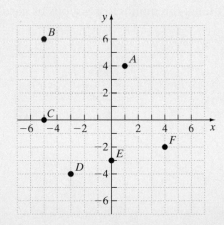

In Problems 19 and 20, plot each point in the xy-plane. Tell in which quadrant or on what coordinate axis each point lies. See Objective 1.

19. $A(3, 5)$

   $B(-2, -6)$

   $C(5, 0)$

   $D(1, -6)$

   $E(0, 3)$

   $F(-4, 1)$

20. $A(-3, 1)$

   $B(-6, 0)$

   $C(2, -5)$

   $D(-6, -2)$

   $E(1, 2)$

   $F(0, -5)$

In Problems 21–26, determine whether the given points are on the graph of the equation. See Objective 2.

21. $2x + 5y = 12$
   (a) $(1, 2)$
   (b) $(-2, 3)$
   (c) $(-4, 4)$
   (d) $\left(-\dfrac{3}{2}, 3\right)$

22. $-4x + 3y = 18$
   (a) $(1, 7)$
   (b) $(0, 6)$
   (c) $(-3, 10)$
   (d) $\left(\dfrac{3}{2}, 4\right)$

23. $y = -2x^2 + 3x - 1$
   (a) $(-2, -15)$
   (b) $(3, 10)$
   (c) $(0, 1)$
   (d) $(2, -3)$

24. $y = x^3 - 3x$
   (a) $(2, 2)$
   (b) $(3, 8)$
   (c) $(-3, -18)$
   (d) $(0, 0)$

25. $y = |x - 3|$
   (a) $(1, 4)$
   (b) $(4, 1)$
   (c) $(-6, 9)$
   (d) $(0, 3)$

26. $x^2 + y^2 = 1$
   (a) $(0, 1)$
   (b) $(1, 1)$
   (c) $\left(\dfrac{1}{2}, \dfrac{1}{2}\right)$
   (d) $\left(\dfrac{\sqrt{3}}{2}, \dfrac{1}{2}\right)$

In Problems 27–54, graph each equation by plotting points. See Objective 3.

27. $y = 4x$

28. $y = 2x$

29. $y = -\dfrac{1}{2}x$

30. $y = -\dfrac{1}{3}x$

31. $y = x + 3$

32. $y = x - 2$

33. $y = -3x + 1$

34. $y = -4x + 2$

35. $y = \dfrac{1}{2}x - 4$

36. $y = -\dfrac{1}{2}x + 2$

37. $2x + y = 7$

38. $3x + y = 9$

39. $y = -x^2$

40. $y = x^2 - 2$

41. $y = 2x^2 - 8$

42. $y = -2x^2 + 8$

43. $y = |x|$

44. $y = |x| - 2$

45. $y = |x - 1|$

46. $y = -|x|$

47. $y = x^3$

48. $y = -x^3$

49. $y = x^3 + 1$

50. $y = x^3 - 2$

51. $x^2 - y = 4$

52. $x^2 + y = 5$

53. $x = y^2 - 1$

54. $x = y^2 + 2$

In Problems 55–58, the graph of an equation is given. List the inter-cepts of the graph. See Objective 4.

55.

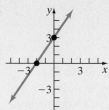

56.

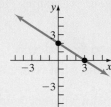

57.

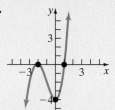

58.

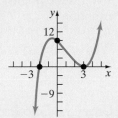

Applying the Concepts

59. If $(a, 4)$ is a point on the graph of $y = 4x - 3$, what is a?

60. If $(a, -2)$ is a point on the graph of $y = -3x + 5$, what is a?

61. If $(3, b)$ is a point on the graph of $y = x^2 - 2x + 1$, what is b?

62. If $(-2, b)$ is a point on the graph of $y = -2x^2 + 3x + 1$, what is b?

63. Area of a Window Bob Villa wishes to put a new window in his home. He wants the perimeter of the window to be 100 feet. The graph above and to the right shows the relation between the width, x, of the opening and the area of the opening.

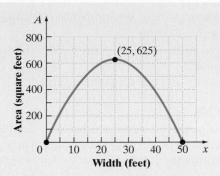

(a) What is the area of the opening if the width is 10 feet?

(b) What is the width of the opening in order for area to be a maximum? What is the maximum area of the opening?

(c) Identify and interpret the intercepts.

64. Projectile Motion The graph below shows the height, in feet, of a ball thrown straight up with an initial speed of 80 feet per second from an initial height of 96 feet after t seconds.

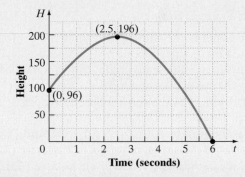

(a) What is the height of the object after 1.5 seconds?

(b) At what time is the height a maximum? What is the maximum height?

(c) Identify and interpret the intercepts.

65. Cell Phones We all struggle with selecting a cellular phone provider. The graph below shows the relation between the monthly cost of a cellular phone and the number of minutes used, m, when using the Sprint PCS 2000-minute plan. (SOURCE: *SprintPCS.com*)

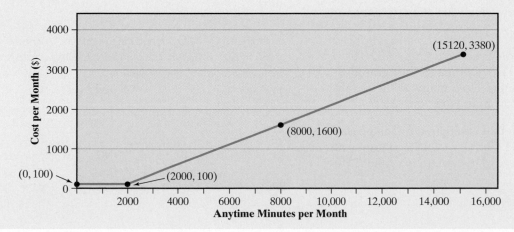

(a) What is the cost of talking for 200 minutes in a month? 500 minutes?

(b) What is the cost of talking 8000 minutes in a month?

(c) Identify and interpret the intercept.

66. **Wind Chill** It is 10° Celsius outside. The wind is calm but then gusts up to 20 meters per second. You feel the chill go right through your bones. The following graph shows the relation between the wind chill temperature (in degrees Celsius) and wind speed (in meters per second).

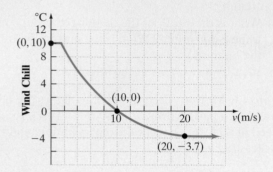

(a) What is the wind chill if the wind is blowing 4 meters per second?

(b) What is the wind chill if the wind is blowing 20 meters per second?

(c) Identify and interpret the intercepts.

67. Plot the points $(4, 0), (4, 2), (4, -3),$ and $(4, -6)$. Describe the set of all points of the form $(4, y)$ where y is a real number.

68. Plot the points $(4, 2), (1, 2), (0, 2),$ and $(-3, 2)$. Describe the set of all points of the form $(x, 2)$ where x is a real number.

Extending the Concepts

69. Draw a graph of an equation that contains two x-intercepts, -2 and 3. At the x-intercept -2, the graph crosses the x-axis; at the x-intercept 3, the graph touches the x-axis. Compare your graph with those of your classmates. How are they similar? How are they different?

70. Draw a graph that contains the points $(-3, -1)$, $(-1, 1), (0, 3),$ and $(1, 5)$. Compare your graph with those of your classmates. How many of the graphs are straight lines? How many are "curved"?

71. Make up an equation that is satisfied by the points $(2, 0), (4, 0),$ and $(1, 0)$. Compare your equation with those of your classmates. How are they similar? How are they different?

72. Make up an equation that contains the points $(0, 3)$, $(1, 3),$ and $(-4, 3)$. Compare your equation with those of your classmates. How many are the same?

Explaining the Concepts

73. Explain what is meant by a complete graph.

74. Explain what the graph of an equation represents.

75. What is the point-plotting method for graphing an equation?

76. What is the y-coordinate of a point that is an x-intercept? What is the x-coordinate of a point that is a y-intercept?

The Graphing Calculator

Just as we have graphed equations using point plotting, the graphing calculator also graphs equations by plotting points. Figure 32 shows the graph of $y = x^2$ and Table 12 shows points on the graph of $y = x^2$ using a TI-84 Plus graphing calculator.

Figure 32

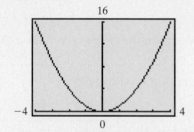

Table 12

In Problems 77–84, use a graphing calculator to draw a complete graph of each equation. Use the TABLE feature to assist in selecting an appropriate viewing window.

77. $y = 3x - 9$ 78. $y = -5x + 8$

79. $y = -x^2 + 8$ 80. $y = 2x^2 - 4$

81. $y + 2x^2 = 13$ 82. $y - x^2 = -15$

83. $y = x^3 - 6x + 1$ 84. $y = -x^3 + 3x$

1.6 Linear Equations in Two Variables

OBJECTIVES

1. Graph Linear Equations Using Point Plotting
2. Graph Linear Equations Using Intercepts
3. Graph Vertical and Horizontal Lines
4. Find the Slope of a Line Given Two Points
5. Interpret Slope as an Average Rate of Change
6. Graph a Line Given a Point and Its Slope
7. Use the Point-Slope Form of a Line
8. Identify the Slope and y-Intercept of a Line from Its Equation
9. Find the Equation of a Line Given Two Points

Preparing for Linear Equations in Two Variables

Before getting started, take this readiness quiz. If you get a problem wrong, go back to the section cited and review the material.

P1. Solve: $3x + 12 = 0$ [Section 1.1, pp. 49–50]
P2. Solve: $2x + 5 = 13$ [Section 1.1, pp. 49–50]
P3. Solve for y: $3x - 2y = 10$ [Section 1.3, pp. 73–76]
P4. Evaluate: $\dfrac{5 - 2}{-2 - 4}$ [Section R.4, pp. 34–35]
P5. Evaluate: $\dfrac{-7 - 2}{-5 - (-2)}$ [Section R.4, pp. 34–35]
P6. Distribute: $-2(x + 3)$ [Section R.3, pp. 29–30]

1 Graph Linear Equations Using Point Plotting

In Section 1.5 we discussed how to graph any equation using the point-plotting method. Remember, the graph of an equation is the set of all ordered pairs (x, y) such that the equation is a true statement.

We are now going to learn methods for graphing a specific type of equation, called a *linear equation in two variables*.

DEFINITION

A **linear equation in two variables** is an equation of the form
$$Ax + By = C$$
where A, B, and C are real numbers. A and B cannot both be 0.

When a linear equation is written in the form $Ax + By = C$, we say that the linear equation is in **standard form.**

Some examples of linear equations in standard form are

$$3x - 4y = 9 \qquad \frac{1}{2}x + \frac{2}{3}y = 4 \qquad 3x = 9 \qquad -2y = 5$$

The graph of a linear equation is a **line.** Let's graph a linear equation using the point-plotting method.

EXAMPLE 1 Graphing a Linear Equation Using the Point-Plotting Method

Graph the linear equation: $4x + 2y = 6$

Solution

To graph the linear equation, we choose various values for x and then use the equation to find the corresponding values of y. For this equation, we will let $x = -2, -1, 0,$ and 1.

$x = -2$:	$4(-2) + 2y = 6$	$x = -1$:	$4(-1) + 2y = 6$
	$-8 + 2y = 6$		$-4 + 2y = 6$
Add 8 to both sides:	$2y = 14$	Add 4 to both sides:	$2y = 10$
Divide both sides by 2:	$y = 7$	Divide both sides by 2:	$y = 5$
$(-2, 7)$ is on the graph.		$(-1, 5)$ is on the graph.	

Preparing for...Answers   **P1.** $\{-4\}$

P2. $\{4\}$ **P3.** $y = \dfrac{3}{2}x - 5$ **P4.** $-\dfrac{1}{2}$

P5. 3   **P6.** $-2x - 6$

In Example 1, we chose to pick x-values and use the equation to find the corresponding y-values; however, we could also have chosen a y-value and used the equation to find the corresponding x-value.

$x = 0$:
$$4(0) + 2y = 6$$
$$0 + 2y = 6$$
$$2y = 6$$
Divide both sides by 2: $y = 3$
$(0, 3)$ is on the graph.

$x = 1$:
$$4(1) + 2y = 6$$
$$4 + 2y = 6$$
Subtract 4 from both sides: $2y = 2$
Divide both sides by 2: $y = 1$
$(1, 1)$ is on the graph.

Table 13 shows the points that are on the graph of $4x + 2y = 6$. We plot the ordered pairs $(-2, 7)$, $(-1, 5)$, $(0, 3)$, and $(1, 1)$ in the Cartesian plane and connect the points in a straight line. See Figure 33.

Table 13		
x	y	(x, y)
-2	7	$(-2, 7)$
-1	5	$(-1, 5)$
0	3	$(0, 3)$
1	1	$(1, 1)$

Figure 33

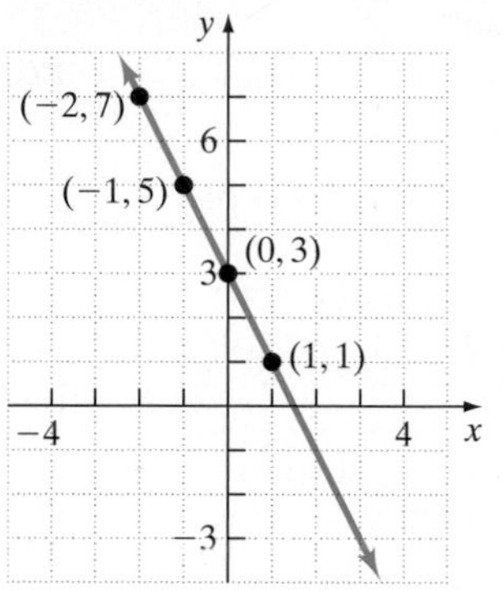

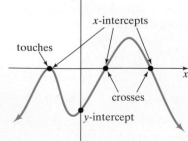

Work Smart

We recommend that you find at least three points to be sure your graph is correct. Also, remember that a complete graph is a graph that shows all the interesting features of the graph, such as its intercepts.

One of the problems with using the point-plotting method to graph equations is determining how many points need to be plotted before we obtain a complete graph. Based on the results of Example 1, we can see that only two points are required to obtain a complete graph of a linear equation. To guard against making an error, however, you should plot at least three points.

Quick ✔

1. A(n) _____ _____ is an equation of the form $Ax + By = C$, where A, B, and C are real numbers. A and B cannot both be 0.

2. The graph of a linear equation is called a _____.

In Problems 3–5, graph each linear equation using the point-plotting method.

3. $y = 2x - 3$

4. $\frac{1}{2}x + y = 2$

5. $-6x + 3y = 12$

2 Graph Linear Equations Using Intercepts

In Section 1.5, we said any complete graph should display the intercepts, if any. Recall, the intercepts of the graph of an equation are the points, if any, where the graph crosses or touches the coordinate axes. See Figure 34.

Now we will explain how to find the intercepts algebraically. From Figure 34 it is apparent that an x-intercept exists when the value of y is 0 and that a y-intercept exists when the value of x is 0. This leads to the following procedure for finding intercepts.

Figure 34

PROCEDURE FOR FINDING INTERCEPTS

- To find the x-intercept(s), if any, of the graph of an equation, let $y = 0$ in the equation and solve for x.
- To find the y-intercept(s), if any, of the graph of an equation, let $x = 0$ in the equation and solve for y.

The procedure given can be used to find the intercepts of any type of equation. Let's use this procedure to find the intercepts of a linear equation.

EXAMPLE 2 Graphing a Linear Equation by Finding Its Intercepts

Graph the linear equation $3x + 2y = 12$ by finding its intercepts.

Solution

To find the y-intercept, we let $x = 0$ and solve the equation $3x + 2y = 12$ for y.

$$\text{Let } x = 0: \quad 3(0) + 2y = 12$$
$$0 + 2y = 12$$
$$2y = 12$$
$$\text{Divide both sides by 2:} \qquad y = 6$$

The y-intercept is 6, so the point $(0, 6)$ is on the graph of the equation.

To find the x-intercept, we let $y = 0$ and solve the equation $3x + 2y = 12$ for x.

$$\text{Let } y = 0: \quad 3x + 2(0) = 12$$
$$3x + 0 = 12$$
$$3x = 12$$
$$\text{Divide both sides by 3:} \qquad x = 4$$

The x-intercept is 4, so the point $(4, 0)$ is on the graph of the equation.

We obtain one additional point on the graph by letting $x = 2$ (or any other value of x besides 0 or 4), and find y to be 3. Table 14 shows the points that are on the graph of $3x + 2y = 12$. We plot the points $(0, 6)$, $(4, 0)$, and $(2, 3)$. Connect the points in a straight line and obtain the graph in Figure 35.

Work Smart

Linear equations in one variable have no solution, one solution, or infinitely many solutions. Because the procedure for finding intercepts of linear equations in two variables results in a linear equation in one variable, linear equations can have no x-intercepts, one x-intercept, or infinitely many x-intercepts. The same applies to y-intercepts.

Figure 35

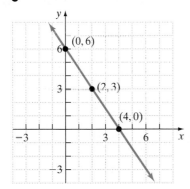

Table 14		
x	y	(x, y)
0	6	$(0, 6)$
4	0	$(4, 0)$
2	3	$(2, 3)$

Quick ✔

6. *True or False:* To find the x-intercept(s), if any, of the graph of an equation, let $y = 0$ in the equation and solve for x.

In Problems 7 and 8, graph each linear equation by finding its intercepts.

7. $x + y = 4$ **8.** $4x - 5y = 20$

EXAMPLE 3 Graphing a Linear Equation by Finding Its Intercepts

Graph the linear equation $x + 3y = 0$ by finding its intercepts.

Solution

To find the y-intercept, we let $x = 0$ and solve the equation $x + 3y = 0$ for y.

$$\text{Let } x = 0: \quad 0 + 3y = 0$$
$$3y = 0$$
$$\text{Divide both sides by 3:} \qquad y = 0$$

The y-intercept is 0, so the point $(0, 0)$ is on the graph of the equation.

To find the x-intercept, we let $y = 0$ and solve the equation $x + 3y = 0$ for x.

$$\text{Let } y = 0: \quad x + 3(0) = 0$$
$$x + 0 = 0$$
$$x = 0$$

The x-intercept is 0, so the point $(0, 0)$ is on the graph of the equation.

Work Smart

We chose $x = -3$ and $x = 3$, to avoid fractions. This makes plotting the points easier.

Because both the x- and y-intercepts are 0, we will find *two* additional points on the graph of the equation. By letting $x = 3$, we find that $y = -1$. By letting $x = -3$, we find that $y = 1$. We plot the points $(0, 0)$, $(-3, 1)$, and $(3, -1)$, connect the points in a straight line and obtain the graph in Figure 36.

Figure 36

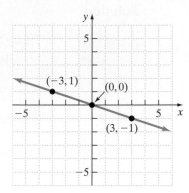

From Example 3, we learn that any equation of the form $Ax + By = 0$, where $A \neq 0$ and $B \neq 0$, has only one intercept at $(0, 0)$. Therefore, to graph equations of this form, we find two additional points on the graph.

> **Quick** ✔ *In Problem 9, graph the equation by finding its intercepts.*
>
> **9.** $3x - 2y = 0$

⌐3⌐ Graph Vertical and Horizontal Lines

In the equation of a line, $Ax + By = C$, we said that A and B cannot both be zero. But what if $A = 0$ or $B = 0$?

⌐EXAMPLE 4⌐ Graphing a Vertical Line

Graph the equation $x = 3$ using the point-plotting method.

Solution

Because the equation $x = 3$ can be written as $1x + 0y = 3$, we know that the graph is a line. When you look at the equation $x = 3$, it should be clear to you that no matter what value of y we choose, the corresponding value of x is going to be 3. Therefore, the points $(3, -2)$, $(3, -1)$, $(3, 0)$, $(3, 1)$, and $(3, 2)$ are all points on the line. See Figure 37.

Figure 37

$x = 3$

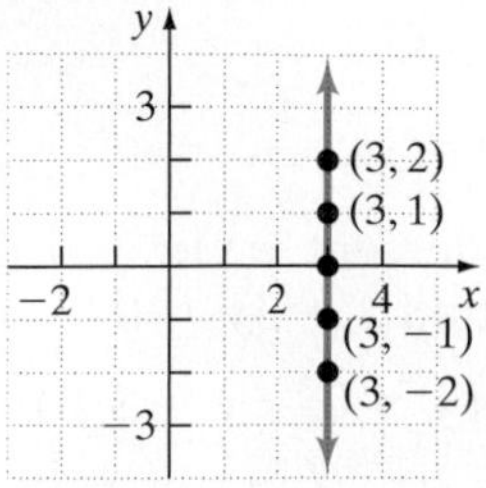

Based on the results of Example 4, we can write the equation of a vertical line:

> **EQUATION OF A VERTICAL LINE**
>
> A **vertical line** is given by an equation of the form
> $$x = a$$
> where a is the x-intercept.

Now let's look at equations that lead to graphs that are horizontal lines.

EXAMPLE 5 Graphing a Horizontal Line

Graph the equation $y = -2$ using the point-plotting method.

Solution

Because the equation $y = -2$ can be written as $0x + 1y = -2$, we know that the graph is a line. In looking at the equation $y = -2$, it should be clear that no matter what value of x we choose, the corresponding value of y is going to be -2. Therefore, the points $(-2, -2)$, $(-1, -2)$, $(0, -2)$, $(1, -2)$, and $(2, -2)$ are all points on the line. See Figure 38.   ■

Figure 38

$y = -2$

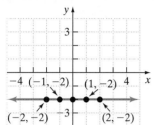

Based on the results of Example 5, we can generalize:

EQUATION OF A HORIZONTAL LINE

A **horizontal line** is given by an equation of the form

$$y = b$$

where b is the y-intercept.

Quick ✔ *In Problems 10–12, graph each equation.*

10. $x = 5$ **11.** $y = -4$ **12.** $-3x + 4 = 1$

4 Find the Slope of a Line Given Two Points

Up to this point, we have given you a linear equation and asked you to graph the line. Now we want to discuss an interesting property of linear equations. Look back at Table 13 and Figure 33 from Example 1. Notice that for each 1-unit increase in x, the value of y decreases by 2. For example, as x increases from -1 to 0, y decreases from 5 to 3; as x increases from 0 to 1, y decreases from 3 to 1. This property of linear equations is referred to as *slope*.

Consider the staircase drawn in Figure 39(a). If we draw a line at the top of each riser on the staircase (in blue), we can see that each step contains exactly the same horizontal **run** and the same vertical **rise**. We call the ratio of the rise to the run the *slope* of the line. It is a numerical measure of the steepness of the line. For example, suppose that the staircase in Figure 39(a) has a run of 7 inches and a rise of 6 inches. Then the slope of the line is $\dfrac{\text{rise}}{\text{run}} = \dfrac{6 \text{ inches}}{7 \text{ inches}}$. If the run of the stair is increased to 10 inches, while the rise remains the same, then the slope of the line is $\dfrac{\text{rise}}{\text{run}} = \dfrac{6 \text{ inches}}{10 \text{ inches}}$. See Figure 39(b). If the run is decreased to 4 inches and the rise remains the same, then the slope of the line is $\dfrac{\text{rise}}{\text{run}} = \dfrac{6 \text{ inches}}{4 \text{ inches}}$. See Figure 39(c).

Figure 39

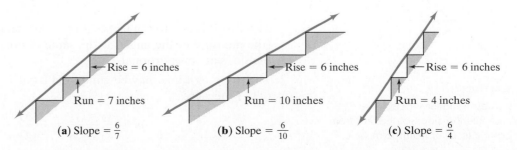

(a) Slope $= \frac{6}{7}$ (b) Slope $= \frac{6}{10}$ (c) Slope $= \frac{6}{4}$

We can define the slope of a line using rectangular coordinates.

DEFINITION

Let $P = (x_1, y_1)$ and $Q = (x_2, y_2)$ be two distinct points. If $x_1 \neq x_2$, the **slope** m of the nonvertical line L containing P and Q is defined by the formula

$$m = \frac{y_2 - y_1}{x_2 - x_1}, \quad x_1 \neq x_2$$

If $x_1 = x_2$, then L is a vertical line and the slope m of L is **undefined** (since this results in division by 0).

The accepted symbol for the slope of a line is m. It comes from the French word *monter*, which means to ascend or climb. Figure 40(a) provides an illustration of the slope of a nonvertical line; Figure 40(b) illustrates a vertical line.

Figure 40

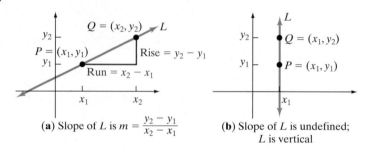

(a) Slope of L is $m = \dfrac{y_2 - y_1}{x_2 - x_1}$ (b) Slope of L is undefined; L is vertical

From Figure 40(a) we can see that the slope m of a nonvertical line may be viewed as

$$m = \frac{y_2 - y_1}{x_2 - x_1} = \frac{\text{Rise}}{\text{Run}}$$

We can also write the slope m of a nonvertical line as

$$m = \frac{y_2 - y_1}{x_2 - x_1} = \frac{\text{Change in } y}{\text{Change in } x} = \frac{\Delta y}{\Delta x}$$

In Words

Slope is the change in y divided by the change in x.

The symbol Δ is the Greek letter delta, which comes from the Greek word *diaphora*, which means "difference." In mathematics, we read the symbol Δ as "change in." So the notation $\dfrac{\Delta y}{\Delta x}$ is read "change in y divided by change in x."

The slope m of a nonvertical line measures the amount that y changes (the vertical change) as x changes from x_1 to x_2 (the horizontal change). The slope m of a vertical line is undefined since it results in division by zero.

Figure 41

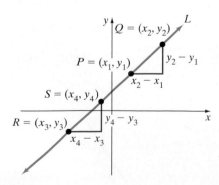

Comments Regarding the Slope of a Nonvertical Line

1. Any two different points on the line can be used to compute the slope of the line shown in Figure 41. The slope m of the line L is given by

$$m = \frac{y_2 - y_1}{x_2 - x_1} \quad \text{or} \quad m = \frac{y_4 - y_3}{x_4 - x_3}$$

This result is due to the fact that the two triangles formed in Figure 41 are similar (the measure of the angles is the same in both triangles). Therefore, the ratios of the sides are proportional.

2. The slope of a line may be computed from $P = (x_1, y_1)$ to $Q = (x_2, y_2)$ or from Q to P because

$$m = \frac{y_2 - y_1}{x_2 - x_1} = \frac{-(y_1 - y_2)}{-(x_1 - x_2)} = \frac{y_1 - y_2}{x_1 - x_2}$$

Work Smart

It doesn't matter whether we compute the slope of the line from point P to Q or from point Q to P.

EXAMPLE 6 Finding and Interpreting the Slope of a Line

Find and interpret the slope of the line containing the points $(3, 6)$ and $(-2, 2)$.

Solution

We plot the points $P = (x_1, y_1) = (3, 6)$ and $Q = (x_2, y_2) = (-2, 2)$ and draw a line through the points as shown in Figure 42. The slope of the line drawn in Figure 42 is

$$m = \frac{y_2 - y_1}{x_2 - x_1} = \frac{2 - 6}{-2 - 3} = \frac{-4}{-5} = \frac{4}{5}$$

We could also compute the slope as

$$m = \frac{y_1 - y_2}{x_1 - x_2} = \frac{6 - 2}{3 - (-2)} = \frac{4}{5}$$

Figure 42

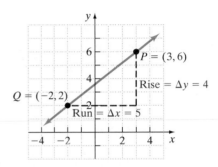

A slope of $\frac{4}{5}$ can be interpreted as: For every 5-unit increase in x, y will increase by 4 units. Or for every 5-unit decrease in x, y will decrease by 4 units. ∎

Quick ✔

13. If a line is vertical, then its slope is _____ .

14. On a line, for every 10-foot run there is a 4-foot rise. The slope of the line is ____ .

15. *True or False:* If $P = (x_1, y_1)$ and $Q = (x_2, y_2)$ are two distinct points with $x_1 \neq x_2$, the slope m of the nonvertical line L containing P and Q is defined by the formula
$$m = \frac{x_2 - x_1}{y_2 - y_1}, \quad y_1 \neq y_2.$$

16. *True or False:* If the slope of a line is $\frac{1}{2}$, then if x increases by 2, y will increase by 1.

In Problems 17–20, find and interpret the slope of the line containing the points.

17. $(0, 3); (3, 12)$ 18. $(-1, 3); (3, -4)$

19. $(3, 2); (-3, 2)$ 20. $(-2, 4); (-2, -1)$

EXAMPLE 7 Finding Slopes of Different Lines Each of Which Contains (3, 5)

Find the slope of the lines $L_1, L_2, L_3,$ and L_4 containing the following pairs of points. Graph the lines in the Cartesian plane.

$$\begin{array}{lll}
L_1: & P(3, 5) & Q_1(5, 8) \\
L_2: & P(3, 5) & Q_2(6, 5) \\
L_3: & P(3, 5) & Q_3(5, -2) \\
L_4: & P(3, 5) & Q_4(3, 0)
\end{array}$$

Solution

Let m_1, m_2, m_3, and m_4 denote the slopes of the lines L_1, L_2, L_3, and L_4, respectively. Then

$$m_1 = \frac{8 - 5}{5 - 3} = \frac{3}{2} \qquad m_2 = \frac{5 - 5}{6 - 3} = \frac{0}{3} = 0$$

$$m_3 = \frac{-2 - 5}{5 - 3} = \frac{-7}{2} = -\frac{7}{2} \qquad m_4 = \frac{0 - 5}{3 - 3} = \frac{-5}{0} \quad \text{undefined}$$

The graphs of the four lines are shown in Figure 43.

Figure 43

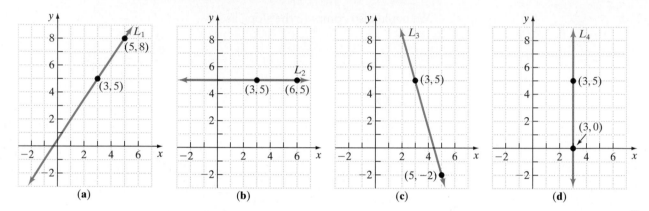

(a) (b) (c) (d)

Relying on Figure 43, we have the following properties of slope:

> **PROPERTIES OF SLOPE**
>
> - When the slope of a line is positive, the line slants upward from left to right, as shown by L_1 in Figure 43(a).
> - When the slope of a line is zero, the line is horizontal, as shown by L_2 in Figure 43(b).
> - When the slope of a line is negative, the line slants downward from left to right, as shown by L_3 in Figure 43(c).
> - When the slope of a line is undefined, the line is vertical, as shown by L_4 in Figure 43(d).

Quick ✔

21. *True or False:* If the slope of a line is negative, then the line slants downward from left to right.

22. Find the slope of the lines L_1, L_2, L_3, and L_4 containing the following pairs of points. Graph all four lines on the same Cartesian plane.

$L_1: P(1, 3) \ Q_1(6, 4)$ $L_2: P(1, 3) \ Q_2(1, 8)$

$L_3: P(1, 3) \ Q_3(-3, 7)$ $L_4: P(1, 3) \ Q_4(-4, 3)$

5 Interpret Slope as an Average Rate of Change

The slope m of a nonvertical line measures the amount that y changes as x changes from x_1 to x_2. The slope of a line is also called the **average rate of change** of y with respect to x.

In applications, we are often interested in knowing how the change in one variable might impact some other variable. For example, if your income increases by $1000, how much will your spending (on average) change? Or, if the speed of your car increases by 10 miles per hour, how much (on average) will your car's gas mileage change?

EXAMPLE 8   Slope as an Average Rate of Change

A strain of *E. coli* Beu 397-recA441 is placed into a Petri dish at 30° Celsius and allowed to grow. The data shown in Table 15 are collected. The population is measured in grams and the time in hours. The population growth is shown in Figure 44.

Table 15

Time (hours), x	Population (grams), y
0	0.09
1	0.12
2	0.16
3	0.22
4	0.29
5	0.39

SOURCE: *Dr. Polly Lavery, Joliet Junior College*

Figure 44

Growth of E-coli

(a) Compute and interpret the average rate of change in the population between 0 and 1 hour.

(b) Compute and interpret the average rate of change in the population between 3 and 4 hours.

(c) Based upon your results to parts (a) and (b), do you think that the population grows linearly? Why?

Solution

(a) To find the average rate of change, we compute the slope of the line between the points $(0, 0.09)$ and $(1, 0.12)$.

$$m = \text{average rate of change} = \frac{0.12 - 0.09}{1 - 0} = 0.03 \text{ gram per hour}$$

The population of *E. coli* was growing at the rate of 0.03 gram per hour between 0 and 1 hour.

(b) We want to compute the slope of the line between the points $(3, 0.22)$ and $(4, 0.29)$.

$$m = \text{average rate of change} = \frac{0.29 - 0.22}{4 - 3} = 0.07 \text{ gram per hour}$$

The population of *E. coli* was growing at the rate of 0.07 gram per hour between 3 and 4 hours.

(c) The population is not growing linearly because the average rate of change (slope) is not constant. In fact, because the average rate of change is increasing as time passes, the population is growing more rapidly over time. ■

Quick ✔

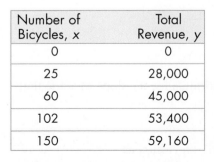

Number of Bicycles, x	Total Revenue, y
0	0
25	28,000
60	45,000
102	53,400
150	59,160

23. The data to the left represent the total revenue that would be received from selling *x* bicycles at Gibson's Bicycle Shop.

(a) Plot the ordered pairs (x, y) on a graph and connect the points with straight lines.

(b) Compute and interpret the average rate of change in the revenue between 0 and 25 bicycles sold.

(c) Compute and interpret the average rate of change in the revenue between 102 and 150 bicycles sold.

(d) Based upon your results to parts (a), (b), and (c), do you think that the revenue grows linearly? Why?

6 Graph a Line Given a Point and Its Slope

One reason we care so much about slope is that it can be used to help graph lines.

EXAMPLE 9 Graphing a Line Given a Point and Its Slope

Draw a graph of the line that contains the point $(1, 2)$ and has a slope of

(a) 3   (b) $-\dfrac{3}{2}$

Solution

(a) Because the slope $= \dfrac{\text{Rise}}{\text{Run}} = \dfrac{\Delta y}{\Delta x}$, we have that $3 = \dfrac{3}{1} = \dfrac{\Delta y}{\Delta x}$. This means that if x increases by 1 unit, then y will increase by 3 units. So, if we start at $(1, 2)$ and move 1 unit to the right and then 3 units up, we end up at the point $(2, 5)$. We then draw a line through the points $(1, 2)$ and $(2, 5)$ to obtain the graph of the line. See Figure 45.

(b) Because the slope $= \dfrac{\text{Rise}}{\text{Run}} = \dfrac{\Delta y}{\Delta x}$, we have that $-\dfrac{3}{2} = \dfrac{-3}{2} = \dfrac{\Delta y}{\Delta x}$. This means that if x increases by 2 units, then y will decrease by 3 units. So, if we start at $(1, 2)$ and move 2 units to the right and then 3 units down, we end up at the point $(3, -1)$. We then draw a line through the points $(1, 2)$ and $(3, -1)$ to obtain the graph of the line. See Figure 46.

It is perfectly acceptable to set $\dfrac{\Delta y}{\Delta x} = -\dfrac{3}{2} = \dfrac{3}{-2}$ so that we move left 2 units from $(1, 2)$ and then up 3 units. We would then end up at $(-1, 5)$, which is also on the graph of the line as indicated in Figure 46. ∎

Figure 45

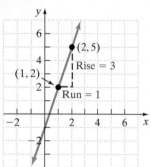

Figure 46

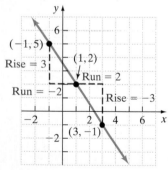

> **Quick ✔**
>
> **24.** Draw a graph of the line that contains the point $(-1, 3)$ and has a slope of
>
> (a) $\dfrac{1}{3}$ (b) -4 (c) 0

7 Use the Point-Slope Form of a Line

A second reason we care so much about slope is that it can be used to help us find the equation of a line. Suppose that L is a nonvertical line with slope m containing the point (x_1, y_1). See Figure 47.

Figure 47

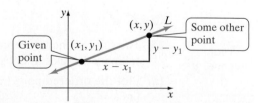

For any other point (x, y) on L, we know from the formula for the slope of a line that

$$m = \frac{y - y_1}{x - x_1}$$

Multiplying both sides by $x - x_1$, we can rewrite this expression as

$$y - y_1 = m(x - x_1)$$

POINT-SLOPE FORM OF AN EQUATION OF A LINE

An equation of a nonvertical line with slope m that contains the point (x_1, y_1) is

Slope
↓
$$y - y_1 = m(x - x_1)$$
↑   ↑
Given Point

EXAMPLE 10   Using the Point-Slope Form of an Equation of a Line

Find the equation of a line whose slope is 3 and that contains the point $(-2, 5)$.
Graph the line.

Solution

Because we are given the slope and a point on the line, we use the point-slope form of
a line with $m = 3$ and $(x_1, y_1) = (-2, 5)$.

$$y - y_1 = m(x - x_1)$$
$$m = 3,\ x_1 = -2,\ y_1 = 5: \quad y - 5 = 3(x - (-2))$$
$$y - 5 = 3(x + 2)$$

Figure 48

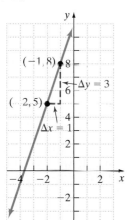

See Figure 48 for a graph of the line. ∎

Quick ✔ *In Problems 25–28, find an equation of the line with the given properties.*
Graph the line.

25. $m = 2, (x_1, y_1) = (3, 5)$

26. $m = -4, (x_1, y_1) = (-2, 3)$

27. $m = \dfrac{1}{3}, (x_1, y_1) = (3, -4)$

28. $m = 0, (x_1, y_1) = (4, -2)$

8 Identify the Slope and y-Intercept of a Line from Its Equation

If we solve the equation in Example 10 for y, we obtain the following:

$$y - 5 = 3(x + 2)$$
Distribute the 3 to remove parentheses: $y - 5 = 3x + 6$
Add 5 to both sides of the equation: $y = 3x + 11$

The coefficient of x, 3, is the slope of the line and the y-intercept of the line is
$y = 3(0) + 11 = 11$. When an equation is written in the form $y = mx + b$, we say the
equation is in *slope-intercept form*.

SLOPE-INTERCEPT FORM OF AN EQUATION OF A LINE

An equation of a line L with slope m and y-intercept b is
$$y = mx + b$$

EXAMPLE 11   Finding the Slope and y-Intercept of a Line
from Its Equation

Write the equation $x - 3y = 9$ in slope-intercept form. Find the slope m and
y-intercept b of the line. Graph the line.

Solution

To put the equation in slope-intercept form, $y = mx + b$, we solve the equation for y.

$$x - 3y = 9$$

Subtract x from both sides of the equation: $\quad -3y = -x + 9$

Divide both sides of the equation by -3: $\quad y = \dfrac{-x + 9}{-3}$

Divide -3 into both terms in the numerator: $\quad y = \dfrac{1}{3}x - 3$

Comparing $y = \dfrac{1}{3}x - 3$ to $y = mx + b$, we see that the coefficient of x, $\dfrac{1}{3}$, is the slope, and the y-intercept is -3.

We graph the line by plotting a point at $(0, -3)$. We then use the slope to find an additional point on the graph by moving right 3 units and up 1 unit from the point $(0, -3)$ to the point $(3, -2)$. Draw a line through the two points and obtain the graph shown in Figure 49.

Figure 49

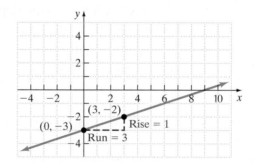

Quick ✓ *In Problems 29–32, find the slope and y-intercept of each line. Graph the line.*

29. $3x - y = 2$ **30.** $6x + 2y = 8$

31. $3x - 2y = 7$ **32.** $7x + 3y = 0$

Work Smart

In Step 2 of Example 12, we chose to use $x_1 = -1$ and $y_1 = 4$, but we could also have used $x_1 = 2$ and $y_1 = -5$. Choose the values of x and y that make the algebra easiest.

9 Find the Equation of a Line Given Two Points

We know that two points are all that is needed to graph a line. If we are given two points, we can find an equation of the line through the points by first finding the slope of the line and then using the point-slope form of a line.

EXAMPLE 12 How to Find an Equation of a Line from Two Points

Find the equation of a line through the points $(-1, 4)$ and $(2, -5)$. If possible, write the equation in slope-intercept form. Graph the line.

Step-by-Step Solution

Step 1: Find the slope of the line containing the points.	Let $(x_1, y_1) = (-1, 4)$ and $(x_2, y_2) = (2, -5)$. Substitute these values into the formula for the slope of a line. $$m = \dfrac{y_2 - y_1}{x_2 - x_1} = \dfrac{-5 - 4}{2 - (-1)} = \dfrac{-9}{3} = -3$$
Step 2: Use the point-slope form of a line to find the equation.	With $m = -3$, $x_1 = -1$, and $y_1 = 4$, we have $$y - y_1 = m(x - x_1)$$ $$y - 4 = -3(x - (-1))$$ $$y - 4 = -3(x + 1)$$
Step 3: Solve the equation for y.	Distribute the -3: $\quad y - 4 = -3x - 3$ Add 4 to both sides: $\quad y = -3x + 1$

Figure 50

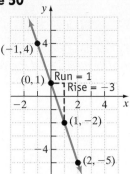

The slope of the line is -3 and the y-intercept is 1. See Figure 50 for the graph.   ∎

Quick ✔ *In Problems 33–35, find the equation of the line containing the given points. If possible, write the equation in slope-intercept form. Graph the line.*

33. $(1, 3); (4, 9)$ **34.** $(-2, 4); (2, 2)$

35. $(-4, 6); (3, 6)$

EXAMPLE 13 Finding an Equation of a Line from Two Points

Find the equation of a line through the points $(-3, 2)$ and $(-3, -2)$. If possible, write the equation in slope-intercept form. Graph the line.

Solution

Let $(x_1, y_1) = (-3, 2)$ and $(x_2, y_2) = (-3, -2)$. Substitute these values into the formula for the slope of a line.

$$m = \frac{y_2 - y_1}{x_2 - x_1} = \frac{-2 - 2}{-3 - (-3)} = \frac{-4}{0} \quad \text{undefined}$$

The slope is undefined, so the line is vertical. The equation of the line is $x = -3$. See Figure 51 for the graph.

Work Smart

If you plot the points first, it will be clear that the line through the points is vertical.

Figure 51

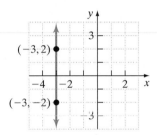

∎

Quick ✔

36. Find an equation of the line containing the points $(3, 2)$ and $(3, -4)$. If possible, write the answer in slope-intercept form. Graph the line.

The presentation of lines dealt with two types of problems.

1. Given an equation, classify and graph it. (See Examples 1–5.)

2. Given a graph, or information about a graph, find its equation. (See Examples 10, 12, and 13.)

This text deals with both types of problems.

SUMMARY EQUATIONS OF LINES

Form of Line	Formula	Comments
Horizontal Line	$y = b$	Graph is a horizontal line (slope is 0) with y-intercept b.
Vertical Line	$x = a$	Graph is a vertical line (undefined slope) with x-intercept a.
Point-slope	$y - y_1 = m(x - x_1)$	Useful for finding the equation of a line given a point and a slope or two points.
Slope-intercept	$y = mx + b$	Useful for quickly determining the slope and y-intercept of the line.
Standard	$Ax + By = C$	Straightforward to find the x- and y-intercepts.

Work Smart: Study Skills

To determine which equation of a line to use, ask yourself "What information do I know?"

If you know (1) the slope and a point that isn't the y-intercept, then use the point-slope form (2) the slope and the y-intercept, then use the slope-intercept form (3) two points, then use the slope formula with the point-slope form (4) and if the slope is undefined, use the vertical line.

1.6 EXERCISES

MathXL   PRACTICE   WATCH   DOWNLOAD   READ   REVIEW

1–36. are the **Quick ✔s** *that follow each* **EXAMPLE**

Building Skills

In Problems 37–44, graph each linear equation by plotting points. See Objective 1.

37. $x - 2y = 6$ **38.** $2x - y = -8$

39. $3x + 2y = 12$ **40.** $-5x + y = 10$

41. $\frac{2}{3}x + y = 6$ **42.** $2x - \frac{3}{2}y = 10$

43. $5x - 3y = 6$ **44.** $-7x + 3y = 9$

In Problems 45–54, graph each linear equation by finding its intercepts. See Objective 2.

45. $3x + y = 6$ **46.** $-2x + y = 4$

47. $5x - 3y = 15$ **48.** $-4x + 3y = 24$

49. $\frac{1}{3}x - \frac{1}{2}y = 1$ **50.** $\frac{1}{4}x + \frac{1}{5}y = 2$

51. $2x + y = 0$ **52.** $4x + 3y = 0$

53. $\frac{2}{3}x - \frac{1}{2}y = 0$ **54.** $-\frac{3}{2}x + \frac{3}{4}y = 0$

In Problems 55–60, graph each linear equation. See Objective 3.

55. $x = -5$ **56.** $x = 5$

57. $y = 1$ **58.** $y = 6$

59. $2y + 8 = -6$ **60.** $3y + 20 = -10$

In Problems 61–64, (a) find the slope of the line and (b) interpret the slope. See Objective 4.

61.
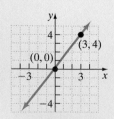

62.
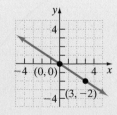

63.
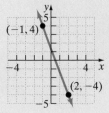

64.
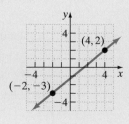

In Problems 65–76, plot each pair of points and graph the line containing them. Determine the slope of the line. See Objective 4.

65. $(0, 0); (1, 5)$

66. $(0, 0); (-2, 5)$

67. $(-2, 3); (1, -6)$

68. $(3, -1); (-2, 11)$

69. $(-2, 3); (3, 7)$

70. $(1, -4); (-1, 3)$

71. $(-3, 2); (4, 2)$

72. $(-3, 1); (2, 1)$

73. $(10, 2); (10, -3)$

74. $(4, 1); (4, -3)$

75. $\left(\frac{1}{2}, \frac{5}{3}\right); \left(\frac{9}{4}, \frac{11}{6}\right)$

76. $\left(\frac{7}{3}, \frac{5}{2}\right); \left(\frac{13}{9}, \frac{13}{4}\right)$

In Problems 77–86, graph the line containing the given point and having slope m. Do not find the equation of the line. See Objective 6.

77. $m = 3; (1, 2)$ **78.** $m = 2; (-1, 4)$

79. $m = -2; (-3, 1)$ **80.** $m = -4; (-1, 5)$

81. $m = \frac{1}{3}; (-3, 4)$ **82.** $m = \frac{4}{3}; (-2, -5)$

83. $m = -\frac{3}{2}; (2, 5)$ **84.** $m = -\frac{1}{2}; (3, 3)$

85. $m = 0; (1, 2)$ **86.** m is undefined; $(-5, 2)$

In Problems 87 and 88, the slope and a point on a line are given. Use the information to find three additional points on the line. Answers may vary.

87. $m = \frac{5}{2}; (-2, 3)$ **88.** $m = -\frac{2}{3}; (1, -3)$

In Problems 89–92, find an equation of the line. Express your answer in slope-intercept form. See Objective 7.

89.   **90.**
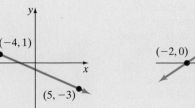

91. 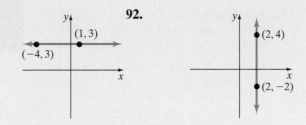   **92.**

In Problems 93–102, find an equation of the line with the given slope and containing the given point. Express your answer in slope-intercept form, if possible. See Objective 7.

93. $m = 2$; $(0, 0)$

94. $m = -1$; $(0, 0)$

95. $m = -3$; $(-1, 1)$

96. $m = 4$; $(2, -1)$

97. $m = \dfrac{4}{3}$; $(3, 2)$

98. $m = \dfrac{1}{2}$; $(2, 1)$

99. $m = -\dfrac{5}{4}$; $(-2, 4)$ *Test*

100. $m = -\dfrac{4}{3}$; $(1, -3)$

101. m undefined; $(6, 1)$

102. $m = 0$; $(3, -2)$

In Problems 103–114, find an equation of the line containing the given points. Express your answer in slope-intercept form, if possible. See Objective 9.

103. $(0, 0)$; $(5, 7)$

104. $(0, 0)$; $(4, -3)$

105. $(3, 2)$; $(4, 7)$

106. $(1, 3)$; $(3, 7)$

107. $(-2, 1)$; $(5, -2)$

108. $(-3, 1)$; $(1, 6)$

109. $(-1, -3)$; $(-1, 5)$

110. $(-3, -4)$; $(1, -4)$

111. $(1, 3)$; $(-3, -7)$

112. $(-5, 1)$; $(1, -1)$

113. $(2, 4)$; $(-4, 4)$

114. $(3, 1)$; $(3, -4)$

In Problems 115–126, find the slope and y-intercept of each line. Graph the line. See Objective 8.

115. $y = 2x - 1$

116. $y = 3x + 2$

117. $y = -4x$

118. $y = -7x$

119. $2x + y = 3$

120. $-3x + y = 1$

121. $4x + 2y = 8$

122. $3x + 6y = 12$

123. $x - 4y - 2 = 0$ *Test*

124. $2x - 5y - 10 = 0$

125. $x = 3$

126. $y = -4$

Applying the Concepts

127. Find an equation for the x-axis.

128. Find an equation for the y-axis.

129. Maximum Heart Rate   The data below represent the maximum number of heartbeats that a healthy individual should have during a 15-second interval of time while exercising for different ages.

(a) Plot the ordered pairs (x, y) on a graph and connect the points with straight lines.

(b) Compute and interpret the average rate of change in the maximum number of heartbeats between 20 and 30 years of age.

(c) Compute and interpret the average rate of change in the maximum number of heartbeats between 50 and 60 years of age.

(d) Based upon your results to parts (a), (b), and (c), do you think that the maximum number of heartbeats is linearly related to age? Why?

Age, x	Maximum Number of Heartbeats, y
20	50
30	47.5
40	45
50	42.5
60	40
70	37.5

SOURCE: *American Heart Association*

130. Raisins The following data represent the weight (in grams) of a box of raisins and the number of raisins in the box.

(a) Plot the ordered pairs (x, y) on a graph and connect the points with straight lines.

(b) Compute and interpret the average rate of change in the number of raisins between 42.3 and 42.5 grams.

(c) Compute and interpret the average rate of change in the number of raisins between 42.7 and 42.8 grams.

(d) Based upon your results to parts (a), (b), and (c), do you think that the number of raisins is linearly related to weight? Why?

Weight (in grams), x	Number of Raisins, y
42.3	82
42.5	86
42.6	89
42.7	91
42.8	93

SOURCE: *Jennifer Maxwell, student at Joliet Junior College*

131. Average Income An individual's income varies with age. The following data show the average income of individuals of different ages in the United States for 2005.

(a) Plot the ordered pairs (x, y) on a graph and connect the points with straight lines.

(b) Compute and interpret the average rate of change in average income between 20 and 30 years of age.

(c) Compute and interpret the average rate of change in average income between 50 and 60 years of age.

(d) Based upon your results to parts (a), (b), and (c), do you think that average income is linearly related to age? Why?

Age, x	Average Income, y
20	$10,469
30	$31,161
40	$40,964
50	$43,627
60	$40,654
70	$21,784

SOURCE: *Statistical Abstract, 2008*

132. U.S. Population The following data represent the population of the United States between 1930 and 2000.

(a) Plot the ordered pairs (x, y) on a graph and connect the points with straight lines.

(b) Compute and interpret the average rate of change in population between 1930 and 1940.

(c) Compute and interpret the average rate of change in population between 1990 and 2000.

(d) Based upon your results to parts (a), (b), and (c), do you think that population is linearly related to the year? Why?

Year, x	Population, y
1930	123,202,624
1940	132,164,569
1950	151,325,798
1960	179,323,175
1970	203,302,031
1980	226,542,203
1990	248,709,873
2000	281,421,906

SOURCE: *U.S. Census Bureau*

133. Measuring Temperature The relationship between Celsius (°C) and Fahrenheit (°F) degrees for measuring temperature is linear. Find an equation relating °C and °F if 0°C corresponds to 32°F and 100°C corresponds to 212°F. Use the equation to find the Celsius measure of 60°F.

134. Building Codes As a result of the Americans with Disabilities Act (ADA, 1990), the building code states that access ramps must have a slope not steeper than $\frac{1}{12}$. Interpret what this result means.

135. Which of the following equations might have the graph shown? (More than one answer is possible.)

(a) $y = 3x - 1$
(b) $y = -2x + 3$
(c) $y = 2x + 3$
(d) $3x - 2y = 4$
(e) $-3x + 2y = -4$

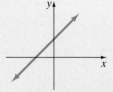

136. Which of the following equations might have the graph shown? (More than one answer is possible.)

(a) $y = 2x - 5$
(b) $y = -x + 2$
(c) $y = -\frac{2}{3}x - 3$
(d) $4x + 3y = -5$
(e) $-2x + y = -4$

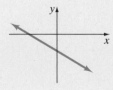

Explaining the Concepts

137. Name the five forms of equations of lines given in this section.

138. What type of line has one x-intercept, but no y-intercept?

139. What type of line has one y-intercept, but no x-intercept?

140. What type of line has one x-intercept and one y-intercept?

141. Are there any lines that have no intercepts? Explain your answer.

142. Exploration Graph $y = 2x$, $y = 2x + 3$, $y = 2x + 7$, and $y = 2x - 4$ on the same Cartesian plane. What pattern do you observe? In general, describe the graph of $y = 2x + b$.

143. Exploration Graph $y = \frac{1}{2}x$, $y = x$, and $y = 2x$ on the same Cartesian plane. What pattern do you observe? In general, describe the graph of $y = ax$ with $a > 0$.

144. Exploration Graph $y = -\frac{1}{2}x$, $y = -x$, and $y = -2x$ on the same Cartesian plane. What pattern do you observe? In general, describe the graph of $y = ax$ with $a < 0$.

The Graphing Calculator

145. To see the role that the slope m plays in the graph of a linear equation $y = mx + b$, graph the following lines on the same screen.

$$Y_1 = 0x + 2 \qquad Y_2 = \frac{1}{2}x + 2$$

$$Y_3 = 2x + 2 \qquad Y_4 = 6x + 2$$

State some general conclusions about the graph of $y = mx + b$ for $m \geq 0$. Now graph

$$Y_1 = -\frac{1}{2}x + 2 \quad Y_2 = -2x + 2 \quad Y_3 = -6x + 2$$

State some general conclusions about the graph of $y = mx + b$ for $m < 0$.

146. To see the role that the y-intercept b plays in the graph of a linear equation $y = mx + b$, graph the following lines on the same screen.

$$Y_1 = 2x \qquad Y_2 = 2x + 2$$

$$Y_3 = 2x + 5 \qquad Y_4 = 2x - 4$$

State some general conclusions about the graph of $y = 2x + b$.

1.7 Parallel and Perpendicular Lines

OBJECTIVES

1 Define Parallel Lines
2 Find Equations of Parallel Lines
3 Define Perpendicular Lines
4 Find Equations of Perpendicular Lines

Work Smart

The words "if and only if" given in the definition mean that there are two statements being made.

If two nonvertical lines are parallel, then their slopes are equal and they have different y-intercepts.

If two nonvertical lines have equal slopes and different y-intercepts, then they are parallel.

Preparing for...Answers **P1.** $\frac{1}{3}$

P2. $-\frac{5}{3}$

Preparing for Parallel and Perpendicular Lines

Before getting started, take this readiness quiz. If you get a problem wrong, go back to the section cited and review the material.

P1. Determine the reciprocal of 3. [Section R.3, pp. 23–24]

P2. Determine the reciprocal of $-\frac{3}{5}$. [Section R.3, pp. 23–24]

1 Define Parallel Lines

When two lines (in the Cartesian plane) do not intersect (that is, they have no points in common), they are said to be *parallel*.

> **PARALLEL LINES**
>
> Two nonvertical lines are **parallel** if and only if their slopes are equal and they have different y-intercepts. Vertical lines are parallel if they have different x-intercepts.

Figure 52(a) on the next page shows nonvertical parallel lines. Figure 52(b) on the next page shows vertical parallel lines.

Figure 52
Parallel lines

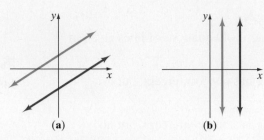

(a)   (b)

EXAMPLE 1 Determining Whether Two Lines Are Parallel

Determine whether the given lines are parallel.

(a) L_1: $4x + y = 8$

   L_2: $6x + 2y = 12$

(b) L_1: $-3x + 2y = 6$

   L_2: $6x - 4y = 8$

Solution

To determine whether two lines are parallel, we determine the slope and y-intercept of each line by putting the equation of the line in slope-intercept form. If the slopes are the same, but the y-intercepts are different, then the lines are parallel.

(a)   Solve L_1 for y: $4x + y = 8$
   Subtract $4x$
   from both sides: $y = -4x + 8$

The slope of L_1 is -4 and the y-intercept is 8.

Solve L_2 for y: $6x + 2y = 12$
   Subtract $6x$ from
       both sides: $2y = -6x + 12$
   Divide both sides
           by 2: $y = \dfrac{-6x + 12}{2}$
   Divide each term in
   the numerator by 2: $y = -3x + 6$

The slope of L_2 is -3 and the y-intercept is 6.

Because the lines have different slopes, they are not parallel.

(b)   Solve L_1 for y: $-3x + 2y = 6$

Add $3x$ to both sides: $2y = 3x + 6$

Divide both sides by 2: $y = \dfrac{3x + 6}{2}$

Divide each term in
the numerator by 2: $y = \dfrac{3}{2}x + 3$

The slope of L_1 is $\dfrac{3}{2}$ and the y-intercept is 3.

Solve L_2 for y: $6x - 4y = 8$
Subtract $6x$ from
   both sides: $-4y = -6x + 8$

Divide both
sides by -4: $y = \dfrac{-6x + 8}{-4}$
Divide each term in
the numerator by -4: $y = \dfrac{3}{2}x - 2$

The slope of L_2 is $\dfrac{3}{2}$ and the y-intercept is -2.

Because the lines have the same slope, $\dfrac{3}{2}$, but different y-intercepts, the lines are parallel. ∎

Quick ✔

1. Two lines are parallel if and only if they have the same _____ and different _____ .

In Problems 2–4, determine whether the two lines are parallel.

2. L_1: $y = 3x + 1$

   L_2: $y = -3x - 3$

3. L_1: $6x + 3y = 3$

   L_2: $-8x - 4y = 12$

4. L_1: $-3x + 5y = 10$

   L_2: $6x + 10y = 10$

2 Find Equations of Parallel Lines

Now that we know how to identify parallel lines, let's discuss how to find the equation of a line that is parallel to a given line.

EXAMPLE 2 How to Find the Equation of a Line That Is Parallel to a Given Line

Find an equation for the line that is parallel to $4x + 2y = 2$ and contains the point $(-2, 3)$. Graph the lines in the Cartesian plane.

Step-by-Step Solution

Step 1: Find the slope of the given line by putting the equation in slope-intercept form.	$4x + 2y = 2$ Subtract 4x from both sides: $\quad 2y = -4x + 2$ Divide both sides by 2: $\quad y = -2x + 1$ The slope of the line is -2.
Step 2: Use the point-slope form of a line with the given point and the slope found in Step 1 to find the equation of the parallel line.	$y - y_1 = m(x - x_1)$ $m = -2, x_1 = -2, y_1 = 3: \quad y - 3 = -2(x - (-2))$
Step 3: Put the equation in slope-intercept form by solving for y.	$y - 3 = -2(x + 2)$ Distribute the -2: $\quad y - 3 = -2x - 4$ Add 3 to both sides: $\quad y = -2x - 1$

The line parallel to $4x + 2y = 2$ containing $(-2, 3)$ is $y = -2x - 1$. Notice that the slopes of the two lines are the same, but the y-intercepts are different. Figure 53 shows the graph of the parallel lines.

Figure 53

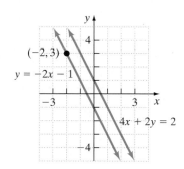

Quick ✔ *In Problems 5 and 6, find the equation of the line that contains the given point and is parallel to the given line. Write the line in slope-intercept form. Graph the lines.*

5. $(5, 8); y = 3x + 1$ **6.** $(-2, 4); 3x + 2y = 10$

3 Define Perpendicular Lines

When two lines intersect at a right angle $(90°)$, they are said to be **perpendicular.** See Figure 54.

We use the slopes of the lines to determine whether two lines are perpendicular.

Figure 54
Perpendicular lines

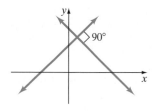

Work Smart

If m_1 and m_2 are negative reciprocals of each other, then

$$m_1 = \frac{-1}{m_2}.$$

PERPENDICULAR LINES

Two nonvertical lines are **perpendicular** if and only if the product of their slopes is -1. Alternatively, two nonvertical lines are perpendicular if their slopes are negative reciprocals of each other. Any vertical line is perpendicular to any horizontal line.

EXAMPLE 3 Finding the Slope of a Line Perpendicular to a Given Line

Find the slope of any line perpendicular to a line whose slope is $\frac{5}{4}$.

Solution

The negative reciprocal of $\frac{5}{4}$ is $\frac{-1}{\frac{5}{4}} = -1 \cdot \frac{4}{5} = -\frac{4}{5}$. Any line whose slope is $-\frac{4}{5}$ will be

perpendicular to the line whose slope is $\frac{5}{4}$ because $-\frac{4}{5} \cdot \left(\frac{5}{4}\right) = -1$. ∎

Quick ✔

7. Two lines are perpendicular if and only if the product of their slopes is __.

8. Find the slope of any line perpendicular to a line whose slope is -3.

EXAMPLE 4 Determining Whether Two Lines Are Perpendicular

Determine whether the given lines are perpendicular.

(a) $L_1: y = 4x + 1$
    $L_2: y = -4x - 3$

(b) $L_1: y = \frac{2}{3}x - 5$
    $L_2: y = -\frac{3}{2}x + 2$

Solution

(a) The slope of L_1 is $m_1 = 4$. The slope of L_2 is $m_2 = -4$. Because the product of the slopes, $m_1 m_2 = 4 \cdot (-4) = -16 \neq -1$, the lines are not perpendicular. Notice that the slopes are not negative reciprocals of each other.

(b) The slope of L_1 is $m_1 = \frac{2}{3}$. The slope of L_2 is $m_2 = -\frac{3}{2}$. Because the

product of the slopes is $m_1 \cdot m_2 = \frac{2}{3} \cdot \left(-\frac{3}{2}\right) = -1$, the lines are perpendicular.

Notice that the slopes are negative reciprocals of each other. ∎

Quick ✔ *In Problems 9–11, determine whether the given lines are perpendicular.*

9. $L_1: y = 5x - 3$
    $L_2: y = -\frac{1}{5}x - 4$

10. $L_1: 4x - y = 3$
    $L_2: x - 4y = 2$

11. $L_1: 2y + 4 = 0$
    $L_2: 3x - 6 = 0$

---

4 Find Equations of Perpendicular Lines

Now that we know how to find the slope of a line perpendicular to a second line, we can find the equation of a line perpendicular to a second line.

EXAMPLE 5 How to Find the Equation of a Line Perpendicular to a Given Line

Find an equation of the line that is perpendicular to the line $2x + 5y = 10$ and contains the point $(4, -1)$. Write the equation in slope-intercept form. Graph the two lines.

Step-by-Step Solution

Step 1: Find the slope of the given line by putting the equation in slope-intercept form.	$2x + 5y = 10$
	Subtract 2x from both sides: $5y = -2x + 10$
	Divide both sides by 5: $y = -\dfrac{2}{5}x + 2$
	The slope of the line is $-\dfrac{2}{5}$.
Step 2: Find the slope of the perpendicular line.	The slope of the perpendicular line is the negative reciprocal of $-\dfrac{2}{5}$, which is $\dfrac{5}{2}$.
Step 3: Use the point-slope form of a line with the given point and the slope found in Step 2 to find the equation of the perpendicular line.	$y - y_1 = m(x - x_1)$ $m = \dfrac{5}{2}, x_1 = 4, y_1 = -1:$ $y - (-1) = \dfrac{5}{2}(x - 4)$
Step 4: Put the equation in slope-intercept form by solving for y.	$y + 1 = \dfrac{5}{2}(x - 4)$
	Distribute the $\dfrac{5}{2}$: $y + 1 = \dfrac{5}{2}x - 10$
	Subtract 1 from both sides: $y = \dfrac{5}{2}x - 11$

The equation of the line perpendicular to $2x + 5y = 10$ through $(4, -1)$ is $y = \dfrac{5}{2}x - 11$. Figure 55 shows the graphs of the two lines.

Figure 55

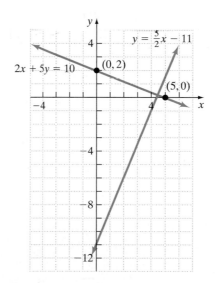

Quick ✔ *In Problems 12–14, find the equation of the line that contains the given point and is perpendicular to the given line. Write the line in slope-intercept form. Graph the lines.*

12. $(-4, 2); y = 2x + 1$

13. $(-3, -4); 3x - 4y = 8$

14. $(3, -2); x = 3$

1.7 EXERCISES

1–14. *are the* **Quick ✔s** *that follow each* **EXAMPLE**

Building Skills

In Problems 15–18, a slope of a line is given. Determine (a) the slope of any line parallel to the line whose slope is given and (b) the slope of any line perpendicular to the line whose slope is given. See Objectives 1 and 3.

15. $m = 5$

16. $m = -\dfrac{8}{5}$

17. $m = -\dfrac{5}{6}$

18. $m = 0$

In Problems 19–26, determine whether the given linear equations are parallel, perpendicular, or neither. See Objectives 1 and 3.

19. $y = 5x + 4$
  $y = 5x - 7$

20. $y = 3x - 1$
  $y = -\dfrac{1}{3}x - 5$

21. $8x + y = 12$
  $2x - 8y = 3$

22. $-3x - y = 3$
  $6x + 2y = 9$

23. $-4x + 2y = 12$
  $x + 2y = 6$

24. $10x - 3y = 5$
  $5x + 6y = 3$

25. $-x + \dfrac{1}{3}y = \dfrac{1}{3}$
  $x - \dfrac{1}{3}y = \dfrac{5}{3}$

26. $\dfrac{1}{2}x - \dfrac{3}{2}y = 3$
  $2x + \dfrac{2}{3}y = 1$

In Problems 27–32, find an equation of the line L. Express your answer in slope-intercept form. See Objectives 2 and 4.

27.

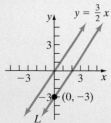

L is parallel to $y = \dfrac{3}{2}x$

28.

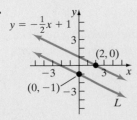

L is parallel to $y = -\dfrac{1}{2}x + 1$

29.

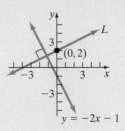

L is perpendicular to $y = -2x - 1$

30.

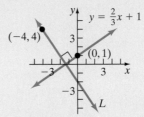

L is perpendicular to $y = \dfrac{2}{3}x + 1$

31.

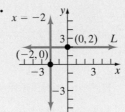

L is perpendicular to $x = -2$

32.

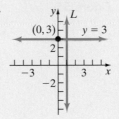

L is perpendicular to $y = 3$

In Problems 33–46, find an equation of the line with the given properties. Express your answer in slope-intercept form. Graph the lines. See Objectives 2 and 4.

33. Parallel to $y = 2x + 3$ through the point $(3, 1)$

34. Parallel to $y = -3x + 1$ through the point $(2, 5)$

35. Perpendicular to $y = -2x + 1$ through the point $(2, 3)$

36. Perpendicular to $y = 4x + 3$ through the point $(4, 1)$

37. Parallel to $y = 1$ through the point $(-1, -3)$

38. Parallel to $x = -2$ through the point $(2, 5)$

39. Perpendicular to $x = 1$ through the point $(1, 3)$

40. Perpendicular to $y = 8$ through the point $(2, -4)$

41. Parallel to $3x - y = 2$ through the point $(1, 5)$

42. Parallel to $2x + y = 5$ through the point $(-4, 3)$

43. Perpendicular to $4x + 3y - 1 = 0$ through the point $(-4, 1)$

44. Perpendicular to $-2x + 5y - 3 = 0$ through the point $(2, -3)$

45. Parallel to $5x + 2y = 1$ through the point $(-2, -3)$

46. Perpendicular to $3x + y = 1$ through the point $(3, -1)$

Mixed Practice

In Problems 47–52, two points on L_1 and two points on L_2 are given. Plot the points in the Cartesian plane and draw a line through the points. Compute the slope of the line containing these points and determine whether the lines are parallel, perpendicular, or neither.

47. L_1: $(1, 2)$; $(6, 5)$
L_2: $(-2, 3)$; $(1, -2)$

48. L_1: $(1, 1)$; $(4, 3)$
L_2: $(-1, 3)$; $(3, -3)$

49. L_1: $(-2, 4)$; $(1, -3)$
L_2: $(-1, -6)$; $(-4, 1)$

50. L_1: $(-3, 0)$; $(0, 2)$
L_2: $(4, 8)$; $(2, 5)$

51. L_1: $(0, 5)$; $(1, 3)$
L_2: $(-4, 6)$; $(0, 14)$

52. L_1: $(1, -3)$; $(5, -4)$
L_2: $(0, 4)$; $(8, 2)$

Applying the Concepts

△ **53. Geometry** Given the points $A = (1, 1)$, $B = (4, 3)$, and $C = (2, 6)$,

(a) Plot the points in a Cartesian plane. Connect the points to form a triangle.
(b) Verify that the triangle is a right triangle by showing that the line segment $\overline{AB}$ is perpendicular to the line segment $\overline{BC}$ and therefore forms a right angle.

△ **54. Geometry** Given the points $A = (-2, -2)$, $B = (3, 1)$, and $C = (-5, 3)$,

(a) Plot the points in a Cartesian plane. Connect the points to form a triangle.
(b) Verify that the triangle is a right triangle by showing that the line segment $\overline{AB}$ is perpendicular to the line segment $\overline{AC}$ and therefore forms a right angle.

△ **55. Geometry** In geometry, we learn that a **parallelogram** is a quadrilateral in which both pairs of opposite sides are parallel. Given the points $A = (2, 2)$, $B = (7, 3)$, $C = (8, 6)$, and $D = (3, 5)$,

(a) Plot the points in a Cartesian plane. Connect the points to form a quadrilateral.
(b) Verify that the quadrilateral is a parallelogram by showing that the opposite sides are parallel.

△ **56. Geometry** In geometry, we learn that a parallelogram is a quadrilateral in which both pairs of opposite sides are parallel. Given the points $A = (-2, -1)$, $B = (4, 1)$, $C = (5, 5)$, and $D = (-1, 3)$,

(a) Plot the points in a Cartesian plane. Connect the points to form a quadrilateral.
(b) Verify that the quadrilateral is a parallelogram by showing that the opposite sides are parallel.

Extending the Concepts

57. Find A so that $Ax + 4y = 12$ is perpendicular to $4x + y = 3$.

58. Find B so that $-6x + By = 3$ is perpendicular to $2x - 3y = 8$.

59. The figure shows the graph of two parallel lines. Which of the following pairs of equations might have such a graph?

(a) $y = x + 3$
$y = -x - 1$
(b) $y = 2x + 3$
$y = 2x + 1$
(c) $x - 2y = 4$
$x - 2y = -3$
(d) $-2x + y = 5$
$-2x + y = 2$
(e) $x - y = 3$
$3x - 3y = 9$

60. The figure shows the graph of two perpendicular lines. Which of the following pairs of equations might have such a graph?

(a) $y = 3x + 4$
$y = -\dfrac{1}{3}x - 2$
(b) $-2x + y = 3$
$x + 2y = 1$
(c) $2x + 3y = -2$
$3x - 2y = 5$
(d) $3x + 4y = 5$
$-3x + 4y = -2$
(e) $x - 2y = 6$
$2y + x = 2$

Explaining the Concepts

61. If two nonvertical lines have the same x-intercept, but different y-intercepts, can they be parallel? Explain your answer.

62. Why don't we say that a horizontal line is perpendicular to a vertical line if they have slopes that are negative reciprocals of each other?

CHAPTER 1 Activity: Pass the Paper

Focus: Solving equations and inequalities
Time: 15 minutes
Group size: 4
Materials needed: One blank piece of notebook paper per group member

To the right are two equations and two inequalities. In this activity you will work together to solve these problems by following the procedure below. Be sure to read through the entire procedure together before beginning the activity so all group members will understand the procedure.

Procedure

1. Write one of the problems shown at the top of your paper. Be sure that each group member chooses a different problem.

2. Two lines below the original problem, write out the first step for solving the problem.

3. Fold the top of the paper down to cover the original problem, leaving your first step visible.

4. Pass your paper to a different group member. You might want to arrange your seats so that the papers can be passed around in a circle.

5. Continue solving the problems one step at a time, covering the step above yours, and passing the paper to the next group member, until all problems are solved.

6. As a group, discuss the solutions and decide whether or not they are correct. If any of the solutions are incorrect, solve them correctly together.

Problems

(a) $4 - (x - 3) = -10 + 5(x + 1)$
(b) $3(x - 2) + 8 = 5x - 2(x - 1)$
(c) $3(x - 4) - 5x > 2x + 12$
(d) $4(x + 1) - 2x \geq 5x - 11$

CHAPTER 1 Review

Section 1.1 Linear Equations	
KEY CONCEPTS	**KEY TERMS**
• **Linear Equation in One Variable** An equation equivalent to one of the form $ax + b = 0$, where a and b are real numbers with $a \neq 0$. • **Addition Property of Equality** For real numbers $a, b,$ and $c,$ if $a = b,$ then $a + c = b + c.$ • **Multiplication Property of Equality** For real numbers $a, b,$ and c where $c \neq 0,$ if $a = b,$ then $ac = bc.$	Equation in one variable Sides of the equation Solution Satisfies Solve an equation Solution set Equivalent equations Conditional equation Contradiction Identity

YOU SHOULD BE ABLE TO...	EXAMPLE	REVIEW EXERCISES
1 Determine whether a number is a solution to an equation (p. 48)	Example 1	1–4
2 Solve linear equations (p. 49)	Examples 2 through 6	5–18
3 Determine whether an equation is a conditional equation, identity, or contradiction (p. 54)	Examples 7 and 8	5–14

In Problems 1–4, determine which of the numbers, if any, are solutions to the given equation.

1. $3x - 4 = 6 + x$; $x = 5$, $x = 6$

2. $-1 - 4x = 2(3 - 2x) - 7$; $x = -2$, $x = -1$

3. $4y - (1 - y) + 5 = -6 - 2(3y - 5) - 2y$;
  $y = -2$, $y = 0$

4. $\dfrac{w - 7}{3} - \dfrac{w}{4} = -\dfrac{7}{6}$; $w = -14$, $w = 7$

In Problems 5–14, solve the linear equation. State whether the equation is an identity, contradiction, or conditional equation.

5. $2w + 9 = 15$

6. $-4 = 8 - 3y$

7. $2x + 5x - 1 = 20$

8. $7x + 5 - 8x = 13$

9. $-2(x - 4) = 8 - 2x$

10. $3(2r + 1) - 5 = 9(r - 1) - 3r$

11. $\dfrac{2y + 3}{4} - \dfrac{y}{2} = 5$

12. $\dfrac{x}{3} + \dfrac{2x}{5} = \dfrac{x - 20}{15}$

13. $0.2(x - 6) + 1.75 = 4.25 + 0.1(3x + 10)$

14. $2.1w - 3(2.4 - 0.2w) = 0.9(3w - 5) - 2.7$

In Problems 15 and 16, determine which values of the variable must be excluded from the domain.

15. $\dfrac{8}{2x + 3}$

16. $\dfrac{6x - 5}{6(x - 1) + 3}$

17. State Income Tax A resident of Missouri completes her state tax return and determines that she paid $2370 in state income tax in 2007. The solution to the equation $2370 = 0.06(x - 9000) + 315$ represents her Missouri taxable income x in 2007. Solve the equation to determine her Missouri taxable income. (SOURCE: *Missouri Department of Revenue*)

18. Movie Club The DVD club to which you belong offers unlimited DVDs at $10 off the regular price if you buy 1 at the regular price. You purchase 5 DVDs through this offer and spend $69.75 (not including tax and shipping). The solution to the equation $x + 4(x - 10) = 69.75$ represents the regular club price x for a DVD. Solve the equation to determine the regular club price for a DVD.

Section 1.2 An Introduction to Problem Solving

KEY CONCEPTS

- **Simple Interest Formula**
  $I = Prt$, where I is interest, P is principal, r is the per annum interest rate expressed as a decimal, t is time in years
- **Uniform Motion Formula**
  $d = rt$, where d is distance, r is average speed, t is time

KEY TERMS

Problem solving	Principal
Mathematical modeling	Rate of interest
Modeling process	Simple interest
Mathematical model	Mixture problems
Direct translation	Uniform motion
Interest	

YOU SHOULD BE ABLE TO...	EXAMPLE	REVIEW EXERCISES
1 Translate English sentences into mathematical statements (p. 58)	Example 1	19–22
2 Model and solve direct translation problems (p. 61)	Examples 2 through 6	23–28
3 Model and solve mixture problems (p. 65)	Examples 7 and 8	29–32
4 Model and solve uniform motion problems (p. 68)	Example 9	33–34

In Problems 19–22, translate each of the following English statements into a mathematical statement. Do not solve the equation.

19. The sum of three times a number and 7 is 22.

20. The difference of a number and 3 is equivalent to the quotient of the number and 2.

21. 20% of a number equals the difference of the number and 12.

22. The product of six and a number is the same as 4 less than twice the number.

For Problems 23 and 24, translate each English statement into a mathematical statement. Then solve the equation.

23. Shawn is 8 years older than Payton and the sum of their ages is 18. What are their ages?

24. The sum of five consecutive odd integers is 125. Find the integers.

25. Computing Grades Logan is in an elementary statistics course and has test scores of 85, 81, 84, and 77. If the final exam counts the same as two tests, what score does Logan need on the final to have an average of 80?

26. Home Equity Loans On January 15, 2008, Bank of America offered a home equity line of credit at a rate of 6.24% annual simple interest. If Cherie has such a credit line with a balance of $3200, how much interest will she accrue at the end of 1 month?

27. Discounted Price Suppose that REI sells a 0° sleeping bag at the discounted price of $94.50. If this price represents a discount of 30% off the original selling price, find the original price.

28. Minimum Wage On July 24, 2008, the federal minimum wage was increased 12% to $6.55. Determine the federal minimum wage prior to July 24, 2008.

29. Making a Mixture CoffeeAM sells chocolate-covered blueberries for $10.95 per pound and chocolate-covered strawberries for $13.95 per pound. The company wants to sell a mix of the two that would sell for $12.95 per pound with no loss in revenue. How many pounds of each treat should be used to make 12 pounds of the mix?

30. A Sports Mix The Candy Depot sells baseball gumballs for $3.50 per pound and soccer gumballs for $4.50 per pound. The company wants to sell a "sports mix" that sells for $3.75 per pound with no loss in revenue. How many pounds of each gumball type should be included to make 10 pounds of the mix?

31. Investments Angie received an $8000 bonus and wants to invest the money. She can invest part of the money at 8% simple interest with a moderate risk and the rest at 18% simple interest with a high risk. She wants an overall annual return of 12% but does not want to risk losing any more than necessary. How much should she invest at 18% to reach her goal?

32. Antifreeze A 2008 Chevrolet Malibu has an engine coolant system capacity of 7.5 quarts. If the system is currently filled with a mixture that is 30% antifreeze, how much of this mixture should be drained and replaced with pure antifreeze so that the system is filled with a mixture that is 50% antifreeze?

33. Road Trip On a 300-mile trip to Chicago, Josh drove part of the time at 60 miles per hour and the remainder of the trip at 70 miles per hour. If the total trip took 4.5 hours, for how many miles did Josh drive at a rate of 60 miles per hour?

34. Uniform Motion An F15 Strike Eagle near New York City and an F14 Tomcat near San Diego are about 2200 miles apart and traveling towards each other. The F15 is traveling 200 miles per hour faster than the F14 and the planes pass each other after 50 minutes. How fast is each plane traveling?

Section 1.3   Using Formulas to Solve Problems

KEY CONCEPTS	KEY TERMS
• **Geometry Formulas (see pages 74–75)**	Formula Golden rectangle Supplementary angles Complementary angles

YOU SHOULD BE ABLE TO...	EXAMPLE	REVIEW EXERCISES
① Solve for a variable in a formula (p. 73)	Examples 2 and 3	35–44
② Use formulas to solve problems (p. 76)	Examples 4 and 5	45–52

In Problems 35–40, solve for the indicated variable.

35. Solve $y = \dfrac{k}{x}$ for x.

36. Solve $F = \dfrac{9}{5}C + 32$ for C.

37. Solve $P = 2L + 2W$ for W.

38. Solve $\rho = m_1 v_1 + m_2 v_2$ for m_2.

39. Solve $PV = nRT$ for T.

40. Solve $S = 2LW + 2LH + 2WH$ for W.

In Problems 41–44, solve for y.

41. $3x + 4y = 2$

42. $-5x + 4y = 10$

43. $48x - 12y = 60$

44. $\dfrac{2}{5}x + \dfrac{1}{3}y = 8$

45. Temperature Conversions To convert temperatures from Fahrenheit to Celsius, we can use the formula.

$C = \dfrac{5}{9}(F - 32)$. If the melting point for platinum is

3221.6°F, convert this temperature to degrees Celsius.

46. Angles in a Triangle The measure of each congruent angle in an isosceles triangle is 30 degrees larger than the measure of the remaining angle. Determine the measures of all three angles.

47. Window Dimensions The perimeter of a rectangular window is 76 feet. The window is 8 feet longer than it is wide. Find the dimensions of the window.

48. Long-Distance Phone Calls A long-distance telephone company charges a monthly fee of $2.95 and a per-minute charge of $0.04. The monthly cost for long distance is given by $C = 2.95 + 0.04x$ where x is the number of minutes used.

(a) Solve the equation for x.

(b) How many full minutes can Debbie use in one month on this plan if she does not want to spend more than $20 in long distance in one month?

49. Concrete Rick has 80 cubic feet of concrete to pour for his new patio. If the patio is rectangular and Rick wants it to be 12 feet by 18 feet, how thick will the patio be if he uses all the concrete?

50. Right Circular Cones The lateral surface area for a frustum of a right circular cone is given by $A = \pi s(R + r)$ where s is the slant height of the frustum, R is the radius of the base, and r is the radius of the top.

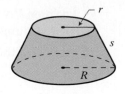

(a) Solve the equation for r.

(b) If the frustum of a right circular cone has a lateral surface area of 10π square feet, a slant height of 2 feet, and a base whose radius is 3 feet, what is the radius of the top of the frustum?

51. Heating Bills On January 15, 2008, the winter energy charge C for Illinois Power residential service was computed using the formula $C = 7.48 + 0.08674x$ for x kilowatt hours (kwh).

(a) Solve the equation for x.

(b) How many kwh were used if the winter energy charge was $206.03? Round to the nearest whole number.

52. Supplementary and Complementary Angles The supplement of an angle and the complement of the same angle sum to 150°. What is the measure of the angle?

Section 1.4 Linear Inequalities

KEY CONCEPTS

- **Linear Inequality in One Variable**
  An inequality of the form $ax + b < c$, $ax + b \le c$, $ax + b > c$, or $ax + b \ge c$, where a, b, and c are real numbers with $a \ne 0$.

- **Interval Notation versus Inequality Notation**

INTERVAL NOTATION	INEQUALITY NOTATION	GRAPH
The open interval (a, b)	$\{x \mid a < x < b\}$	
The closed interval $[a, b]$	$\{x \mid a \le x \le b\}$	
The half-open interval $[a, b)$	$\{x \mid a \le x < b\}$	
The half-open interval $(a, b]$	$\{x \mid a < x \le b\}$	
The interval $[a, \infty)$	$\{x \mid x \ge a\}$	
The interval (a, ∞)	$\{x \mid x > a\}$	
The interval $(-\infty, a]$	$\{x \mid x \le a\}$	
The interval $(-\infty, a)$	$\{x \mid x < a\}$	
The interval $(-\infty, \infty)$	$\{x \mid x \text{ is a real number}\}$	

KEY TERMS

Solve an inequality
Solutions
Solution set
Interval notation
Closed interval
Open interval
Half-open or half-closed interval
Left endpoint
Right endpoint
Equivalent inequalities

- **Addition Property of Inequalities**
  For real numbers a, b, and c

  If $a < b$, then $a + c < b + c$.

  If $a > b$, then $a + b > b + c$.

- **Multiplication Properties of Inequalities**
  For real numbers a, b, and c

  If $a < b$ and if $c > 0$, then $ac < bc$.

  If $a > b$ and if $c > 0$, then $ac > bc$.

  If $a < b$ and if $c < 0$, then $ac > bc$.

  If $a > b$ and if $c < 0$, then $ac < bc$.

YOU SHOULD BE ABLE TO...	EXAMPLE	REVIEW EXERCISES
1 Represent inequalities using the real number line and interval notation (p. 81)	Examples 1 through 4	53–56
2 Understand the properties of inequalities (p. 84)		57–58
3 Solve linear inequalities (p. 85)	Examples 5 through 8	59–68
4 Solve problems involving linear inequalities (p. 88)	Example 9	69–72

In Problems 53 and 54, write each inequality using interval notation and graph the inequality.

53. $2 < x \leq 7$

54. $x > -2$

In Problems 55 and 56, write each interval as an inequality involving x and graph the inequality.

55. $(-\infty, 4]$

56. $[-1, 3)$

In Problems 57 and 58, use the Addition Property and/or Multiplication Property to find a and b.

57. If $5 \leq x \leq 9$, then $a \leq 2x - 3 \leq b$.

58. If $-2 < x < 0$, then $a < 3x + 5 < b$.

In Problems 59–68, solve each linear inequality. Express your solution using set-builder notation and interval notation. Graph the solution set.

59. $3x + 12 \leq 0$

60. $2 < 1 - 3x$

61. $-7 \leq 3(h + 1) - 8$

62. $-7x - 8 < -22$

63. $3(p - 2) + (5 - p) > 2 - (p - 3)$

64. $2(x + 1) + 1 > 2(x - 2)$

65. $5(x - 1) - 7x > 2(2 - x)$

66. $0.03x + 0.10 > 0.52 - 0.07x$

67. $-\dfrac{4}{9}w + \dfrac{7}{12} < \dfrac{5}{36}$

68. $\dfrac{2}{5}y - 20 > \dfrac{2}{3}y + 12$

69. Octoberfest The German Club plans to rent a hall for their annual Octoberfest banquet. The hall costs $150 to rent plus $7.50 for each person who attends. If the club does not want to spend more than $600 for the event, how many people can attend the banquet?

70. Car Rentals A Ford Taurus at Enterprise Rent-a-Car rents for $43.46 per day. You receive 150 free miles per day but are charged $0.25 per mile for any additional miles. How many miles can you drive per day, on average, and not exceed your daily budget of $60.00?

71. Fund Raising A middle school band sells $1 candy bars at a carnival to raise money for new instruments. The band pays $50.00 to rent a booth and must pay the candy company $0.60 for each bar sold. How many bars must the band sell to be making a profit?

72. Movie Club A DVD club offers unlimited DVDs for $9.95 if you purchase one for $24.95. How many DVDs can you purchase without spending more than $72.00?

Section 1.5 Rectangular Coordinates and Graphs of Equations

KEY CONCEPTS	KEY TERMS	
• **Graph of an Equation in Two Variables** The set of all ordered pairs (x, y) in the xy-plane that satisfy the equation • **Intercepts** The points, if any, where a graph crosses or touches the coordinate axes	x-axis y-axis Origin Rectangular or Cartesian coordinate system xy-plane Coordinate axes Ordered pair Coordinates x-coordinate y-coordinate Abscissa Ordinate	Quadrants Equation in two variables Sides Satisfy Graph of an equation in two variables Point-plotting method Complete graph Intercept x-intercept y-intercept

YOU SHOULD BE ABLE TO...	EXAMPLE	REVIEW EXERCISES
1 Plot points in the rectangular coordinate system (p. 93)	Example 1	73, 74
2 Determine whether an ordered pair is a point on the graph of an equation (p. 95)	Example 2	75, 76
3 Graph an equation using the point-plotting method (p. 97)	Examples 3 through 5	77–82
4 Identify the intercepts from the graph of an equation (p. 99)	Example 6	83
5 Interpret graphs (p. 100)	Example 7	84

In Problems 73 and 74, plot each point in the same xy-plane. Tell in which quadrant or on what coordinate axis each point lies.

73. $A(2, -4)$
$\quad B(-1, -3)$
$\quad C(0, 4)$
$\quad D(-5, 1)$
$\quad E(1, 0)$
$\quad F(4, 3)$

74. $A(3, 0)$
$\quad B(1, 5)$
$\quad C(-3, -5)$
$\quad D(-1, 4)$
$\quad E(5, -2)$
$\quad F(0, -5)$

In Problems 75 and 76, determine whether the given points are on the graph of the equation.

75. $3x - 2y = 7$
  (a) $(3, 1)$
  (b) $(2, -1)$
  (c) $(4, 0)$
  (d) $\left(\dfrac{1}{3}, -3\right)$

76. $y = 2x^2 - 3x + 2$
  (a) $(-1, 3)$
  (b) $(1, 1)$
  (c) $(-2, 16)$
  (d) $\left(\dfrac{1}{2}, \dfrac{3}{2}\right)$

In Problems 77–82, graph each equation by plotting points.

77. $y = x + 2$ **78.** $2x + y = 3$

79. $y = -x^2 + 4$ **80.** $y = |x + 2| - 1$

81. $y = x^3 + 2$ **82.** $x = y^2 + 1$

In Problem 83, the graph of an equation is given. List the intercepts of the graph.

83.

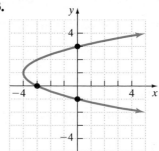

84. Cell Phones A cellular phone company offers a plan for $40 per month for 3000 minutes with additional minutes costing $0.05 per minute. The graph below shows the monthly cost, in dollars, when x minutes are used.

(a) If you talk for 2250 minutes in a month, how much is your monthly bill?

(b) Use the graph to estimate your monthly bill if you talk for 12 thousand minutes.

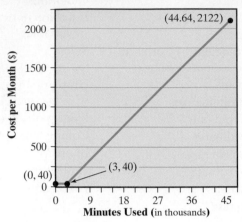

Section 1.6   Linear Equations in Two Variables

KEY CONCEPTS	KEY TERMS

KEY CONCEPTS

- **Standard Form of a Line**

  $Ax + By = C$, where A, B, and C are real numbers. A and B are not both 0.

- **Finding Intercepts**

  x-intercept(s): Let $y = 0$ in the equation and solve for x

  y-intercept(s): Let $x = 0$ in the equation and solve for y

- **Equation of a Vertical Line**

  $x = a$, where a is the x-intercept

- **Equation of a Horizontal Line**

  $y = b$, where b is the y-intercept

- **Slope of a Line**

  Let $P = (x_1, y_1)$ and $Q = (x_2, y_2)$ be two distinct points. If $x_1 \neq x_2$, the slope m of the nonvertical line L containing P and Q is defined by the formula

  $$m = \frac{y_2 - y_1}{x_2 - x_1}, \quad x_1 \neq x_2$$

  If $x_1 = x_2$, then L is a vertical line and the slope m of L is undefined (since this results in division by 0).

- When the slope of a line is positive, the line slants upward from left to right.

- When the slope of a line is negative, the line slants downward from left to right.

- When the slope of a line is zero, the line is horizontal.

- When the slope of a line is undefined, the line is vertical.

- **Point-slope Form of a Line**

  An equation of a nonvertical line of slope m that contains the point (x_1, y_1) is $y - y_1 = m(x - x_1)$.

- **Slope-intercept Form of a Line**

  An equation of a nonvertical line with slope m and y-intercept b is $y = mx + b$.

KEY TERMS

Linear equation
Standard form
Line
Vertical line
Horizontal line
Run
Rise
Slope
Undefined slope
Average rate of change

YOU SHOULD BE ABLE TO...	EXAMPLE	REVIEW EXERCISES
1 Graph linear equations using point plotting (p. 105)	Example 1	85–88
2 Graph linear equations using intercepts (p. 106)	Examples 2 and 3	89–92
3 Graph vertical and horizontal lines (p. 108)	Examples 4 and 5	93–95
4 Find the slope of a line given two points (p. 109)	Examples 6 and 7	96–99
5 Interpret slope as an average rate of change (p. 112)	Example 8	100
6 Graph a line given a point and its slope (p. 114)	Example 9	101–104
7 Use the point-slope form of a line (p. 114)	Example 10	105–108
8 Identify the slope and y-intercept of a line from its equation (p. 115)	Example 11	113–114
9 Find the equation of a line given two points (p. 116)	Examples 12 and 13	109–112

In Problems 85–88, graph each linear equation by plotting points.

85. $x + y = 7$ **86.** $x - y = -4$

87. $5x - 2y = 6$ **88.** $-3x + 2y = 8$

In Problems 89–92, graph each linear equation by finding its intercepts.

89. $5x + 3y = 30$ **90.** $4x + 3y = 0$

91. $\dfrac{3}{4}x - \dfrac{1}{2}y = 1$ **92.** $4x + y = 8$

In Problems 93–95, graph each linear equation.

93. $x = 4$

94. $y = -8$

95. $3x + 5 = -1$

In Problems 96 and 97, (a) find the slope of the line and (b) interpret the slope.

96.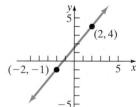

97.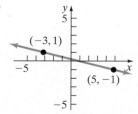

In Problems 98 and 99, plot each pair of points and determine the slope of the line containing them. Graph the line.

98. $(-1, 5); (2, -1)$

99. $(4, 5); (0, -1)$

100. Illinois's Population The following data represent the population of Illinois between 1940 and 2000.

Year, x	Population, y
1940	7,897,241
1950	8,712,176
1960	10,081,158
1970	11,110,285
1980	11,427,409
1990	11,430,602
2000	12,419,293

SOURCE: *U.S. Census Bureau*

(a) Plot the ordered pairs (x, y) on a graph and connect the points with straight lines.

(b) Compute and interpret the average rate of change in population between 1940 and 1950.

(c) Compute and interpret the average rate of change in population between 1980 and 1990.

(d) Compute and interpret the average rate of change in population between 1990 and 2000.

(e) Based upon the results to parts **(a)**, **(b)**, **(c)**, and **(d)**, do you think that population is linearly related to the year? Why?

In Problems 101–104, graph the line containing the point P and having slope m. Do not find the equation of the line.

101. $m = 4; P(-1, -5)$

102. $m = -\dfrac{2}{3}; P(3, 2)$

103. m is undefined; $P(2, -4)$

104. $m = 0; P(-3, 1)$

In Problems 105 and 106, find an equation of the line. Express your answer in either slope-intercept or standard form, whichever you prefer.

105.

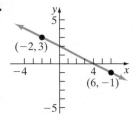

106.

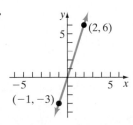

In Problems 107 and 108, find an equation of the line with the given slope and containing the given point. Express your answer in either slope-intercept or standard form, whichever you prefer.

107. $m = -1; (3, 2)$

108. $m = \dfrac{3}{5}; (-10, -4)$

In Problems 109–112, find an equation of the line containing the given points. Express your answer in either slope-intercept or standard form, whichever you prefer.

109. $(6, 2); (-3, 5)$

110. $(-2, 3); (4, 3)$

111. $(4, -1); (1, -7)$

112. $(-1, 2); (8, -1)$

In Problems 113–114, find the slope and y-intercept of each line. Graph the line.

113. $y = 4x - 6$

114. $2x + 3y = 12$

Section 1.7   Parallel and Perpendicular Lines

KEY CONCEPTS	KEY TERMS
• **Parallel Lines** Two lines are parallel if they have the same slope, but different *y*-intercepts. • **Slopes of Perpendicular Lines** Two lines are perpendicular if the product of their slopes is -1. Alternatively, two lines are perpendicular if their slopes are negative reciprocals of each other.	Parallel lines Perpendicular lines

YOU SHOULD BE ABLE TO...	EXAMPLE	REVIEW EXERCISES
☐1 Define parallel lines (p. 121)	Example 1	115, 117–120
☐2 Find equations of parallel lines (p. 123)	Example 2	121–123
☐3 Define perpendicular lines (p. 123)	Examples 3 and 4	116, 117–120
☐4 Find equations of perpendicular lines (p. 124)	Example 5	124–126

In Problems 115–116, the slope of a line L is $m = -\dfrac{3}{8}$.

115. Determine the slope of a line that is parallel to *L*.

116. Determine the slope of a line that is perpendicular to *L*.

In Problems 117–120, determine whether the given pairs of linear equations are parallel, perpendicular, or neither.

117. $x - 3y = 9$
$9x + 3y = -3$

118. $6x - 8y = 16$
$3x + 4y = 28$

119. $2x - y = 3$
$-6x + 3y = 0$

120. $x = 2$
$y = 2$

In Problems 121–126, find an equation of the line with the given properties. Express your answer in slope-intercept form, if possible. Graph the lines.

121. Parallel to $y = -2x - 5$ through $(1, 2)$

122. Parallel to $5x - 2y = 8$ through $(4, 3)$

123. Parallel to $x = -3$ through $(1, -4)$

124. Perpendicular to $y = 3x + 7$ through $(6, 2)$

125. Perpendicular to $3x + 4y = 6$ through $(-3, -2)$

126. Perpendicular to $x = 2$ through $(5, -4)$

Section 1.8   Linear Inequalities in Two Variables

KEY CONCEPT	KEY TERMS
• Linear inequalities in two variables are inequalities in one of the forms $$Ax + By < C \qquad Ax + By > C \qquad Ax + By \le C \qquad Ax + By \ge C$$ where A, B, and C are real numbers and A and B are not both zero.	Half-planes Satisfied Graph of a linear inequality in two variables

YOU SHOULD BE ABLE TO...	EXAMPLE	REVIEW EXERCISES
1 Determine whether an ordered pair is a solution to a linear inequality (p. 128)	Example 1	127–128
2 Graph linear inequalities (p. 129)	Examples 2 and 3	129–134
3 Solve problems involving linear inequalities (p. 131)	Example 4	135–136

In Problems 127 and 128, determine whether the given points are solutions to the linear inequality.

127. $5x + 3y \le 15$
   (a) $(4, -2)$
   (b) $(-6, 15)$
   (c) $(5, -1)$

128. $x - 2y > -4$
   (a) $(2, 3)$
   (b) $(5, -2)$
   (c) $(-1, 3)$

In Problems 129–134, graph each inequality.

129. $y < 3x - 2$

130. $2x - 4y \le 12$

131. $3x + 4y > 20$

132. $y \ge 5$

133. $2x + 3y < 0$

134. $x > -8$

135. Entertainment Budget Ethan's entertainment budget permits him to spend a maximum of $60 per month on movie tickets and music CDs. Movie tickets cost on average $7.50 each. Music CDs average $15.00 each.

   (a) Write a linear inequality that describes Ethan's options for spending the $60 maximum budget.

   (b) Can Ethan buy 5 movie tickets and 2 music CDs?

   (c) Can Ethan buy 2 movie tickets and 2 music CDs?

136. Fund Raising For a fund raiser, the Math Club agrees to sell candy bars and candles. The club's profit will be 50¢ for each candy bar and $2.00 for each candle it sells. The club needs to earn at least $1000 in order to pay for an upcoming field trip.

   (a) Write a linear inequality that describes the combination of candy bars and candles that must be sold.

   (b) Will selling 500 candy bars and 350 candles earn enough for the trip?

   (c) Will selling 600 candy bars and 400 candles earn enough for the trip?

CHAPTER 1 TEST

Remember to use your Chapter Test Prep Video CD to see fully worked-out solutions to any problems you would like to review.

1. Determine which, if any, of the following are solutions to $3(x - 7) + 5 = x - 4$.

   (a) $x = 6$

   (b) $x = -2$

2. Write the following inequalities in interval notation and graph on a real number line.

   (a) $x > -4$

   (b) $3 < x \le 7$

In Problems 3 and 4, translate the English statement into a mathematical statement. Do not attempt to solve.

3. Three times a number, decreased by 8, is 4 more than the number.

4. Two-thirds of a number, increased by twice the difference of the number and 5, is more than 7.

In Problems 5 and 6, solve the equation. Determine if the equation is an identity, a contradiction, or a conditional equation.

5. $5x - (x - 2) = 6 + 2x$

6. $7 + x - 3 = 3(x + 1) - 2x$

In Problems 7–9, solve the inequality and graph the solution set on a real number line.

7. $x + 2 \le 3x - 4$

8. $4x + 7 > 2x - 3(x - 2)$

9. $-x + 4 \le x + 3$

10. Solve $7x + 4y = 3$ for y.

11. **Computer Sales** Glen works as a computer salesman and earns $400 weekly plus 8% commission on his weekly sales. If he wants to make at least $750 in a week, how much must his sales be?

12. **Party Costs** A recreational center offers a children's birthday party for $75 plus $5 for each child. How many children were at Payton's birthday party if the total cost for the party was $145?

13. **Sandbox** Rick is building a rectangular sandbox for his daughter. He wants the length of the sandbox to be 2 feet more than the width and he has 20 feet of lumber to build the frame. Find the dimensions of the sandbox.

14. **Mixture** Two acid solutions are available to a chemist. One is a 10% nitric acid solution and the other is a 40% nitric acid solution. How much of each type of solution should be mixed together to form 12 liters of a 20% nitric acid solution?

15. **Ironman Race** The last leg of the Ironman competition is a 26.2-mile run. Contestant A runs at a constant rate of 8 miles per hour. If Contestant B starts the run 30 minutes after Contestant A and runs at a constant rate of 10 miles per hour, how long will it take Contestant B to catch up to Contestant A?

16. Plot the following ordered pairs in the same xy-plane. Tell in which quadrant or on what coordinate axis each point lies.

    $A(3, -4), B(0, 2), C(3, 0), D(2, 1), E(-1, -4), F(-3, 5)$

17. Determine whether the ordered pair is a point on the graph of the equation $y = 3x^2 + x - 5$.

    (a) $(-2, 4)$

    (b) $(-1, -3)$

    (c) $(2, 9)$

In Problems 18 and 19, graph the equations by plotting points.

18. $y = 4x - 1$

19. $y = 4x^2$

20. Identify the intercepts from the graph below.

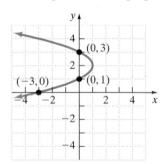

21. The following graph represents the speed of a car over time.

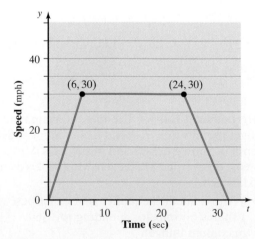

    (a) What is the speed of the car at 6 seconds?

    (b) Identify and interpret the intercepts.

In Problems 22–26, graph each linear equation, using any appropriate method.

22. $x - y = 8$

23. $3x + 5y = 0$

24. $3x + 2y = 12$

25. $\dfrac{3}{2}x - \dfrac{1}{4}y = 1$

26. $x = -7$

27. Find and interpret the slope of the line containing the points $(5, -2)$ and $(-1, 6)$.

28. Draw a graph of the line that contains the point $(2, -4)$ and has a slope of $-\dfrac{3}{5}$. Do not find the equation of the line.

29. Determine whether the graphs of the following pair of linear equations are parallel, perpendicular, or neither.

$$8x - 2y = 1$$
$$x + 4y = -2$$

In Problems 30–33, find the equation of the line with the given properties. Express your answer in either slope-intercept or standard form, whichever you prefer.

30. Through the point $(-3, 1)$ and having a slope of 4

31. Through the points $(6, 1)$ and $(-3, 7)$

32. Parallel to $x - 5y = 15$ and through the point $(10, -1)$

33. Perpendicular to $3x - y = 4$ and through the point $(6, 2)$

34. Determine whether the given points are solutions to the linear inequality $3x - y > 10$.

(a) $(3, -1)$ (b) $(4, 5)$ (c) $(5, 3)$

In Problems 35 and 36, graph each linear inequality.

35. $y \leq -2x + 1$

36. $5x - 2y < 0$

37. Area of a Circle The following data show the relationship between the diameter of a circle and the area of that circle.

Diameter (feet), x	Area (square feet), y
1	0.79
3	7.07
6	28.27
7	38.48
8	50.27
10	78.54
13	132.73

(a) Plot the ordered pairs (x, y) on a graph and connect the points with straight lines.

(b) Compute and interpret the average rate of change in area between diameter lengths of 1 and 3 feet.

(c) Compute and interpret the average rate of change in area between diameter lengths of 10 and 13 feet.

(d) Based upon the results to parts (a), (b), and (c), do you think that the area of the circle is linearly related to the diameter? Why?

CUMULATIVE REVIEW Chapters R–1

1. Approximate each number by (i) truncating and (ii) rounding to the indicated number of decimal places.

(a) 27.2357; 3 decimal places.

(b) 1.0729; 1 decimal place.

2. Plot the points -4, $-\dfrac{5}{2}$, 0, and $\dfrac{7}{2}$ on a real number line.

In Problems 3–8, evaluate the expressions.

3. $-|-14|$

4. $-3 + 4 - 7$

5. $\dfrac{-3(12)}{-6}$

6. $(-3)^4$

7. $5 - 2(1 - 4)^3 + 5 \cdot 3$

8. $\dfrac{2}{3} + \dfrac{1}{2} - \dfrac{1}{4}$

9. Evaluate $3x^2 + 2x - 7$ when $x = 2$.

10. Simplify: $4a^2 - 6a + a^2 - 12 + 2a - 1$

11. Determine if the given values are in the domain of x for the expression $\dfrac{x + 3}{x^2 + x - 2}$.

(a) $x = -2$ (b) $x = 0$

12. Use the Distributive Property to remove parentheses and then simplify: $3(x + 2) - 4(2x - 1) + 8$

13. Determine whether $x = 3$ is a solution to the equation $x - (2x + 3) = 5x - 1$.

In Problems 14 and 15, solve the equation.

14. $4x - 3 = 2(3x - 2) - 7$

15. $\dfrac{x + 1}{3} = x - 4$

16. Solve $2x - 5y = 6$ for y.

In Problems 17 and 18, solve the inequality and graph the solution set on a real number line.

17. $\dfrac{x + 3}{2} \leq \dfrac{3x - 1}{4}$

18. $5(x - 3) \geq 7(x - 4) + 3$

19. Plot the following ordered pairs in the same Cartesian plane.

$$A(-3, 0), \quad B(4, -2), \quad C(1, 5),$$
$$D(0, 3), \quad E(-4, -5), \quad F(-5, 2)$$

In Problems 20 and 21, graph the linear equation using the method you prefer.

20. $y = -\dfrac{1}{2}x + 4$ **21.** $4x - 5y = 15$

In Problems 22 and 23, find the equation of the line with the given properties. Express your answer in either slope-intercept or standard form, whichever you prefer.

22. Through the points $(3, -2)$ and $(-6, 10)$

23. Parallel to $y = -3x + 10$ and through the point $(-5, 7)$

24. Graph $x - 3y > 12$.

25. Computing Grades Shawn really wants an A in his geometry class. His four exam scores are 94, 95, 90, and 97. The final exam is worth two exam scores. To have an A, his average must be at least 93. For what range of scores on the final exam will Shawn be able to earn an A in the course?

26. Body Mass Index The body mass index (BMI) of a person 62 inches tall and weighing x pounds is given by $0.2x - 2$. A BMI of 30 or more is considered to be obese. For what weights would a person 62 inches tall be considered obese?

27. Supplementary Angles Two angles are supplementary. The measure of the larger angle is 15 degrees more than twice the measure of the smaller angle. Find the angle measures.

28. Cylinders Max has 100 square inches of aluminum with which to make a closed cylinder. If the radius of the cylinder must be 2 inches, how tall will the cylinder be? (Round to the nearest hundredth of an inch.)

29. Consecutive Integers Find three consecutive even integers such that the sum of the first two is 22 more than the third.

2

Relations, Functions, and More Inequalities

Everyone knows that diamonds are a girl's best friend. The word *diamond* comes from the Greek word *adamas*, which means "unconquerable." Diamonds were first discovered in India in 800 B.C. Ancient Greeks thought diamonds were parts of stars that fell to earth. Diamonds are the hardest of all gemstones. The quality of diamonds is assessed by the four "Cs"—Cut, Color, Clarity, and Carats. Carats is a measure of the weight of a diamond. Did you know that the price of a diamond is linearly related to the number of carats? See Problem 67 on page 187.

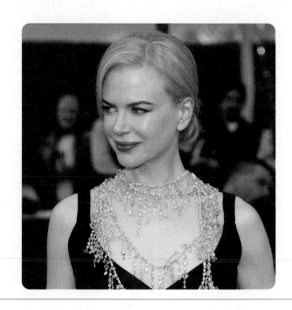

OUTLINE

The Big Picture: Putting It Together

In Chapter 1 we studied linear equations in two variables. We represented the solution of a linear equation in two variables using the rectangular coordinate system. The rectangular coordinate system provides the connection between algebra and geometry. Prior to the introduction of the rectangular coordinate system, algebra and geometry were thought to be separate subjects.

We begin this chapter with an introduction to the concept of a function. The function is arguably the single most important concept of algebra. We then discuss compound inequalities and absolute value equations and inequalities. The rectangular coordinate system will help us to visualize solutions to these equations and inequalities.

2.1 Relations

OBJECTIVES

1. Understand Relations
2. Find the Domain and the Range of a Relation
3. Graph a Relation Defined by an Equation

Preparing for Relations

Before getting started, take this readiness quiz. If you get a problem wrong, go back to the section cited and review the material.

P1. Write the inequality $-4 \leq x \leq 4$ in interval notation. [Section 1.4, pp. 81–84]

P2. Write the interval $[2, \infty)$ using an inequality. [Section 1.4, pp. 81–84]

P3. Plot the ordered pairs $(-2, 4), (3, -1),$ $(0, 5),$ and $(4, 0)$ in the rectangular coordinate system. [Section 1.5, pp. 93–95]

P4. Graph the equation: $2x + 5y = 10$ [Section 1.6, pp. 105–108]

P5. Graph the equation $y = x^2 - 3$ by plotting points. [Section 1.5, pp. 97–99]

1 Understand Relations

We often see situations where one variable is somehow linked to the value of some other variable. For example, an individual's level of education is linked to annual income. Engine size is linked to gas mileage. When the value of one variable is related to the value of a second variable, we have a *relation.*

> **DEFINITION**
>
> When the elements in one set are associated with elements in a second set, we have a **relation.** If x and y are two elements in these sets and if a relation exists between x and y, then we say that x **corresponds** to y or that y **depends on** x, and we write $x \rightarrow y$. We may also write a relation where y depends on x as an ordered pair (x, y).

EXAMPLE 1 Illustrating a Relation

Consider the data presented in Figure 1, where a correspondence between states and senators in 2008 is shown for randomly selected senators. We might name the relation "is represented in the U.S. Senate by." So, we would say "Indiana is represented by Evan Bayh."

Figure 1

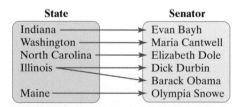

By representing the relation as in Figure 1, we are using **mapping,** in which we draw an arrow from an element in the set "state" to an element in the set "senator." We could also represent the relation in Figure 1 using ordered pairs in the form (state, senator) as follows:

{(Indiana, Evan Bayh), (Washington, Maria Cantwell),
(North Carolina, Elizabeth Dole), (Illinois, Dick Durbin),
(Illinois, Barack Obama), (Maine, Olympia Snowe)}

∎

Preparing for...Answers **P1.** $[-4, 4]$
P2. $x \geq 2$
P3. **P4.**

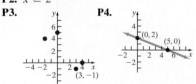

P5.

Quick ✔

1. If a relation exists between x and y, then we say that x _____ to y or that y _____ on x, and we write $x \rightarrow y$.

2. Use the map to represent the relation as a set of ordered pairs.

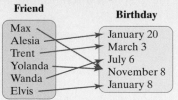

3. Use the set of ordered pairs to represent the relation as a map.

$$\{(1, 3), (5, 4), (8, 4), (10, 13)\}$$

2 Find the Domain and the Range of a Relation

In a relation we say that y depends on x and can write the relation as a set of ordered pairs (x, y). We can think of the set of all x as the **inputs** of the relation. The set of all y can be thought of as the **outputs** of the relation. We use this interpretation of a relation to define *domain* and *range*.

> **DEFINITION**
>
> The **domain** of a relation is the set of all inputs of the relation. The **range** is the set of all outputs of the relation.

EXAMPLE 2 Finding the Domain and the Range of a Relation

Find the domain and the range of the relation presented in Figure 1 from Example 1.

Solution

The domain is the set of all inputs and the range is the set of all outputs. The inputs, and therefore the domain, of the relation are

$$\{\text{Indiana, Washington, North Carolina, Illinois, Maine}\}$$

The outputs, and therefore the range, of the relation are

$$\{\text{Evan Bayh, Maria Cantwell, Elizabeth Dole, Dick Durbin,}$$
$$\text{Barack Obama, Olympia Snowe}\}$$

The careful reader will notice that we did not list Illinois twice in the domain because the domain and the range are sets and we never list elements in a set more than once. Also, it does not matter in what order we list the elements in the domain or range.

Work Smart

Never list elements in the domain or range more than once.

> **Quick ✔**
>
> **4.** The _____ of a relation is the set of all inputs of the relation. The _____ is the set of all outputs of the relation.
>
> **5.** State the domain and the range of the relation.
>
>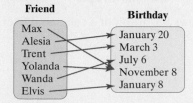
>
> **6.** State the domain and the range of the relation.
>
> $$\{(1, 3), (5, 4), (8, 4), (10, 13)\}$$

Relations can also be represented by plotting a set of ordered pairs. The set of all x-coordinates represents the domain of the relation and the set of all y-coordinates represents the range of the relation.

EXAMPLE 3 Finding the Domain and the Range of a Relation

Figure 2 shows the graph of a relation. Identify the domain and the range of the relation.

Figure 2

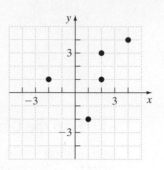

Solution

Work Smart

Write the points as ordered pairs to assist in finding the domain and range.

First, we notice that the ordered pairs in the graph are $(-2, 1)$, $(1, -2)$, $(2, 1)$, $(2, 3)$, and $(4, 4)$. The domain is the set of all x-coordinates: $\{-2, 1, 2, 4\}$. The range is the set of all y-coordinates: $\{-2, 1, 3, 4\}$. ∎

Quick ✔

7. Identify the domain and the range of the relation shown in the figure.

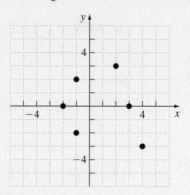

We have learned that a relation can be defined by a map or by a set of ordered pairs. A relation can also be defined by a graph. Remember that the graph of an equation is the set of all ordered pairs (x, y) such that the equation is a true statement. If a graph exists for some ordered pair (x, y), then the x-coordinate is in the domain and the y-coordinate is in the range. Think of it this way: When a graph of a relation is given, its domain may be viewed as the shadow created by the graph on the x-axis by vertical beams of light. Its range can be viewed as the shadow created by the graph on the y-axis by horizontal beams of light.

EXAMPLE 4 Identifying the Domain and the Range of a Relation from Its Graph

Figure 3 shows the graph of a relation. Determine the domain and the range of the relation.

Figure 3

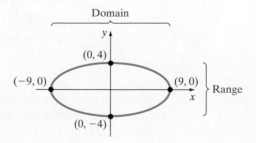

Solution

To find the domain of the relation, we determine the x-coordinates for which the graph exists. The graph exists for all x-values between -9 and 9, inclusive. Therefore, the domain is $\{x \mid -9 \le x \le 9\}$ or, using interval notation, $[-9, 9]$.

To find the range of the relation, we determine the y-coordinates for which the graph exists. The graph exists for all y-values between -4 and 4, inclusive. Therefore, the range is $\{y \mid -4 \le y \le 4\}$ or, using interval notation $[-4, 4]$. ◼

Quick ✔

8. *True or False:* If the graph of a relation does not exist at $x = 3$, then 3 is not in the domain of the relation.

9. *True or False:* The range of a relation is always the set of all real numbers.

In Problems 10 and 11, identify the domain and the range of the relation from its graph.

10.   **11.**

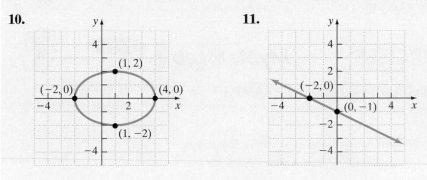

Work Smart

We can define relations by
1. Mapping
2. Sets of ordered pairs
3. Graphs
4. Equations

3 Graph a Relation Defined by an Equation

Another approach to defining a relation (instead of a map, a set of ordered pairs, or a graph) is to define relations through equations such as $x + y = 4$ or $x = y^2$. When relations are defined by equations, we typically graph the relation so that we can visualize how y depends upon x. As was seen in Example 4, the graph of the relation is also useful for helping us to identify the domain and the range of the relation.

EXAMPLE 5 Relations Defined by Equations

Graph the relation $y = -x^2 + 4$. Use the graph to determine the domain and the range of the relation.

Solution

The relation says to take the input x, square it, multiply this result by -1, and then add 4 to get the output y. We use the point-plotting method to graph the relation. Table 1 shows some points on the graph. Figure 4 shows a graph of the relation.

Table 1		
x	$y = -x^2 + 4$	(x, y)
-3	$-(-3)^2 + 4 = -5$	$(-3, -5)$
-2	$-(-2)^2 + 4 = 0$	$(-2, 0)$
-1	3	$(-1, 3)$
0	4	$(0, 4)$
1	3	$(1, 3)$
2	0	$(2, 0)$
3	-5	$(3, -5)$

Figure 4

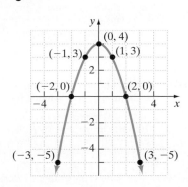

From the graph, we can see that the graph extends indefinitely to the left and to the right (that is, the graph exists for all x-values). Therefore, the domain of the relation is the set of all real numbers, or $\{x \mid x \text{ is any real number}\}$, or using interval notation, $(-\infty, \infty)$. We also notice from the graph that there are no y-values greater than 4, but the graph exists everywhere for y-values less than or equal to 4. The range of the relation is $\{y \mid y \leq 4\}$, or using interval notation $(-\infty, 4]$. ■

Quick ✔ *In Problems 12–14, graph each relation. Use the graph to identify the domain and the range.*

12. $y = 3x - 8$ **13.** $y = x^2 - 8$ **14.** $x = y^2 + 1$

Work Smart: Study Skills

Selected problems in the exercise sets are identified by a 🔘 symbol. For extra help, view the worked solutions to these problems on the book's CD Lecture Series.

2.1 EXERCISES

PRACTICE   WATCH   DOWNLOAD   READ   REVIEW

1–14. *are the* **Quick ✔s** *that follow each* **EXAMPLE**

Building Skills

In Problems 15–18, write each relation as a set of ordered pairs. Then identify the domain and the range of the relation. See Objectives 1 and 2.

15.

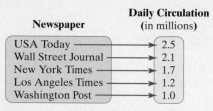

Daily Circulation
Newspaper | (in millions)
USA Today → 2.5
Wall Street Journal → 2.1
New York Times → 1.7
Los Angeles Times → 1.2
Washington Post → 1.0

SOURCE: *Information Please Almanac*

16.

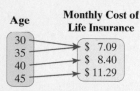

Age | Monthly Cost of Life Insurance
30 →
35 → $ 7.09
40 → $ 8.40
45 → $ 11.29

SOURCE: *eterm.com*

🔘 **17.**

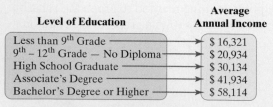

Level of Education | Average Annual Income
Less than 9th Grade → $ 16,321
9th – 12th Grade — No Diploma → $ 20,934
High School Graduate → $ 30,134
Associate's Degree → $ 41,934
Bachelor's Degree or Higher → $ 58,114

SOURCE: *United States Census Bureau*

18.

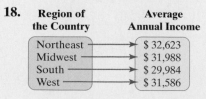

Region of the Country | Average Annual Income
Northeast → $ 32,623
Midwest → $ 31,988
South → $ 29,984
West → $ 31,586

SOURCE: *United States Census Bureau*

In Problems 19–24, write each relation as a map. Then identify the domain and the range of the relation. See Objectives 1 and 2.

19. $\{(-3, 4), (-2, 6), (-1, 8), (0, 10), (1, 12)\}$

20. $\{(-2, 6), (-1, 3), (0, 0), (1, -3), (2, 6)\}$

🔘 **21.** $\{(-2, 4), (-1, 2), (0, 0), (1, 2), (2, 4)\}$

22. $\{(-2, -8), (-1, -1), (0, 0), (1, 1), (2, 8)\}$

23. $\{(0, -4), (-1, -1), (-2, 0), (-1, 1), (0, 4)\}$

24. $\{(-3, 0), (0, 3), (3, 0), (0, -3)\}$

In Problems 25–32, identify the domain and the range of the relation from the graph. See Objective 2.

25.

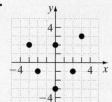

26.

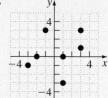

27.

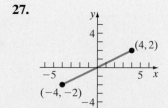

28.

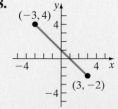

29.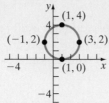

30.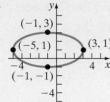

31.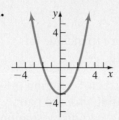

32.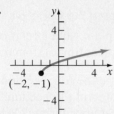

In Problems 33–54, use the graph of the relation obtained in Problems 33–54 from Section 1.5 to identify the domain and the range of the relation. See Objective 3.

33. $y = -3x + 1$

34. $y = -4x + 2$

35. $y = \frac{1}{2}x - 4$

36. $y = -\frac{1}{2}x + 2$

37. $2x + y = 7$

38. $3x + y = 9$

39. $y = -x^2$

40. $y = x^2 - 2$

41. $y = 2x^2 - 8$

42. $y = -2x^2 + 8$

43. $y = |x|$

44. $y = |x| - 2$

45. $y = |x - 1|$

46. $y = -|x|$

47. $y = x^3$

48. $y = -x^3$

49. $y = x^3 + 1$

50. $y = x^3 - 2$

51. $x^2 - y = 4$

52. $x^2 + y = 5$

53. $x = y^2 - 1$

54. $x = y^2 + 2$

Applying the Concepts

55. Area of a Window Bob Villa wishes to put a new window in his home. He wants the perimeter of the window to be 100 feet. The graph below shows the relation between the width, x, of the opening and the area of the opening.

(a) Determine the domain and the range of the relation.

(b) Provide an explanation as to why the domain obtained in part (a) is reasonable.

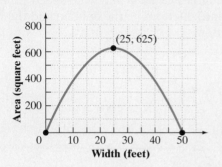

56. Projectile Motion The graph below shows the height, in feet, of a ball thrown straight up with an initial speed of 80 feet per second from an initial height of 96 feet after t seconds. Determine the domain and the range of the relation.

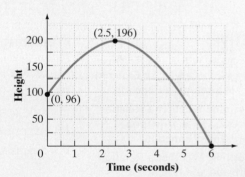

57. Cell Phones We all struggle with selecting a cellular phone provider. The graph below shows the relation between the monthly cost, C, of a cellular phone and the number of anytime minutes used, m, when using the Sprint PCS 2000-minute plan. (SOURCE: *SprintPCS.com*)

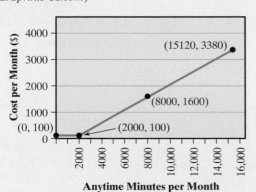

(a) Determine the domain and the range of the relation.

(b) If anytime minutes are from 7:00 A.M. to 7:00 P.M. Monday through Friday, provide an explanation as to why the domain obtained in part (a) is reasonable assuming there are 21 nonweekend days.

58. Wind Chill It is 10° Celsius outside. The wind is calm but then gusts up to 20 meters per second. You feel the chill go right through your bones. The graph below shows the relation between the wind chill temperature (in degrees Celsius) and wind speed (in meters per second). Determine the domain and the range of the relation.

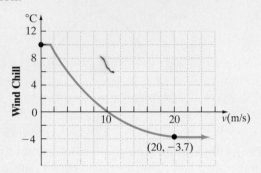

(20, −3.7)

Extending the Concepts

59. Draw the graph of a relation whose domain is all real numbers, but whose range is a single real number. Compare your graph with those of your classmates. How are they similar?

60. Draw the graph of a relation whose domain is a single real number, but whose range is all real numbers. Compare your graph with those of your classmates. How are they similar?

Explaining the Concepts

61. Explain what a relation is. Be sure to include an explanation of domain and range.

62. State the four methods for describing a relation presented in this section. When is using ordered pairs most appropriate? When is using a graph most appropriate? Support your opinion.

2.2 An Introduction to Functions

OBJECTIVES

- **1** Determine Whether a Relation Expressed as a Map or Ordered Pairs Represents a Function
- **2** Determine Whether a Relation Expressed as an Equation Represents a Function
- **3** Determine Whether a Relation Expressed as a Graph Represents a Function
- **4** Find the Value of a Function
- **5** Work with Applications of Functions

Preparing for an Introduction to Functions
Before getting started, take this readiness quiz. If you get a problem wrong, go back to the section cited and review the material.

P1. Evaluate the expression $2x^2 - 5x$ for
  (a) $x = 1$ **(b)** $x = 4$ **(c)** $x = -3$ [Section R.5, pp. 40–41]

P2. Express the inequality $x \le 5$ using interval notation.   [Section 1.4, pp. 81–84]

P3. Express the interval $(2, \infty)$ using set-builder notation.   [Section 1.4, pp. 81–84]

1 Determine Whether a Relation Expressed as a Map or Ordered Pairs Represents a Function

We now present what is one of the most important concepts in algebra—the *function*. A function is a special type of relation. To understand the idea behind a function, let's revisit the relation presented in Example 1 from Section 2.1, shown again in Figure 5. Recall, this is a correspondence between states and their senators. We named the relation "is represented in the U.S. Senate by."

Figure 5

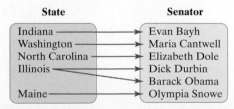

State   Senator

For the relation in Figure 5, if someone were asked to name the senator who represents Illinois, some would respond "Dick Durbin," while others would respond "Barack Obama." In other words, the input "state" does not correspond to a single output "senator."

Preparing for...Answers **P1. (a)** −3
(b) 12   **(c)** 33
P2. $(-\infty, 5]$ **P3.** $\{x \mid x > 2\}$

Let's consider a second relation where we have a correspondence between states and their population presented in Figure 6(a). If asked for the population that corresponds to North Carolina, everyone would respond "8857 thousand." In other words, each input "state" corresponds to exactly one output "population."

Figure 6(b) is a relation that shows a correspondence between "animals" and "life expectancy." If asked to determine the life expectancy of a dog, we would all respond "11 years." If asked to determine the life expectancy of a cat, we would all respond "11 years."

Figure 6

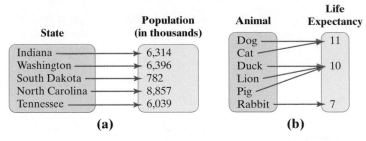

(a)   (b)

Looking carefully at the three relations, we should notice that the relations presented in Figures 6(a) and 6(b) have something in common, while the relation in Figure 5 is different. What is it? The common link between the relations in Figure 6(a) and 6(b) is that each input corresponds to only one output. However, in Figure 5 the input Illinois corresponds to two outputs—Dick Durbin and Barack Obama. This leads to the definition of a *function*.

In Words

For a relation to be classified as a function, each input may have only one output.

DEFINITION

A **function** is a relation in which each element in the domain (the inputs) of the relation corresponds to exactly one element in the range (the outputs) of the relation.

The idea behind functions is predictability. If an input is known, a function can be used to determine the output with 100% certainty (Figures 6(a) and (b)). With nonfunctions, we don't have this predictability (Figure 5).

EXAMPLE 1   Determining Whether a Relation Represents a Function

Determine whether the following relations represent functions. If the relation is a function, then state its domain and range.

(a) See Figure 7(a). For this relation, the domain represents the length (mm) of the right humerus and the range represents the length (mm) of the right tibia for each of five rats sent to space. The lengths were measured once the rats returned from their trip.

(b) See Figure 7(b). For this relation, the domain represents the weight of pear-cut diamonds and the range represents their price.

(c) See Figure 7(c). For this relation, the domain represents the age of 5 males and the range represents their HDL (good) cholesterol (mg/dL).

Figure 7

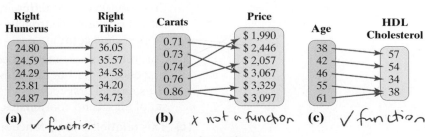

(a) ✓ function

(b) ✗ not a function   (c) ✓ function

SOURCE: *NASA Life Sciences Data Archive*   SOURCE: *diamonds.com*

Solution

(a) The relation in Figure 7(a) is a function because each element in the domain corresponds to exactly one element in the range. The domain of the function is {24.80, 24.59, 24.29, 23.81, 24.87}. The range of the function is {36.05, 35.57, 34.58, 34.20, 34.73}.

(b) The relation in Figure 7(b) is not a function because there is an element in the domain, 0.86, that corresponds to two elements in the range. If 0.86 is chosen from the domain, a single price cannot be determined for the diamond.

(c) The relation in Figure 7(c) is a function because each element in the domain corresponds to exactly one element in the range. Notice that it is okay for more than one element in the domain to correspond to the same element in the range (both 55 and 61 correspond to 38). The domain of the function is {38, 42, 46, 55, 61}. The range of the function is {57, 54, 34, 38}. ∎

Work Smart

All functions are relations, but not all relations are functions!

Quick ✔

1. A _____ is a relation in which each element in the domain of the relation corresponds to exactly one element in the range of the relation.

2. *True or False:* Every relation is a function.

In Problems 3 and 4, determine whether the relation represents a function. If the relation is a function, state its domain and range.

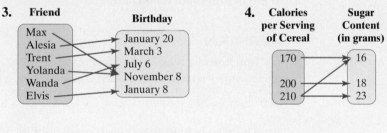

We may also think of a function as a set of ordered pairs (x, y) in which no ordered pairs have the same first coordinate, but different second coordinates.

EXAMPLE 2 Determining Whether a Relation Represents a Function

Determine whether each relation represents a function. If the relation is a function, then state its domain and range.

(a) {(1, 3), (−1, 4), (0, 6), (2, 8)}

(b) {(−2, 6), (−1, 3), (0, 2), (1, 3), (2, 6)}

(c) {(0, 3), (1, 4), (4, 5), (9, 5), (4, 1)}

Solution

(a) This relation is a function because there are no ordered pairs with the same first coordinate, but different second coordinates. The domain of the function is the set of all first coordinates, {−1, 0, 1, 2}. The range of the function is the set of all second coordinates, {3, 4, 6, 8}.

(b) This relation is a function because there are no ordered pairs with the same first coordinate, but different second coordinates. The domain of the function is the set of all first coordinates, {−2, −1, 0, 1, 2}. The range of the function is the set of all second coordinates, {2, 3, 6}.

(c) This relation is not a function because there are two ordered pairs, (4, 5) and (4, 1), with the same first coordinate, but different second coordinates. ∎

Work Smart

In a function, two different inputs can correspond to the same output, but two different outputs cannot be the result of a single input.

In Example 2(b), notice that -2 and 2 in the domain each correspond to 6 in the range. This does not violate the definition of a function—two different first coordinates can have the same second coordinate. A violation of the definition occurs when two ordered pairs have the same first coordinate and different second coordinates as in Example 2(c).

Quick ✔ *In Problems 5 and 6, determine whether each relation represents a function. If the relation is a function, then state its domain and range.*

5. $\{(-3, 3), (-2, 2), (-1, 1), (0, 0), (1, 1)\}$

6. $\{(-3, 2), (-2, 5), (-1, 8), (-3, 6)\}$

2 Determine Whether a Relation Expressed as an Equation Represents a Function

At this point, we have shown how to identify when a relation defined by a map or ordered pairs is a function. In Section 2.1, we also learned how to express relations as equations and graphs. We will now address the circumstances under which equations are functions.

To determine whether an equation, where y depends upon x, is a function, it is often easiest to solve the equation for y. If a value of x corresponds to exactly one y, the equation defines a function; otherwise it does not define a function.

EXAMPLE 3 Determining Whether an Equation Represents a Function

Determine whether the equation $y = 3x + 5$ shows y as a function of x.

Solution

The rule for getting from x to y is to multiply x by 3 and then add 5. Since there is only one output y that can result by performing these operations on any given input x, the equation is a function.

EXAMPLE 4 Determining Whether an Equation Represents a Function

Determine whether the equation $y = \pm x^2$ shows y as a function of x.

Solution

In Words

The symbol $\pm$ is a shorthand device and is read "plus or minus." For example, ± 4 means "negative four or positive four."

Notice that for any single value of x (other than 0), two values of y result. For example, if $x = 2$, then $y = \pm 4$ (-4 or $+4$). Since a single x corresponds to more than one y, the equation is not that of a function.

Quick ✔ *In Problems 7–9, determine whether each equation shows y as a function of x.*

7. $y = -2x + 5$ **8.** $y = \pm 3x$ **9.** $y = x^2 + 5x$

3 Determine Whether a Relation Expressed as a Graph Represents a Function

Remember that the graph of an equation is the set of all ordered pairs (x, y) that satisfy the equation. For a relation to be a function, each number x in the domain can correspond to only one y in the range. This means that the graph of an equation will *not* represent a function if two points with the same x-coordinate have different y-coordinates. This leads to the following test.

VERTICAL LINE TEST

A set of points in the xy-plane is the graph of a function if and only if every vertical line intersects the graph in at most one point.

EXAMPLE 5 Using the Vertical Line Test to Identify Graphs of Functions

Which of the graphs in Figure 8 are graphs of functions?

Figure 8

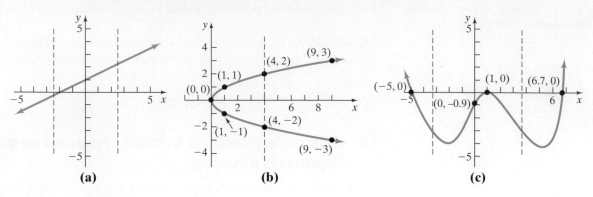

(a)   (b)   (c)

Solution

The graph in Figure 8(a) is a function, because every vertical line intersects the graph in at most one point. The graph in Figure 8(b) is not a function, because a vertical line intersects the graph in more than one point. The graph in Figure 8(c) is a function, because a vertical line intersects the graph in at most one point. ∎

Based on the results of Example 5, do you see why the vertical line test works? If a vertical line intersects the graph of an equation in two or more points, then the same x-coordinate corresponds to two or more different y-coordinates and we have violated the definition of a function.

Quick ✔

10. *True or False:* For a graph to be a function, any vertical line can intersect the graph in at most one point.

In Problems 11 and 12, use the vertical line test to determine whether the graph is that of a function.

11.

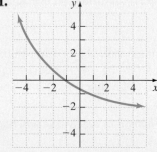

12.

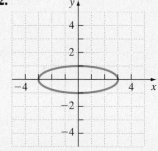

4 Find the Value of a Function

Functions are often denoted by letters such as f, F, g, G, and so on. If f is a function, then for each number x in its domain, the corresponding value in the range is denoted $f(x)$, read as "f of x" or as "f at x." We call $f(x)$ the **value of f at the number x;** $f(x)$ is the number that results when the function is applied to x; $f(x)$ does not mean "f times x." For example, the function $y = 3x + 5$ given in Example 3 may be written as $f(x) = 3x + 5$.

For a function $y = f(x)$, the variable x is called the **independent variable,** because it can be assigned any of the numbers in the domain. The variable y is called the **dependent variable,** because its value depends on x.

Any symbol can be used to represent the independent variable. For example, if f is the *square function,* then f can be defined by $f(x) = x^2$, $f(t) = t^2$, or $f(z) = z^2$. All three functions are the same: Each tells us to square the independent variable.

In practice, the symbols used for the independent and dependent variables should remind us of what they represent. For example, in economics, we use C for cost and q

Work Smart

Be careful with function notation. In the expression $y = f(x)$, y is the dependent variable, x is the independent variable, and f is the name given to a rule that relates the input x to the output y.

for quantity, so that $C(q)$ represents the cost of manufacturing q units of a good. Here, C is the dependent variable, q is the independent variable, and $C(q)$ is the rule that tells us how to get the output C from the input q.

The independent variable is also called the **argument** of the function. Thinking of the independent variable as an argument can sometimes make it easier to find the value of a function. For example, if f is the function defined by $f(x) = x^2$, then f tells us to square the argument. So, $f(2)$ means to square 2, $f(a)$ means to square a, and $f(x + h)$ means to square the quantity $x + h$.

EXAMPLE 6   Finding Values of a Function

For the function defined by $f(x) = x^2 + 6x$, evaluate:

(a) $f(3)$ (b) $f(-2)$

Solution

(a) Wherever we see an x in the equation defining the function f we substitute 3 to get

$$f(3) = 3^2 + 6(3)$$
$$= 9 + 18$$
$$= 27$$

(b) We substitute -2 for x in the expression $x^2 + 6x$ to get

$$f(-2) = (-2)^2 + 6(-2)$$
$$= 4 + (-12)$$
$$= -8$$

The notation $f(x)$ plays a dual role—it represents the rule for getting from the input to the output and its value represents the output y of the function. For example, in Example 6(a), the rule for getting from the input to the output is given by $f(x) = x^2 + 6x$. In words, the function says to "take some input x, square it, and add the result to six times the input x." If the input is 3, then $f(3)$ represents the output, 27.

EXAMPLE 7   Finding Values of a Function

For the function $F(z) = 4z + 7$, evaluate:

(a) $F(z + 3)$ (b) $F(z) + F(3)$

Solution

(a) Wherever we see a z in the equation defining F, we substitute $z + 3$ to get

$$F(z + 3) = 4(z + 3) + 7$$
$$= 4z + 12 + 7$$
$$= 4z + 19$$

(b)
$$F(z) + F(3) = \underbrace{4z + 7}_{F(z)} + \underbrace{4 \cdot 3 + 7}_{F(3)}$$
$$= 4z + 7 + 12 + 7$$
$$= 4z + 26$$

Quick ✔

13. In the function $H(q) = 2q^2 - 5q + 1$, H is called the _____ variable and q is called the _____ variable or _____.

In Problems 14–17, let $f(x) = 3x + 2$ and $g(x) = -2x^2 + x - 3$ to evaluate each function.

14. $f(4)$ **15.** $g(-2)$ **16.** $f(x - 2)$ **17.** $f(x) - f(2)$

> ## SUMMARY IMPORTANT FACTS ABOUT FUNCTIONS
>
> 1. For each x in the domain there corresponds exactly one y in the range.
> 2. f is a symbol that we use to denote the function. It represents the equation that we use to get from an x in the domain to $f(x)$ in the range.
> 3. If $y = f(x)$, then x is called the independent variable or argument of f, and y is called the dependent variable or the value of f at x.

⌐5 Work with Applications of Functions

EXAMPLE 8 Life Cycle Hypothesis

The Life Cycle Hypothesis from Economics was presented by Franco Modigliani in 1954. It states that income is a function of age. The function $I(a) = -55a^2 + 5119a - 54{,}448$ represents the relation between average annual income I and age a.

(a) Identify the dependent and independent variables.

(b) Evaluate $I(20)$. Provide a verbal explanation of the meaning of $I(20)$.

Solution

(a) Because income depends upon age, we have that the dependent variable is income, I, and the independent variable is age, a.

(b) We let $a = 20$ in the function.

$$I(20) = -55(20)^2 + 5119(20) - 54{,}448$$
$$= 25{,}932$$

The average annual income of an individual who is 20 years of age is \$25,932. ∎

> ### Quick ✔
>
> 18. In 2002, the *Prestige* oil tanker sank and started leaking oil off the coast of Spain. The oil slick takes the shape of a circle. Suppose that the area A (in square miles) of the circle contaminated with oil can be determined using the function $A(t) = 0.25\pi t^2$, where t represents the number of days since the tanker sprung a leak.
>
>   (a) Identify the dependent and independent variables.
>
>   (b) Evaluate $A(30)$. Provide a verbal explanation of the meaning of $A(30)$.

2.2 EXERCISES

PRACTICE   WATCH   DOWNLOAD   READ   REVIEW

1–18. are the Quick ✔s that follow each EXAMPLE

Building Skills

In Problems 19–28, determine whether each relation represents a function. State the domain and the range of each relation. See Objective 1.

19.

State	Number of Representatives
Virginia	11
Nevada	3
New Mexico	
Tennessee	9
Texas	32

20.

Animal	Gestation Period (days)
Cat	63
Dog	
Goat	151
Pig	115
Rabbit	31

21.

Horse-power	Top Speed
150	118
180	130
174	140

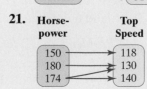

22.

Grade on Exam		Study Time (hours)

A B C D → 5, 6, 4, 3.5, 1

23. $\{(0, 3), (1, 4), (2, 5), (3, 6)\}$

24. $\{(-1, 4), (0, 1), (1, -2), (2, -5)\}$

25. $\{(-3, 5), (1, 5), (4, 5), (7, 5)\}$

26. $\{(-2, 3), (-2, 1), (-2, -3), (-2, 9)\}$

27. $\{(-10, 1), (-5, 4), (0, 3), (-5, 2)\}$

28. $\{(-5, 3), (-2, 1), (5, 1), (7, -3)\}$

In Problems 29–38, determine whether each equation shows y as a function of x. See Objective 2.

29. $y = 2x + 9$

30. $y = -6x + 3$

31. $2x + y = 10$

32. $6x - 3y = 12$

33. $y = \pm 5x$

34. $y = \pm 2x^2$

35. $y = x^2 + 2$

36. $y = x^3 - 3$

37. $x + y^2 = 10$

38. $y^2 = x$

In Problems 39–46, determine whether the graph is that of a function. See Objective 3.

39.

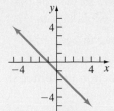

40.

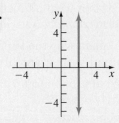

41.

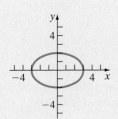

42.

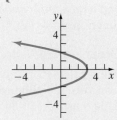

43.

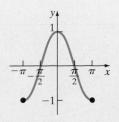

44.

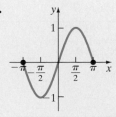

45.

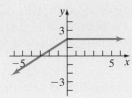

46.

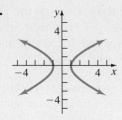

In Problems 47–50, find the following values for each function. See Objective 4.

(a) $f(0)$ **(b)** $f(3)$ **(c)** $f(-2)$ **(d)** $f(-x)$

(e) $-f(x)$ **(f)** $f(x + 2)$ **(g)** $f(2x)$ **(h)** $f(x + h)$

47. $f(x) = 2x + 3$ **48.** $f(x) = 3x + 1$

49. $f(x) = -5x + 2$ **50.** $f(x) = -2x - 3$

In Problems 51–58, find the value of each function. See Objective 4.

51. $f(x) = x^2 + 3; f(2)$

52. $f(x) = -2x^2 + x + 1; f(-3)$

53. $s(t) = -t^3 - 4t; s(-2)$

54. $g(h) = -h^2 + 5h - 1; g(4)$

55. $F(x) = |x - 2|; F(-3)$

56. $G(z) = 2|z + 5|; G(-6)$

57. $F(z) = \dfrac{z + 2}{z - 5}; F(4)$

58. $h(q) = \dfrac{3q^2}{q + 2}; h(2)$

Applying the Concepts

59. If $f(x) = 3x^2 - x + C$ and $f(3) = 18$, what is the value of C?

60. If $f(x) = -2x^2 + 5x + C$ and $f(-2) = -15$, what is the value of C?

61. If $f(x) = \dfrac{2x + 5}{x - A}$ and $f(0) = -1$, what is the value of A?

62. If $f(x) = \dfrac{-x + B}{x - 5}$ and $f(3) = -1$, what is the value of B?

△ **63. Geometry** Express the area A of a circle as a function of its radius, r. Determine the area of a circle whose radius is 4 inches. That is, find $A(4)$.

△ **64. Geometry** Express the area A of a triangle as a function of its height h assuming that the length of the base is 8 centimeters. Determine the area of this triangle if its height is 5 centimeters. That is, find $A(5)$.

65. Salary Express the gross salary G of Jackie, who earns $15 per hour as a function of the number of hours worked, h. Determine the gross salary of Jackie if she works 25 hours. That is, find $G(25)$.

66. Commissions Roberta is a commissioned salesperson. She earns a base weekly salary of $250 per week plus 15% of the sales price of items sold. Express her gross salary G as a function of the price p of items sold. Determine the weekly gross salary of Roberta if the value of items sold is $10,000. That is, find $G(10,000)$.

67. Population as a Function of Age The function $P(a) = 18.75a^2 - 5309.62a + 321{,}783.32$ represents the population (in thousands) of Americans in 2007, P, that are a years of age or older. (SOURCE: *United States Census Bureau*)

(a) Identify the dependent and independent variables.

(b) Evaluate $P(20)$. Provide a verbal explanation of the meaning of $P(20)$.

(c) Evaluate $P(0)$. Provide a verbal explanation of the meaning of $P(0)$.

68. Number of Rooms The function $N(r) = -1.33r^2 + 14.68r - 17.09$ represents the number of housing units (in millions), N, in 2005 that have r rooms, where $1 \le r \le 9$. (SOURCE: *United States Census Bureau*)

(a) Identify the dependent and independent variables.

(b) Evaluate $N(3)$. Provide a verbal explanation of the meaning of $N(3)$.

(c) Why is it unreasonable to evaluate $N(0)$?

69. Revenue Function The function $R(p) = -p^2 + 200p$ represents the daily revenue R earned from selling personal digital assistants (PDAs) at p dollars for $0 \le p \le 200$.

(a) Identify the dependent and independent variables.

(b) Evaluate $R(50)$. Provide a verbal explanation of the meaning of $R(50)$.

(c) Evaluate $R(120)$. Provide a verbal explanation of the meaning of $R(120)$.

70. Average Trip Length The function $T(x) = 0.01x^2 - 0.12x + 8.89$ represents the average vehicle trip length T (in miles) x years since 1969.

(a) Identify the dependent and independent variables.

(b) Evaluate $T(35)$. Provide a verbal explanation of the meaning of $T(35)$.

(c) Evaluate $T(0)$. Provide a verbal explanation of the meaning of $T(0)$.

Extending the Concepts

71. Math for the Future: College Algebra A **piecewise-defined function** is a function defined by more than one equation. For example, the absolute value function $f(x) = |x|$ is actually defined by two equations: $f(x) = x$ if $x \ge 0$ and $f(x) = -x$ if $x < 0$. We can combine these equations into one expression as

$$f(x) = \begin{cases} x & x \ge 0 \\ -x & x < 0 \end{cases}$$

To evaluate $f(3)$, we recognize that $3 \ge 0$, so we use the rule $f(x) = x$ and obtain $f(3) = 3$. To evaluate $f(-4)$, we recognize that $-4 < 0$, so we use the rule $f(x) = -x$ and obtain $f(-4) = -(-4) = 4$.

(a) $f(x) = \begin{cases} x + 3 & x < 0 \\ -2x + 1 & x \ge 0 \end{cases}$

(i) Find $f(3)$.   (ii) Find $f(-2)$.   (iii) Find $f(0)$.

(b) $f(x) = \begin{cases} -3x + 1 & x < -2 \\ x^2 & x \ge -2 \end{cases}$

(i) Find $f(-4)$.   (ii) Find $f(2)$.   (iii) Find $f(-2)$.

72. Math for the Future: Calculus

(a) If $f(x) = 3x + 7$, find $\dfrac{f(x + h) - f(x)}{h}$.

(b) If $f(x) = -2x + 1$, find $\dfrac{f(x + h) - f(x)}{h}$.

Explaining the Concepts

73. Investigate when the use of function notation $y = f(x)$ first appeared. Start by researching Lejeune Dirichlet.

74. Are all relations functions? Are all functions relations? Explain your answers.

75. Explain what a function is. Be sure to include the terms *domain* and *range* in your explanation.

76. Explain why the vertical line test can be used to identify the graph of a function.

77. What are the four forms of a function presented in this section?

78. Explain why the terms *independent variable* for x and *dependent variable* for y make sense in the function $y = f(x)$.

The Graphing Calculator

Graphing calculators have the ability to evaluate any function you wish. Figure 9 shows the results obtained in Example 6 using a TI-84 Plus graphing calculator.

Figure 9

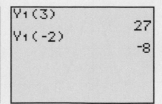

In Problems 79–86, use a graphing calculator to find the value of each function.

79. $f(x) = x^2 + 3; f(2)$

80. $f(x) = -2x^2 + x + 1; f(-3)$

81. $F(x) = |x - 2|; F(-3)$

82. $g(h) = \sqrt{2h + 1}; g(4)$

83. $H(x) = \sqrt{4x - 3}; H(7)$

84. $G(z) = 2|z + 5|; G(-6)$

85. $F(z) = \dfrac{z + 2}{z - 5}; F(4)$

86. $h(q) = \dfrac{3q^2}{q + 2}; h(2)$

2.3 Functions and Their Graphs

OBJECTIVES

1. Find the Domain of a Function
2. Graph a Function
3. Obtain Information from the Graph of a Function
4. Graph Functions in the Library of Functions
5. Interpret Graphs of Functions

In Words

The domain of a function is the set of all inputs for which the function gives an output that is a real number or makes sense.

Preparing for Functions and Their Graphs

Before getting started, take this readiness quiz. If you get a problem wrong, go back to the section cited and review the material.

P1. Solve: $3x - 12 = 0$ [Section 1.1, pp. 49–52]

P2. Graph $y = x^2$ by point-plotting.   [Section 1.5, pp. 97–99]

1 Find the Domain of a Function

When working with functions, we need to determine the set of inputs for which a function makes sense. Often the set of inputs for which the function makes sense is not specified; instead, only the equation defining the function is given.

DEFINITION

When only the equation of a function is given, we agree that the **domain of f** is the largest set of real numbers for which $f(x)$ is a real number.

When identifying the domain of a function don't forget that division by zero is undefined, so exclude values of the variable that cause division by zero.

EXAMPLE 1   Finding the Domain of a Function

Find the domain of each of the following functions:

(a) $G(x) = x^2 + 1$ (b) $g(z) = \dfrac{z - 3}{z + 1}$

Solution

(a) The function G tells us to square a number x and then add 1 to the result. These operations can be performed on any real number, so the domain of G is the set of all real numbers. We can express the domain as $\{x | x$ is a real number$\}$ or, using interval notation, $(-\infty, \infty)$.

(b) The function g tells us to divide $z - 3$ by $z + 1$. Since division by 0 is not defined, the denominator $z + 1$ can never be 0. Therefore, z can never equal -1. The domain of g is $\{z | z \neq -1\}$. ∎

Quick ✔

1. When only the equation of a function f is given, we agree that the _____ of f is the largest set of real numbers for which $f(x)$ is a real number.

In Problems 2 and 3, find the domain of each function.

2. $f(x) = 3x^2 + 2$ **3.** $h(x) = \dfrac{x + 1}{x - 3}$

Preparing for...Answers   **P1.** {4}

P2.

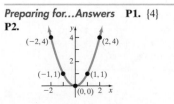

When we use functions in applications, the domain may be restricted by physical or geometric considerations, rather than by pure mathematical restrictions. For example, the domain of the function defined by $f(x) = x^2$ is the set of all real numbers. However, if f is used to obtain the area of a square when the length x of a side is known, then we must restrict the domain of f to the positive real numbers, since the length of a side can never be 0 or negative.

EXAMPLE 2 Finding the Domain of a Function

The number N of computers produced at one of Dell Computers manufacturing facilities in one day after t hours is given by the function, $N(t) = 336t - 7t^2$. What is the domain of this function?

Solution

The independent variable in this function is t, where t represents the number of hours in the day. Therefore, the domain of the function is $\{t | 0 \le t \le 24\}$, or the interval $[0, 24]$. ▪

> **Quick ✓**
> 4. The function $A(r) = \pi r^2$ gives the area of a circle A as a function of the radius r. What is the domain of the function?

2 Graph a Function

Figure 10 shows the graph of the linear equation $y = -2x + 4$. The graph passes the vertical line test so the equation $y = -2x + 4$ is a function. Therefore, we can express the relation using function notation as $f(x) = -2x + 4$. The graph of an equation is the same as the graph of the function where the horizontal axis represents the independent variable and the vertical axis represents the dependent variable. When we graph functions, we label the vertical axis either by y or by the name of the function.

> **DEFINITION**
>
> When a function is defined by an equation in x and y, the **graph of the function** is the set of *all* ordered pairs (x, y) such that $y = f(x)$.

So, if $f(3) = 8$, then the point whose ordered pair is $(3, 8)$ is on the graph of $y = f(x)$.

EXAMPLE 3 Graphing a Function

Graph the function $f(x) = |x|$.

Solution

To graph the function $f(x) = |x|$, we first determine some ordered pairs $(x, f(x)) = (x, y)$ such that $y = |x|$. See Table 2. We now plot the ordered pairs (x, y) from Table 2 in an xy-plane and connect the points as shown in Figure 11.

Figure 10

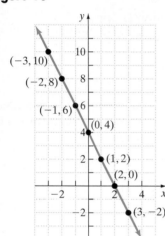

Table 2		
x	$f(x)$	$(x, f(x))$
-3	$|-3| = 3$	$(-3, 3)$
-2	$|-2| = 2$	$(-2, 2)$
-1	$|-1| = 1$	$(-1, 1)$
0	$|0| = 0$	$(0, 0)$
1	$|1| = 1$	$(1, 1)$
2	$|2| = 2$	$(2, 2)$
3	$|3| = 3$	$(3, 3)$

Figure 11
$f(x) = |x|$

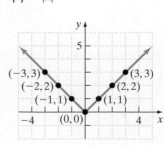

▪

Quick ✔ *In Problems 5–7, graph each function.*

5. $f(x) = -2x + 9$ **6.** $f(x) = x^2 + 2$ **7.** $f(x) = |x - 2|$

⌐3⌐ Obtain Information from the Graph of a Function

Remember, the domain of a function is the set of all allowed values of the variable and the range is the set of outputs of the function. We can find the domain and the range of a function from its graph. The approach to finding the domain and the range of a function from its graph is identical to the approach taken to find the domain and the range of a relation from its graph.

⌐EXAMPLE 4⌐ Determining the Domain and the Range of a Function from Its Graph

Figure 12 shows the graph of a function.

(a) Determine the domain and the range of the function.

(b) Identify the intercepts.

Figure 12

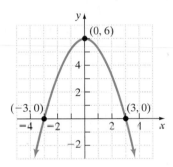

In Words

When the graph of a function is given, its domain may be viewed as the shadow created by the graph on the *x*-axis by vertical beams of light. Its range can be viewed as the shadow created by the graph on the *y*-axis by horizontal beams of light.

Solution

(a) To find the domain of the function, we determine the *x*-coordinates for which the graph of the function exists. Because the graph exists for all real numbers *x*, the domain is $\{x \mid x$ is any real number$\}$, or using interval notation, $(-\infty, \infty)$.

  To find the range of the function, we determine the *y*-coordinates for which the graph of the function exists. Because the graph exists for all real numbers *y* less than or equal to 6, the range is $\{y \mid y \le 6\}$, or using interval notation, $(-\infty, 6]$.

(b) The intercepts are the points $(-3, 0)$, $(0, 6)$, and $(3, 0)$. The *x*-intercepts are -3 and 3. The *y*-intercept is 6.   ∎

Quick ✔

8. Use the graph of the function to answer parts (a) and (b).

(a) Determine the domain and the range of the function.

(b) Identify the intercepts.

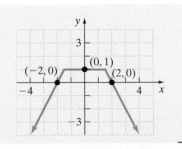

Remember, if (x, y) is a point on the graph of a function f, then y is the value of f at *x*, that is, $y = f(x)$. So, if $(1, 5)$ is a point on the graph of f, then $f(1) = 5$. The next example illustrates how to obtain information about a function if its graph is known.

EXAMPLE 5 Obtaining Information from the Graph of a Function

The Wonder Wheel is a Ferris wheel located in Coney Island. See Figure 13. Let f be the distance above the ground of a person riding on the Wonder Wheel as a function of time x (in minutes). Figure 14 represents the graph of the function f. Use the graph to answer the following questions.

Figure 13

Figure 14

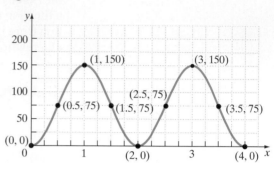

(a) What are $f(1.5)$ and $f(3)$? Interpret these values.

(b) What is the domain of f?

(c) What is the range of f?

(d) List the intercepts.

(e) For what values of x does $f(x) = 75$? That is, solve $f(x) = 75$.

Solution

(a) Since $(1.5, 75)$ is on the graph of f, then $f(1.5) = 75$. After 1.5 minutes, an individual on the Wonder Wheel is 75 feet in the air. Similarly, we find that since $(3, 150)$ is on the graph we have that $f(3) = 150$. After 3 minutes, an individual on the Wonder Wheel is 150 feet in the air.

(b) To determine the domain of f, we notice that for each number x between 0 and 4, inclusive, there are points $(x, f(x))$ on the graph of f. Therefore, the domain of f is $\{x \mid 0 \le x \le 4\}$, or the interval $[0, 4]$.

(c) The points on the graph have y-coordinates between 0 and 150, inclusive. Therefore, the range of f is $\{y \mid 0 \le y \le 150\}$, or the interval $[0, 150]$.

(d) The intercepts are $(0, 0)$, $(2, 0)$, and $(4, 0)$.

(e) Since $(0.5, 75)$, $(1.5, 75)$, $(2.5, 75)$, and $(3.5, 75)$ are the only points on the graph for which $y = f(x) = 75$, the solution set to the equation $f(x) = 75$ is $\{0.5, 1.5, 2.5, 3.5\}$. ∎

Quick ✔

9. If the point $(3, 8)$ is on the graph of a function f, then $f(\underline{\quad}) = \underline{\quad}$. If $g(-2) = 4$, then $(\underline{\quad}, \underline{\quad})$ is a point on the graph of g.

10. Use the graph of $y = f(x)$ to answer the following questions.

(a) What are $f(-3)$ and $f(1)$?

(b) What is the domain of f?

(c) What is the range of f?

(d) List the intercepts.

(e) For what value of x does $f(x) = 15$? That is, solve $f(x) = 15$.

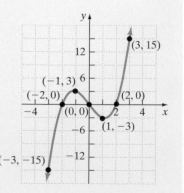

EXAMPLE 6 Obtaining Information about the Graph of a Function

Consider the function $f(x) = 2x - 5$.

(a) Is the point $(3, -1)$ on the graph of the function?

(b) If $x = 1$, what is $f(x)$? What point is on the graph of the function?

(c) If $f(x) = 3$, what is x? What point is on the graph of f?

Solution

(a) When $x = 3$, then

$$f(x) = 2x - 5$$
$$f(3) = 2(3) - 5 = 6 - 5 = 1$$

Since $f(3) = 1$, the point $(3, 1)$ is on the graph; the point $(3, -1)$ is not on the graph.

(b) If $x = 1$, then

$$f(x) = 2x - 5$$
$$f(1) = 2(1) - 5 = 2 - 5 = -3$$

The point $(1, -3)$ is on the graph of f.

(c) If $f(x) = 3$, then

$$f(x) = 3$$
$$2x - 5 = 3$$

Add 5 to both sides: $2x = 8$

Divide both sides by 2: $x = 4$

If $f(x) = 3$, then $x = 4$. The point $(4, 3)$ is on the graph of f. ■

Work Smart: Study Skills

Do not confuse the directions "Find $f(3)$" with "If $f(x) = 3$, what is x?" Write down and study errors that you commonly make so that you can avoid them.

> **Quick ✔**
>
> **11.** Consider the function $f(x) = -3x + 7$.
>
> (a) Is the point $(-2, 1)$ on the graph of the function?
>
> (b) If $x = 3$, what is $f(x)$? What point is on the graph of the function?
>
> (c) If $f(x) = -8$, what is x? What point is on the graph of f?

The Zero of a Function

If $f(r) = 0$ for some number r, then r is called a **zero** of f. For example, if $f(x) = x^2 - 4$, then -2 and 2 are zeros of f because $f(-2) = 0$ and $f(2) = 0$. We can identify the zeros of a function from its graph. To see how, we must remember that $y = f(x)$ means that the point (x, y) is on the graph of f. So, if r is a zero of f, then $f(r) = 0$, which means the point $(r, 0)$ is on the graph of f. If $(r, 0)$ is on the graph of f, then r is an x-intercept. So, the x-intercepts of the graph of a function are also the zeros of the function.

Figure 15

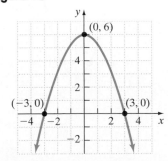

EXAMPLE 7 Finding the Zeros of a Function from Its Graph

Find the zeros of the function f whose graph is shown in Figure 15.

Solution

We look for the x-intercepts of the graph because these are also the zeros of the function. The x-intercepts are -3 and 3, so the zeros of f are -3 and 3. ■

Quick ✔

In problems 12–14, determine if the value is a zero of the function.

12. $f(x) = 2x + 6; -3$ **13.** $g(x) = x^2 - 2x - 3; 1$

14. $h(z) = -z^3 + 4z; 2$

15. Find the zeros of the function f whose graph is shown.

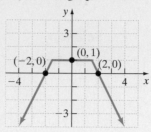

⌐4⌐ Graph Functions in the Library of Functions

In Table 3, we list a number of basic functions, their properties, and their graphs.

Table 3		
Function	**Properties**	**Graph**
Linear Function $f(x) = mx + b$ m and b are real numbers	• Domain and range are all real numbers. • Graph is nonvertical line with slope $= m$ y intercept $= b$.	$f(x) = mx + b, m > 0$ $(0, b)$
Identity Function (special type of linear function) $f(x) = x$	• Domain and range are all real numbers. • Graph is a line with slope of $m = 1$ y-intercept $= 0$. • The line consists of all points for which the x-coordinate equals the y-coordinate.	$f(x) = x$ $(1, 1)$ $(0, 0)$ $(-1, -1)$
Constant Function (special type of linear function) $f(x) = b$ b is a real number	• Domain is the set of all real numbers and range is the set consisting of a single number b. • Graph is a horizontal line with slope $m = 0$ y-intercept of b.	$f(x) = b$ $(0, b)$
Square Function $f(x) = x^2$	• Domain is the set of all real numbers; its range is the set of nonnegative real numbers. • The intercept of the graph is $(0, 0)$.	y $f(x) = x^2$ $(-2, 4)$ $(2, 4)$ $(-1, 1)$ $(1, 1)$ $(0, 0)$

(continued)

Function	Properties	Graph
Cube Function $f(x) = x^3$	• Domain and range are the set of all real numbers. • The intercept of the graph is at $(0, 0)$.	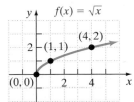
Square Root Function $f(x) = \sqrt{x}$	• Domain and range are the set of nonnegative real numbers. • The intercept of the graph is at $(0, 0)$.	
Cube Root Function $f(x) = \sqrt[3]{x}$	• Domain and range are the set of real numbers. • The intercept of the graph is at $(0, 0)$.	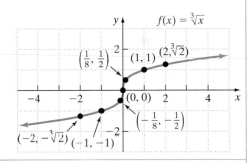
Reciprocal Function $f(x) = \dfrac{1}{x}$	• Domain and range are the set of all nonzero real numbers. • The graph has no intercepts.	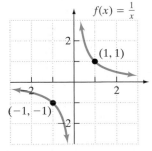
Absolute Value Function $f(x) = |x|$	• Domain is the set of all real numbers; its range is the set of nonnegative real numbers. • The intercept of the graph is at $(0, 0)$. • If $x \geq 0$, then $f(x) = x$, and the graph of f is part of the line $y = x$; if $x < 0$, then $f(x) = -x$, and the graph of f is part of the line $y = -x$.	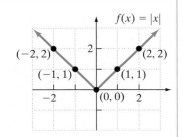

⌈5⌉ Interpret Graphs of Functions

We can use the graph of a function to give a visual description of many different scenarios. Consider the following example.

⌈EXAMPLE 8⌉ Graphing a Verbal Description

Maria decides to take a walk. She leaves her house and walks 3 blocks in 2 minutes at a constant speed. She realizes that she left her front door unlocked, so she runs home in 1 minute. It takes Maria 1 minute to find her keys and lock the door. She then decides to run 10 blocks in 3 minutes. She is a little tired now, so she rests for 1 minute and then walks an additional 4 blocks in 10 minutes. She hitches a ride home with her neighbor who happens to drive by and gets home in 2 minutes. Draw a graph of Maria's distance from home (in blocks) as a function of time.

Solution

First, we recognize that distance from home is a function of time. Therefore, we draw a Cartesian Plane with the horizontal axis representing the independent variable, time, and the vertical axis representing the dependent variable, distance from home.

The ordered pair $(0, 0)$ corresponds to starting the walk at home. The ordered pair $(2, 3)$ corresponds to being 3 blocks from home after 2 minutes. We start the graph at the origin and then draw a straight line from $(0, 0)$ to $(2, 3)$. From the point $(2, 3)$, we draw a straight line to $(3, 0)$, which represents the return trip home to lock the door. Draw a line segment from $(3, 0)$ to $(4, 0)$ to represent the time it takes to lock the door. Draw a line segment from $(4, 0)$ to $(7, 10)$, which represents the 10 blocks run in 3 minutes. Now we draw a horizontal line from $(7, 10)$ to $(8, 10)$. This represents the resting period. Draw a line from $(8, 10)$ to $(18, 14)$ to represent the 4-block walk in 10 minutes. Finally, draw a line segment from $(18, 14)$ to $(20, 0)$ to represent the ride home. See Figure 16.

Figure 16

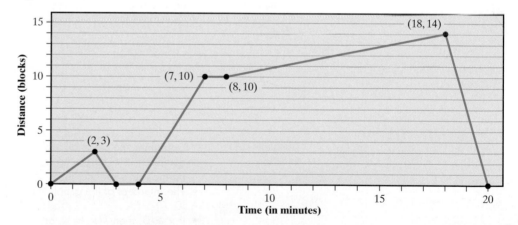

Quick ✔

16. Maria decides to take a walk. She leaves her house and walks 5 blocks in 5 minutes at a constant speed. She realizes that she left her front door unlocked, so she runs home in 2 minutes. It takes Maria 1 minute to find her keys and lock the door. She then decides to jog 8 blocks in 5 minutes. She then runs 3 blocks in 1 minute. She is a little tired now, so she rests for 2 minutes and then walks home in 10 minutes. Draw a graph of Maria's distance from home (in blocks) as a function of time.

2.3 EXERCISES

MyMathLab
Powered by CourseCompass™ and MathXL™

PRACTICE WATCH DOWNLOAD READ REVIEW

1–16. *are the* Quick ✔s *that follow each* EXAMPLE

Building Skills

In Problems 17–24, find the domain of each function. See Objective 1.

17. $f(x) = 4x + 7$

18. $G(x) = -8x + 3$

19. $F(z) = \dfrac{2z + 1}{z - 5}$

20. $H(x) = \dfrac{x + 5}{2x + 1}$

21. $f(x) = 3x^4 - 2x^2$

22. $s(t) = 2t^2 - 5t + 1$

23. $G(x) = \dfrac{3x - 5}{3x + 1}$

24. $H(q) = \dfrac{1}{6q + 5}$

In Problems 25–32, graph each function. See Objective 2.

25. $f(x) = 4x - 6$

26. $g(x) = -3x + 5$

27. $h(x) = x^2 - 2$

28. $F(x) = x^2 + 1$

29. $G(x) = |x - 1|$

30. $H(x) = |x + 1|$

31. $g(x) = x^3$

32. $h(x) = x^3 - 3$

In Problems 33–42, for each graph of a function, find (a) the domain and the range, (b) the intercepts, if any, and (c) the zeros, if any. See Objective 3.

33.

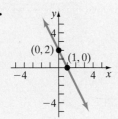

34.

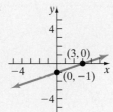

35.

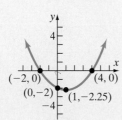

36.

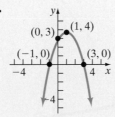

37.

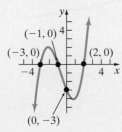

38.

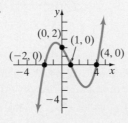

39.

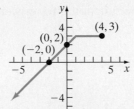

40.

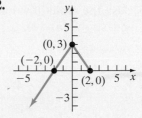

41.

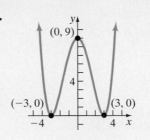

42.

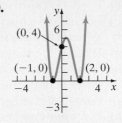

43. Use the graph of the function f shown to answer parts **(a)**–**(l)**.

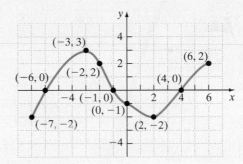

(a) Find $f(-7)$.

(b) Find $f(-3)$.

(c) Find $f(6)$.

(d) Is $f(2)$ positive or negative?

(e) For what numbers x is $f(x) = 0$?

(f) What is the domain of f?

(g) What is the range of f?

(h) What are the x-intercepts?

(i) What is the y-intercept?

(j) For what numbers x is $f(x) = -2$?

(k) For what number x is $f(x) = 3$?

(l) What are the zeros of f?

44. Use the graph of the function g shown to answer parts **(a)**–**(l)**.

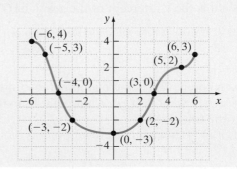

(a) Find $g(-3)$.
(b) Find $g(5)$.
(c) Find $g(6)$.
(d) Is $g(-5)$ positive or negative?
(e) For what numbers x is $g(x) = 0$?
(f) What is the domain of g?
(g) What is the range of g?
(h) What are the x-intercepts?
(i) What is the y-intercept?
(j) For what numbers x is $g(x) = -2$?
(k) For what number x is $g(x) = 3$?
(l) What are the zeros of g?

45. Use the table of values for the function F to answer questions **(a)–(e)**.

x	F(x)
−4	0
−2	3
−1	5
0	2
3	−6

(a) What is $F(-2)$?
(b) What is $F(3)$?
(c) For what number(s) x is $F(x) = 5$?
(d) What is the x-intercept of the graph of F?
(e) What is the y-intercept of the graph of F?

46. Use the table of values for the function G to answer questions **(a)–(e)**.

x	G(x)
−5	−3
−4	0
0	5
3	8
7	5

(a) What is $G(3)$?
(b) What is $G(7)$?
(c) For what number(s) x is $G(x) = 5$?
(d) What is the x-intercept of the graph of G?
(e) What is the y-intercept of the graph of G?

In Problems 47–50, answer the questions about the given function. See Objective 3.

47. $f(x) = 4x - 9$

(a) Is the point $(2, 1)$ on the graph of the function?
(b) If $x = 3$, what is $f(x)$? What point is on the graph of the function?
(c) If $f(x) = 7$, what is x? What point is on the graph of f?
(d) Is 2 a zero of f?

48. $f(x) = 3x + 5$

(a) Is the point $(-2, 1)$ on the graph of the function?
(b) If $x = 4$, what is $f(x)$? What point is on the graph of the function?
(c) If $f(x) = -4$, what is x? What point is on the graph of f?
(d) Is -2 a zero of f?

49. $g(x) = -\dfrac{1}{2}x + 4$

(a) Is the point $(4, 2)$ on the graph of the function?
(b) If $x = 6$, what is $g(x)$? What point is on the graph of the function?
(c) If $g(x) = 10$, what is x? What point is on the graph of g?
(d) Is 8 a zero of g?

50. $H(x) = \dfrac{2}{3}x - 4$

(a) Is the point $(3, -2)$ on the graph of the function?
(b) If $x = 6$, what is $H(x)$? What point is on the graph of the function?
(c) If $H(x) = -4$, what is x? What point is on the graph of H?
(d) Is 6 a zero of H?

In Problems 51–58, match each graph to the function listed whose graph most resembles the one given. See Objective 4.

(a) Constant function   (b) Linear function
(c) Square function   (d) Cube function
(e) Square root function   (f) Reciprocal function
(g) Absolute value function   (h) Cube root function

51. 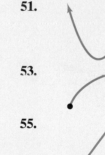   **52.**

53.    **54.**

55. 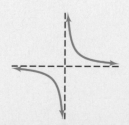   **56.**

57.   **58.**

In Problems 59–64, sketch the graph of each function. Label at least three points. See Objective 4.

59. $f(x) = x^2$ **60.** $f(x) = x^3$ **61.** $f(x) = \sqrt{x}$

62. $f(x) = \sqrt[3]{x}$ **63.** $f(x) = \dfrac{1}{x}$ **64.** $f(x) = |x|$

Applying the Concepts

△ **65. Geometry** The volume V of a sphere as a function of its radius r is given by $V(r) = \dfrac{4}{3}\pi r^3$. What is the domain of this function?

△ **66. Geometry** The area A of a triangle as a function of its height h assuming that the length of the base is 5 centimeters is $A = \dfrac{5}{2}h$. What is the domain of the function?

67. Salary The gross salary G of Jackie as a function of the number of hours worked, h, is given by $G(h) = 22.5h$. What is the domain of the function if she can work up to 60 hours per week?

68. Commissions Roberta is a commissioned salesperson. She earns a base weekly salary of $350 plus 12% of the sales price of items sold. Her gross salary G as a function of the price p of items sold is given by $G(p) = 350 + 0.12p$. What is the domain of the function?

69. Demand for Hot Dogs Suppose the function $D(p) = 1200 - 10p$ represents the demand for hot dogs, whose price is p, at a baseball game. Find the domain of the function.

70. Revenue Function The function $R(p) = -p^2 + 200p$ represents the daily revenue earned from selling personal digital assistants (PDAs) at p dollars for $0 \le p \le 200$. Explain why any p greater than $200 is not in the domain of the function.

---

71. Match each of the following functions with the graph that best describes the situation.

(a) The distance from ground level of a person who is jumping on a trampoline as a function of time
(b) The cost of a telephone call as a function of time
(c) The height of a human as a function of time
(d) The revenue earned from selling cars as a function of price
(e) The book value of a machine that is depreciated by equal amounts each year as a function of the year

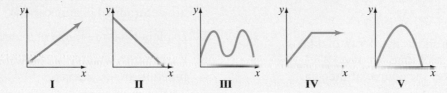

72. Match each of the following functions with the graph that best describes the situation.

(a) The average high temperature each day as a function of the day of the year
(b) The number of bacteria in a Petri dish as a function of time
(c) The distance that a person rides her bicycle at a constant speed as a function of time
(d) The temperature of a pizza after it is removed from the oven as a function of time
(e) The value of a car as a function of time

---

73. Pulse Rate Consider the following scenario: Zach starts jogging on a treadmill. His resting pulse rate is 70. As he continues to jog on the treadmill, his pulse increases at a constant rate until, after 10 minutes, his pulse is 120. He then starts jogging faster and his pulse increases at a constant rate for 2 minutes, at which time his pulse is up to 150. He then begins a cooling-off period for 7 minutes until his pulse backs down to 110. He then gets off the treadmill and his pulse returns to 70 after 12 minutes. Draw a graph of Zach's pulse as a function of time.

74. Altitude of an Airplane Suppose that a plane is flying from Chicago to New Orleans. The plane leaves the gate and taxis for 5 minutes. The plane takes off and gets up to 10,000 feet after 5 minutes. The plane continues to ascend at a constant rate until it reaches its cruising altitude of 35,000 feet after another 25 minutes. For the next 80 minutes, the plane maintains a constant height of 35,000 feet. The plane then descends at a constant rate until it lands after 20 minutes. It requires 5 minutes to taxi to the gate. Draw a graph of the height of the plane as a function of time.

75. Height of a Swing An 8-year-old girl gets on a swing and starts swinging for 10 minutes. Draw a graph that represents the height of the child from the ground as a function of time.

76. Temperature of Pizza Marissa is hungry and would like a pizza. Her mother pulls a frozen pizza out of the freezer and puts it in the oven. After 12 minutes the pizza is done, but Mom lets the pizza cool for 5 minutes before serving it to Marissa. Draw a graph that represents the temperature of the pizza as a function of time.

77. The graph below shows the weight of a person as a function of his age. Describe the weight of the individual over the course of his life.

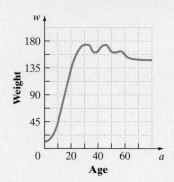

78. The following graph shows the depth of a lake (in feet) as a function of time (in days). Describe the depth of the lake over the course of the year.

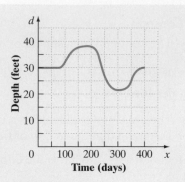

Extending the Concepts

79. Draw a graph of a function f with the following characteristics: x-intercepts: $-4, -1, 2$; y-intercept: -2; $f(-3) = 7$ and $f(3) = 8$.

80. Draw a graph of a function f with the following characteristics: x-intercepts: $-3, 2$, and 5; y-intercept: 3; $f(3) = -2$.

Explaining the Concepts

81. Using the definition of a function, explain why the graph of a function can have at most one y-intercept.

82. Explain what the domain of a function is. In your explanation, provide a discussion as to how domains are determined in applications.

83. Explain what the range of a function is.

84. Explain the relationship between the x-intercepts of a function and its zeros.

PUTTING THE CONCEPTS TOGETHER (Sections 2.1–2.3)

These problems cover important concepts from Sections 2.1 through 2.3. We designed these problems so that you can review the chapter so far and show your mastery of the concepts. Take time to work these problems before proceeding with the next section. The answers to these problems are located at the back of the text on page AN-13.

1. Explain why the following relation is a function. Then express the function as a set of ordered pairs.

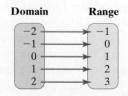

2. Determine which of the following relations represent functions.

(a) $y = x^3 - 4x$ (b) $y = \pm 4x + 3$

3. Is the following relation a function? If so, state the domain and range.

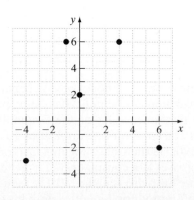

4. Explain why the relation whose graph is on the following page is a function. If the name of the function is f, find $f(5)$.

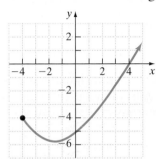

5. What is the zero of the function whose graph is shown?

6. Let $f(x) = -5x + 3$ and $g(x) = -2x^2 + 5x - 1$.
    Find the value of each of the following.

    (a) $f(4)$ (b) $g(-3)$

    (c) $f(x) - f(4)$ (d) $f(x - 4)$

7. Find the domain of each of the following functions.

    (a) $G(h) = h^2 + 4$ (b) $F(w) = \dfrac{w - 4}{3w + 1}$

8. Graph $f(x) = |x| - 2$. Use the graph to state the domain and the range of f.

9. **Vertical Motion** The graph below shows the height, h, in feet, of a ball thrown straight up with an initial speed of 40 feet per second from an initial height of 80 feet after t seconds.

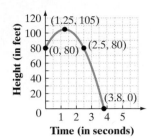

    (a) Find and interpret $h(2.5)$.
    (b) What is the domain of h?
    (c) What is the range of h?
    (d) For what value of t does $h(t) = 105$?

10. Consider the function $f(x) = 5x - 2$.

    (a) Is the point $(3, 12)$ on the graph of the function?
    (b) If $x = -2$, what is $f(x)$? What point is on the graph of the function?
    (c) If $f(x) = -22$, what is x? What point is on the graph of f?
    (d) Is $\dfrac{2}{5}$ a zero of f?

2.4 Linear Functions and Models

OBJECTIVES

1 Graph Linear Functions
2 Find the Zero of a Linear Function
3 Build Linear Models from Verbal Descriptions
4 Build Linear Models from Data

Preparing for...Answers

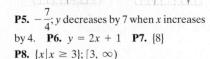

P5. $-\dfrac{7}{4}$; y decreases by 7 when x increases by 4.   P6. $y = 2x + 1$ P7. $\{8\}$
P8. $\{x \mid x \geq 3\}$; $[3, \infty)$

Preparing for Linear Functions and Models

Before getting started, take this readiness quiz. If you get a problem wrong, go back to the section cited and review the material.

P1. Graph: $y = 2x - 3$ [Section 1.6, pp. 115–116]

P2. Graph: $\dfrac{1}{2}x + y = 2$ [Section 1.6, pp. 106–107]

P3. Graph: $y = -4$ [Section 1.6, pp. 108–109]

P4. Graph: $x = 5$ [Section 1.6, pp. 108–109]

P5. Find and interpret the slope of the line through
     $(-1, 3)$ and $(3, -4)$.   [Section 1.6, pp. 109–111]

P6. Find the equation of the line through $(1, 3)$ and $(4, 9)$.   [Section 1.6, pp. 109–111]

P7. Solve: $0.5(x - 40) + 100 = 84$ [Section 1.1, pp. 49–54]

P8. Solve: $4x + 20 \geq 32$ [Section 1.4, pp. 85–88]

1 Graph Linear Functions

In Chapter 1, we discussed linear equations in two variables. Recall, a linear equation in two variables is an equation of the form $Ax + By = C$ where A, B, and C are real numbers. In addition, A and B cannot both be zero.

Remember, lines can have four basic forms: (1) they can rise from left to right; (2) they can fall from left to right; (3) they can be horizontal; or (4) they can be vertical. Figure 17 shows these four basic forms. Notice that lines that rise from left to right have a positive slope, lines that fall from left to right have a negative slope, horizontal lines have a 0 slope, and vertical lines have undefined slope.

Figure 17

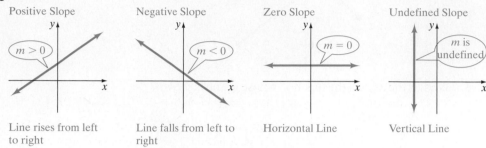

Positive Slope	Negative Slope	Zero Slope	Undefined Slope
Line rises from left to right	Line falls from left to right	Horizontal Line	Vertical Line

If you look at the graphs shown in Figure 17, you should notice that all except one pass the vertical line test for identifying graphs of functions. Which one does not pass? We conclude the following: **All linear equations except equations of the form $x = a$, vertical lines, are functions.**

Because all linear equations except those of the form $x = a$ are functions, we can write any linear equation that is in the form $Ax + By = C$ using function notation provided that $B \neq 0$ as follows:

$$Ax + By = C \qquad B \neq 0$$

Subtract Ax from both sides: $\quad By = -Ax + C$

Divide both sides by B: $\quad \dfrac{By}{B} = \dfrac{-Ax + C}{B}$

Simplify: $\quad y = -\dfrac{A}{B}x + \dfrac{C}{B}$

$$\updownarrow \qquad \updownarrow \qquad \updownarrow$$

$$f(x) \;=\; mx \;+\; b$$

This leads to the following definition:

DEFINITION

A **linear function** is a function of the form

$$f(x) = mx + b$$

where m and b are real numbers. The graph of a linear function is called a **line**.

We can graph linear functions using the same techniques we used to graph linear equations that are written in slope-intercept form, $y = mx + b$ (See Section 1.6).

Figure 18

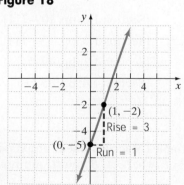

EXAMPLE 1 Graphing a Linear Function

Graph the linear function: $f(x) = 3x - 5$

Solution

Comparing $f(x) = 3x - 5$ to $f(x) = mx + b$, we see that the slope m is 3 and the y-intercept b is -5. We begin by plotting the point $(0, -5)$. Because $m = 3 = \dfrac{3}{1} = \dfrac{\Delta y}{\Delta x} = \dfrac{\text{Rise}}{\text{Run}}$, from the point $(0, -5)$ we go to the right 1 unit and up 3 units and end up at $(1, -2)$. We draw a line through these two points and obtain the graph of $f(x) = 3x - 5$ shown in Figure 18.

Quick ✔

1. For the graph of a linear function $f(x) = mx + b$, m is the _____ and b is the _____ .

2. The graph of a linear function is called a _____ .

3. *True or False:* All linear equations are functions.

4. For the linear function $G(x) = -2x + 3$, the slope is ___ and the y-intercept is ___ .

In Problems 5–8, graph each linear function.

5. $f(x) = 2x - 3$ 6. $G(x) = -5x + 4$ 7. $h(x) = \dfrac{3}{2}x + 1$ 8. $f(x) = 4$

⌐2 Find the Zero of a Linear Function

In Section 2.3 we stated that if r is a zero of a function f, then $f(r) = 0$. To find the zero of any function f, we solve the equation $f(x) = 0$. So, to find the zero of a linear function $f(x) = mx + b$, we solve the equation $mx + b = 0$.

EXAMPLE 2 Finding the Zero of a Linear Function

Find the zero of $f(x) = -4x + 12$.

Solution

We find the zero by solving $f(x) = 0$.

$$f(x) = 0$$
$$f(x) = -4x + 12: \quad -4x + 12 = 0$$

Subtract 12 from both sides of the equation: $\quad -4x = -12$

Divide both sides of the equation by -4: $\quad x = 3$

Check: Since $f(3) = -4(3) + 12 = 0$, the zero of f is 3. ∎

Quick ✔ *In Problems 9–11, find the zero of each linear function.*

9. $f(x) = 3x - 15$ 10. $G(x) = \dfrac{1}{2}x + 4$ 11. $F(p) = -\dfrac{2}{3}p + 8$

Applications of Linear Functions

There are many applications of linear functions. For example, the cost of cab fare, sales commissions, or the cost of breakfast as a function of the number of eggs ordered can each be modeled by a linear function.

EXAMPLE 3 Sales Commissions

Tony's weekly salary at Apple Chevrolet is 0.75% of his weekly sales plus $450. The linear function $S(x) = 0.0075x + 450$ describes Tony's weekly salary S as a linear function of his weekly sales x.

(a) What is the implied domain of the function?

(b) If Tony sells cars worth a total of $50,000 one week, what is his salary?

(c) If Tony earned $600 one week, what was the value of the cars that he sold?

(d) Draw a graph of the function.

(e) For what value of cars sold will Tony's weekly salary exceed $1200?

Solution

(a) The independent variable is weekly sales, x. Because it does not make sense to talk about negative weekly sales, we have that the domain of the function is $\{x \mid x \geq 0\}$ or, using interval notation, $[0, \infty)$.

(b) We evaluate the function at $x = \$50,000$ to obtain

$$S(50,000) = 0.0075(50,000) + 450$$
$$= \$825$$

Tony will earn $825 for the week if he sells $50,000 worth of cars.

(c) Here, we need to solve the equation $S(x) = 600$.

$$0.0075x + 450 = 600$$

Subtract 450 from both sides: $0.0075x = 150$

Divide both sides by 0.0075: $x = \$20,000$

If Tony earned $600, then he sold $20,000 worth of cars in a week.

(d) We plot the independent variable, *weekly sales,* on the horizontal axis and the dependent variable, *salary,* on the vertical axis. We graph the equation by plotting points. From part (b), we know the point $(50,000, 825)$ is on the graph. From part (c), we know the point $(20,000, 600)$ is on the graph. We also know the point $(0, 450)$ is on the graph. Do you see why? We plot these points and obtain the graph shown in Figure 19.

Figure 19

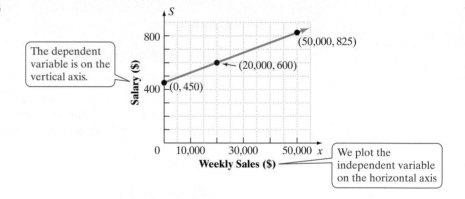

(e) We need to solve the inequality $S(x) > 1200$.

$$0.0075x + 450 > 1200$$

Subtract 450 from both sides: $0.0075x > 750$

Divide both sides of the inequality by 0.0075: $x > 100,000$

If Tony sells more than $100,000 worth of cars for the week, his salary will exceed $1200.

Notice a few details regarding the graph of the linear function in Figure 19. First, we only graph the function over its domain, $[0, \infty)$, so that in this case we only graph in quadrant I. Also notice that we labeled the horizontal axis x for the independent variable, *weekly sales,* and we labeled the vertical axis S for the dependent variable, *salary.* For this reason, the intercept on the vertical axis is the S-intercept, not the y-intercept. We also indicated what the independent and dependent variables represent on each coordinate axis. It is always a good practice to label your axes.

Quick ✔

12. The cost, C, of renting a 12-foot moving truck for a day is $40 plus $0.35 times the number of miles driven. The linear function $C(x) = 0.35x + 40$ describes the cost C of driving the truck x miles.

(a) What is the implied domain of this linear function?

(b) Determine the C-intercept of the graph of the linear function.

(c) What is the rental cost if the truck is driven 80 miles?

(d) How many miles was the truck driven if the rental cost is $85.50?

(e) Graph the linear function.

(f) How many miles can you drive if you can spend up to $127.50?

⎡3⎤ Build Linear Models from Verbal Descriptions

A linear function is a function of the form $f(x) = mx + b$, where m is the slope of the linear function and b is its y-intercept. In Section 1.6, we said that the slope m can be thought of as an average rate of change. The slope describes by how much a dependent variable changes for a given change in the independent variable. For example, in the linear function $f(x) = 4x + 3$, the slope is $4 = \dfrac{4}{1} = \dfrac{\Delta y}{\Delta x}$ so that the dependent variable y will increase by 4 units for every 1-unit increase in x (the independent variable). When the average rate of change of a function is constant, then we can use a linear function to model the situation. For example, if your phone company charges you $0.05 per minute to talk regardless of the number of minutes on the phone, then we can use a linear function to model the cost of talking with slope $m = \dfrac{0.05 \text{ dollar}}{1 \text{ minute}}$.

EXAMPLE 4 Cost Function

The simplest cost function is the linear cost function $C(x) = ax + b$, where b represents the fixed costs of operating a business and a represents the costs associated with manufacturing one additional item. Suppose that a small bicycle manufacturer has daily fixed costs of $2000 and each bicycle costs $80 to manufacture.

(a) Write a linear function that expresses the cost of manufacturing x bicycles in a day.

(b) What is the cost of manufacturing 5 bicycles in a day?

(c) How many bicycles can be manufactured for $2800?

(d) Graph the linear function.

Solution

(a) Because each additional bicycle costs $80 to manufacture, we have that $a = 80$. The fixed costs are $2000 so that $b = 2000$. Therefore, the cost function is

$$C(x) = 80x + 2000$$

(b) We evaluate the function for $x = 5$ and obtain

$$C(5) = 80(5) + 2000$$
$$= \$2400$$

It will cost $2400 to manufacture 5 bicycles.

(c) We solve $C(x) = 2800$.

$$C(x) = 2800$$
$$80x + 2000 = 2800$$

Subtract 2000 from both sides: $80x = 800$

Divide both sides by 80: $x = 10$

So 10 bicycles can be manufactured for a cost of $2800.

(d) Label the horizontal axis x and the vertical axis C. Figure 20 shows the graph of the cost function. ∎

Figure 20

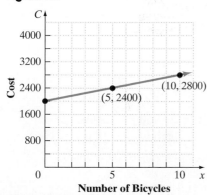

Number of Bicycles

Quick ✔

13. Suppose that the government imposes a tax of $1 per bicycle manufactured for the business presented in Example 4.

    (a) Write a linear function that expresses the cost C of manufacturing x bicycles in a day.

    (b) What is the cost of manufacturing 5 bicycles in a day?

    (c) How many bicycles can be manufactured for $2810?

    (d) Graph the linear function.

EXAMPLE 5 Straight-Line Depreciation

Book value is the value of an asset such as a building or piece of machinery that a company uses to create its balance sheet. Some companies will use straight-line depreciation to depreciate their assets so that the value of the asset declines by a constant amount each year. The amount of the decline depends upon the useful life that the company places on the asset. Suppose that Pearson Publishing Company just purchased a new fleet of cars for its sales force at a cost of $29,400 per car. The company will depreciate the cars using the straight-line method over 7 years, so that each car depreciates by $\dfrac{\$29{,}400}{7} = \$4200$ per year.

(a) Write a linear function that expresses the book value V of each car as a function of its age, x.

(b) What is the implied domain of this linear function?

(c) What is the book value of each car after 3 years?

(d) When will the book value of each car be $12,600?

(e) Graph the linear function.

Solution

(a) We let $V(x)$ represent the book value of each car after x years, so $V(x) = mx + b$. The original value of the car is $29,400, so $V(0) = 29,400$. The V-intercept of the linear function is $29,400. Because each car depreciates by $4200 per year, the slope of the linear function is -4200. The linear function that represents the book value of each car after x years is given by

$$V(x) = -4200x + 29{,}400$$

(b) Because a car cannot have a negative age, we know that the age, x, must be greater than or equal to zero. In addition, each car is depreciated over 7 years. After 7 years the book value of each car is $V(7) = 0$. Therefore, the implied domain of the function is $\{x \mid 0 \leq x \leq 7\}$, or using interval notation, $[0, 7]$.

(c) The book value of each car after $x = 3$ years is given by $V(3)$.

$$V(3) = -4200(3) + 29{,}400$$
$$= \$16{,}800$$

(d) To find when the book value is $12,600, we solve the equation

$$V(x) = 12{,}600$$
$$-4200x + 29{,}400 = 12{,}600$$

Subtract 29,400 from both sides: $\qquad -4200x = -16{,}800$

Divide both sides by 4: $\qquad\qquad x = 4$

Each car will have a book value of $12,600 after 4 years.

(e) Label the horizontal axis x and the vertical axis V. Since $V(0) = 29,400$, we know that $(0, 29400)$ is on the graph. Since $V(7) = 0$, we know that $(7, 0)$ is on the graph. To graph the function, we use these points (the intercepts), along with points $(3, 16800)$ and $(4, 12600)$ found in parts (c) and (d). See Figure 21.

Figure 21

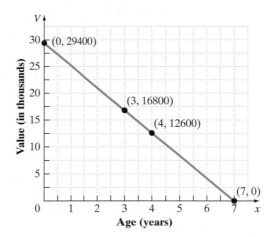

Quick ✔

14. Roberta just purchased a new car. Her monthly payments are $250 per month. She estimates that maintenance and gas cost her $0.18 per mile.

   (a) Write a linear function that relates the monthly cost C of operating the car as a function of miles driven, x.

   (b) What is the implied domain of this linear function?

   (c) What is the monthly cost of driving 320 miles?

   (d) How many miles can Roberta drive each month if she can afford the monthly cost to be $282.40?

   (e) Graph the linear function.

⌐4 Build Linear Models from Data

We know from Section 1.6 that only two points are required to find the equation of a line. But what if we have a set of data with more than two points? How can we tell if the data (the two variables) are related linearly? While there are some rather sophisticated methods for determining whether two variables are linearly related (and beyond the scope of this course), we can draw a picture of the data and learn whether the variables might be linearly related. This picture is called a *scatter diagram.*

Scatter Diagrams

Often, we are interested in finding an equation that can describe the relation between two variables. The first step in determining the type of equation that could be used to describe the relation is to plot the ordered pairs that make up the relation in the Cartesian plane. The graph that results is called a **scatter diagram.**

⌐EXAMPLE 6 Drawing a Scatter Diagram

In baseball, the on-base percentage for a team represents the percentage of time that the team safely reaches base. The data given in Table 4 represent the number of runs scored and the on-base percentage for various teams during the 2007 baseball season.

Table 4			
Team	On-Base Percentage, x	Runs Scored, y	(x, y)
NY Yankees	36.6	968	(36.6, 968)
Los Angeles Angels	34.5	822	(34.5, 822)
Texas Rangers	32.8	816	(32.8, 816)
Toronto Blue Jays	32.7	753	(32.7, 753)
Minnesota Twins	33.0	718	(33.0, 718)
Oakland A's	33.8	741	(33.8, 741)
Kansas City Royals	32.2	706	(32.2, 706)
Baltimore Orioles	33.3	756	(33.3, 756)

SOURCE: *espn.com*

(a) Draw a scatter diagram of the data, treating on-base percentage as the independent variable.

(b) Describe what happens as the on-base percentage increases.

Figure 22

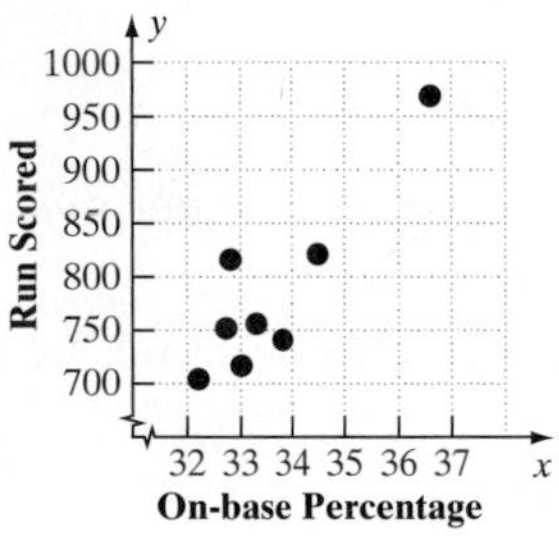

Run Scored / On-base Percentage

Solution

(a) To draw a scatter diagram we plot the ordered pairs listed in Table 4. See Figure 22.

(b) From the scatter diagram, we can see that as the on-base percentage increases, the number of runs scored also increases. While the relation between on-base percentage and number of runs scored does not follow a perfect linear relation (because the points don't all fall on a straight line), we can agree that the pattern of the data is linear. ∎

Quick ✔

15. The data listed below represent the total cholesterol (in mg/dL) and age of males.

Age, x	Total Cholesterol, y	Age, x	Total Cholesterol, y
25	180	38	239
25	195	48	204
28	186	51	243
32	180	62	228
32	197	65	269

(a) Draw a scatter diagram treating age as the independent variable.

(b) Describe the relation between age and total cholesterol.

Figure 23

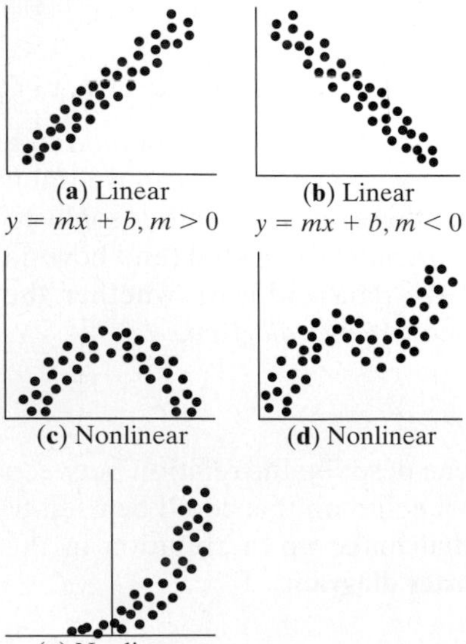

(a) Linear
$y = mx + b, m > 0$

(b) Linear
$y = mx + b, m < 0$

(c) Nonlinear

(d) Nonlinear

(e) Nonlinear

Recognizing the Type of Relation That Appears to Exist between Two Variables

We use scatter diagrams to help us see the type of relation that exists between two variables. In this text, we will look at a few different types of relations between two variables. For now, however, our only goal is to distinguish between linear and nonlinear relations. See Figure 23.

EXAMPLE 7 Distinguishing between Linear and Nonlinear Relations

Determine whether the relation between the two variables in each graph of Figure 24 is linear or nonlinear. If the relation is linear, indicate whether the slope is positive or negative.

Figure 24

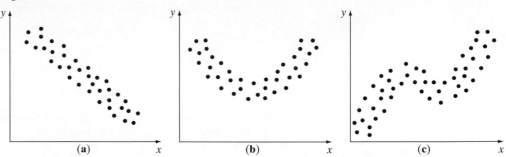

| (a) | (b) | (c) |

Solution

(a) Linear with negative slope   (b) Nonlinear   (c) Nonlinear   ■

Quick ✔ *In Problems 16 and 17, determine whether the relation between the two variables is linear or nonlinear. If it is linear, determine whether the slope is positive or negative.*

16.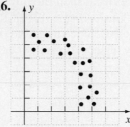

17.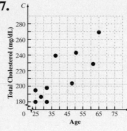

Fitting a Line to Data

Suppose that the scatter diagram of a set of data appears to be linearly related as in Figure 23(a) or (b). We might wish to find an equation of a line that relates the two variables. One way to obtain an equation for data that appears to follow a linear pattern is to draw a line through two points on the scatter diagram and determine the equation of the line through these points using the point-slope form of a line, $y - y_1 = m(x - x_1)$. To review using this formula work "*Preparing for . . .*" Problem P6 at the beginning of this section, if you haven't already done so.

EXAMPLE 8   Finding a Model for Linearly Related Data

Using the data in Table 4 from Example 6,

(a) Select two points and find a linear model that describes the relation between the points.

(b) Graph the line on the scatter diagram obtained in Example 6(a).

(c) Use the linear model found in part (a) to predict the number of runs scored by a team whose on-base percentage is 34.6%.

(d) Interpret the slope. Does it make sense to interpret the y-intercept?

Solution

(a) Select two points, for example, (32.2, 706) and (36.6, 968). (You should select your own two points and complete the solution.) The slope of the line joining the points (32.2, 706) and (36.6, 968) is

$$m = \frac{968 - 706}{36.6 - 32.2} = \frac{262}{4.4} = 59.55$$

The equation of the line with slope 59.55 and passing through $(32.2, 706)$ is found using the point-slope form with $m = 59.55$, $x_1 = 32.2$, and $y_1 = 706$.

$$\text{Point-slope form:} \quad y - y_1 = m(x - x_1)$$
$$m = 59.55; x_1 = 32.2, y_1 = 706: \quad y - 706 = 59.55(x - 32.2)$$
$$\text{Distribute } 59.55: \quad y - 706 = 59.55x - 1917.51$$
$$\text{Add 706 to both sides:} \quad y = f(x) = 59.55x - 1211.51$$

Figure 25

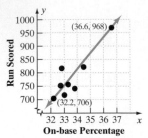

On-base Percentage

(b) Figure 25 shows the scatter diagram with the graph of the line found in part (a). We obtain the graph of the line by drawing the line through the two points selected in part (a).

(c) We evaluate $f(x) = 59.55x - 1211.51$ at $x = 34.6$.

$$f(34.6) = 59.55(34.6) - 1211.51$$
$$= 848.92$$

We round this to the nearest whole number. We predict that a team whose on-base percentage is 34.6% will score 849 runs.

(d) The slope of the linear function is 59.55. This means that if the on-base percentage increases by 1, then the number of runs scored will increase by about 60 runs. The y-intercept, -1211.51, represents the runs scored when the on-base percentage is 0. Since negative runs scored does not make sense and we do not have any observations near zero, it does not make sense to interpret the y-intercept. ∎

Quick ✔

18. Using the data from Quick Check Problem 15 on page 182,

   (a) Select two points and find a linear model that describes the relation between the points.

   (b) Graph the line on the scatter diagram obtained in Quick Check Problem 15 (page 182).

   (c) Predict the total cholesterol of a 39-year-old male.

   (d) Interpret the slope. Does it make sense to interpret the y-intercept?

2.4 EXERCISES

PRACTICE   WATCH   DOWNLOAD   READ   REVIEW

1–18. are the **Quick ✔***s that follow each* **EXAMPLE**

Building Skills

For Problems 19–30, graph each linear function. See Objective 1.

19. $F(x) = 5x - 2$

20. $F(x) = 4x + 1$

21. $G(x) = -3x + 7$

22. $G(x) = -2x + 5$

23. $H(x) = -2$

24. $P(x) = 5$

25. $f(x) = \frac{1}{2}x - 4$

26. $f(x) = \frac{1}{3}x - 3$

27. $F(x) = -\frac{5}{2}x + 5$

28. $P(x) = -\frac{3}{5}x - 1$

29. $G(x) = -\frac{3}{2}x$

30. $f(x) = \frac{4}{5}x$

In Problems 31–38, find the zero of the linear function. See Objective 2.

31. $f(x) = 2x + 10$

32. $f(x) = 3x + 18$

33. $G(x) = -5x + 40$

34. $H(x) = -4x + 36$

35. $s(t) = \frac{1}{2}t - 3$

36. $p(q) = \frac{1}{4}q + 2$

37. $P(z) = -\frac{4}{3}z + 12$

38. $F(t) = -\frac{3}{2}t + 6$

In Problems 39–42, determine whether the scatter diagram indicates that a linear relation may exist between the two variables. If a linear relation does exist, indicate whether the slope is positive or negative. See Objective 4.

39.

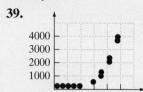

40.

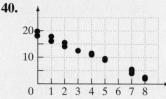

41.

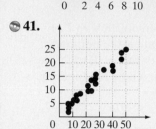

42.

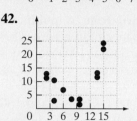

In Problems 43–46,

(a) Draw a scatter diagram of the data.
(b) Select two points from the scatter diagram and find the equation of the line containing the points selected.*
(c) Graph the line found in part (b) on the scatter diagram. See Objective 4.

43.

x	2	4	5	8	9
y	1.4	1.8	2.1	2.3	2.6

44.

x	2	3	5	6	7
y	5.7	5.2	2.8	1.9	1.8

45.

x	1.2	1.8	2.3	3.5	4.1
y	8.4	7.0	7.3	4.5	2.4

46.

x	0	0.5	1.4	2.1	3.9
y	0.8	1.3	1.9	2.5	5.0

Mixed Practice

47. Suppose that $f(x) = 3x + 2$.

(a) What is the slope?
(b) What is the y-intercept?
(c) What is the zero of f?
(d) Solve $f(x) = 5$. What point is on the graph of f?
(e) Solve $f(x) \leq -1$.
(f) Graph f.

48. Suppose that $g(x) = 8x + 3$.

(a) What is the slope?
(b) What is the y-intercept?
(c) What is the zero of g?
(d) Solve $g(x) = 19$. What point is on the graph of g?
(e) Solve $g(x) > -5$.
(f) Graph g.

*Answers will vary.

49. Suppose that $f(x) = x - 5$ and $g(x) = -3x + 7$.

(a) Solve $f(x) = g(x)$. What is the value of f at the solution? What point is on the graph of f? What point is on the graph of g?
(b) Solve $f(x) > g(x)$.
(c) Graph f and g in the same Cartesian plane. Label the intersection point.

50. Suppose that $f(x) = \frac{4}{3}x + 5$ and $g(x) = \frac{1}{3}x + 1$.

(a) Solve $f(x) = g(x)$. What is the value of f at the solution? What point is on the graph of f? What point is on the graph of g?
(b) Solve $f(x) \leq g(x)$.
(c) Graph f and g in the same Cartesian plane. Label the intersection point.

51. Find a linear function f such that $f(2) = 6$ and $f(5) = 12$. What is $f(-2)$?

52. Find a linear function g such that $g(1) = 5$ and $g(5) = 17$. What is $g(-3)$?

53. Find a linear function h such that $h(3) = 7$ and $h(-1) = 14$. What is $h\left(\frac{1}{2}\right)$?

54. Find a linear function F such that $F(2) = 5$ and $F(-3) = 9$. What is $F\left(-\frac{3}{2}\right)$?

55. In parts **(a)–(e)**, use the figure shown below.

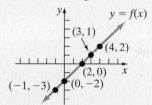

(a) Solve $f(x) = 1$.   **(b)** Solve $f(x) = -3$.
(c) What is $f(4)$?
(d) What are the intercepts of the function $y = f(x)$?
(e) Write the equation of the function whose graph is given in the form $f(x) = mx + b$.

56. In parts **(a)–(e)**, use the figure shown below.

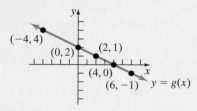

(a) Solve $g(x) = 1$.   **(b)** Solve $g(x) = -1$.
(c) What is $g(-4)$?
(d) What are the intercepts of the function $y = g(x)$?
(e) Write the equation of the function whose graph is given in the form $g(x) = mx + b$.

Applying the Concepts

57. Taxes The function $T(x) = 0.15(x - 8025) + 802.50$ represents the federal income tax bill T of a single person whose adjusted gross income in 2008 was x dollars for income between \$8025 and \$32,550, inclusive. (SOURCE: *Internal Revenue Service*)

(a) What is the domain of this linear function?

(b) What was a single filer's tax bill if adjusted gross income was \$20,000?

(c) Which variable is independent and which is dependent?

(d) Graph the linear function over the domain specified in part **(a).**

(e) What was a single filer's adjusted gross income if his or her tax bill was \$3352.50?

58. Sales Commissions Tanya works for Pearson Education as a book representative. The linear function $I(s) = 0.01s + 20,000$ describes the annual income I of Tanya when she has total sales s.

(a) What is the implied domain of this linear function?

(b) What is $I(0)$? Explain what this result means.

(c) What is Tanya's salary if she sells \$500,000 in books for the year?

(d) Graph the linear function.

(e) At what level of sales will Tanya's income be \$45,000?

59. Cab Fare The linear function $C(m) = 1.5m + 2$ describes the cab fare C for a ride of m miles.

(a) What is the implied domain of this linear function?

(b) What is $C(0)$? Explain what this result means.

(c) What is cab fare for a 5-mile ride?

(d) Graph the linear function.

(e) How many miles can you ride in a cab if you have \$13.25?

(f) Over what range of miles can you ride if you can spend no more than \$39.50?

60. Luxury Tax In 2002, Major League Baseball signed a labor agreement with the players. In this agreement, any team whose payroll exceeded \$128 million in 2005 will have to pay a luxury tax of 22.5% (for first-time offenses). The linear function $T(p) = 0.225(p - 128)$ describes the luxury tax T of a team whose payroll was p (in millions).

(a) What is the implied domain of this linear function?

(b) What was the luxury tax for a team whose payroll \$160 million?

(c) Graph the linear function.

(d) What was the payroll of a team that paid luxury tax of \$11.7 million?

61. Health Costs The annual cost of health insurance H as a function of age a is given by the function

$H(a) = 22.8a - 117.5$ for $15 \leq a \leq 90$.

(SOURCE: *Statistical Abstract, 2005*)

(a) What are the independent and dependent variables?

(b) What is the domain of this linear function?

(c) What is the health insurance premium of a 30-year-old?

(d) Graph the linear function over its domain.

(e) What is the age of an individual whose health insurance premium is \$976.90?

62. Birth Rate A multiple birth is any birth with 2 or more children born. The birth rate is the number of births per 1000 women. The birth rate B of multiple births as a function of age a is given by the function $B(a) = 1.73a - 14.56$ for $15 \leq a \leq 44$.

(SOURCE: *Centers for Disease Control*)

(a) What are the independent and dependent variables?

(b) What is the domain of this linear function?

(c) What is the multiple birth rate of women who are 22 years of age according to the model?

(d) Graph the linear function over its domain.

(e) What is the age of women whose multiple birth rate is 49.45?

63. Phone Charges Sprint has a long-distance phone plan that charges a monthly fee of \$5.95 plus \$0.05 per minute. (SOURCE: *Sprint.com*)

(a) Find a linear function that expresses the monthly bill B as a function of minutes used m.

(b) What are the independent and dependent variables?

(c) What is the implied domain of this linear function?

(d) What is the monthly bill if 300 minutes are used for long-distance phone calls?

(e) How many minutes were used for long distance if the long-distance phone bill was \$17.95?

(f) Graph the linear function.

(g) Over what range of minutes can you talk each month if you don't want to spend more than \$18.45?

64. RV Rental The rental cost R of a class C 20-foot recreational vehicle is \$129.50 plus \$0.15 per mile.

(SOURCE: *westernrv.com*)

(a) Find a linear function that expresses the cost R as a function of miles driven m.

(b) What are the independent and dependent variables?

(c) What is the implied domain of this linear function?

(d) What is the rental cost if 860 miles are driven?

(e) How many miles were driven if the rental cost is \$213.80?

(f) Graph the linear function.

(g) Over what range of miles can you drive if you have a budget of $287?

65. Depreciation Suppose that a company has just purchased a new computer for $2700. The company chooses to depreciate the computer using the straight-line method over 3 years.

(a) Find a linear function that expresses the book value V of the computer as a function of its age x.

(b) What is the implied domain of this linear function?

(c) What is the book value of the computer after the first year?

(d) What are the intercepts of the graph of the linear function?

(e) When will the book value of the computer be $900?

(f) Graph the linear function.

66. Depreciation Suppose that a company just purchased a new machine for its manufacturing facility for $1,200,000. The company chooses to depreciate the machine using the straight-line method over 20 years.

(a) Find a linear function that expresses the book value V of the machine as a function of its age x.

(b) What is the implied domain of this linear function?

(c) What is the book value of the machine after three years?

(d) What are the intercepts of the graph of the linear function?

(e) When will the book value of the machine be $480,000?

(f) Graph the linear function.

67. Diamonds The relation between the cost of a diamond and its weight is linear. In looking at two diamonds, we find that one of the diamonds weighs 0.7 carat and costs $3543, while the other diamond weighs 0.8 carat and costs $4378. (SOURCE: *diamonds.com*)

(a) Find a linear function that relates the price of a diamond, C, to its weight, x, treating weight as the independent variable.

(b) Predict the price of a diamond that weighs 0.77 carat.

(c) Interpret the slope.

(d) If a diamond costs $5300, what do you think it should weigh?

68. Apartments In the North Chicago area, an 820-square-foot apartment rents for $1507 per month. A 970-square-foot apartment rents for $1660. (SOURCE: *apartments.com*) Suppose that the relation between area and rent is linear.

(a) Find a linear function that relates the rent of a North Chicago apartment, R, to its area, x, treating area as the independent variable.

(b) Predict the rent of a 900-square-foot apartment in North Chicago.

(c) Interpret the slope.

(d) If the rent of a North Chicago apartment is $1300 per month, how big would you expect it to be?

69. The Consumption Function A famous theory in economics developed by John Maynard Keynes states that personal consumption expenditures are a linear function of disposable income. An economist wishes to develop a model that relates income and consumption and obtains the following information from the United States Bureau of Economic Analysis. In 2000, personal disposable income was $7194 billion and personal consumption expenditures were $6739 billion. In 2006, personal disposable income was $9523 billion and personal consumption expenditures were $9269 billion.

(a) Find a linear function that relates personal consumption expenditures, C, to disposable income, x, treating disposable income as the independent variable.

(b) In 2007, personal disposable income was $9742 billion. Use this information to predict personal consumption expenditures in 2007.

(c) Interpret the slope. In economics, this slope is called the **marginal propensity to consume.**

(d) If personal consumption expenditures were $9520 billion, what do you think that disposable income was?

70. According to the National Center for Health Statistics, the average birth weight of babies born to 22-year-old mothers is 3280 grams. The average birth weight of babies born to 32-year-old mothers is 3370 grams. Suppose that the relation between age of mother and birth weight is linear.

(a) Find a linear function that relates age of mother a to birth weight W treating age of mother as the independent variable.

(b) Predict the birth weight of a baby born to a mother who is 30 years old.

(c) Interpret the slope.

(d) If a baby weighs 3310 grams, how old do you expect the mother to be?

71. Concrete As concrete cures, it gains strength. The following data represent the 7-day and 28-day strength (in pounds per square inch) of a certain type of concrete.

7-day Strength, x	28-day Strength, y
2300	4070
3390	5220
2430	4640
2890	4620
3330	4850
2480	4120
3380	5020
2660	4890
2620	4190
3340	4630

(a) Draw a scatter diagram of the data treating 7-day strength as the independent variable.
(b) What type of relation appears to exist between 7-day strength and 28-day strength?
(c) Select two points and find an equation of the line containing the points.
(d) Graph the line on the scatter diagram drawn in part (a).
(e) Predict the 28-day strength of a slab of concrete if its 7-day strength is 3000 psi.
(f) Interpret the slope of the line found in part (c).

72. Candy The following data represent the weight (in grams) of various candy bars and the corresponding number of calories.

Candy Bar	Weight, x	Calories, y
Hershey's Milk Chocolate	44.28	230
Nestle Crunch	44.84	230
Butterfinger	61.30	270
Baby Ruth	66.45	280
Almond Joy	47.33	220
Twix (with Caramel)	58.00	280
Snickers	61.12	280
Heath	39.52	210

SOURCE: Megan Pocius, student at Joliet Junior College

(a) Draw a scatter diagram of the data treating weight as the independent variable.
(b) What type of relation appears to exist between the weight of a candy bar and the number of calories?
(c) Select two points and find an equation of the line containing the points.
(d) Graph the line on the scatter diagram drawn in part (a).
(e) Predict the number of calories in a candy bar that weighs 62.3 grams.
(f) Interpret the slope of the line found in part (c).

73. Raisins The following data represent the weight (in grams) of a box of raisins and the number of raisins in the box.

Weight, w	Number of Raisins, N
42.3	87
42.7	91
42.8	93
42.4	87
42.6	89
42.4	90
42.3	82
42.5	86
42.7	86
42.5	86

SOURCE: Jennifer Maxwell, student at Joliet Junior College

(a) Does the relation defined by the set of ordered pairs (w, N) represent a function?
(b) Draw a scatter diagram of the data treating weight as the independent variable.
(c) Select two points and find the equation of the line containing the points.
(d) Graph the line on the scatter diagram drawn in part (b).
(e) Express the relationship found in part (c) using function notation.
(f) Predict the number of raisins in a box that weighs 42.5 grams.
(g) Interpret the slope of the line found in part (c).

74. Height versus Head Circumference The following data represent the height (in inches) and head circumference (in inches) of 9 randomly selected children.

Height, h	Head Circumference, C
25.25	16.4
25.75	16.9
25	16.9
27.75	17.6
26.50	17.3
27.00	17.5
26.75	17.3
26.75	17.5
27.5	17.5

SOURCE: Denise Slucki, student at Joliet Junior College

(a) Does the relation defined by the set of ordered pairs (h, C) represent a function?
(b) Draw a scatter diagram of the data treating height as the independent variable.

(c) Select two points and find the equation of the line containing the points.

(d) Graph the line on the scatter diagram drawn in part **(b)**.

(e) Express the relationship found in part **(c)** using function notation.

(f) Predict the head circumference of a child who is 26.5 inches tall.

(g) Interpret the slope of the line found in part **(c)**.

Extending the Concepts

75. **Math for the Future: Calculus** The **average rate of change** of a function $y = f(x)$ from c to x is defined as

$$\text{Average rate of change} = \frac{\Delta y}{\Delta x} = \frac{f(x) - f(c)}{x - c}, \quad x \neq c$$

provided that c is in the domain of f. The average rate of change of a function is simply the slope of the line joining the points $(c, f(c))$ and $(x, f(x))$. We call the line joining these points a **secant line.** The slope of the secant line is

$$m_{\text{sec}} = \frac{f(x) - f(c)}{x - c}$$

The figure illustrates the idea.

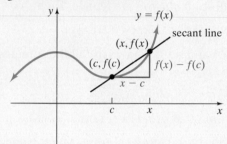

Below, we show the graph of the function $f(x) = 2x^2 - 4x + 1$.

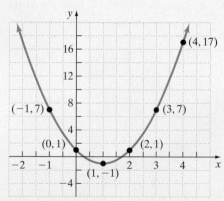

(a) On the graph of $f(x) = 2x^2 - 4x + 1$ draw a line through the points $(1, f(1))$ and $(x, f(x))$ where $x = 4$.

(b) Find the slope of the secant line through $(1, f(1))$ and $(x, f(x))$ where $x = 4$.

(c) Find the equation of the secant line through $(1, f(1))$ and $(x, f(x))$ where $x = 4$

(d) Repeat parts **(a)–(c)** for $x = 3$, $x = 2$, $x = 1.5$, and $x = 1.1$.

(e) What happens to the slope of the secant line as x gets closer to 1?

76. A strain of *E. coli* Beu 397-recA441 is placed into a Petri dish at 30° Celsius and allowed to grow. The population is estimated by means of an optical device in which the amount of light that passes through the Petri dish is measured. The data below are collected. Do you think that a linear function could be used to describe the relation between the two variables? Why or why not?

Time, x	Population, y
0	0.09
2.5	0.18
3.5	0.26
4.5	0.35
6	0.50

SOURCE: *Dr. Polly Lavery, Joliet Junior College*

The Graphing Calculator

The equation of the line obtained in Example 8 depends on the points selected, which will vary from person to person. So the line we found might be different from the line that you found. Although the line that we found in Example 8 fits the data well, there may be a line that "fits it better." Do you think that your line fits the data better? Is there a line of *best fit*? As it turns out, there is a method for finding the line that best fits linearly related data (called the *line of best fit*).*

Graphing utilities can be used to draw scatter diagrams and find the line of best fit. Figure 26(a) shows a scatter diagram of the data presented in Table 4 from Example 6 drawn on a TI-84 Plus graphing calculator. Figure 26(b) shows the line of best fit from a TI-84 Plus graphing calculator.

The line of best fit is $y = 53.8x - 1022.1$.

Figure 26

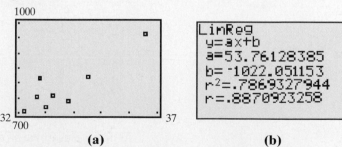

(a)   (b)

In Problems 77–80,

(a) *Draw a scatter diagram using a graphing calculator*

(b) *Find the line of best fit using a graphing calculator for the data in the problem specified.*

77. Problem 71   78. Problem 72

79. Problem 73   80. Problem 74

---

*We shall not discuss in this book the underlying mathematics of lines of best fit. Books in elementary statistics discuss this topic.

2.5 Compound Inequalities

OBJECTIVES

1 Determine the Intersection or Union of Two Sets

2 Solve Compound Inequalities Involving "and"

3 Solve Compound Inequalities Involving "or"

4 Solve Problems Using Compound Inequalities

Preparing for Compound Inequalities

Before getting started, take the following readiness quiz. If you get a problem wrong, go back to the section cited and review the material.

P1. Use set-builder notation and interval notation to name the set of all real numbers x such that $-2 \le x \le 5$. [Section 1.4, pp. 81–84]

P2. Graph the inequality $x \ge 4$. [Section 1.4, pp. 81–84]

P3. Use interval notation to express the inequality shown in the graph. [Section 1.4, pp. 81–84]

P4. Solve: $2(x + 3) - 5x = 15$ [Section 1.1, pp. 49–52]

P5. Solve: $2x + 3 > 11$ [Section 1.4, pp. 85–88]

P6. Solve: $x + 8 \ge 4(x - 1) - x$ [Section 1.4, pp. 85–88]

1 Determine the Intersection or Union of Two Sets

Consider the information presented in Table 5 regarding students enrolled in an Intermediate Algebra course. We can classify the people in the course in a set. For example, suppose we define set A as the set of all students whose age is less than 25. Then

$$A = \{\text{Grace, Sophia, Kevin, Jack, George, Teresa}\}$$

Suppose we define set B as the set of all students who are female. Then

$$B = \{\text{Grace, Sophia, Mary, Nancy, Teresa}\}$$

Now list all the students who are in set A and set B. That is, list all the students who are less than 25 years of age and female.

$$A \text{ and } B = \{\text{Grace, Sophia, Teresa}\}$$

Now list all the students who are either in set A or set B or both.

$$A \text{ or } B = \{\text{Grace, Sophia, Kevin, Jack, George, Teresa, Mary, Nancy}\}$$

Figure 27 shows a Venn diagram illustrating the relation among A, B, A and B, and A or B. Notice that Grace, Sophia, and Teresa are in both A and B, while Robert is neither in A nor B.

Table 5		
Student	Age	Gender
Grace	19	Female
Sophia	23	Female
Kevin	20	Male
Robert	32	Male
Jack	19	Male
Mary	35	Female
Nancy	40	Female
George	22	Male
Teresa	20	Female

Figure 27

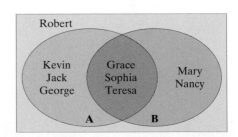

When we used the word *and* to obtain the set, we listed elements that were common to both set A and set B. When we used the word *or* to obtain the set, we listed elements that were in either set A or set B or both. These results lead us to the following definitions.

Preparing for...Answers

P1. $\{x \mid -2 \le x \le 5\}$; $[-2, 5]$

P2.
0 1 2 3 4 5 6

P3. $(-1, 3]$ **P4.** $\{-3\}$

P5. $\{x \mid x > 4\}$; $(4, \infty)$;
2 3 4 5 6 7

P6. $\{x \mid x \le 6\}$; $(-\infty, 6]$;
2 3 4 5 6 7

DEFINITIONS

- The **intersection** of two sets A and B, denoted $A \cap B$, is the set of all elements that belong to both set A and set B.

- The **union** of two sets A and B, denoted $A \cup B$, is the set of all elements that are in the set A or in the set B or in both A and B.

- The word **and** implies intersection, while the word **or** implies union.

EXAMPLE 1 Finding the Intersection and Union of Sets

Let $A = \{1, 3, 5, 7, 9\}$ and let $B = \{1, 2, 3, 4, 5\}$. Find

(a) $A \cap B$ **(b)** $A \cup B$

Solution

(a) $A \cap B$ is the set of all elements that are in both A and B. So, $A \cap B = \{1, 3, 5\}$.

(b) $A \cup B$ is the set of all elements that are in A or B, or both. So,
$A \cup B = \{1, 2, 3, 4, 5, 7, 9\}$. ∎

Work Smart

When finding the union of two sets, we list each element only once, even if it occurs in both sets.

Quick ✔

1. The _____ of two sets A and B, denoted $A \cap B$, is the set of all elements that belong to both set A and set B.

2. The word ___ implies intersection. The word ___ implies union.

3. *True or False:* The intersection of two sets can be the empty set.

4. *True or False:* The symbol for the union of two sets is $\cap$.

In Problems 5–10, let $A = \{1, 2, 3, 4, 5, 6\}$, $B = \{1, 3, 5, 7\}$, and $C = \{2, 4, 6, 8\}$.

5. Find $A \cap B$.   6. Find $A \cap C$.

7. Find $A \cup B$.   8. Find $A \cup C$.

9. Find $B \cap C$.   10. Find $B \cup C$.

Let's look at the intersection and union of two sets involving inequalities.

EXAMPLE 2 Finding the Intersection and Union of Two Sets

Suppose $A = \{x | x \le 5\}$, $B = \{x | x \ge 1\}$, and $C = \{x | x < -2\}$.

(a) Determine $A \cap B$. Graph the set on a real number line. Write the set $A \cap B$ using both set-builder notation and interval notation.

(b) Determine $B \cup C$. Graph the set on a real number line. Write the set $B \cup C$ using both set-builder notation and interval notation.

Solution

(a) $A \cap B$ is the set of all real numbers that are less than or equal to 5 and greater than or equal to 1. We can identify this set by determining where the graphs of the inequalities overlap. See Figure 28.

Figure 28

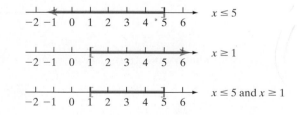

We can represent the set $A \cap B$ using set-builder notation as $\{x | 1 \le x \le 5\}$ or interval notation as $[1, 5]$.

(b) $B \cup C$ is the set of all real numbers that are greater than or equal to 1 or less than -2. The union of these two sets would be all real numbers less than -2 or greater than or equal to 1. See Figure 29. We can represent the set $B \cup C$ using set-builder notation as $\{x | x < -2 \text{ or } x \ge 1\}$ or interval notation as $(-\infty, -2) \cup [1, \infty)$. ∎

Figure 29

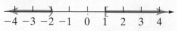

Work Smart

Throughout the text, we will use the word "or" when using set-builder notation and we will use the union symbol, ∪, when using interval notation.

Quick ✔ *Let $A = \{x | x > 2\}$, $B = \{x | x < 7\}$, and $C = \{x | x \le -3\}$.*

11. Determine $A \cap B$. Graph the set on a real number line. Write the set $A \cap B$ using both set-builder notation and interval notation.

12. Determine $A \cup C$. Graph the set on a real number line. Write the set $A \cup C$ using both set-builder notation and interval notation.

⌐2 Solve Compound Inequalities Involving "and"

A **compound inequality** is formed by joining two inequalities with the word "and" or "or." For example,

$$3x + 1 > 4 \quad \text{and} \quad 2x - 3 < 7$$
$$5x - 2 \le 13 \quad \text{or} \quad 2x - 5 > 3$$

are examples of compound inequalities. To **solve a compound inequality** means to find all possible values of the variable such that the compound inequality results in a true statement. For example, the compound inequality

$$3x + 1 > 4 \quad \text{and} \quad 2x - 3 < 7$$

is true for $x = 2$, but false for $x = 0$.

Let's look at an example that illustrates how to solve compound inequalities involving the word "and."

⌐EXAMPLE 3 How to Solve a Compound Inequality Involving "and"

Solve $3x + 2 > -7$ and $4x + 1 \le 9$. Graph the solution set.

Step-by-Step Solution

Step 1: Solve each inequality separately.		
	$3x + 2 > -7$	$4x + 1 \le 9$
Subtract 2 from both sides:	$3x > -9$	Subtract 1 from both sides: $\quad 4x \le 8$
Divide both sides by 3:	$x > -3$	Divide both sides by 4: $\quad x \le 2$

Step 2: Find the intersection of the solution sets, which will represent the solution set to the compound inequality.

To find the intersection of the two solution sets, we graph each inequality separately. See Figure 30.

Figure 30

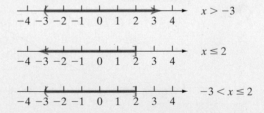

The intersection of $x > -3$ and $x \le 2$ is $-3 < x \le 2$.

The solution set is $\{x | -3 < x \le 2\}$ or, using interval notation, $(-3, 2]$.

The steps below summarize the procedure for solving compound inequalities involving "and."

STEPS FOR SOLVING COMPOUND INEQUALITIES INVOLVING "AND"

Step 1: Solve each inequality separately.

Step 2: Find the INTERSECTION of the solution sets of each inequality.

EXAMPLE 4 Solving a Compound Inequality with "and"

Solve $-2x + 5 > -1$ and $5x + 6 \leq -4$. Graph the solution set.

Solution

We solve each inequality separately:

$$-2x + 5 > -1 \qquad\qquad\qquad 5x + 6 \leq -4$$

Subtract 5 from both sides: $\quad -2x > -6$ Subtract 6 from both sides: $\quad 5x \leq -10$

Divide both sides by -2; $\qquad x < 3$ Divide both sides by 5: $\qquad x \leq -2$
don't forget to reverse the
direction of the inequality!

Find the intersection of the solution sets, which will represent the solution set to the compound inequality. See Figure 31.

Figure 31

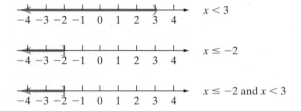

The intersection of $x < 3$ and $x \leq -2$ is $x \leq -2$. The solution set is $\{x | x \leq -2\}$ or, using interval notation, $(-\infty, -2]$.

Quick ✔ *In Problems 13–15, solve each compound inequality. Express your solution using set-builder notation and interval notation. Graph the solution set.*

13. $2x + 1 \geq 5$ and $-3x + 2 < 5$

14. $4x - 5 < 7$ and $3x - 1 > -10$

15. $-8x + 3 < -5$ and $\dfrac{2}{3}x + 1 < 3$

EXAMPLE 5 Solving a Compound Inequality with "and"

Solve $x - 5 > -1$ and $2x - 3 \leq -5$. Graph the solution set.

Solution

We solve each inequality separately:

$$x - 5 > -1 \qquad\qquad\qquad 2x - 3 \leq -5$$

Add 5 to both sides: $\qquad x > 4$ Add 3 to both sides: $\qquad 2x \leq -2$

                            Divide both sides by 2: $\qquad x \leq -1$

Figure 32

Find the intersection of the solution sets, which will represent the solution set to the compound inequality. See Figure 32.

The intersection of $x > 4$ and $x \leq -1$ is the empty set. The solution set is $\{\ \}$ or $\varnothing$.

Quick ✔ *In Problems 16 and 17, solve each compound inequality. Express your solution using set-builder notation and interval notation. Graph the solution set.*

16. $3x - 5 < -8$ and $2x + 1 > 5$

17. $5x + 1 \leq 6$ and $3x + 2 \geq 5$

Sometimes, we can combine "and" inequalities into a more streamlined notation.

WRITING INEQUALITIES INVOLVING "AND" COMPACTLY

If $a < b$, then we can write

$$a < x \quad \text{and} \quad x < b$$

more compactly as

$$a < x < b$$

For example, we can write

$$-3 < -4x + 1 \quad \text{and} \quad -4x + 1 < 13$$

as

$$-3 < -4x + 1 < 13$$

When compound inequalities come in this form, we solve the inequality by getting the variable by itself in the "middle" with a coefficient of 1.

EXAMPLE 6 Solving a Compound Inequality

Solve $-3 < -4x + 1 < 13$ and graph the solution set.

Solution

Our goal is to get the variable by itself in the "middle" with a coefficient of 1.

$$-3 < -4x + 1 < 13$$

Subtract 1 from all three parts (Addition Property): $-3 - 1 < -4x + 1 - 1 < 13 - 1$

$$-4 < -4x < 12$$

Divide all three parts by -4. Don't forget to reverse the direction of the inequalities. $\dfrac{-4}{-4} > \dfrac{-4x}{-4} > \dfrac{12}{-4}$

$$1 > x > -3$$

If $b > x > a$, then $a < x < b$: $-3 < x < 1$

The solution using set-builder notation is $\{x | -3 < x < 1\}$. The solution using interval notation is $(-3, 1)$. Figure 33 shows the graph of the solution set.

Figure 33

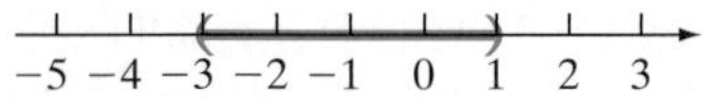

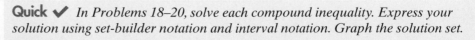

To visualize the results of Example 6, look at Figure 34, which shows the graph of $f(x) = -3$, $g(x) = -4x + 1$, and $h(x) = 13$. Notice the graph of $g(x) = -4x + 1$ is between the graphs of $f(x) = -3$ and $h(x) = 13$ for $-3 < x < 1$. So, the solution set of $-3 < -4x + 1 < 13$ is $\{x | -3 < x < 1\}$.

Figure 34

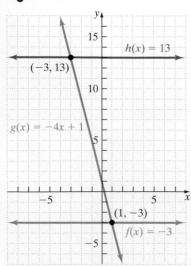

Quick ✔ *In Problems 18–20, solve each compound inequality. Express your solution using set-builder notation and interval notation. Graph the solution set.*

18. $-2 < 3x + 1 < 10$

19. $0 < 4x - 5 \le 3$

20. $3 \le -2x - 1 \le 11$

3 Solve Compound Inequalities Involving "or"

We now address compound inequalities involving the word "or." The solution to these types of inequalities is the union of the solutions to each inequality.

EXAMPLE 7 How to Solve a Compound Inequality Involving "or"

Solve $3x - 5 < -2$ or $4 - 5x \leq -16$. Graph the solution set.

Step-by-Step Solution

Step 1: Solve each inequality separately.		$3x - 5 < -2$		$4 - 5x \leq -16$
	Add 5 to each side:	$3x < 3$	Subtract 4 from both sides:	$-5x \leq -20$
	Divide both sides by 3:	$x < 1$	Divide both sides by -5: Don't forget to reverse the direction of the inequality.	$x \geq 4$

Step 2: Find the union of the solution sets, which will represent the solution set to the compound inequality.

The union of the two solution sets is $x < 1$ or $x \geq 4$. The solution set using set-builder notation is $\{x \mid x < 1$ or $x \geq 4\}$. The solution set using interval notation is $(-\infty, 1) \cup [4, \infty)$. Figure 35 shows the graph of the solution set.

Figure 35

Below is a summary of the steps for solving compound inequalities involving "or."

STEPS FOR SOLVING COMPOUND INEQUALITIES INVOLVING "OR"

Step 1: Solve each inequality separately.

Step 2: Find the UNION of the solution sets of each inequality.

Quick ✔ *In Problems 21–24, solve each compound inequality. Express your solution using set-builder notation and interval notation. Graph the solution set.*

21. $x + 3 < 1$ or $x - 2 > 3$

22. $3x + 1 \leq 7$ or $2x - 3 > 9$

23. $2x - 3 \geq 1$ or $6x - 5 \geq 1$

24. $\dfrac{3}{4}(x + 4) < 6$ or $\dfrac{3}{2}(x + 1) > 15$

Work Smart

A common error to avoid is to write the solution $x < 1$ or $x > 4$ as $1 > x > 4$, which is incorrect. There are no real numbers that are less than 1 *and* greater than 4. Another common error is to "mix" symbols as in $1 < x > 4$. This makes no sense!

EXAMPLE 8 Solving Compound Inequalities Involving "or"

Solve $\dfrac{1}{2}x - 1 < 1$ or $\dfrac{2x - 1}{3} \geq -1$. Graph the solution set.

Solution

First, we solve each inequality separately.

	$\dfrac{1}{2}x - 1 < 1$			$\dfrac{2x - 1}{3} \geq -1$
Add 1 to each side:	$\dfrac{1}{2}x < 2$		Multiply both sides by 3:	$2x - 1 \geq -3$
Multiply both sides by 2:	$x < 4$		Add 1 to both sides:	$2x \geq -2$
			Divide both sides by 2:	$x \geq -1$

Find the union of the solution sets of each inequality. If we graph the solution set of each inequality separately, we notice that the union of the two solution sets is the set of all real numbers. See Figure 36.

Figure 36

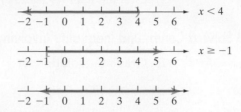

$$x < 4$$

$$x \geq -1$$

The solution set using set-builder notation is $\{x \mid x \text{ is any real number}\}$. The solution set using interval notation is $(-\infty, \infty)$. ∎

> **Quick ✔** *In Problems 25 and 26, solve each compound inequality. Express your solution using set-builder notation and interval notation. Graph the solution set.*
>
> **25.** $3x - 2 > -5$ or $2x - 5 \leq 1$
>
> **26.** $-5x - 2 \leq 3$ or $7x - 9 > 5$

⌐4 Solve Problems Using Compound Inequalities

We now look at an application involving compound inequalities.

⌐EXAMPLE 9 Federal Income Taxes

In 2008, a married couple filing a joint federal tax return whose income placed them in the 25% tax bracket paid federal income taxes between $8962.50 and $25,550, inclusive. The couple had to pay federal income taxes equal to $8962.50 plus 25% of the amount over $65,100. Find the range of taxable income in order for a married couple to have been in the 25% tax bracket. (SOURCE: *Internal Revenue Service*)

Solution

Step 1: Identify We want to find the range of the taxable income for a married couple in the 25% tax bracket. This is a direct translation problem involving an inequality.

Step 2: Name We let t represent the taxable income.

Step 3: Translate The federal tax bill equals $8962.50 plus 25% of the taxable income over $65,100. If the couple had taxable income equal to $66,100, their tax bill was $8962.50 plus 25% of $1000 ($1000 is the amount over $65,100). In general, if the couple has taxable income t, then their tax bill will be

$$\underbrace{8962.50}_{\$8962.50} \quad \underbrace{\text{plus}}_{+} \quad \underbrace{25\%}_{0.25} \quad \underbrace{\text{of the amount over } \$65,100}_{(t - \$65,100)}$$

Because the tax bill was between $8962.50 and $25,550, we have

$$8962.50 \leq 8962.50 + 0.25(t - 65,100) \leq 25,550 \quad \text{The Model}$$

Step 4: Solve

$$8962.50 \leq 8962.50 + 0.25(t - 65,100) \leq 25,550$$

Remove the parentheses by distributing 0.25: $8962.50 \leq 8962.50 + 0.25t - 16,275 \leq 25,550$

Combine like terms: $8962.50 \leq -7312.50 + 0.25t \leq 25,550$

Add 7312.50 to all three parts: $16,275 \leq 0.25t \leq 32,862.50$

Divide all three parts by 0.25: $65,100 \leq t \leq 131,450$

Step 5: Check If a married couple had taxable income of $65,100, then their tax bill was be $8962.50 + 0.25($65,100 - $65,100) = $8962.50. If a married couple had taxable income of $131,450, then their tax bill was $8962.50 + 0.25($131,450 - $65,100) = $25,550.

Work Smart

The word "range" tells us that an inequality is to be solved.

Step 6: Answer the Question A married couple who filed a federal joint income tax return with a tax bill between \$8962.50 and \$25,550 had taxable income between \$65,100 and \$131,450.

Quick ✔

27. In 2008, an individual filing a federal tax return whose income placed him or her in the 25% tax bracket paid federal income taxes between \$4481.25 and \$16,056.25. The individual had to pay federal income taxes equal to \$4481.25 plus 25% of the amount over \$32,550. Find the range of taxable income in order for an individual to have been in the 25% tax bracket. (SOURCE: *Internal Revenue Service*)

28. AT&T offers a long-distance phone plan that charges \$2.00 per month plus \$0.10 per minute. During the course of a year, Sophia's long-distance phone bill ranges from \$6.50 to \$26.50. What was the range of monthly minutes?

2.5 EXERCISES

PRACTICE   WATCH   DOWNLOAD   READ   REVIEW

1–28. *are the* Quick ✔*s that follow each* EXAMPLE

Building Skills

In Problems 29–34, use $A = \{4, 5, 6, 7, 8, 9\}$, $B = \{1, 5, 7, 9\}$, *and* $C = \{2, 3, 4, 6\}$ *to find each set. See Objective 1.*

29. $A \cup B$

30. $A \cup C$

31. $A \cap B$

32. $A \cap C$

33. $B \cap C$

34. $B \cup C$

In Problems 35–38, use the graph of the inequality to find each set. See Objective 1.

35. $A = \{x | x \le 5\}$; $B = \{x | x > -2\}$
Find (a) $A \cap B$ and (b) $A \cup B$.

-3 -2 -1 0 1 2 3 4 5 6

-3 -2 -1 0 1 2 3 4 5 6

36. $A = \{x | x \ge 4\}$; $B = \{x | x < 1\}$
Find (a) $A \cap B$ and (b) $A \cup B$.

-1 0 1 2 3 4 5 6

-1 0 1 2 3 4 5 6

37. $E = \{x | x > 3\}$; $F = \{x | x < -1\}$
Find (a) $E \cap F$ and (b) $E \cup F$.

-3 -2 -1 0 1 2 3 4

-3 -2 -1 0 1 2 3 4

38. $E = \{x | x \le 2\}$; $F = \{x | x \ge -2\}$
Find (a) $E \cap F$ and (b) $E \cup F$.

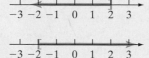

-3 -2 -1 0 1 2 3

In Problems 39–42, use the graph to solve the compound inequality. Graph the solution set. See Objective 2.

39. $-5 \le 2x - 1 \le 3$

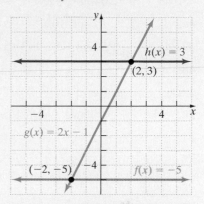

40. $-1 \le \dfrac{1}{2}x + 1 \le 3$

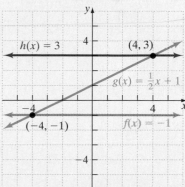

41. $-4 < -\dfrac{5}{3}x + 1 < 6$

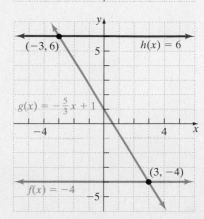

42. $-3 < \frac{5}{4}x + 2 < 7$

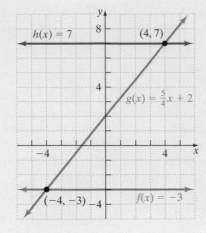

In Problems 43–66, solve each compound inequality. Graph the solution set. See Objective 2.

43. $x < 3$ and $x \geq -2$

44. $x \leq 5$ and $x > 0$

45. $4x - 4 < 0$ and $-5x + 1 \leq -9$

46. $6x - 2 \leq 10$ and $10x > -20$

47. $4x - 3 < 5$ and $-5x + 3 > 13$

48. $x - 3 \leq 2$ and $6x + 5 \geq -1$

49. $7x + 2 \geq 9$ and $4x + 3 \leq 7$

50. $-4x - 1 < 3$ and $-x - 2 > 3$

51. $-3 \leq 5x + 2 < 17$

52. $-10 < 6x + 8 \leq -4$

53. $-3 \leq 6x + 1 \leq 10$

54. $-12 < 7x + 2 \leq 6$

55. $3 \leq -5x + 7 < 12$

56. $-6 < -3x + 6 \leq 4$

57. $-1 \leq \frac{1}{2}x - 1 \leq 3$

58. $0 < \frac{3}{2}x - 3 \leq 3$

59. $3 \leq -2x - 1 \leq 11$

60. $-3 < -4x + 1 < 17$

61. $\frac{2}{3}x + \frac{1}{2} < \frac{5}{6}$ and $-\frac{1}{5}x + 1 < \frac{3}{10}$

62. $x - \frac{3}{2} \leq \frac{5}{4}$ and $-\frac{2}{3}x - \frac{2}{9} < \frac{8}{9}$

63. $-2 < \frac{3x + 1}{2} \leq 8$

64. $-4 \leq \frac{4x - 3}{3} < 3$

65. $-8 \leq -2(x + 1) < 6$

66. $-6 < -3(x - 2) < 15$

In Problems 67–80, solve each compound inequality. Graph the solution set. See Objective 3.

67. $x < -2$ or $x > 3$

68. $x < 0$ or $x \geq 6$

69. $x - 2 < -4$ or $x + 3 > 8$

70. $x + 3 \leq 5$ or $x - 2 \geq 3$

71. $6(x - 2) < 12$ or $4(x + 3) > 12$

72. $4x + 3 > -5$ or $8x - 5 < 3$

73. $-8x + 6x - 2 > 0$ or $5x > 3x + 8$

74. $3x \geq 7x + 8$ or $x < 4x - 9$

75. $2x + 5 \leq -1$ or $\frac{4}{3}x - 3 > 5$

76. $-\frac{4}{5}x - 5 > 3$ or $7x - 3 > 4$

77. $\frac{1}{2}x < 3$ or $\frac{3x - 1}{2} > 4$

78. $\frac{2}{3}x + 2 \leq 4$ or $\frac{5x - 3}{3} \geq 4$

79. $3(x - 1) + 5 < 2$ or $-2(x - 3) < 1$

80. $2(x + 1) - 5 \leq 4$ or $-(x + 3) \leq -2$

Mixed Practice

In Problems 81–94, solve each compound inequality. Graph the solution set.

81. $3a + 5 < 5$ and $-2a + 1 \leq 7$

82. $5x - 1 < 9$ and $5x > -20$

83. $5(x + 2) < 20$ or $4(x - 4) > -20$

84. $3(x + 7) < 24$ or $6(x - 4) > -30$

85. $-4 \leq 3x + 2 \leq 10$

86. $-8 \leq 5x - 3 \leq 4$

87. $2x + 7 < -13$ or $5x - 3 > 7$

88. $3x - 8 < -14$ or $4x - 5 > 7$

89. $5 < 3x - 1 < 14$

90. $-5 < 2x + 7 \leq 5$

91. $\frac{x}{3} \leq -1$ or $\frac{4x - 1}{2} > 7$

92. $\frac{x}{2} \leq -4$ or $\frac{2x - 1}{3} \geq 2$

93. $-3 \leq -2(x + 1) < 8$

94. $-15 < -3(x + 2) \leq 1$

Applying the Concepts

In Problems 95–100, use the Addition Property and/or Multiplication Properties to find a and b.

95. If $-3 < x < 4$, then $a < x + 4 < b$.

96. If $-2 < x < 3$, then $a < x - 3 < b$.

97. If $4 < x < 10$, then $a < 3x < b$.

98. If $2 < x < 12$, then $a < \dfrac{1}{2}x < b$.

99. If $-2 < x < 6$, then $a < 3x + 5 < b$.

100. If $-4 < x < 3$, then $a < 2x - 7 < b$.

101. Systolic Blood Pressure Blood pressure is measured using two numbers. One of the numbers measures systolic blood pressure. The systolic blood pressure represents the pressure while the heart is beating. In a healthy person, the systolic blood pressure should be greater than 90 and less than 140. If we let the variable x represent a person's systolic blood pressure, express the systolic blood pressure of a healthy person using a compound inequality.

102. Diastolic Blood Pressure Blood pressure is measured using two numbers. One of the numbers measures diastolic blood pressure. The diastolic blood pressure represents the pressure while the heart is resting between beats. In a healthy person, the diastolic blood pressure should be greater than 60 and less than 90. If we let the variable x represent a person's diastolic blood pressure, express the diastolic blood pressure of a healthy person using a compound inequality.

103. Computing Grades Joanna desperately wants to earn a B in her history class. Her current test scores are 74, 86, 77, and 89. Her final exam is worth 2 test scores. In order to earn a B, Joanna's average must lie between 80 and 89, inclusive. What range of scores can Joanna receive on the final and earn a B in the course?

104. Computing Grades Jack needs to earn a C in his sociology class. His current test scores are 67, 72, 81, and 75. His final exam is worth 3 test scores. In order to earn a C, Jack's average must lie between 70 and 79, inclusive. What range of scores can Jack receive on the final exam and earn a C in the course?

105. Federal Tax Withholding The percentage method of withholding for federal income tax (2007) states that a single person whose weekly wages, after subtracting withholding allowances, are over $645, but not over $1482, shall have $81.90 plus 25% of the excess over $645 withheld. Over what range does the amount withheld vary if the weekly wages vary from $700 to $800, inclusive? (SOURCE: *Internal Revenue Service*)

106. Federal Tax Withholding Rework Problem 105 if the weekly wages vary from $900 to $1000, inclusive.

107. Gas Bill Pacific Gas and Electric Company charges $65.05 plus $1.15855 per therm for gas usage in excess of 70 therms. In the winter of 2007/2008, one homeowner's bill ranged from a low of $157.73 to a high of $175.11. Over what range did gas usage vary (in therms)? (SOURCE: *Pacific Gas and Electric Company*)

108. Electric Bills In North Carolina, Duke Energy charges $31.52 plus $0.075895 for each additional kilowatt hour (kwh) used during the months from November through June for usage in excess of 350 kwh. Suppose one homeowner's electric bill ranged from a high of $69.47 to a low of $39.11 during this time period. Over what range did the usage vary (in kwh)? (SOURCE: *Duke Energy*)

109. The Arithmetic Mean If $a < b$, show that $a < \dfrac{a + b}{2} < b$. We call $\dfrac{a + b}{2}$ the **arithmetic mean** of a and b.

△ **110. Identifying Triangles** A triangle has the property that the length of the longest side is greater than the difference of the other sides and the length of the longest side is less than the sum of the other sides. That is, if a, b, and c are sides such that $a \le b \le c$, then $b - a < c < b + a$. Determine which of the following could be lengths of the sides of a triangle.

(a) 3, 4, 5   (c) 3, 3, 5

(b) 4, 7, 12   (d) 1, 9, 10

Extending the Concepts

111. Solve $2x + 1 \le 5x + 7 \le x - 5$.

112. Solve $x - 3 \le 3x + 1 \le x + 11$.

113. Solve $4x + 1 > 2(2x + 1)$. Provide an explanation that generalizes the result.

114. Solve $4x + 1 > 2(2x - 1)$. Provide an explanation that generalizes the result.

115. Consider the following analysis assuming that $x < 2$.

$$5 > 2$$
$$5(x - 2) > 2(x - 2)$$
$$5x - 10 > 2x - 4$$
$$3x > 6$$
$$x > 2$$

How can it be that the final line in the analysis states that $x > 2$, when the original assumption stated that $x < 2$?

2.6 Absolute Value Equations and Inequalities

OBJECTIVES

1. Solve Absolute Value Equations
2. Solve Absolute Value Inequalities Involving < or ≤
3. Solve Absolute Value Inequalities Involving > or ≥
4. Solve Applied Problems Involving Absolute Value Inequalities

Preparing for Absolute Value Equations and Inequalities

Before getting started, take the following readiness quiz. If you get a problem wrong, go back to the section cited and review the material.

In Problems P1–P4, evaluate each expression. [Section R.3, pp. 19–20]

P1. $|3|$ **P2.** $|-4|$ **P3.** $|-1.6|$ **P4.** $|0|$

P5. Express the distance between the origin, 0, and 5 as an absolute value. [Section R.3, pp. 19–20]

P6. Express the distance between the origin, 0, and −8 as an absolute value. [Section R.3, pp. 19–20]

P7. Solve: $4x + 5 = -9$ [Section 1.1, pp. 49–52]

P8. Solve: $-2x + 1 > 5$ [Section 1.4, pp. 85–88]

Figure 37

$|-5| = 5$

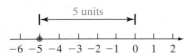

Recall from Section R.3 that we defined the absolute value of a number as the distance between the number and the origin on the real number line. For example, $|-5| = 5$ because the distance on the real number line from 0 to −5 is 5 units. See Figure 37 for a geometric interpretation of absolute value.

This interpretation of absolute value forms the basis for solving absolute value equations.

1 Solve Absolute Value Equations

We begin with an example.

EXAMPLE 1 Solving an Absolute Value Equation

Solve the equation $|x| = 4$.

Solution

We will present three versions of the solution. The first two present a geometric solution; the third presents an algebraic solution.

Geometric Solution 1: The equation $|x| = 4$ is asking, "Tell me all real numbers x such that the distance from the origin to x on the real number line is 4 units." There are two such numbers as indicated in Figure 38, −4 and 4. The solution set is $\{-4, 4\}$.

Geometric Solution 2: We can visualize the solution to $|x| = 4$ by graphing $f(x) = |x|$ and $g(x) = 4$ on the same xy-plane. Figure 39 shows the graphs of $f(x) = |x|$ and $g(x) = 4$. The x-coordinates of the points of intersection are −4 and 4, which represent the solutions to the equation $f(x) = g(x)$.

Figure 38

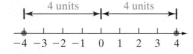

Figure 39

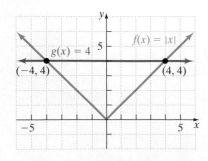

Algebraic Solution: The algebraic definition of $|a|$ is that $|a| = a$ if $a \geq 0$ and $|a| = -a$ if $a < 0$. Since we do not know whether $|x|$ is positive or negative in the equation $|x| = 4$, we solve the problem for $x \geq 0$ or $x < 0$.

If $x \geq 0$		If $x < 0$	
$|x| = 4$			$|x| = 4$
$|x| = x$ since $x \geq 0$: $x = 4$		$|x| = -x$ since $x < 0$: $-x = 4$	
		Multiply both sides by −1: $x = -4$	

Preparing for...Answers **P1.** 3 **P2.** 4
P3. 1.6 **P4.** 0 **P5.** $|5|$
P6. $|-8|$ **P7.** $\left\{-\dfrac{7}{2}\right\}$
P8. $\{x | x < -2\}; (-\infty, -2)$

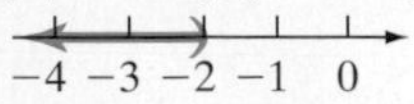

$\overset{\longleftarrow}{\underset{-4\ -3\ -2\ -1\ \ 0}{}}$

Quick ✔ *In Problems 1 and 2, solve the equation geometrically and algebraically.*

1. $|x| = 7$ **2.** $|z| = 1$

The results of Example 1 and Quick Checks 1 and 2 lead us to the following result.

Figure 40

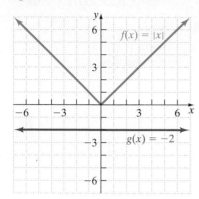

EQUATIONS INVOLVING ABSOLUTE VALUE

If a is a positive real number and if u is any algebraic expression, then

$$|u| = a \quad \text{is equivalent to} \quad u = a \quad \text{or} \quad u = -a$$

Note: If $a = 0$, the equation $|u| = 0$ is equivalent to $u = 0$. If $a < 0$, the equation $|u| = a$ has no solution.

In the equation $|u| = a$, we require that a be non-negative (greater than or equal to 0). If a is negative, the equation has no real solution. To see why, consider the equation $|x| = -2$. Figure 40 shows the graph of $f(x) = |x|$ and $g(x) = -2$. Notice that the graphs do not intersect, which implies that the equation $|x| = -2$ has no real solution. The solution set is the empty set, $\varnothing$ or $\{\,\}$.

Example 2 illustrates how to solve an equation involving absolute value.

EXAMPLE 2 How to Solve an Equation Involving Absolute Value

Solve the equation: $|2x - 1| + 3 = 12$

Step-by-Step Solution

Step 1: Isolate the expression containing the absolute value.	$|2x - 1| + 3 = 12$ Subtract 3 from both sides: $|2x - 1| = 9$
Step 2: Rewrite the absolute value equation as two equations: $u = a$ and $u = -a$, where u is the algebraic expression in the absolute value symbol. Here $u = 2x - 1$ and $a = 9$.	$2x - 1 = 9 \qquad\qquad$ or $\qquad\qquad 2x - 1 = -9$
Step 3: Solve each equation.	$\qquad 2x - 1 = 9 \qquad\qquad\qquad\qquad\qquad 2x - 1 = -9$ Add 1 to each side: $2x = 10 \qquad$ Add 1 to each side: $2x = -8$ Divide both sides by 2: $x = 5 \qquad$ Divide both sides by 2: $x = -4$
Step 4: Check: Verify each solution.	Let $x = 5$: $\qquad\qquad\qquad\qquad$ Let $x = -4$: $\quad |2x - 1| + 3 = 12 \qquad\qquad\qquad |2x - 1| + 3 = 12$ $\quad |2(5) - 1| + 3 \overset{?}{=} 12 \qquad\qquad |2(-4) - 1| + 3 \overset{?}{=} 12$ $\quad |10 - 1| + 3 \overset{?}{=} 12 \qquad\qquad\ |-8 - 1| + 3 \overset{?}{=} 12$ $\qquad\quad 9 + 3 \overset{?}{=} 12 \qquad\qquad\qquad\quad\ 9 + 3 \overset{?}{=} 12$ $\qquad\quad 12 = 12 \ \ \text{True} \qquad\qquad\qquad 12 = 12 \ \ \text{True}$

Both solutions check, so the solution set is $\{-4, 5\}$. ∎

The following steps can be used to solve an absolute value equation.

STEPS FOR SOLVING ABSOLUTE VALUE EQUATIONS WITH ONE ABSOLUTE VALUE

Step 1: Isolate the expression containing the absolute value.

Step 2: Rewrite the absolute value equation as two equations: $u = a$ and $u = -a$, where u is the algebraic expression in the absolute value symbol.

Step 3: Solve each equation.

Step 4: Verify your solution.

Quick ✔

3. $|u| = a$ is equivalent to $u = \underline{\quad}$ or $u = \underline{\quad}$.

In Problems 4–7, solve each equation.

4. $|2x - 3| = 7$ **5.** $|3x - 2| + 3 = 10$

6. $|-5x + 2| - 2 = 5$ **7.** $3|x + 2| - 4 = 5$

EXAMPLE 3 **Solving an Equation Involving Absolute Value with No Solution**

Solve the equation: $|x + 5| + 7 = 5$

Solution

$$|x + 5| + 7 = 5$$

Subtract 7 from both sides: $\qquad |x + 5| = -2$

Since the absolute value of any real number is always nonnegative (greater than or equal to zero), the equation has no real solution. The solution set is $\{ \ \}$ or $\varnothing$. ∎

Work Smart

The equation $|u| = a$, where a is a negative real number, has no real solution. See Figure 40 to see why.

Quick ✔

8. *True or False:* $|x| = -4$ has no real solution.

In Problems 9–11, solve each equation.

9. $|5x + 3| = -2$

10. $|2x + 5| + 7 = 3$

11. $|x + 1| + 3 = 3$

What if an absolute value equation has two absolute values as in $|3x - 1| = |x + 5|$? How do we handle this situation? Well, there are four possibilities for the algebraic expressions in the absolute value symbol:

1. both algebraic expressions are positive,

2. both are negative,

3. the left is positive, and the right is negative, or

4. the left is negative and the right is positive.

To see how the solution works, we need to consider the algebraic definition for absolute value. This definition states that $|a| = a$, if $a \geq 0$ and $|a| = -a$ if $a < 0$.

So, if $3x - 1 \geq 0$, then $|3x - 1| = 3x - 1$. However, if $3x - 1 < 0$, then $|3x - 1| = -(3x - 1)$. This leads us to a method for solving absolute value equations with two absolute values.

Work Smart

$|3x - 1| \neq 3x + 1$

Case 1: Both Algebraic Expressions Are Positive	Case 2: Both Algebraic Expressions Are Negative	Case 3: The Algebraic Expression on the Left Is Positive, and the Right Is Negative	Case 4: The Algebraic Expression on the Left Is Negative, and the Right Is Positive
$|3x - 1| = |x + 5|$	$|3x - 1| = |x + 5|$	$|3x - 1| = |x + 5|$	$|3x - 1| = |x + 5|$
$3x - 1 = x + 5$	$-(3x - 1) = -(x + 5)$	$3x - 1 = -(x + 5)$	$-(3x - 1) = x + 5$
	$3x - 1 = x + 5$		

When both algebraic expressions are positive, or both negative, we end up with equivalent equations. Therefore, Case 1 and Case 2 result in equivalent equations. Also, if one side is positive and the other is negative, we end up with equivalent equations. Therefore, Case 3 and Case 4 result in equivalent equations. The four possibilities reduce to two possibilities.

EQUATIONS INVOLVING TWO ABSOLUTE VALUES

If u and v are any algebraic expression, then

$$|u| = |v| \quad \text{is equivalent to} \quad u = v \quad \text{or} \quad u = -v$$

EXAMPLE 4 Solving an Absolute Value Equation Involving Two Absolute Values

Solve the equation: $|2x - 3| = |x + 6|$

Solution

The equation is in the form $|u| = |v|$, where $u = 2x - 3$ and $v = x + 6$. We rewrite the equation as two equations that do not involve absolute value:

$$2x - 3 = x + 6 \quad \text{or} \quad 2x - 3 = -(x + 6)$$

Now, we solve each equation.

$$2x - 3 = x + 6 \qquad\qquad\qquad 2x - 3 = -(x + 6)$$

Distribute the -1: $2x - 3 = -x - 6$

Add 3 to both sides: $\quad 2x = x + 9 \qquad$ Add 3 to both sides: $\quad 2x = -x - 3$

Add x to both sides: $\quad 3x = -3$

Subtract x from both sides: $\quad x = 9 \qquad$ Divide both sides by 3: $\quad x = -1$

Check

$x = 9$: $\qquad |2(9) - 3| \overset{?}{=} |9 + 6| \qquad x = -1$: $\qquad |2(-1) - 3| \overset{?}{=} |-1 + 6|$

$$|18 - 3| \overset{?}{=} |15| \qquad\qquad\qquad |-2 - 3| \overset{?}{=} |5|$$

$$|15| \overset{?}{=} 15 \qquad\qquad\qquad\qquad |-5| \overset{?}{=} 5$$

$$15 = 15 \quad \text{True} \qquad\qquad\qquad 5 = 5 \quad \text{True}$$

Both solutions check, so the solution set is $\{-1, 9\}$. ■

Quick ✔ *In Problems 12–15, solve each equation.*

12. $|x - 3| = |2x + 5|$ **13.** $|8z + 11| = |6z + 17|$

14. $|3 - 2y| = |4y + 3|$ **15.** $|2x - 3| = |5 - 2x|$

⎡2 Solve Absolute Value Inequalities Involving $<$ or $\le$

The method for solving absolute value equations relies on the geometric interpretation of absolute value. Namely, the absolute value of a real number x is the distance from the origin to x on the real number line. We use this same interpretation to solve absolute value inequalities.

EXAMPLE 5 Solving an Absolute Value Inequality

Solve the inequality $|x| < 4$. Graph the solution set.

Solution

The inequality $|x| < 4$ is asking, "Tell me all real numbers x such that the distance from the origin to x on the real number line is less than 4." Figure 41 illustrates the

Figure 41

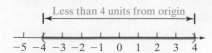

situation. We can see from the figure that any number between -4 and 4 satisfies the inequality. The solution set consists of all real numbers x for which $-4 < x < 4$ or, using interval notation, $(-4, 4)$.

We could also visualize these results by graphing $f(x) = |x|$ and $g(x) = 4$. See Figure 42. Because we are solving $f(x) < g(x)$, we look for all x-coordinates such that the graph of $f(x)$ is below the graph of $g(x)$. From the graph, we can see that the graph of $f(x) = |x|$ is below the graph of $g(x) = 4$ for all x between -4 and 4. So the solution set consists of all x for which $-4 < x < 4$, or all x in the interval $(-4, 4)$. ∎

The results of Example 5 lead to the following.

Figure 42

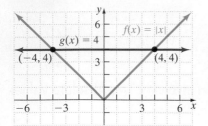

INEQUALITIES OF THE FORM $<$ OR $\leq$ INVOLVING ABSOLUTE VALUE

If a is a positive real number and if u is an algebraic expression, then

$$|u| < a \qquad \text{is equivalent to} \qquad -a < u < a$$
$$|u| \leq a \qquad \text{is equivalent to} \qquad -a \leq u \leq a$$

Note: If $a = 0$, $|u| < 0$ has no solution; $|u| \leq 0$ is equivalent to $u = 0$. If $a < 0$, the inequality has no solution.

Quick ✔

16. If $a > 0$, then $|u| < a$ is equivalent to _____.

17. $|u| < a$ will have no real solution if a ___ 0.

In Problems 18 and 19, solve each inequality. Graph the solution set.

18. $|x| \leq 5$ **19.** $|x| < \dfrac{3}{2}$

EXAMPLE 6 How to Solve an Absolute Value Inequality Involving $\leq$

Solve the inequality $|2x + 3| \leq 5$. Graph the solution set.

Step-by-Step Solution

Step 1: The inequality is in the form $|u| \leq a$, where $u = 2x + 3$ and $a = 5$. We rewrite the inequality as a compound inequality that does not involve absolute value.	$|2x + 3| \leq 5$ Use the fact that $|u| \leq a$ means $-a \leq u \leq a$: $-5 \leq 2x + 3 \leq 5$

Step 2: Solve the resulting compound inequality.

Subtract 3 from all three parts: $\quad -5 - 3 \leq 2x + 3 - 3 \leq 5 - 3$
$$-8 \leq 2x \leq 2$$

Divide all three parts of the inequality by 2: $\quad \dfrac{-8}{2} \leq \dfrac{2x}{2} \leq \dfrac{2}{2}$
$$-4 \leq x \leq 1$$

Figure 43

The solution using set-builder notation is $\{x \mid -4 \leq x \leq 1\}$. The solution using interval notation is $[-4, 1]$. Figure 43 shows the graph of the solution set. ∎

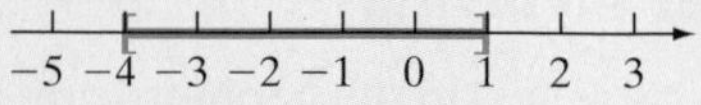

Work Smart

Although not a complete check of the solution of Example 6, we can choose a number in the interval and see if it works. Let's try $x = -3$.

$$|2(-3) + 3| \overset{?}{\leq} 5$$
$$|-6 + 3| \overset{?}{\leq} 5$$
$$|-3| \overset{?}{\leq} 5$$
$$3 \leq 5$$

Quick ✔ *In Problems 20–22, solve each inequality. Graph the solution set.*

20. $|x + 3| < 5$

21. $|2x - 3| \leq 7$

22. $|7x + 2| < -3$

EXAMPLE 7 Solving an Absolute Value Inequality Involving <

Solve the inequality $|-3x + 2| + 4 < 14$. Graph the solution set.

Solution

First, we want to isolate the absolute value by subtracting 4 from both sides of the inequality.

$$|-3x + 2| + 4 < 14$$

Subtract 4 from both sides: $\qquad\qquad\qquad |-3x + 2| < 10$

$|u| < a$ means $-a < u < a$: $\qquad\qquad -10 < -3x + 2 < 10$

Subtract 2 from all three parts: $\quad -10 - 2 < -3x + 2 - 2 < 10 - 2$

$$-12 < -3x < 8$$

Divide all three parts by -3. Be sure to
reverse the direction of the inequalities.
$$\frac{-12}{-3} > \frac{-3x}{-3} > \frac{8}{-3}$$

$$4 > x > -\frac{8}{3}$$

$b > x > a$ is equivalent to $a < x < b$:
$$-\frac{8}{3} < x < 4$$

Figure 44

The solution using set-builder notation is $\left\{ x \,\middle|\, -\dfrac{8}{3} < x < 4 \right\}$. The solution using interval notation is $\left(-\dfrac{8}{3}, 4 \right)$. Figure 44 shows the graph of the solution set. ∎

Quick ✔ *In Problems 23–26, solve each inequality. Graph the solution set.*

23. $|x| + 4 < 6$ $\qquad\qquad\qquad$ **24.** $|x - 3| + 4 \leq 8$

25. $3|2x + 1| \leq 9$ $\qquad\qquad\qquad$ **26.** $|-3x + 1| - 5 < 3$

⌐3 Solve Absolute Value Inequalities Involving > or ≥

Now let's look at absolute value inequalities involving $>$ or $\geq$.

EXAMPLE 8 Solving an Absolute Value Inequality Involving >

Solve the inequality $|x| > 3$. Graph the solution set.

Solution

The inequality $|x| > 3$ is asking, "Tell me all real numbers x such that the distance from the origin to x on the real number line is more than 3 units." Figure 45 illustrates the situation.

Figure 45

More than 3 units from origin, 0. $\qquad$ More than 3 units from origin, 0.

Figure 46

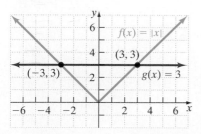

We can see from the figure that any number less than -3 or greater than 3 satisfies the inequality. The solution set consists of all real numbers x for which $x < -3$ or $x > 3$ or, using interval notation, $(-\infty, -3) \cup (3, \infty)$.

We could also visualize these results by graphing $f(x) = |x|$ and $g(x) = 3$. See Figure 46. Because we are solving $f(x) > g(x)$, we look for all x-coordinates such that the graph of $f(x)$ is above the graph of $g(x)$. From the graph, we can see that the graph of $f(x) = |x|$ is above the graph of $g(x) = 3$ for all x less than -3 or all x greater than 3. So the solution set consists of all x for which $x < -3$ or $x > 3$, that is, all x in the interval $(-\infty, -3) \cup (3, \infty)$. ∎

Based upon Example 8, we are led to the following results.

INEQUALITIES OF THE FORM > OR ≥ INVOLVING ABSOLUTE VALUE

If a is a positive real number and u is an algebraic expression, then

$$|u| > a \qquad \text{is equivalent to} \qquad u < -a \quad \text{or} \quad u > a$$
$$|u| \geq a \qquad \text{is equivalent to} \qquad u \leq -a \quad \text{or} \quad u \geq a$$

Quick ✔

27. $|u| > a$ is equivalent to _____ or _____.

28. *True or False: $|x| > -2$ has no real solution.*

In Problems 29 and 30, solve each inequality. Graph the solution set.

29. $|x| \geq 6$ 　　　　　　　　**30.** $|x| > \dfrac{5}{2}$

EXAMPLE 9 How to Solve an Inequality Involving >

Solve the inequality $|2x - 5| > 3$. Graph the solution set.

Step-by-Step Solution

Step 1: The inequality is in the form $|u| > a$, where $u = 2x - 5$ and $a = 3$. We rewrite the inequality as a compound inequality that does not involve absolute value.

$$|2x - 5| > 3$$
$$2x - 5 < -3 \qquad \text{or} \qquad 2x - 5 > 3$$

Step 2: Solve each inequality separately.

	$2x - 5 < -3$		$2x - 5 > 3$
Add 5 to both sides:	$2x < 2$	Add 5 to both sides:	$2x > 8$
Divide both sides by 2:	$x < 1$	Divide both sides by 2:	$x > 4$

Step 3: Find the union of the solution sets of each inequality.

The solution set is $\{x \,|\, x < 1 \text{ or } x > 4\}$, or using interval notation, $(-\infty, 1) \cup (4, \infty)$. See Figure 47 for the graph of the solution set.

Figure 47

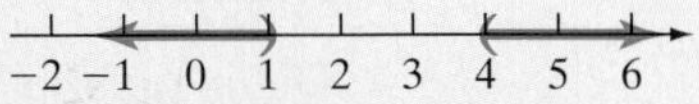

∎

Quick ✔ *In Problems 31–36, solve each inequality. Graph the solution set.*

31. $|x + 3| > 4$ 　　　　　　　　**32.** $|4x - 3| \geq 5$

33. $|-3x + 2| > 7$ 　　　　　　　**34.** $|2x + 5| - 2 > -2$

35. $|6x - 5| \geq 0$ 　　　　　　　**36.** $|2x + 1| > -3$

Work Smart

$$|u| > a$$

CANNOT be written as

$$-a > u > a$$

SUMMARY   SOLVING ABSOLUTE VALUE EQUATIONS AND INEQUALITIES

Absolute Value Form	Equation/Inequality Form	Example	
		Algebraic Solution	**Graphical Solution**
$\lvert u \rvert = a$	$u = a$ or $u = -a$	$\lvert x + 3 \rvert = 5$ $x + 3 = 5$ or $x + 3 = -5$ $x = 2$ or $x = -8$ Solution set: $\{-8, 2\}$	
$\lvert u \rvert = \lvert v \rvert$	$u = v$ or $u = -v$	$\lvert x - 2 \rvert = \lvert 2x \rvert$ $x - 2 = 2x$ $x - 2 = -2x$ $-2 = x$ $3x = 2$ $x = -2$ $x = \dfrac{2}{3}$ Solution set: $\left\{-2, \dfrac{2}{3}\right\}$	
$\lvert u \rvert < a$ $\lvert u \rvert \le a$	$-a < u < a$ $-a \le u \le a$	$\lvert x - 1 \rvert \le 4$ $-4 \le x - 1 \le 4$ $-3 \le x \le 5$ Solution set: $\{x \mid -3 \le x \le 5\}$ or $[-3, 5]$	
$\lvert u \rvert > a$ $\lvert u \rvert \ge a$	$u < -a$ or $u > a$ $u \le -a$ or $u \ge a$	$\lvert x + 1 \rvert > 3$ $x + 1 < -3$ or $x + 1 > 3$ $x < -4$ or $x > 2$ Solution set: $\{x \mid x < -4 \text{ or } x > 2\}$ or $(-\infty, -4) \cup (2, \infty)$	

4 Solve Applied Problems Involving Absolute Value Inequalities

You may frequently read phrases such as "margin of error" and "tolerance" in the newspaper or on the Internet. For example, according to a Gallup poll conducted September, 2007, 82% of Americans indicated they were willing to spend more for children's toys manufactured in the United States. The poll had a margin of error of 4%. The 82% reported is an estimate of the true percentage of Americans who are willing to spend more for children's toys manufactured in the United States. If we let p represent the true percentage of Americans willing to spend more on children's toys manufactured in the United States, then we can represent the poll's margin of error mathematically as

$$\lvert p - 82 \rvert \le 4$$

As another example, the tolerance of a belt used in a pulley system whose width is 6 inches is $\dfrac{1}{16}$ inch. If x represents the actual width of the belt, then we can represent the acceptable belt widths as

$$\lvert x - 6 \rvert \le \dfrac{1}{16}$$

⌐EXAMPLE 10 Analyzing the Margin of Error in a Poll

The inequality

$$|p - 82| \leq 4$$

represents the percentage of Americans who indicated they were willing to spend more for children's toys manufactured in the United States. Solve the inequality and interpret the results.

Solution

$$|p - 82| \leq 4$$

$|u| \leq a$ means $-a \leq u \leq a$: $\quad -4 \leq p - 82 \leq 4$

Add 82 to all three parts of the inequality: $\quad 78 \leq p \leq 86$

The percentage of Americans who are willing to spend more for children's toys manufactured in the United States is between 78% and 86%, inclusive. ∎

Quick ✔

37. The inequality $|x - 4| \leq \dfrac{1}{32}$ represents the acceptable belt widths x (in inches) for a belt that is manufactured for a pulley system. Determine the acceptable belt widths.

38. In a poll conducted by ABC News, 9% of Americans stated that they have been shot at. The margin of error in the poll was 1.7%. If we let p represent the true percentage of people who have been shot at, we can represent the margin of error as

$$|p - 9| \leq 1.7$$

Solve the inequality and interpret the results.

2.6 EXERCISES

PRACTICE   WATCH   DOWNLOAD   READ   REVIEW

1–38. are the **Quick ✔**s that follow each **EXAMPLE**

Building Skills

In Problems 39–60, solve each absolute value equation. See Objective 1.

◎ 39. $|x| = 10$

40. $|z| = 9$

41. $|y - 3| = 4$

42. $|x + 3| = 5$

◎ 43. $|-3x + 5| = 8$

44. $|-4y + 3| = 9$

45. $|y| - 7 = -2$

46. $|x| + 3 = 5$

47. $|2x + 3| - 5 = 3$

48. $|3y + 1| - 5 = -3$

◎ 49. $-2|x - 3| + 10 = -4$

50. $3|y - 4| + 4 = 16$

51. $|-3x| - 5 = -5$

52. $|-2x| + 9 = 9$

53. $\left|\dfrac{3x - 1}{4}\right| = 2$

54. $\left|\dfrac{2x - 3}{5}\right| = 2$

55. $|3x + 2| = |2x - 5|$

56. $|5y - 2| = |4y + 7|$

◎ 57. $|8 - 3x| = |2x - 7|$

58. $|5x + 3| = |12 - 4x|$

59. $|4y - 7| = |9 - 4y|$

60. $|5x - 1| = |9 - 5x|$

In Problems 61–74, solve each absolute value inequality. Graph the solution set on a real number line. See Objective 2.

61. $|x| < 9$

62. $|x| \leq \dfrac{5}{4}$

63. $|x - 4| \leq 7$

64. $|y + 4| < 6$

65. $|3x + 1| < 8$

66. $|4x - 3| \leq 9$

67. $|6x + 5| < -1$

68. $|4x + 3| \leq 0$

69. $2|x - 3| + 3 < 9$

70. $3|y + 2| - 2 < 7$

71. $|2 - 5x| + 3 < 10$

72. $|-3x + 2| - 7 \leq -2$

73. $|(2x - 3) - 1| < 0.01$

74. $|(3x + 2) - 8| < 0.01$

In Problems 75–86, solve each absolute value inequality. Graph the solution set on the real number line. See Objective 3.

75. $|y - 5| > 2$

76. $|x + 4| \geq 7$

77. $|-4x - 3| \geq 5$

78. $|-5y + 3| > 7$

79. $2|y| + 3 > 1$

80. $3|z| + 8 > 2$

81. $|-5x - 3| - 7 > 0$

82. $|-9x + 2| - 11 \geq 0$

83. $4|-2x + 1| > 4$

84. $3|8x + 3| \geq 9$

85. $|1 - 2x| \geq |-5|$

86. $|3 - 5x| > |-7|$

Mixed Practice

In Problems 87–90, use the graphs of the functions given to solve each problem.

87. $f(x) = |x|$, $g(x) = 5$

   (a) $f(x) = g(x)$
   (b) $f(x) \leq g(x)$
   (c) $f(x) > g(x)$

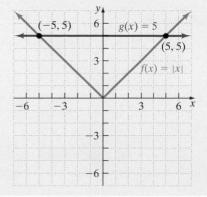

88. $f(x) = |x|$, $g(x) = 6$

   (a) $f(x) = g(x)$
   (b) $f(x) \leq g(x)$
   (c) $f(x) > g(x)$

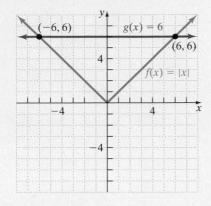

89. $f(x) = |x + 2|$, $g(x) = 3$

   (a) $f(x) = g(x)$
   (b) $f(x) < g(x)$
   (c) $f(x) \geq g(x)$

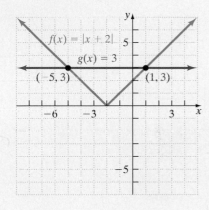

90. $f(x) = |2x|$, $g(x) = 10$

   (a) $f(x) = g(x)$
   (b) $f(x) < g(x)$
   (c) $f(x) \geq g(x)$

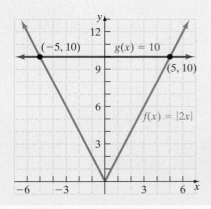

In Problems 91–110, solve each absolute value equation or inequality. For absolute value inequalities, graph the solution set on a real number line.

91. $|x| > 5$

92. $|x| \geq \dfrac{8}{3}$

93. $|2x + 5| = 3$

94. $|4x + 3| = 1$

95. $7|x| = 35$

96. $8|y| = 32$

97. $|5x + 2| \leq 8$

98. $|7y - 3| < 11$

99. $|-2x + 3| = -4$

100. $|3x - 4| = -9$

101. $|3x + 2| \geq 5$

102. $|5y + 3| > 2$

103. $|3x - 2| + 7 > 9$

104. $|4y + 3| - 8 \geq -3$

105. $|5x + 3| = |3x + 5|$

106. $|3z - 2| = |z + 6|$

107. $|4x + 7| + 6 < 5$

108. $|4x + 1| > 0$

109. $\left| \dfrac{x - 2}{4} \right| = \left| \dfrac{2x + 1}{6} \right|$

110. $\left| \dfrac{1}{2}x - 3 \right| = \left| \dfrac{2}{3}x + 1 \right|$

Applying the Concepts

111. Express the fact that x differs from 5 by less than 3 as an inequality involving absolute value. Solve for x.

112. Express the fact that x differs from -4 by less than 2 as an inequality involving absolute value. Solve for x.

113. Express the fact that twice x differs from -6 by more than 3 as an inequality involving absolute value. Solve for x.

114. Express the fact that twice x differs from 7 by more than 3 as an inequality involving absolute value. Solve for x.

115. Tolerance A certain rod in an internal combustion engine is supposed to be 5.7 inches. The tolerance on the rod is 0.0005 inches. If x represents the

length of a rod, the acceptable lengths of a rod can be expressed as $|x - 5.7| \leq 0.0005$. Determine the acceptable lengths of the rod. (SOURCE: *WiseCo Piston*)

116. Tolerance A certain rod in an internal combustion engine is supposed to be 6.125 inches. The tolerance on the rod is 0.0005 inches. If x represents the length of a rod, the acceptable lengths of a rod can be expressed as $|x - 6.125| \leq 0.0005$. Determine the acceptable lengths of the rod.

117. IQ Scores According to the Stanford-Binet IQ test, a normal IQ score is 100. It can be shown that anyone with an IQ x that satisfies the inequality $\left| \dfrac{x - 100}{15} \right| > 1.96$ has an unusual IQ score. Determine the IQ scores that would be considered unusual.

118. Gestation Period The length of human pregnancy is about 266 days. It can be shown that a mother whose gestation period x satisfies the inequality $\left| \dfrac{x - 266}{16} \right| > 1.96$ has an unusual length of pregnancy. Determine the length of pregnancy that would be considered unusual.

Extending the Concepts

In Problems 119–126, solve each equation.

119. $|x| - x = 5$

120. $|y| + y = 3$

121. $z + |-z| = 4$

122. $y - |-y| = 12$

123. $|4x + 1| = x - 2$

124. $|2x + 1| = x - 3$

125. $|x + 5| = -(x + 5)$

126. $|y - 4| = y - 4$

Explaining the Concepts

127. Explain why $|2x - 3| + 1 = 0$ has no solution.

128. Explain why the solution set of $|5x - 3| > -5$ is the set of all real numbers.

129. Explain why $|4x + 3| + 3 < 0$ has the empty set as the solution set.

130. Solve $|x - 5| = |5 - x|$. Explain why the result is reasonable. What do we call this type of equation?

2.7 Variation

OBJECTIVES

1. Model and Solve Problems Involving Direct Variation
2. Model and Solve Problems Involving Inverse Variation
3. Model and Solve Problems Involving Combined or Joint Variation

Preparing for Variation

Before getting started, take this readiness quiz. If you get a problem wrong, go back to the section cited and review the material.

P1. Solve: $30 = 5x$ [Section 1.1, pp. 49–52]

P2. Solve: $4 = \dfrac{k}{3}$ [Section 1.1, pp. 49–52]

P3. Graph: $y = 3x$ [Section 1.6, pp. 115–116]

1 Model and Solve Problems Involving Direct Variation

Often two variables are related in terms of proportions. For example, we say "Revenue is proportional to sales" or "Force is proportional to acceleration." When we say that one variable is proportional to another variable, we are talking about *variation*. **Variation** refers to how one quantity varies in relation to some other quantity. Quantities may vary *directly*, *inversely*, or *jointly*. We will discuss direct variation first.

> **DEFINITION**
>
> Suppose we let x and y represent two quantities. We say that y **varies directly** with x, or y is **directly proportional to** x, if there is a nonzero number k such that
>
> $$y = kx$$
>
> The number k is called the **constant of proportionality**.

Figure 48

$y = kx,\ k > 0,\ x \ge 0$

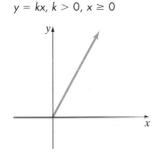

If y varies directly with x, then y is a linear function of x. The graph in Figure 48 illustrates the relationship between y and x if y varies directly with x and $k > 0, x \ge 0$. Notice that the constant of proportionality is the slope of the line and the y intercept is 0.

If we know that two quantities vary directly, then knowing the value of each quantity in one instance allows us to write a formula that is true in all cases.

EXAMPLE 1 Hooke's Law

Hooke's Law states that the force (or weight) on a spring is directly proportional to the length that the spring stretches from its "at rest" position. That is, $F = kx$, where F is the force exerted, x is the extension of the spring, and k is the proportionality constant that varies from spring to spring.

(a) Suppose that a 20-pound weight causes a spring to stretch 10 inches. See Figure 49. Find the constant of proportionality, k.

Figure 49

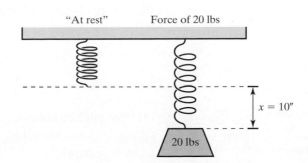

Preparing for...Answers **P1.** {6}
P2. {12}
P3.

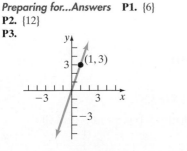

(b) Write the relation between force and stretch length using function notation.

(c) Suppose a weight is attached to the spring and it stretches 8 inches. What is the weight attached to the spring?

(d) Graph the relation between force and length that the spring stretches.

Solution

(a) We know that $F = kx$ and that $F = 20$ pounds when $x = 10$ inches. Substituting, we have that

$$F = kx$$
$$20 = k(10)$$
$$k = 2$$

(b) With $k = 2$, we have that $F = 2x$. We write this using function notation as
$$F(x) = 2x$$

(c) If the spring stretches $x = 8$ inches, the force exerted is
$$F(8) = 2(8) = 16 \text{ pounds}$$

(d) Figure 50 shows the relation between force and length of the spring.

Figure 50

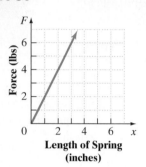

EXAMPLE 2 Car Payments

Suppose that Dulce just purchased a used car for $10,000. She decides to put $1000 down on the car and borrow the remaining $9000. The bank lends Dulce $9000 at 4.9% interest for 48 months. Her payments are $206.86. The monthly payment p on a car varies directly with the amount borrowed b.

(a) Find a function that relates the monthly payment p to the amount borrowed b for any car loan with the same terms.

(b) Suppose that Dulce put $2000 down on the car instead. What would her monthly payment be?

(c) Graph the relation between monthly payment and amount borrowed.

Solution

(a) Because p varies directly with b, we know that
$$p = kb$$
for some constant k. Because $p = \$206.86$ when $b = \$9000$, it follows that
$$206.86 = k(9000)$$
Solving this equation for k by dividing both sides of the equation by 9000, we find that
$$k = 0.022984$$
So, we have that
$$p = 0.022984b$$

We can write this as a linear function:
$$p(b) = 0.022984b$$

(b) When $b = \$8000$, we have that
$$p(8000) = 0.022984(8000)$$
$$= \$183.87$$

If Dulce put $2000 down, her payment would be $183.87.

(c) Figure 51 shows the relationship between the monthly payment p and the amount borrowed b.

Work Smart

To avoid round-off error, do not round the value of k to fewer than 5 decimal places.

Figure 51

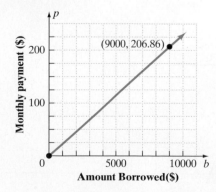

Quick ✔

1. _____ refers to how one quantity varies in relation to some other quantity.

2. If x and y are two quantities, then y is directly proportional to x if there is a nonzero number k such that _____.

3. The cost of gas C varies directly with the number of gallons pumped, g. Suppose that the cost of pumping 8 gallons of gas is \$33.60.

   (a) Find a function that relates the cost of gas C to the number of gallons pumped g.

   (b) Suppose that 5.6 gallons are pumped into your car. What would the cost be?

   (c) Graph the relation between cost and number of gallons pumped.

Figure 52

$$y = \frac{k}{x}, \, k > 0, \, x > 0$$

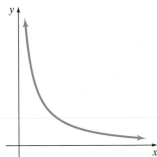

2 Model and Solve Problems Involving Inverse Variation

We now turn our attention to another kind of variation.

DEFINITION

Suppose x and y represent two quantities. We say that y **varies inversely** with x, or y is **inversely proportional to** x, if there is a nonzero number k such that

$$y = \frac{k}{x}$$

The graph in Figure 52 illustrates the relationship between y and x if y varies inversely with x with $k > 0$ and $x > 0$. Notice from the graph that as x increases, the value of y decreases.

EXAMPLE 3 Weight That Can Be Supported by a Beam

The weight W that can be safely supported by a 2-inch by 4-inch (2-by-4) piece of lumber varies inversely with its length l. See Figure 53.

Figure 53

(a) Experiments indicate that the maximum weight a 12-foot pine 2-by-4 can support is 400 pounds. Find a function that relates the maximum weight to the length l for any pine 2-by-4.

(b) Determine the maximum weight that a 15-foot pine 2-by-4 can sustain.

Solution

(a) Because W varies inversely with l, we know that

$$W = \frac{k}{l}$$

for some constant k. Because $W = 400$ when $l = 12$, it follows that

$$400 = \frac{k}{12}$$

Solving this equation for k by multiplying both sides of the equation by 12, we find that

$$k = 4800$$

So we have that

$$W = \frac{4800}{l}$$

We can write this as a function:

$$W(l) = \frac{4800}{l}$$

(b) When $l = 15$ feet, we have that

$$W(15) = \frac{4800}{15}$$
$$= 320 \text{ pounds}$$

The maximum weight that a 15-foot pine 2-by-4 can sustain is 320 pounds. ■

Quick ✔

4. Suppose we let x and y represent two quantities. We say that y varies inversely with x, or y is inversely proportional to x, if there is a nonzero number k such

that _____.

5. The rate of vibration (in oscillations per second) V of a string under constant tension varies inversely with the length l.

   (a) If a string is 30 inches long and vibrates 500 times per second, find a function that relates the rate of vibration to the length of a string.

   (b) What is the rate of vibration of a string that is 50 inches long?

3 Model and Solve Problems Involving Combined or Joint Variation

When a variable quantity Q is proportional to the product of two or more other variables, we say that Q **varies jointly** with these quantities. For example, the equation $y = kxz$ can be read as "y varies jointly with x and z." When direct and inverse variation occur at the same time, we have **combined variation**. For example, the equation $y = \dfrac{kx}{z}$ can be read as "y varies directly with x and inversely with z." The equation $y = \dfrac{kmn}{p}$ can be read "y varies jointly with m and n and inversely with p."

EXAMPLE 4 Force of the Wind—Joint Variation

The force F of the wind on a flat surface positioned at a right angle to the direction of the wind varies jointly with the area A of the surface and the square of the speed v of the wind. A wind of 30 miles per hour blowing on a window measuring 4 feet by 5 feet has a force of 150 pounds. What is the force on a window measuring 2 feet by 6 feet caused by a hurricane-force wind of 100 miles per hour?

Solution

Because F varies jointly with A and the square of v, we know that

$$F = kAv^2$$

for some constant k. The dimensions of the window are 4 feet by 5 feet, so the area A of the window is (4 feet)(5 feet) = 20 square feet. Because $F = 150$ when $A = 20$ and $v = 30$, it follows that

$$150 = k(20)(30^2)$$

We solve this equation for k.

$$150 = 18{,}000k$$

$$k = \frac{1}{120}$$

So we have that

$$F = \frac{1}{120}Av^2$$

For a wind of 100 miles per hour blowing on a window whose area is $A = (2 \text{ feet})(6 \text{ feet}) = 12$ square feet, the force F is

$$F = \frac{1}{120}(12)(100)^2$$

$$= 1000 \text{ pounds} \qquad \blacksquare$$

Quick ✔

6. When direct and inverse variation occur at the same time, we have _____
_____.

7. The kinetic energy K of an object varies jointly with its mass and the square of its velocity. The kinetic energy of a 110-kg linebacker running at 9 meters per second is 4455 joules. Determine the kinetic energy of a 140-kg linebacker running at 5 meters per second.

EXAMPLE 5 Centripetal Force—Combined Variation

The force required to keep an object traveling in a circular motion is called the centripetal force. The centripetal force F required to keep an object of a fixed mass in circular motion varies directly to the square of the velocity v of the object and inversely to the radius r of the circle. See Figure 54.

The force required to keep a car traveling 30 meters per second on a circular road with radius 50 meters is 21,600 newtons. Determine the force required to keep the same car on a circular road if it is traveling 40 meters per second on a road whose radius is 30 meters.

Solution

Because the force varies directly with the square of the velocity of the object and inversely to the radius of the circle, we have combined variation with

$$F = \frac{kv^2}{r}$$

Figure 54

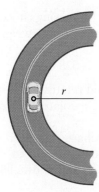

for some constant k. Because $F = 21{,}600$ when $v = 30$ and $r = 50$, it follows that

$$21{,}600 = \frac{k \cdot 30^2}{50}$$

Solving for k, we find that $k = 1200$. So we have that

$$F = \frac{1200v^2}{r}$$

For a car traveling 40 meters per second on a circular road with radius 30 meters, the force required to keep the car on the road is

$$F = \frac{1200 \cdot 40^2}{30}$$

$$= 64{,}000 \text{ newtons} \qquad \blacksquare$$

Quick ✔

8. The electrical resistance of a wire R varies directly with the length of the wire l and inversely with the square of the diameter of the wire d. If a wire 432 feet long and 4 millimeters in diameter has a resistance of 1.24 ohms, find the resistance in a wire that is 282 feet long with a diameter of 3 millimeters. Round your answer to two decimal places.

2.7 EXERCISES

MyMathLab

PRACTICE   WATCH   DOWNLOAD   READ   REVIEW

1–8. are the **Quick ✓s** *that follow each* **EXAMPLE**

Building Skills

In Problems 9–14, (a) find the constant of proportionality k,
(b) write the linear function relating the two variables, and (c) find
the quantity indicated. See Objective 1.

9. Suppose that y varies directly with x. When $x = 5$,
   then $y = 30$. Find y when $x = 7$.

10. Suppose that y varies directly with x. When $x = 3$,
    then $y = 15$. Find y when $x = 5$.

11. Suppose that y is directly proportional to x. When
    $x = 7$, then $y = 3$. Find y when $x = 28$.

12. Suppose that y is directly proportional to x. When
    $x = 20$, then $y = 4$. Find y when $x = 35$.

13. Suppose that y is directly proportional to x. When
    $x = 8$, then $y = 4$. Find y when $x = 30$.

14. Suppose that y is directly proportional to x. When
    $x = 12$, then $y = 8$. Find y when $x = 20$.

In Problems 15–18, (a) find the constant of proportionality k,
(b) write the function relating the two variables, and (c) find the
quantity indicated. See Objective 2.

15. Suppose that y varies inversely with x. When $x = 10$,
    $y = 2$. Find y if $x = 5$.

16. Suppose that y varies inversely with x. When $x = 3$,
    $y = 15$. Find y if $x = 5$.

17. Suppose that y is inversely proportional to x. When
    $x = 7$, $y = 3$. Find y if $x = 28$.

18. Suppose that y is inversely proportional to x. When
    $x = 20$, $y = 4$. Find y if $x = 35$.

In Problems 19–22 (a) find the constant of proportionality k,
(b) write the function relating the variables, and (c) find the quantity
indicated. See Objective 3.

19. Suppose that y varies jointly with x and z. When
    $y = 10$, $x = 8$ and $z = 5$. Find y if $x = 12$ and
    $z = 9$.

20. Suppose that y varies jointly with x and z. When
    $y = 20$, $x = 6$ and $z = 10$. Find y if $x = 8$ and
    $z = 15$.

21. Suppose that Q varies directly with x and inversely
    with y. When $Q = \dfrac{13}{12}$, $x = 5$ and $y = 6$. Find Q if
    $x = 9$ and $y = 4$.

22. Suppose that Q varies directly with x and inversely
    with y. When $Q = \dfrac{14}{5}$, $x = 4$ and $y = 3$. Find Q if
    $x = 8$ and $y = 3$.

Applying the Concepts

23. **Mortgage Payments** The monthly payment p on a
    mortgage varies directly with the amount borrowed b.
    Suppose that you decide to borrow $120,000 using a
    30-year mortgage at 5.75% interest. You are told that
    your payment is $700.29.

    (a) Write a linear function that relates the monthly
    payment p to the amount borrowed b for a
    mortgage with the same terms.
    (b) Assume that you have decided to buy a more
    expensive home that requires you to borrow
    $140,000. What will your monthly payment be?
    (c) Graph the relation between monthly payment
    and amount borrowed.

24. **Mortgage Payments** The monthly payment p on a
    mortgage varies directly with the amount borrowed b.
    Suppose that you decide to borrow $120,000 using a
    15-year mortgage at 5.5% interest. You are told that
    your payment is $980.50.

    (a) Write a linear function that relates the monthly
    payment p to the amount borrowed b for a
    mortgage with the same terms.
    (b) Assume that you have decided to buy a more
    expensive home that requires you to borrow
    $150,000. What will your monthly payment be?
    (c) Graph the relation between monthly payment
    and amount borrowed.

25. **Cost Function** The cost C of purchasing chocolate-
    covered almonds varies directly with the weight w in
    pounds. Suppose that the cost of purchasing 5 pounds
    of chocolate-covered almonds is $28.

    (a) Write a linear function that relates the cost C to
    the number of pounds of chocolate-covered
    almonds purchased w.
    (b) What would it cost to purchase 3.5 pounds of
    chocolate-covered almonds?
    (c) Graph the relation between cost and weight.

26. **Conversion** Suppose that you are planning a trip to
    Europe so you need to obtain some euros. The
    amount received in euros varies directly with the
    amount in U.S. dollars. Your friend just converted
    $600 into 405 euros.

    (a) Write a linear function that relates the number of
    euros E to the number of U.S. dollars d.

(b) If you wish to convert $700 into euros, how many euros would you receive?

(c) Graph the relation between euros and U.S. dollars.

27. **Falling Objects** The velocity of a falling object (ignoring air resistance) v is directly proportional to the time t of the fall. If, after 2 seconds, the velocity of the object is 64 feet per second, what will its velocity be after 3 seconds?

28. **Circumference of a Circle** The circumference of a circle C is directly proportional to its radius r. If the circumference of a circle whose radius is 5 inches is 10π inches, what is the circumference of a circle whose radius is 8 inches?

29. **Demand** Suppose that the demand D for candy at the movie theater is inversely related to the price p.

(a) When the price of candy is $2.50 per bag, the theater sells 150 bags of candy. Express the demand of candy as a function of its price.

(b) Determine the number of bags of candy that will be sold if the price is raised to $3 a bag.

30. **Driving to School** The time t that it takes to get to school varies inversely with your average speed s.

(a) Suppose that it takes you 30 minutes to drive to school when your average speed is 35 miles per hour. Express the driving time to school as a function of average speed.

(b) Suppose that your average speed driving to school is 30 miles per hour. How long will it take you to get to school?

31. **Pressure** The volume of a gas V held at a constant temperature in a closed container varies inversely with its pressure P. If the volume of a gas is 600 cubic centimeters (cc) when the pressure is 150 millimeters of mercury (mm Hg), find the volume when the pressure is 200 mm Hg.

32. **Resistance** The current i in a circuit is inversely proportional to its resistance R measured in ohms. Suppose that when the current in a circuit is 30 amperes, the resistance is 8 ohms. Find the current in the same circuit when the resistance is 10 ohms.

33. **Weight** The weight of an object above the surface of Earth varies inversely with the square of the distance from the center of Earth. If Maria weighs 120 pounds when she is on the surface of Earth (3960 miles from the center), determine Maria's weight if she is at the top of Mount McKinley (3.8 miles from the surface of Earth).

34. **Intensity of Light** The intensity I of light (measured in foot-candles) varies inversely with the square of the

distance from the bulb. Suppose the intensity of a 100-watt light bulb at a distance of 2 meters is 0.075 foot-candles. Determine the intensity of the bulb at a distance of 3 meters.

35. **Drag Force** When an object moves through air, a frictionlike drag force tends to slow the object down. The drag force D on a parachutist free-falling varies jointly with the surface area of the parachutist and the square of his velocity. The drag force on a parachutist with surface area 2 square meters falling at 40 meters per second is 1152 newtons. Find the drag force on a parachutist whose surface area is 2.5 square meters falling at 50 meters per second.

36. **Kinetic Energy** The kinetic energy K (measured in joules) of a moving object varies jointly with the mass of the object and the square of its velocity v. The kinetic energy of a linebacker weighing 110 kilograms and running at a speed of 8 meters per second is 3520 joules. Find the kinetic energy of a wide receiver weighing 90 kilograms and running at a speed of 10 meters per second.

37. **Newton's Law of Gravitation** According to Newton's law of universal gravitation, the force F of gravity between any two objects varies jointly with the masses of the objects m_1 and m_2 and inversely with the square of the distance between the objects r. The force of gravity between a 105-kg man and his 80-kg wife when they are separated by a distance of 5 meters is 2.24112×10^{-8} newtons. Find the force of gravity between the man and his wife when they are 2 meters apart.

38. **Electrical Resistance** The electrical resistance of a wire varies directly with the length of the wire and inversely with the square of the diameter of the wire. If a wire 50 feet long and 3 millimeters in diameter has a resistance of 0.255 ohms, find the length of a wire of the same material whose resistance is 0.147 ohms and whose diameter is 2.5 millimeters.

39. **Stress of Material** The stress in the material of a pipe subject to internal pressure varies jointly with the internal pressure and internal diameter of the pipe and inversely with the thickness of the pipe. The stress is 100 pounds per square inch when the diameter is 5 inches, the thickness is 0.75 inch, and the internal pressure is 25 pounds per square inch. Find the stress when the internal pressure is 50 pounds per square inch, the diameter is 6 inches, and the thickness is 0.5 inch.

40. **Gas Laws** The volume V of an ideal gas varies directly with the temperature T and inversely with the pressure P. If a cylinder contains oxygen at a temperature of 300 kelvin (K) and a pressure of 15 atmospheres in

a volume of 100 liters, what is the constant of proportionality k? If a piston is lowered into the cylinder, decreasing the volume occupied by the gas to 70 liters and raising the temperature to 315 K, what is the pressure?

Extending the Concepts

41. **David and Goliath** The force F (in newtons) required to maintain an object in a circular path varies jointly with the mass m (in kilograms) of the object and the square of its speed (measured in meters per second) and inversely with the radius r (in meters) of the circular path. Suppose that David has a rope that is 3 meters long. On the end of the rope he has attached a pouch that holds a 0.5-kilogram stone. Suppose that David is able to spin the rope in a circular motion at the rate of 50 revolutions per minute.

(a) The spinning rate of 50 revolutions per minute can be converted to an *angular velocity* ω (lowercase Greek letter omega) using the formula $\omega = 2\pi \cdot$ revolutions per minute. Write

the spinning rate as an angular velocity rounded to two decimal places.

(b) Use the fact that $v = \omega r$, where r is the radius of the circle, to find the linear velocity (in meters per minute) of the stone if it were released. Now convert the linear velocity to meters per second.

(c) Suppose that the force on the rope required to keep the rock in a circular motion is 2.3 newtons. Use the result from part (b) to find the constant of proportionality k.

(d) David is fairly certain that he will require more force than this to beat Goliath in a battle, so he increases the circular motion to 80 revolutions per minute and increases the length of the rope to 4 meters. What is the force required to keep the stone in a circular motion?

42. Suppose that y is directly proportional to x^2. If x is doubled, what happens to the value of y?

CHAPTER 2 Activity: Shifting Discovery

Focus: Using graphing skills, discover the possible "rules" for graphing functions.

Time: 30–35 minutes

Group size: 4

Materials Needed: Graph paper (2–3 pieces)

Each member of the group needs to

1. Draw a coordinate plane and label the x-axis and y-axis.

2. By plotting points, graph the primary function: $f(x) = x^2$.

3. On the same coordinate plane, each group member graphs *one* of the following functions by plotting points. Be sure to graph the primary function and one of the functions (a)–(d) on the same coordinate plane.

(a) $f(x) = x^2 + 3$
(b) $f(x) = (x - 3)^2$
(c) $f(x) = x^2 - 3$
(d) $f(x) = (x + 3)^2$

As a group, discuss the following:

4. What shape are the graphs?

5. Each member of the group should share the difference between the graph of your primary function and the other function you chose.

6. As a group, can you develop rules for these differences?

With this possible rule in mind, each member of the group needs to

7. Draw a coordinate plane and label x-axis, y-axis, and -10 to 10 on each axis.

8. Graph the primary function by plotting points: $f(x) = |x|$.

9. On the same coordinate plane, each group member graphs *one* of the following functions by plotting points. Be sure to graph the primary function and one of the functions (a)–(d) on the same coordinate plane.

(a) $f(x) = |x| + 4$
(b) $f(x) = |x - 4|$
(c) $f(x) = |x| - 4$
(d) $f(x) = |x + 4|$

10. Did your rules developed in Problem 6 hold true? Discuss.

CHAPTER 2 Review

Section 2.1 Relations

KEY CONCEPT	KEY TERMS	
• **Relation** A correspondence between two variables x and y where y depends on x. Relations can be represented through maps, sets of ordered pairs, equations, or graphs.	Relation Corresponds Depends on Mapping	Inputs Outputs Domain Range

YOU SHOULD BE ABLE TO...	EXAMPLE	REVIEW EXERCISES
1 Understand relations (p. 148)	Example 1	1–4
2 Find the domain and the range of a relation (p. 149)	Examples 2 through 4	1–16
3 Graph a relation defined by an equation (p. 151)	Example 5	9–14

In Problems 1 and 2, write each relation as a set of ordered pairs. Then identify the domain and range of the relation.

1.

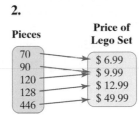

SOURCE: *U.S. Mint website*

2.

Pieces	Price of Lego Set
70	$ 6.99
90	$ 9.99
120	$ 12.99
128	$ 49.99
446	

SOURCE: *Lego website*

In Problems 3 and 4, write each relation as a map. Then identify the domain and the range of the relation.

3. $\{(2, 7), (-4, 8), (3, 5), (6, -1), (-2, -9)\}$

4. $\{(3, 1), (3, 7), (5, 1), (-2, 8), (1, 4)\}$

In Problems 5–8, identify the domain and range of the relation from the graph.

5.

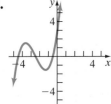

6.

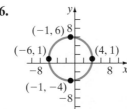

7.

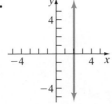

8.

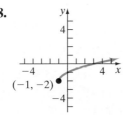

In Problems 9–14, graph the relation. Use the graph of the relation to identify the domain and the range of the relation.

9. $y = x + 2$ **10.** $2x + y = 3$ **11.** $y = -x^2 + 4$

12. $y = |x + 2| - 1$ **13.** $y = x^3 + 2$ **14.** $x = y^2 + 1$

15. Cell Phones A cellular phone company offers a plan for $40 per month for 3000 minutes with additional minutes costing $0.05 per minute. The graph below shows the monthly cost, in dollars, when x minutes are used.

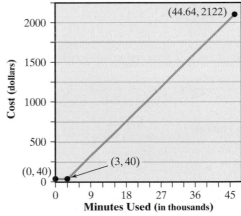

(a) What is the domain and the range of the relation?

(b) Explain why the domain obtained in part **(a)** is reasonable.

16. Vertical Motion The graph below shows the height, in feet, of a ball thrown straight up with an initial speed of 40 feet per second from an initial height of 96 feet after t seconds. What is the domain and the range of the relation?

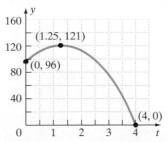

Section 2.2 An Introduction to Functions

KEY CONCEPTS	KEY TERMS
• **Functions** A special type of relation where any given input, x, corresponds to only one output y. Functions can be represented through maps, sets of ordered pairs, equations, or graphs. • **Vertical Line Test** A set of points in the xy-plane is the graph of a function if and only if every vertical line intersects the graph in at most one point.	Function Vertical Line Test Value of f at the number x Independent variable Dependent variable Argument Graph of the function

YOU SHOULD BE ABLE TO...	EXAMPLE	REVIEW EXERCISES
1 Determine whether a relation expressed as a map or ordered pairs represents a function (p. 154)	Examples 1 and 2	17, 18
2 Determine whether a relation expressed as an equation represents a function (p. 157)	Examples 3 and 4	19–22
3 Determine whether a relation expressed as a graph represents a function (p. 157)	Example 5	23–26
4 Find the value of a function (p. 158)	Examples 6 and 7	27–30
5 Work with applications of functions (p. 160)	Example 8	31, 32

In Problems 17 and 18, determine whether the given relation represents a function. State the domain and the range of each relation.

17. (a) $\{(-1, -2), (-1, 3), (5, 0), (7, 2), (9, 4)\}$

(b)

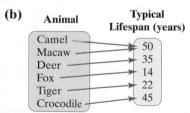

18. (a) $\{(-2, 4), (2, 3), (-3, -1), (5, 7), (4, 7)\}$

(b)

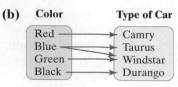

In Problems 19–22, determine whether each relation shows y as a function of x.

19. $3x - 5y = 18$

20. $x^2 + y^2 = 81$

21. $y = \pm 10x$

22. $y = x^2 - 14$

In Problems 23–26, determine whether the graph is that of a function.

23.
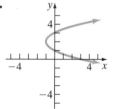

24.
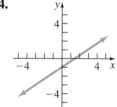

25.
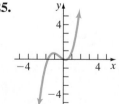

26.
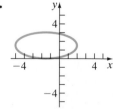

In Problems 27–30, find the indicated values for the given functions.

27. $f(x) = x^2 + 2x - 5$
   (a) $f(-2)$
   (b) $f(3)$

28. $g(z) = \dfrac{2z + 1}{z - 3}$
   (a) $g(0)$
   (b) $g(2)$

29. $F(x) = -2x + 7$

   (a) $F(5)$

   (b) $F(-x)$

30. $G(x) = 2x + 1$

   (a) $G(7)$

   (b) $G(x + h)$

31. Population Using census data from 1900 to 2006, the function $P(t) = 0.213t^2 - 18.474t + 597.372$ represents the population, P, of Orange County in Florida (in thousands) t years after 1900.

   (a) Identify the dependent and independent variables.

   (b) Evaluate $P(110)$ and explain what it represents.

   (c) Evaluate $P(-70)$ and explain what it represents. Is the result reasonable? Explain.

32. Education The function $P(a) = -0.0064a^2 + 0.6826a - 6.82$ represents the percent of the population a years of age with an advanced degree where $a \geq 25$. SOURCE: *Current Population Survey*

   (a) Identify the dependent and independent variables.

   (b) Evaluate $P(30)$ and explain what it represents.

Section 2.3 Functions and Their Graphs

KEY CONCEPTS	KEY TERM
• **Domain of a Function** When only an equation of a function is given, the domain of the function is the largest set of real numbers for which $f(x)$ is a real number. However, in applications, the domain of a function is the largest set of real numbers for which the output of the function is reasonable. • **Graph of a Function** The graph of a function, f, is the set of all ordered pairs $(x, f(x))$.	Domain of f

YOU SHOULD BE ABLE TO...	EXAMPLE	REVIEW EXERCISES
1 Find the domain of a function (p. 163)	Examples 1 and 2	33–36
2 Graph a function (p. 164)	Example 3	37–40
3 Obtain information from the graph of a function (p. 165)	Examples 4 through 7	41–45, 47, 48
4 Graph functions in the Library of Functions (p. 168)	pp. 168–169	46
5 Interpret graphs of functions (p. 170)	Example 8	49, 50

For Problems 33–36, find the domain of each function.

33. $f(x) = -\dfrac{3}{2}x + 5$

34. $g(w) = \dfrac{w - 9}{2w + 5}$

35. $h(t) = \dfrac{t + 2}{t - 5}$

36. $G(t) = 3t^2 + 4t - 9$

In Problems 37–40, graph each function.

37. $f(x) = 2x - 5$

38. $g(x) = x^2 - 3x + 2$

39. $h(x) = (x - 1)^3 - 3$

40. $f(x) = |x + 1| - 4$

For Problems 41–44, for each function whose graph is shown, find (a) the domain and the range, and (b) the intercepts, if any,

41.

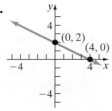

42.

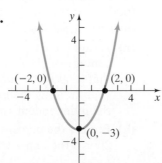

43.

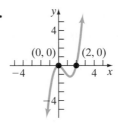

44.

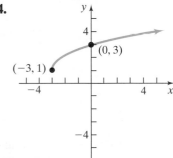

45. The graph of $y = f(x)$ is shown.

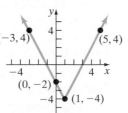

   (a) What is $f(-3)$?

   (b) For what value of x does $f(x) = -4$?

   (c) What are the zeros of f?

46. Graph each of the following functions.

   (a) $f(x) = x^2$

   (b) $f(x) = \sqrt{x}$

In Problems 47 and 48, answer the questions about the given function.

47. $h(x) = 2x - 7$

    (a) Is the point $(3, -1)$ on the graph of the function?

    (b) If $x = -2$, what is $h(x)$? What point is on the graph of the function?

    (c) If $h(x) = 4$, what is x? What point is on the graph of h?

48. $g(x) = \dfrac{3}{5}x + 4$

    (a) Is the point $(-5, 2)$ on the graph of the function?

    (b) If $x = 3$, what is $g(x)$? What point is on the graph of the function?

    (c) If $g(x) = -2$, what is x? What point is on the graph of g?

49. Travel by Train A Metrolink train leaves L.A. Union Station and travels 6 miles at a constant speed for 10 minutes, arriving at the Glendale station, where it waits 1 minute for passengers to board and depart. The train continues traveling at the same speed for 5 more minutes to reach downtown Burbank, which is 3 miles from Glendale. Sketch a graph that represents the distance of the train as a function of time until it reaches downtown Burbank.

50. Filling a Tub With the faucet running at a constant rate, it takes Angie 7 minutes to fill her bathtub. She turns off the faucet when the tub is full and realizes the water is too hot. She then opens the drain, letting water out at a constant rate that is half the rate of the faucet. After draining for 2 minutes, she stops the drain and turns on the faucet at the same rate as before (but at a cooler temperature) until the tub is full. Sketch a graph that represents the amount of water in the tub as a function of time.

Section 2.4 Linear Functions

KEY CONCEPT	KEY TERMS
• **Linear Function** A linear function is a function of the form $f(x) = mx + b$ where m is the slope and b is the y-intercept of the graph.	Linear function Line Scatter diagram

YOU SHOULD BE ABLE TO...	EXAMPLE	REVIEW EXERCISES
1 Graph linear functions (p. 175)	Example 1	51–54
2 Find the zero of a linear function (p. 177)	Example 2	51–54
3 Build linear models from verbal descriptions (p. 179)	Examples 4 and 5	57–60
4 Build linear models from data (p. 181)	Examples 6 through 8	61–64

In Problems 51–54, graph each linear function. Find the zero of each function.

51. $g(x) = 2x - 6$

52. $H(x) = -\dfrac{4}{3}x + 5$

53. $F(x) = -x - 3$

54. $f(x) = \dfrac{3}{4}x - 3$

55. Long Distance A phone company offers a plan for long-distance calls that charges $5.00 per month plus 7¢ per minute. The monthly long-distance cost C for talking x minutes is given by the linear function $C(x) = 0.07x + 5$.

    (a) What is the implied domain of this linear function?

    (b) What is the cost if a person made 235 minutes worth of long-distance calls during one month?

    (c) Graph the linear function.

    (d) In one month, how many minutes of long-distance can be purchased for $75?

56. Straight-Line Depreciation Using straight-line depreciation, the value V of a particular computer x years after purchase is given by the linear function $V(x) = 1800 - 360x$ for $0 \le x \le 5$.

    (a) What are the independent and dependent variables?

    (b) What is the domain of this linear function?

    (c) What is the initial value of the computer?

    (d) What is the value of the computer 2 years after purchase?

    (e) Graph the linear function over its domain.

    (f) After how long will the value of the computer be $0?

57. Federal Tax Returns In 1996, approximately 12.6% of U.S. federal tax returns were filed electronically. In 2005, approximately 30.1% were filed electronically.

(SOURCE: *Internal Revenue Service*)

    (a) Assuming a linear relation between year and percentage of electronic filings, find a linear function that relates the percentage of electronic filings to year, treating the number of years since 1996 as the independent variable, x.

    (b) Predict the percentage of electronic filings in 2008 if the linear trend continues.

(c) Interpret the slope.

(d) Assuming the linear trend continues, in what year will the percentage of electronic returns be 47.52%?

58. Heart Rates According to the American Geriatric Society, the maximum recommended heart rate for a 20-year-old man under stress is 200 beats per minute. The maximum recommended heart rate for a 60-year-old man under stress is 160 beats per minute.

(a) Find a linear function that relates the maximum recommended heart rate for men to age.

(b) Predict the maximum recommended heart rate for a 45-year-old man under stress.

(c) Interpret the slope.

(d) For what age would the maximum recommended heart rate under stress be 168 beats per minute?

59. Car Rental The daily rental charge for a particular car is $35 plus $0.12 per mile.

(a) Find a linear function that expresses the rental cost C as a function of the miles driven m.

(b) What are the independent and dependent variables?

(c) What is the implied domain of this linear function?

(d) For a one-day rental, what is the rental cost if 124 miles are driven?

(e) For a one-day rental, how many miles were driven if the rental cost was $67.16?

(f) Graph the linear function.

60. Satellite Television Bill A satellite television company charges $33.99 per month for a 100-channel package, plus $3.50 for each pay-per-view movie watched that month.

(a) Find a linear function that expresses the monthly bill B as a function of x, the number of pay-per-view movies watched that month.

(b) What are the independent and dependent variables?

(c) What is the implied domain of this linear function?

(d) What is the monthly bill if 5 pay-per-view movies are watched that month?

(e) For one month, how many pay-per-view movies were watched if the bill was $58.49?

(f) Graph the linear function.

In Problems 61 and 62,

(a) *Draw a scatter diagram of the data.*

(b) *Select two points from the scatter diagram and find the equation of the line containing the points selected.* *

(c) *Graph the line found in part (b) on the scatter diagram.*

*Answers will vary.

61.

x	2	5	8	11	14
y	13.3	11.6	8.4	7.2	4.6

62.

x	0	0.4	1.5	2.3	4.2
y	0.6	1.1	1.3	1.8	3.0

63. The table below gives the number of calories and the total carbohydrates (in grams) for a one-cup serving of seven name-brand cereals (not including milk).

Cereal	Calories, x	Total Carbohydrates (in grams), y
Rice Krispies®	96	23.2
Life®	160	33.3
Lucky Charms®	120	25.0
Kellogg's Complete®	120	30.7
Wheaties®	110	24.0
Cheerios®	110	22.0
Honey Nut Chex®	160	34.7

SOURCE: *Quaker Oats, General Mills, and Kellogg*

(a) Draw a scatter diagram of the data treating calories as the independent variable.

(b) What type of relation appears to exist between calories and total carbohydrates in a one-cup serving of cereal?

(c) Select two points and find an equation of the line containing the points.*

(d) Graph the line on the scatter diagram drawn in part (a).

(e) Predict the total carbohydrates in a one-cup serving of cereal that has 140 calories.

(f) Interpret the slope of the line found in part (c).

64. Second-Day Delivery Costs The table below lists some selected prices charged by Federal Express for FedEx 2Day delivery, depending on the weight of the package.

Weight (in pounds), x	FedEx 2Day® Delivery Charge, y
1	$15.88
3	$18.60
6	$26.19
8	$31.17
9	$33.42
11	$38.10

SOURCE: *Federal Express Corporation*

(a) Draw a scatter diagram of the data treating weight as the independent variable.

(b) What type of relation appears to exist between the weight of the package and the FedEx 2Day delivery charge?

(c) Select two points and find an equation of the line containing the points.*

(d) Graph the line on the scatter diagram drawn in part **(a).**

(e) Predict the FedEx 2Day delivery charge for shipping a 5-pound package.

(f) Interpret the slope of the line found in part **(c).**

*Answers will vary.

Section 2.5 Compound Inequalities		
KEY CONCEPT		**KEY TERMS**
• If $a < b$, then we can write $a < x$ and $x < b$ as $a < x < b$.	Intersection Union	Compound inequality Solve a compound inequality

YOU SHOULD BE ABLE TO...	EXAMPLE	REVIEW EXERCISES
1 Determine the intersection or union of two sets (p. 190)	Examples 1 and 2	65–70
2 Solve compound inequalities involving "and" (p. 192)	Examples 3 through 6	71, 72, 75, 76, 80
3 Solve compound inequalities involving "or" (p. 195)	Examples 7 and 8	73, 74, 77, 78, 79
4 Solve problems using compound inequalities (p. 196)	Example 9	81, 82

In Problems 65–68, use $A = \{2, 4, 6, 8\}$,
$B = \{-1, 0, 1, 2, 3, 4\}$, *and* $C = \{1, 2, 3, 4\}$ *to find each set.*

65. $A \cup B$ **66.** $A \cap C$

67. $B \cap C$ **68.** $A \cup C$

In Problems 69 and 70, use the graph of the inequality to find each set.

69. $A = \{x | x \le 4\}$; $B = \{x | x > 2\}$. Find **(a)** $A \cap B$ and **(b)** $A \cup B$.

70. $E = \{x | x \ge 3\}$; $F = \{x | x < -2\}$. Find **(a)** $E \cap F$ and **(b)** $E \cup F$.

In Problems 71–80, solve each compound inequality. Graph the solution set.

71. $x < 4$ and $x + 3 > 2$

72. $3 < 2 - x < 7$

73. $x + 3 < 1$ or $x > 2$

74. $x + 6 \ge 10$ or $x \le 0$

75. $3x + 2 \le 5$ and $-4x + 2 \le -10$

76. $1 \le 2x + 5 < 13$

77. $x - 3 \le -5$ or $2x + 1 > 7$

78. $3x + 4 > -2$ or $4 - 2x \ge -6$

79. $\frac{1}{3}x > 2$ or $\frac{2}{5}x < -4$

80. $x + \frac{3}{2} \ge 0$ and $-2x + \frac{3}{2} > \frac{1}{4}$

81. Heart Rates The normal heart rate for healthy adults between the ages of 21 and 60 should be between 70 and 75 beats per minute (inclusive). If we let x represent the heart rate of an adult between the ages of 21 and 60, express the normal range of values using a compound inequality.

82. Heating Bills For usage above 300 kilowatt hours, the non–space heat winter energy charge for Illinois Power residential service was $23.12 plus $0.05947 per kilowatt hour over 300. During one winter, a customer's charge ranged from a low of $50.28 to a high of $121.43. Over what range of values did electric usage vary (in kilowatt hours)? Express answers rounded to the nearest tenth of a kilowatt.

Section 2.6 Absolute Value Equations and Inequalities

KEY CONCEPTS

- **Equations Involving Absolute Value**
  If a is a positive real number and if u is any algebraic expression, then $|u| = a$ is equivalent to $u = a$ or $u = -a$.

- **Equations Involving Two Absolute Values**
  If u and v are any algebraic expression, then $|u| = |v|$ is equivalent to $u = v$ or $u = -v$.

- **Inequalities of the Form $<$ or $\leq$ Involving Absolute Value**
  If a is a positive real number and if u is any algebraic expression, then $|u| < a$ is equivalent to $-a < u < a$ and $|u| \leq a$ is equivalent to $-a \leq u \leq a$.

- **Inequalities of the Form $>$ or $\geq$ Involving Absolute Value**
  If a is a positive real number and if u is any algebraic expression, then $|u| > a$ is equivalent to $u < -a$ or $u > a$ and $|u| \geq a$ is equivalent to $u \leq -a$ or $u \geq a$.

YOU SHOULD BE ABLE TO...	EXAMPLE	REVIEW EXERCISES
1 Solve absolute value equations (p. 200)	Examples 1 through 4	83–88
2 Solve absolute value inequalities involving $<$ or $\leq$ (p. 203)	Examples 5 through 7	89, 91, 94, 95
3 Solve absolute value inequalities involving $>$ or $\geq$ (p. 205)	Examples 8 and 9	90, 92, 93, 96
4 Solve applied problems involving absolute value inequalities (p. 207)	Example 10	97, 98

In Problems 83–88, solve the absolute value equation.

83. $|x| = 4$

84. $|3x - 5| = 4$

85. $|-y + 4| = 9$

86. $-3|x + 2| - 5 = -8$

87. $|2w - 7| = -3$

88. $|x + 3| = |3x - 1|$

In Problems 89–96, solve each absolute value inequality. Graph the solution set on a real number line.

89. $|x| < 2$

90. $|x| \geq \dfrac{7}{2}$

91. $|x + 2| \leq 3$

92. $|4x - 3| \geq 1$

93. $3|x| + 6 \geq 1$

94. $|7x + 5| + 4 < 3$

95. $|(x - 3) - 2| \leq 0.01$

96. $\left|\dfrac{2x - 3}{4}\right| > 1$

97. Tolerance The diameter of a certain ball bearing is required to be 0.503 inches. The tolerance on the bearing is 0.001 inches. If x represents the diameter of a bearing, the acceptable diameters of the bearing can be expressed as $|x - 0.503| \leq 0.001$. Determine the acceptable diameters of the bearing.

98. Tensile Strength The tensile strength of paper used to make grocery bags is about 40 lb/in.^{2} A paper grocery bag whose tensile strength satisfies the inequality $\left|\dfrac{x - 40}{2}\right| > 1.96$ has an unusual tensile strength. Determine the tensile strengths that would be considered unusual.

Section 2.7 Variation

YOU SHOULD BE ABLE TO...	EXAMPLE	REVIEW EXERCISES
1 Model and solve problems involving direct variation (p. 211)	Examples 1 and 2	99, 100, 105, 106
2 Model and solve problems involving inverse variation (p. 213)	Example 3	101, 103, 107, 108
3 Model and solve problems involving joint or combined variation (p. 214)	Examples 4 and 5	102, 104, 109, 110

In Problems 99–104, (a) find the constant of proportionality k, (b) write the function relating the variables, and (c) find the quantity indicated.

99. Suppose that y varies directly with x. If $y = 30$ when $x = 6$, find y when $x = 10$.

100. Suppose that y varies directly with x. If $y = 18$ when $x = -3$, find y when $x = 8$.

101. Suppose that y varies inversely with x. If $y = 15$ when $x = 4$, find y when $x = 5$.

102. Suppose that y varies jointly with x and z. If $y = 45$ when $x = 6$ and $z = 10$, find y when $x = 8$ and $z = 7$.

103. Suppose that s varies inversely with the square of t. If $s = 18$ when $t = 2$, find s when $t = 3$.

104. Suppose that w varies directly with x and inversely with z. If $w = \dfrac{4}{3}$ when $x = 10$ and $z = 12$, find w when $x = 9$ and $z = 16$.

105. Snow-Water Equivalent The amount of water in snow is directly proportional to the depth of the snow. Suppose the amount of water in 40 inches of snow is 4.8 inches. How much water is contained in 50 inches of snow?

106. Car Payments Roberta is buying a car. The monthly payment p for the car varies directly with the amount borrowed b. Suppose the dealership tells her that if she borrows $15,000, her payment will be $293.49. What would be Roberta's payment if she borrows $18,000?

107. Radio Signals The frequency of a radio signal varies inversely with the wavelength. A signal of 800 kilohertz has a wavelength of 375 meters. What frequency has a signal of wavelength 250 meters?

108. Ohm's Law The electrical current flowing through a wire varies inversely with the resistance of the wire. If the current is 8 amperes when the resistance is 15 ohms, for what resistance will the current be 10 amperes?

109. Volume of a Cylinder The volume V of a right circular cylinder varies jointly with the height h and the square of the diameter d. If the volume of a cylinder is 231 cubic centimeters when the diameter is 7 centimeters and the height is 6 centimeters, find the volume when the diameter is 8 centimeters and the height is 14 centimeters.

110. Volume of a Pyramid The volume V of a pyramid varies jointly with the base area B and the height h. If the volume of a pyramid is 270 cubic inches when the base area is 81 square inches and the height is 10 inches, find the volume of a pyramid with base area 125 square inches and height 9 inches.

CHAPTER 2 TEST

Remember to use your Chapter Test Prep Video CD to see fully worked-out solutions to any of these problems you would like to review.

1. Write the relation as a map. Then identify the domain and the range of the relation.

$$\{(2, 8), (5, -2), (7, 12), (-4, -7), (7, 3), (5, -1)\}$$

2. Identify the domain and range of the relation from the graph.

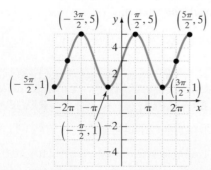

3. Graph the relation $y = x^2 - 3$ by plotting points. Use the graph of the relation to identify the domain and range.

In Problems 4 and 5, determine whether the relations represent functions. Identify the domain and the range of each relation.

4.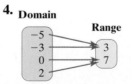

5.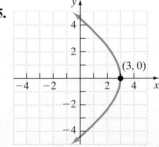

6. Does the equation $y = \pm 5x$ represent a function? Why or why not?

7. For $f(x) = -3x + 11$, find $f(x + h)$.

8. For $g(x) = 2x^2 + x - 1$, find the indicated values.
   (a) $g(-2)$ **(b)** $g(0)$ **(c)** $g(3)$

9. Sketch the graph of $f(x) = x^2 + 3$.

10. Using data from 1989 to 2006, the function $P(x) = 0.16x + 3.63$ approximates the average movie ticket price (in dollars) x years after 1989. (SOURCE: *National Association of Theater Owners*)

   (a) Identify the dependent and independent variables.

   (b) Evaluate $P(20)$ and explain what it represents.

   (c) In what year will the average movie ticket be $7.63?

11. Find the domain of $f(x) = \dfrac{-15}{x + 2}$.

12. $h(x) = -5x + 12$

   (a) Is the point $(2, 2)$ on the graph of the function?

   (b) If $x = 3$, what is $h(x)$? What point is on the graph of the function?

   (c) If $h(x) = 27$, what is x? What point is on the graph of h?

   (d) What is the zero of h?

13. The following graph represents the speed of a car as a function of time.

   (a) When does the car stop accelerating?

   (b) For how long does the car maintain a constant speed?

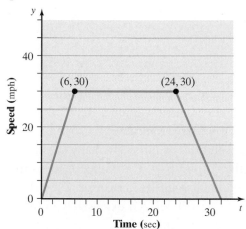

14. Crafts Fair Sales Henry plans to sell small wooden shelves at a crafts fair for $30 each. A booth at the fair costs $100 to rent. Henry estimates his expenses for producing the shelves to be $12 each, so his profit will be $18 per shelf.

   (a) Write a function that expresses Henry's profit P as a function of the number of shelves x sold.

   (b) What is the implied domain of this linear function?

   (c) What is the profit if Henry sells 34 shelves?

   (d) Graph the linear function.

   (e) If Henry's profit is $764, how many shelves did he sell?

15. Shetland Pony Weights The table below lists the average weight of a Shetland pony, depending on the age of the pony.

Age (months), x	Average Weight (kilograms), y
3	60
6	95
12	140
18	170
24	185

SOURCE: *The Merck Veterinary Manual*

   (a) Draw a scatter diagram of the data treating age as the independent variable.

   (b) What type of relation appears to exist between the age and the weight of the Shetland pony?

   (c) Select two points and find an equation of the line containing the points.*

   (d) Graph the line on the scatter diagram drawn in part **(a)**.

   (e) Predict the weight of a 9-month-old Shetland pony.

   (f) Interpret the slope of the line found in part **(c)**.

16. Solve: $|2x + 5| - 3 = 0$

In Problems 17–20, solve each inequality and graph the solution set on a real number line.

17. $x + 2 < 8$ and $2x + 5 > 1$

18. $x > 4$ or $2(x - 1) + 3 < -2$

19. $2|x - 5| + 1 < 7$

20. $|-2x + 1| > 5$

21. Using a Lever Using a lever, the force F required to lift a weight is inversely proportional to the length l of the force arm of the lever (assuming all other factors are constant). If a force of 50 pounds is required to lift a granite boulder when the force arm length is 4 feet, how much force will be required to lift the boulder if the force arm length is 10 feet?

22. Lateral Surface Area of a Cylinder The lateral surface area L of a right circular cylinder varies jointly with its radius r and height h. If the lateral surface area of a cylinder with radius 7 centimeters and height 12 centimeters is 528 square centimeters, what would be the lateral surface area if the radius is 9 centimeters and the height is 14 centimeters?

---

*Answers will vary.

3 Systems of Linear Equations and Inequalities

Why does it take longer to fly west than east? The answer is the jet stream. But what impact does the jet stream have on flight time? Is it the same for all airplanes? See Example 7 in Section 3.2 and Quick Check Problem 7 on page 250.

OUTLINE

The Big Picture: Putting It Together

In the first part of Chapter 1, we solved linear equations and inequalities in one variable. Recall that linear equations in one variable can have no solution (a contradiction), one solution, or infinitely many solutions (an identity). In the second part of Chapter 1, we graphed linear equations and inequalities in two variables. The graph of a linear equation will be used extensively in this chapter to help us visualize results.

In this chapter, we will discuss solving two or more linear equations involving two or more variables (called *systems of equations*). We are going to learn a variety of techniques that can be used to solve these systems. We also will learn that these systems can have no solution, one solution, or infinitely many solutions, just like linear equations in one variable. We conclude the chapter by looking at systems of linear inequalities. These systems require us to determine the region of a Cartesian plane that satisfies two or more linear inequalities simultaneously.

3.1 Systems of Linear Equations in Two Variables

OBJECTIVES

1. Determine Whether an Ordered Pair Is a Solution to a System of Linear Equations
2. Solve a System of Two Linear Equations Containing Two Unknowns by Graphing
3. Solve a System of Two Linear Equations Containing Two Unknowns by Substitution
4. Solve a System of Two Linear Equations Containing Two Unknowns by Elimination
5. Identify Inconsistent Systems
6. Express the Solution of a System of Dependent Equations

Preparing for Systems of Linear Equations in Two Variables

Before getting started, take the following readiness quiz. If you get a problem wrong, go back to the section cited and review the material.

P1. Evaluate $2x - 3y$ for $x = 5$, $y = 4$.   [Section R.5, pp. 40–41]

P2. Determine whether the point $(4, -1)$ is on the graph of the equation $2x - 3y = 11$.   [Section 1.5, pp. 95–96]

P3. Graph: $y = 3x - 7$ [Section 1.6, p. 116]

P4. Find the equation of the line parallel to $y = -3x + 1$ containing the point $(2, 3)$.   [Section 1.7, p. 123]

P5. Determine the slope and y-intercept of $4x - 3y = 15$.   [Section 1.6, pp. 115–116]

P6. What is the additive inverse of 4?   [Section R.3, p. 21]

P7. Solve: $2x - 3(-3x + 1) = -36$ [Section 1.1, pp. 49–52]

Recall, from Section 1.6, that an equation in two variables is linear provided that it can be written in the form $Ax + By = C$, where A, B, and C are real numbers and A and B are not both zero. However, linear equations can have more than two variables. Some examples of linear equations are

Linear equation in two variables, x and y	Linear equation in three variables, x, y, and z	Linear equation in four variables, w, x, y, and z
$4x - 3y = 9$	$-2x + y - 5z = -3$	$3w - x + 5y - 2z = 12$

A **system of linear equations** is a grouping of two or more linear equations, each of which contains one or more variables.

EXAMPLE 1   Examples of Systems of Linear Equations

(a) $\begin{cases} 2x + y = 5 \\ x - 5y = -10 \end{cases}$ Two equations containing two variables, x and y

(b) $\begin{cases} x + 3y + z = 8 \\ 3x - y + 6z = 12 \\ -4x - y + 2z = -1 \end{cases}$ Three equations containing three variables, x, y, and z ∎

We use a brace, as shown in the systems in Example 1, to remind us that we are dealing with a *system* of equations. In this section, we concentrate on systems of two linear equations containing two variables such as the system in Example 1(a).

1   Determine Whether an Ordered Pair Is a Solution to a System of Linear Equations

A **solution** of a system of equations consists of values for the variables that are solutions of each equation of the system. When we are solving systems of two linear equations containing two unknowns, we represent the solution as an ordered pair, (x, y).

EXAMPLE 2   Determining Whether Values Are a Solution to a System of Linear Equations

Determine whether the given ordered pairs are solutions to the system of equations.

$$\begin{cases} 2x + 3y = 9 \\ -5x - 3y = 0 \end{cases}$$

(a) $(6, -1)$ **(b)** $(-3, 5)$

Preparing for...Answers   **P1.** -2
P2. Yes

P3.

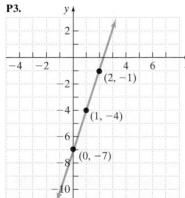

P4. $y = -3x + 9$ **P5.** slope $= 4/3$; y-intercept $= -5$ **P6.** -4 **P7.** $\{-3\}$

Solution

To help us organize our thoughts, we name $2x + 3y = 9$ equation (1) and $-5x - 3y = 0$ equation (2).

$$\begin{cases} 2x + 3y = 9 & (1) \\ -5x - 3y = 0 & (2) \end{cases}$$

(a) Let $x = 6$ and $y = -1$ in both equations (1) and (2). If both equations are true, then $(6, -1)$ is a solution.

Equation (1): $2x + 3y = 9$ Equation (2): $-5x - 3y = 0$

$x = 6, y = -1$: $2(6) + 3(-1) \stackrel{?}{=} 9$ $x = 6, y = -1$: $-5(6) - 3(-1) \stackrel{?}{=} 0$

$12 - 3 \stackrel{?}{=} 9$ $-30 + 3 \stackrel{?}{=} 0$

$9 = 9$ True $-27 = 0$ False

> **Work Smart**
>
> A solution to a system must satisfy all of the equations in the system.

Although $x = 6$, $y = -1$ satisfy equation (1), they do not satisfy equation (2); therefore, $(6, -1)$ is not a solution of the system of equations.

(b) Let $x = -3$ and $y = 5$ in both equations (1) and (2). If both equations are true, then $(-3, 5)$ is a solution.

Equation (1): $2x + 3y = 9$ Equation (2): $-5x - 3y = 0$

$x = -3, y = 5$: $2(-3) + 3(5) \stackrel{?}{=} 9$ $x = -3, y = 5$: $-5(-3) - 3(5) \stackrel{?}{=} 0$

$-6 + 15 \stackrel{?}{=} 9$ $15 - 15 \stackrel{?}{=} 0$

$9 = 9$ True $0 = 0$ True

> **Work Smart**
>
> It is a good idea to number the equations in a system so that it is easier to keep track of your work.

Because $x = -3$, $y = 5$ satisfy both equations (1) and (2), the ordered pair $(-3, 5)$ is a solution of the system of equations. ■

For the remainder of the chapter, we shall number each equation as we did in Example 1. When solving homework problems, you should do the same.

Quick ✔

1. A _____ is a grouping of two or more linear equations, each of which contains one or more variables.

2. Which of the following points is a solution to the system of equations?

$$\begin{cases} 2x + 3y = 7 \\ 3x + y = -7 \end{cases}$$

  (a) $(2, 1)$ **(b)** $(-4, 5)$ **(c)** $(-2, -1)$

Visualizing the Solutions in a System of Two Linear Equations Containing Two Unknowns

We can view the problem of solving a system of two linear equations containing two variables as a geometry problem. The graph of each equation in the system is a line. So, a system of two equations containing two variables represents a pair of lines. The graphs of the two lines can appear in one of three ways:

1. **INTERSECT:** If the lines intersect, then the system of equations has one solution given by the point of intersection. The system is **consistent** and the equations are **independent.** See Figure 1(a).

2. **PARALLEL:** If the lines are parallel, then the system of equations has no solution because the lines never intersect. The system is **inconsistent.** See Figure 1(b).

3. **COINCIDENT:** If the lines lie on top of each other (are coincident), then the system of equations has infinitely many solutions. The solution set is the set of all points on the line. The system is **consistent** and the equations are **dependent.** See Figure 1(c).

Figure 1

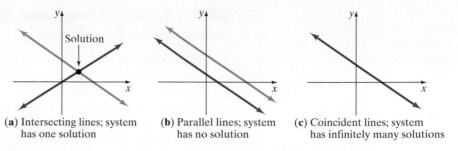

(**a**) Intersecting lines; system has one solution

(**b**) Parallel lines; system has no solution

(**c**) Coincident lines; system has infinitely many solutions

Quick ✔

3. If a system of equations has no solution, it is said to be _____.

4. If a system of equations has infinitely many solutions, the system is said to be _____ and the equations are _____.

5. *True or False:* A system of two linear equations containing two variables always has at least one solution.

6. *True or False:* When the lines in a system of equations are parallel, then the system is inconsistent and has no solution.

For now, we will concentrate on solving systems for which there is a single solution.

2 Solve a System of Two Linear Equations Containing Two Unknowns by Graphing

Let's look at an example where we use graphing to solve a system. Remember, the ordered pair of the point of intersection of the two graphs represents the solution to the system.

EXAMPLE 3 Solving a System of Two Linear Equations Using Graphing

Solve the following system by graphing: $\begin{cases} x + y = -1 \\ -2x + y = -7 \end{cases}$

Solution

First, we name $x + y = -1$ equation (1) and $-2x + y = -7$ equation (2).

$$\begin{cases} x + y = -1 & (1) \\ -2x + y = -7 & (2) \end{cases}$$

Figure 2

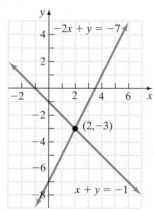

In order to graph each equation, we put them in slope-intercept form. Equation (1) in slope-intercept form is $y = -x - 1$, which has slope -1 and y-intercept -1. Equation (2) in slope-intercept form is $y = 2x - 7$, which has slope 2 and y-intercept -7. Figure 2 shows their graphs. (Note that we could also have graphed the lines using the intercepts.) The lines appear to intersect at $(2,-3)$, so we believe that the ordered pair $(2,-3)$ is the solution to the system.

Check Let $x = 2$ and $y = -3$ in both equations in the system:

Equation (1): $x + y = -1$ Equation (2): $-2x + y = -7$

$x = 2, y = -3$: $2 + (-3) \overset{?}{=} -1$ $x = 2, y = -3$: $-2(2) + (-3) \overset{?}{=} -7$

$\qquad\qquad\qquad 2 - 3 \overset{?}{=} -1$ $\qquad\qquad\qquad\qquad -4 - 3 \overset{?}{=} -7$

$\qquad\qquad\qquad\quad -1 = -1$ True $\qquad\qquad\qquad\qquad\quad -7 = -7$ True

Both equations are true, so the solution is the ordered pair $(2, -3)$. ∎

Quick ✔ *In Problems 7 and 8, solve the system by graphing.*

7. $\begin{cases} y = -3x + 10 \\ y = \quad 2x - 5 \end{cases}$

8. $\begin{cases} 2x + \quad y = -1 \\ -2x + 2y = 10 \end{cases}$

Work Smart

Obtaining exact solutions using graphical methods can be difficult. Therefore, algebraic methods should be used.

3 Solve a System of Two Linear Equations Containing Two Unknowns by Substitution

If the x- and y-coordinates of the point of intersection between two lines are not integers, then obtaining an exact result graphically can be difficult. Therefore, rather than using graphical methods to obtain solutions to systems of two linear equations, we prefer to use algebraic methods. The first algebraic method that we present is the *method of substitution*. The goal of the method of substitution is to obtain a single linear equation involving a single unknown.

Let's look at an example that illustrates how to solve a system of equations using substitution.

EXAMPLE 4 How to Solve a System of Two Equations Containing Two Unknowns by Substitution

Solve the following system by substitution: $\begin{cases} 3x + y = -9 & (1) \\ -2x + 3y = 17 & (2) \end{cases}$

Step-by-Step Solution

Step 1: Solve one of the equations for one of the unknowns.	It is easiest to solve equation (1) for y since the coefficient of y is 1. Subtract $3x$ from both sides:	$3x + y = -9$ $y = -3x - 9$
Step 2: Substitute $-3x - 9$ for y in equation (2).	Equation (2):	$-2x + 3y = 17$ $-2x + 3(-3x - 9) = 17$
Step 3: Solve the equation for x.	Distribute the 3: Combine like terms: Add 27 to both sides: Divide both sides by -11:	$-2x - 9x - 27 = 17$ $-11x - 27 = 17$ $-11x = 44$ $x = -4$
Step 4: We substitute -4 for x in the equation from Step 1.		$y = -3x + 9$ $y = -3(-4) - 9$ $y = 12 - 9$ $y = 3$
Step 5: Check: We check our answer that $x = -4$ and $y = 3$.	Equation (1): $\quad 3x + y = -9$ $x = -4, y = 3:\quad 3(-4) + 3 \overset{?}{=} -9$ $-12 + 3 \overset{?}{=} -9$ $-9 = -9$ True	Equation (2): $\quad -2x + 3y = 17$ $-2(-4) + 3(3) \overset{?}{=} 17$ $8 + 9 \overset{?}{=} 17$ $17 = 17$ True

Both equations are satisfied so the solution is the ordered pair $(-4, 3)$. ∎

Work Smart

When using substitution solve for the variable whose coefficient is 1 or -1 in order to simplify the algebra.

STEPS FOR SOLVING A SYSTEM OF TWO LINEAR EQUATIONS CONTAINING TWO UNKNOWNS BY SUBSTITUTION

Step 1: Solve one of the equations for one of the unknowns. For example, we might solve equation (1) for y in terms of x. Choose the equation that is easiest to solve for a variable. Typically, this would be an equation that has a variable whose coefficient is 1 or -1.

Step 2: Substitute the expression that equals the variable solved for in Step 1 into the other equation. The result will be a single linear equation in one unknown. For example, if we solved equation (1) for y in terms of x in Step 1, then we would replace y in equation (2) with the algebraic expression in x.

Step 3: Solve the linear equation in one unknown found in Step 2.

Step 4: Substitute the value of the variable into the expression found in Step 1 to find the value of the other variable.

Step 5: Check your answer.

EXAMPLE 5 Solving a System of Two Equations Containing Two Unknowns by Substitution

Solve the following system by substitution: $\begin{cases} 2x - 3y = -6 & (1) \\ -8x + 3y = 3 & (2) \end{cases}$

Solution

We choose to solve equation (1) for x because it seems easiest.

$$\text{Equation (1):} \quad 2x - 3y = -6$$
$$\text{Add } 3y \text{ to both sides:} \quad 2x = 3y - 6$$
$$\text{Divide both sides by 2:} \quad x = \frac{3y - 6}{2}$$
$$\text{Divide 2 into both terms in the numerator:} \quad x = \frac{3}{2}y - 3$$

Work Smart

Notice how we use substitution to reduce a system of two linear equations involving two unknowns down to one linear equation involving one unknown. Again, we use algebraic techniques to reduce a problem down to one we already know how to solve!

Now substitute $\frac{3}{2}y - 3$ for x in equation (2) and then solve for y.

$$\text{Equation (2):} \quad -8x + 3y = 3$$
$$-8\left(\frac{3}{2}y - 3\right) + 3y = 3$$
$$\text{Distribute the } -8: \quad -8 \cdot \frac{3}{2}y - (-8) \cdot 3 + 3y = 3$$
$$\text{Multiply:} \quad -12y + 24 + 3y = 3$$
$$\text{Combine like terms:} \quad -9y + 24 = 3$$
$$\text{Subtract 24 from both sides:} \quad -9y = -21$$
$$\text{Divide both sides by } -9: \quad y = \frac{-21}{-9}$$
$$y = \frac{7}{3}$$

Now we substitute $\frac{7}{3}$ for y into $x = \frac{3}{2}y - 3$ to find the value of x.

$$x = \frac{3}{2}\left(\frac{7}{3}\right) - 3$$
$$\text{Multiply:} \quad x = \frac{7}{2} - 3$$
$$x = \frac{1}{2}$$

Check We check our answer that $x = \frac{1}{2}$ and $y = \frac{7}{3}$.

Equation (1):	$2x - 3y = -6$	Equation (2):	$-8x + 3y = 3$
$x = \frac{1}{2}, y = \frac{7}{3}$:	$2\left(\frac{1}{2}\right) - 3\left(\frac{7}{3}\right) \overset{?}{=} -6$		$-8\left(\frac{1}{2}\right) + 3\left(\frac{7}{3}\right) \overset{?}{=} 3$
	$1 - 7 \overset{?}{=} -6$		$-4 + 7 \overset{?}{=} 3$
	$-6 = -6$ True		$3 = 3$ True

Both equations are satisfied so the solution is the ordered pair $\left(\frac{1}{2}, \frac{7}{3}\right)$. ∎

Quick ✔ *In Problems 9 and 10, solve the system using substitution.*

9. $\begin{cases} y = -3x - 5 \\ 5x + 3y = 1 \end{cases}$

10. $\begin{cases} 2x + y = -2 \\ -3x - 2y = -2 \end{cases}$

Work Smart

Substitution is a method to use if one of the variables has a coefficient of 1 or if one of the variables is already solved for; otherwise use elimination.

⎡4⎤ Solve a System of Two Linear Equations Containing Two Unknowns by Elimination

Using substitution to solve the system in Example 5 led to some rather complicated equations containing fractions. A second algebraic method for solving a system of linear equations is the *method of elimination*. This method is usually preferred over the method of substitution if substitution leads to fractions.

The basic idea in using elimination is to get the coefficients of one of the variables to be additive inverses, such as 5 and −5, so that we can add the equations together and get a single linear equation involving one unknown. Remember that this is the same goal we had when using the method of substitution.

Let's go over an example to illustrate how to solve a system of linear equations by elimination.

EXAMPLE 6 How to Solve a System of Linear Equations by Elimination

Solve: $\begin{cases} 5x + 2y = -5 & (1) \\ -2x - 4y = -14 & (2) \end{cases}$

Step-by-Step Solution

Step 1: Our first goal is to get the coefficients on one of the variables to be additive inverses.

In looking at this system, we can make the coefficients of y to be additive inverses by multiplying equation (1) by 2.

$$\begin{cases} 5x + 2y = -5 & (1) \\ -2x - 4y = -14 & (2) \end{cases}$$

Multiply both sides of (1) by 2:

$$\begin{cases} 2(5x + 2y) = 2(-5) & (1) \\ -2x - 4y = -14 & (2) \end{cases}$$

Use the Distributive Property:

$$\begin{cases} 10x + 4y = -10 & (1) \\ -2x - 4y = -14 & (2) \end{cases}$$

Step 2: We now add equations (1) and (2) to eliminate the variable y and then solve for x.

$$\begin{cases} 10x + 4y = -10 & (1) \\ -2x - 4y = -14 & (2) \end{cases}$$

Add (1) and (2): $\quad 8x = -24$

Divide both sides by 8: $\quad x = -3$

Step 3: Substitute −3 for x into either equation (1) or (2) and solve for y. We will back-substitute −3 for x into equation (1).

Equation (1): $\quad 5x + 2y = -5$

$x = -3$: $\quad 5(-3) + 2y = -5$

$-15 + 2y = -5$

Add 15 to both sides: $\quad 2y = 10$

Divide both sides by 2: $\quad y = 5$

We have that $x = -3$ and $y = 5$.

Step 4: Check

Equation (1): $\quad 5x + 2y = -5$

$x = -3, y = 5$: $\quad 5(-3) + 2(5) \overset{?}{=} -5$

$-15 + 10 \overset{?}{=} -5$

$-5 = -5$ True

Equation (2): $\quad -2x - 4y = -14$

$-2(-3) - 4(5) \overset{?}{=} -14$

$6 - 20 \overset{?}{=} -14$

$-14 = -14$ True

The solution is the ordered pair $(-3, 5)$. ∎

The following steps can be used to solve a system of linear equations by elimination.

> **STEPS FOR SOLVING A SYSTEM OF LINEAR EQUATIONS BY ELIMINATION**
>
> **Step 1:** Multiply both sides of one equation or both equations by a nonzero constant so that the coefficients of one of the variables are additive inverses.
>
> **Step 2:** Add equations (1) and (2) to eliminate the variable whose coefficients are now additive inverses. Solve the resulting equation for the unknown.
>
> **Step 3:** Substitute the value of the variable found in Step 2 into one of the original equations to find the value of the remaining variable.
>
> **Step 4:** Check your answer.

What allows us to add two equations and use the result to replace an equation? Remember, an equation is a statement that the left side equals the right side. When we add equation (2) to equation (1), we are adding the same quantity to both sides of equation (1).

EXAMPLE 7 Solving a System of Linear Equations by Elimination

Solve: $\begin{cases} \dfrac{5}{2}x + 2y = 5 & (1) \\[2mm] \dfrac{3}{2}x + \dfrac{3}{2}y = \dfrac{9}{4} & (2) \end{cases}$

Solution

Because both equations (1) and (2) have fractions, our first goal is to get rid of the fractions by multiplying both sides of equation (1) by 2 and both sides of equation (2) by 4.

$$\begin{cases} \dfrac{5}{2}x + 2y = 5 & (1) \\[2mm] \dfrac{3}{2}x + \dfrac{3}{2}y = \dfrac{9}{4} & (2) \end{cases}$$

Multiply both sides of (1) by 2: $\begin{cases} 2\left(\dfrac{5}{2}x + 2y\right) = 2 \cdot 5 & (1) \end{cases}$

Multiply both sides of (2) by 4: $\begin{cases} 4\left(\dfrac{3}{2}x + \dfrac{3}{2}y\right) = 4 \cdot \dfrac{9}{4} & (2) \end{cases}$

Use the Distributive Property: $\begin{cases} 5x + 4y = 10 & (1) \\ 6x + 6y = 9 & (2) \end{cases}$

Divide both sides of equation (2) by 3: $\begin{cases} 5x + 4y = 10 & (1) \\ 2x + 2y = 3 & (2) \end{cases}$

Multiply both sides of equation (2) by -2: $\begin{cases} 5x + 4y = 10 & (1) \\ -4x - 4y = -6 & (2) \end{cases}$

Add (1) and (2): $x = 4$

Work Smart

If you are not afraid of fractions, you could eliminate x by multiplying both sides of equation (1) by -3 and both sides of equation (2) by 5. Try it!

Work Smart

Although it is not necessary to divide both sides of equation (2) by 3, it makes solving the problem easier. Do you see why?

Back-substitute 4 for x into the original equation (1).

$$\text{Equation (1):} \quad \frac{5}{2}x + 2y = 5$$

$$x = 4: \quad \frac{5}{2}(4) + 2y = 5$$

$$10 + 2y = 5$$

$$\text{Subtract 10 from both sides:} \quad 2y = -5$$

$$\text{Divide both sides by 2:} \quad y = -\frac{5}{2}$$

We have that $x = 4$ and $y = -\dfrac{5}{2}$.

We leave the check to you. The solution is the ordered pair $\left(4, -\dfrac{5}{2}\right)$. ∎

> **Quick** ✔ *In Problems 11–13, solve the system using elimination.* **Note:** *Problem 11 is the system solved using substitution in Example 5.*
>
> **11.** $\begin{cases} 2x - 3y = -6 \\ -8x + 3y = 3 \end{cases}$ **12.** $\begin{cases} -2x + y = 4 \\ -5x + 3y = 7 \end{cases}$
>
> **13.** $\begin{cases} -3x + 2y = 3 \\ 4x - 3y = -6 \end{cases}$

SUMMARY WHICH METHOD SHOULD I USE?

We have presented three methods for solving systems of two linear equations containing two unknowns. A question that remains unanswered is "When should I use each method?" Below, we present a summary of the methods, the advantages of each method, and when each method should be used.

Method	Advantages/Disadvantages	When Should I Use It?
Graphical	Allows us to "see" the answer but if the solutions are not integers, it can be difficult to determine the solution.	When a visual solution is required.
Substitution	Method gives exact solutions. The algebra can be easy provided one of the variables has a coefficient of 1. If none of the coefficients are 1, the algebra can get messy.	If one of the coefficients of the variables is 1 or one of the variables is already solved for (as in $x =$ or $y =$).
Elimination	Method gives exact solutions. It is easy to use when none of the variables has a coefficient of 1.	If both equations are in standard form ($Ax + By = C$).

Work Smart

The figure below shows a consistent and independent system.

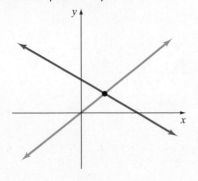

⌐5⌐ Identify Inconsistent Systems

Examples 2–7 dealt only with consistent and independent systems of equations. That is, we only discussed systems of equations with a single solution. Remember that there are two other possibilities for the solution of a system of linear equations: (1) The system could be inconsistent, which means that the lines in the system are parallel, or (2) the system could be consistent, but dependent, which means that the lines in the system are coincident (the same line).

In this next example, we look at an inconsistent system of equations.

EXAMPLE 8   An Inconsistent System

Solve: $\begin{cases} 3x + 2y = 2 & (1) \\ -6x - 4y = 8 & (2) \end{cases}$

Solution

It seems easiest to use the method of elimination to solve this system because none of the variables has a coefficient of 1.

In looking at this system, we can make the coefficients on the variable x additive inverses by multiplying equation (1) by 2.

$$\begin{cases} 3x + 2y = 2 & (1) \\ -6x - 4y = 8 & (2) \end{cases}$$

Multiply (1) by 2: $\begin{cases} 2(3x + 2y) = 2(2) & (1) \\ -6x - 4y = 8 & (2) \end{cases}$

Use the Distributive Property: $\begin{cases} 6x + 4y = 4 & (1) \\ -6x - 4y = 8 & (2) \end{cases}$

Add (1) and (2): $0 = 12$

The equation $0 = 12$ is false. We conclude that the system has no solution, so the solution set is $\varnothing$ or $\{\ \}$. The system is inconsistent.   ■

Figure 3 shows the pair of lines whose equations form the system in Example 8. Notice that the graphs of the two equations are lines, each with slope $-\frac{3}{2}$. Equation (1) has a y-intercept of 1, while equation (2) has a y-intercept of -2. Therefore, the lines are parallel and do not intersect. This geometric statement is equivalent to the algebraic statement that the system has no solution.

Work Smart

When solving a system of equations, if you end up with a statement "0 = some nonzero constant," the system is inconsistent. Graphically, the lines in the system are parallel.

Figure 3

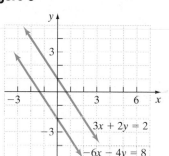

$3x + 2y = 2$

$-6x - 4y = 8$

> **Quick** ✔ *In Problem 14, show that the system is inconsistent. Draw a graph to support your result.*
>
> **14.** $\begin{cases} -3x + y = 2 \\ 6x - 2y - 1 \end{cases}$

6   Express the Solution of a System of Dependent Equations

The next example illustrates a system with infinitely many solutions.

EXAMPLE 9   Solving a System of Dependent Equations

Solve: $\begin{cases} 3x + y = 1 & (1) \\ -6x - 2y = -2 & (2) \end{cases}$

Solution

We choose to use the substitution method because solving equation (1) for y is straightforward.

Equation (1): $3x + y = 1$

Subtract $3x$ from both sides: $y = -3x + 1$

Substitute $-3x + 1$ for y in equation (2).

Equation (2): $-6x - 2y = -2$

$-6x - 2(-3x + 1) = -2$

Distribute the -2: $-6x + 6x - 2 = -2$

$-2 = -2$

The equation $-2 = -2$ is true. This means that as long as y is chosen so that it equals $-3x + 1$, we will have a solution to the system. For example, if $x = 0$, then $y = -3(0) + 1 = 1$; if $x = 1$, then $y = -3(1) + 1 = -2$; if $x = 2$, then $y = -3(2) + 1 = -5$.

In Words

The solution to a dependent system is "the set of all ordered pairs such that one of the equations in the system is true."

The system of equations is consistent, but dependent (the value of y that makes the equation true *depends* on the value of x) so that there are infinitely many solutions. We will write the solution as

$$\{(x, y)\,|\,3x + y = 1\}$$

Figure 4 illustrates the situation presented in Example 9. The graphs of the two equations are lines, each with slope -3 and y-intercept 1. The lines are coincident.

Look back at the equations in Example 9. Notice that the terms in equation (2) are -2 times the terms in equation (1). This is another way to identify dependent systems when you have two equations with two unknowns.

Figure 4

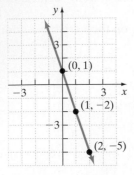

(0, 1)

(1, −2)

(2, −5)

> **Quick ✔** *In Problems 15 and 16, solve the system. Draw a graph to support your result.*
>
> **15.** $\begin{cases} -3x + 2y = 8 \\ 6x - 4y = -16 \end{cases}$
>
> **16.** $\begin{cases} 2x - 3y = -16 \\ -3x + 2y = 19 \end{cases}$

3.1 EXERCISES

MyMathLab

PRACTICE   WATCH   DOWNLOAD   READ   REVIEW

1–16. are the Quick ✔s that follow each EXAMPLE

Building Skills

In Problems 17–20, determine whether the given ordered pairs listed are solutions of the system of linear equations. See Objective 1.

17. $\begin{cases} 2x + y = 13 \\ -5x + 3y = 6 \end{cases}$

  (a) $(5, 3)$
  (b) $(3, 7)$

18. $\begin{cases} x - 2y = -11 \\ 3x + 2y = -1 \end{cases}$

  (a) $(-5, 3)$
  (b) $(-3, 4)$

19. $\begin{cases} 5x + 2y = 9 \\ -10x - 4y = -18 \end{cases}$

  (a) $(1, 2)$
  (b) $\left(2, -\dfrac{1}{2}\right)$

20. $\begin{cases} -3x + y = 5 \\ 6x - 2y = 6 \end{cases}$

  (a) $(-2, -1)$
  (b) $(2, 0)$

In Problems 21–24, use the graph of the system to determine whether the system is consistent or inconsistent. If consistent, indicate whether the system is independent or dependent. See Objective 1.

21. $\begin{cases} x + y = 1 \\ x + 2y = 0 \end{cases}$

22. $\begin{cases} -2x + y = 4 \\ 2x + y = 0 \end{cases}$

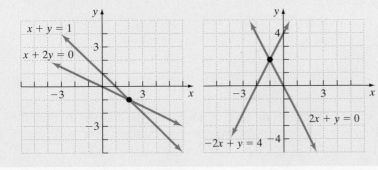

23. $\begin{cases} x - 2y = -2 \\ x - 2y = 2 \end{cases}$

24. $\begin{cases} 3x + y = 1 \\ -6x - 2y = -2 \end{cases}$

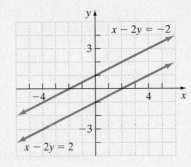 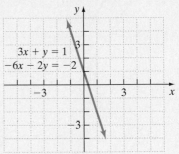

In Problems 25–28, solve the system of equations by graphing. See Objective 2.

25. $\begin{cases} y = 3x \\ y = -2x + 5 \end{cases}$

26. $\begin{cases} y = -2x + 4 \\ y = 2x - 4 \end{cases}$

27. $\begin{cases} 2x + y = 2 \\ x + 3y = -9 \end{cases}$

28. $\begin{cases} -x + 2y = -9 \\ 2x + y = -2 \end{cases}$

In Problems 29–36, solve the system of equations using substitution. See Objective 3.

29. $\begin{cases} y = -\dfrac{1}{2}x + 1 \\ y + 2x = 10 \end{cases}$

30. $\begin{cases} y + 3x = -4 \\ y = 4x + 17 \end{cases}$

31. $\begin{cases} x = \dfrac{2}{3}y \\ 3x - y = -3 \end{cases}$

32. $\begin{cases} y = \dfrac{1}{2}x \\ x - 4y = -4 \end{cases}$

33. $\begin{cases} 2x - 4y = 2 \\ x + 2y = 0 \end{cases}$ **34.** $\begin{cases} 3x + 2y = 0 \\ 6x + 2y = 5 \end{cases}$

35. $\begin{cases} x + y = 10{,}000 \\ 0.05x + 0.07y = 650 \end{cases}$

36. $\begin{cases} x + y = 5000 \\ 0.04x + 0.08y = 340 \end{cases}$

In Problems 37–44, solve the system of equations using elimination. See Objective 4.

37. $\begin{cases} x + y = -5 \\ -x + 2y = 14 \end{cases}$ **38.** $\begin{cases} x + y = -6 \\ -2x - y = 0 \end{cases}$

39. $\begin{cases} x + 2y = -5 \\ 3x + 3y = 9 \end{cases}$ **40.** $\begin{cases} -3x + 2y = -5 \\ 2x - y = 10 \end{cases}$

41. $\begin{cases} 2x + 5y = -3 \\ x + \dfrac{5}{4}y = -\dfrac{1}{2} \end{cases}$ **42.** $\begin{cases} x + 2y = -\dfrac{8}{3} \\ 3x - 3y = 5 \end{cases}$

43. $\begin{cases} 0.05x + 0.1y = 5.25 \\ 0.08x - 0.02y = 1.2 \end{cases}$ **44.** $\begin{cases} 0.04x + 0.06y = 2.1 \\ 0.06x - 0.03y = 0.15 \end{cases}$

In Problems 45–48, use either the method of substitution or elimination to show that the system is inconsistent. Draw a graph to support your result. See Objective 5.

45. $\begin{cases} 3x + y = 1 \\ -6x - 2y = -4 \end{cases}$ **46.** $\begin{cases} -2x + 4y = 9 \\ x - 2y = -3 \end{cases}$

47. $\begin{cases} 5x - 2y = 2 \\ -10x + 4y = 3 \end{cases}$ **48.** $\begin{cases} 6x - 4y = 6 \\ -3x + 2y = 3 \end{cases}$

In Problems 49–54, use either the method of substitution or elimination to show that the system is consistent, but dependent. Solve the system and draw a graph to support your solution. See Objective 6.

49. $\begin{cases} y = \dfrac{1}{2}x + 1 \\ 2x - 4y = -4 \end{cases}$ **50.** $\begin{cases} y = -\dfrac{2}{3}x + 3 \\ 2x + 3y = 9 \end{cases}$

51. $\begin{cases} x + 3y = 6 \\ -\dfrac{x}{3} - y = -2 \end{cases}$ **52.** $\begin{cases} -4x + y = 8 \\ x - \dfrac{y}{4} = -2 \end{cases}$

53. $\begin{cases} \dfrac{1}{3}x - 2y = 6 \\ -\dfrac{1}{2}x + 3y = -9 \end{cases}$ **54.** $\begin{cases} \dfrac{5}{4}x - \dfrac{1}{2}y = 6 \\ -\dfrac{5}{3}x + \dfrac{2}{3}y = -8 \end{cases}$

Mixed Practice

In Problems 55–62, solve the system of equations using either substitution or elimination.

55. $\begin{cases} x + 3y = 0 \\ -2x + 4y = 30 \end{cases}$ **56.** $\begin{cases} 2x + y = -1 \\ -3x - 2y = 7 \end{cases}$

57. $\begin{cases} x = 5y - 3 \\ -3x + 15y = 9 \end{cases}$ **58.** $\begin{cases} y = \dfrac{1}{2}x + 2 \\ x - 2y = -4 \end{cases}$

59. $\begin{cases} 2x - 4y = 18 \\ 3x + 5y = -3 \end{cases}$ **60.** $\begin{cases} 12x + 45y = 0 \\ 8x + 6y = 24 \end{cases}$

61. $\begin{cases} \dfrac{5}{6}x - \dfrac{1}{3}y = -5 \\ -x + \dfrac{2}{5}y = 1 \end{cases}$ **62.** $\begin{cases} \dfrac{1}{3}x - \dfrac{1}{2}y = -5 \\ -\dfrac{4}{5}x + \dfrac{6}{5}y = 1 \end{cases}$

Applying the Concepts

In Problems 63–66, write each equation in the system of equations in slope-intercept form. Use the slope-intercept form to determine the number of solutions the system has.

63. $\begin{cases} 2x + y = -5 \\ 5x + 3y = 1 \end{cases}$ **64.** $\begin{cases} 4x - 2y = 8 \\ -10x + 5y = 5 \end{cases}$

65. $\begin{cases} 3x - 2y = -2 \\ -6x + 4y = 4 \end{cases}$ **66.** $\begin{cases} 2x - y = -5 \\ -4x + 3y = 9 \end{cases}$

△**67. Parallelogram** Use the parallelogram shown to the right to answer parts (a) and (b).

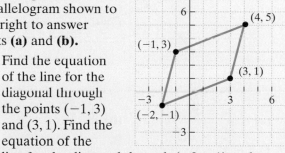

   (a) Find the equation of the line for the diagonal through the points $(-1, 3)$ and $(3, 1)$. Find the equation of the line for the diagonal through $(-2, -1)$ and $(4, 5)$.

   (b) Find the point of intersection of the diagonals.

△**68. Rhombus** A rhombus is a parallelogram whose adjacent sides are congruent. Use the rhombus to the right to answer parts (a), (b), and (c).

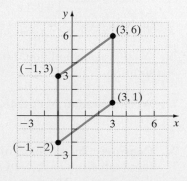

   (a) Find the equation of the line for the diagonal through the points $(-1, 3)$ and $(3, 1)$. Find the equation of the line for the diagonal through $(-1, -2)$ and $(3, 6)$.

   (b) Find the point of intersection of the diagonals.

   (c) Compare the slopes of the diagonals. What can be said about the diagonals of a rhombus?

Extending the Concepts

69. Which of the following ordered pairs could be a solution to the system graphed below?

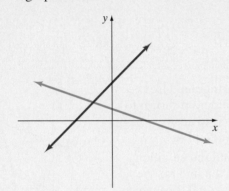

(a) $(2, 4)$ (b) $(-2, 0)$ (c) $(-3, 1)$

(d) $(5, -2)$ (e) $(-1, -3)$ (f) $(-1, 3)$

70. Which of the following systems of equations could have the graph below?

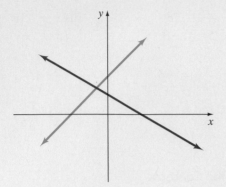

(a) $\begin{cases} 2x + 3y = 12 \\ 2x + y = -2 \end{cases}$ (b) $\begin{cases} 2x + 3y = 3 \\ -2x + y = 2 \end{cases}$

(c) $\begin{cases} 2x - 3y = 12 \\ x + 2y = 2 \end{cases}$

71. For the system $\begin{cases} Ax + 3By = 2 \\ -3Ax + By = -11 \end{cases}$, find A and B such that $x = 3$, $y = 1$ is a solution.

72. Write a system of equations that has $(3, 5)$ as a solution.

73. Write a system of equations that has $(-1, 4)$ as a solution.

△**74.** **Centroid** The medians of a triangle are the line segments from each vertex to the midpoint of the opposite side. The centroid of a triangle is the point where the medians of the triangle intersect. Use the information given in the figure of the triangle to find its centroid.

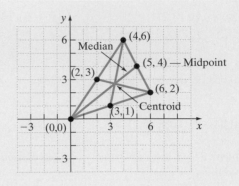

In Problems 75–78, solve each system using either substitution or elimination. Draw a graph to support your solution.

75. $\begin{cases} 3x + y = 5 \\ x + y = 3 \\ x + 3y = 7 \end{cases}$ **76.** $\begin{cases} x + y = -2 \\ -3x + 2y = 16 \\ 2x - 4y = -16 \end{cases}$

77. $\begin{cases} y = \dfrac{2}{3}x - 5 \\ 4x - 6y = 30 \\ x - 5y = 11 \end{cases}$

78. $\begin{cases} -4x + 3y = 33 \\ 3x - 4y = -37 \\ 2x - 3y = 15 \end{cases}$

Explaining the Concepts

79. In this section, we presented two algebraic methods for solving a system of linear equations. Are there any circumstances where one method is preferable to the other? What are these circumstances?

80. Describe geometrically the three possibilities for a solution to a system of two linear equations containing two variables.

81. The solution to a system of two linear equations in two unknowns is $x = 3$, $y = -2$. Where do the lines in the system intersect? Why?

82. In the process of solving a system of linear equations, what tips you off that the system is consistent but dependent? What tips you off that the system is inconsistent?

The Graphing Calculator

A graphing calculator can be used to approximate the point of intersection between two equations using its INTERSECT command. We illustrate this feature of the graphing calculator by doing Example 3. Start by graphing each equation in the system as shown in Figure 5(a). Then use the INTERSECT command and find that the lines intersect at $x = 2$, $y = -3$. See Figure 5(b). The solution is the ordered pair $(2, -3)$.

Figure 5

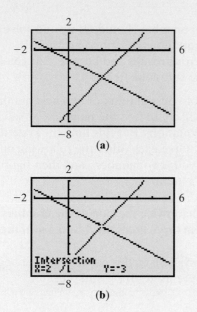

(a)

(b)

In Problems 83–90, use a graphing calculator to solve each system of equations. If necessary, express your solution rounded to two decimal places.

83. $\begin{cases} y = 3x - 1 \\ y = -2x + 5 \end{cases}$

84. $\begin{cases} y = \dfrac{3}{2}x - 4 \\ y = -\dfrac{1}{4}x + 3 \end{cases}$

85. $\begin{cases} 3x - y = -1 \\ -4x + y = -3 \end{cases}$

86. $\begin{cases} -6x - 2y = 4 \\ 5x + 3y = -2 \end{cases}$

87. $\begin{cases} 4x - 3y = 1 \\ -8x + 6y = -2 \end{cases}$

88. $\begin{cases} -2x + 5y = -2 \\ 4x - 10y = 1 \end{cases}$

89. $\begin{cases} 2x - 3y = 12 \\ 5x + y = -2 \end{cases}$

90. $\begin{cases} x - 3y = 21 \\ x + 6y = -2 \end{cases}$

CHAPTER 3 Activity: Find the Numbers

Focus: Solving systems of equations
Time: 15 minutes
Group size: 2

Consider the following dialogue between two students.

   Michele: Think of two numbers between 1 and 10, and don't tell me what they are.

   Rafael: OK, I've thought of two numbers.

   Michele: Now tell me the sum of the two numbers and the difference of the two numbers, and I'll tell you what your two numbers are.

   Rafael: Their sum is 14 and their difference is 6.

   Michele: Your numbers are 10 and 4.

   Rafael: That's right! How did you do that?

   Michele: I set up a system of equations using the sum and difference that you gave me, along with the variables x and y.

1. Each group member should set up and solve the system of equations described by Michele.

    Discuss your results and be sure that you both arrive at the solutions 10 and 4.

2. Now each of you will think of two new numbers and the other will try to find the numbers by solving a system of equations. But this time the system will be a bit trickier! Give each other the following information about your two numbers, and then figure out each other's numbers:

    five more than twice the sum of the numbers
    four less than three times the difference of the numbers

3. Would the systems in this activity work if negative numbers were used? Try it and see!

CHAPTER 3 Review

Section 3.1   Systems of Linear Equations in Two Variables

KEY CONCEPTS	KEY TERMS
• **Recognizing Solutions to Systems of Two Linear Equations with Two Unknowns** • If the lines in a system of two linear equations containing two unknowns intersect, then the point of intersection is the solution and the system is consistent and independent. • If the lines in a system of two linear equations containing two unknowns are parallel, then the system has no solution and the system is inconsistent. • If the lines in a system of two linear equations containing two unknowns lie on top of each other, then the system has infinitely many solutions. The solution set is the set of all points on the line and the system is consistent, but dependent.	System of linear equations Solution Consistent and independent Inconsistent Consistent and dependent

YOU SHOULD BE ABLE TO...	EXAMPLE	REVIEW EXERCISES
1 Determine whether an ordered pair is a solution to a system of linear equations (p. 229)	Example 2	1–4
2 Solve a system of two linear equations containing two unknowns by graphing (p. 231)	Example 3	5–10
3 Solve a system of two linear equations containing two unknowns by substitution (p. 232)	Examples 4 and 5	11–14, 19–24
4 Solve a system of two linear equations containing two unknowns by elimination (p. 234)	Examples 6 and 7	15–24
5 Identify inconsistent systems (p. 236)	Example 8	9, 23
6 Express the solution of a system of dependent equations (p. 237)	Example 9	12, 17

In Problems 1–4, determine whether the given values of the variables listed are solutions to the system of equations.

1. $\begin{cases} x + 3y = -2 \\ 2x - y = 10 \end{cases}$

(a) $x = 3, y = -1$

(b) $x = 4, y = -2$

2. $\begin{cases} -2x + 5y = 4 \\ 4x - 5y = -3 \end{cases}$

(a) $x = \dfrac{1}{2}, y = 1$

(b) $x = -1, y = \dfrac{1}{3}$

3. $\begin{cases} 6x - 5y = -12 \\ x - y = -3 \end{cases}$

(a) $x = 3, y = 6$

(b) $x = 1, y = 4$

4. $\begin{cases} 3x - y = 9 \\ 8x + 3y = 7 \end{cases}$

(a) $x = 3, y = 0$

(b) $x = 2, y = -3$

In Problems 5 and 6, use the graph of the system to determine the solution.

5. $\begin{cases} x + 4y = 12 \\ 2x - y = 6 \end{cases}$

6. $\begin{cases} 3x + 2y = 4 \\ x - 2y = 4 \end{cases}$

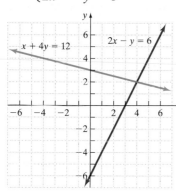

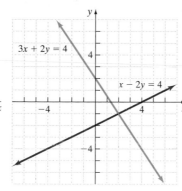

In Problems 7–10, solve each system of linear equations by graphing.

7. $\begin{cases} y = -3x + 1 \\ y = \dfrac{1}{2}x - 6 \end{cases}$

8. $\begin{cases} -2x + 3y = -9 \\ 3x + y = 8 \end{cases}$

9. $\begin{cases} y = -\dfrac{1}{3}x + 2 \\ x + 3y = -9 \end{cases}$

10. $\begin{cases} 2x - 3y = 0 \\ 2x - y = -4 \end{cases}$

In Problems 11–14, solve each system of linear equations using substitution.

11. $\begin{cases} y = -\dfrac{1}{4}x + 2 \\ y = 4x - 32 \end{cases}$

12. $\begin{cases} y = -\dfrac{3}{4}x + 2 \\ 3x + 4y = 8 \end{cases}$

13. $\begin{cases} y = 3x - 9 \\ 4x + 3y = -1 \end{cases}$

14. $\begin{cases} x - 2y = 7 \\ 3x - y = -4 \end{cases}$

In Problems 15–18, solve each system of linear equations using elimination.

15. $\begin{cases} 2x - y = 9 \\ 3x + y = 11 \end{cases}$

16. $\begin{cases} -x + 3y = 4 \\ 3x - 4y = -2 \end{cases}$

17. $\begin{cases} 2x - 4y = 8 \\ -3x + 6y = -12 \end{cases}$

18. $\begin{cases} 3x - 4y = -11 \\ 2x - 3y = -7 \end{cases}$

In Problems 19–24, solve each system of linear equations using either substitution or elimination.

19. $\begin{cases} x + y = -4 \\ 2x - 3y = 12 \end{cases}$

20. $\begin{cases} 5x - 3y = 2 \\ x + 2y = -10 \end{cases}$

21. $\begin{cases} 3x - 2y = 5 \\ 4x - 5y = 9 \end{cases}$

22. $\begin{cases} 12x + 20y = 21 \\ 3x - 2y = 0 \end{cases}$

23. $\begin{cases} 6x + 9y = -3 \\ 8x + 12y = 7 \end{cases}$

24. $\begin{cases} 6x + 11y = 2 \\ 5x + 8y = -3 \end{cases}$

CHAPTER 3 TEST

Remember to use your Chapter Test Prep Video CD to see fully worked-out solutions to any of these problems you would like to review.

1. Solve the system of linear equations by graphing.

$$\begin{cases} 2x - y = 0 \\ 4x - 5y = 12 \end{cases}$$

In Problems 2–5, solve the system of linear equations using either substitution or elimination.

2. $\begin{cases} 5x + 2y = -3 \\ y = 2x - 6 \end{cases}$

3. $\begin{cases} 9x + 3y = 1 \\ x - 2y = 4 \end{cases}$

4. $\begin{cases} 6x - 9y = 5 \\ 8x - 12y = 7 \end{cases}$

5. $\begin{cases} 2x + y = -4 \\ \dfrac{1}{3}x + \dfrac{1}{2}y = 2 \end{cases}$

In Problems 6 and 7, solve each system of three linear equations containing three unknowns.

6. $\begin{cases} x - 2y + 3z = 1 \\ x + y - 3z = 7 \\ 3x - 4y + 5z = 7 \end{cases}$

7. $\begin{cases} 2x + 4y + 3z = 5 \\ 3x - y + 2z = 8 \\ x + y + 2z = 0 \end{cases}$

In Problems 8 and 9, perform each row operation on the given augmented matrix.

8. $\begin{bmatrix} 1 & -3 & | & -2 \\ 2 & -4 & | & 8 \end{bmatrix}$

   (a) $R_2 = -2r_1 + r_2$
      followed by

   (b) $R_2 = \dfrac{1}{2}r_2$

9. $\begin{bmatrix} 1 & -2 & 1 & | & -2 \\ 3 & -5 & 2 & | & 1 \\ 0 & -4 & 5 & | & -32 \end{bmatrix}$

   (a) $R_2 = -3r_1 + r_2$
      followed by

   (b) $R_3 = 4r_2 + r_3$

In Problems 10 and 11, write the augmented matrix for each system of linear equations. Then, use the matrix to solve the system.

10. $\begin{cases} x - 5y = 2 \\ 2x + y = 4 \end{cases}$

11. $\begin{cases} x + 2y + z = 3 \\ 4y + 3z = 5 \\ 2x + 3y = 1 \end{cases}$

In Problems 12 and 13, find the value of each determinant.

12. $\begin{vmatrix} 3 & -5 \\ 4 & -8 \end{vmatrix}$

13. $\begin{vmatrix} 0 & 1 & 2 \\ 3 & 3 & -1 \\ -2 & 1 & 2 \end{vmatrix}$

In Problems 14 and 15, solve each system of linear equations using Cramer's Rule, if applicable.

14. $\begin{cases} x - y = -2 \\ 5x + 3y = -8 \end{cases}$

15. $\begin{cases} x + y + z = -2 \\ x + y - 2z = 1 \\ 4x + 2y + 3z = -15 \end{cases}$

In Problems 16 and 17, graph each system of linear inequalities. Label the corner points.

16. $\begin{cases} 2x - y > -2 \\ x - 3y < 9 \end{cases}$

17. $\begin{cases} 3x + 2y \le 12 \\ x - 2y \ge -4 \\ x \ge 0 \\ y \ge 0 \end{cases}$

18. Grain Storage A grain-storage warehouse has a total of 50 bins. Some of the bins hold 25 tons of grain each, and the rest hold 20 tons each. How many of each type of bin are there if the capacity of the warehouse is 1160 tons?

△ **19. Triangle** In the triangle shown below, the measure of angle z is 10° larger than the measure of angle y. Five times the measure of angle x equals the sum of the measures of angles y and z. Find the measures of angles x, y, and z.

20. Shopping It's Margaret's lucky day. While shopping, she happened onto a sale where designer blouses were being sold for $12 each and designer sweaters were being sold for $18 each. Unfortunately, Margaret has no more than $180 to spend. She also decides that she can buy at most 13 items.

(a) Let x denote the number of blouses and y denote the number of sweaters that Margaret will buy. Write a system of linear inequalities that represents the possible combinations of purchases.

(b) Graph the system and label the corner points.

CUMULATIVE REVIEW Chapters R-3

1. Consider the following set of numbers:

$$\left\{-13, -\frac{7}{8}, 0, \frac{\pi}{2}, 2.7, 4\sqrt{2}, 11\right\}.$$ List the numbers that are:

(a) Counting numbers

(b) Integers

(c) Rational numbers

(d) Irrational numbers

(e) Real numbers

2. Translate the following statement into a mathematical statement: Twice the sum of a number and four equals three times the number decreased by six.

3. Evaluate: $\dfrac{3 - 7(5)}{4}$

4. Evaluate $\dfrac{x^2 - 5x + 4}{x - 1}$ for $x = 7$.

5. Simplify: $x(x - 4) - 7(x + 5) + 2(x^2 + 4)$

6. Solve: $3|x + 7| - 4 = 20$

7. Solve: $\dfrac{x + 1}{5} \geq \dfrac{5x + 29}{10}$

8. Solve: $|2x - 7| > 3$

9. For $A = \{0, 2, 4, 6, 8, 10, 12\}$ and $B = \{0, 3, 6, 9, 12, 15\}$ find each of the following.

(a) $A \cap B$

(b) $A \cup B$

10. Graph: $y = 2|x| - 5$

11. Find the zero of $f(x) = \dfrac{2}{3}x - 4$.

12. Determine which, if any, of the following graphs are graphs of functions.

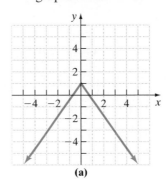

(a)

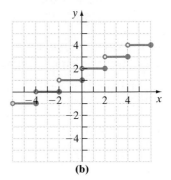

(b)

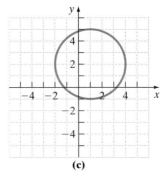

(c)

13. Determine the domain of $f(x) = \dfrac{2x + 7}{2x - 1}$.

14. For $g(x) = 3x^2 + 4x - 7$, find each of the following.

(a) $g(-4)$ **(b)** $g\left(\dfrac{2}{3}\right)$ **(c)** $g(-x)$

15. Graph the linear equation $2x - 5y = 20$.

16. Determine whether the graphs of the following linear equations are parallel, perpendicular, or neither.

$$\begin{cases} 3x - 9y = 5 \\ 5x - 15y = -27 \end{cases}$$

17. Find the equation of the line passing through the points $(-6, 14)$ and $(9, -11)$. Write your answer in either slope-intercept or standard form, whichever you prefer.

18. The weight of a collection of quarters varies directly with the number of quarters in the collection. If 50 quarters weigh 281 grams, determine the weight of 35 quarters.

19. Using data from the U.S. Census Bureau, the projected population of the state of Alabama x years after 1995 is given by $P(x) = -275.8x^2 + 40{,}628.4x + 4{,}253{,}440.3$. The model is only valid for years 1995 through 2025.

   (a) Identify the dependent and independent variables.

   (b) What is the domain of this function?

   (c) Find $P(20)$ and explain what this value represents.

   (d) Use the function to find the projected population of Alabama in the year 2020.

20. Long Distance Earth Tones offers the Green Saver long-distance plan that charges \$4.95 per month plus 8¢ per minute.

   (a) Write the monthly long-distance cost C as a function of long-distance minutes talked x.

   (b) What is the implied domain of this linear function?

   (c) What is the cost if a person makes 645 minutes of long-distance calls during one month?

   (d) During one month, how many minutes of long-distance calls can be made for \$130.95?

In Problems 21 and 22, solve each system of equations.

21. $\begin{cases} y = \dfrac{1}{2}x + 9 \\ 5x + 4y = -20 \end{cases}$

22. $\begin{cases} 6x - 4y + 3z = 3 \\ 3x + 10y + z = -4 \\ 9x + 2y + 4z = 1 \end{cases}$

In Problems 23 and 24, find the value of each determinant.

23. $\begin{vmatrix} -4 & 2 \\ -5 & 3 \end{vmatrix}$

24. $\begin{vmatrix} 2 & 3 & 0 \\ -1 & 4 & 2 \\ 2 & -2 & -3 \end{vmatrix}$

25. Graph the following system of linear inequalities.

$$\begin{cases} x + 3y < 12 \\ x \geq 3 \end{cases}$$

Getting Ready for Chapter 4
Laws of Exponents and Scientific Notation

Work Smart

We read a^n as "a raised to the power n" or "a raised to the nth power." We usually read a^2 as "a squared" and a^3 as "a cubed."

In Words

When multiplying two exponential expressions with the same base, add the exponents. Then write the common base to the power of this sum.

A quick review of positive integer exponents is in order. Recall that if a is a real number and n is a positive integer, then the symbol a^n means that we should use a as a factor n times. That is,

$$a^n = \underbrace{a \cdot a \cdot \cdots \cdot a}_{n \text{ factors}}$$

For example,

$$4^3 = \underbrace{4 \cdot 4 \cdot 4}_{3 \text{ factors}}$$

In the notation a^n, we call a the **base** and n the **power** or **exponent.**

1 Simplify Exponential Expressions Using the Product Rule

Several general rules can be discovered for simplifying expressions involving *positive* integer exponents. The first rule that we introduce is used when multiplying two exponential expressions that have the same base. Consider the following:

$$x^2 \cdot x^4 = \underbrace{(x \cdot x)}_{2 \text{ factors}} \underbrace{(x \cdot x \cdot x \cdot x)}_{4 \text{ factors}} = \underbrace{x \cdot x \cdot x \cdot x \cdot x \cdot x}_{6 \text{ factors}} = x^6$$

Sum of powers 2 and 4. Same base. Same base.

Based on the above, we have the following result:

PRODUCT RULE FOR EXPONENTS (POSITIVE INTEGER EXPONENTS)

If a is a real number and m and n are positive integers, then

$$a^m \cdot a^n = a^{m+n}$$

EXAMPLE 1 Using the Product Rule to Simplify Expressions Involving Exponents

Simplify each expression. All answers should contain only positive integer exponents.

   (a) $2^2 \cdot 2^3$ (b) $3z^2 \cdot 4z^4$

Solution

   (a) $2^2 \cdot 2^3 = 2^{2+3}$ (b) $3z^2 \cdot 4z^4 = 3 \cdot 4 \cdot z^2 \cdot z^4$

               $= 2^5$ $= 12z^{2+4}$

               $= 32$ $= 12z^6$ ∎

Quick ✔

1. In the notation a^n we call a the _____ and n the _____ or _____.
2. Using a Law of Exponents, $a^m \cdot a^n =$ _____.

In Problems 3–7, simplify each expression. All answers should contain only positive integer exponents.

3. $5^2 \cdot 5$ 4. $(-3)^2 \cdot (-3)^3$ 5. $y^4 \cdot y^3$

6. $(5x^2) \cdot (-2x^5)$ 7. $6y^3 \cdot (-y^2)$

2 Simplify Exponential Expressions Using the Quotient Rule

To find a general rule for the quotient of two exponential expressions with *positive* integer exponents, we use the Reduction Property to divide out common factors. Consider the following:

$$\frac{y^6}{y^2} = \frac{\overbrace{y \cdot y \cdot y \cdot y \cdot \cancel{y} \cdot \cancel{y}}^{6 \text{ factors}}}{\underbrace{\cancel{y} \cdot \cancel{y}}_{2 \text{ factors}}} = \underbrace{y \cdot y \cdot y \cdot y}_{4 \text{ factors}} = y^4$$

Difference of powers 6 and 2

We conclude from this result that

$$\frac{y^6}{y^2} = y^{6-2} = y^4$$

This result is true in general.

In Words

When dividing two exponential expressions with a common base, subtract the exponent in the denominator from the exponent in the numerator. Then write the common base to the power of this difference.

QUOTIENT RULE FOR EXPONENTS (POSITIVE INTEGER EXPONENTS)

If a is a real number and if m and n are positive integers, then

$$\frac{a^m}{a^n} = a^{m-n} \qquad \text{if } a \neq 0$$

EXAMPLE 2 Using the Quotient Rule to Simplify Expressions Involving Exponents

Simplify each expression. Answers should contain only positive integer exponents.

(a) $\dfrac{8^5}{8^3}$

(b) $\dfrac{27z^9}{12z^4}$

Solution

(a) $\dfrac{8^5}{8^3} = 8^{5-3}$

$= 8^2$

$= 64$

(b) $\dfrac{27z^9}{12z^4} = \dfrac{9 \cdot 3}{4 \cdot 3} z^{9-4}$

$= \dfrac{9}{4} z^5$

■

Quick ✔

8. *True or False:* To divide two exponential expressions having the same base, keep the base and subtract the exponents.

In Problems 9–12, simplify each expression. All answers should contain only positive integer exponents.

9. $\dfrac{5^6}{5^4}$

10. $\dfrac{y^8}{y^6}$

11. $\dfrac{16a^6}{10a^5}$

12. $\dfrac{-24b^5}{16b^3}$

3 Evaluate Exponential Expressions with a Zero or Negative Exponent

To this point, we have considered only exponential expressions with positive integer exponents. We now wish to extend the definition of exponential expressions to *all* integer exponents. That is, we wish to evaluate exponential expressions where the exponent can be a positive integer, zero, or a negative integer. We begin with raising a real number to the 0 power.

DEFINITION ZERO-EXPONENT RULE

If a is a nonzero real number, we define

$$a^0 = 1 \quad \text{if } a \neq 0$$

The reason that $a^0 = 1$ is easy to see based upon the Product Rule and the Identity Property of Multiplication. From the Product Rule for Exponents we have that

$$a^0 a^n = a^{0+n}$$
$$= a^n$$
$$= 1 \cdot a^n$$

From the Identity Property of Multiplication, it must be that $a^0 = 1$.

Suppose that we wanted to simplify $\dfrac{z^3}{z^5}$. If we use the Quotient Rule for Exponents, we obtain

$$\frac{z^3}{z^5} = z^{3-5} = z^{-2}$$

We could also simplify this expression using the Reduction Property.

$$\frac{z^3}{z^5} = \frac{\cancel{z} \cdot \cancel{z} \cdot \cancel{z}}{\cancel{z} \cdot \cancel{z} \cdot \cancel{z} \cdot z \cdot z} = \frac{1}{z^2}$$

This implies that $z^{-2} = \dfrac{1}{z^2}$. Based upon this result, we define a raised to a negative power as follows:

DEFINITION NEGATIVE-EXPONENT RULE

If n is a positive integer and if a is a nonzero real number, then we define

$$a^{-n} = \frac{1}{a^n} \quad \text{or} \quad \frac{1}{a^{-n}} = a^n \quad \text{if } a \neq 0$$

$\overline{\text{EXAMPLE 3}}$ **Evaluating Exponential Expressions Containing Integer Exponents**

Simplify each expression. All exponents should be positive integers.

    (a) 3^{-4} **(b)** $\dfrac{1}{3^{-2}}$ **(c)** $5x^0$ **(d)** $4x^{-5}$

Solution

    (a) $3^{-4} = \dfrac{1}{3^4} = \dfrac{1}{81}$ **(b)** $\dfrac{1}{3^{-2}} = 3^2 = 9$ **(c)** $5x^0 = 5 \cdot 1 = 5$ **(d)** $4x^{-5} = \dfrac{4}{x^5}$ ■

Quick ✔

13. $a^0 =$ __ , provided $a \neq$ __ .   **14.** $a^{-n} =$ __ , provided $a \neq$ __ .

In Problems 15–20, simplify each expression. All exponents should be positive integers.

15. 5^{-3} **16.** $5z^{-7}$ **17.** $\dfrac{1}{x^{-4}}$ **18.** $\dfrac{5}{y^{-3}}$ **19.** -4^0 **20.** $(-10)^0$

EXAMPLE 4 Evaluating Exponential Expressions Containing Integer Exponents

Simplify each expression. All exponents should be positive integers.

(a) $\left(\dfrac{2}{3}\right)^{-3}$

(b) $\left(\dfrac{1}{7}\right)^{-2}$

Solution

(a) $\left(\dfrac{2}{3}\right)^{-3} = \dfrac{1}{\left(\dfrac{2}{3}\right)^3}$

$= \dfrac{1}{\dfrac{2}{3} \cdot \dfrac{2}{3} \cdot \dfrac{2}{3}}$

$= \dfrac{1}{\dfrac{8}{27}}$

$= \dfrac{27}{8}$

(b) $\left(\dfrac{1}{7}\right)^{-2} = \dfrac{1}{\left(\dfrac{1}{7}\right)^2}$

$= \dfrac{1}{\dfrac{1}{7} \cdot \dfrac{1}{7}}$

$= \dfrac{1}{\dfrac{1}{49}}$

$= 49$

The following shortcut is based upon the results of Example 4:

In Words

To evaluate $\left(\dfrac{a}{b}\right)^{-n}$, determine the reciprocal of the base and then raise it to the nth power.

If a and b are real numbers and n is an integer, then

$$\left(\frac{a}{b}\right)^{-n} = \left(\frac{b}{a}\right)^{n} \qquad \text{if } a \neq 0, b \neq 0$$

Quick ✔ *In Problems 21–24, simplify each expression. All exponents should be positive integers.*

21. $\left(\dfrac{4}{3}\right)^{-2}$

22. $\left(-\dfrac{1}{4}\right)^{-3}$

23. $\left(\dfrac{3}{x}\right)^{-2}$

24. $\dfrac{5}{2^{-2}}$

Now that we have definitions for 0 as an exponent and negative exponents, we restate the Product Rule and Quotient Rule for Exponents assuming that the exponent is any integer (positive, negative, or zero).

PRODUCT RULE FOR EXPONENTS

If a is a real number and m and n are integers, then

$$a^m \cdot a^n = a^{m+n}$$

If m, n, or $m + n$ is 0 or negative, then a cannot be 0.

QUOTIENT RULE FOR EXPONENTS

If a is a real number and if m and n are integers, then

$$\frac{a^m}{a^n} = a^{m-n} \qquad \text{if } a \neq 0$$

You should notice that allowing the exponents to be any integer (instead of just positive integers) requires that we include restrictions on the value of the base.

EXAMPLE 5 Using the Product Rule to Simplify Expressions Containing Exponents

Simplify each expression. All exponents should be positive integers.

(a) $(-3)^2(-3)^{-4}$

(b) $\dfrac{3}{4}y^5 \cdot \dfrac{20}{9}y^{-2}$

Solution

(a) $(-3)^2(-3)^{-4} = (-3)^{2+(-4)}$

$= (-3)^{-2}$

$= \dfrac{1}{(-3)^2}$

$= \dfrac{1}{9}$

(b) $\dfrac{3}{4}y^5 \cdot \dfrac{20}{9}y^{-2} = \dfrac{3}{4} \cdot \dfrac{20}{9}y^{5+(-2)}$

$= \dfrac{5}{3}y^3$

EXAMPLE 6 Using the Quotient Rule to Simplify Expressions Involving Exponents

(a) $\dfrac{w^{-2}}{w^{-5}}$

(b) $\dfrac{20a^3b}{4ab^4}$

Solution

(a) $\dfrac{w^{-2}}{w^{-5}} = w^{-2-(-5)}$

$= w^{-2+5}$

$= w^3$

(b) $\dfrac{20a^3b}{4ab^4} = 5a^{3-1}b^{1-4}$

$= 5a^2b^{-3}$

$a^{-n} = \dfrac{1}{a^n}: \quad = \dfrac{5a^2}{b^3}$

Quick ✔ *In Problems 25–30, simplify each expression. All exponents should be positive integers.*

25. $6^3 \cdot 6^{-5}$

26. $\dfrac{10^{-3}}{10^{-5}}$

27. $(4x^2y^3) \cdot (5xy^{-4})$

28. $\left(\dfrac{3}{4}a^3b\right) \cdot \left(\dfrac{8}{9}a^{-2}b^3\right)$

29. $\dfrac{-24b^5}{16b^{-3}}$

30. $\dfrac{50s^2t}{15s^5t^{-4}}$

⌐4⌐ Simplify Exponential Expressions Using the Power Rule

Another law of exponents applies when an exponential expression containing a power is itself raised to a power.

$$(3^2)^4 = \underbrace{3^2 \cdot 3^2 \cdot 3^2 \cdot 3^2}_{\text{4 factors}} = \underbrace{(3 \cdot 3) \cdot (3 \cdot 3) \cdot (3 \cdot 3) \cdot (3 \cdot 3)}_{\substack{\text{2 factors 2 factors 2 factors 2 factors} \\ 2 \cdot 4 = 8 \text{ factors}}} = 3^8$$

We have the following result:

In Words

If an exponential expression contains a power raised to a power, keep the base and multiply the powers.

POWER RULE FOR EXPONENTIAL EXPRESSIONS

If a is a real number and m and n are integers, then

$$(a^m)^n = a^{m \cdot n}$$

If m or n is 0 or negative, then a must not be 0.

EXAMPLE 7 Using the Power Rule to Simplify Exponential Expressions

Simplify each expression. All exponents should be positive integers.

(a) $(4^3)^5$

(b) $[(-3)^3]^2$

(c) $(6^3)^0$

Solution

(a) $(4^3)^5 = 4^{3 \cdot 5}$
$$= 4^{15}$$

(b) $[(-3)^3]^2 = (-3)^{3 \cdot 2}$
$$= (-3)^6$$
$$= 729$$

(c) $(6^3)^0 = 6^{3 \cdot 0}$
$$= 6^0$$
$$= 1$$ ■

Quick ✔ *In Problems 31–36, simplify each expression. All exponents should be positive integers.*

31. $(2^2)^3$

32. $(5^8)^0$

33. $[(-4)^3]^2$

34. $(a^3)^5$

35. $(z^3)^{-6}$

36. $(s^{-3})^{-7}$

5 Simplify Exponential Expressions Containing Products or Quotients

We will now look at two additional laws of exponents. The first deals with raising a product to a power, while the second deals with raising a quotient to a power. Consider the following where we have a product to a power:

$$(x \cdot y)^3 = (x \cdot y) \cdot (x \cdot y) \cdot (x \cdot y)$$
$$= (x \cdot x \cdot x) \cdot (y \cdot y \cdot y)$$
$$= x^3 \cdot y^3$$

We have the following result:

Work Smart

Do not use this rule to try and simplify $(a + b)^2$ as $a^2 + b^2$ or $(a + b)^3$ as $a^3 + b^3$. To use this rule the base must be the *product* of two numbers—not a sum.

PRODUCT TO A POWER RULE

If a and b are real numbers and n is an integer, then

$$(a \cdot b)^n = a^n \cdot b^n$$

If n is 0 or negative, neither a nor b can be 0.

EXAMPLE 8 Using the Product to a Power Rule to Simplify Exponential Expressions

Simplify each expression. All exponents should be positive integers.

(a) $(3z)^4$

(b) $(-5y^{-2})^{-3}$

(c) $(-4a^2)^{-2}$

Solution

(a) $(3z)^4 = 3^4 z^4$
$$= 81z^4$$

(b) $(-5y^{-2})^{-3} = (-5)^{-3}(y^{-2})^{-3}$
$$= \frac{y^{-2(-3)}}{(-5)^3}$$
$$= \frac{y^6}{-125}$$
$$= -\frac{y^6}{125}$$

(c) $(-4a^2)^{-2} = \frac{1}{(-4a^2)^2}$
$$= \frac{1}{(-4)^2(a^2)^2}$$
$$= \frac{1}{16a^4}$$ ■

Quick ✔ *In Problems 37–40, simplify each expression. All exponents should be positive integers.*

37. $(5y)^3$

38. $(6y)^0$

39. $(3x^2)^4$

40. $(4a^3)^{-2}$

Now let's look at a quotient raised to a power:

$$\left(\frac{2}{3}\right)^4 = \left(\frac{2}{3}\right) \cdot \left(\frac{2}{3}\right) \cdot \left(\frac{2}{3}\right) \cdot \left(\frac{2}{3}\right) = \frac{2^4}{3^4}$$

We have the following result:

QUOTIENT TO A POWER RULE

If a and b are real numbers and n is an integer, then

$$\left(\frac{a}{b}\right)^n = \frac{a^n}{b^n} \qquad \text{if } b \neq 0$$

If n is negative or 0, then a cannot be 0.

EXAMPLE 9 Using the Quotient to a Power Rule to Simplify Exponential Expressions

Simplify each expression. All exponents should be positive integers.

(a) $\left(\dfrac{w}{4}\right)^3$ (b) $\left(\dfrac{2x^2}{y^3}\right)^4$

Solution

(a) $\left(\dfrac{w}{4}\right)^3 = \dfrac{w^3}{4^3}$

$= \dfrac{w^3}{64}$

(b) $\left(\dfrac{2x^2}{y^3}\right)^4 = \dfrac{(2x^2)^4}{(y^3)^4}$

$= \dfrac{2^4(x^2)^4}{(y^3)^4}$

$= \dfrac{16x^{2\cdot4}}{y^{3\cdot4}}$

$= \dfrac{16x^8}{y^{12}}$

Quick ✔ *In Problems 41–44, simplify each expression. All exponents should be positive integers.*

41. $\left(\dfrac{z}{3}\right)^4$ **42.** $\left(\dfrac{x}{2}\right)^{-5}$ **43.** $\left(\dfrac{x^2}{y^3}\right)^4$ **44.** $\left(\dfrac{3a^{-2}}{b^4}\right)^3$

---

6 Simplify Exponential Expressions Using the Laws of Exponents

We now summarize the Laws of Exponents.

THE LAWS OF EXPONENTS

If a and b are real numbers and if m and n are integers, then assuming the expression is defined,

Zero Exponent Rule:	$a^0 = 1$	if $a \neq 0$
Negative Exponent Rule:	$a^{-n} = \dfrac{1}{a^n}$	if $a \neq 0$
Product Rule:	$a^m \cdot a^n = a^{m+n}$	
Quotient Rule:	$\dfrac{a^m}{a^n} = a^{m-n}$	if $a \neq 0$

THE LAWS OF EXPONENTS (*continued*)

Power Rule: $(a^m)^n = a^{m \cdot n}$

Product to Power Rule: $(a \cdot b)^n = a^n \cdot b^n$

Quotient to Power Rule: $\left(\dfrac{a}{b}\right)^n = \dfrac{a^n}{b^n}$ if $b \neq 0$

Quotient to a Negative Power Rule: $\left(\dfrac{a}{b}\right)^{-n} = \left(\dfrac{b}{a}\right)^n$ if $a \neq 0, b \neq 0$

Now let's do some examples where we use one or more of the preceding rules.

EXAMPLE 10 Using the Laws of Exponents

Simplify each expression. All exponents should be positive integers. None of the variables is zero.

(a) $\dfrac{a^3 b^{-1}}{(a^2 b)^3}$ **(b)** $\left(\dfrac{3xy}{x^2 y^{-2}}\right)^2 \cdot \left(\dfrac{9x^2 y^{-3}}{x^3 y^2}\right)^{-1}$

Solution

$$(a \cdot b)^n = a^n \cdot b^n$$
$$\downarrow$$

(a) $\dfrac{a^3 b^{-1}}{(a^2 b)^3} = \dfrac{a^3 b^{-1}}{(a^2)^3 b^3}$

$(a^m)^n = a^{m \cdot n}$: $= \dfrac{a^3 b^{-1}}{a^6 b^3}$

$\dfrac{a^m}{a^n} = a^{m-n}$: $= a^{3-6} b^{-1-3}$

                                            $= a^{-3} b^{-4}$

$a^{-n} = \dfrac{1}{a^n}$: $= \dfrac{1}{a^3 b^4}$

$$\dfrac{a^m}{a^n} = a^{m-n}$$
$$\downarrow$$

Work Smart: Study Skills

Many different approaches may be taken to simplify exponential expressions. In Example 10(b), we could have used the Quotient to Power Rule first and then continued to simplify, for example. Try working a problem one way and then working it again a second way to see if you obtain the same answer.

(b) $\left(\dfrac{3xy}{x^2 y^{-2}}\right)^2 \cdot \left(\dfrac{9x^2 y^{-3}}{x^3 y^2}\right)^{-1} = (3x^{1-2} y^{1-(-2)})^2 \cdot (9x^{2-3} y^{-3-2})^{-1}$

                                            $= (3x^{-1} y^3)^2 \cdot (9x^{-1} y^{-5})^{-1}$

$(a \cdot b)^n = a^n \cdot b^n$: $= 3^2 \cdot (x^{-1})^2 (y^3)^2 \cdot 9^{-1} \cdot (x^{-1})^{-1} (y^{-5})^{-1}$

$(a^m)^n = a^{m \cdot n}$: $= 9x^{-2} y^6 \cdot \dfrac{1}{9} \cdot xy^5$

$a^m a^n = a^{m+n}$: $= x^{-2+1} y^{6+5}$

$a^{-n} = \dfrac{1}{a^n}$: $= x^{-1} y^{11} = \dfrac{y^{11}}{x}$

Quick ✔ *In Problems 45–47, simplify each expression. All exponents should be positive integers.*

45. $\dfrac{(3x^2 y)^2}{12xy^{-2}}$ **46.** $(3ab^3)^3 \cdot (6a^2 b^2)^{-2}$ **47.** $\left(\dfrac{2x^2 y^{-1}}{x^{-2} y^2}\right)^2 \cdot \left(\dfrac{4x^3 y^2}{xy^{-2}}\right)^{-1}$

7 Convert Between Scientific Notation and Decimal Notation

Figure 1

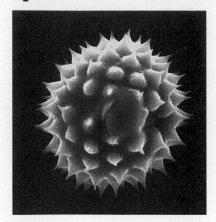

Measurements of physical quantities can range from very small to very large. For example, the mass of an electron (Figure 1) is approximately 0.00000000000000000000000000000911 gram and the mass of Earth (Figure 2) is about 5,980,000,000,000,000,000,000,000 kilograms. These numbers are difficult to write and difficult to read, so we use exponents to write them.

> **DEFINITION** SCIENTIFIC NOTATION
>
> When a number has been written as the product of a number a, where $1 \le |a| < 10$, and a power of 10, it is said to be written in **scientific notation.** That is, a number is written in scientific notation when it is of the form
>
> $$a \times 10^N$$
>
> where
>
> $$1 \le |a| < 10 \quad \text{and} \quad N \text{ is an integer}$$

Figure 2

For example, in scientific notation,

$$\text{Mass of an Electron} = 9.11 \times 10^{-28} \text{ gram}$$

$$\text{Mass of Earth} = 5.98 \times 10^{24} \text{ kilograms}$$

> **CONVERTING A DECIMAL TO SCIENTIFIC NOTATION**
>
> To change a number into scientific notation
>
> **Step 1:** Count the number N of decimal places that the decimal point must be moved in order to arrive at a number a, where $1 \le |a| < 10$.
>
> **Step 2:** If the absolute value of the original number is greater than or equal to 1, the scientific notation is $a \times 10^N$. If the absolute value of the original number is between 0 and 1, the scientific notation is $a \times 10^{-N}$.

EXAMPLE 11 How to Convert from Decimal Notation to Scientific Notation

Write each number in scientific notation.

(a) 94,873

(b) 0.042

Step-by-Step Solution

For a number to be in scientific notation, the decimal must be moved so there is a single nonzero digit to the left of the decimal point. All remaining digits must appear to the right of the decimal point.

(a)

Step 1: The decimal point in 94,873 follows the 3. Therefore, we will move the decimal to the left until it is between the 9 and the 4. Do you see why? This requires that we move the decimal $N = 4$ places.

$9\,4\,8\,7\,3.$

Step 2: The original number is greater than 1, so we write 94,873 in scientific notation as

9.4873×10^4

(b)

Step 1: Because 0.042 is less than 1, we move the decimal point to the right until it is between the 4 and the 2. This requires that we move the decimal N = 2 places.

0.042

Step 2: The original number is between 0 and 1, so we write 0.042 in scientific notation as

4.2×10^{-2}

Work Smart

In Example 11(a), we move the decimal four places to the left because, when the number is written in scientific notation, we are multiplying 9.4873 by $10^4 = 10,000$—which, if simplified, would move the decimal four places to the right.

EXAMPLE 12 Converting a Negative Number from Decimal Notation to Scientific Notation

Write $-520,000,000$ in scientific notation.

Solution

Because the absolute value of the number is greater than 1, we move the decimal to the left $N = 8$ places. Therefore,

$$-520,000,000 = -5.2 \times 10^8$$

Quick ✔ *In Problems 48–51, write each number in scientific notation.*

48. 532 **49.** $-1,230,000$ **50.** 0.034 **51.** -0.0000845

Now we are going to convert a number from scientific notation to decimal notation.

CONVERTING A NUMBER FROM SCIENTIFIC NOTATION TO DECIMAL NOTATION

Determine the exponent on the number 10. If the exponent is negative, then move the decimal $|N|$ decimal places to the left. If the exponent is positive, then move the decimal N decimal places to the right.

EXAMPLE 13 Converting from Scientific Notation to Decimal Notation

Write each number in decimal notation.

(a) 3.2×10^3 (b) 7.54×10^{-5}

Solution

(a) The exponent on the 10 is 3 so we will move the decimal three places to the right.
$$3.2 \times 10^3 = 3.200 \times 10^3 = 3200$$

Work Smart

We move the decimal three places to the right in Example 13(a) because $10^3 = 1000$. So, we are really multiplying 3.2 by 1000. We move the decimal five places to the left in Example 13(b) because
$$10^{-5} = \frac{1}{10^5} = \frac{1}{100,000} = 0.00001$$

(b) The exponent on the 10 is -5 so we will move the decimal five places to the left.
$$7.54 \times 10^{-5} = 000007.54 \times 10^{-5} = 0.0000754$$

Quick ✔ *In Problems 52–55, write each number in decimal notation.*

52. 5×10^2 **53.** 9.1×10^5 **54.** 1.8×10^{-4} **55.** 1×10^{-6}

8 Use Scientific Notation to Multiply and Divide

Once a number is presented in scientific notation, the Laws of Exponents make it relatively straightforward to multiply and divide the numbers. The two Laws of Exponents that we make use of are

$$a^m \cdot a^n = a^{m+n} \quad \text{and} \quad \frac{a^m}{a^n} = a^{m-n}$$

We will use these laws where the base is 10.

EXAMPLE 14 Multiplying Using Scientific Notation

Perform the indicated operation. Express the answer in scientific notation.

(a) $(5 \times 10^2) \cdot (3 \times 10^8)$

(b) $(2.5 \times 10^{-3}) \cdot (4.3 \times 10^{-4})$

Solution

(a) $(5 \times 10^2) \cdot (3 \times 10^8) = (5 \cdot 3) \times (10^2 \cdot 10^8)$

$= 15 \times 10^{10}$

$15 = 1.5 \times 10^1: \quad = (1.5 \times 10^1) \times 10^{10}$

$= 1.5 \times 10^{11}$

(b) $(2.5 \times 10^{-3}) \cdot (4.3 \times 10^{-4}) = (2.5 \cdot 4.3) \times (10^{-3} \cdot 10^{-4})$

$= 10.75 \times 10^{-7}$

$= (1.075 \times 10^1) \times 10^{-7}$

$= 1.075 \times 10^{-6}$ ∎

Quick ✔ *In Problems 56–58, perform the indicated operation. Express the solution in scientific notation.*

56. $(3 \times 10^3) \cdot (2 \times 10^5)$ **57.** $(2 \times 10^{-4}) \cdot (4 \times 10^{-7})$

58. $(6 \times 10^{-5}) \cdot (4 \times 10^8)$

EXAMPLE 15 Dividing Using Scientific Notation

Perform the indicated operation. Express the answer in scientific notation.

(a) $\dfrac{8 \times 10^5}{2 \times 10^3}$ (b) $\dfrac{2.5 \times 10^5}{5 \times 10^{-3}}$

Solution

(a) $\dfrac{8 \times 10^5}{2 \times 10^3} = \dfrac{8}{2} \times \dfrac{10^5}{10^3} = 4 \times 10^2$

(b) $\dfrac{2.5 \times 10^5}{5 \times 10^{-3}} = \dfrac{2.5}{5} \times \dfrac{10^5}{10^{-3}}$

$= 0.5 \times 10^{5-(-3)}$

$= 0.5 \times 10^8$

$= (5 \times 10^{-1}) \times 10^8$

$= 5 \times 10^7$ ∎

Quick ✔ *In Problems 59–62, perform the indicated operation. Express the solution in scientific notation.*

59. $\dfrac{6 \times 10^8}{3 \times 10^6}$ **60.** $\dfrac{6.8 \times 10^{-8}}{3.4 \times 10^{-5}}$ **61.** $\dfrac{4.8 \times 10^7}{9.6 \times 10^3}$ **62.** $\dfrac{3 \times 10^{-5}}{8 \times 10^7}$

EXAMPLE 16   Using Scientific Notation to Multiply and Divide

Perform the indicated operation. Express the answer in decimal notation.

(a) $(3,000,000) \cdot (90,000)$

(b) $\dfrac{0.00000075}{0.00015}$

Solution

In each of these problems, we will first write the numbers in scientific notation and then perform the indicated operation.

(a)
$$
\begin{aligned}
(3,000,000) \cdot (90,000) &= (3 \times 10^6) \cdot (9 \times 10^4) \\
&= 27 \times 10^{10} \\
&= 2.7 \times 10^{11} \\
&= 270,000,000,000
\end{aligned}
$$

(b)
$$
\begin{aligned}
\frac{0.00000075}{0.00015} &= \frac{7.5 \times 10^{-7}}{1.5 \times 10^{-4}} \\
&= \frac{7.5}{1.5} \times \frac{10^{-7}}{10^{-4}} \\
&= 5 \times 10^{-7-(-4)} \\
&= 5 \times 10^{-3} \\
&= 0.005
\end{aligned}
$$

Quick ✔ *In Problems 63–66, perform the indicated operation. Express the solution in decimal notation.*

63. $(8,000,000) \cdot (30,000)$

64. $\dfrac{0.000000012}{0.000004}$

65. $(25,000,000) \cdot (0.00003)$

66. $\dfrac{0.000039}{13,000,000}$

GETTING READY FOR CHAPTER 4 EXERCISES

 *Powered by CourseCompass™ and MathXL*
MyMathLab

 Math XL

 PRACTICE   WATCH   DOWNLOAD   READ   REVIEW

1–66. *are the* **Quick ✔s** *that follow each* **EXAMPLE**

Mixed Practice

In Problems 67–112, simplify each expression. All exponents should be positive integers.

67. -5^2

68. 5^{-2}

69. -5^{-2}

70. -5^0

71. $-8^2 \cdot 8^{-2}$

72. $\dfrac{8^7}{8^5} \cdot 8^{-2}$

73. $\left(\dfrac{4}{9}\right)^{-2}$

74. $\left(\dfrac{3}{4}\right)^{-3}$

75. $(-3)^2 \cdot (-3)^{-5}$

76. $(-4)^{-5} \cdot (-4)^3$

77. $\dfrac{(-4)^2}{(-4)^{-1}}$

78. $\dfrac{(-3)^3}{(-3)^{-2}}$

79. $\dfrac{2^3 \cdot 3^{-2}}{2^{-2} \cdot 3^{-4}}$

80. $\dfrac{3^{-2} \cdot 5^3}{3^2 \cdot 5}$

81. $(6x)^3 (6x)^{-3}$

82. $(5a^2)^5 (5a^2)^{-5}$

83. $(2s^{-2}t^4)(-5s^2t)$

84. $(6ab) \cdot (3a^3b^{-4})$

85. $\left(\dfrac{1}{4}xy\right) \cdot (20xy^{-2})$

86. $(3xy^3) \cdot \left(\dfrac{1}{9}x^2y\right)$

87. $\dfrac{36x^7y^3}{9x^5y^2}$

88. $\dfrac{25a^2b^3}{5ab^6}$

89. $\dfrac{21a^2b}{14a^3b^{-2}}$

90. $\dfrac{25x^{-2}y}{10xy^3}$

91. $(x^{-2})^4$

92. $(z^2)^{-6}$

93. $(3x^2y)^3$

94. $(5a^2b^{-1})^2$

95. $\left(\dfrac{z}{4}\right)^{-3}$

96. $\left(\dfrac{x}{y}\right)^{-8}$

97. $(3a^{-3})^{-2}$

98. $(2y^{-2})^{-4}$

99. $(-2a^2b^3)^{-4}$

100. $(-4a^{-2}b^2)^{-2}$

101. $\dfrac{2^3 \cdot xy^{-2}}{12(x^2)^{-2}y}$

102. $\dfrac{3^2 \cdot x^{-3}(y^2)^3}{15x^2y^8}$

103. $\left(\dfrac{15a^2b^3}{3a^{-4}b^5}\right)^{-2}$

104. $\left(\dfrac{15x^4y^7}{18x^{-3}y}\right)^{-1}$

105. $(4x^4y^{-2})^{-1} \cdot (2x^2y^{-1})^2$

106. $(9a^2b^{-4})^{-1} \cdot (3ab^{-2})^2$

107. $\dfrac{(-2)^2x^3(yz)^2}{-4xy^{-2}z}$

108. $\dfrac{(-3)^3a^3(ab)^{-2}}{9ab^4}$

109. $\dfrac{(3x^{-1}yz^2)^2}{(xy^{-2}z)^3}$

110. $\dfrac{(2ab^2c)^{-1}}{(a^{-1}b^3c^2)^{-2}}$

111. $\dfrac{(6a^3b^{-2})^{-1}}{(2a^{-2}b)^{-2}} \cdot \left(\dfrac{3ab^3}{2a^2b^{-3}}\right)^2$

112. $\left(\dfrac{a^{-3}b^{-1}}{2a^4b^{-2}}\right)^2 \cdot \dfrac{(4a^2b)^2}{(2a^{-2}b)^3}$

In Problems 113–122, perform the indicated operation. Express the solution in scientific notation.

113. $(-5.3 \times 10^{-4}) \cdot (2.8 \times 10^{-3})$

114. $(6.2 \times 10^3) \cdot (-3.8 \times 10^5)$

115. $(4 \times 10^6)^3$

116. $(5 \times 10^8)^2$

117. $\dfrac{5 \times 10^{-6}}{8 \times 10^{-4}}$

118. $\dfrac{1 \times 10^7}{5 \times 10^{-4}}$

119. $\dfrac{(4 \times 10^3)(6 \times 10^7)}{3 \times 10^4}$

120. $\dfrac{(3 \times 10^9)(8 \times 10^{-6})}{4 \times 10^4}$

121. $\dfrac{6.2 \times 10^{-3}}{(3.1 \times 10^4) \cdot (2 \times 10^{-7})}$

122. $\dfrac{1.5 \times 10^{13}}{(3 \times 10^4) \cdot (5 \times 10^8)}$

In Problems 123–128, perform the indicated operation by changing to scientific notation first. Express the solution in decimal notation.

123. $(4{,}000{,}000) \cdot (3{,}000{,}000)$

124. $(15{,}000) \cdot (3{,}000{,}000)$

125. $\dfrac{0.00008}{0.002}$

126. $\dfrac{0.00012}{0.0000002}$

127. $\dfrac{(0.000004) \cdot 1{,}600{,}000}{(0.0008) \cdot (0.002)}$

128. $\dfrac{(0.0001) \cdot (3{,}500{,}000)}{(0.0005) \cdot (1{,}400{,}000)}$

Applying the Concepts

△ **129. Cubes** Suppose the length of a side of a cube is x^2. Find the volume of the cube in terms of x.

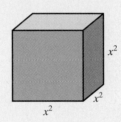

△ **130. Circles** The radius r of a circle is $\dfrac{d}{2}$, where d is the diameter. The area of a circle is given by the formula $A = \pi r^2$. Find the area of a circle in terms of its diameter d.

131. Diameter of a Plant Cell The diameter of a plant cell is 0.00001276 meter. Express this number in scientific notation.

132. Diameter of an Atom The diameter of an atom is about 0.0000000001 meter. Express this diameter as a number in scientific notation.

133. Diameter of Earth The diameter of Earth is 12,760,000 meters. Express this number in scientific notation.

134. National Debt As of July 21, 2008, the debt of the United States federal government was $9,524,000,000,000. Express this number in scientific notation.

135. A Nanometer One nanometer is 1×10^{-9} meter. Express this number in decimal notation.

136. A Lightyear One lightyear is 1×10^{16} meters. Express this number in decimal notation.

137. Rubik Cube The Rubik's Cube has 4×10^{19} possible states. Express this number in decimal notation.

138. Hair Growth Human hair grows at a rate of 1×10^{-8} mile per hour. Express this number in decimal notation. What is the growth rate in miles per year?

139. Per Capita GDP The per capita Gross Domestic Product (GDP) is the GDP divided by the United States population. It represents the average output of each resident of the United States and is measured in dollars per person. In 2007, the Gross Domestic Product of the United States was $\$1.38 \times 10^{13}$. In 2007, the United States population was 3.0×10^{8} people. Determine the per capita GDP of the United States in 2007. Express your answer in decimal notation.

140. Astronomy The speed of light is 186,000 miles per second. How long does it take a beam of light to reach Earth from the Sun when the Sun is 93,000,000 miles from Earth? Express your answer in seconds, using scientific notation.

141. Population Density Population density is the number of people living per some unit of land. In other words, Population Density $= \dfrac{\text{Population}}{\text{Area of Land}}$. The United States is 3.54×10^{6} square miles. In 1990, the United States population was 2.49×10^{8} people. In 2007, the United States population was 3.02×10^{8} people.

(a) Determine the population density of the United States in 1990. Interpret the result.
(b) Determine the population density of the United States in 2007. Interpret the result.
(c) By how much did the population density increase? What does this result mean?

142. Fossil Fuels In 2006, the United States imported 5.0×10^{9} barrels of oil. The United States population was 3.0×10^{8} people in 2006.

(a) Determine the per capita number of barrels of oil imported into the United States in 2007.
(b) One barrel of oil contains 42 gallons. Determine the number of gallons of oil imported into the United States in 2007.
(c) Use the result from part (b) to compute the per capita number of gallons of oil imported into the United States in 2007.

In Problems 143–146, simplify each algebraic expression by rewriting each factor with a common base. (Hint: Consider that $8 = 2^3$.)

143. $\dfrac{2^{x+3}}{4}$

144. $\dfrac{3^{2x}}{27}$

145. $3^x \cdot 27^{3x+1}$

146. $9^{-x} \cdot 3^{x+1}$

147. If $3^x = 5$, what does 3^{4x} equal?

148. If $4^x = 6$, what does 4^{5x} equal?

149. If $2^x = 7$, what does 2^{-4x} equal?

150. If $5^x = 3$, what does 5^{-3x} equal?

Explaining the Concepts

151. A friend of yours has a homework problem in which he must simplify $(x^4)^3$. He tells you that he thinks the answer is x^7. Is he right? If not, explain where he went wrong.

152. A friend of yours is convinced that x^0 must equal 0. Write an explanation that details why $x^0 = 1$. Include any restrictions that must be placed on x.

153. Explain why a cannot be 0 when m, n, or $m + n$ is negative or 0 in the expression a^{m+n}. Use examples to support your explanation.

154. Explain why a cannot be 0 when n is negative or 0 in the expression $(a^m)^n$. Use examples to support your explanation.

155. Explain why neither a nor b can be 0 when n is 0 or negative in the expression $(a \cdot b)^n = a^n \cdot b^n$.

156. Provide a justification for the product rule for exponential expressions.

157. Provide a justification for the quotient rule for exponential expressions.

158. Provide a justification for the power rule for exponential expressions.

159. Provide a justification for the product to a power rule for exponential expressions.

160. Explain how to convert a decimal number to scientific notation. Explain how to convert a number in scientific notation to decimal notation.

161. Explain the benefits of using scientific notation to multiply or divide very large or very small numbers.

4 Polynomials and Polynomial Functions

Did you know that your late 40s and early 50s are your so-called "peak earning years"? In fact, economists develop models that can be used to describe your earnings over your lifetime. Not surprisingly, your earnings will rise from your early 20s to your mid-40s. Then, from your mid-50s and beyond, your earnings start to decrease. See Problem 92 in Section 4.1.

OUTLINE

The Big Picture: Putting It Together

In Chapter 2, we presented a discussion of functions and, in particular, linear functions. We learned properties of linear functions and how to graph them.

We are now going to generalize our discussion of functions a little more. It turns out that linear functions belong to a class of functions called *polynomial functions*. Polynomial functions are arguably the simplest of all functions because they require only addition and repeated multiplication to evaluate. In this chapter, we learn how to add, subtract, multiply, and divide polynomials and polynomial functions. We then learn techniques for "undoing" polynomial multiplication, called factoring. You will find that the Distributive Property comes in handy in many of these operations. Finally, we learn how to use factoring to solve equations that have polynomial expressions or equations that involve polynomial functions.

4.1 Adding and Subtracting Polynomials

OBJECTIVES

1. Define Monomial and Determine the Coefficient and Degree of a Monomial
2. Define Polynomial and Determine the Degree of a Polynomial
3. Simplify Polynomials by Combining Like Terms
4. Evaluate Polynomial Functions
5. Add and Subtract Polynomial Functions

Preparing for Adding and Subtracting Polynomials

Before getting started, take the following readiness quiz. If you get a problem wrong, go back to the section cited and review the material.

P1. What is the coefficient of $-4x^5$? [Section R.5, p. 41]

P2. Combine like terms: $5x^2 - 3x + 1 - 2x^2 - 6x + 3$ [Section R.5, pp. 41–43]

P3. Use the Distributive Property to remove the parentheses: $-4(x - 3)$ [Section R.3, pp. 29–30]

P4. Given $f(x) = -4x + 3$, find $f(3)$. [Section 2.2, pp. 158–159]

1 Define Monomial and Determine the Coefficient and Degree of a Monomial

Recall from Section R.5 that a term is a number or the product of a number and one or more variables raised to a power. The numerical factor of a term is the coefficient. For example, consider Table 1, where various algebraic expressions are given and the terms of each expression identified.

Table 1	
Algebraic Expression	Terms
$5x + 4$	$5x, 4$
$7x^2 - 8x + 3 = 7x^2 + (-8x) + 3$	$7x^2, -8x, 3$
$3x^2 + 7y^{-1}$	$3x^2, 7y^{-1}$

In this chapter, we study *polynomials*. Polynomials have terms that are *monomials*.

Work Smart

The nonnegative integers are $0, 1, 2, 3, \ldots$.

DEFINITION

A **monomial in one variable** is the product of a constant and a variable raised to a nonnegative integer power. A monomial in one variable is of the form

$$ax^k$$

where a is a constant, x is a variable, and $k \geq 0$ is an integer. The constant a is called the **coefficient** of the monomial. If $a \neq 0$, then k is called the **degree** of the monomial.

What if $a = 0$? Since $0 = 0x = 0x^2 = 0x^3 = \ldots$, we cannot assign a degree to 0. Therefore, we say 0 has no degree.

EXAMPLE 1 Identifying the Coefficient and Degree of Monomials

	MONOMIAL	COEFFICIENT	DEGREE
(a)	$5x^3$	5	3
(b)	$-\dfrac{2}{3}x^6$	$-\dfrac{2}{3}$	6
(c)	$8 = 8x^0$	8	0
(d)	$x^2 = 1x^2$	1	2
(e)	$-x = -1 \cdot x$	-1	1
(f)	0	0	no degree

Now let's look at some expressions that are not monomials.

EXAMPLE 2 Expressions That Are Not Monomials

(a) $4x^{\frac{1}{2}}$ is not a monomial because the exponent of the variable x is $\dfrac{1}{2}$ and $\dfrac{1}{2}$ is not a nonnegative integer.

(b) $5x^{-3}$ is not a monomial because the exponent of the variable x is -3 and -3 is not a nonnegative integer.

Quick ✔

1. In a monomial ax^k, what are the possible values of k?

In Problems 2–5, determine whether the expression is a monomial. For those that are monomials, name the coefficient and give the degree.

2. $8x^5$ **3.** $5x^{-2}$

4. 12 **5.** $x^{\frac{1}{3}}$

A monomial may contain more than one variable factor, such as $ax^m y^n$, where a is a constant (called the coefficient), x and y are variables, and m and n are nonnegative integers. The **degree of the monomial** $ax^m y^n$ is the sum of the exponents, $m + n$.

EXAMPLE 3 Monomials in More than One Variable

(a) $-4x^3 y^4$ is a monomial in x and y of degree $3 + 4 = 7$. The coefficient is -4.

(b) $10ab^5$ is a monomial in a and b of degree $1 + 5 = 6$. The coefficient is 10. ∎

Quick ✔ *In Problems 6–9, determine whether the expression is a monomial. For those that are monomials, determine the coefficient and degree.*

6. $3x^5 y^2$ **7.** $-2m^3 n$

8. $4ab^{\frac{1}{2}}$ **9.** $-xy$

⌐2 Define Polynomial and Determine the Degree of a Polynomial

We begin with a definition.

DEFINITION

A **polynomial** is a monomial or the sum of monomials.

A polynomial is in **standard form** if it is written with the terms in descending order according to degree. The **degree of a polynomial** is the highest degree of all the terms of the polynomial. Remember, the degree of a nonzero constant is 0 and the number 0 has no degree.

EXAMPLE 4 Examples of Polynomials

POLYNOMIAL	DEGREE
(a) $7x^3 - 2x^2 + 6x + 4$	3
(b) $3 - 8x + x^2 = x^2 - 8x + 3$	2
(c) $-7x^4 + 24$	4
(d) $x^3 y^4 - 3x^3 y^2 + 2x^3 y$	7
(e) $p^2 q - 8p^3 q^2 + 3 = -8p^3 q^2 + p^2 q + 3$	5
(f) 6	0
(g) 0	No Degree

∎

EXAMPLE 5 Is the Algebraic Expression a Polynomial?

(a) $4x^{-2} - 5x + 1$ is not a polynomial because the exponent on the first term, -2, is negative.

(b) $\dfrac{4}{x^3}$ is not a polynomial because it can be written as $4x^{-3}$ and -3 is less than 0. Remember, the exponents on polynomials must be integers greater than or equal to 0.

(c) $\dfrac{8x^2 + 16}{2}$ is a polynomial of degree 2 because it can be written as $4x^2 + 8$ after dividing 2 into each term in the numerator.

(d) $\dfrac{3xy + 1}{xy - 2}$ is not a polynomial because it is the quotient of two polynomials, and the expression cannot be simplified to a polynomial. ∎

Quick ✔ *In Problems 10–14, determine whether the algebraic expression is a polynomial. For those that are polynomials, determine the degree.*

10. $-3x^3 + 7x^2 - x + 5$

11. $5z^{-1} + 3$

12. $\dfrac{x - 1}{x + 1}$

13. $\dfrac{3x^2 - 9x + 27}{3}$

14. $5p^3q - 8pq^2 + pq$

Work Smart

The prefix "bi" means "two," as in bicycle. The prefix "tri" means "three," as in tricycle. The prefix "poly" means "many."

A polynomial with exactly one term is a monomial; a polynomial that has two monomials that are not like terms is called a **binomial;** and a polynomial that contains three monomials that are not like terms is called a **trinomial.** So

$-14x$ is a polynomial	but more specifically	$-14x$ is a monomial
$2x^3 - 5x$ is a polynomial	but more specifically	$2x^3 - 5x$ is a binomial
$-x^3 - 4x + 11$ is a polynomial	but more specifically	$-x^3 - 4x + 11$ is a trinomial
$3x^2 + 6xy - 2y^2$ is a polynomial	but more specifically	$3x^2 + 6xy - 2y^2$ is a trinomial

We use the term *monomial* to describe a polynomial with a *single* term, and the term *polynomial* to describe the sum of two or more monomials.

⎡3⎤ Simplify Polynomials by Combining Like Terms

In Section R.5, we learned how to combine like terms. To simplify a polynomial means to perform all indicated operations and combine like terms. One operation we perform on polynomials is addition. **To add polynomials, combine the like terms of the polynomials.**

⎡EXAMPLE 6⎤ Simplifying Polynomials: Addition

Simplify: $(-4x^3 + 9x^2 + x - 3) + (2x^3 + 6x + 5)$

Solution

We can find the sum using either horizontal addition or vertical addition.

Work Smart

Remember, like terms have the same variable and the same exponent on the variable.

Horizontal Addition:

The idea here is to combine like terms.

$$(-4x^3 + 9x^2 + x - 3) + (2x^3 + 6x + 5)$$

$$\text{Remove parentheses:} \quad = -4x^3 + 9x^2 + x - 3 + 2x^3 + 6x + 5$$

$$\text{Rearrange terms:} \quad = -4x^3 + 2x^3 + 9x^2 + x + 6x - 3 + 5$$

$$\text{Distributive Property:} \quad = (-4 + 2)x^3 + 9x^2 + (1 + 6)x + (-3 + 5)$$

$$\text{Simplify:} \quad = -2x^3 + 9x^2 + 7x + 2$$

Vertical Addition:

The idea here is to line up like terms in each polynomial vertically and then add the coefficients.

$$
\begin{array}{r}
-4x^3 + 9x^2 + x - 3 \\
2x^3 + 6x + 5 \\
\hline
-2x^3 + 9x^2 + 7x + 2
\end{array}
$$

∎

Quick ✔ *In Problems 15 and 16, simplify by adding the polynomials.*
15. $(2x^2 - 3x + 1) + (4x^2 + 5x - 3)$
16. $(5w^4 - 3w^3 + w - 8) + (-2w^4 + w^3 - 7w^2 + 3)$

EXAMPLE 7 Simplifying Polynomials in Two Variables: Addition

Simplify: $(5a^2b - 3ab + 2ab^2) + (a^2b + 5ab - 4ab^2)$

Solution

Although you have the choice of the horizontal or vertical format, we only present the horizontal format. The first step is to remove the parentheses.

$$(5a^2b - 3ab + 2ab^2) + (a^2b + 5ab - 4ab^2) = 5a^2b - 3ab + 2ab^2 + a^2b + 5ab - 4ab^2$$

Rearrange terms: $= 5a^2b + a^2b - 3ab + 5ab + 2ab^2 - 4ab^2$

Distributive Property: $= (5 + 1)a^2b + (-3 + 5)ab + (2 - 4)ab^2$

Simplify: $= 6a^2b + 2ab - 2ab^2$ ∎

Quick ✔ *In Problem 17, simplify by adding the polynomials.*
17. $(8x^2y + 2x^2y^2 - 7xy^2) + (-3x^2y + 5x^2y^2 + 3xy^2)$

We can subtract polynomials using either the horizontal or vertical approach as well. Remember,

$$a - b = a + (-b)$$

So, to subtract one polynomial from another, we add the opposite of each term in the polynomial following the subtraction sign and then combine like terms.

EXAMPLE 8 Simplifying Polynomials: Subtraction

Simplify: $(5z^3 + 3z^2 - 3) - (-2z^3 + 7z^2 - z + 2)$

Solution

Horizontal Subtraction:
Recall that $a - b = a + (-1) \cdot b$.

$$(5z^3 + 3z^2 - 3) - (-2z^3 + 7z^2 - z + 2) = 5z^3 + 3z^2 - 3 + (-1)(-2z^3 + 7z^2 - z + 2)$$

Distribute the -1: $= 5z^3 + 3z^2 - 3 + 2z^3 - 7z^2 + z - 2$

Rearrange terms: $= 5z^3 + 2z^3 + 3z^2 - 7z^2 + z - 3 - 2$

Combine like terms: $= 7z^3 - 4z^2 + z - 5$

Vertical Subtraction:
We line up like terms, change the sign of each coefficient of the second polynomial, and add.

$$
\begin{array}{rrrr}
z^3 & z^2 & z^1 & z^0 \\
5z^3 + 3z^2 & & - 3 \\
-(-2z^3 + 7z^2 - z + 2) \\
\end{array}
\qquad
\begin{array}{rrrr}
z^3 & z^2 & z^1 & z^0 \\
5z^3 + 3z^2 & & - 3 \\
+ 2z^3 - 7z^2 + z - 2 \\
\hline
7z^3 - 4z^2 + z - 5 \\
\end{array}
$$
∎

Quick ✔ *In Problems 18–20, simplify by subtracting the polynomials.*

18. $(5x^3 - 6x^2 + x + 9) - (4x^3 + 10x^2 - 6x + 7)$

19. $(8y^3 - 5y^2 + 3y + 1) - (-3y^3 + 6y + 8)$

20. $(8x^2y + 2x^2y^2 - 7xy^2) - (-3x^2y + 5x^2y^2 + 3xy^2)$

4 Evaluate Polynomial Functions

Up to now, we have only discussed polynomial expressions, such as $4x^3 + x^2 - 7x + 1$. If we write $f(x) = 4x^3 + x^2 - 7x + 1$, then we have a *polynomial function*.

DEFINITION

A **polynomial function** is a function whose rule is a polynomial. The domain of all polynomial functions is the set of all real numbers. The **degree** of a polynomial function is the value of the largest exponent on the variable.

In Chapter 2, we studied linear functions. Recall, a linear function is a function of the form $f(x) = mx + b$. Table 2 illustrates some specific types of polynomial functions, their functional forms, and specific examples.

Table 2

Polynomial	Functional Form	Examples	Degree
Linear	$f(x) = a_1x + a_0$ where a_1 is the slope and a_0 is the y-intercept	$f(x) = 4x + 5$	1
		$f(x) = -6x$	1
		$f(x) = 3$	0
Quadratic	$f(x) = a_2x^2 + a_1x + a_0, \ a_2 \neq 0$	$f(x) = 3x^2 - 5x + 1$	2
Cubic	$f(x) = a_3x^3 + a_2x^2 + a_1x + a_0, \ a_3 \neq 0$	$f(x) = -2x^3 + 4x - 1$	3

To **evaluate** a polynomial function, we substitute the value of the variable and simplify, just as we did in Section 2.2.

EXAMPLE 9 Evaluating a Polynomial Function

For the polynomial function $P(x) = 2x^3 - 5x^2 + x - 3$, find

(a) $P(3)$ **(b)** $P(-1)$

Solution

(a) We substitute 3 for x in the expression $2x^3 - 5x^2 + x - 3$ to get

$$P(3) = 2(3)^3 - 5(3)^2 + 3 - 3$$
$$= 2 \cdot 27 - 5 \cdot 9 + 3 - 3$$
$$= 54 - 45 + 3 - 3$$
$$= 9$$

(b) We substitute -1 for x in the expression $2x^3 - 5x^2 + x - 3$ to get

$$P(-1) = 2(-1)^3 - 5(-1)^2 + (-1) - 3$$
$$= 2 \cdot (-1) - 5 \cdot 1 + (-1) - 3$$
$$= -2 - 5 - 1 - 3$$
$$= -11$$

Quick ✔

21. Find the following values of the polynomial function $g(x) = -2x^3 + 7x + 1$.

(a) $g(0)$ (b) $g(2)$ (c) $g(-3)$

Polynomial functions can be used to model a variety of situations.

EXAMPLE 10 A Polynomial Model for Higher Education

The scatter diagram shown in Figure 1 shows the percentage of the population of the United States with an advanced degree (more than a bachelor's degree) for various ages. The polynomial function

$$D(a) = -0.006a^2 + 0.683a - 6.82$$

can be used to approximate the percent of the population whose age is a who have an advanced degree, D.

(a) Use the function to estimate the percentage of the population of 35-year-olds with an advanced degree.

(b) Use the function to estimate the percentage of the population of 65-year-olds with an advanced degree.

Figure 1

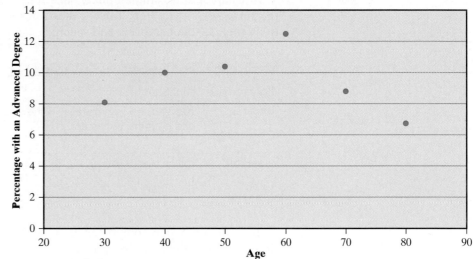

SOURCE: *Statistical Abstract, 2008*

Solution

(a) The independent variable a represents the age, so $a = 35$. We evaluate $D(35)$.

$$D(a) = -0.006a^2 + 0.683a - 6.82$$
$$D(35) = -0.006(35)^2 + 0.683(35) - 6.82$$
$$= -7.35 + 23.905 - 6.82$$
$$= 9.735$$

We estimate that the percentage of the population who are 35 years of age with an advanced degree is 9.735%. This looks to be close to the pattern in the scatter diagram.

(b) We evaluate $D(65)$.

$$D(a) = -0.006a^2 + 0.683a - 6.82$$
$$D(65) = -0.006(65)^2 + 0.683(65) - 6.82$$
$$= -25.35 + 44.395 - 6.82$$
$$= 12.225$$

We estimate that the percentage of the population who are 65 years of age with an advanced degree is 12.225%. This also looks to be close to the pattern in the scatter diagram. ∎

Quick ✔

22. The polynomial function $B(a) = -1399a^2 + 70,573a - 495,702$ represents the number of first births of women who were a years of age in the United States in 2006.

(a) Use the function to predict the number of first births to 25-year-old women.

(b) Use the function to predict the number of first births to 40-year-old women.

⌈5⌉ Add and Subtract Polynomial Functions

Functions, just like numbers, can be added, subtracted, multiplied, and divided. In this section, we concentrate on adding and subtracting polynomial functions.

DEFINITION

If f and g are two functions,
The **sum $f + g$** is the function defined by
$$(f + g)(x) = f(x) + g(x)$$
The **difference $f - g$** is the function defined by
$$(f - g)(x) = f(x) - g(x)$$

⌈EXAMPLE 11⌉ Finding the Sum and Difference of Two Polynomial Functions

Let f and g be two functions defined as
$$f(x) = 3x^2 - x + 1 \quad \text{and} \quad g(x) = -x^2 + 5x - 6$$
Find the following:

(a) $(f + g)(x)$ (b) $(f - g)(x)$ (c) $(f + g)(2)$ (d) $(f - g)(-1)$

Solution

(a) $(f + g)(x) = f(x) + g(x)$
$$= (3x^2 - x + 1) + (-x^2 + 5x - 6)$$
$$= 3x^2 - x + 1 - x^2 + 5x - 6$$
$$= 3x^2 - x^2 - x + 5x + 1 - 6$$
$$= 2x^2 + 4x - 5$$

(b) $(f - g)(x) = f(x) - g(x)$
$$= (3x^2 - x + 1) - (-x^2 + 5x - 6)$$
$$= 3x^2 - x + 1 + x^2 - 5x + 6$$
$$= 3x^2 + x^2 - x - 5x + 1 + 6$$
$$= 4x^2 - 6x + 7$$

(c) Because $(f + g)(x) = 2x^2 + 4x - 5$, we have
$$(f + g)(2) = 2(2)^2 + 4(2) - 5$$
$$= 8 + 8 - 5$$
$$= 11$$
We could also have evaluated $(f + g)(2)$ as follows:
$$(f + g)(2) = f(2) + g(2)$$
$$= 11 + 0$$
$$= 11$$

(d) Because $(f - g)(x) = 4x^2 - 6x + 7$, we have
$$(f - g)(-1) = 4(-1)^2 - 6(-1) + 7$$
$$= 4 + 6 + 7$$
$$= 17$$

Quick ✔

23. Let f and g be two functions defined as

$$f(x) = 3x^2 - x + 1 \quad \text{and} \quad g(x) = -x^2 + 5x - 6$$

Find the following:

(a) $(f + g)(x)$ (b) $(f - g)(x)$ (c) $(f + g)(1)$ (d) $(f - g)(-2)$

Let's look at an application of the difference of two functions.

EXAMPLE 12 The Profit Function

Profit is defined as total revenue minus total cost. The profit function of a company that manufactures and sells x units of a product is given by

$$P(x) = R(x) - C(x)$$

where P represents the company's profits
   R represents the company's revenue
   C represents the company's cost

(a) If a company sells a scientific calculator for $12, its revenue function is $R(x) = 12x$. If the cost of each additional calculator manufactured is $7 and fixed costs are $1200 per week, its cost is given by $C(x) = 7x + 1200$. Find the company's profit function, $P(x)$.

(b) Determine and interpret $P(800)$.

Solution

(a) The profit function is

$$P(x) - R(x) - C(x)$$
$$= 12x - (7x + 1200)$$
$$= 12x - 7x - 1200$$
$$= 5x - 1200$$

(b) $P(800) = 5(800) - 1200$
$$= 4000 - 1200$$
$$= 2800$$

If the company manufactures and sells 800 calculators in a week, its profit will be $2800. ∎

Quick ✔

24. The calculator company presented in Example 12 just gave its employees a raise that increases the cost of each additional calculator manufactured to $8. In addition, it renewed its lease on the plant so that weekly fixed costs increased to $1250.

(a) Determine the new profit function.

(b) Determine and interpret $P(800)$.

4.1 EXERCISES

1–24. *are the* Quick ✔*s that follow each* **EXAMPLE**

Building Skills

In Problems 25–32, determine the coefficient and degree of each monomial. See Objective 1.

25. $3x^2$

26. $5x^4$

27. $-8x^2y^3$

28. $-12xy$

29. $\frac{4}{3}x^6$

30. $-\frac{5}{3}z^5$

31. 2

32. -7

In Problems 33–36, state why each of the following is not a polynomial. See Objective 2.

33. $2x^{-1} + 3x$

34. $6p^{-3} - p^{-2} + 3p^{-1}$

35. $\frac{4}{z-1}$

36. $\frac{x^2+2}{x}$

In Problems 37–52, determine whether the algebraic expression is a polynomial (Yes or No). If it is a polynomial, write the polynomial in standard form, determine the degree, and state if it is a monomial, binomial, or trinomial. If it is a polynomial with more than 3 terms, identify the expression as a polynomial. See Objective 2.

37. $5x^2 - 9x + 1$

38. $-3y^2 + 8y + 1$

39. $\frac{-20}{n}$

40. $\frac{1}{x}$

41. $3y^{\frac{1}{3}} + 2$

42. $8m - 4m^{\frac{1}{2}}$

43. $\frac{5}{8}$

44. -12

45. $5 - 8y + 2y^2$

46. $7 - 5p + 2p^2 - p^3$

47. $7x^{-1} + 4$

48. $4y^{-2} + 6y - 1$

49. $3x^2y^2 + 2xy^4 + 4$

50. $4mn^3 - 2m^2n^3 + mn^8$

51. $4pqr + 2p^2q + 3pq^{\frac{1}{4}}$

52. $-2xyz^2 + 7x^3z - 8y^{\frac{1}{2}}z$

In Problems 53–72, simplify each polynomial by adding or subtracting, as indicated. Express your answer as a single polynomial in standard form. See Objective 3.

53. $5z^3 + 8z^3$

54. $10y^4 - 6y^4$

55. $(x^2 + 5x + 1) + (3x^2 - 2x - 3)$

56. $(x^2 - 4x + 1) + (5x^2 + 2x + 7)$

57. $(6p^3 - p^2 + 3p - 4) + (2p^3 - 7p + 3)$

58. $(2w^3 - w^2 + 6w - 5) + (-3w^3 + 5w^2 + 9)$

59. $(5x^2 + 9x + 4) - (3x^2 + 5x + 1)$

60. $(7y^2 + 9y + 12) - (4y^2 + 8y - 3)$

61. $(7s^2t^3 + st^2 - 5t - 8) - (4s^2t^3 + 5st^2 - 7)$

62. $(-2x^3y^3 + 7xy - 3) - (x^3y^3 + 5y^2 + xy - 3)$

63. $(3 - 5x + x^2) + (-2 + 3x - 5x^2)$

64. $(-3 - 5z + 3z^2) + (1 + 2z + z^2)$

65. $(6 - 2y + y^3) - (-2 + y^2 - 2y^3)$

66. $(8 - t^3) - (1 + 3t + 3t^2 + t^3)$

67. $\left(\frac{1}{4}x^2 + \frac{3}{2}x + 3\right) + \left(\frac{1}{2}x^2 - \frac{1}{4}x - 2\right)$

68. $\left(\frac{3}{4}y^3 - \frac{1}{8}y + \frac{2}{3}\right) + \left(\frac{1}{2}y^3 + \frac{5}{12}y - \frac{5}{6}\right)$

69. $(5x^2y^2 - 8x^2y + xy^2) + (3x^2y^2 + x^2y - 4xy^2)$

70. $(7a^3b + 9ab^2 - 4a^2b) + (-4a^3b + 3a^2b - 8ab^2)$

71. $(3x^2y + 7xy^2 + xy) - (2x^2y - 4xy^2 - xy)$

72. $(-5xy^2 + 3xy - 9y^2) - (5xy^2 + 7xy - 8y^2)$

In Problems 73–78, find the following values for each polynomial function. See Objective 4.

    (a) $f(0)$ **(b)** $f(2)$ **(c)** $f(-3)$

73. $f(x) = x^2 - 4x + 1$ **74.** $f(x) = x^2 + 5x - 3$

75. $f(x) = 2x^3 - 7x + 3$ **76.** $f(x) = -2x^3 + 3x - 1$

77. $f(x) = -x^3 + 3x^2 - 2x + 3$

78. $f(x) = -2x^3 + x^2 + 5x - 3$

In Problems 79–84, for the given functions f and g, find the following. See Objective 5.

(a) $(f + g)(x)$ (b) $(f - g)(x)$

(c) $(f + g)(2)$ (d) $(f - g)(1)$

79. $f(x) = 2x + 5; g(x) = -5x + 1$

80. $f(x) = 4x + 3; g(x) = 2x - 3$

81. $f(x) = x^2 - 5x + 3; g(x) = 2x^2 + 3$

82. $f(x) = 3x^2 + x + 2; g(x) = x^2 - 3x - 1$

83. $f(x) = x^3 + 6x^2 + 12x + 2; g(x) = x^3 - 8$

84. $f(x) = 8x^3 + 1; g(x) = x^3 + 3x^2 + 3x + 1$

Applying the Concepts

85. Add $5x^3 - 5x + 3$ to $-4x^3 + x^2 - 2x + 1$.

86. Add $2x^3 - 3x^2 - 5x + 7$ to $x^3 + 3x^2 - 6x - 4$.

87. Subtract $4b^3 - b^2 + 3b - 1$ from $2b^3 + 5b^2 - b + 3$.

88. Subtract $2q^3 - 3q^2 + 7q - 2$ from $-5q^3 + q^2 + 2q - 1$.

△**89. Area** A rectangle has one corner on the graph of $y = 6 - 2x$, another at the origin, a third on the positive y-axis, and the fourth on the positive x-axis (see the figure).

The polynomial function $A(x) = -2x^2 + 6x$ can be used to find the area A of the rectangle whose vertex is at (x, y).

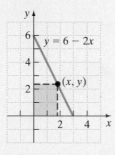

(a) Find the area of the rectangle whose vertex is at $(2, 2)$.

(b) Find the area of the rectangle whose vertex is at $(1, 4)$.

(c) How can the coordinates of the vertex be used to find the area? What is the area?

△**90. Area** A rectangle has one corner on the graph of $y = 10 - 2x$, another at the origin, a third on the positive y-axis, and the fourth on the positive x-axis (see the figure).

The polynomial function $A(x) = -2x^2 + 10x$ can be used to find the area A of the rectangle whose vertex is at (x, y).

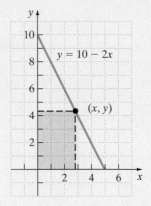

(a) Find the area of the rectangle whose vertex is at $(3, 4)$.

(b) Find the area of the rectangle whose vertex is at $(4, 2)$.

91. Price per Square Foot of a New Home The bar graph shown represents the average price per square foot for a new single-family home in the United States for the years 1992–2006.

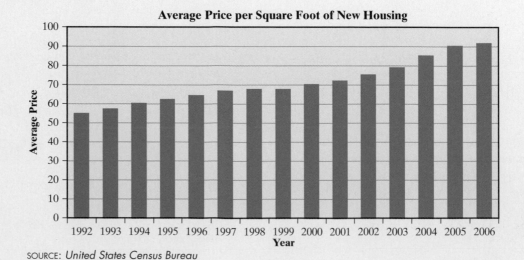

SOURCE: *United States Census Bureau*

The polynomial function $P(t) = 0.019t^3 - 0.292t^2 + 3.068t + 55.140$ can be used to approximate the average price per square foot P, where t is the number of years since 1992.

(a) Use the function to estimate the average price per square foot in 1992.
(b) Use the function to predict the average price per square foot in 2012.

92. **Income** The bar graph shown represents the average per-capita income for residents of the United States by age in 2005.

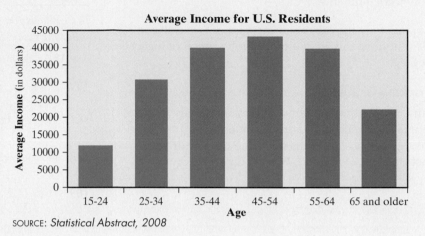

Average Income for U.S. Residents

SOURCE: *Statistical Abstract, 2008*

The polynomial function $I(a) = -44.45a^2 + 4251.02a - 56,879.54$ can be used to approximate the average income I, where a is the age of the individual.

(a) Use the function to estimate the average income of a 20-year-old in 2002.
(b) Use the function to estimate the average income of a 55-year-old in 2002.

---

93. **Profit Function** Suppose that the revenue R from selling x cell phones is $R(x) = -1.2x^2 + 220x$. The cost C of selling x cell phones is $C(x) = 0.05x^3 - 2x^2 + 65x + 500$.
   (a) Find the profit function, $P(x)$.
   (b) Find the profit if $x = 15$ cell phones are sold.
   (c) Determine and interpret $P(100)$.

94. **Profit Function** Suppose that the revenue R from selling x clocks is $R(x) = -0.3x^2 + 30x$. The cost C of selling x clocks is $C(x) = 0.1x^2 + 7x + 400$.
   (a) Find the profit function, $P(x)$.
   (b) Find the profit if $x = 15$ clocks are sold.
   (c) Determine and interpret $P(40)$.

Extending the Concepts

95. If $f(x) = 3x + 2$ and $g(x) = ax - 5$, find a such that $(f + g)(3) = 12$.

96. If $f(x) = -5x + 1$ and $g(x) = ax - 3$, find a such that $(f - g)(2) = 10$.

97. The graph of two functions, f and g, is shown to the right. Use the graph to answer parts **(a)**–**(d)**.

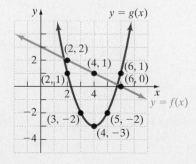

(a) $(f + g)(2)$
(b) $(f + g)(4)$
(c) $(f - g)(6)$
(d) $(g - f)(6)$

98. **Work-Related Disability** Suppose that $M(a)$ represents the number of American males with a work-related disability who are a years of age. Suppose that $F(a)$ represents the number of American females with a work-related disability who are a years of age. Determine a function T that represents the total number of Americans with work-related disabilities who are a years of age.

99. **Taxes** Let $T(x)$ represent the total taxes paid by everyone who worked in the United States in year x. Let $F(x)$ represent the taxes paid to the federal government in year x. Write a function S that represents the total taxes paid other than federal (state, property, sales, and so on) in year x.

Explaining the Concepts

100. Explain the difference between a term and a monomial term.

101. What is the degree of a polynomial that is linear?

102. How many terms are in a binomial? How many terms are in a trinomial?

103. Give a definition of *polynomial* using your own words. Provide examples of polynomials that are monomials, binomials, and trinomials. In addition, give examples of polynomials that are linear.

104. What is the difference between a polynomial and a polynomial function?

105. Explain why the degree of the sum of two polynomials is at most the degree of the polynomial of highest degree.

The Graphing Calculator

Graphing calculators can be used to evaluate any function. Figure 2 shows the result obtained in Example 9(b) on a TI-84 Plus graphing calculator with the function to be evaluated, $P(x) = 2x^3 - 5x^2 + x - 3$ in Y_1.

Figure 2

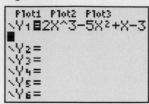 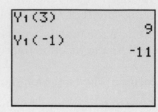

In Problems 106–109, use a graphing calculator to find the following values for each polynomial function.

(a) $f(4)$ (b) $f(-2)$ (c) $f(6)$

106. $f(x) = -2x^2 + 5x + 3$

107. $f(x) = 4x^2 - 7x + 1$

108. $f(x) = -3x^3 + 5x^2 - 8x + 1$

109. $f(x) = 2x^3 - 5x^2 + x + 5$

4.2 Multiplying Polynomials

OBJECTIVES

1. Multiply a Monomial and a Polynomial
2. Multiply a Binomial by a Binomial
3. Multiply a Polynomial by a Polynomial
4. Multiply Special Products
5. Multiply Polynomial Functions

Preparing for Multiplying Polynomials

Before getting started, take the following readiness quiz. If you get a problem wrong, go back to the section cited and review the material.

P1. Simplify: $4x^2 \cdot 3x^3$ [Getting Ready, p. 306]

P2. Simplify: $(-3x)^2$ [Getting Ready, p. 311]

P3. Use the Distributive Property to remove the parentheses: $4(x - 5)$ [Section R.3, pp. 29–30]

Multiplying polynomials is based on two concepts learned earlier: the Product Rule for Exponents (Getting Ready, p. 306) and the Distributive Property (Section R.3, p. 29). The following example will help you to review these concepts.

EXAMPLE 1   Review the Product Rule for Exponents and the Distributive Property

(a) Simplify: $(2a^3b)(-6a^2b^4)$

(b) Remove the parentheses: $2(z - 3)$

Solution

(a)
$$(2a^3b)(-6a^2b^4) = (2 \cdot (-6))(a^3 \cdot a^2)(b \cdot b^4)$$

Product Rule: $a^m \cdot a^n = a^{m+n}$: $= -12a^{3+2}b^{1+4}$

$$= -12a^5b^5$$

(b) The Distributive Property is used to remove parentheses:

$$2(z - 3) = 2 \cdot z - 2 \cdot 3 = 2z - 6$$

Quick ✔ *In Problems 1–4, simplify each expression completely. All exponents should be positive.*

1. $(3x^5)(2x^2)$ **2.** $(-7a^3b^2)(3ab^4)$

3. $\left(\dfrac{2}{3}x^4\right)\left(\dfrac{15}{8}x\right)$ **4.** $-3(x + 2)$

1   Multiply a Monomial and a Polynomial

From Example 1(b), we can see that when we multiply a binomial by a monomial, we use the Distributive Property to remove the parentheses. In general, when we multiply a polynomial by a monomial, we use the *Extended Form of the Distributive Property.*

In Words

The Extended Form of the Distributive Property says to multiply each term in parentheses by a.

EXTENDED FORM OF THE DISTRIBUTIVE PROPERTY

$$a(b_1 + b_2 + \cdots + b_n) = a \cdot b_1 + a \cdot b_2 + \cdots + a \cdot b_n$$

where $a, b_1, b_2, \ldots, b_n$ are real numbers.

EXAMPLE 2   Using the Extended Form of the Distributive Property

Multiply and simplify each of the following expressions:

   (a) $3x^2(x^2 + 4x + 2)$

   (b) $\dfrac{1}{2}xy^3\left(\dfrac{2}{3}xy^2 + \dfrac{6}{5}y + \dfrac{3}{4}\right)$

Solution

   (a) $3x^2(x^2 + 4x + 2) = 3x^2 \cdot x^2 + 3x^2 \cdot 4x + 3x^2 \cdot 2$

$$= 3x^4 + 12x^3 + 6x^2$$

   (b) $\dfrac{1}{2}xy^3\left(\dfrac{2}{3}xy^2 + \dfrac{6}{5}y + \dfrac{3}{4}\right) = \dfrac{1}{2}xy^3 \cdot \dfrac{2}{3}xy^2 + \dfrac{1}{2}xy^3 \cdot \dfrac{6}{5}y + \dfrac{1}{2}xy^3 \cdot \dfrac{3}{4}$

$$= \dfrac{1}{3}x^2y^5 + \dfrac{3}{5}xy^4 + \dfrac{3}{8}xy^3 \quad\blacksquare$$

Quick ✔ *In Problems 5–7, multiply and simplify each of the expressions.*

5. $5x(x^2 + 3x + 2)$

6. $2xy(3x^2 - 5xy + 2y^2)$

7. $\dfrac{3}{4}y^2\left(\dfrac{4}{3}y^2 + \dfrac{2}{9}y + \dfrac{16}{3}\right)$

2   Multiply a Binomial by a Binomial

When we find the product of two binomials, we use the Distributive Property by distributing the first binomial to each term in the second binomial. Just as with addition and subtraction of polynomials, we can use either a horizontal or vertical format.

EXAMPLE 3 Multiplying Two Binomials

Find the product: $(3x + 4)(2x - 5)$

Solution

VERTICAL MULTIPLICATION

$$
\begin{array}{r}
3x + 4 \\
\times\ 2x - 5 \\
\hline
-15x - 20 \quad \leftarrow -5(3x + 4) \\
6x^2 + 8x \quad \longleftarrow 2x(3x + 4) \\
\hline
6x^2 - 7x - 20
\end{array}
$$

HORIZONTAL MULTIPLICATION

We distribute the first binomial to each term in the second binomial.

$$
\begin{aligned}
(3x + 4)(2x - 5) &= (3x + 4)(2x) + (3x + 4)(-5) \\
&= 3x \cdot 2x + 4 \cdot 2x + 3x \cdot (-5) + 4 \cdot (-5) \\
&= 6x^2 + 8x - 15x - 20
\end{aligned}
$$

Combine like terms: $= 6x^2 - 7x - 20$

In either case, $(3x + 4)(2x - 5) = 6x^2 - 7x - 20$. ∎

The FOIL Method

When multiplying two binomials, we can use a method referred to as the **FOIL method.** The acronym FOIL stands for **First, Outer, Inner, Last** and is illustrated below.

$$
(ax + b)(cx + d) = ax \cdot cx + ax \cdot d + b \cdot cx + b \cdot d
$$

EXAMPLE 4 Using the FOIL Method to Multiply Two Binomials

Find the product:

(a) $(4y - 3)(2y + 5)$ **(b)** $(2m + n)(m - 3n)$

Solution

$$
\begin{aligned}
\textbf{(a)}\ (4y - 3)(2y + 5) &= 4y \cdot 2y + 4y \cdot 5 - 3 \cdot 2y - 3 \cdot 5 \\
&= 8y^2 + 20y - 6y - 15 \\
&= 8y^2 + 14y - 15
\end{aligned}
$$

$$
\begin{aligned}
\textbf{(b)}\ (2m + n)(m - 3n) &= 2m \cdot m - 2m \cdot 3n + n \cdot m - n \cdot 3n \\
&= 2m^2 - 6mn + mn - 3n^2 \\
&= 2m^2 - 5mn - 3n^2
\end{aligned}
$$

∎

Quick ✔

8. The acronym FOIL stands for ____ , ____ , ____ , ____ .

In Problems 9–11, find the product.

9. $(x + 4)(x + 1)$ **10.** $(3v + 5)(2v - 3)$

11. $(2a - b)(a + 5b)$

⌐3 Multiply a Polynomial by a Polynomial

Work Smart

When multiplying polynomials, it is a good idea to write the polynomials in descending order of degree.

When multiplying a trinomial by a binomial or a trinomial by a trinomial, we make repeated use of the Distributive Property. The approach is similar to that taken in Example 3 presented earlier. It is a good idea to write each polynomial in standard form. Although you also have the choice of the horizontal or vertical format, we only present the horizontal format.

EXAMPLE 5 Multiplying Two Polynomials

Find the product:

   (a) $(3x + 1)(x^2 + 4x - 3)$ (b) $(x^2 + 5x + 2)(2x^2 - x + 3)$

Solution

   (a) We begin by distributing the binomial $3x + 1$ to each term in the trinomial.

$$(3x + 1)(x^2 + 4x - 3) = (3x + 1) \cdot x^2 + (3x + 1) \cdot 4x + (3x + 1) \cdot (-3)$$

Distributive Property: $= 3x^3 + x^2 + 12x^2 + 4x - 9x - 3$

Combine like terms: $= 3x^3 + 13x^2 - 5x - 3$

   (b) Distribute $x^2 + 5x + 2$ to each term in the second trinomial.

$$(x^2 + 5x + 2)(2x^2 - x + 3) = (x^2 + 5x + 2) \cdot 2x^2 + (x^2 + 5x + 2) \cdot (-x)$$
$$+ (x^2 + 5x + 2) \cdot 3$$

Distributive Property: $= x^2 \cdot 2x^2 + 5x \cdot 2x^2 + 2 \cdot 2x^2 + x^2 \cdot (-x)$
$$+ 5x \cdot (-x) + 2 \cdot (-x) + x^2 \cdot 3 + 5x \cdot 3 + 2 \cdot 3$$
$$= 2x^4 + 10x^3 + 4x^2 - x^3 - 5x^2 - 2x + 3x^2$$
$$+ 15x + 6$$

Combine like terms: $= 2x^4 + 9x^3 + 2x^2 + 13x + 6$ ∎

Quick ✔ *In Problems 12 and 13, find the product.*

12. $(2y - 3)(y^2 + 4y + 5)$ **13.** $(z^2 - 3z + 2)(2z^2 + z + 6)$

4 Multiply Special Products

There are certain products, called **special products,** which occur quite frequently. Because these products are special, we give them names.

EXAMPLE 6 Products of the Form $(A - B)(A + B)$

Find the product: $(x - 7)(x + 7)$

Solution

We use FOIL and obtain

$$\overset{\text{F}}{} \quad \overset{\text{O}}{} \quad \overset{\text{I}}{} \quad \overset{\text{L}}{}$$

$$(x - 7)(x + 7) = x \cdot x + x \cdot 7 - 7 \cdot x - 7 \cdot 7$$
$$= x^2 + 7x - 7x - 49$$
$$= x^2 - 49 \quad ∎$$

Work Smart

When multiplying products of the form $(A - B)(A + B)$, the "middle terms" will always be "opposites" and therefore sum to 0. Also, don't forget multiplication is commutative. So,

$(A + B)(A - B) = (A - B)(A + B)$
$= A^2 - B^2$

We have the following based upon the results of Example 6.

> **DIFFERENCE OF TWO SQUARES**
>
> $$(A - B)(A + B) = A^2 - B^2$$

EXAMPLE 7 Using the Difference of Two Squares Formula

   (a) $(A + B)(A - B) = A^2 - B^2$

$$(3x + 2)(3x - 2) = (3x)^2 - 2^2$$
$$= 9x^2 - 4$$

(b)
$$A = 2m \text{ and } B = 5n^2$$
$$\downarrow$$
$$(2m - 5n^2)(2m + 5n^2) = (2m)^2 - (5n^2)^2$$
$$= 4m^2 - 25n^4$$

■

Quick ✔

14. *True or False:* The product of a binomial and a binomial is always a trinomial.

15. $(A - B)(A + B) = \underline{\hspace{2cm}}$.

In Problems 16 and 17, find each product.

16. $(5y + 2)(5y - 2)$ **17.** $(7y + 2z^3)(7y - 2z^3)$

⌐EXAMPLE 8 **Products of the Form** $(A + B)^2$ **or** $(A - B)^2$

Find each product:

   (a) $(4x + 3)^2$ **(b)** $(3z - 5)^2$

Solution

(a) $(4x + 3)^2 = (4x + 3)(4x + 3)$
$$= (4x)^2 + \underbrace{(4x)(3) + (4x)(3)}_{= 2(4x)(3)} + 3^2$$
$$= 16x^2 + 24x + 9$$

Work Smart

$$(A + B)^2 \neq A^2 + B^2$$
$$(A - B)^2 \neq A^2 - B^2$$

Whenever you feel the urge to perform an operation that you're not quite sure about, try it with actual numbers. For example, does

$$(3 + 2)^2 = 3^2 + 2^2?$$
NO! So
$$(A + B)^2 \neq A^2 + B^2$$

(b) $(3z - 5)^2 = (3z - 5)(3z - 5)$
$$= (3z)^2 \underbrace{- (3z)(5) - (3z)(5)}_{= -2(3z)(5)} + 5^2$$
$$= 9z^2 - 30z + 25$$

■

Example 8 leads to some general results.

SQUARES OF BINOMIALS, OR PERFECT SQUARE TRINOMIALS
$$(A + B)^2 = A^2 + 2AB + B^2$$
$$(A - B)^2 = A^2 - 2AB + B^2$$

⌐EXAMPLE 9 **Using the Perfect Square Trinomial Formulas**

$$(A + B)^2 = A^2 + 2 \ A \ B + B^2$$
$$\downarrow$$
(a) $(w + 5)^2 = w^2 + 2 \cdot w \cdot 5 + 5^2$
$$= w^2 + 10w + 25$$

$$(A - B)^2 = A^2 - 2 \ A \ B + B^2$$
$$\downarrow$$
(b) $(6p - 5)^2 = (6p)^2 - 2 \cdot 6p \cdot 5 + 5^2$
$$= 36p^2 - 60p + 25$$

(c) $(3x + 5y^2)^2 = (3x)^2 + 2 \cdot 3x \cdot 5y^2 + (5y^2)^2$
$$= 9x^2 + 30xy^2 + 25y^4$$

■

Work Smart

If you can't remember the formulas for a perfect square, don't panic! Use the fact that

$$(A + B)^2 = (A + B)(A + B)$$

and then FOIL. The same reasoning applies to perfect squares of the form $(A - B)^2$.

Quick ✔

18. *True or False:* $(x + a)^2 = x^2 + a^2$

In Problems 19–21, find each product.

19. $(z - 8)^2$ **20.** $(6p + 5)^2$ **21.** $(4a - 3b)^2$

⎡5⎤ Multiply Polynomial Functions

In Section 4.1, we introduced adding and subtracting functions. We now present the multiplication of functions.

DEFINITION

Let f and g be two functions. The **product** $f \cdot g$ is the function defined by

$$(f \cdot g)(x) = f(x) \cdot g(x)$$

EXAMPLE 10 Finding the Product of Two Functions

Suppose that $f(x) = 2x + 5$ and $g(x) = x^2 - 7x + 5$.

(a) Find $f(4) \cdot g(4)$.

(b) Find $(f \cdot g)(x)$.

(c) Use the result from part (b) to determine $(f \cdot g)(4)$.

Solution

(a) We will evaluate the functions at $x = 4$ separately.

$$f(4) = 2(4) + 5 \qquad\qquad g(4) = (4)^2 - 7(4) + 5$$
$$= 13 \qquad\qquad\qquad\quad = 16 - 28 + 5$$
$$= -7$$
$$f(4) \cdot g(4) = (13)(-7) - -91$$

(b)
$$(f \cdot g)(x) - f(x) \cdot g(x)$$
$$= (2x + 5)(x^2 - 7x + 5)$$

Distribute:
$$= (2x + 5)x^2 + (2x + 5)(-7x) + (2x + 5) \cdot 5$$

Distribute:
$$= 2x \cdot x^2 + 5x^2 + (2x)(-7x) + 5(-7x) + 2x \cdot 5 + 5 \cdot 5$$

Simplify:
$$= 2x^3 + 5x^2 - 14x^2 - 35x + 10x + 25$$

Combine like terms:
$$= 2x^3 - 9x^2 - 25x + 25$$

(c)
$$(f \cdot g)(4) = 2(4)^3 - 9(4)^2 - 25(4) + 25$$
$$= 2(64) - 9(16) - 100 + 25$$
$$= 128 - 144 - 100 + 25$$
$$= -91$$

Notice that $(f \cdot g)(4) = f(4) \cdot g(4)$, as we would expect.   ∎

Quick ✔

22. $(f \cdot g)(x) = $ _____ · _____.

23. Suppose that $f(x) = 5x - 3$ and $g(x) = x^2 + 3x + 1$.

(a) Find $f(2) \cdot g(2)$.

(b) Find $(f \cdot g)(x)$.

(c) Use the result from part (b) to determine $(f \cdot g)(2)$.

Back in Section 2.2, we learned to evaluate functions when the argument (the value at which we are evaluating the function) was, itself, an algebraic expression.

EXAMPLE 11 Evaluating Functions

For the function $f(x) = x^2 + 5x$, find

(a) $f(x + 3)$ (b) $f(x + h) - f(x)$

Solution

$$f(\text{input}) = (\text{input})^2 + 5(\text{input})$$

(a) $f(x + 3) = (x + 3)^2 + 5(x + 3)$

$$= x^2 + 6x + 9 + 5x + 15$$

$$= x^2 + 11x + 24$$

(b) To evaluate $f(x + h) - f(x)$, we first evaluate $f(x + h)$ by replacing x in $f(x)$ with $x + h$. We then subtract $f(x)$ from this result.

$$f(x + h) - f(x) = \overbrace{(x + h)^2 + 5(x + h)}^{f(x + h)} - \overbrace{(x^2 + 5x)}^{f(x)}$$

$$= x^2 + 2xh + h^2 + 5x + 5h - x^2 - 5x$$

Combine like terms: $= 2xh + h^2 + 5h$ ∎

Quick ✔

24. For the function $f(x) = x^2 - 2x$, find

(a) $f(x - 3)$

(b) $f(x + h) - f(x)$.

4.2 EXERCISES

PRACTICE   WATCH   DOWNLOAD   READ   REVIEW

1–24. are the Quick ✔*s that follow each* EXAMPLE

Building Skills

In Problems 25–36, find the product. See Objective 1.

25. $(5xy^2)(-3x^2y^3)$ **26.** $(9a^3b^2)(-3a^2b^5)$

27. $\left(\frac{3}{4}yz^3\right)\left(\frac{20}{9}y^3z^2\right)$ **28.** $\left(\frac{12}{5}x^2y\right)\left(\frac{15}{4}x^4y^3\right)$

29. $5x(x^2 + 4x + 2)$ **30.** $6y(y^2 - 4y + 3)$

31. $-4a^2b(3a^2 + 2ab - b^2)$

32. $-3mn^3(4m^2 - mn + 5n^2)$

33. $\frac{2}{3}ab\left(\frac{3}{4}a^2b - \frac{9}{8}ab^3 + 6ab\right)$

34. $\frac{5}{2}xy\left(\frac{4}{15}x^2y - \frac{6}{5}xy + \frac{3}{10}xy^2\right)$

35. $0.4x^2(1.2x^2 - 0.8x + 1.5)$

36. $0.8y(0.4y^2 + 1.1y - 2.5)$

In Problems 37–50, find the product of the two binomials. See Objective 2.

37. $(x + 3)(x + 5)$ **38.** $(y - 2)(y - 6)$

39. $(a + 5)(a - 3)$

40. $(z - 8)(z + 3)$

41. $(4a + 3)(3a - 1)$

42. $(5x - 3)(x + 4)$

43. $(-3x + 1)(2x + 7)$

44. $(-x + 4)(6x + 1)$

45. $(4 - 5x)(3 + 2x)$

46. $(2 - 7y)(5 + 2y)$

47. $\left(\frac{2}{3}x + 2\right)\left(\frac{1}{2}x - 4\right)$

48. $\left(\frac{3}{2}y + 4\right)\left(\frac{4}{3}y - 1\right)$

49. $(4a + 3b)(a - 5b)$

50. $(3m - 5n)(m + 2n)$

In Problems 51–66, find the product of the polynomials. See Objective 3.

51. $(x + 1)(x^2 + 4x + 2)$

52. $(y - 2)(y^2 + 5y - 3)$

53. $(3a - 2)(2a^2 + a - 5)$

54. $(2b + 3)(3b^2 - 2b + 1)$

55. $(5z^2 + 3z + 2)(4z + 3)$

56. $(3p^2 - 5p + 3)(7p - 2)$

57. $(x - 3)(x^3 - 4x^2 + 2x - 7)$

58. $(w + 2)(w^3 - 6w^2 - 3w + 2)$

59. $(4 + y)(2y^2 - 3 + 5y)$

60. $(3 + 2z)(z^2 + 5 - 3z)$

61. $(w^2 + 2w + 1)(2w^2 - 3w + 1)$

62. $(a^2 + 4a + 4)(3a^2 - a - 2)$

63. $(x + y)(3x^2 - 2xy + 4y^2)$

64. $(a + 2b)(2a^2 - 5ab + 3b^2)$

65. $(2ab + 5)(4a^2 - 2ab + b^2)$

66. $(xy - 2)(x^2 + 2xy + 4y^2)$

In Problems 67–84, find the special product. See Objective 4.

67. $(x - 6)(x + 6)$

68. $(y + 9)(y - 9)$

69. $(a + 8)^2$

70. $(b + 3)^2$

71. $(3y - 1)^2$

72. $(4z - 5)^2$

73. $(5a + 3b)(5a - 3b)$

74. $(8y + 3z)(8y - 3z)$

75. $(8z + y)^2$

76. $(4a + 7b)^2$

77. $(10x - y)^2$

78. $(7p - 3q)^2$

79. $(a^3 + 2b)(a^3 - 2b)$

80. $(m^2 \quad 2n^3)(m^2 + 2n^3)$

81. $[3x - (y + 1)][3x + (y + 1)]$

82. $[5 - (a + b)][5 + (a + b)]$

83. $[2a + (b - 3)]^2$

84. $[(m + 4) - n]^2$

In Problems 85–90, for the given functions find

    (a) $(f \cdot g)(x)$ **(b)** $(f \cdot g)(3)$

See Objective 5.

85. $f(x) = x + 4; g(x) = x - 1$

86. $f(x) = x + 5; g(x) = 2x + 1$

87. $f(x) = 4x - 3; g(x) = 2x + 5$

88. $f(x) = 5x - 1; g(x) = 4x + 5$

89. $f(x) = x - 2; g(x) = x^2 + 5x - 3$

90. $f(x) = x + 5; g(x) = x^2 - 2x + 3$

In Problems 91–96, for the given functions, find

    (a) $f(x + 2)$ **(b)** $f(x + h) - f(x)$

See Objective 5.

91. $f(x) = x^2 + 1$

92. $f(x) = x^2 - 4$

93. $f(x) = x^2 + 5x - 2$

94. $f(x) = x^2 - 2x + 3$

95. $f(x) = 3x^2 - x + 1$

96. $f(x) = -2x^2 + x - 5$

Mixed Practice

In Problems 97–116, simplify the expression.

97. $5ab(a - b)^2$

98. $-3x(x - 3)^2$

99. $(5y + 1)(5y - 1)$

100. $(9b + 2)^2$

101. $(8z + 3)(3z - 1)$

102. $(4x + 3)(3x - 7)$

103. $(2m - 3n)(4m + n) - (m - 2n)^2$

104. $(6p + q)(5p - 2q) - (p + 3q)^2$

105. $(x + 3)(x^2 - 3x + 9)$

106. $(2y + 3)(4y^2 - 6y + 9)$

107. $\left(2x - \dfrac{1}{2}\right)^2$

108. $\left(3x + \dfrac{1}{3}\right)^2$

109. $(p + 2)^3$

110. $(z - 3)^3$

111. $(7x - 5y + 2)(3x - 2y + 1)$

112. $(2a + b - 5)(4a - 2b + 1)$

113. $(2p - 1)(p + 3) + (p - 3)(p + 3)$

114. $(3z + 2)(z - 2) + (z + 2)(z - 2)$

115. $(x + 3)(x - 3)(x^2 - 9) - (x + 1)(x^2 - 3)$

116. $(a + 2)(a - 2)(a^2 - 4) - (a + 3)(a^2 - 3)$

Applying the Concepts

△ *We can visualize the product of polynomials by using area of rectangles. In Problems 117–120, find a polynomial expression for the total area of each of the following figures.*

117.

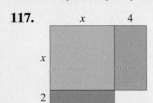

118.

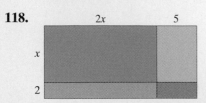

119.

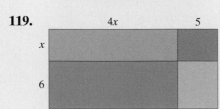

120.

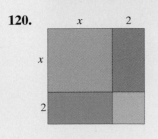

△ *In Problems 121 and 122, write a polynomial expression for the area of the shaded region of the figure.*

121.

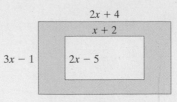

122.

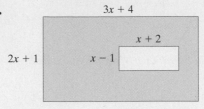

△ **123. Perfect Square** Why is the expression $(a + b)^2$ called a perfect square? Consider the figure below.

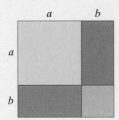

   (a) Find the area of each of the four quadrilaterals.
   (b) Use the result from part **(a)** to find the area of the entire region.
   (c) Find the length and width of the entire region in terms of a and b. Use this result to find the area of the entire region. What do you notice?

△ **124. Area** Express the area of the shaded region in the figure shown as a polynomial in standard form.

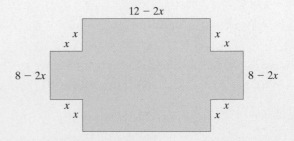

Extending the Concepts

In Problems 125–128, find the product.

125. $(2^x + 3)(2^x - 4)$ **126.** $(3^x - 1)(3^x - 9)$

127. $(5^y - 1)^2$ **128.** $(2^z - 4)^2$

4.3 Dividing Polynomials; Synthetic Division

OBJECTIVES

1. Divide a Polynomial by a Monomial
2. Divide Polynomials Using Long Division
3. Divide Polynomials Using Synthetic Division
4. Divide Polynomial Functions
5. Use the Remainder and Factor Theorems

Preparing for Dividing Polynomials and Synthetic Division

Before getting started, take the following readiness quiz. If you get a problem wrong, go back to the section cited and review the material.

P1. Simplify: $\dfrac{15x^5}{12x^3}$ [Getting Ready, p. 307]

P2. Add: $\dfrac{2}{7} + \dfrac{5}{7}$ [Section R.3, pp. 26–27]

We have now presented a discussion of adding, subtracting, and multiplying polynomials. All that's left is to discuss polynomial division! We begin with dividing a polynomial by a monomial.

When we added, subtracted, and multiplied polynomials, the result was also a polynomial. This is not true for polynomial division—a polynomial divided by a polynomial may not be a polynomial.

1 Divide a Polynomial by a Monomial

Dividing a polynomial by a monomial is based on the Quotient Rule for Exponents (see Getting Ready, p. 307). For example,

$$\frac{24z^5}{18z^2} = \frac{6\cdot4}{6\cdot3}z^{5-2}$$
$$= \frac{4}{3}z^3$$

Recall that

$$\frac{A}{C} + \frac{B}{C} = \frac{A+B}{C}$$

We reverse this process when dividing a polynomial by a monomial.

For example, if A, B, and C are monomials, we can write $\dfrac{A+B}{C}$ as shown below.

$$\frac{A+B}{C} = \frac{A}{C} + \frac{B}{C}$$

We can extend this result to polynomials with three or more terms.

EXAMPLE 1 Dividing a Polynomial by a Monomial

Divide and simplify:

(a) $\dfrac{12p^4 + 15p^3 + 3p^2}{3p^2}$ (b) $\dfrac{6a^2b^2 - 4a^2b + 3ab^2}{2a^2b^2}$

Solution

For each of the problems, we divide the monomial in the denominator into each term in the numerator.

(a) $\dfrac{12p^4 + 15p^3 + 3p^2}{3p^2} = \dfrac{12p^4}{3p^2} + \dfrac{15p^3}{3p^2} + \dfrac{3p^2}{3p^2}$

$\dfrac{a^m}{a^n} = a^{m-n}: \quad = \dfrac{12}{3}p^{4-2} + \dfrac{15}{3}p^{3-2} + \dfrac{3}{3}\cdot p^{2-2}$

Simplify: $= 4p^2 + 5p + 1$

(b)
$$\frac{6a^2b^2 - 4a^2b + 3ab^2}{2a^2b^2} = \frac{6a^2b^2}{2a^2b^2} - \frac{4a^2b}{2a^2b^2} + \frac{3ab^2}{2a^2b^2}$$

$$\frac{a^m}{a^n} = a^{m-n}: \quad = \frac{6}{2}a^{2-2}b^{2-2} - \frac{4}{2}a^{2-2}b^{1-2} + \frac{3}{2}a^{1-2}b^{2-2}$$

$$\text{Simplify:} \quad = 3a^0b^0 - 2a^0b^{-1} + \frac{3}{2}a^{-1}b^0$$

$$a^0 = 1; \ b^0 = 1; \ a^{-1} = \frac{1}{a}; \ b^{-1} = \frac{1}{b}: \quad = 3 - \frac{2}{b} + \frac{3}{2a}$$

Quick ✔ *In Problems 1–3, find the quotient.*

1. $\dfrac{9p^4 - 12p^3 + 3p^2}{3p}$ 2. $\dfrac{20a^5 - 10a^2 + 1}{5a^3}$ 3. $\dfrac{x^4y^4 + 8x^2y^2 - 4xy}{4x^3y}$

2 Divide Polynomials Using Long Division

The procedure for dividing two polynomials is similar to the procedure for dividing two integers. Although this procedure should be familiar to you, we review it in the following example.

EXAMPLE 2 Dividing an Integer by an Integer

Divide 645 by 14.

Solution

$$
\begin{array}{r}
46 \quad \leftarrow \text{Quotient} \\
\text{Divisor} \rightarrow 14\overline{)645} \quad \leftarrow \text{Dividend} \\
-56 \quad \leftarrow 4 \cdot 14 \ (\text{Subtract}) \\
\hline
85 \\
-84 \quad \leftarrow 6 \cdot 14 \ (\text{Subtract}) \\
\hline
1 \quad \leftarrow \text{Remainder}
\end{array}
$$

So 645 divided by 14 is 46 with a remainder of 1. We write this as follows:

$$\frac{645}{14} = 46 + \frac{1}{14}$$ ∎

In Example 2, the number 14 is called the **divisor,** the number 645 is called the **dividend,** the number 46 is called the **quotient,** and the number 1 is called the **remainder.**

We can always check our work after completing a division problem by multiplying the quotient by the divisor and adding this product to the remainder. The result should be the dividend. That is,

$$(\text{Quotient})(\text{Divisor}) + \text{Remainder} = \text{Dividend}$$

For example, we can check the results of Example 2 as follows:

$$(46)(14) + 1 = 644 + 1 = 645$$

To divide two polynomials, we must first write each polynomial in standard form (descending order of degree). Use the pattern in Example 2 to guide your work.

EXAMPLE 3 How to Divide Two Polynomials

Find the quotient and remainder when

$$4x^2 + 7x + 3 \text{ is divided by } x + 3$$

Step-by-Step Solution

Each polynomial is in standard form. The dividend is $4x^2 + 7x + 3$ and the divisor is $x + 3$.

Step 1: Divide the leading term of the dividend, $4x^2$, by the leading term of the divisor, x. Enter the result over the term $4x^2$.

$$\frac{4x^2}{x} = 4x$$

$$
\begin{array}{r}
4x \\
x + 3\overline{)4x^2 + 7x + 3}
\end{array}
$$

Step 2: Multiply $4x$ by $x + 3$. Be sure to vertically align like terms.

$$
\begin{array}{r}
4x \phantom{{}+ 7x + 3} \\
x + 3\overline{)4x^2 + 7x + 3} \\
\underline{4x^2 + 12x} \qquad \leftarrow 4x(x + 3) = 4x^2 + 12x
\end{array}
$$

Step 3: Subtract $4x^2 + 12x$ from $4x^2 + 7x + 3$.

$$
\begin{array}{r}
4x \phantom{{}+ 7x + 3} \\
x + 3\overline{)4x^2 + 7x + 3} \\
\underline{-(4x^2 + 12x)} \\
-5x + 3
\end{array}
$$

Step 4: Repeat Steps 1–3 treating $-5x + 3$ as the dividend by dividing x into $-5x$ to obtain -5.

$$
\begin{array}{r}
4x - 5 \qquad \leftarrow \dfrac{-5x}{x} = -5 \\
x + 3\overline{)4x^2 + 7x + 3} \\
\underline{-(4x^2 + 12x)} \\
-5x + 3 \\
\underline{-(-5x - 15)} \quad \leftarrow -5(x + 3) = -5x - 15 \\
18
\end{array}
$$

Work Smart

When the degree of the remainder is less than the degree of the divisor, you are finished dividing.

Because 18 is a lower degree than the divisor, $x + 3$, the process ends. The quotient is $4x - 5$ and the remainder is 18.

Step 5: Check Verify that (Quotient)(Divisor) + Remainder = Dividend.

$$(4x - 5)(x + 3) + 18 = 4x^2 + 12x - 5x - 15 + 18$$
$$\text{Combine like terms:} \quad = 4x^2 + 7x + 3$$

The answer checks, so

$$\frac{4x^2 + 7x + 3}{x + 3} = 4x - 5 + \frac{18}{x + 3}$$

Always write the results of polynomial division as follows:

$$\frac{\text{Dividend}}{\text{Divisor}} = \text{Quotient} + \frac{\text{Remainder}}{\text{Divisor}}$$

EXAMPLE 4   Dividing Two Polynomials

Simplify by performing long division: $\dfrac{6x^3 - 11x^2 - 7x + 2}{3x + 2}$

Solution

$$
\begin{array}{r}
2x^2 - 5x + 1 \\
3x + 2\overline{)6x^3 - 11x^2 - 7x + 2} \\
\underline{-(6x^3 + 4x^2)} \qquad \leftarrow 2x^2(3x + 2) \\
-15x^2 - 7x + 2 \\
\underline{-(-15x^2 - 10x)} \qquad \leftarrow -5x(3x + 2) \\
3x + 2 \\
\underline{-(3x + 2)} \quad \leftarrow 1(3x + 2) \\
0 \quad \leftarrow \text{Remainder}
\end{array}
$$

$$\frac{6x^3}{3x} = 2x^2; \quad \frac{-15x^2}{3x} = -5x; \quad \frac{3x}{3x} = 1$$

The quotient is $2x^2 - 5x + 1$ and the remainder is 0. We now check our work.

Check (Quotient)(Divisor) + Remainder = Dividend

$$(2x^2 - 5x + 1)(3x + 2) + 0 = 6x^3 - 11x^2 - 7x + 2$$

Our answer checks, so

$$\frac{6x^3 - 11x^2 - 7x + 2}{3x + 2} = 2x^2 - 5x + 1$$ ∎

In Example 4, the remainder was 0. Therefore,

$$6x^3 - 11x^2 - 7x + 2 = (2x^2 - 5x + 1)(3x + 2)$$

which means that $2x^2 - 5x + 1$ and $3x + 2$ are *factors* of $6x^3 - 11x^2 - 7x + 2$. This result is true in general: If the remainder is zero, then the divisor and quotient are factors of the dividend.

EXAMPLE 5 Dividing Two Polynomials

Simplify by performing long division: $\dfrac{8 - 15x + x^2 + 4x^3 + 3x^5}{3 + x^2}$

Solution

When setting up this division problem, you should write the dividend and divisor in standard form. Write the missing x^4 term in the dividend as $0x^4$.

$$
\begin{array}{r}
3x^3 \qquad\quad -5x\ +1 \\
x^2 + 3\overline{)3x^5 + 0x^4 + 4x^3 + x^2 - 15x + 8} \\
-(3x^5 \qquad\quad + 9x^3) \qquad\qquad \leftarrow 3x^3(x^2 + 3) \\
\overline{-5x^3 + x^2 - 15x + 8} \\
-(-5x^3 \qquad - 15x) \qquad \leftarrow -5x(x^2 + 3) \\
\overline{x^2 \qquad\quad + 8} \\
-(x^2 \qquad\quad + 3) \quad \leftarrow 1(x^2 + 3) \\
\overline{5} \quad \leftarrow \text{Remainder}
\end{array}
$$

The quotient is $3x^3 - 5x + 1$ and the remainder is 5. We now check our work.

Check (Quotient)(Divisor) + Remainder = Dividend

$$(3x^3 - 5x + 1)(x^2 + 3) + 5 = 3x^5 + 4x^3 + x^2 - 15x + 8$$

Our answer checks, so

$$\frac{8 - 15x + x^2 + 4x^3 + 3x^5}{3 + x^2} = 3x^3 - 5x + 1 + \frac{5}{3 + x^2}$$ ∎

Quick ✔

4. Because $\dfrac{3x^2 + 2x - 1}{x + 1} = 3x - 1$, the remainder when dividing $3x^2 + 2x - 1$ by $x + 1$ is _____ and $3x^2 + 2x - 1 =$ _____ · _____. We call $x + 1$ and $3x - 1$ _____ of $3x^2 + 2x - 1$.

5. Given that $\dfrac{6x^3 - x^2 - 9x + 8}{x + 1} = 6x^2 - 7x - 2 + \dfrac{10}{x + 1}$, we call $6x^3 - x^2 - 9x + 8$ the _____, $x + 1$ the _____, and 10 the _____.

6. To check a division problem, we verify _____ · _____ + _____ = _____.

In Problems 7–9, simplify by performing long division.

7. $\dfrac{x^3 + 3x^2 - 31x + 21}{x - 4}$

8. $\dfrac{2x^3 + 7x^2 - 7x - 12}{2x - 3}$

9. $\dfrac{2 + 12x^2 - 2x^3 - 5x^4 + x^5}{x^2 - 2}$

3 Divide Polynomials Using Synthetic Division

To find the quotient and remainder when a polynomial of degree 1 or higher is divided by $x - c$, a shortened version of long division called **synthetic division** makes the task easier.

Work Smart

Synthetic division can be used only when the divisor is of the form $x - c$ or $x + c$.

To see how synthetic division works, we will use long division to divide the polynomial $2x^3 - 5x^2 - 7x + 20$ by $x - 3$. Synthetic division comes from rewriting the long division in a more compact form. For example, in the long division below, the terms in red ink are not really necessary because they are identical to the terms directly above them. The subtraction signs are not necessary, because subtraction is understood. With these items removed, we have the division shown on the right.

$$
\begin{array}{r}
2x^2 + x - 4 \quad\longleftarrow \text{Quotient} \\
x - 3\overline{)2x^3 - 5x^2 - 7x + 20} \\
-(2x^3 - 6x^2) \\
\hline
x^2 - 7x \\
-(x^2 - 3x) \\
\hline
-4x + 20 \\
-(-4x + 12) \\
\hline
8 \quad\longleftarrow \text{Remainder}
\end{array}
$$

$$
\begin{array}{r}
2x^2 + x - 4 \\
x - 3\overline{)2x^3 - 5x^2 - 7x + 20} \\
-6x^2 \\
\hline
x^2 \\
- 3x \\
\hline
-4x \\
12 \\
\hline
8
\end{array}
$$

The x's that appear in the division on the right are not necessary if we are careful about positioning each coefficient. As long as the right-most number under the division symbol is the constant, the number to its left is the coefficient of x and so on, we can remove the x's. Now we have

$$
\begin{array}{r}
2x^2 + x - 4 \\
x - 3\overline{)2 \quad 5 \quad 7 \quad 20} \\
-6 \\
\hline
\boxed{1} \\
-3 \\
\hline
\boxed{-4} \\
12 \\
\hline
\boxed{8}
\end{array}
$$

We can make this display more compact by moving the lines up until the "boxed" numbers align horizontally.

$$
\begin{array}{r}
2x^2 + x - 4 \\
x - 3\overline{)2 \quad -5 \quad -7 \quad 20} \\
-6 \quad -3 \quad 12 \\
\hline
\square \quad 1 \quad -4 \quad 8
\end{array}
$$

Because the leading coefficient of the divisor is always 1, we know that the leading coefficient of the dividend will always be the leading coefficient of the quotient. So, we place the leading coefficient of the quotient, 2, in the boxed position.

$$
\begin{array}{r}
2x^2 + x - 4 \\
x - 3\overline{)2 \quad -5 \quad -7 \quad 20} \\
-6 \quad -3 \quad 12 \\
\hline
2 \quad 1 \quad -4 \quad 8
\end{array}
$$

The first three numbers in the bottom row are the coefficients of the quotient. The last number in the bottom row is the remainder. Now, the top row above is not needed.

$$
\begin{array}{r}
x - 3\overline{)2 \quad -5 \quad -7 \quad 20} \quad \text{Row 1}\\
-6 \quad -3 \quad 12 \quad \text{Row 2}\\
\hline
2 \quad 1 \quad -4 \quad 8 \quad \text{Row 3}
\end{array}
$$

Remember, the entries in Row 3 are obtained by subtracting the entries in Row 2 from the entries in Row 1. Rather than subtracting the entries in Row 2, we can change the sign of each entry and then add. With this modification, our display becomes

$$
\begin{array}{r}
x-3\overline{)2 \quad -5 \quad -7 \quad \quad 20} \quad \text{Row 1} \\
\underline{6 \quad \;\; 3 \quad -12} \quad \text{Row 2 (add)} \\
2 \quad \;\; 1 \quad -4 \quad \quad 8 \quad \text{Row 3}
\end{array}
$$

Notice that the entries in Row 2 are three times the entries one column to the left in Row 3 (for example, the 6 in Row 2 is 3 times 2; the 3 in Row 2 is 3 times 1, and so on). We remove the $x - 3$ and replace it with 3. The entries in Row 3 give us the quotient and remainder.

$$
\begin{array}{r}
3\overline{)2 \quad -5 \quad -7 \quad \quad 20} \quad \text{Row 1} \\
\underline{6 \quad \;\; 3 \quad -12} \quad \text{Row 2 (add)} \\
2 \quad \;\; 1 \quad -4 \quad \quad 8 \quad \text{Row 3} \\
\underline{2x^2 + x - 4} \quad 8 \quad\quad\quad \boxed{\text{Remainder}} \\
\text{Quotient}
\end{array}
$$

Let's go over an example step by step.

Work Smart

If there are any missing powers of x in the dividend, you must insert a coefficient of 0 for the missing term when doing synthetic division.

EXAMPLE 6 How to Use Synthetic Division to Divide Polynomials

Use synthetic division to find the quotient and remainder when $3x^3 + 11x^2 + 14$ is divided by $x + 4$.

Step-by-Step Solution

Step 1: Write the dividend in descending powers of x. Then copy the coefficients of the dividend. Remember to insert a 0 for any missing power of x.	$3x^3 + 11x^2 + 14 = 3x^3 + 11x^2 + 0x + 14$ $\quad 3 \quad\quad 11 \quad\quad 0 \quad\quad 14 \;\text{Row 1}$
Step 2: Insert the division symbol. Rewrite the divisor in the form $x - c$ and insert the value of c to the left of the division symbol.	$x + 4 = x - (-4)$ $-4\overline{)3 \quad\quad 11 \quad\quad 0 \quad\quad 14} \;\text{Row 1}$
Step 3: Bring the 3 down two rows and enter it in Row 3.	$-4\overline{)3 \quad\quad 11 \quad\quad 0 \quad\quad 14} \;\text{Row 1}$ $\downarrow \quad\quad\quad\quad\quad\quad\quad\quad\quad \text{Row 2}$ $3 \quad\quad\quad\quad\quad\quad\quad\quad\quad \text{Row 3}$
Step 4: Multiply the latest entry in Row 3 by -4 and place the result in Row 2, one column over to the right.	$-4\overline{)3 \quad\quad 11 \quad\quad 0 \quad\quad 14} \;\text{Row 1}$ $\downarrow \quad\; -12 \quad\quad\quad\quad\quad \text{Row 2}$ $3^{\,-4(3)\nearrow} \quad\quad\quad\quad\quad\quad \text{Row 3}$
Step 5: Add the entry in Row 2 to the entry above it in Row 1. Enter the sum in Row 3.	$-4\overline{)3 \quad\quad 11 \quad\quad 0 \quad\quad 14} \;\text{Row 1}$ $\downarrow \quad\; -12 \quad\quad\quad\quad\quad \text{Row 2}$ $3^{\,-4(3)\nearrow} \;\; -1 \quad\quad\quad\quad \text{Row 3}$
Step 6: Repeat Steps 4 and 5 until no more entries are available in Row 1.	$-4\overline{)3 \quad\quad 11 \quad\quad 0 \quad\quad 14} \;\text{Row 1}$ $\downarrow \quad\; -12 \quad\quad 4 \quad\; -16 \;\text{Row 2}$ $3^{\,-4(3)\nearrow} \; -1^{\,-4(-1)\nearrow} \; 4^{\,-4(4)\nearrow} \; -2 \;\text{Row 3}$

Step 7: The final entry in Row 3, -2, is the remainder;
the other entries in Row 3, 3, -1, and 4, are the
coefficients of the quotient, in descending order of degree.
The quotient is a polynomial whose degree is one less than
the degree of the dividend.

Quotient: $3x^2 - x + 4$
Remainder: -2

Step 8: Check

(Quotient)(Divisor) + Remainder = Dividend

$$(3x^2 - x + 4)(x + 4) + (-2)$$
$$= 3x^3 + 12x^2 - x^2 - 4x + 4x + 16 - 2$$
$$= 3x^3 + 11x^2 + 14$$

So $\dfrac{3x^3 + 11x^2 + 14}{x + 4} = 3x^2 - x + 4 - \dfrac{2}{x + 4}$.

Let's do one more example where we consolidate all the steps given in Example 6.

EXAMPLE 7 Dividing Two Polynomials Using Synthetic Division

Use synthetic division to find the quotient and remainder when $x^4 - 5x^3 - 6x^2 + 33x - 15$ is divided by $x - 5$.

Solution

The divisor is $x - 5$ so that $c = 5$.

$$
\begin{array}{r|rrrrr}
5) & 1 & -5 & -6 & 33 & -15 \\
\downarrow & & 5 & 0 & -30 & 15 \\
\hline
& 1 & 0 & -6 & 3 & 0
\end{array}
$$

The dividend is a fourth-degree polynomial, so the quotient is a third-degree polynomial. The quotient is $x^3 + 0x^2 - 6x + 3 = x^3 - 6x + 3$ and the remainder is 0. So

$$\frac{x^4 - 5x^3 - 6x^2 + 33x - 15}{x - 5} = x^3 - 6x + 3$$

In Example 7, because $\dfrac{x^4 - 5x^3 - 6x^2 + 33x - 15}{x - 5} = x^3 - 6x + 3$, we know that $x - 5$ and $x^3 - 6x + 3$ are factors of $x^4 - 5x^3 - 6x^2 + 33x - 15$. Therefore, we can write

$$x^4 - 5x^3 - 6x^2 + 33x - 15 = (x - 5)(x^3 - 6x + 3)$$

Work Smart: Study Skills

Knowing when a method **does not** apply is as essential as knowing when the method **does** apply. When can synthetic division be used to divide polynomials? When can't synthetic division be used?

Quick ✔

10. *True or False:* We can divide $-4x^3 + 5x^2 + 10x - 3$ by $x^2 - 2$ using synthetic division.

11. *True or False:* We can divide $-4x^3 + 5x^2 + 10x - 3$ by $2x + 1$ using synthetic division.

In Problems 12 and 13, use synthetic division to find the quotient.

12. $\dfrac{2x^3 + x^2 - 7x - 13}{x - 2}$

13. $\dfrac{x^4 + 8x^3 + 15x^2 - 2x - 6}{x + 3}$

⌈4⌉ Divide Polynomial Functions

We have discussed adding, subtracting, and multiplying polynomial functions. All that is left is dividing polynomial functions.

DEFINITION

If f and g are functions, then the **quotient** $\dfrac{f}{g}$ is the function defined by

$$\left(\frac{f}{g}\right)(x) = \frac{f(x)}{g(x)} \quad g(x) \neq 0$$

EXAMPLE 8 Dividing Two Polynomial Functions

If $f(x) = 2x^4 - x^3 - 3x^2 + 13x - 4$ and $g(x) = x^2 - 2$, find

(a) $\left(\dfrac{f}{g}\right)(x)$ **(b)** $\left(\dfrac{f}{g}\right)(2)$

Solution

(a) $\left(\dfrac{f}{g}\right)(x) = \dfrac{f(x)}{g(x)} = \dfrac{2x^4 - x^3 - 3x^2 + 13x - 4}{x^2 - 2}$

We use long division to find the quotient because the divisor is not of the form $x - c$.

$$
\begin{array}{r}
2x^2 - x + 1 \\
x^2 - 2 \overline{)2x^4 - x^3 - 3x^2 + 13x - 4} \\
-(2x^4 \qquad - 4x^2) \\
\hline
-x^3 + x^2 + 13x - 4 \\
-(-x^3 \qquad + 2x) \\
\hline
x^2 + 11x - 4 \\
-(x^2 \qquad - 2) \\
\hline
11x - 2
\end{array}
$$

So $\left(\dfrac{f}{g}\right)(x) = \dfrac{f(x)}{g(x)} = 2x^2 - x + 1 + \dfrac{11x - 2}{x^2 - 2}$.

(b) $\left(\dfrac{f}{g}\right)(2) = 2(2)^2 - 2 + 1 + \dfrac{11(2) - 2}{(2)^2 - 2}$

$= 8 - 2 + 1 + \dfrac{20}{2}$

$= 17$ ∎

Quick ✔

In Problem 14, find (a) $\left(\dfrac{f}{g}\right)(x)$ *and (b)* $\left(\dfrac{f}{g}\right)(3)$.

14. $f(x) = 3x^4 - 4x^3 - 3x^2 + 10x - 5;\ g(x) = x^2 - 2$

5 Use the Remainder and Factor Theorems

Look back at Example 6, where we used synthetic division to find the quotient and remainder when $3x^3 + 11x^2 + 14$ is divided by $x + 4$. If we let $f(x) = 3x^3 + 11x^2 + 14$, we find that $f(-4) = -2$. Looking back at Example 6, we find that the remainder when $3x^3 + 11x^2 + 14$ is divided by $x + 4$ is -2. The value of the function f at $x = -4$ is the same as the remainder when f is divided by $x + 4 = x - (-4)$. This result is not a coincidence and is true in general! It is called the *Remainder Theorem*.

In Words

A theorem is a big idea that can be shown to be true in general. The word comes from a Greek verb meaning "to view."

THE REMAINDER THEOREM

Let f be a polynomial function. If $f(x)$ is divided by $x - c$, then the remainder is $f(c)$.

EXAMPLE 9 Using the Remainder Theorem

Use the Remainder Theorem to find the remainder if $f(x) = 2x^3 - 3x + 8$ is divided by $x + 3$.

Solution

The divisor is $x + 3 = x - (-3)$, so the Remainder Theorem says that the remainder is $f(-3)$.

$$f(x) = 2x^3 - 3x + 8$$
$$f(-3) = 2(-3)^3 - 3(-3) + 8$$
$$= 2(-27) + 9 + 8$$
$$= -54 + 9 + 8$$
$$= -37$$

When $f(x) = 2x^3 - 3x + 8$ is divided by $x + 3$, the remainder is -37.

Check Using synthetic division, we find that the remainder is, in fact, -37.

$$
\begin{array}{r|rrrr}
-3 & 2 & 0 & -3 & 8 \\
   &   & -6 & 18 & -45 \\
\hline
   & 2 & -6 & 15 & -37 \\
\end{array}
\quad \leftarrow \text{Remainder}
$$

■

Quick ✔

15. Use the Remainder Theorem to find the remainder if
$f(x) = 3x^3 + 10x^2 - 9x - 4$ is divided by

(a) $x - 2$ **(b)** $x + 4$

We saw from Example 7 that when the remainder is 0, then the quotient and divisor are factors of the dividend. The Remainder Theorem can be used to determine whether an expression of the form $x - c$ is a factor of the dividend. This result is called the *Factor Theorem*.

Work Smart

"If and only if" statements are used to compress two statements into one. The Factor Theorem is two statements:

1. If $f(c) = 0$, then $x - c$ is a factor of f.
2. If $x - c$ is a factor of f, then $f(c) = 0$.

THE FACTOR THEOREM

Let f be a polynomial function. Then $x - c$ is a factor of $f(x)$ if and only if $f(c) = 0$.

We can use the Factor Theorem to determine whether a polynomial has a particular factor.

EXAMPLE 10 Using the Factor Theorem

Use the Factor Theorem to determine whether the function
$f(x) = 2x^3 - 3x^2 - 18x - 8$ has the factor

(a) $x - 3$ **(b)** $x + 2$

Solution

The Factor Theorem states that if $f(c) = 0$, then $x - c$ is a factor of f.

(a) Because $x - 3$ is of the form $x - c$ with $c = 3$, we find the value of $f(3)$.
$$f(3) = 2(3)^3 - 3(3)^2 - 18(3) - 8 = -35 \neq 0$$

Since $f(3) \neq 0$, we know that $x - 3$ is not a factor of f.

(b) Because $x + 2 = x - (-2)$ is of the form $x - c$ with $c = -2$, we find the value of $f(-2)$. Rather than evaluating the function using substitution, we use synthetic division.

$$
\begin{array}{r|rrrr}
-2 & 2 & -3 & -18 & -8 \\
   &   & -4 & 14 & 8 \\
\hline
   & 2 & -7 & -4 & 0 \\
\end{array}
\quad \leftarrow \text{Remainder}
$$

In Words

If $f(c) = 0$, then $f(x)$ can be written in factored form as

$$f(x) = (x - c)\,(\text{quotient})$$

The remainder is 0, so that $f(-2) = 0$. Because $f(-2) = 0$, we know that $x + 2$ is a factor of f. This means the dividend can be written as the product of the quotient and divisor. The quotient is $2x^2 - 7x - 4$ and the divisor is $x + 2$, so

$$2x^3 - 3x^2 - 18x - 8 = (x + 2)(2x^2 - 7x - 4) \qquad \blacksquare$$

Quick ✔

16. Use the Factor Theorem to determine whether $x - c$ is a factor of $f(x) = 2x^3 - 9x^2 - 6x + 5$ for the given values of c. If $x - c$ is a factor, then write f in factored form. That is, write $f(x) = (x - c)(\text{quotient})$.

(a) $c = -2$ **(b)** $c = 5$

4.3 EXERCISES

MyMathLab   PRACTICE   WATCH   DOWNLOAD   READ   REVIEW

1–16. *are the* Quick ✔*s that follow each* EXAMPLE

Building Skills

In Problems 17–24, divide and simplify. See Objective 1.

17. $\dfrac{8x^2 + 12x}{4x}$

18. $\dfrac{6z^3 + 9z^2}{3z^2}$

19. $\dfrac{2a^3 - 15a^2 + 10a}{5a}$

20. $\dfrac{4b^3 + 12b^2 + 24b}{6b}$

21. $\dfrac{2y^3 + 6y}{4y^2}$

22. $\dfrac{3z^4 + 12z^2}{6z^3}$

23. $\dfrac{4m^2n^2 + 6m^2n - 18mn^2}{4m^2n^2}$

24. $\dfrac{2x^2y^3 - 9xy^3 + 16x^2y}{2x^2y^2}$

In Problems 25–42, divide using long division. See Objective 2.

25. $\dfrac{x^2 + 5x + 6}{x + 2}$

26. $\dfrac{x^2 - 4x - 21}{x + 3}$

27. $\dfrac{2x^2 + x - 4}{x - 2}$

28. $\dfrac{3z^2 - 7z - 28}{z - 4}$

29. $\dfrac{2w^2 + 5w - 49}{2w - 7}$

30. $\dfrac{4x^2 - 17x - 33}{4x + 7}$

31. $\dfrac{x^3 + 8x^2 + x - 42}{x + 3}$

32. $\dfrac{x^3 + x^2 - 22x - 40}{x + 2}$

33. $\dfrac{w^3 - 21w - 20}{w + 4}$

34. $\dfrac{a^3 - 49a + 120}{a + 8}$

35. $\dfrac{6x^3 - 13x^2 - 80x - 25}{2x + 5}$

36. $\dfrac{4p^3 + 20p^2 + 19p - 15}{2p + 5}$

37. $\dfrac{x^3 - 7x^2 + 3x - 21}{x^2 + 3}$

38. $\dfrac{x^3 - 5x^2 - 2x + 10}{x^2 - 2}$

39. $\dfrac{3z^3 + 21z^2 + 5z + 2}{3z^2 + 1}$

40. $\dfrac{2k^3 + 10k^2 - 6k - 8}{2k^2 - 3}$

41. $\dfrac{2x^4 - 11x^3 + 8x^2 - 22x + 144}{x^2 + 2x + 5}$

42. $\dfrac{2x^4 - 7x^3 - 50x^2 - 10x + 96}{x^2 + x - 3}$

In Problems 43–56, divide using synthetic division. See Objective 3.

43. $\dfrac{x^2 - 3x - 10}{x - 5}$

44. $\dfrac{x^2 + 4x - 12}{x - 2}$

45. $\dfrac{2x^2 + 11x + 12}{x + 4}$

46. $\dfrac{3x^2 + 19x - 40}{x + 8}$

47. $\dfrac{x^2 - 3x - 14}{x - 6}$

48. $\dfrac{x^2 + 2x - 17}{x - 4}$

49. $\dfrac{x^3 - 19x - 15}{x - 5}$

50. $\dfrac{x^3 - 13x - 17}{x + 3}$

51. $\dfrac{3x^4 - 5x^3 - 21x^2 + 17x + 25}{x - 3}$

52. $\dfrac{2x^4 - x^3 - 38x^2 + 16x + 103}{x + 4}$

53. $\dfrac{x^4 - 40x^2 + 109}{x + 6}$

54. $\dfrac{a^4 - 65a^2 + 55}{a - 8}$

55. $\dfrac{2x^3 + 3x^2 - 14x - 15}{x - \dfrac{5}{2}}$

56. $\dfrac{3x^3 + 13x^2 + 8x - 12}{x - \dfrac{2}{3}}$

In Problems 57–66, find (a) $\left(\dfrac{f}{g}\right)(x)$, *(b)* $\left(\dfrac{f}{g}\right)(2)$. *See Objective 4.*

57. $f(x) = 4x^3 - 8x^2 + 12x;\ g(x) = 4x$

58. $f(x) = 3x^3 - 9x^2 + 12x;\ g(x) = 3x$

59. $f(x) = x^2 - x - 12; g(x) = x - 4$

60. $f(x) = x^2 + 3x - 4; g(x) = x + 4$

61. $f(x) = 2x^2 + 5x - 1; g(x) = x + 3$

62. $f(x) = 3x^2 - 6x + 5; g(x) = 2x + 1$

63. $f(x) = 2x^3 + 9x^2 + x - 12; g(x) = 2x + 3$

64. $f(x) = 3x^3 - 2x^2 - 19x - 6; g(x) = 3x + 1$

65. $f(x) = x^3 - 13x - 12; g(x) = x^2 - 9$

66. $f(x) = x^3 - 19x + 30; g(x) = x^2 - x - 6$

In Problems 67–74, use the Remainder Theorem to find the remainder. See Objective 5.

67. $f(x) = x^2 - 5x + 1$ is divided by $x - 2$

68. $f(x) = x^2 + 4x - 5$ is divided by $x + 2$

69. $f(x) = x^3 - 2x^2 + 5x - 3$ is divided by $x + 4$

70. $f(x) = x^3 + 3x^2 - x + 1$ is divided by $x - 3$

71. $f(x) = 2x^3 - 4x + 1$ is divided by $x - 5$

72. $f(x) = 3x^3 + 2x^2 - 5$ is divided by $x + 3$

73. $f(x) = x^4 + 1$ is divided by $x - 1$

74. $f(x) = x^4 - 1$ is divided by $x - 1$

In Problems 75–82, use the Factor Theorem to determine whether $x - c$ is a factor of the given function for the given values of c. If $x - c$ is a factor, then write f in factored form. That is, write $f(x) = (x - c)(quotient)$. See Objective 5.

75. $f(x) = x^2 - 3x + 2; c = 2$

76. $f(x) = x^2 + 5x + 6; c = 3$

77. $f(x) = 2x^2 + 5x + 2; c = -2$

78. $f(x) = 3x^2 + x - 2; c = -1$

79. $f(x) = 4x^3 - 9x^2 - 49x - 30; c = 3$

80. $f(x) = 2x^3 - 9x^2 - 2x + 24; c = 1$

81. $f(x) = 4x^3 - 7x^2 - 5x + 6; c = -1$

82. $f(x) = 5x^3 + 8x^2 - 7x - 6; c = -2$

Mixed Practice

In Problems 83–96, divide using any appropriate method.

83. $\dfrac{3a^3b^2 - 9a^2b + 18ab}{3ab}$

84. $\dfrac{5s^4t^3 - 15s^3t^2 + 50s^2t}{5s^2t}$

85. $\dfrac{3y^2 + 11y + 6}{3y + 2}$

86. $\dfrac{4a^2 + 23a + 15}{4a + 3}$

87. $\dfrac{x^3 + 6x^2 + 8x + 32}{x^2 + 5}$

88. $\dfrac{x^3 - 3x^2 + 5x - 12}{x^2 + 3}$

89. $\dfrac{8x^3 + 6x}{12x^2}$

90. $\dfrac{3x^4 + 6x^2}{9x^3}$

91. $\dfrac{x^3 + 7x^2 + 2x - 46}{x + 4}$

92. $\dfrac{x^3 + 5x^2 - 29x - 97}{x - 5}$

93. $\dfrac{3x^3 + 5x^2 - 24x - 40}{3x + 5}$

94. $\dfrac{4b^3 + 11b^2 - 28b - 17}{4b + 3}$

95. $\dfrac{8x^3 - 27}{2x - 3}$

96. $\dfrac{8a^3 + 125}{2a + 5}$

97. If $\dfrac{f(x)}{x - 5} = 3x + 5$, find $f(x)$.

98. If $\dfrac{f(x)}{x + 3} = 2x + 7$, find $f(x)$.

99. If $\dfrac{f(x)}{x - 3} = x + 8 + \dfrac{4}{x - 3}$, find $f(x)$.

100. If $\dfrac{f(x)}{x - 3} = x^2 + 2 + \dfrac{7}{x - 3}$, find $f(x)$.

Applying the Concepts

△ **101.** **Area** The area of a rectangle is $15x^2 + x - 2$ square feet. If the width of the rectangle is $3x - 1$ feet, find the length.

△ **102.** **Area** The area of a rectangle is $10x^2 + 9x - 9$ square centimeters. If the width of the rectangle is $2x + 3$ centimeters, find the length.

△ **103.** **Volume** The volume of the box shown is $2x^3 + 9x^2 - 20x - 75$ cubic centimeters. Find the length if the width is $x + 5$ centimeters and the height is $x - 3$ centimeters.

$x - 3$

$x + 5$

△**104. Volume** The volume of the box shown is $4x^3 + 35x^2 + 52x + 21$ cubic feet. Find the height if the width is $4x + 3$ feet and the length is $x + 1$ feet.

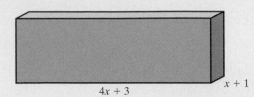

4x + 3   x + 1

105. Average Cost The average cost function is defined in economics as $\overline{C}(x) = \dfrac{C(x)}{x}$, where C is the cost of manufacturing x units of a good. Suppose that $C(x) = 0.01x^3 - 0.4x^2 + 13x + 400$, where x is the number of wristwatches manufactured in a day.

(a) What is $\overline{C}(x) = \dfrac{C(x)}{x}$?

(b) What is the average cost of manufacturing $x = 50$ wristwatches in a day?

106. Average Cost The average cost function is defined in economics as $\overline{C}(x) = \dfrac{C(x)}{x}$, where C is the cost of manufacturing x units of a good. Suppose that $C(x) = 0.01x^3 - 0.45x^2 + 16.5x + 600$, where x is the number of wagons manufactured in a day.

(a) What is $\overline{C}(x) = \dfrac{C(x)}{x}$?

(b) What is the average cost of manufacturing $x = 50$ wagons in a day?

Extending the Concepts

107. Find the sum of $a, b, c,$ and d if
$$\frac{2x^3 - 3x^2 - 26x - 37}{x + 2} = ax^2 + bx + c + \frac{d}{x + 2}.$$

108. What is the remainder when $f(x) = 2x^{30} - 3x^{20} + 4x^{10} - 2$ is divided by $x - 1$?

Explaining the Concepts

109. If f is a polynomial of degree n and it is divided by $x + 4$, the quotient will be a polynomial of degree $n - 1$. Explain why.

110. Explain the Remainder Theorem in your own words. Explain the Factor Theorem in your own words.

111. Given that $\dfrac{6x^3 - x^2 - 9x + 4}{3x + 4} = 2x^2 - 3x + 1$, is $3x + 4$ a factor of $6x^3 - x^2 - 9x + 4$? If so, write $6x^3 - x^2 - 9x + 4$ in factored form.

112. Suppose that you were asked to divide $8x^3 - 3x + 1$ by $x + 3$. Would you use long division or synthetic division? Why?

PUTTING THE CONCEPTS TOGETHER (Sections 4.1–4.3)

These problems cover important concepts from Sections 4.1 through 4.3. We designed these problems so that you can review the chapter so far and show your mastery of the concepts. Take time to work these problems before proceeding with the next section. The answers to these problems are located at the back of the text on page AN-27.

1. Write the polynomial in standard form and determine its degree:
$$3m + 5m^4 - 2m^3 + 8$$

2. Add: $(7a^2 - 4a^3 + 7a - 1) + (2a^2 - 6a - 7)$

3. Subtract: $\left(\frac{1}{5}y^2 + 2y - 6\right) - (4y^2 - y + 2)$

4. For $f(x) = 2x^3 - x^2 + 4x + 9$, find $f(2)$.

5. For $f(x) = 6x + 5$ and $g(x) = -x^2 + 2x + 3$, find $(f + g)(-3)$.

6. For $f(x) = 2x^2 + 7$ and $g(x) = x^2 - 4x - 3$, find $(f - g)(x)$.

7. Multiply: $2mn^3(m^2n - 4mn + 6)$

8. Multiply: $(3a - 5b)^2$

9. Multiply: $(7n^2 + 3)(7n^2 - 3)$

10. Multiply: $(3a + 2b)(6a^2 - 2ab + b^2)$

11. For $f(x) = x + 2$ and $g(x) = x^2 - 4x + 11$, find $(f \cdot g)(x)$.

12. Divide using long division: $\dfrac{10z^3 + 41z^2 + 7z - 49}{2z + 7}$

13. Divide using synthetic division:
$$\frac{2x^3 + 25x^2 + 62x - 6}{x + 9}$$

14. For $f(x) = x^3 + 2x^2 - 4x + 5$ and $g(x) = x - 1$, find $\left(\dfrac{f}{g}\right)(x)$.

15. Use the Factor Theorem to determine if $x + 5$ is a factor of $f(x) = 3x^3 + 8x^2 - 23x + 60$. If so, write the function in factored form—that is, in the form $f(x) = (x + 5)(\text{quotient})$.

4.4 Greatest Common Factor; Factoring by Grouping

Preparing for Greatest Common Factor; Factoring by Grouping

Before getting started, take the following readiness quiz. If you get a problem wrong, go back to the section cited and review the material.

P1. Write 24 as the product of prime factors.   [Section R.3, p. 28]

P2. Distribute: $4(3x - 5)$ [Section R.3, pp. 29–30]

Consider the following products:

$$5y(y^2 - 2y + 5) = 5y^3 - 10y^2 + 25y$$

$$(3x + 1)(x - 5) = 3x^2 - 14x - 5$$

The polynomials on the left side are called **factors** of the polynomial on the right side. Expressing a polynomial with integer coefficients as the product of two or more other polynomials with integer coefficients is called **factoring over the integers.**

A polynomial with integer coefficients is **prime** if it cannot be written as the product of two other polynomials with integer coefficients (excluding 1 and −1). When a polynomial has been written as a product consisting only of prime factors, it is said to be **factored completely.** The word *prime* has the same meaning as it does for integers. For example, 3, 7, and 13 are prime numbers while $4 (= 2 \cdot 2)$, $12 (= 2 \cdot 6)$, and $35 (= 5 \cdot 7)$ are not prime. If we write 4 as $2 \cdot 2$, we have factored 4 completely. If we write 12 as $2 \cdot 6$, we have not factored completely, because 6 can be further factored as $2 \cdot 3$. So, 12 factored completely would be written $2 \cdot 2 \cdot 3$.

In Words

Factoring is "undoing" multiplication.

1 Factor Out the Greatest Common Factor

The first step in factoring any polynomial is to look for the *greatest common factor*. The **greatest common factor (GCF)** of a polynomial is the largest polynomial that is a factor of all the terms in the polynomial. To find the GCF of a polynomial, find the largest polynomial that is a factor of (or divides evenly into) each term in the polynomial.

EXAMPLE 1 Finding the Greatest Common Factor

Find the greatest common factor (GCF) of the terms.

    (a) $4x, 12$ **(b)** $6x^3, 12x^2, 15x$ **(c)** $4x^3y^4, 8x^2y^3, 12xy^2$

Solution

In each case, we look for the largest polynomial that is a factor of each polynomial.

    (a) Look at the coefficients first. The largest number that divides into 4 and 12 evenly is 4, so 4 is part of the GCF. Because 12 does not have a variable factor, the GCF is 4.

    (b) The largest number that divides evenly into 6, 12, and 15 is 3, so 3 is part of the GCF. Now, look at the variable expressions, x^3, x^2, and x. Since $x^3 = x \cdot x \cdot x$, $x^2 = x \cdot x$, and $x = x$, we choose the variable expression with the smallest exponent, $x(= x^1)$ as part of the GCF. The GCF is $3x$.

    (c) The largest number that divides into 4, 8, and 12 is 4, so 4 is part of the GCF. Look at the expression involving x. The smallest exponent involving x is 1, so x is part of the GCF. The smallest exponent involving y is y^2, so y^2 is part of the GCF. The GCF is $4xy^2$.   ▪

Quick ✔

1. In $(3x + 1)(x - 5) = 3x^2 - 14x - 5$, the polynomials on the left side are called _____ of the polynomial on the right side.

2. If a polynomial cannot be written as the product of two other polynomials (excluding 1 and −1), then the polynomial is said to be _____.

Preparing for...Answers
P1. $24 = 2 \cdot 2 \cdot 2 \cdot 3$ **P2.** $12x - 20$

3. The _____ of a polynomial is the largest polynomial that is a factor of all the terms in the polynomial.

4. *True or False:* The number 17 is prime.

5. *True or False:* If we write 8 as $2 \cdot 4$, it is factored completely.

In Problems 6–8, find the greatest common factor (GCF) of the terms.

6. $5y, 15$ 7. $4z^3, 10z^2, 12z$ 8. $6x^3y^5, 9x^2y^3, 12xy^4$

Once the GCF is identified, we use the Distributive Property to factor the GCF out.

EXAMPLE 2   How to Factor Out the Greatest Common Factor

Factor out the greatest common factor: $4a^2b^2 - 10ab^3 + 18a^3b^4$

Step-by-Step Solution

Step 1: Find the GCF.	$GCF = 2ab^2$
Step 2: Rewrite each term as the product of the GCF and remaining factor.	$4a^2b^2 - 10ab^3 + 18a^3b^4 = 2ab^2 \cdot 2a - 2ab^2 \cdot 5b + 2ab^2 \cdot 9a^2b^2$
Step 3: Factor out GCF.	$= 2ab^2(2a - 5b + 9a^2b^2)$
Step 4: Check	$2ab^2(2a - 5b + 9a^2b^2) = 2ab^2 \cdot 2a - 2ab^2 \cdot 5b + 2ab^2 \cdot 9a^2b^2$
	$= 4a^2b^2 - 10ab^3 + 18a^3b^4$

So $4a^2b^2 - 10ab^3 + 18a^3b^4 = 2ab^2(2a - 5b + 9a^2b^2)$.   ■

FACTORING OUT THE GREATEST COMMON FACTOR

Step 1: Identify the greatest common factor (GCF) of the terms.

Step 2: Rewrite each term as the product of the GCF and remaining factor.

Step 3: Use the Distributive Property to factor out the GCF.

Step 4: Use the Distributive Property to verify that the factorization is correct.

Quick ✔ *In Problems 9–11, factor out the greatest common factor.*

9. $7z^2 - 14z$ 10. $6y^3 - 14y^2 + 10y$ 11. $2m^4n^2 + 8m^3n^4 - 6m^2n^5$

When the coefficient of the term of highest degree is negative, we often prefer to factor the negative out of the polynomial as part of the GCF.

EXAMPLE 3   Factoring Out a Negative Number as Part of the GCF

Factor out the greatest common factor.

(a) $-8a + 16$ (b) $-2b^3 + 10b^2 + 8b$

Solution

$$GCF = -8$$

(a) $-8a + 16 = -8 \cdot a + (-8) \cdot (-2)$

$= -8(a - 2)$

Check $-8(a - 2) = -8 \cdot a + (-8) \cdot (-2)$
$$= -8a + 16$$

$$\overset{\text{GCF} = -2b}{\overbrace{}}$$

(b) $-2b^3 + 10b^2 + 8b = -2b \cdot b^2 + (-2b) \cdot (-5b) + (-2b) \cdot (-4)$
$$= -2b(b^2 - 5b - 4)$$

Check $-2b(b^2 - 5b - 4) = -2b \cdot b^2 + (-2b) \cdot (-5b) + (-2b) \cdot (-4)$
$$= -2b^3 + 10b^2 + 8b \qquad \blacksquare$$

Quick ✔ *In Problems 12 and 13, factor out the greatest common factor.*

12. $-5y^2 + 10y$ **13.** $-3a^3 + 6a^2 - 12a$

Sometimes the greatest common factor is a binomial.

EXAMPLE 4 Factoring Out a Binomial as the Greatest Common Factor

Factor out the greatest common binomial factor.

(a) $4x(x - 3) + 5(x - 3)$

(b) $3y(2y + 1) - 5(2y + 1)^2$

(c) $(c + 4)(c - 1) + (5c - 2)(c - 1)$

Solution

$$\overset{\text{GCF} = (x - 3)}{\overbrace{}}$$

(a) $4x(x - 3) + 5(x - 3) = (x - 3) \cdot 4x + (x - 3) \cdot 5$
$$= (x - 3)(4x + 5)$$

(b) $3y(2y + 1) - 5(2y + 1)^2 = (2y + 1) \cdot 3y - (2y + 1) \cdot 5(2y + 1)$
$$= (2y + 1)(3y - 5(2y + 1))$$
$$= (2y + 1)(3y - 10y - 5)$$
$$= (2y + 1)(-7y - 5)$$
Factor out -1: $= -(2y + 1)(7y + 5)$

(c) $(c + 4)(c - 1) + (5c - 2)(c - 1) = (c - 1) \cdot (c + 4) + (c - 1) \cdot (5c - 2)$
$$= (c - 1)(c + 4 + 5c - 2)$$
$$= (c - 1)(6c + 2)$$
GCF $= 2$ in $6c + 2$: $= 2(c - 1)(3c + 1)$ $\blacksquare$

Quick ✔ *In Problems 14 and 15, factor out the greatest common factor.*

14. $4a(a - 3) + 3(a - 3)$ **15.** $(w + 2)(w - 5) + (2w + 1)(w - 5)$

2   Factor by Grouping

Sometimes a common factor does not occur in every term of the polynomial, but a common factor does occur in some of the terms of the polynomial (one group of polynomials) and a second common factor occurs in the remaining terms of the polynomial (a second group of polynomials). When this happens, the common factor can be factored out of each group using the Distributive Property. This technique is called **factoring by grouping** and is used often when a polynomial contains four terms.

EXAMPLE 5 How to Factor by Grouping

Factor by grouping: $4x - 4y + ax - ay$

Step-by-Step Solution

Step 1: Group terms with common factors. In this problem the first two terms have a common factor of 4 and the last two terms have a common factor of a.	$4x - 4y + ax - ay = (4x - 4y) + (ax - ay)$
Step 2: In each grouping, factor out the common factor.	$= 4(x - y) + a(x - y)$
Step 3: Factor out the common factor that remains.	$= (x - y)(4 + a)$

Step 4: **Check**

$$\overset{\text{FOIL}}{\downarrow}$$
$$(x - y)(4 + a) = 4x + ax - 4y - ay$$
$$\text{Rearrange terms: } = 4x - 4y + ax - ay$$

So $4x - 4y + ax - ay = (x - y)(4 + a)$. ∎

Based on Example 5, the following steps should be followed to factor by grouping.

> **STEPS TO FACTOR BY GROUPING**
>
> **Step 1:** Group the terms with common factors. Sometimes it will be necessary to rearrange the terms.
> **Step 2:** In each grouping, factor out the common factor.
> **Step 3:** Factor out the common factor that remains.
> **Step 4:** Check your work.

EXAMPLE 6 Factoring by Grouping

Factor by grouping:

  (a) $x^3 + 3x^2 + 2x + 6$ **(b)** $6x^2 + 9x - 10x - 15$

Solution

  (a) First, we group terms with common factors. Notice the first two terms, x^3 and $3x^2$, have a common factor of x^2; the last two terms have a common factor of 2.

$$x^3 + 3x^2 + 2x + 6 = (x^3 + 3x^2) + (2x + 6)$$
$$\text{Factor out common factor: } = x^2(x + 3) + 2(x + 3)$$
$$= (x + 3)(x^2 + 2)$$
$$\textbf{Check} \quad (x + 3)(x^2 + 2) = x^3 + 2x + 3x^2 + 6$$
$$\text{Rearrange terms: } = x^3 + 3x^2 + 2x + 6$$

So $x^3 + 3x^2 + 2x + 6 = (x + 3)(x^2 + 2)$.

Work Smart

In Example 6(a), grouping the first three terms would result in a common factor of x, but factoring out an x would not result in a common factor, such as x + 3.

  (b) $$6x^2 + 9x - 10x - 15 = (6x^2 + 9x) + (-10x - 15)$$
$$\text{Factor out } -5 \text{ in the second grouping: } = 3x(2x + 3) + (-5)(2x + 3)$$
$$= (2x + 3)(3x - 5)$$

We leave the check to you. ∎

> **Quick** ✔ *In Problems 16–18, factor by grouping.*
> **16.** $5x + 5y + bx + by$ **17.** $w^3 - 3w^2 + 4w - 12$ **18.** $2x^2 + x - 10x - 5$

4.4 EXERCISES

PRACTICE   WATCH   DOWNLOAD   READ   REVIEW

1–18. *are the* Quick ✔s *that follow each* **EXAMPLE**

Building Skills

In Problems 19–36, factor out the greatest common factor. See Objective 1.

19. $5a + 35$

20. $8z + 48$

21. $-3y + 21$

22. $-4b + 32$

23. $14x^2 - 21x$

24. $12a^2 + 45a$

25. $3z^3 - 6z^2 + 18z$

26. $2w^3 + 10w^2 - 14$

27. $-5p^4 + 10p^3 - 25p^2$

28. $-6q^3 + 36q^2 - 48q$

29. $49m^3n + 84mn^3 - 35m^4n^2$

30. $64x^4y^2 - 40x^3y^4 + 96xy^5$

31. $-18z^3 + 14z^2 + 4z$

32. $-18b^3 + 10b^2 + 6b$

33. $5c(3c - 2) - 3(3c - 2)$

34. $6z(5z + 3) + 5(5z + 3)$

35. $(4a + 3)(a - 3) + (2a - 7)(a - 3)$

36. $(5b + 3)(b + 4) + (3b + 1)(b + 4)$

In Problems 37–48, factor by grouping. See Objective 2.

37. $5x + 5y + ax + ay$

38. $8x - 8y + bx - by$

39. $2z^3 + 10z^2 - 5z - 25$

40. $3y^3 + 9y^2 - 5y - 15$

41. $w^2 - 5w + 3w - 15$

42. $p^2 - 3p + 8p - 24$

43. $2x^2 - 8x - 4x + 16$

44. $3a^2 - 15a - 9a + 45$

45. $3x^3 + 15x^2 - 12x^2 - 60x$

46. $2y^3 + 14y^2 - 4y^2 - 28y$

47. $2ax - 2ay - bx + by$

48. $15x^2 - 5xy + 18xy - 6y^2$

Mixed Practice

In Problems 49–58, factor each polynomial completely.

49. $(w + 3)(w - 3) - (w - 2)(w - 3)$

50. $(x + 5)(x - 3) - (x - 1)(x - 3)$

51. $2y^2 + 5y - 4y - 10$

52. $3q^2 + 5q - 12q - 20$

53. $6x^3y^3 + 9x^2y - 21x^3y^2$ **54.** $8a^4b^2 + 12a^3b^3 - 36ab^4$

55. $x^3 + x^2 + 3x + 3$

56. $c^3 - c^2 + 5c - 5$

57. $x(x - 2) + 3(x - 2)^2$ **58.** $2y(y + 4) + 3(y + 4)^2$

Math for the Future *In Problems 59–66, expressions that occur in calculus are given. Factor and simplify each expression.*

59. $3x^2(4x + 1)^2 + 8x^3(4x + 1)$

60. $2x(3x + 5)^2 + 6x^2(3x + 5)$

61. $3(x + 9)^2(2x + 5) + 2(x + 9)^3$

62. $4(x - 3)^3(3x + 1) + 3(x - 3)^4$

63. $4(2x - 1)(x - 5)^3 + 3(x - 5)^2(2x - 1)^2$

64. $2(x + 3)(6x + 5)^3 + 18(6x + 5)^2(x + 3)^2$

65. $2(x^2 + 1) \cdot 2x(4x - 3)^3 + 3(4x - 3)^2 \cdot 4(x^2 + 1)^2$

66. $3(x^2 + 3)^2 \cdot 2x(2x + 1)^2 + 2(2x + 1) \cdot 2(x^2 + 3)^3$

Applying the Concepts

△ **67.** **Area** Write the area of the shaded region in factored form.

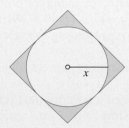

△ **68.** **Area** Write the area of the shaded region in factored form.

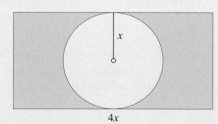

69. Surface Area The surface area of a cylindrical can whose radius is r inches and height is 4 inches is given by $S = 2\pi r^2 + 8\pi r$. Express the surface area in factored form.

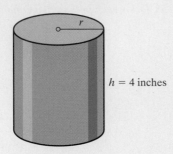

$h = 4$ inches

70. Volume The volume of a right circular cylinder of height h and radius r inscribed in a sphere of fixed radius R is given by $V = \pi h R^2 - \dfrac{\pi h^3}{4}$. Express the volume of the cylinder in factored form.

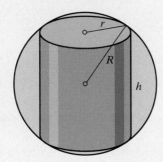

71. Markups and Discounts Suppose that a clothing store marks up its clothes 40% when it buys them from the supplier.

(a) Let x represent the cost of designer shirts purchased from the supplier. Write an algebraic expression representing the selling price of the shirt.

(b) After 1 month, the manager of the clothing store discounts the shirts by 40%. Write an algebraic expression representing the sale price of the shirt in terms of x.

(c) Write the algebraic expression in factored form.

(d) Based on your answer to part (c), is the store selling the shirt for the same price that it paid for it?

72. Summer Clearance Suppose that an electronics store decides to sell last year's model 35-inch televisions for a 20% discount.

(a) Let x represent the original price of the television. Write an algebraic expression representing the selling price of the television.

(b) After 1 month, the manager of the store discounts the TVs by another 15%. Write an algebraic expression representing the sale price of the televisions in terms of x, the original selling price.

(c) Write the algebraic expression in factored form.

(d) If the original price of the television was $650, what is the sale price after the second discount?

73. Stock Prices Suppose that Christina purchased a stock for x dollars. During the first year, the stock's price rose 15%.

(a) Write an algebraic expression for the price of the stock after the first year in terms of x.

(b) During the second year, the stock's price rose 10%. Write an algebraic expression for the price of the stock after the second year in terms of x.

(c) Write the algebraic expression found in part (b) in factored form.

(d) If the stock was originally purchased for $x = \$20$, what is the value of the stock after two years?

Extending the Concepts

In this section, we discussed factoring polynomials over the integers. This means that factors of a polynomial can only have polynomials with integer coefficients. However, we could also discuss polynomials with, say, rational coefficients such as $\dfrac{1}{3}x + \dfrac{2}{3}$. A polynomial such as this can be factored over the rational numbers by factoring out the greatest common factor $\dfrac{1}{3}$, so that $\dfrac{1}{3}x + \dfrac{2}{3} = \dfrac{1}{3}(x + 2)$. Use this idea to factor out the greatest common factor in Problems 74–77.

74. $\dfrac{1}{2}x + \dfrac{3}{2}$ **75.** $\dfrac{1}{4}x - \dfrac{7}{4}$

76. $\dfrac{2}{3}x^2 + \dfrac{4}{9}x$ **77.** $\dfrac{1}{5}b^3 + \dfrac{8}{25}b$

78. The Better Deal Which is the better deal: (a) receiving a 30% discount or (b) receiving a 15% discount and then another 15% discount after the first 15% discount was applied? Prove it!

In Problems 79–81, factor out the greater common factor of each expression. Assume n is a positive integer.

79. $x^n + 3x^{n+1} + 6x^{2n}$

80. $2x^{3n} - 8x^{4n} + 16x^{2n}$

81. $4y^{n+3} - 8y^{n+2} + 6y^{n+5}$

4.5 Factoring Trinomials

OBJECTIVES

$\boxed{1}$ Factor Trinomials of the Form $x^2 + bx + c$

$\boxed{2}$ Factor Trinomials of the Form $ax^2 + bx + c, a \neq 1$

$\boxed{3}$ Factor Trinomials Using Substitution

Preparing for Factoring Trinomials

Before getting started, take the following readiness quiz. If you get a problem wrong, go back to the section cited and review the material.

P1. Determine the coefficients of $4x^2 - 9x + 2$.   [Section R.5, p. 41]

P2. Find two integers whose sum is 5 and product is 6.

P3. Find two integers whose sum is -4 and product is -32.

P4. Find two integers whose sum is 6 and product is -40.

P5. Find two integers whose sum is -12 and product is 32.

P6. List the factors of 18 whose sum is 11.

P7. List the factors of -24 whose sum is -2.

In this section, we are going to factor trinomials of the form $ax^2 + bx + c$, where a, b, and c are integers. We begin by looking at trinomials where the leading coefficient is 1.

$\boxed{1}$ Factor Trinomials of the Form $x^2 + bx + c$

The idea behind factoring a second-degree polynomial of the form $x^2 + bx + c$ is to see whether it can be written as the product of two first-degree polynomials.

For example,

Multiplication
$\longrightarrow$

Factored Form $\longrightarrow (x - 5)(x + 2) = x^2 - 3x - 10 \longleftarrow$ Product

$\longleftarrow$

Factoring

The factors of $x^2 - 3x - 10$ are $x - 5$ and $x + 2$. Notice the following:

$$x^2 - 3x - 10 = (x - 5)(x + 2)$$

The sum of -5 and 2 is -3

The product of -5 and 2 is -10

Preparing for...Answers **P1.** 4, 9, 2
P2. 2, 3   **P3.** $-8, 4$ **P4.** $-4, 10$
P5. $-8, -4$ **P6.** 9 and 2   **P7.** -6 and 4

In general, if $x^2 + bx + c = (x + m)(x + n)$, then $mn = c$ and $m + n = b$.

EXAMPLE 1 How to Factor a Trinomial of the Form $x^2 + bx + c$

Factor: $x^2 + 8x + 12$

Step-by-Step Solution

Step 1: We are looking for factors of $c = 12$ whose sum is $b = 8$. We begin by listing all factors of 12 and computing the sum of these factors.

Integers Whose Product Is 12	1, 12	2, 6	3, 4	$-1, -12$	$-2, -6$	$-3, -4$
Sum	13	8	7	-13	-8	-7

We can see that $2 \cdot 6 = 12$ and $2 + 6 = 8$, so $m = 2$ and $n = 6$.

Step 2: We write the trinomial in the form $(x + m)(x + n)$.

$$x^2 + 8x + 12 = (x + 2)(x + 6)$$

Step 3: Check We FOIL $(x + 2)(x + 6)$ to verify our solution.

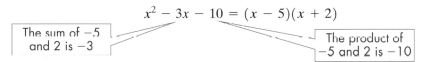

$$(x + 2)(x + 6) = x^2 + 6x + 2x + 2(6) = x^2 + 8x + 12$$

So $x^2 + 8x + 12 = (x + 2)(x + 6)$. Because multiplication is commutative, the order in which we list the factors does not matter. So $x^2 + 8x + 12$ is also equal to $(x + 6)(x + 2)$. ∎

We summarize the steps used in Example 1 below.

FACTORING A TRINOMIAL OF THE FORM $x^2 + bx + c$

Step 1: Find the pair of integers whose product is c and whose sum is b. That is, determine m and n such that $mn = c$ and $m + n = b$.

Step 2: Write $x^2 + bx + c = (x + m)(x + n)$.

Step 3: Check your work by multiplying out the factored form.

Work Smart

In a trinomial $x^2 + bx + c$, if both b and c are positive, then m and n must both be positive.

In Example 1, notice that the coefficient of the middle term is positive and the constant is positive. If the coefficient of the middle term and constant are both positive, then m and n must both be positive.

Quick ✔

1. When factoring a trinomial of the form $x^2 + bx + c$, we need to find pairs of integers m and n such that _____ $= c$ and _____ $= b$.

2. *True or False:* $x^2 + 12x + 11 = (x + 11)(x + 1)$

In Problems 3 and 4, factor each trinomial.

3. $y^2 + 9y + 18$ 4. $p^2 + 14p + 24$

EXAMPLE 2 Factoring a Trinomial of the Form $x^2 + bx + c$

Factor: $p^2 - 10p + 24$

Solution

We are looking for factors of $c = 24$ whose sum is $b = -10$. We begin by listing all factors of 24 and computing the sum of these factors.

Integers Whose Product Is 24	1, 24	2, 12	3, 8	4, 6	−1, −24	−2, −12	−3, −8	−4, −6
Sum	25	14	11	10	−25	−14	−11	−10

We can see that $-4 \cdot (-6) = 24$ and $-4 + (-6) = -10$, so $m = -4$ and $n = -6$. We write the trinomial in the form $(p + m)(p + n)$.

$$p^2 - 10p + 24 = (p + (-4))(p + (-6))$$
$$= (p - 4)(p - 6)$$

Check We FOIL $(p - 4)(p - 6)$ to verify our solution.

$$(p - 4)(p - 6) = p^2 - 6p - 4p + (-4)(-6)$$
$$= p^2 - 10p + 24$$ ∎

Work Smart

In a trinomial $x^2 + bx + c$, if b is negative and c is positive, then m and n must both be negative.

In Example 2, notice that the coefficient of the middle term is negative and the constant is positive. If the coefficient of the middle term is negative and constant is positive, then m and n must both be negative.

Quick ✔ *In Problems 5 and 6, factor each trinomial.*

5. $q^2 - 6q + 8$ 6. $x^2 - 8x + 12$

EXAMPLE 3 Factoring a Trinomial of the Form $x^2 + bx + c, c < 0$

Factor: $z^2 - 3z - 28$

Solution

We are looking for factors of $c = -28$ whose sum is $b = -3$. We begin by listing all factors of -28 and computing the sum of these factors.

Integers Whose Product Is −28	−1, 28	−2, 14	−4, 7	1, −28	2, −14	4, −7
Sum	27	12	3	−27	−12	−3

We can see that $4 \cdot (-7) = -28$ and $4 + (-7) = -3$, so $m = 4$ and $n = -7$. We write the trinomial in the form $(z + m)(z + n)$.

$$z^2 - 3z - 28 = (z + 4)(z + (-7))$$
$$= (z + 4)(z - 7)$$

Check We FOIL $(z + 4)(z - 7)$ to verify our solution.

$$(z + 4)(z - 7) = z^2 - 7z + 4z + 4(-7) = z^2 - 3z - 28 \qquad \blacksquare$$

In Example 3, notice that the coefficient of the middle term is negative and the constant is also negative. If the coefficient of the middle term is negative and constant is negative, then m and n must be opposite in sign. The factor with the larger absolute value must be negative.

Work Smart

In a trinomial $x^2 + bx + c$, if both b and c are negative, then m and n must have opposite signs.

Quick ✔ *In Problems 7 and 8, factor each trinomial.*

7. $w^2 - 4w - 21$ **8.** $q^2 - 9q - 36$

Remember, a polynomial whose coefficients are integers that cannot be written as the product of two other polynomials whose coefficients are integers (other than 1 or −1) is said to be prime.

EXAMPLE 4 Identifying a Prime Trinomial

Factor: $y^2 + 4y + 12$

Solution

We are looking for factors of $c = 12$ whose sum is $b = 4$. Because both b and c are positive, we know that m and n must both be positive, so we only list positive factors of 12 and compute the sum of these factors.

Integers Whose Product Is 12	1, 12	2, 6	3, 4
Sum		13	8	7

There are no factors of 12 whose sum is 4. Therefore, $y^2 + 4y + 12$ is prime. $\qquad \blacksquare$

Quick ✔

9. Show that $t^2 - 5t + 8$ is prime by listing all factors of 8 and showing none of the factors sum to −5.

Sometimes we need to factor out a common factor before factoring the trinomial.

EXAMPLE 5 Factoring Trinomials with a Common Factor

Factor: $3u^3 - 9u^2 - 120u$

Solution

Work Smart

What's the first thing to look for when factoring any polynomial? A greatest common factor!

We start by noticing that there is a common factor of $3u$ in the trinomial. We factor the $3u$ out:

$$3u^3 - 9u^2 - 120u = 3u(u^2 - 3u - 40)$$

We now concentrate on factoring the trinomial in parentheses, $u^2 - 3u - 40$. We are looking for factors of $c = -40$ whose sum is $b = -3$. We begin by listing all factors of -40. Because $c = -40$ and $b = -3$, we know the larger factor (in absolute value) will be negative.

Integers Whose Product Is -40	$1, -40$	$2, -20$	$4, -10$	$5, -8$
Sum	-39	-18	-6	-3

We can see that $5 \cdot (-8) = -40$ and $5 + (-8) = -3$, so $m = 5$ and $n = -8$. We write the trinomial in the form $(u + m)(u + n)$.

$$u^2 - 3u - 40 = (u + 5)(u + (-8))$$
$$= (u + 5)(u - 8)$$

Remember, we already factored out a common factor, so we have that

$$3u^3 - 9u^2 - 120u = 3u(u^2 - 3u - 40)$$
$$= 3u(u + 5)(u - 8)$$

Check
$$3u(u + 5)(u - 8) = 3u(u^2 - 8u + 5u - 40)$$
$$= 3u(u^2 - 3u - 40)$$
$$= 3u^3 - 9u^2 - 120u$$ ■

Quick ✔ *In Problems 10 and 11, factor each trinomial completely.*

10. $2x^3 - 12x^2 - 54x$ **11.** $-3z^2 - 21z - 30$

If a trinomial has more than one variable, we take the same approach as that used for trinomials with one variable. So trinomials of the form

$$x^2 + bxy + cy^2$$

will factor as

$$(x + \_y)(x + \_y)$$

where the blanks need to be determined.

EXAMPLE 6 Factoring Trinomials with Two Variables

Factor: $p^2 + 6pq - 16q^2$

Solution

The trinomial $p^2 + 6pq - 16q^2$ will factor as $(p + mq)(p + nq)$ where $mn = -16$ and $m + n = 6$. We are looking for factors of $c = -16$ whose sum is $b = 6$. We list factors of -16, but because $c = -16$ and $b = 6$, we know the larger factor of 16 will be positive.

Integers Whose Product Is -16	$-1, 16$	$-2, 8$	$-4, 4$
Sum	15	6	0

We can see that $-2 \cdot 8 = -16$ and $-2 + 8 = 6$, so $m = -2$ and $n = 8$. We write the trinomial in the form $(p + mq)(p + nq)$.

$$p^2 + 6pq - 16q^2 = (p + (-2)q)(p + 8q)$$
$$= (p - 2q)(p + 8q)$$

Check
$$(p - 2q)(p + 8q) = p^2 + 8pq - 2pq - 16q^2$$
$$= p^2 + 6pq - 16q^2$$ ∎

Quick ✔ *In Problems 12 and 13, factor completely each trinomial.*

12. $x^2 + 8xy + 15y^2$ **13.** $m^2 + mn - 20n^2$

⎡2 Factor Trinomials of the Form $ax^2 + bx + c$, $a \neq 1$

When it comes to factoring trinomials of the form $ax^2 + bx + c$, where a is not 1, we have two methods that can be used:

1. Factoring by grouping
2. Trial and error

There are pros and cons to both methods. We will point out these pros and cons as we proceed. We start with factoring by grouping.

Factoring $ax^2 + bx + c$, $a \neq 1$, by Grouping

Example 7 illustrates how to factor $ax^2 + bx + c$, $a \neq 1$, by grouping.

⎡**EXAMPLE 7** How to Factor $ax^2 + bx + c$, $a \neq 1$, by Grouping

Factor: $3x^2 + 14x + 8$

Step-by-Step Solution

First, we notice that $3x^2 + 14x + 8$ has no common factors and that $a = 3$, $b = 14$, and $c = 8$.

Step 1: Find the value of ac.	The value of $a \cdot c = 3 \cdot 8 = 24$.

Step 2: We want to determine the integers whose product is 24 and whose sum is 14. Because both 24 and 14 are positive, we only list the positive factors of 24.

Integers Whose Product Is 24	1, 24	2, 12	3, 8	4, 6
Sum	25	14	11	10

The integers whose product is 24 and sum is 14 are 2 and 12.

Step 3: Write
$ax^2 + bx + c = ax^2 + mx + nx + c.$

Write $3x^2 + 14x + 8$ as $3x^2 + 2x + 12x + 8$

$14x = 2x + 12x$

Step 4: Factor the expression in Step 3 by grouping.

$$3x^2 + 2x + 12x + 8 = (3x^2 + 2x) + (12x + 8)$$
$$= x(3x + 2) + 4(3x + 2)$$
Factor out $3x + 2$: $= (3x + 2)(x + 4)$

Step 5: Check

$$(3x + 2)(x + 4) = 3x^2 + 12x + 2x + 8$$
$$= 3x^2 + 14x + 8$$

So $3x^2 + 14x + 8 = (3x + 2)(x + 4)$. ∎

To factor a second-degree polynomial $ax^2 + bx + c$ when $a \neq 1$ and there are no common factors in the polynomial, we use the steps on the following page.

FACTORING $ax^2 + bx + c, a \neq 1$, BY GROUPING: a, b, AND c HAVE NO COMMON FACTORS

Step 1: Find the value of ac.

Step 2: Find the pair of integers whose product is ac and whose sum is b. That is, find m and n so that $mn = ac$ and $m + n = b$.

Step 3: Write $ax^2 + bx + c = ax^2 + mx + nx + c$.

Step 4: Factor the expression in Step 3 by grouping.

Step 5: Multiply out the factored form to verify your answer.

EXAMPLE 8 Factoring $ax^2 + bx + c, a \neq 1$, by Grouping

Factor: $12x^2 - x - 6$

Solution

First, we notice that $12x^2 - x - 6$ has no common factors and that $a = 12$, $b = -1$, and $c = -6$. The value of $a \cdot c = 12 \cdot (-6) = -72$.

We want to determine the integers whose product is -72 and whose sum is -1. Because $-72 < 0$, we know that one integer will be positive and the other negative. Because $-1 < 0$, we know the factor of -72 with the larger absolute value will be negative.

Integers Whose Product Is -72	1, -72	2, -36	3, -24	4, -18	6, -12	8, -9
Sum	-71	-34	-21	-14	-6	-1

The integers whose product is -72 and sum is -1 are 8 and -9.

$$-x = 8x - 9x$$

$$12x^2 - x - 6 = 12x^2 + 8x - 9x - 6$$
$$= (12x^2 + 8x) + (-9x - 6)$$
$$= 4x(3x + 2) - 3(3x + 2)$$
Factor out $3x + 2$: $= (3x + 2)(4x - 3)$

Work Smart

Be careful with the negative sign on $-9x$.

Check $(3x + 2)(4x - 3) = 12x^2 - 9x + 8x - 6$
$$= 12x^2 - x - 6$$

So $12x^2 - x - 6 = (3x + 2)(4x - 3)$.

Quick ✔ *In Problems 14 and 15, factor each trinomial completely.*

14. $2b^2 + 7b - 15$ **15.** $10x^2 + 27x + 18$

The advantage of factoring by grouping to factor trinomials of the form $ax^2 + bx + c, a \neq 1$, is that it is algorithmic (that is, step by step). However, if the product $a \cdot c$ gets large, then there are a lot of factors of ac whose sum must be determined. This can get overwhelming. Under these circumstances, it may be better to try the second method, trial and error.

Using Trial and Error to Factor $ax^2 + bx + c, a \neq 1$

The idea behind using trial and error is to list various binomials and use FOIL to find their product until the combination of binomials that results in the original trinomial is found. While this method may sound haphazard, experience and logic play a role in minimizing the number of possibilities that must be tried before a factored form is found.

EXAMPLE 9 How to Factor $ax^2 + bx + c$, $a \neq 1$ Using Trial and Error

Factor: $10x^2 + 19x + 6$

Step-by-Step Solution

We always check for common factors first. There are no common factors in $10x^2 + 19x + 6$.

| Step 1: List the possibilities for the first terms of each binomial whose product is ax^2. | We list all possible ways of representing the first term, $10x^2$. $(10x + \underline{})(x + \underline{})$ $(5x + \underline{})(2x + \underline{})$ |

| Step 2: List the possibilities for the last terms of each binomial whose product is c. | The last term, 6, has the factors: $1 \cdot 6, 2 \cdot 3, -1 \cdot (-6),$ or $-2 \cdot (-3)$. |

Step 3: Write out all the combinations of factors found in Steps 1 and 2. Multiply the binomials out until a product is found that equals the trinomial.

Possible Factorization	Product	Possible Factorization	Product
$(10x + 1)(x + 6)$	$10x^2 + 61x + 6$	$(5x + 1)(2x + 6)$	$10x^2 + 32x + 6$
$(10x + 6)(x + 1)$	$10x^2 + 16x + 6$	$(5x + 6)(2x + 1)$	$10x^2 + 17x + 6$
$(10x + 2)(x + 3)$	$10x^2 + 32x + 6$	$(5x + 2)(2x + 3)$	$10x^2 + 19x + 6$
$(10x + 3)(x + 2)$	$10x^2 + 23x + 6$	$(5x + 3)(2x + 2)$	$10x^2 + 16x + 6$
$(10x - 1)(x - 6)$	$10x^2 - 61x + 6$	$(5x - 1)(2x - 6)$	$10x^2 - 32x + 6$
$(10x - 6)(x - 1)$	$10x^2 - 16x + 6$	$(5x - 6)(2x - 1)$	$10x^2 - 17x + 6$
$(10x - 2)(x - 3)$	$10x^2 - 32x + 6$	$(5x - 2)(2x - 3)$	$10x^2 - 19x + 6$
$(10x - 3)(x - 2)$	$10x^2 - 23x + 6$	$(5x - 3)(2x - 2)$	$10x^2 - 16x + 6$

The highlighted row is the factorization that works, so $10x^2 + 19x + 6 = (5x + 2)(2x + 3)$. ∎

In looking at the solution to Example 9, you may feel a little overwhelmed—so many possibilities! However, many of the possibilities could have been eliminated with a little thought. For example, we notice that the middle and last terms are both positive. This means that the factors of c must be positive—this alone would eliminate half of the combinations listed in Example 9. Further, because the original polynomial has no common factors, the binomials in the factored form cannot have common factors either. This would eliminate four additional possibilities.

If we had employed these hints, the list in Example 9 would become

Possible Factorization	Product
$(10x + 1)(x + 6)$	$10x^2 + 61x + 6$
$(10x + 3)(x + 2)$	$10x^2 + 23x + 6$
$(5x + 6)(2x + 1)$	$10x^2 + 17x + 6$
$(5x + 2)(2x + 3)$	$10x^2 + 19x + 6$

Not too bad! There are only four possibilities. We summarize the steps to factor using trial and error and some helpful hints on the next page.

STEPS TO FACTOR $ax^2 + bx + c$, $a \neq 1$, USING TRIAL AND ERROR: a, b, AND c HAVE NO COMMON FACTORS

Step 1: List the possibilities for the first terms of each binomial whose product is ax^2.

$$(\underline{}x + \,)(\underline{}x + \,) = ax^2 + bx + c$$

Step 2: List the possibilities for the last terms of each binomial whose product is c.

$$(\underline{}x + \square)(\underline{}x + \square) = ax^2 + bx + c$$

Step 3: Write out all the combinations of factors found in Steps 1 and 2. Multiply the binomials out until a product is found that equals the trinomial.

HELPFUL HINTS IN USING TRIAL AND ERROR TO FACTOR $ax^2 + bx + c$, $a \neq 1$

- If $a < 0$, factor out -1 as a GCF so that $a > 0$.
- If the constant c is positive, then the factors of c must be the same sign as b.
- If $ax^2 + bx + c$ has no common factor, then the binomials in the factored form cannot have common factors either.
- If the value of b is small, then choose factors of ac that are close to each other. If the value of b is large, then choose factors of ac that are far from each other.
- If the value of b is correct except for the sign, then interchange the signs in the binomial factors.

EXAMPLE 10 Factoring $ax^2 + bx + c$, $a \neq 1$, Using Trial and Error

Factor: $18x^2 + 3x - 10$

Solution

There are no common factors in $18x^2 + 3x - 10$. We list all possible ways of representing the first term, $18x^2$.

$$(18x + \underline{})(x + \underline{})$$
$$(9x + \underline{})(2x + \underline{})$$
$$(6x + \underline{})(3x + \underline{})$$

The last term, -10, has the factors: $1 \cdot (-10)$, $2 \cdot (-5)$, $-1 \cdot 10$, or $-2 \cdot 5$.

We list some possible combinations of factors found in Steps 1 and 2. We should notice that the middle term is $+3x$. Because this middle term is positive and small, the binomial factors we list should have outer and inner products that sum to a positive, small number. Therefore, we will start with $(6x + \underline{})(3x + \underline{})$ and the factors $2 \cdot (-5)$ and $-2 \cdot 5$. We do not use $6x + 2$ or $6x - 2$ as a possible factor because there is a common factor in these binomials.

Let's try $(6x - 5)(3x + 2)$.

$$(6x - 5)(3x + 2) = 18x^2 + 12x - 15x - 10$$
$$= 18x^2 - 3x - 10$$

Close! The only problem is that the middle term is the opposite sign that we want. Therefore, let's change the signs on -5 and 2 in the binomial and try $(6x + 5)(3x - 2)$.

$$(6x + 5)(3x - 2) = 18x^2 - 12x + 15x - 10$$
$$= 18x^2 + 3x - 10$$

So $18x^2 + 3x - 10 = (6x + 5)(3x - 2)$. ∎

The moral of the story in Example 10 is that the name *trial and error* is a bit misleading. You won't have to haphazardly choose binomial factors "until the cows come home" provided you use the helpful hints and some careful thought.

Quick ✔ *In Problems 16 and 17, factor each trinomial completely.*

16. $8x^2 + 14x + 5$

17. $12y^2 + 32y - 35$

EXAMPLE 11 Factoring Trinomials with Two Variables

Factor: $24x^2 + 13xy - 2y^2$

Solution

There are no common factors in $24x^2 + 13xy - 2y^2$. The trinomial will factor in the form $24x^2 + 13xy - 2y^2 = (\_x + \_y)(\_x + \_y)$.

We list all possible ways of representing the first term, $24x^2$.

$$(24x + \_y)(x + \_y)$$
$$(12x + \_y)(2x + \_y)$$
$$(8x + \_y)(3x + \_y)$$
$$(6x + \_y)(4x + \_y)$$

The last term, -2, has the factors: $1 \cdot (-2)$ or $2 \cdot (-1)$.

We should notice that the middle term is $+13xy$. Because this middle term is positive and neither large nor small, the binomial factors we list should have outer and inner products that sum to a positive, midsize number. The only coefficients on y in the factored form are 1 and 2 (ignoring their sign for a second). We cannot have 2 as a factor in the forms $(12x + \_y)(2x + \_y)$ or $(6x + \_y)(4x + \_y)$ because 2 creates a common factor and a common factor does not exist in the original trinomial. Therefore, we will start with $(8x + \_y)(3x + \_y)$ and the factors $1 \cdot (-2)$ and $2 \cdot (-1)$.

Let's try $(8x + 1y)(3x - 2y)$.

$$(8x + 1y)(3x \quad 2y) = 24x^2 - 16xy + 3xy - 2y^2$$
$$= 24x^2 - 13xy - 2y^2$$

Close! The only problem is that the middle term is the opposite sign that we want. Therefore, let's change the signs on 1 and -2 in the binomial and try $(8x - 1y)(3x + 2y)$.

$$(8x - 1y)(3x + 2y) = 24x^2 + 16xy - 3xy - 2y^2$$
$$= 24x^2 + 13xy - 2y^2$$

So $24x^2 + 13xy - 2y^2 = (8x - y)(3x + 2y)$. ■

Quick ✔ *In Problems 18 and 19, completely factor the trinomial.*

18. $30x^2 + 7xy - 2y^2$

19. $8x^2 - 10xy - 42y^2$

EXAMPLE 12 Factoring Trinomials with a Negative Leading Coefficient

Factor: $-14x^2 + 29x + 15$

Solution

While there are no common factors in $-14x^2 + 29x + 15$, we do notice that the coefficient of the square term is negative. It is easier to factor trinomials when the leading coefficient is positive. Therefore, we can factor -1 out of the trinomial to obtain

$$-14x^2 + 29x + 15 = -1(14x^2 - 29x - 15)$$

Now we factor the expression in parentheses using either the grouping technique or trial and error and obtain

$$-14x^2 + 29x + 15 = -1(14x^2 - 29x - 15)$$

Remember the -1 that was factored out: $= -1(7x + 3)(2x - 5)$ ∎

Quick ✔ *In Problems 20 and 21, factor each trinomial completely.*

20. $-6y^2 + 23y + 4$ **21.** $-9x^2 - 21xy - 10y^2$

⎾3⏌ Factor Trinomials Using Substitution

Sometimes it is possible to factor a complicated-looking polynomial through a substitution of one variable for another. When this approach is used, we say that we are **factoring by substitution.**

⎾EXAMPLE 13⏌ Factoring by Substitution

Factor: $2n^6 - n^3 - 15$

Solution

Notice that $2n^6 - n^3 - 15$ can be written as $2(n^3)^2 - n^3 - 15$ so that the trinomial is in the form $au^2 + bu + c$, where $u = n^3$. If we substitute u for n^3, we obtain

$$2n^6 - n^3 - 15 = 2(n^3)^2 - n^3 - 15$$

Let $n^3 = u$: $= 2u^2 - u - 15$

Factor: $= (2u + 5)(u - 3)$

Let $u = n^3$: $= (2n^3 + 5)(n^3 - 3)$

So $2n^6 - n^3 - 15 = (2n^3 + 5)(n^3 - 3)$. ∎

> **Work Smart**
>
> To see if a trinomial can be factored using substitution, check to see if the trinomial can be written in the form
>
> $a(☺)^2 + b(☺) + c$
>
> where ☺ is some algebraic expression.

⎾EXAMPLE 14⏌ Factoring by Substitution

Factor: $3(x - 3)^2 + 11(x - 3) - 4$

Solution

Notice that $3(x - 3)^2 + 11(x - 3) - 4$ can be written in the form $au^2 + bu + c$ where $u = x - 3$. If we substitute u for $x - 3$, we obtain

$$3(x - 3)^2 + 11(x - 3) - 4 = 3u^2 + 11u - 4$$

Factor: $= (3u - 1)(u + 4)$

We do not want to factor an expression in u, we want to factor an expression in x. So, we substitute $x - 3$ for u and obtain

$$3u^2 + 11u - 4 = (3u - 1)(u + 4)$$

Let $u = x - 3$: $= [3(x - 3) - 1][(x - 3) + 4]$

$= (3x - 9 - 1)(x + 1)$

$= (3x - 10)(x + 1)$

So $3(x - 3)^2 + 11(x - 3) - 4 = (3x - 10)(x + 1)$. ∎

Quick ✔

22. When factoring $3(2x - 3)^2 + 5(2x - 3) + 2$ by substitution, we would let $u = $ _____.

In Problems 23 and 24, factor each trinomial by substitution.

23. $y^4 - 2y^2 - 24$ **24.** $4(x - 3)^2 + 5(x - 3) - 6$

4.5 EXERCISES

PRACTICE   WATCH   DOWNLOAD   READ   REVIEW

1–24. are the Quick ✔*s that follow each* EXAMPLE

Building Skills

In Problems 25–40, factor each trinomial completely.
See Objective 1.

25. $x^2 + 8x + 15$ **26.** $x^2 + 8x + 12$

27. $p^2 + 3p - 18$ **28.** $z^2 + 3z - 28$

29. $r^2 + 10r + 25$ **30.** $y^2 - 12y + 36$

31. $s^2 + 7s - 60$ **32.** $q^2 + 2q - 80$

33. $x^2 - 15x + 56$ **34.** $z^2 - 16z + 48$

35. $-w^2 - 2w + 24$ **36.** $-p^2 + 3p + 54$

37. $x^2 + 7xy + 12y^2$ **38.** $m^2 + 7mn + 10n^2$

39. $p^2 + 2pq - 24q^2$ **40.** $x^2 - 4xy - 21y^2$

In Problems 41–56, factor each trinomial completely.
See Objective 2.

41. $2p^2 - 15p - 8$ **42.** $3z^2 - 13z - 10$

43. $4y^2 - 11y + 6$ **44.** $6x^2 - 37x + 6$

45. $8s^2 + 2s - 3$ **46.** $12r^2 + 11r - 15$

47. $16z^2 + 8z - 15$ **48.** $18y^2 + 43y - 5$

49. $18y^2 + 17y + 4$ **50.** $20r^2 + 23r + 6$

51. $2x^2 + 11xy - 21y^2$ **52.** $3m^2 + 7mn - 6n^2$

53. $4r^2 - 23rs + 15s^2$ **54.** $6r^2 - 25rs + 4s^2$

55. $24r^2 + 23rs - 12s^2$ **56.** $18x^2 + 37xy - 20y^2$

In Problems 57–66, factor each trinomial completely.
See Objective 3.

57. $x^4 + 3x^2 + 2$ **58.** $y^4 + 5y^2 + 6$

59. $m^2n^2 + 5mn - 14$ **60.** $r^2s^2 + 8rs - 48$

61. $(x + 1)^2 - 6(x + 1) - 16$

62. $(y - 3)^2 + 3(y - 3) + 2$

63. $(3r - 1)^2 - 9(3r - 1) + 20$

64. $(5z - 3)^2 - 12(5z - 3) + 32$

65. $2(y - 3)^2 + 13(y - 3) + 15$

66. $3(z + 3)^2 + 14(z + 3) + 8$

Mixed Practice

In Problems 67–98, factor each polynomial completely. If the poly-
nomial cannot be factored, say it is prime. Be sure to look for a
greatest common factor.

67. $10w^2 + 41w + 21$

68. $8q^2 + 26q + 11$

69. $4(2y + 1)^2 - 3(2y + 1) - 1$

70. $2(3z - 1)^2 + 3(3z - 1) + 1$

71. $12x^2 + 23xy + 10y^2$

72. $24m^2 + 58mn + 9n^2$

73. $y^2 + 2y - 27$

74. $t^2 - 5t + 8$

75. $x^4 + 6x^2 + 8$

76. $a^6 + 7a^3 + 12$

77. $z^6 + 9z^3 + 20$

78. $r^6 - 6r^3 + 8$

79. $r^2 - 12rs + 32s^2$

80. $p^2 - 14pq + 45q^2$

81. $8(z + 1)^2 + 2(z + 1) - 1$

82. $9(a + 2)^2 - 10(a + 2) + 1$

83. $3x^2 - 7x - 12$

84. $5w^2 - 10w + 12$

85. $2x^2 + 12x - 54$

86. $3y^2 - 6y - 189$

87. $-3r^2 + 39r - 120$

88. $-4s^2 - 32s - 48$

89. $-16m^2 + 12m + 70$

90. $-24y^2 - 39y + 18$

91. $48z^2 + 124z + 28$

92. $48w^2 + 20w - 42$

93. $3x^3 - 6x^2 - 240x$

94. $4x^3 - 52x^2 + 144x$

95. $8x^3y^2 - 76x^2y^2 + 140xy^2$

96. $-24m^3n - 18m^2n + 27mn$

97. $70r^4s - 36r^3s - 16r^2s$

98. $54x^3y + 33x^2y - 72xy$

Applying the Concepts

99. **How to Make an Open Box** The volume of an open box with a rectangular base is to be made from a piece of cardboard that is 24 by 30 inches by cutting a square piece of cardboard from each corner and turning up the sides. See the illustration. The volume V of the box as a function of the length x of the side of the square cut from each corner is

$$V(x) = 4x^3 - 108x^2 + 720x$$

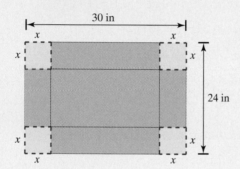

(a) Find and interpret $V(3)$.
(b) Completely factor the function
   $V(x) = 4x^3 - 108x^2 + 720x$.
(c) Find $V(3)$ using the factored form found in part **(b)**.
(d) Did you find it easier to evaluate $V(3)$ in part **(a)** or in part **(c)**?

100. **Projectile Motion** A boy is standing on a cliff that is 240 feet high and throws a rock out toward the ocean. The height of the rock above the sea can be described by the function in which t is time in seconds and s is the height in feet:

$$s(t) = -16t^2 + 32t + 240$$

(a) Find and interpret $s(3)$.
(b) Completely factor the function
   $s(t) = -16t^2 + 32t + 240$.
(c) Find $s(3)$ using the factored form found in part **(b)**.
(d) Did you find it easier to evaluate $s(3)$ in part **(a)** or in part **(c)**?

101. Suppose that we know one factor of $6x^2 - 11x - 10$ is $3x + 2$. What is the other factor?

102. Suppose that we know one factor of $8x^2 + 22x - 21$ is $2x + 7$. What is the other factor?

Extending the Concepts

In this section, we discussed factoring polynomials whose coefficients are integers (factoring over the integers). We can also factor polynomials whose coefficients are rational numbers in which case we factor over the rational numbers. One technique for doing this is to first factor out the coefficient of the highest degree term as a greatest common factor as follows:

$$\frac{1}{3}x^2 + \frac{4}{3}x + 1 = \frac{1}{3}(x^2 + 4x + 3)$$
$$= \frac{1}{3}(x + 3)(x + 1)$$

Use this technique in Problems 103–108.

103. $\frac{1}{2}x^2 + 3x + 4$

104. $\frac{1}{4}x^2 + 2x + 3$

105. $\frac{1}{3}p^2 - \frac{2}{3}p - 1$

106. $\frac{1}{4}z^2 + \frac{1}{2}z - \frac{15}{4}$

107. $\frac{4}{3}a^2 - \frac{8}{3}a - 32$

108. $\frac{3}{8}b^2 - \frac{15}{8}b - 9$

Math for the Future *In College Algebra, you will be required to factor expressions such as those found in Problems 109–112. Completely factor the following expressions. Hint: Factor by substitution.*

109. $2^{2n} - 4 \cdot 2^n - 5$

110. $3^{2x} - 11 \cdot 3^x + 10$

111. $4^{2x} - 12 \cdot 4^x + 32$

112. $4^x - 6 \cdot 2^x + 8$

Explaining the Concepts

113. State the circumstances for which trial and error is a better approach than grouping when factoring $ax^2 + bx + c, a \neq 1$.

114. When factoring any polynomial, what is always the first step?

115. A student factored the trinomial $3p^2 - 9p - 30$ as $(3p + 6)(p - 5)$ on an exam, but only received partial credit. Can you explain why?

116. How can you tell if a trinomial is prime? Make up an example to demonstrate your reasoning.

4.6 Factoring Special Products

OBJECTIVES

1. Factor Perfect Square Trinomials
2. Factor the Difference of Two Squares
3. Factor the Sum or Difference of Two Cubes

Preparing for Factoring Special Products

Before getting started, take the following readiness quiz. If you get a problem wrong, go back to the section cited and review the material.

P1. What is 1^2? 2^2? 3^2? 4^2? 5^2?   [Section R.4, pp. 33–34]

P2. What is $\left(-\dfrac{3}{2}\right)^2$?   [Section R.4, pp. 33–34]

In this section, we look at polynomials that can be categorized as having "special formulas" for factoring. We begin with perfect square trinomials.

1 Factor Perfect Square Trinomials

Recall from Section 4.2 that

$$(A + B)^2 = A^2 + 2AB + B^2$$
$$(A - B)^2 = A^2 - 2AB + B^2$$

We call these perfect square trinomials. Reversing the formulas, we obtain a method for factoring perfect square trinomials.

PERFECT SQUARE TRINOMIALS

$$A^2 + 2AB + B^2 = (A + B)^2$$
$$A^2 - 2AB + B^2 = (A - B)^2$$

Work Smart

The perfect squares are $1^2 = 1$, $2^2 = 4$, $3^2 = 9$, and so on. Any variable raised to an even exponent is a perfect square. So x^2, $x^4 = (x^2)^2$, $x^6 = (x^3)^2$ are all perfect squares.

In order for a polynomial to be a perfect square trinomial, two conditions must be satisfied.

1. The first and last terms must be perfect squares. Examples of perfect squares are

   81 because $9^2 = 81$ $4x^2$ because $(2x)^2 = 4x^2$

   144 because $12^2 = 144$ $25a^4$ because $(5a^2)^2 = 25a^4$

2. The "middle term" must equal 2 or -2 times the product of the expressions being squared in the first and last term.

   Perfect square trinomials can be factored using the methods introduced in the last section, however, they can be factored much quicker using the above formulas when they are recognized.

EXAMPLE 1 Factoring Perfect Square Trinomials

Factor:

   (a) $z^2 - 10z + 25$ **(b)** $9x^2 + 48xy + 64y^2$ **(c)** $32m^4 - 48m^2 + 18$

Solution

   (a) The first term, z^2, and the third term, $25 = 5^2$, are perfect squares. Because the middle term, $-10z$, is -2 times the product of z and 5, we have a perfect square trinomial. So

$$z^2 - 10z + 25 = z^2 - 2 \cdot z \cdot 5 + 5^2$$

$$A = z,\ B = 5,\ A^2 - 2AB + B^2 = (A - B)^2: \quad = (z - 5)^2$$

(b) The first term, $9x^2 = (3x)^2$, and the third term, $64y^2 = (8y)^2$, are perfect squares. Because the middle term, $48xy$, is 2 times the product of $3x$ and $8y$, we have a perfect square trinomial. So

$$9x^2 + 48xy + 64y^2 = (3x)^2 + 2 \cdot 3x \cdot 8y + (8y)^2$$

$A = 3x, B = 8y, A^2 + 2AB + B^2 = (A + B)^2: \quad = (3x + 8y)^2$

(c) Remember, the first step in any factoring problem is to look for a common factor.

$$32m^4 - 48m^2 + 18 = 2(16m^4 - 24m^2 + 9)$$

Look at the expression in parentheses. The first term, $16m^4 = (4m^2)^2$, and the third term, $9 = 3^2$, are perfect squares. Because the middle term is -2 times the product of $4m^2$ and 3, we have a perfect square trinomial. So

$$16m^4 - 24m^2 + 9 = (4m^2)^2 - 2 \cdot 4m^2 \cdot 3 + 3^2$$
$$= (4m^2 - 3)^2$$

Therefore,

$$32m^4 - 48m^2 + 18 = 2(16m^4 - 24m^2 + 9)$$
$$= 2(4m^2 - 3)^2 \qquad \blacksquare$$

Quick ✔

1. A trinomial of the form $A^2 + 2AB + B^2$ or $A^2 - 2AB + B^2$ is called a _____ _____.

2. *True or False:* $4x^2 + 6x + 9$ is a perfect square trinomial.

In Problems 3–5, factor each trinomial completely.

3. $x^2 - 18x + 81$ 4. $4x^2 + 20xy + 25y^2$ 5. $18p^4 - 84p^2 + 98$

⌐2 Factor the Difference of Two Squares

Another "special product" introduced in Section 4.2 was

$$(A - B)(A + B) = A^2 - B^2$$

We call this product the difference of two squares.

DIFFERENCE OF TWO SQUARES

$$A^2 - B^2 = (A - B)(A + B)$$

⌐EXAMPLE 2 Factoring the Difference of Two Squares

Factor:

(a) $y^2 - 100$ **(b)** $9x^2 - 16y^4$

Solution

(a) We notice that $y^2 - 100$ is the difference of two squares, y^2 and $100 = 10^2$. So

$$y^2 - 100 = y^2 - 10^2$$
$$= (y - 10)(y + 10)$$

Work Smart

Don't forget that you can always check your answer by multiplying out the factored form.

(b) We notice that $9x^2 - 16y^4$ is the difference of two squares, $9x^2 = (3x)^2$ and $16y^4 = (4y^2)^2$. So

$$9x^2 - 16y^4 = (3x)^2 - (4y^2)^2$$
$$= (3x - 4y^2)(3x + 4y^2) \qquad \blacksquare$$

Quick ✔ *In Problems 6–8, factor completely.*
6. $z^2 - 16$ **7.** $16m^2 - 81n^2$ **8.** $4a^2 - 9b^4$

EXAMPLE 3   Factoring the Difference of Two Squares

Factor:

(a) $32x^4 - 2$

(b) $x^2 + 10x + 25 - y^2$

Solution

(a) Remember, the first step in any factoring problem is to look for a common factor. In this polynomial, we have a common factor of 2.

$$32x^4 - 2 = 2(16x^4 - 1)$$

Difference of Two Squares, $16x^4 = (4x^2)^2$, $1 = 1^2$: $= 2((4x^2)^2 - 1^2)$

$A^2 - B^2 = (A - B)(A + B),$

where $A = 4x^2$ and $B = 1$: $= 2(4x^2 - 1)(4x^2 + 1)$

We are not quite finished. Notice that $4x^2 - 1$ is the
difference of two squares, $4x^2 = (2x)^2$ and $1 = 1^2$: $= 2((2x)^2 - 1^2)(4x^2 + 1)$

$A^2 - B^2 = (A - B)(A + B)$, where $A = 2x$ and $B = 1$: $= 2(2x - 1)(2x + 1)(4x^2 + 1)$

Work Smart

$4x^2 + 1$ is the **sum** of two squares. Remember that the sum of two squares does not factor over the integers.

Check $2(2x - 1)(2x + 1)(4x^2 + 1) = 2(4x^2 - 1)(4x^2 + 1)$

$$= 2(16x^4 + 4x^2 - 4x^2 - 1)$$
$$= 2(16x^4 - 1)$$
$$= 32x^4 - 2$$

So $32x^4 - 2 = 2(2x - 1)(2x + 1)(4x^2 + 1)$.

(b) Remember, when we have four or more terms, we should try to factor by grouping. In Section 4.4, we grouped two terms in each group. Any attempt to group two terms in each group in this problem will fail because we won't have a common factor in each group (try it!). However, if we look closely, we should notice that the first three terms, $x^2 + 10x + 25$, form a perfect square trinomial (which factors into a perfect square) and the last term, y^2, is a perfect square.

Work Smart

Perfect square trinomials are trinomials of the form

$A^2 + 2AB + B^2 = (A + B)^2$
$A^2 - 2AB + B^2 = (A - B)^2$

$$x^2 + 10x + 25 - y^2 = (x^2 + 10x + 25) - y^2$$

$x^2 + 10x + 25 = x^2 + 2(5)x + 5^2$
$= (x + 5)^2$: $= (x + 5)^2 - y^2$

$(x + 5)^2 - y^2$ is the difference of two
squares, where $A = (x + 5)$ and $B = y$: $= (\overset{A}{\overbrace{x + 5}} - \overset{B}{\overbrace{y}})(\overset{A}{\overbrace{x + 5}} + \overset{B}{\overbrace{y}})$

Check

$$(x + 5 - y)(x + 5 + y) = (x + 5 - y) \cdot x + (x + 5 - y) \cdot 5 + (x + 5 - y) \cdot y$$
$$= x^2 + 5x - xy + 5x + 25 - 5y + xy + 5y - y^2$$
$$= x^2 + 10x + 25 - y^2$$

So $x^2 + 10x + 25 - y^2 = (x + 5 - y)(x + 5 + y)$.   ∎

Quick ✔ *In Problems 9 and 10, factor completely.*
9. $3b^4 - 48$ **10.** $p^2 - 8p + 16 - q^2$

You may be asking yourself, "What about the sum of two squares—how does it factor?" The answer is that **the sum of two squares, $a^2 + b^2$, is prime and does not factor over the integers.** In fact, the sum of two squares cannot be factored for any real numbers! So binomials such as $x^2 + 4$ or $4y^2 + 81$ are prime.

Work Smart

The perfect cubes are $1^3 = 1$, $2^3 = 8$, $3^3 = 27$, and so on. Any variable raised to a multiple of 3 is a perfect cube. So x^3, $x^6 = (x^2)^3$, $x^9 = (x^3)^3$ are all perfect cubes.

⎡3⎤ Factor the Sum or Difference of Two Cubes

Consider the following products:

$$(A + B)(A^2 - AB + B^2) = A^3 - A^2B + AB^2 + A^2B - AB^2 + B^3$$
$$= A^3 + B^3$$
$$(A - B)(A^2 + AB + B^2) = A^3 + A^2B + AB^2 - A^2B - AB^2 - B^3$$
$$= A^3 - B^3$$

These products show us that we can factor the sum or difference of two cubes as follows:

THE SUM OF TWO CUBES

$$A^3 + B^3 = (A + B)(A^2 - AB + B^2)$$

THE DIFFERENCE OF TWO CUBES

$$A^3 - B^3 = (A - B)(A^2 + AB + B^2)$$

⎡EXAMPLE 4⎤ Factoring the Sum or Difference of Two Cubes

Factor:

(a) $x^3 - 27$ **(b)** $8m^3 + 125n^6$

Solution

(a) We have the difference of two cubes, x^3 and $27 = 3^3$. We let $A = x$ and $B = 3$ in the factoring formula for the difference of two cubes.

$$A^3 - B^3 = (A - B)(A^2 + AB + B^2)$$
$$x^3 - 27 = x^3 - 3^3 = (x - 3)(x^2 + x(3) + 3^2)$$
$$= (x - 3)(x^2 + 3x + 9)$$

So $x^3 - 27 = (x - 3)(x^2 + 3x + 9)$.

(b) We have the sum of two cubes, $8m^3 = (2m)^3$ and $125n^6 = (5n^2)^3$. We let $A = 2m$ and $B = 5n^2$ in the factoring formula for the sum of two cubes.

$$8m^3 + 125n^6 = ((2m)^3 + (5n^2)^3)$$
$$= (2m + 5n^2)((2m)^2 - (2m)(5n^2) + (5n^2)^2)$$
$$= (2m + 5n^2)(4m^2 - 10mn^2 + 25n^4)$$

So $8m^3 + 125n^6 = (2m + 5n^2)(4m^2 - 10mn^2 + 25n^4)$. ∎

Quick ✔

11. $A^3 + B^3 = ($_____$)($_____$)$.

12. $A^3 - B^3 = ($_____$)($_____$)$.

In Problems 13 and 14, completely factor.

13. $z^3 + 64$ **14.** $125p^3 - 216q^6$

EXAMPLE 5 Factoring the Sum or Difference of Two Cubes

Factor:

(a) $27x^3 - 216y^6$ (b) $(x - 4)^3 + 8x^3$

Solution

(a) We see that $27x^3 = (3x)^3$ and $216y^6 = (6y^2)^3$ is the difference of two cubes. However, there is a common factor of 27 in the binomial $27x^3 - 216y^6$. How did we recognize this common factor? Well, $27x^3 = (3x)^3$ and $216y^6 = (6y^2)^3$. Now, there is a common factor of 3 between 3 and 6. Because this common factor is being cubed, we know $3^3 = 27$ is a common factor. Therefore, we factor out the 27.

$$27x^3 - 216y^6 = 27(x^3 - 8y^6)$$
$$= 27(x^3 - (2y^2)^3)$$

Let $A = x$ and $B = 2y^2$ in the factoring
formula for the difference of two cubes: $= 27(x - 2y^2)(x^2 + 2xy^2 + 4y^4)$

(b) We notice that we have the sum of two cubes, $(x - 4)^3$ and $8x^3 = (2x)^3$. We let $A = x - 4$ and $B = 2x$ in the factoring formula for the sum of two cubes.

$$(x - 4)^3 + 8x^3 = (x - 4)^3 + (2x)^3$$
$$= (x - 4 + 2x)((x - 4)^2 - (x - 4) \cdot 2x + (2x)^2)$$

Combine like terms; multiply: $= (3x - 4)(x^2 - 8x + 16 - 2x^2 + 8x + 4x^2)$

Combine like terms: $= (3x - 4)(3x^2 + 16)$

So $(x - 4)^3 + 8x^3 = (3x - 4)(3x^2 + 16)$.   ∎

Quick ✔ *In Problems 15 and 16, factor completely.*

15. $32m^3 + 500n^6$ **16.** $(x + 1)^3 - 27x^3$

4.6 EXERCISES

MyMathLab
Powered by CourseCompass™ and MathXL®

 PRACTICE   WATCH   DOWNLOAD   READ   REVIEW

1–16. are the Quick ✔s *that follow each* EXAMPLE

Building Skills

In Problems 17–36, factor each perfect square trinomial completely. See Objective 1.

17. $x^2 + 4x + 4$
18. $y^2 + 6y + 9$
19. $36 + 12w + w^2$
20. $49 - 14d + d^2$
21. $4x^2 + 4x + 1$
22. $9z^2 - 6z + 1$
23. $9p^2 - 30p + 25$
24. $16y^2 - 24y + 9$
25. $25a^2 + 90a + 81$
26. $36b^2 + 84b + 49$
27. $9x^2 + 24xy + 16y^2$
28. $4a^2 + 20ab + 25b^2$
29. $3w^2 - 30w + 75$
30. $4c^2 - 24c + 36$

31. $-5t^2 - 70t - 245$
32. $-2a^2 - 32a - 128$
33. $32a^2 - 80ab + 50b^2$
34. $12x^2 - 84xy + 147y^2$
35. $z^4 - 6z^2 + 9$
36. $b^4 + 8b^2 + 16$

In Problems 37–52, factor the difference of two squares completely. See Objective 2.

37. $x^2 - 9$
38. $z^2 - 64$
39. $4 - y^2$
40. $81 - a^2$
41. $4z^2 - 9$
42. $16y^2 - 81$
43. $100m^2 - 81n^2$
44. $x^4 - 9y^2$
45. $m^4 - 36n^2$
46. $x^4 - 100y^2$
47. $8p^2 - 18q^2$
48. $12m^2 - 75n^2$

49. $80p^2r - 245b^2r$

50. $36x^2z - 64y^2z$

51. $(x + y)^2 - 9$

52. $16 - (x - y)^2$

In Problems 53–70, factor the sum or difference of two cubes completely. See Objective 3.

53. $x^3 - 8$

54. $z^3 + 64$

55. $125 + m^3$

56. $216 - n^3$

57. $x^6 - 64y^3$

58. $m^6 - 27n^3$

59. $24x^3 - 375y^3$

60. $16m^3 + 54n^3$

61. $(p + 1)^3 - 27$

62. $(y - 2)^3 - 8$

63. $(3y + 1)^3 + 8y^3$

64. $(2z + 3)^3 + 27z^3$

65. $(x + 3)^3 - (x - 3)^3$

66. $(y + 5)^3 + (y - 5)^3$

67. $y^6 + z^9$

68. $m^9 + n^{12}$

69. $y^9 - 1$

70. $x^{12} - 1$

Mixed Practice

In Problems 71–96, factor each polynomial completely.

71. $25x^2 - y^2$

72. $9a^2 - b^2$

73. $8x^3 + 27$

74. $64x^3 - 125$

75. $z^2 - 8z + 16$

76. $p^2 - 20p + 100$

77. $5x^4 - 40xy^3$

78. $3m^4 - 81mn^3$

79. $49m^2 - 42mn + 9n^2$

80. $81p^2 - 72pq + 16q^2$

81. $4x^2 + 16$

82. $-3y^2 - 27$

83. $y^4 - 8y^2 + 16$

84. $p^4 - 18p^2 + 81$

85. $4a^2b^2 + 12ab + 9$

86. $9m^2n^2 - 30mn + 25$

87. $p^2 + 2p + 4$

88. $y^2 - 3y + 9$

89. $x^2 - 4x + 4 - y^2$

90. $p^2 + 8p + 16 - q^2$

91. $2n^2 - 2m^2 + 40m - 200$

92. $2a^2 - 2b^2 - 24b - 72$ **93.** $3y^3 - 24$

94. $-5a^3 - 40$

95. $16x^2 + 24xy + 9y^2 - 100$

96. $36m^2 + 12mn + n^2 - 81$

Applying the Concepts

△ *In Problems 97–100, find an expression in factored form for the area of the shaded region.*

97.

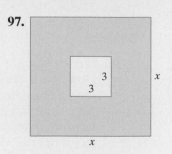

98.

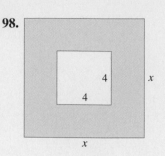

99.

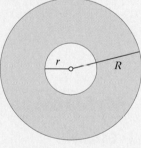

100.

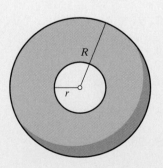

△ *In Problems 101–104, find an expression in factored form for the area or volume of the shaded region.*

101. Circle: $Area = \pi r^2$

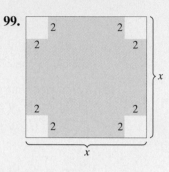

102. Cylinder: $Volume = \pi r^2 h$

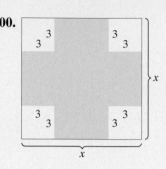

103. Rectangular solid: $Volume = lwh$

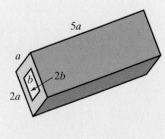

104. Sphere: $Volume = \dfrac{4}{3}\pi r^3$

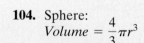
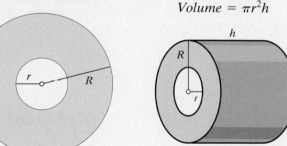

△ **105. A Perfect Square** What is a perfect square? The figure below shows a square whose dimensions are $(a + b)$ by $(a + b)$. The area of the square is therefore $(a + b)^2$. Write the area of the square as the sum of the areas of the four quadrilaterals in the figure. Then show that this sum is equal to $(a + b)^2$.

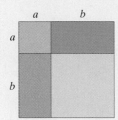

△ **106. Difference of Two Squares** What is the difference of two squares? The figure below shows two squares. The length of the sides on the "outer" square is a and the length of the sides on the "inner" square is b. The area of the shaded region is $a^2 - b^2$. Express the area of the blue shaded region as the sum of the two shaded regions in terms of a and b. Conclude that $a^2 - b^2 = (a + b)(a - b)$.

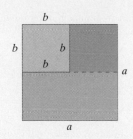

Extending the Concepts

107. Determine two values of b that will make $4x^2 + bx + 81$ a perfect square trinomial. How did you find these values?

108. Determine the value of c that will make $16y^2 + 24y + c$ a perfect square trinomial. How did you find this value?

109. What has to be added to $x^2 + 18x$ to make it a perfect square trinomial?

110. What has to be added to $4x^2 + 36x$ to make it a perfect square trinomial?

In this section, we discussed factoring polynomials whose coefficients are integers (factoring over the integers). We can also factor polynomials whose coefficients are rational numbers in which case we factor over the rational numbers. For example,

$$\frac{x^2}{25} - \frac{1}{4} = \left(\frac{x}{5}\right)^2 - \left(\frac{1}{2}\right)^2$$
$$= \left(\frac{x}{5} - \frac{1}{2}\right)\left(\frac{x}{5} + \frac{1}{2}\right)$$

Use this technique to factor Problems 111–118.

111. $b^2 - 0.4b + 0.04$ **112.** $x^2 + 0.6x + 0.09$

113. $9b^2 - \dfrac{1}{25}$ **114.** $100x^2 - \dfrac{1}{81}$

115. $\dfrac{x^2}{9} - \dfrac{y^2}{25}$ **116.** $\dfrac{a^2}{36} - \dfrac{b^2}{49}$

117. $\dfrac{x^3}{8} - \dfrac{y^3}{27}$ **118.** $\dfrac{a^3}{27} + \dfrac{b^3}{64}$

4.7 Factoring: A General Strategy

OBJECTIVES

1. Factor Polynomials Completely
2. Write Polynomial Functions in Factored Form

1 Factor Polynomials Completely

We begin this special section by putting together all the various factoring techniques we have discussed in Sections 4.4–4.6. The following steps should be followed for any factoring problem.

STEPS FOR FACTORING

Step 1: Factor out the greatest common factor (GCF), if any exists.

Step 2: Count the number of terms.

Step 3: (a) 2 terms

- Is it the difference of two squares? If so,
$$A^2 - B^2 = (A - B)(A + B)$$
- Is it the sum of two squares? If so, stop! The expression is prime.

- Is it the difference of two cubes? If so,

$$A^3 - B^3 = (A - B)(A^2 + AB + B^2)$$

- Is it the sum of two cubes? If so,

$$A^3 + B^3 = (A + B)(A^2 - AB + B^2)$$

(b) 3 terms

- Is it a perfect square trinomial? If so,

$$A^2 + 2AB + B^2 = (A + B)^2 \quad \text{or} \quad A^2 - 2AB + B^2 = (A - B)^2$$

- Is the coefficient of the square term 1? If so,

$$x^2 + bx + c = (x + m)(x + n) \text{ where } mn = c \text{ and } m + n = b$$

- Is the coefficient of the square term different from 1? If so,
  a. Use factoring by grouping
  b. Use trial and error

(c) 4 terms

- Use factoring by grouping

Step 4: Check your work by multiplying out the factored form.

EXAMPLE 1 How to Factor Completely

Factor: $8x^2 - 16x - 42$

Step-by-Step Solution

Step 1: Factor out the greatest common factor (GCF), if any exists.	The GCF is 2, so we factor 2 out of the expression.	$8x^2 - 16x - 42 = 2(4x^2 - 8x - 21)$
Step 2: Count the number of terms.	There are three terms in the polynomial in parentheses.	

Step 3: We concentrate on the trinomial in parentheses, $4x^2 - 8x - 21$. It is not a perfect square trinomial. Because the coefficient on the square term, 4, and the constant, -21, aren't that big, we choose to factor by grouping.

$$ac = 4(-21) = -84$$

Because $6 \cdot (-14) = -84$ and $6 + (-14) = -8$, we rewrite $4x^2 - 8x - 21$ as

$$4x^2 + 6x - 14x - 21 = (4x^2 + 6x) + (-14x - 21)$$

GCF in 1st grouping: $2x$;
GCF in 2nd grouping: $-7 \quad = 2x(2x + 3) - 7(2x + 3)$

Factor out $2x + 3$: $\quad = (2x + 3)(2x - 7)$

Step 4: Check

$$2(2x + 3)(2x - 7) = 2(4x^2 - 14x + 6x - 21)$$
$$= 2(4x^2 - 8x - 21)$$

Distribute: $\quad = 8x^2 - 16x - 42$

The answer checks, so $8x^2 - 16x - 42 = 2(2x + 3)(2x - 7)$. ∎

Quick ✔ *In Problems 1 and 2, factor the polynomial completely.*
1. $2p^2q - 8pq^2 - 90q^3$
2. $-45x^2y + 66xy + 27y$

EXAMPLE 2   How to Factor Completely

Factor: $9p^2 - 25q^2$

Step-by-Step Solution

Step 1: Factor out the greatest common factor (GCF), if any exists.	There is no GCF.
Step 2: Count the number of terms.	There are two terms.

Step 3: Because the first term, $9p^2 = (3p)^2$, and the second term, $25q^2 = (5q)^2$, are both perfect squares, we have the difference of two squares.

$$9p^2 - 25q^2 = \overset{A}{\overbrace{(3p)^2}} - \overset{B}{\overbrace{(5q)^2}}$$
$$A^2 - B^2 = (A - B)(A + B): \; = (3p - 5q)(3p + 5q)$$

Step 4: Check

$$(3p - 5q)(3p + 5q) = 9p^2 + 15pq - 15pq - 25q^2$$
$$\text{Combine like terms:} \; = 9p^2 - 25q^2$$

So $9p^2 - 25q^2 = (3p - 5q)(3p + 5q)$. ∎

Quick ✔ *In Problems 3 and 4, factor the polynomial completely.*

3. $81x^2 - 100y^2$ **4.** $-3m^2n + 147n$

EXAMPLE 3   Factoring Completely

Factor: $16x^2 + 112xy + 196y^2$

Solution

We first look for a common factor. Each term has a factor of 4, so the GCF is 4.

$$16x^2 + 112xy + 196y^2 = 4(4x^2 + 28xy + 49y^2)$$

We concentrate on the polynomial in parentheses. There are three terms in the parentheses. Notice that the first term is a perfect square, $4x^2 = (2x)^2$. The third term is also a perfect square, $49y^2 = (7y)^2$. The middle term is 2 times the product of $2x$ and $7y$. The polynomial in parentheses is a perfect square trinomial.

$$4(4x^2 + 28xy + 49y^2) = 4((2x)^2 + 2(2x)(7y) + (7y)^2)$$
$$A = 2x; B = 7y;$$
$$A^2 + 2AB + B^2 = (A + B)^2: \; = 4(2x + 7y)^2$$

Check
$$4(2x + 7y)^2 = 4(2x + 7y)(2x + 7y)$$
$$\text{FOIL:} \; = 4(4x^2 + 14xy + 14xy + 49y^2)$$
$$\text{Combine like terms:} \; = 4(4x^2 + 28xy + 49y^2)$$
$$\text{Distribute:} \; = 16x^2 + 112xy + 196y^2$$

So $16x^2 + 112xy + 196y^2 = 4(2x + 7y)^2$. ∎

Quick ✔ *In Problems 5 and 6, factor each polynomial completely.*

5. $p^2 - 16pq + 64q^2$ **6.** $20x^2 + 60x + 45$

EXAMPLE 4 Factoring Completely

Factor: $8m^3 + 27n^6$

Solution

We notice that the polynomial does not have a common factor and it has two terms. Because the first term is a perfect cube, $8m^3 = (2m)^3$, and the second term is a perfect cube, $27n^6 = (3n^2)^3$, we have the sum of two cubes.

$$8m^3 + 27n^6 = (2m)^3 + (3n^2)^3$$

$A = 2m;\ B = 3n^2;$

$A^3 + B^3 = (A + B)(A^2 - AB + B^2):\ = (2m + 3n^2)((2m)^2 - (2m)(3n^2) + (3n^2)^2)$

$$= (2m + 3n^2)(4m^2 - 6mn^2 + 9n^4)$$

Check $(2m + 3n^2)(4m^2 - 6mn^2 + 9n^4) = 8m^3 - 12m^2n^2 + 18mn^4$

$$+ 12m^2n^2 - 18mn^4 + 27n^6$$

Combine like terms: $= 8m^3 + 27n^6$

So $8m^3 + 27n^6 = (2m + 3n^2)(4m^2 - 6mn^2 + 9n^4)$. ∎

> **Quick** ✔ *In Problems 7 and 8, factor each polynomial completely.*
> **7.** $64y^3 - 125$ **8.** $-16m^3 - 2n^3$

EXAMPLE 5 Factoring Completely

Factor: $-4xy^2 + 12xy + 132x$

Solution

We notice that each term has a common factor of $-4x$. Factor out the GCF of $-4x$.

$$-4xy^2 + 12xy + 132x = -4x(y^2 - 3y - 33)$$

There are three terms in the polynomial in parentheses, $y^2 - 3y - 33$. Because 33 is not a perfect square, $y^2 - 3y - 33$ is not a perfect square trinomial. We need to find two factors of -33 whose sum is -3. There are no such factors. Therefore, $y^2 - 3y - 33$ is prime. So

$$-4xy^2 + 12xy + 132x = -4x(y^2 - 3y - 33)$$ ∎

> **Quick** ✔ *In Problems 9 and 10, factor each polynomial completely.*
> **9.** $10z^2 - 15z + 35$ **10.** $6xy^2 + 81x^3$

EXAMPLE 6 Factoring Completely

Factor: $6x^3 - 4x^2 - 24x + 16$

Solution

Each term has a common factor of 2. Factor out the GCF of 2.

$$6x^3 - 4x^2 - 24x + 16 = 2(3x^3 - 2x^2 - 12x + 8)$$

Because there are four terms remaining in the parentheses, we attempt to factor by grouping. Group the first two terms and the last two terms. Watch out for the subtraction sign in front of the third term!

$$2(3x^3 - 2x^2 - 12x + 8) = 2[(3x^3 - 2x^2) + (-12x + 8)]$$

Common factor of x^2 in 1st grouping;

Common factor of -4 in 2nd grouping: $= 2[x^2(3x - 2) - 4(3x - 2)]$

Factor out $3x - 2$ as a common factor: $= 2(3x - 2)(x^2 - 4)$

$x^2 - 4$ is the difference of two squares: $= 2(3x - 2)(x - 2)(x + 2)$

Check
$$2(3x - 2)(x - 2)(x + 2) = 2(3x - 2)(x^2 - 4)$$
$$\text{FOIL:} \quad = 2(3x^3 - 12x - 2x^2 + 8)$$
$$\text{Distribute; Rearrange terms:} \quad = 6x^3 - 4x^2 - 24x + 16$$

It checks, so $6x^3 - 4x^2 - 24x + 16 = 2(3x - 2)(x - 2)(x + 2)$.   ∎

Quick ✔ *In Problems 11 and 12, factor each polynomial completely.*

11. $2x^3 + 5x^2 + 4x + 10$ **12.** $9x^3 + 3x^2 - 9x - 3$

EXAMPLE 7 Factoring Completely

Factor: $x^2 - 6xy + 9y^2 - 25$

Solution

There are no common factors and there are four terms, so we try factoring by grouping. Attempts to form two groups of two terms fail. Before thinking that the polynomial is prime, consider that the first three terms form a perfect square trinomial that factors to a perfect square. And the last term is a perfect square. We group the first three terms.

$$x^2 - 6xy + 9y^2 - 25 = (x^2 - 6xy + 9y^2) - 25$$
$$= [x^2 - 2x(3y) + (3y)^2] - 25$$
$$A = x; B = 3y;$$
$$A^2 - 2AB + B^2 = (A - B)^2: \quad = (x - 3y)^2 - 5^2$$
$$A = x - 3y; B = 5;$$
$$A^2 - B^2 = (A - B)(A + B): \quad = (x - 3y - 5)(x - 3y + 5)$$

Check
$$(x - 3y - 5)(x - 3y + 5) = x^2 - 3xy + 5x - 3xy + 9y^2$$
$$-15y - 5x + 15y - 25$$
$$= x^2 - 6xy + 9y^2 - 25$$ ∎

So, $x^2 - 6xy + 9y^2 - 25 = (x - 3y - 5)(x - 3y + 5)$.

Quick ✔ *In Problems 13 and 14, factor each polynomial completely.*

13. $4x^2 + 4xy + y^2 - 81$ **14.** $16 - m^2 - 8mn - 16n^2$

---

2 Write Polynomial Functions in Factored Form

Later in this course and in other mathematics courses, you will be required to write polynomial functions in factored form.

EXAMPLE 8 Writing a Polynomial Function in Factored Form

Write each of the following polynomial functions in factored form.

  (a) $f(x) = 8x^2 + 14x - 15$ **(b)** $H(z) = -3z^3 - 15z^2 - 27z - 135$

Solution

  (a) To write $f(x) = 8x^2 + 14x - 15$ in factored form, we factor $8x^2 + 14x - 15$.
  First, we see that there are three terms in the polynomial and the polynomial has no common factor. We will factor the polynomial using trial and error. We can represent the first term $8x^2$ as

$$(x + \underline{\quad})(8x + \underline{\quad}) \quad \text{or} \quad (2x + \underline{\quad})(4x + \underline{\quad})$$

The last term, -15, has the factors: $1 \cdot (-15), 3 \cdot (-5), -1 \cdot 15, -5 \cdot 3$. We want the middle term's coefficient to be 14, which is positive, but not too big. As we look for the correct combination of factors to obtain this result, we will start with $(2x + \underline{})(4x + \underline{})$. Since the middle term's coefficient is positive, let's try $+5$ and -3.

$$(2x + 5)(4x - 3) = 8x^2 - 6x + 20x - 15$$
$$= 8x^2 + 14x - 15$$

It works! Therefore,

$$f(x) = 8x^2 + 14x - 15$$
$$= (2x + 5)(4x - 3)$$

(b) To write $H(z) = -3z^3 - 15z^2 - 27z - 135$ in factored form, we factor $-3z^3 - 15z^2 - 27z - 135$.

$$H(z) = -3z^3 - 15z^2 - 27z - 135$$

Factor out common factor of -3: $\quad = -3(z^3 + 5z^2 + 9z + 45)$

Four terms; factor by grouping: $\quad = -3[(z^3 + 5z^2) + (9z + 45)]$

Common factor of z^2 in 1st grouping;
Common factor of 9 in 2nd grouping: $\quad = -3[z^2(z + 5) + 9(z + 5)]$

Factor out $z + 5$ as a common factor: $\quad = -3(z + 5)(z^2 + 9)$

So, $H(z) = -3(z + 5)(z^2 + 9)$. We leave the check to you. ∎

Quick ✔ *In Problems 15 and 16, write each polynomial function in factored form.*

15. $G(x) = 2x^2 + 3x - 14$ **16.** $F(p) = 27p^2 - 12$

4.7 EXERCISES

PRACTICE   WATCH   DOWNLOAD   READ   REVIEW

1–16. *are the* **Quick** ✔*s that follow each* **EXAMPLE**

Building Skills

In Problems 17–64, factor each polynomial completely.
See Objective 1.

17. $2x^2 - 12x - 144$

18. $3x^2 + 6x - 105$

19. $-3y^2 + 27$

20. $-5a^2 + 80$

21. $4b^2 + 20b + 25$

22. $8m^2 - 42m + 49$

23. $16w^3 + 2y^6$

24. $54p^6 - 2q^3$

25. $-3z^2 + 12z - 18$

26. $-4c^3 + 16c^2 - 28c$

27. $20y^2 - 9y - 18$

28. $18t^2 - 9t - 20$

29. $x^3 - 4x^2 + 5x - 20$

30. $p^3 + 7p^2 - 3p - 21$

31. $200x^2 + 18y^2$

32. $12p^2 + 50q^2$

33. $x^4 - 81$

34. $16w^4 - 1$

35. $3x^2 - 7x - 16$

36. $4w^2 - 3w - 6$

37. $36q^3 + 24q^2 + 4q$

38. $20k^3 - 60k^2 + 45k$

39. $24m^3n - 66m^2n - 63mn$

40. $20p^3q - 2p^2q - 4pq$

41. $3r^5 - 24r^2s^3$

42. $54p^5 + 16p^2q^3$

43. $2x^3 + 8x^2 - 18x - 72$

44. $3x^3 - 6x^2 - 48x + 96$

45. $9x^4 - 1$

46. $4z^4 - 25$

47. $3w^4 + 4w^2 - 15$

48. $4b^4 + 4b^2 - 15$

49. $(2y + 3)^2 - 5(2y + 3) + 6$

50. $(3x + 5)^2 + 4(3x + 5) - 21$

51. $p^2 - 10p + 25 - 36q^2$

52. $a^2 + 12a + 36 - 4b^2$

53. $y^6 + 6y^3 - 16$

54. $w^6 + 4w^3 - 5$

55. $p^6 - 1$

56. $q^6 + 1$

57. $-3x^3 - 15x^2 + 27x + 135$

58. $-2y^3 - 4y^2 + 32y + 64$

59. $3a - 27a^3$

60. $-5z - 20z^3$

61. $8t^5 + 14t^3 - 72t$

62. $18h^5 + 154h^3 - 72h$

63. $2x^4y + 10x^3y - 18x^2y - 90xy$

64. $2p^4q + 14p^3q - 32p^2q - 224pq$

In Problems 65–74, factor each polynomial function. See Objective 2.

65. $f(x) = x^2 - 2x - 63$

66. $F(x) = x^2 + 3x - 40$

67. $P(m) = 7m^2 + 31m + 12$

68. $H(p) = 5p^2 + 28p - 12$

69. $G(x) = -12x^2 + 147$

70. $g(x) = -100x^2 + 36$

71. $s(t) = -16t^2 + 96t + 256$

72. $S(y) = 2y^3 - 8y^2 - 42y$

73. $H(a) = 2a^3 + 5a^2 - 32a - 80$

74. $G(x) = 2x^3 - x^2 - 18x + 9$

Applying the Concepts

△ *In Problems 75–78, write an algebraic expression in completely factored form for the area that is shaded.*

75.

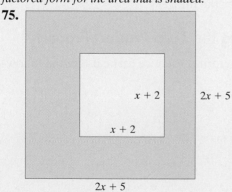

76.

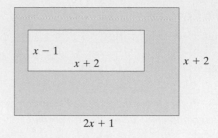

77.

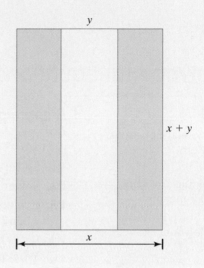

78.

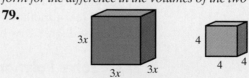

△ *In Problems 79 and 80, find an algebraic expression in factored form for the difference in the volumes of the two cubes shown.*

79.

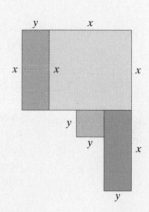

80.

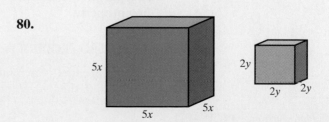

Extending the Concepts

81. Show that $x^2 + 9$ is prime.

82. Show that $x^2 - 4x - 8$ is prime.

In Problems 83–86, factor out the indicated common factor of the expression. Then completely factor the expression.

83. $x^{\frac{5}{2}} - 9x^{\frac{1}{2}}; x^{\frac{1}{2}}$ **84.** $x^{\frac{3}{2}} - 4x^{-\frac{1}{2}}; x^{-\frac{1}{2}}$

85. $1 + 6x^{-1} + 8x^{-2}; x^{-2}$ **86.** $3 - 2x^{-1} - x^{-2}; x^{-2}$

Explaining the Concepts

87. Write out the steps for factoring any polynomial.

88. What does factored completely mean?

4.8 Polynomial Equations

OBJECTIVES

1. Solve Polynomial Equations Using the Zero-Product Property
2. Solve Equations Involving Polynomial Functions
3. Model and Solve Problems Involving Polynomials

Preparing for Polynomial Equations

Before getting started, take the following readiness quiz. If you get a problem wrong, go back to the cited section and review the material.

P1. Solve: $x + 4 = 0$ [Section 1.1, pp. 49–51]

P2. Solve: $3(x - 2) - 12 = 0$ [Section 1.1, pp. 49–52]

P3. Evaluate $2x^2 + 3x + 1$
when (a) $x = 2$ (b) $x = -1$. [Section R.5, pp. 40–41]

P4. If $f(x) = 4x + 3$, solve $f(x) = 11$.
What point is on the graph of f? [Section 2.3, p. 167]

P5. If $f(x) = -2x + 8$, find $f(4)$.
What point is on the graph of f? [Section 2.3, p. 164]

P6. Find the zero of $f(x) = \dfrac{2}{3}x - 6$. [Section 2.4, p. 177]

In Sections 4.4–4.7, we learned how to factor polynomial expressions. Why is factoring an important skill? As we progress through the course you will see that there are many uses of factoring. We can present one important use now. It turns out that factoring is really handy for solving *polynomial equations*. A **polynomial equation** is any equation that contains a polynomial expression. The **degree of a polynomial equation** is the degree of the polynomial expression in the equation. Some examples of polynomial equations are

$4x + 5 = 17$	$2x^2 - 5x - 3 = 0$	$y^3 + 4y^2 = 3y + 18$
Polynomial equation of degree 1	Polynomial equation of degree 2	Polynomial equation of degree 3

The polynomial equation $4x + 5 = 17$ is, more specifically, a linear or first-degree equation. Remember, we studied linear equations back in Section 1.1. In this section, we will learn methods for solving polynomial equations when the polynomial expression is of degree 2 or higher and factorable over the integers.

Work Smart

Remember, the degree of a polynomial is the value of the largest exponent on the variable. For example, the degree of $4x^3 - 9x^2 + 1$ is 3.

1 Solve Polynomial Equations Using the Zero-Product Property

If a polynomial equation can be solved using factoring, then we make use of the following property.

THE ZERO-PRODUCT PROPERTY

If the product of two numbers is zero, then at least one of the numbers is 0. That is, if $ab = 0$, then $a = 0$ or $b = 0$ or both a and b are 0.

Preparing for...Answers **P1.** $\{-4\}$
P2. $\{6\}$ **P3.** (a) 15 (b) 0 **P4.** $\{2\}$;
$(2, 11)$ **P5.** $0; (4, 0)$ **P6.** 9

For example, if $2x = 0$, then either $2 = 0$ or $x = 0$. Since $2 \neq 0$, it must be that $x = 0$.

EXAMPLE 1 Using the Zero-Product Property

Solve: $(x + 5)(2x - 3) = 0$

Solution

We have the product of two numbers, $x + 5$ and $2x - 3$, set equal to 0. By the Zero-Product Property, at least one of the numbers must equal 0. Therefore, we set each of the expressions to 0 and solve each equation separately:

$$x + 5 = 0 \quad \text{or} \quad 2x - 3 = 0$$

Subtract 5 from both sides: $x = -5$ Add 3 to both sides: $2x = 3$

Divide both sides by 2: $x = \dfrac{3}{2}$

Check

$x = -5$: $(x + 5)(2x - 3) = 0$
$$(-5 + 5)(2(-5) - 3) \stackrel{?}{=} 0$$
$$0(-13) \stackrel{?}{=} 0$$
$$0 = 0 \quad \text{True}$$

$x = \dfrac{3}{2}$: $(x + 5)(2x - 3) = 0$
$$\left(\dfrac{3}{2} + 5\right)\left(2 \cdot \left(\dfrac{3}{2}\right) - 3\right) \stackrel{?}{=} 0$$
$$\left(\dfrac{13}{2}\right) \cdot (3 - 3) \stackrel{?}{=} 0$$
$$\dfrac{13}{2} \cdot 0 \stackrel{?}{=} 0$$
$$0 = 0 \quad \text{True}$$

The solution set is $\left\{-5, \dfrac{3}{2}\right\}$.   ■

Quick ✔

1. A _____ _____ is any equation that contains a polynomial expression.
2. The Zero-Product Property states that if $a \cdot b = 0$, then _____ or _____.

In Problems 3 and 4, use the Zero-Product Property to solve the equation.

3. $x(x + 7) = 0$ 4. $(x - 3)(4x + 3) = 0$

Using the Zero-Product Property to Solve Quadratic Equations

The Zero-Product Property can be used to solve *quadratic equations*.

Work Smart

Why can't a equal 0? If a is equal to zero, the equation would be $bx + c = 0$, a linear equation.

DEFINITION

A **quadratic equation** is an equation equivalent to one of the form

$$ax^2 + bx + c = 0$$

where a, b, and c are real numbers and $a \neq 0$.

Quadratic equations are equations such as

$$3x^2 + 5x + 2 = 0 \qquad -7z^2 + 14z = 0 \qquad y^2 - 16 = 0 \qquad p^2 + 8p = 16$$

A quadratic equation written in the form $ax^2 + bx + c = 0$ is said to be in **standard form.** The first three equations listed above are in standard form; the equation $p^2 + 8p = 16$ is not in standard form.

Sometimes, a quadratic equation is called a **second-degree equation** because the left side is a polynomial of degree 2.

When a quadratic equation is written in standard form, $ax^2 + bx + c = 0$, it may be possible to factor the expression $ax^2 + bx + c$ as the product of two first-degree polynomials. We will present methods for solving $ax^2 + bx + c = 0$ when we cannot factor the expression on the left side in Sections 7.2 and 7.3.

EXAMPLE 2 How to Solve a Quadratic Equation by Factoring

Solve: $2x^2 - 5x = 3$

Step-by-Step Solution

Step 1: Write the quadratic equation in standard form, $ax^2 + bx + c = 0$.	$2x^2 - 5x = 3$ Subtract 3 from both sides: $2x^2 - 5x - 3 = 0$
Step 2: Factor the expression on the left side of the equation.	$(2x + 1)(x - 3) = 0$
Step 3: Set each factor to 0.	$2x + 1 = 0$ or $x - 3 = 0$
Step 4: Solve each first-degree equation.	$2x = -1$ or $x = 3$ $x = -\dfrac{1}{2}$
Step 5: **Check:** Substitute $-\dfrac{1}{2}$ for x and 3 for x into the original equation.	$x = -\dfrac{1}{2}$: $2x^2 - 5x = 3$ $\qquad$ $x - 3$: $2x^2 - 5x = 3$ $2\left(-\dfrac{1}{2}\right)^2 - 5\left(-\dfrac{1}{2}\right) \overset{?}{=} 3$ $\qquad$ $2(3)^2 - 5(3) \overset{?}{=} 3$ $2\left(\dfrac{1}{4}\right) + \dfrac{5}{2} \overset{?}{=} 3$ $\qquad\qquad$ $18 - 15 \overset{?}{=} 3$ $\dfrac{1}{2} + \dfrac{5}{2} \overset{?}{=} 3$ $\qquad\qquad\qquad$ $3 = 3$ True $3 = 3$ True

The solution set is $\left\{ -\dfrac{1}{2}, 3 \right\}$.

We summarize the steps to solve a quadratic equation by factoring below.

STEPS FOR SOLVING A QUADRATIC EQUATION BY FACTORING

Step 1: Write the quadratic equation in standard form, $ax^2 + bx + c = 0$.

Step 2: Factor the expression on the left side of the equation.

Step 3: Set each factor found in Step 2 equal to zero using the Zero-Product Property.

Step 4: Solve each first-degree equation for the variable.

Step 5: Be sure to check your answers by substituting into the *original* equation.

Quick ✔

5. A _____ _____ is an equation equivalent to one of the form $ax^2 + bx + c = 0$ where a, b, and c are real numbers and $a \neq 0$.

In Problems 6–8, solve each quadratic equation by factoring.

6. $p^2 - 5p + 6 = 0$ $\qquad\qquad$ **7.** $3t^2 - 14t = 5$

8. $4y^2 + 8y + 3 = y^2 - 1$

EXAMPLE 3   Solving a Quadratic Equation by Factoring

Solve: $(m - 1)(3m + 5) = 16m$

Solution

First, we need to write the equation in standard form.

$$(m - 1)(3m + 5) = 16m$$

FOIL: $\qquad\qquad 3m^2 + 2m - 5 = 16m$

Subtract $16m$ from both sides to put the equation in standard form: $\qquad 3m^2 - 14m - 5 = 0$

Factor: $\qquad (3m + 1)(m - 5) = 0$

Set each factor to 0: $\qquad\qquad 3m + 1 = 0 \quad$ or $\quad m - 5 = 0$

$$3m = -1 \quad \text{or} \quad m = 5$$

$$m = -\frac{1}{3}$$

Work Smart

Do not attempt to solve the equation $(m - 1)(3m + 5) = 16m$ by setting each factor equal to $2m$.

Check   Substitute $m = -\dfrac{1}{3}$ and $m = 5$ into the original equation.

$m = -\dfrac{1}{3}$: $\quad (m - 1)(3m + 5) = 16m$

$$\left(-\frac{1}{3} - 1\right)\left(3 \cdot \left(-\frac{1}{3}\right) + 5\right) \overset{?}{=} 16 \cdot \left(-\frac{1}{3}\right)$$

$$\left(-\frac{4}{3}\right)(-1 + 5) \overset{?}{=} -\frac{16}{3}$$

$$-\frac{16}{3} = -\frac{16}{3} \quad \text{True}$$

$m = 5$: $\quad (m - 1)(3m + 5) = 16m$

$$(5 - 1)(3(5) + 5) \overset{?}{=} 16(5)$$

$$4(20) \overset{?}{=} 80$$

$$80 = 80 \qquad \text{True}$$

The solution set is $\left\{-\dfrac{1}{3}, 5\right\}$. ∎

Quick ✔ *In Problems 9 and 10, solve each quadratic equation by factoring.*
9. $x(x + 3) = -2$ $\qquad\qquad$ **10.** $(x - 3)(x + 5) = 9$

Using the Zero-Product Property to Solve Higher-Degree Equations

Up to now, we have solved only second-degree equations. We can use an extended form of the Zero-Product Property to solve polynomial equations of degree three or higher. The basic idea is to first write the equation so that the right-hand side is zero (that is, write the equation in standard form), factor the expression that equals zero, and then set each factor to zero and solve.

EXAMPLE 4   How to Solve an Equation Using the Zero-Product Property

Solve: $w^3 + 5w^2 - 4w = 20$

Step-by-Step Solution

Step 1: We put the equation in standard form by subtracting 20 from both sides of the equation.	$w^3 + 5w^2 - 4w = 20$ $w^3 + 5w^2 - 4w - 20 = 0$

Step 2: Factor the expression on the left side of the equation. Because there are four terms, we factor by grouping.

Group the 1st two terms; group the last two terms:

$$(w^3 + 5w^2) + (-4w - 20) = 0$$

Factor out the common factor in each group:

$$w^2(w + 5) - 4(w + 5) = 0$$

Factor out $w + 5$:

$$(w + 5)(w^2 - 4) = 0$$

Factor $w^2 - 4$:

$$(w + 5)(w + 2)(w - 2) = 0$$

Step 3: Set each factor to 0. $w + 5 = 0$ or $w + 2 = 0$ or $w - 2 = 0$

Step 4: Solve each first-degree equation.

$w = -5$ or $w = -2$ or $w = 2$

Step 5: Check: Substitute $w = -5$, $w = -2$, and $w = 2$ into the original equation.

$w = -5$:

$$w^3 + 5w^2 - 4w = 20$$
$$(-5)^3 + 5(-5)^2 - 4(-5) \stackrel{?}{=} 20$$
$$-125 + 125 + 20 \stackrel{?}{=} 20$$
$$20 = 20$$
True

$w = -2$:

$$w^3 + 5w^2 - 4w = 20$$
$$(-2)^3 + 5(-2)^2 - 4(-2) \stackrel{?}{=} 20$$
$$-8 + 20 + 8 \stackrel{?}{=} 20$$
$$20 = 20$$
True

$w = 2$:

$$w^3 + 5w^2 - 4w = 20$$
$$(2)^3 + 5(2)^2 - 4(2) \stackrel{?}{=} 20$$
$$8 + 20 - 8 \stackrel{?}{=} 20$$
$$20 = 20$$
True

The solution set is $\{-5, -2, 2\}$. ∎

Quick ✔ *In Problem 11, solve the polynomial equation.*

11. $y^3 - y^2 + 9 = 9y$

⌐2 Solve Equations Involving Polynomial Functions

Suppose that we were given the function $f(x) = x^2 + 6x - 3$ and wanted to know the values of x such that $f(x) = 4$. This requires solving the equation

$$\overbrace{x^2 + 6x - 3}^{f(x)} = 4$$

⌐EXAMPLE 5 Solving an Equation Involving a Polynomial Function

Suppose that $f(x) = x^2 + 6x - 3$. Find the values of x such that $f(x) = 4$. What points are on the graph of f?

Solution

We want to solve $f(x) = 4$. That is, we want to solve $x^2 + 6x - 3 = 4$. We start by putting the equation in standard form.

$$x^2 + 6x - 3 = 4$$

Subtract 4 from both sides:

$$x^2 + 6x - 7 = 0$$

Factor:

$$(x + 7)(x - 1) = 0$$

Set each factor to 0: $x + 7 = 0$ or $x - 1 = 0$

$$x = -7 \quad \text{or} \quad x = 1$$

Check

$$x = -7: \quad x^2 + 6x - 3 = 4 \qquad\qquad x = 1: \quad x^2 + 6x - 3 = 4$$
$$(-7)^2 + 6(-7) - 3 \stackrel{?}{=} 4 \qquad\qquad\qquad (1)^2 + 6(1) - 3 \stackrel{?}{=} 4$$
$$49 - 42 - 3 \stackrel{?}{=} 4 \qquad\qquad\qquad\qquad 1 + 6 - 3 \stackrel{?}{=} 4$$
$$4 = 4 \quad \text{True} \qquad\qquad\qquad\qquad 4 = 4 \quad \text{True}$$

The values of x such that $f(x) = 4$ are -7 and 1. So, the points $(-7, 4)$ and $(1, 4)$ are on the graph of f. ◼

Quick ✔

12. Suppose that $g(x) = x^2 - 8x + 3$. Find the values of x such that

    (a) $g(x) = 12$ **(b)** $g(x) = -4$

    What points are on the graph of g?

In Section 2.4 we discussed how to find the zero of a linear function. Recall, a zero of a function f is any number r such that $f(r) = 0$. In addition, if r is a zero of a function, then r is also an x-intercept of the graph of a function; that is, the point $(r, 0)$ is on the graph of the function. Consider Figure 3, which shows the graph of $y = f(x)$. We can see from the graph that -3 and 3 are x-intercepts. Therefore, the zeros of f are -3 and 3.

Figure 3

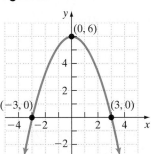

EXAMPLE 6 Finding the Zeros of a Quadratic Function

Find the zeros of $f(x) = 4x^2 - 5x - 6$. What are the x-intercepts of the graph of the function?

Solution

The zeros are found by solving the equation $f(x) = 0$ or $4x^2 - 5x - 6 = 0$. The solutions to this equation are $-\dfrac{3}{4}$ and 2, so the zeros of $f(x) = 4x^2 - 5x - 6$ are $-\dfrac{3}{4}$ and 2. Because the zeros are $-\dfrac{3}{4}$ and 2, the x-intercepts of the graph of the function are also $-\dfrac{3}{4}$ and 2. ◼

Quick ✔

13. Find the zeros of $h(x) = 2x^2 + 3x - 20$. What are the x-intercepts of the graph of the function?

3 Model and Solve Problems Involving Polynomials

Many applied problems require solving polynomial equations by factoring. For example, the height of a projectile over time can be described by a polynomial equation. We can use the equation to determine the time at which the projectile is a certain height. As always, we shall employ the problem-solving strategy first presented in Section 1.2.

EXAMPLE 7 Geometry: Area of a Rectangle

The length of a rectangle is 8 feet more than its width. If the area of the rectangle is 84 square feet, what are the dimensions of the rectangle? See Figure 4.

Figure 4

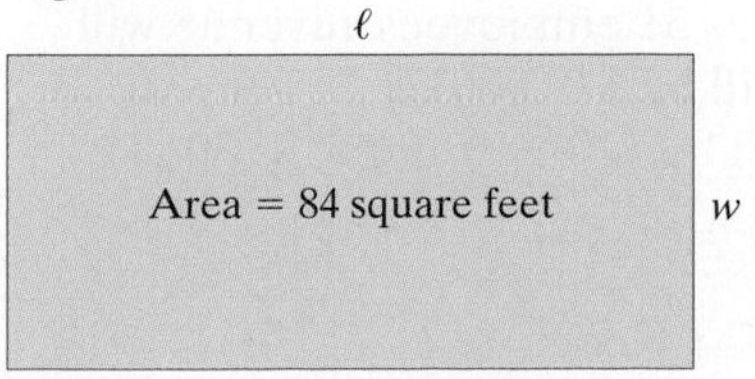

ℓ

| Area = 84 square feet | w |

Solution

Step 1: Identify This is a geometry problem involving the area of a rectangle.

Step 2: Name We let w represent the width of the rectangle and l represent the length of the rectangle.

Step 3: Translate Because the length is 8 feet more than the width, we know that $l = w + 8$. In addition, we are given that the area of the rectangle is 84 square feet.

$$\text{Area} = (\text{length})(\text{width})$$

$$\text{Area} = lw$$

$$84 = (w + 8)w \qquad \text{The Model}$$

Step 4: Solve We now proceed to solve the equation.

$$w(w + 8) = 84$$

Distribute: $\qquad\qquad\qquad\qquad w^2 + 8w = 84$

Subtract 84 from both sides: $\qquad\quad w^2 + 8w - 84 = 0$

Factor: $\qquad\qquad (w + 14)(w - 6) = 0$

Set each factor to 0: $\qquad w + 14 = 0 \quad$ or $\quad w - 6 = 0$

Solve: $\qquad\qquad w = -14 \quad$ or $\qquad w = 6$

Step 5: Check Since w represents the width of the rectangle, we discard the solution $w = -14$. If the width of the rectangle is 6 feet, then the length would be $6 + 8 = 14$ feet. The area of a rectangle that is 6 feet by 14 feet would be $6(14) = 84$ square feet. We have the right answer!

Step 6: Answer The dimensions of the rectangle are 6 feet by 14 feet. ■

Quick ✔

14. The width of a rectangular plot of land is 6 miles less than its length. If the area of the land is 135 square miles, what are the dimensions of the land?

EXAMPLE 8 Pricing a Charter

Chicago Tours offers boat charters along the Chicago coastline on Lake Michigan. John Alfirivich decides to take his company on a tour as a thank-you to his employees. He strikes a deal with Chicago Tours. Normally, a ticket costs $20 per person, but for each person John brings in excess of 30 people, Chicago Tours will lower the price of the ticket by $0.10. Assuming that John knows more than 30 employees will go on the trip and that the capacity of the boat is 120 passengers, how many employees can attend if John is willing to spend $900 for the tour?

Solution

Step 1: Identify This is a direct translation problem involving revenue. Remember, revenue is price times quantity.

Step 2: Name We let x represent the number of employees in excess of 30 that attend.

Step 3: Translate Revenue is price times quantity. If John brings 30 employees, the revenue to Chicago Tours will be $20(30). If John brings 31 employees, revenue will be $19.90(31). If John brings 32 employees, revenue will be $19.80(32). In general, if John brings x employees in excess of 30, revenue will be $(20 - 0.1x)(x + 30)$. Because John wants to spend $900, we have

$$(20 - 0.1x)(x + 30) = 900 \quad \text{The Model}$$

Step 4: Solve We now proceed to solve the equation.

$$(20 - 0.1x)(x + 30) = 900$$

FOIL: $\quad 20x + 600 - 0.1x^2 - 3x = 900$

Combine like terms; rearrange terms: $\quad -0.1x^2 + 17x + 600 = 900$

Subtract 900 from both sides: $\quad -0.1x^2 + 17x - 300 = 0$

Multiply both sides by -10 to make the
coefficient of x^2 equal to 1: $\quad x^2 - 170x + 3000 = 0$

Factor: $\quad (x - 150)(x - 20) = 0$

Set each factor to 0: $\quad x - 150 = 0 \quad$ or $\quad x - 20 = 0$

Solve: $\quad x = 150 \quad$ or $\quad x = 20$

Step 5: Check Remember that x represents the number of passengers in excess of 30. We discard the solution $x = 150$ because it causes the capacity to exceed 120 passengers. Therefore, $30 + 20 = 50$ passengers can go on the trip. The cost per ticket would be $20 - 0.1(20) = \$20 - \$2 = \$18$. Multiplying the cost per ticket by the number of passengers we obtain $\$18(50) = \$900$. We have the right answer!

Step 6: Answer A total of 50 employees can attend. ∎

Quick ✔

15. A compact disk manufacturer charges $100 for each box of CDs ordered. However, for orders in excess of 30 boxes, but less than 65 boxes, it reduces the price by $1 per box. If a customer placed an order that qualified for the discount pricing and the bill was $4200, how many boxes of CDs were ordered?

EXAMPLE 9 Projectile Motion

A ball is thrown off a cliff by a child from a height of 240 feet above sea level, as pictured in Figure 5. The height s of the ball above the water (in feet) as a function of time (in seconds) can be modeled by the function

$$s(t) = -16t^2 + 32t + 240$$

(a) When will the height of the ball be 240 feet?
(b) When will the ball strike the water?

Solution

(a) To determine when the height of the ball will be 240 feet, we solve the equation $s(t) = 240$.

$$s(t) = 240$$

$$-16t^2 + 32t + 240 = 240$$

Subtract 240 from both sides: $\quad -16t^2 + 32t = 0$

Factor out $-16t$: $\quad -16t(t - 2) = 0$

Set each factor to 0: $\quad -16t = 0 \quad$ or $\quad t - 2 = 0$

Solve each equation: $\quad t = 0 \quad$ or $\quad t = 2$

The ball will be at a height of 240 feet the instant the ball leaves the child's hand and after 2 seconds of flight.

Figure 5

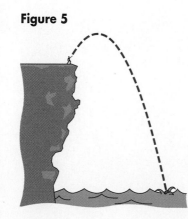

(b) The ball will strike the water at the instant its height is 0. So, we need to solve the equation $s(t) = 0$.

$$s(t) = 0$$
$$-16t^2 + 32t + 240 = 0$$

Factor out -16: $\qquad -16(t^2 - 2t - 15) = 0$

Factor: $\qquad -16(t - 5)(t + 3) = 0$

Set each factor to 0: $\quad -16 = 0 \quad \text{or} \quad t - 5 = 0 \quad \text{or} \quad t + 3 = 0$

Solve each equation: $\qquad\qquad\qquad\qquad t = 5 \quad \text{or} \qquad t = -3$

The equation $-16 = 0$ is false and $t = -3$ makes no sense. Therefore, the ball will strike the water after 5 seconds. ∎

Quick ✓

16. A model rocket is fired straight up from the ground. The height s of the rocket (in feet) as a function of time (in seconds) can be modeled by the function $s(t) = -16t^2 + 160t$.

(a) When will the height of the rocket be 384 feet from the ground?

(b) When will the rocket strike the ground?

4.8 EXERCISES

MyMathLab *Powered by CourseCompass™ and MathXL®*

 MathXL

PRACTICE　WATCH　DOWNLOAD　READ　REVIEW

1–16. are the Quick ✓*s that follow each* EXAMPLE

Building Skills

In Problems 17–56, solve each equation. See Objective 1.

17. $(x - 3)(x + 1) = 0$　**18.** $(x + 3)(x - 8) = 0$

19. $2x(3x + 4) = 0$　**20.** $4x(2x - 3) = 0$

21. $y(y - 5)(y + 3) = 0$　**22.** $3a(a - 9)(a + 11) = 0$

23. $3p^2 - 12p = 0$　**24.** $5c^2 + 15c = 0$

25. $2w^2 = 16w$　**26.** $4t^2 = -20t$

27. $m^2 + 2m - 15 = 0$　**28.** $x^2 + 3x - 40 = 0$

29. $w^2 - 13w = -36$　**30.** $y^2 + 13y = -42$

31. $p^2 - 6p + 9 = 0$　**32.** $a^2 + 12a + 36 = 0$

33. $5x^2 = 2x + 3$　**34.** $4c^2 + 6 = 25c$

35. $6m^2 = 23m - 15$　**36.** $6z^2 + 17z = -5$

37. $3p^2 + 9p - 120 = 0$　**38.** $4y^2 - 20y - 56 = 0$

39. $-4b^2 - 14b + 60 = 0$　**40.** $-6n^2 - 9n + 60 = 0$

41. $\frac{1}{2}x^2 + 2x - 6 = 0$　**42.** $\frac{1}{2}t^2 - 3t - 8 = 0$

43. $\frac{2}{3}x^2 + x = \frac{14}{3}$　**44.** $\frac{2}{3}x^2 + \frac{7}{3}x = 5$

45. $x(x + 8) = 33$　**46.** $y(y + 4) = 45$

47. $(x - 2)(x + 1)(x + 5) = 0$

48. $(y - 4)(y - 1)(3y + 2) = 0$

49. $2z^3 - 5z^2 = 3z$

50. $7q^3 + 31q^2 = -12q$

51. $2p^3 + 5p^2 - 8p - 20 = 0$

52. $w^3 + 5w^2 - 16w - 80 = 0$

53. $-30b^3 - 38b^2 = 12b$

54. $-24b^3 + 27b = 18b^2$

55. $(x - 2)^3 = x^3 - 2x$

56. $(x + 2)^3 = x^3 - 2x$

In Problems 57–62, see Objective 2.

57. Suppose that $f(x) = x^2 + 7x + 12$. Find the values of x such that

(a) $f(x) = 2$ **(b)** $f(x) = 20$

What points are on the graph of f?

58. Suppose that $f(x) = x^2 + 5x + 3$. Find the values of x such that

(a) $f(x) = 3$ **(b)** $f(x) = 17$

What points are on the graph of f?

59. Suppose that $g(x) = 2x^2 - 6x - 5$. Find the values of x such that

(a) $g(x) = 3$ **(b)** $g(x) = 15$

What points are on the graph of g?

60. Suppose that $h(x) = 3x^2 - 9x - 8$. Find the values of x such that

(a) $h(x) = -8$ **(b)** $h(x) = 22$

What points are on the graph of h?

61. Suppose that $F(x) = -3x^2 + 12x + 5$. Find the values of x such that

(a) $F(x) = 5$ **(b)** $F(x) = -10$

What points are on the graph of F?

62. Suppose that $G(x) = -x^2 + 4x + 6$. Find the values of x such that

(a) $G(x) = 1$ **(b)** $G(x) = 9$

What points are on the graph of G?

In Problems 63–68, find the zeros of the function. What are the x-intercepts of the graph of the function? See Objective 2.

63. $f(x) = x^2 + 9x + 14$ **64.** $f(x) = x^2 - 13x + 42$

65. $g(x) = 6x^2 - 25x - 9$

66. $h(x) = 8x^2 - 18x - 35$

67. $s(x) = 2x^3 + 2x^2 - 40x$

68. $f(x) = 3x^3 - 15x^2 - 42x$

Mixed Practice

In Problems 69–84, solve each equation.

69. $(x + 3)(x - 5) = 9$ **70.** $(x + 7)(x - 3) = 11$

71. $2q^2 + 3q - 14 = 0$ **72.** $3t^2 + 7t - 20 = 0$

73. $-3b^2 + 21b = 0$ **74.** $-7z^2 + 42z = 0$

75. $(x + 2)(x + 3) = x(x - 2)$

76. $(x + 7)(x - 6) = x(x + 3)$

77. $x^3 + 5x^2 - 4x - 20 = 0$

78. $2c^3 + 3c^2 - 8c - 12 = 0$

79. $(2x + 1)(x - 3) - x^2 = (x - 2)(x - 3)$

80. $(3x - 2)(x + 4) - x(x + 1) = (2x + 1)(x + 4) - 12$

81. $4x^4 - 17x^2 + 4 = 0$

82. $9z^4 - 13z^2 + 4 = 0$

83. $(a + 3)^2 - 5(a + 3) = -6$

84. $(2b + 1)^2 + 7(2b + 1) = -12$

In Problems 85–88, find the domain of each function.

85. $f(x) = \dfrac{5}{x^2 - 4}$

86. $f(x) = \dfrac{-9}{x^2 + 6x + 5}$

87. $g(x) = \dfrac{4x + 3}{2x^2 - 3x + 1}$

88. $h(x) = \dfrac{x + 4}{3x^2 - 7x - 6}$

Applying the Concepts

△ **89. Area** The length of a rectangle is 8 centimeters less than its width. What are the dimensions of the rectangle if its area is 128 square centimeters?

△ **90. Area** The length of a rectangle is twice the sum of its width and 3. What are the dimensions of the rectangle if its area is 216 square inches?

△ **91. Area** The height of a triangle is 12 feet more than its base. What are the height and base of the triangle if its area is 110 square feet?

△92. **Area** The base of a triangle is 4 meters shorter than its height. What are the height and base of the triangle if its area is 48 square meters?

△93. **Convex Polygons** A **convex polygon** is a polygon whose interior angles are between 0° and 180°. The number of diagonals D in a convex polygon with n sides is given by the formula $D = \dfrac{n(n-3)}{2}$.

Determine the number of sides n in a convex polygon that has 20 diagonals.

94. **Consecutive Integers** The sum S of the consecutive integers $1, 2, 3, \ldots, n$ is given by the formula $S = \dfrac{n(n+1)}{2}$. That is, $1 + 2 + 3 + \cdots + n = \dfrac{n(n+1)}{2}$. How many consecutive integers must be added together to obtain a sum of 36?

95. **Enclosing an Area with a Fence** A farmer has 100 meters of fencing and wants to enclose a rectangular plot that borders a river. If the farmer does not fence the side along the river, what are the dimensions of the land enclosed if the area enclosed is 800 square meters?

96. **Enclosing an Area with a Fence** A farmer has 300 feet of fencing and wants to enclose a rectangular corral that borders his barn on one side and then divide it into two plots with a fence parallel to one of the sides (see the figure). Assuming that the farmer will not fence the side along the barn, what are the lengths of the parts of the fence if the total area enclosed is 4800 square feet?

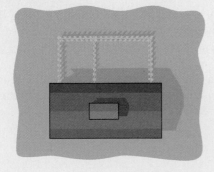

97. **Landscape Design** Robert Boehm just designed a cloister (a rectangular garden surrounded by a covered walkway on all four sides). The outside dimensions of the garden are 12 feet by 8 feet, and the area of the garden and the walkway together are 252 square feet. What is the width of the walkway?

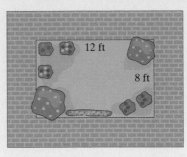

98. **Picture Frame** The outside dimensions of a picture frame are 40 inches by 32 inches. The area of the picture within the frame is 1008 square inches. Find the width of the frame.

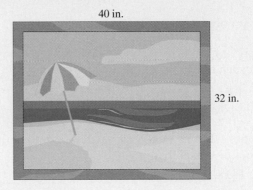

99. **Making a Box** A box is to be made from a rectangular piece of corrugated cardboard where the length is 5 more inches than the width by cutting a square piece 2 inches on each side from each corner. The volume of the box is to be 168 cubic inches. Find the dimensions of the rectangular piece of cardboard.

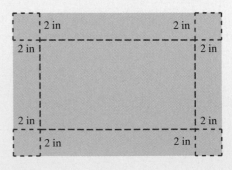

100. **Making a Box** A box is to be made from a rectangular piece of corrugated cardboard where the length is 8 inches more than the width by cutting a square piece 3 inches on each side from each corner. The volume of the box is to be 315 cubic inches. Find the dimensions of the rectangular piece of cardboard.

101. Marginal Cost Marginal cost can be thought of as the cost of producing one additional unit of output. For example, if the marginal cost of producing the 30th unit of output is \$9.30, then it cost \$9.30 to increase production from 29 to 30 units. The marginal cost C (in dollars) to produce x bicycles is given by $C(x) = x^2 - 40x + 600$.

  (a) Find the marginal cost of producing 30 bicycles.
  (b) How many bicycles can be manufactured so that marginal cost equals \$200? That is, solve $C(x) = 200$.
  (c) Economic theory states that, to maximize profit, production should continue until marginal revenue equals marginal cost. Marginal revenue is the additional revenue received for each bicycle sold. In certain situations, the marginal revenue is the price of the product. Assuming that marginal revenue equals \$225, how many bicycles should be manufactured?

102. Marginal Cost (See Problem 101.) Suppose that the marginal cost of manufacturing x cellular telephones is given by

$$C(x) = \frac{1}{2}x^2 - 30x + 475.$$

  (a) Find the marginal cost of producing 30 cell phones.
  (b) How many cell phones can be manufactured so that marginal cost equals \$75? That is, solve $C(x) = 75$.
  (c) Economic theory states that, to maximize profit, production should continue until marginal revenue equals marginal cost. Assuming that marginal revenue equals \$97, how many cell phones should be manufactured?

103. Projectile Motion Tiger Woods hits a golf ball with an initial speed of 240 feet per second. The height s of the ball (in feet) as a function of time (in seconds) can be modeled by the function

$$s(t) = -16t^2 + 120t$$

  (a) When will the height of the ball be 200 feet?
  (b) When will the ball hit the ground?

104. Projectile Motion A cannonball is fired from a cliff that is 260 feet high with an initial speed of 128 feet per second. The height s of the cannonball (in feet) as a function of time (in seconds) can be modeled by

the function

$$s(t) = -16t^2 + 64t + 260$$

  (a) When will the height of the cannonball be 320 feet?
  (b) When will the cannonball hit the ground?

The Graphing Calculator

The graphing calculator can be used to find solutions to any equation. The ZERO (or ROOT) feature of a graphing calculator can be used to find solutions of an equation when one side of the equation is 0. Solving an equation for x when one side of the equation is 0 is equivalent to finding where the graph of the corresponding function crosses or touches the x-axis. For example, to solve the equation in Example 2, $2x^2 - 5x - 3 = 0$, we would graph $Y_1 = 2x^2 - 5x - 3$ and then use ZERO (or ROOT) to determine where $Y_1 = 0$. See Figures 6(a) and (b).

Figure 6

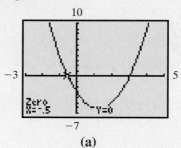

(a)

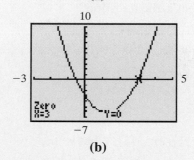

(b)

In Problems 105–110, solve each equation using a graphing calculator. Round your answers to two decimal places, if necessary.

105. $2x^2 - 7x - 5 = 0$

106. $2x^2 - x - 10 = 0$

107. $0.2x^2 - 5.1x + 3 = 0$

108. $0.4x^2 - 2.7x + 1 = 0$

109. $-x^2 + 0.6x = -2$

110. $-3.1x^2 - 0.4x = -3$

CHAPTER 4 Activity: What Is the Question?

Focus: Performing operations and solving equations with polynomials
Time: 15–20 minutes
Group size: 2 or 4

In this activity you will work as a team to solve eight multiple-choice questions. However, these questions are different from most multiple-choice questions. You are given the answer to a problem and must determine which of the multiple-choice options has the correct question for the given answer.

Before beginning the activity, decide how you will approach this task as a team. For example:

- If there are 2 members on your team ... one member will always examine choices (a) and (b) and the other will always examine choices (c) and (d).

- If there are 4 members on your team ... one member will always examine choice (a), another member will always examine choice (b), ... etc.

1. The answer is $-3x^2 - 10x$. What is the question?

   (a) Simplify: $2x - 3x(x^2 + 4)$
   (b) Find the quotient: $(6x^3 - 20x^2) \div (-2x)$
   (c) Simplify: $-3x(x^2 + 3) + 1$
   (d) Find the quotient: $(-6x^4 - 20x^3) \div (2x^2)$

2. The answer is 5. What is the question?
   Find $(f + g)(-1)$.

   (a) $f(x) = 2x + 2, g(x) = -3x - 1$
   (b) $f(x) = 2x + 3, g(x) = -3x + 1$
   (c) $f(x) = -2x + 5, g(x) = -3x + 4$
   (d) $f(x) = -2x - 2, g(x) = 3x - 4$

3. The answer is $(6x + 1)(2x - 3)$. What is the question?

   (a) Factor: $12x^2 - 20x + 3$
   (b) Factor: $12x^2 + 16x - 3$
   (c) Factor: $12x^2 - 16x - 3$
   (d) Factor: $12x^2 + 20x + 3$

4. The answer is $x^2 + 5x + 6$. What is the question?

   (a) Find the product: $(x + 6)(x - 1)$
   (b) Simplify: $2x^2 + 7x + 9 - (x^2 - 2x - 3)$

   (c) Find the product: $(x + 2)(x + 3)$
   (d) Simplify: $(x + 6)^2$

5. The answer is 3. What is the question?

   (a) What is the name of the variable in $16z^2 + 3z - 5$?
   (b) What is the degree of the polynomial $2mn + 6m - 3$?
   (c) How many terms are in the polynomial $2mn + 6m - 3$?
   (d) What is the coefficient of b in the polynomial $3a^2b - 9a + 5b$?

6. The answer is $x = -5$ or $x = 3$. What is the question?

   (a) Solve: $x(x + 2) = 15$
   (b) Find the values of x such that $f(x) = 8$ if $f(x) = x^2 + 4x + 3$.
   (c) Solve: $\dfrac{2}{3}x + 5 = \dfrac{1}{3}x^2$
   (d) Find the x-intercepts of the graph of the function $f(x) = x^2 - 2x - 15$.

7. The answer is $8x^2$. What is the question?

   (a) Simplify: $9x^2(x + 1) - 3x^2(3x + 5)$
   (b) Find the greatest common factor: $16x^2y^2 - 8x^3y - 24x^2$
   (c) Find the quotient: $(-8x^3 - 8x^2) \div (x + 1)$
   (d) Factor by grouping: $8x^3 + 8x^2 - x - 1$

8. The answer is $x + 2$. What is the question?

   (a) Find the quotient: $(x^3 + x^2 - 7x - 2) \div (x^2 + 3x - 1)$
   (b) Find the binomial factor: $x^3 - 8$
   (c) Find the quotient: $(x^2 + 2x - 3) \div (x - 1)$
   (d) Find the binomial factor: $x^3 + 8$

CHAPTER 4 Review

Section 4.1 Adding and Subtracting Polynomials

KEY CONCEPTS	KEY TERMS
• **Monomial** A monomial in one variable is the product of a constant and a variable raised to a nonnegative integer power. A monomial in one variable is of the form ax^k where a is a constant, x is a variable, and $k \geq 0$ is an integer. The constant a is called the **coefficient** of the monomial. If $a \neq 0$, then k is called the **degree** of the monomial. • **Polynomial** A polynomial is a monomial or the sum of monomials. • **Polynomial Function** A polynomial function is a function whose rule is a polynomial. The domain of all polynomial functions is the set of all real numbers. • **Sum or Difference of Two Functions** If f and g are two functions: The sum $f + g$ is the function defined by $(f + g)(x) = f(x) + g(x)$ The difference $f - g$ is the function defined by $(f - g)(x) = f(x) - g(x)$	Monomial Coefficient Degree Polynomial Standard form Binomial Trinomial Polynomial function Evaluate Sum of two functions Difference of two functions

YOU SHOULD BE ABLE TO...	EXAMPLE	REVIEW EXERCISES
1 Define monomial and determine the coefficient and degree of a monomial (p. 321)	Examples 1 through 3	1–2
2 Define polynomial and determine the degree of a polynomial (p. 322)	Examples 4 and 5	3–4
3 Simplify polynomials by combining like terms (p. 323)	Examples 6 through 8	5–10
4 Evaluate polynomial functions (p. 325)	Examples 9 and 10	11–12, 13(b), 14(b), 15(b), 16
5 Add and subtract polynomial functions (p. 327)	Examples 11 and 12	13(a), 14(a), 15(a)

In Problems 1 and 2, determine the coefficient and degree of each monomial.

1. $-7x^4$

2. $\dfrac{1}{9}w^3$

In Problems 3 and 4, write each polynomial in standard form. Then determine the degree of each polynomial.

3. $x + 7x^3 - 8 - 2x^2$

4. $3 + 2y - 3y^2 + y^4$

In Problems 5–10, add or subtract as indicated. Express your answer as a single polynomial in standard form.

5. $(x^2 + 2x - 7) + (3x^2 - x - 4)$

6. $(4x^3 - 3x^2 + x - 5) - (x^4 + 2x^2 - 7x + 1)$

7. $\left(\dfrac{1}{4}x^2 - \dfrac{1}{2}x \right) - \left(4x - \dfrac{1}{6} \right)$

8. $\left(\dfrac{1}{2}x^2 - x + \dfrac{1}{4} \right) + \left(\dfrac{1}{3}x^2 + \dfrac{2}{5} \right)$

9. $(x^3y^2 + 6x^2y^2 - xy) + (-x^3y^2 + 4x^2y^2 + xy)$

10. $(a^2b - 4ab^2 + 3) - (2a^2b + 2ab^2 + 7)$

In Problems 11–14, find the indicated function or function value.

11. $f(x) = -3x^2 + 2x - 8$
    (a) $f(-2)$ **(b)** $f(0)$ **(c)** $f(3)$

12. $f(x) = x^3 - 5x^2 + 3x - 1$
    (a) $f(-3)$ **(b)** $f(0)$ **(c)** $f(2)$

13. $f(x) = 4x - 3; g(x) = x^2 + 3x + 2$
    (a) $(f + g)(x)$ **(b)** $(f + g)(3)$

14. $f(x) = 2x^3 + x^2 - 7; g(x) = 3x^2 - x + 5$
    (a) $(f - g)(x)$ **(b)** $(f - g)(2)$

15. Profit Suppose that the revenue function R from selling x graphing calculators is $R(x) = -1.5x^2 + 180x$. The cost C of selling x graphing calculators is $C(x) = x^2 - 100x + 3290$.

(a) Find the profit function.

(b) Find the profit if $x = 25$ calculators are sold.

16. Area The area A of the region shown in quadrant I is given by $A(x) = -x^2 + 5x$ where (x, y) is a point in quadrant I on the graph of the line $y = -2x + 5$.

(a) Find the area of the region when the given point is $(2, 1)$.

(b) Find the area of the region when the given point is $(1, 3)$.

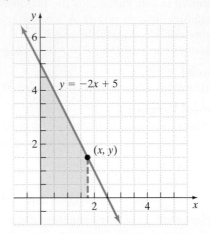

Section 4.2 Multiplying Polynomials

KEY CONCEPTS	KEY TERMS
• **Product Rule for Exponents** If a is a real number and m and n are integers, then $a^m \cdot a^n = a^{m+n}$. If m, n, or $m + n$ is 0 or negative, then a cannot be 0.	FOIL Special products
• **Distributive Property** If a, b, and c are real numbers, then $a \cdot (b + c) = a \cdot b + a \cdot c$ and $(a + b) \cdot c = a \cdot c + b \cdot c$.	
• **Extended Form of the Distributive Property** $a(b_1 + b_2 + \cdots + b_n) = a \cdot b_1 + a \cdot b_2 + \cdots + a \cdot b_n$ where $a, b_1, b_2, \ldots, b_n$ are real numbers.	
• **Difference of Two Squares** $(A - B)(A + B) = A^2 - B^2$	
• **Squares of Binomials or Perfect Square Trinomials** $(A + B)^2 = A^2 + 2AB + B^2$ $(A - B)^2 = A^2 - 2AB + B^2$	
• **Product of Two Functions** Let f and g be two functions. The product $f \cdot g$ is the function defined by $(f \cdot g)(x) = f(x) \cdot g(x)$.	

YOU SHOULD BE ABLE TO...	EXAMPLE	REVIEW EXERCISES
1 Multiply a monomial and a polynomial (p. 333)	Example 2	17–20
2 Multiply a binomial by a binomial (p. 333)	Examples 3 and 4	21–24
3 Multiply a polynomial by a polynomial (p. 334)	Example 5	25–28
4 Multiply special products (p. 335)	Examples 6 through 9	29–34
5 Multiply polynomial functions (p. 337)	Example 10	35–36

In Problems 17 20, find the product.

17. $(-3x^3y)(4xy^2)$ **18.** $\left(\frac{1}{3}mn^4\right)(18m^3n^3)$

19. $5ab(-2a^2b + ab^2 - 3ab)$

20. $0.5c(1.7c^2 + 4.3c + 8.9)$

In Problems 21–24, find the product of the two binomials.

21. $(x + 2)(x - 9)$ **22.** $(-3x + 1)(2x - 8)$

23. $(m - 4n)(2m + n)$ **24.** $(2a + 15)(-a + 3)$

In Problems 25–28, find the product of the polynomials.

25. $(x + 2)(3x^2 - 5x + 1)$

26. $(w - 4)(w^2 + w - 8)$

27. $(m^2 - 2m + 3)(2m^2 + 5m - 7)$

28. $(2p - 3q)(p^2 + 7pq - 4q^2)$

In Problems 29–34, find the special products.

29. $(3w + 1)(3w - 1)$ **30.** $(2x - 5y)(2x + 5y)$

31. $(6k - 5)^2$ **32.** $(3a + 2b)^2$

33. $(x + 2)(x^2 - 2x + 4)$ **34.** $(2x - 3)(4x^2 + 6x + 9)$

In Problems 35–38, find the indicated function or value.

35. $f(x) = 3x - 7; g(x) = 6x + 5$
  (a) $(f \cdot g)(x)$ **(b)** $(f \cdot g)(-2)$

36. $f(x) = x + 2; g(x) = 3x^2 - x + 1$
  (a) $(f \cdot g)(x)$ **(b)** $(f \cdot g)(4)$

37. $f(x - 3)$ when $f(x) = 5x^2 + 8$.

38. $f(x + h) - f(x)$ when $f(x) = -x^2 + 3x - 5$.

Section 4.3   Division of Polynomials and Synthetic Division

KEY CONCEPTS	KEY TERMS
• **Quotient Rule for Exponents** If a is a real number and m and n are integers, then $\dfrac{a^m}{a^n} = a^{m-n}, a \neq 0$. • **Quotient of Two Functions** Let f and g be two functions. The quotient $\dfrac{f}{g}$ is the function defined by $\left(\dfrac{f}{g}\right)(x) = \dfrac{f(x)}{g(x)}, g(x) \neq 0$. • **The Remainder Theorem** Let f be a polynomial function. If $f(x)$ is divided by $x - c$, then the remainder is $f(c)$. • **The Factor Theorem** Let f be a polynomial function. Then $x - c$ is a factor of $f(x)$ if and only if $f(c) = 0$.	Divisor Dividend Quotient Remainder Synthetic division

YOU SHOULD BE ABLE TO...	EXAMPLE	REVIEW EXERCISES
1 Divide a polynomial by a monomial (p. 341)	Example 1	39–42
2 Divide polynomials using long division (p. 342)	Examples 3 through 5	43–48, 63
3 Divide polynomials using synthetic division (p. 345)	Examples 6 and 7	49–54, 64
4 Divide polynomial functions (p. 347)	Example 8	55–58
5 Use the Remainder and Factor Theorems (p. 348)	Examples 9 and 10	59–62

In Problems 39–42, divide and simplify.

39. $\dfrac{12x^3 - 6x^2}{3x}$

40. $\dfrac{15w^5 - 5w^3 + 25w^2 + 10w}{5w}$

41. $\dfrac{7y^3 + 12y^2 - 6y}{2y}$

42. $\dfrac{2m^3n^2 + 8m^2n^2 - 14mn^3}{4m^2n^3}$

In Problems 43–48, divide using long division.

43. $\dfrac{3x^2 - 2x - 8}{x - 2}$

44. $\dfrac{-2x^2 - 3x + 40}{x + 5}$

45. $\dfrac{6z^3 + 9z^2 + 4z - 6}{2z + 3}$

46. $\dfrac{12k^3 - 29k^2 - 14k + 16}{3k - 8}$

47. $\dfrac{16x^4 - 81}{2x - 3}$

48. $\dfrac{2x^4 - 11x^3 + 35x^2 - 54x + 55}{x^2 - 3x + 4}$

In Problems 49–54, divide using synthetic division.

49. $\dfrac{5x^2 + 11x + 8}{x + 2}$

50. $\dfrac{9a^2 - 14a - 8}{a - 2}$

51. $\dfrac{3m^3 + 11m^2 - 5m - 33}{m + 3}$

52. $\dfrac{n^3 + 2n^2 - 39n + 67}{n - 4}$

53. $\dfrac{x^4 + 6x^2 - 7}{x + 1}$

54. $\dfrac{2x^3 + 5x - 8}{x + 2}$

In Problems 55–58, find the indicated function or value.

55. $f(x) = 5x^3 + 25x^2 - 15x; g(x) = 5x$

   (a) $\left(\dfrac{f}{g}\right)(x)$ **(b)** $\left(\dfrac{f}{g}\right)(2)$

56. $f(x) = 9x^2 + 54x - 31; g(x) = 3x - 2$

   (a) $\left(\dfrac{f}{g}\right)(x)$ **(b)** $\left(\dfrac{f}{g}\right)(-3)$

57. $f(x) = 2x^3 + 12x^2 + 9x - 28;$
    $g(x) = x + 4$

   (a) $\left(\dfrac{f}{g}\right)(x)$ **(b)** $\left(\dfrac{f}{g}\right)(-2)$

58. $f(x) = 3x^4 - 14x^3 + 31x^2 - 58x + 22;$
    $g(x) = x^2 - x + 5$

   (a) $\left(\dfrac{f}{g}\right)(x)$ **(b)** $\left(\dfrac{f}{g}\right)(4)$

In Problems 59 and 60, use the Remainder Theorem to find the remainder.

59. $f(x) = 4x^2 - 7x + 23$ is divided by $x - 4$.

60. $f(x) = x^3 - 2x^2 + 12x - 5$ is divided by $x + 2$.

In Problems 61 and 62, use the Factor Theorem to determine whether $x - c$ is a factor of the given function for the given value of c. If $x - c$ is a factor, then write the function in factored form.

61. $f(x) = 3x^2 + x - 14; c = 2$

62. $f(x) = 2x^2 + 13x + 22; c = -4$

63. The area of a rectangle is $20x^2 - 11x - 3$ square meters. If the width of the rectangle is $4x - 3$ meters, find an expression for the length.

64. The volume of a rectangular box is $2x^3 + x^2 - 7x - 6$ cubic centimeters. If the height of the box is $x - 2$ centimeters, find an expression for the area of the top of the box.

Section 4.4   Greatest Common Factor and Factoring by Grouping

KEY CONCEPTS	KEY TERMS

• **Factoring out the greatest common factor**
 Identify the greatest common factor (GCF) of each term. Rewrite each term as the product of the GCF and remaining factor. Use the Distributive Property to factor out the GCF. Check your work using the Distributive Property.
 	
 • **Factoring by grouping**
 Group the terms with common factors. Sometimes it will be necessary to rearrange the terms. In each grouping, factor out the common factor. Factor out the common factor that remains. Check your work.
	Factors
	 Factoring over the
	   integers
	 Prime
	 Factored completely
	 Greatest common factor
	   (GCF)
	 Factoring by grouping

YOU SHOULD BE ABLE TO...	EXAMPLE	REVIEW EXERCISES
1 Factor out the greatest common factor (p. 353)	Examples 1 through 4	65–72, 79, 80
2 Factor by grouping (p. 355)	Examples 5 and 6	73–78

In Problems 65–72, factor out the greatest common factor.

65. $4z + 24$

66. $-7y^2 + 91y$

67. $14x^3y^2 + 2xy^2 - 8x^2y$

68. $30a^4b^3 + 15a^3b - 25a^2b^2$

69. $3x(x + 5) - 4(x + 5)$

70. $-4c(2c + 9) + 3(2c + 9)$

71. $(5x + 3)(x - 5y) + (x + 2)(x - 5y)$

72. $(3a - b)(a + 7) - (a + 1)(a + 7)$

In Problems 73–78, factor by grouping.

73. $x^2 + 6x - 3x - 18$

74. $c^2 + 2c - 5c - 10$

75. $14z^2 + 16z - 21z - 24$

76. $21w^2 - 28w + 6w - 8$

77. $2x^3 + 2x^2 - 18x^2 - 18x$

78. $10a^4 + 15a^3 + 70a^3 + 105a^2$

79. Integers The sum of the first n positive integers is given by $\frac{1}{2}n^2 + \frac{1}{2}n$.

    (a) Write this expression in factored form.
    (b) Use the factored form to determine the sum of the first 32 positive integers.

80. Revenue A computer manufacturer estimates that its revenue for selling x computer systems can be approximated by the function $R(x) = 5200x - 2x^3$. Express the revenue function in factored form.

Section 4.5 Factoring Trinomials

KEY CONCEPTS	KEY TERM
• **Factoring $x^2 + bx + c$** $x^2 + bx + c = (x + m)(x + n)$, where $mn = c$ and $m + n = b$ • **Factoring $ax^2 + bx + c$ by grouping** See page 364 • **Factoring $ax^2 + bx + c$ by trial and error** See page 366	Factoring by substitution

YOU SHOULD BE ABLE TO...	EXAMPLE	REVIEW EXERCISES
1 Factor trinomials of the form $x^2 + bx + c$ (p. 359)	Examples 1 through 6	81–86
2 Factor trinomials of the form $ax^2 + bx + c$, $a \neq 1$ (p. 363)	Examples 7 through 12	87–94
3 Factor trinomials using substitution (p. 368)	Examples 13 and 14	95–98

In Problems 81–98, factor each trinomial completely. If the polynomial cannot be factored, say it is prime.

81. $w^2 - 11w - 26$

82. $x^2 - 9x + 15$

83. $-t^2 + 6t + 72$

84. $m^2 + 10m + 21$

85. $x^2 + 4xy - 320y^2$

86. $r^2 - 5rs + 6s^2$

87. $5x^2 + 13x - 6$

88. $6m^2 + 41m + 44$

89. $4y^2 - 5y + 7$

90. $8t^2 + 22t - 6$

91. $6x^2 - 13x + 5$

92. $21r^2 - rs - 2s^2$

93. $20x^2 - 57xy + 27y^2$

94. $-2s^2 + 12s + 14$

95. $x^4 - 10x^2 - 11$

96. $10x^2y^2 + 41xy + 4$

97. $(a + 4)^2 - 9(a + 4) - 36$

98. $2(w - 1)^2 + 11(w - 1) + 9$

Section 4.6 Factoring Special Products

KEY CONCEPTS	KEY TERM

KEY CONCEPTS

- **Squares of Binomials or Perfect Square Trinomials**
$A^2 + 2AB + B^2 = (A + B)^2$
$A^2 - 2AB + B^2 = (A - B)^2$

- **Difference of Two Squares**
$A^2 - B^2 = (A - B)(A + B)$

- **Sum or Difference of Two Cubes**
$A^3 + B^3 = (A + B)(A^2 - AB + B^2)$
$A^3 - B^3 = (A - B)(A^2 + AB + B^2)$

KEY TERM

Sum of two squares

YOU SHOULD BE ABLE TO...	EXAMPLE	REVIEW EXERCISES
1 Factor perfect square trinomials (p. 371)	Example 1	99–104
2 Factor the difference of two squares (p. 372)	Examples 2 and 3	105–110
3 Factor the sum or difference of two cubes (p. 374)	Examples 4 and 5	111–116

In Problems 99–116, factor completely.

99. $x^2 + 22x + 121$

100. $w^2 - 34w + 289$

101. $144 - 24c + c^2$

102. $x^2 - 8x + 16$

103. $64y^2 + 80y + 25$

104. $12z^2 + 48z + 48$

105. $x^2 - 196$

106. $49 - y^2$

107. $t^2 - 225$

108. $4w^2 - 81$

109. $36x^4 - 25y^2$

110. $80mn^2 - 20m$

111. $x^3 - 343$

112. $729 - y^3$

113. $27x^3 - 125y^3$

114. $8m^6 + 27n^3$

115. $2a^6 - 2b^6$

116. $(y - 1)^3 + 64$

Section 4.7 Factoring: A General Strategy

KEY CONCEPT

Steps for Factoring

Step 1: Factor out the greatest common factor (GCF), if any exists.

Step 2: Count the number of terms.

Step 3: **(a)** 2 terms
- Is it the difference of two squares? If so,
$A^2 - B^2 = (A - B)(A + B)$
- Is it the sum of two squares? If so, stop! The expression is prime.
- Is it the difference of two cubes? If so,
$A^3 - B^3 = (A - B)(A^2 + AB + B^2)$
- Is it the sum of two cubes? If so,
$A^3 + B^3 = (A + B)(A^2 - AB + B^2)$

   (b) 3 terms
- Is it a perfect square trinomial? If so,
$A^2 + 2AB + B^2 = (A + B)^2$ or $A^2 - 2AB + B^2 = (A - B)^2$
- Is the coefficient of the square term 1? If so,
$x^2 + bx + c = (x + m)(x + n)$ where $mn = c$ and $m + n = b$
- Is the coefficient of the square term different from 1? If so,
   (a) Use factoring by grouping
   (b) Use trial and error

   (c) 4 terms
- Use factoring by grouping

Step 4: Check your work by multiplying out the factored form.

YOU SHOULD BE ABLE TO...	EXAMPLE	REVIEW EXERCISES
1 Factor polynomials completely (p. 377)	Examples 1 through 7	117–131
2 Write polynomial functions in factored form (p. 381)	Example 8	132–136

In Problems 117–131, factor each polynomial completely.

117. $x^2 + 7x + 6$

118. $-8x^2y^3 + 12xy^3$

119. $7x^3 - 35x^2 + 28x$

120. $3x^2 - 3x - 18$

121. $4z^2 - 60z + 225$

122. $12x^2 + 7x - 49$

123. $10n^2 - 33n - 7$

124. $8 - 2y - y^2$

125. $2x^3 - 10x^2 + 6x - 30$

126. $(3h + 2)^3 + 64$

127. $5p^3q^2 - 80p$

128. $m^4 - 5m^2 + 4$

129. $686 - 16m^6$

130. $h^3 + 2h^2 - h - 2$

131. $108x^3 + 4y^3$

In Problems 132–136, factor each polynomial function.

132. $F(c) = c^2 - 24c + 144$

133. $f(x) = -3x^2 + 6x + 45$

134. $g(x) = 16x^2 - 100$

135. $G(y) = 16y^3 + 250$

136. $f(x) = -4x^2 - 16$

In Problems 137 and 138, write an expression for the shaded area in factored form.

137.

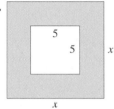

138.

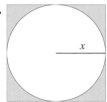

Section 4.8 Polynomial Equations

KEY CONCEPTS

- **The Zero-Product Property**
  If the product of two numbers is zero, then at least one of the numbers is 0.
  That is, if $ab = 0$, then $a = 0$ or $b = 0$ or both a and b are 0.

- **Zero of a Function**
  A zero of a function f is any number r such that $f(r) = 0$. If r is a zero of a function, then r is also an x-intercept of the graph of the function.

KEY TERMS

Polynomial equation
Degree of a polynomial
  equation
Zero-product property
Quadratic equation
Standard form
Second-degree equation
Zero

YOU SHOULD BE ABLE TO...	EXAMPLE	REVIEW EXERCISES
1 Solve polynomial equations using the Zero-Product Property (p. 384)	Examples 1 through 4	139–148
2 Solve equations involving polynomial functions (p. 388)	Examples 5 and 6	149–152
3 Model and solve problems involving polynomials (p. 389)	Examples 7 through 9	153–154

In Problems 139–148, solve each equation.

139. $(w + 5)(w - 13) = 0$

140. $x(2x + 1)(3x - 5) = 0$

141. $5a^2 = -20a$

142. $y^2 + 2y = 15$

143. $x^2 + 21x + 54 = 0$

144. $15x^2 + 29x - 14 = 0$

145. $x(x + 1) = 110$

146. $\frac{1}{2}x^2 + 5x + 12 = 0$

147. $(b + 1)(b - 3) = 5$

148. $(x + 7)^3 = x^3 + 133$

149. Suppose that $f(x) = x^2 + 5x - 18$. Find values of x such that

  (a) $f(x) = 6$ **(b)** $f(x) = -4$

  What points are on the graph of f?

150. Suppose that $f(x) = 5x^2 - 4x + 3$. Find values of x such that

(a) $f(x) = 3$ **(b)** $f(x) = 4$

What points are on the graph of f?

In Problems 151 and 152, find the zeros of the function. What are the x-intercepts of the graph of the function?

151. $f(x) = 3x^3 + 18x^2 + 24x$

152. $f(x) = -4x^2 + 22x + 42$

153. Falling Object At one point, a four-foot flagpole on top of the KXJB-TV mast in Galesburg, North

Dakota, made it the world's tallest structure, standing 2064 feet tall. If an object is dropped from the top of this mast, the height s of the object (in feet) as a function of time (in seconds) can be modeled by the function $s(t) = -16t^2 + 2064$. When will the object be 1280 feet above the ground?

154. Reliability A simple parallel system with two identical components has a reliability given by $R = 1 - (1 - r)^2$, where r is the reliability of the individual components.

(a) What is the reliability of the individual components if the system reliability is $R = 0.96$?

(b) What is the reliability of the individual components if the system reliability is $R = 0.99$?

CHAPTER 4 TEST

Remember to use your Chapter Test Prep Video CD to see fully worked-out solutions to any of these problems you would like to review.

CHAPTER
Test Prep
VIDEOS

1. Write the polynomial in standard form and determine its degree.

$$7x^2 + x^4 - 5x^7 + 1 - x$$

2. Add:

$$(-2a^3b^2 + 5a^2b + ab + 1) + \left(\frac{1}{3}a^3b^2 + 4a^2b - 6ab - 5\right)$$

3. For $f(x) = x^3 + 3x^2 - x + 1$, find $f(-2)$.

4. For $f(x) = 7x^3 - 1$ and $g(x) = 4x^2 + 3x - 2$, find $(f - g)(x)$.

In Problems 5–7, perform the indicated multiplication.

5. $\frac{1}{2}a^2b(4ab^2 - 6ab + 8)$

6. $(3x - 1)(4x + 17)$

7. $(2m - n)^2$

8. Divide using long division: $\dfrac{6z^3 - 14z^2 + z + 4}{2z^2 + 1}$

9. Divide using synthetic division: $\dfrac{5x^2 - 27x - 18}{x - 6}$

10. For $f(x) = 6x^2 + x - 12$ and $g(x) = 2x + 3$, find $\left(\dfrac{f}{g}\right)(2)$.

11. Use the Remainder Theorem to determine the remainder when $f(x) = 2x^3 - 3x^2 - 4x + 7$ is divided by $x - 3$.

12. Factor out the greatest common factor: $12a^3b^2 + 8a^2b^2 - 16ab^3$

In Problems 13–18, factor completely.

13. $6c^2 + 21c - 4c - 14$

14. $x^2 - 13x - 48$

15. $-14p^2 - 17p + 6$

16. $5(z - 1)^2 + 17(z - 1) - 12$

17. $-98x^2 + 112x - 32$

18. $16x^2 - 196$

19. Solve: $3m^2 - 5m = 5m - 7$

20. One side of a rectangular patio is 3 meters longer than the other. If the area of the patio is 108 square meters, what are the dimensions of the patio?

Getting Ready for Chapter 5:
A Review of Operations on Rational Numbers

OBJECTIVES

1. Write Rational Numbers in Lowest Terms
2. Multiply and Divide Rational Numbers
3. Add and Subtract Rational Numbers

The purpose of this "Getting Ready" section is to provide a review of operations on rational numbers. As you go through the section, pay attention to the methods used to perform each operation because these same methods will be used in Chapter 5 when we discuss operations on rational expressions.

1 Write Rational Numbers in Lowest Terms

We prefer to write rational numbers in **lowest terms;** that is, we write rational numbers so that there are not any common factors in the numerator and the denominator of the rational number. We obtain rational numbers in lowest terms using the *Reduction Property*.

REDUCTION PROPERTY

If a, b, and c are real numbers, then

$$\frac{ac}{bc} = \frac{a}{b} \qquad \text{if } b \neq 0, c \neq 0$$

EXAMPLE 1 Writing Rational Numbers in Lowest Terms

Divide out the 9's
$$\frac{45}{18} = \frac{\cancel{9} \cdot 5}{\cancel{9} \cdot 2} = \frac{5}{2}$$

∎

Quick ✔

1. When a rational number is written so that there are not any common factors in the numerator and the denominator, we say that the rational number is in _____ _____ .

In Problems 2 and 3, write each rational number in lowest terms.

2. $\dfrac{13 \cdot 5}{13 \cdot 6}$

3. $\dfrac{80}{12}$

2 Multiply and Divide Rational Numbers

We now review the methods for multiplying and dividing rational numbers.

MULTIPLYING RATIONAL NUMBERS

Step 1: Completely factor each integer in the numerator and denominator.

Step 2: Divide out common factors in the numerator and denominator.

Step 3: Use the fact that if $\dfrac{a}{b}$ and $\dfrac{c}{d}$, $b \neq 0$, $d \neq 0$, are two rational numbers, then

$$\frac{a}{b} \cdot \frac{c}{d} = \frac{ac}{bd}.$$

In Words

To multiply two rational numbers, multiply the numerators and then multiply the denominators. To divide two rational numbers, multiply the rational number in the numerator by the reciprocal of the rational number in the denominator.

DIVIDING RATIONAL NUMBERS

To divide rational numbers, use the fact that if $\dfrac{a}{b}$ and $\dfrac{c}{d}$, $b \neq 0$, $c \neq 0$, $d \neq 0$, are two

rational numbers, then $\dfrac{\dfrac{a}{b}}{\dfrac{c}{d}} = \dfrac{a}{b} \div \dfrac{c}{d} = \dfrac{a}{b} \cdot \dfrac{d}{c} = \dfrac{ad}{bc}$.

EXAMPLE 2 Multiplying and Dividing Rational Numbers

Perform the indicated operation. Be sure to express the result in lowest terms.

(a) $\dfrac{10}{3} \cdot \dfrac{18}{25}$

(b) $\dfrac{\dfrac{14}{5}}{\dfrac{21}{10}}$

Solution

$$10 = 2 \cdot 5; \ 18 = 9 \cdot 2 = 3 \cdot 3 \cdot 2; \ 25 = 5 \cdot 5$$
$$\downarrow$$

(a)
$$\dfrac{10}{3} \cdot \dfrac{18}{25} = \dfrac{2 \cdot 5}{3} \cdot \dfrac{3 \cdot 3 \cdot 2}{5 \cdot 5}$$

Multiply; use the Reduction Property to divide out common factors:
$$= \dfrac{2 \cdot \cancel{5} \cdot \cancel{3} \cdot 3 \cdot 2}{\cancel{3} \cdot \cancel{5} \cdot 5}$$

$$= \dfrac{2 \cdot 3 \cdot 2}{5}$$

Multiply:
$$= \dfrac{12}{5}$$

Work Smart

In Example 2(a), rather than factoring each numerator and denominator individually and then dividing out like factors, we might proceed as follows:

$$\dfrac{10}{3} \cdot \dfrac{18}{25} = \dfrac{\overset{2}{\cancel{10}} \cdot \overset{6}{\cancel{18}}}{\underset{1}{\cancel{3}} \cdot \underset{5}{\cancel{25}}}$$

$$= \dfrac{2 \cdot 6}{1 \cdot 5}$$

Multiply numerators; multiply denominators:
$$= \dfrac{12}{5}$$

Notice that we use slashes in the same direction when writing in lowest terms and put the remaining factor next to the reduced factor.

(b) We rewrite the division problem as a multiplication problem by multiplying the numerator, $\dfrac{14}{5}$, by the reciprocal of the denominator, $\dfrac{21}{10}$. The reciprocal of $\dfrac{21}{10}$ is $\dfrac{10}{21}$.

$$\dfrac{\dfrac{14}{5}}{\dfrac{21}{10}} = \dfrac{14}{5} \cdot \dfrac{10}{21}$$

$$= \dfrac{7 \cdot 2}{5} \cdot \dfrac{5 \cdot 2}{7 \cdot 3}$$

Multiply; use the Reduction Property to divide out common factors:
$$= \dfrac{\cancel{7} \cdot 2 \cdot \cancel{5} \cdot 2}{\cancel{5} \cdot \cancel{7} \cdot 3}$$

$$= \dfrac{2 \cdot 2}{3} = \dfrac{4}{3}$$

Quick ✔ *In Problems 4–7, perform the indicated operation. Express your answer in lowest terms.*

4. $\dfrac{5}{7} \cdot \left(-\dfrac{21}{10}\right)$

5. $\dfrac{35}{15} \cdot \dfrac{3}{14}$

6. $\dfrac{\dfrac{4}{5}}{\dfrac{12}{25}}$

7. $\dfrac{24}{35} \div \left(-\dfrac{8}{7}\right)$

⌈3⌉ Add and Subtract Rational Numbers

We now review addition and subtraction of rational numbers.

In Words

To add two rational numbers with a common denominator, add the numerators and write the sum over the common denominator.

ADDING OR SUBTRACTING RATIONAL NUMBERS

Step 1: If $\dfrac{a}{c}$ and $\dfrac{b}{c}$, $c \neq 0$, are two rational numbers, then $\dfrac{a}{c} + \dfrac{b}{c} = \dfrac{a+b}{c}$ and $\dfrac{a}{c} - \dfrac{b}{c} = \dfrac{a-b}{c}$.

Step 2: Write the result in lowest terms.

EXAMPLE 3 Adding or Subtracting Rational Numbers with Common Denominators

Perform the indicated operation. Be sure to express the result in lowest terms.

(a) $\dfrac{7}{24} + \dfrac{11}{24}$ **(b)** $\dfrac{2}{15} - \dfrac{7}{15}$

Solution

(a)
$$\frac{7}{24} + \frac{11}{24} = \frac{7+11}{24}$$
$$= \frac{18}{24}$$

Factor numerator and denominator: $= \dfrac{6 \cdot 3}{6 \cdot 4}$

Divide out common factors: $= \dfrac{3}{4}$

(b)
$$\frac{2}{15} - \frac{7}{15} = \frac{2-7}{15}$$
$$= \frac{-5}{15}$$

Factor numerator and denominator: $= \dfrac{-1 \cdot 5}{3 \cdot 5}$

Divide out common factors: $= \dfrac{-1}{3} = -\dfrac{1}{3}$

Quick ✔ *In Problems 8 and 9, perform the indicated operation. Express your answer in lowest terms.*

8. $\dfrac{11}{12} + \dfrac{5}{12}$ **9.** $\dfrac{3}{18} - \dfrac{13}{18}$

What if the denominators of the rational numbers to be added or subtracted are not the same? In this case, we must rewrite each rational number over a *least common denominator*. The **least common denominator (LCD)** is the smallest integer that is a multiple of each denominator in the rational numbers to be added or subtracted.

EXAMPLE 4 How to Find the Least Common Denominator

Find the least common denominator of the rational numbers $\frac{7}{30}$ and $\frac{5}{12}$. Then rewrite each rational number with the least common denominator.

Work Smart

Line up the factors vertically to find the LCD.

Step-by-Step Solution

Step 1: Factor each denominator.

It is easier to see the common factors by listing them directly over each other.
$$\downarrow$$
$$30 = 5 \cdot 6 = 5 \cdot 3 \cdot 2$$
$$12 = 3 \cdot 4 = \quad 3 \cdot 2 \cdot 2$$

Step 2: Write down the common factor(s) between each denominator. Then copy the remaining factors. The product of these factors is the least common denominator (LCD).

The common factors are 3 and 2.
The remaining factors are 5 and 2.
$$LCD = 3 \cdot 2 \cdot 5 \cdot 2 = 60$$

We rewrite $\frac{7}{30}$ with a denominator of 60 by multiplying the numerator and denominator by 2. We rewrite $\frac{5}{12}$ with a denominator of 60 by multiplying the numerator and denominator by 5.

Work Smart

When we multiply $\frac{7}{30}$ by $\frac{2}{2}$, we are using the Multiplicative Identity Property of real numbers where $1 = \frac{2}{2}$.

$$\frac{7}{30} = \frac{7}{30} \cdot \frac{2}{2} = \frac{7 \cdot 2}{30 \cdot 2} = \frac{14}{60}$$
$$\frac{5}{12} = \frac{5}{12} \cdot \frac{5}{5} = \frac{5 \cdot 5}{12 \cdot 5} = \frac{25}{60}$$

Quick ✔ *In Problems 10 and 11, find the least common denominator (LCD) of each pair of rational numbers. Then rewrite each rational number with the LCD.*

10. $\frac{3}{25}$ and $\frac{2}{15}$

11. $\frac{5}{18}$ and $-\frac{1}{63}$

Now that we know how to obtain the least common denominator, we can discuss how to add or subtract rational numbers that have unlike denominators.

EXAMPLE 5 How to Add or Subtract Fractions Using the Least Common Denominator

Perform the indicated operation:

(a) $\frac{5}{2} + \frac{4}{3}$

(b) $\frac{5}{28} - \frac{5}{12}$

Step-by-Step Solution

(a) $\frac{5}{2} + \frac{4}{3}$

Step 1: Find the least common denominator.	Each denominator is prime, so the LCD $= 2 \cdot 3 = 6$.

Step 2: Rewrite each rational number with the common denominator.	$\dfrac{5}{2} + \dfrac{4}{3} = \dfrac{5}{2} \cdot \dfrac{3}{3} + \dfrac{4}{3} \cdot \dfrac{2}{2}$ $\qquad\qquad = \dfrac{15}{6} + \dfrac{8}{6}$

Step 3: Add the rational numbers found in Step 2.	$\qquad\qquad = \dfrac{15 + 8}{6}$ $\qquad\qquad = \dfrac{23}{6}$

Step 4: Write the result in lowest terms.	The rational number is already in lowest terms.

$$\text{So, } \frac{5}{2} + \frac{4}{3} = \frac{23}{6}$$

(b) $\dfrac{5}{28} - \dfrac{5}{12}$

Step 1: Find the least common denominator.	$28 = 7 \cdot 4$ $12 = 4 \cdot 3$ The LCD $= 4 \cdot 7 \cdot 3 = 84$

Step 2: Rewrite each rational number with the common denominator.	$\dfrac{5}{28} - \dfrac{5}{12} = \dfrac{5}{28} \cdot \dfrac{3}{3} - \dfrac{5}{12} \cdot \dfrac{7}{7}$ $\qquad\qquad = \dfrac{15}{84} - \dfrac{35}{84}$

Step 3: Subtract the rational numbers found in Step 2.	$\qquad\qquad = \dfrac{15 - 35}{84}$ $\qquad\qquad = \dfrac{-20}{84}$

Step 4: Write the result in lowest terms.	$\qquad\qquad = \dfrac{-5 \cdot 4}{21 \cdot 4}$ $\qquad\qquad = \dfrac{-5}{21} = -\dfrac{5}{21}$

$$\text{So, } \frac{5}{28} - \frac{5}{12} = -\frac{5}{21}$$

We summarize the steps used in Example 5 below.

> **ADDING OR SUBTRACTING RATIONAL NUMBERS WITH UNLIKE DENOMINATORS**
>
> **Step 1:** Find the least common denominator.
> **Step 2:** Rewrite each rational number with the common denominator.
> **Step 3:** Add or subtract the rational numbers found in Step 2.
> **Step 4:** Write the result in lowest terms.

Quick ✔ *In Problems 12–14, perform the indicated operation. Express your answer in lowest terms.*

12. $\dfrac{3}{4} + \dfrac{1}{5}$

13. $\dfrac{3}{20} + \dfrac{2}{15}$

14. $\dfrac{5}{14} - \dfrac{11}{21}$

GETTING READY FOR CHAPTER 5 EXERCISES

PRACTICE WATCH DOWNLOAD READ REVIEW

1–14. *are the* **Quick** ✔**s** *that follow each* **EXAMPLE**

Building Skills

In Problems 15–20, write each rational number in lowest terms. See Objective 1.

15. $\dfrac{4}{12}$

16. $\dfrac{6}{18}$

17. $-\dfrac{15}{35}$

18. $-\dfrac{12}{28}$

19. $\dfrac{-50}{-10}$

20. $\dfrac{81}{-27}$

In Problems 21–32, multiply or divide the rational numbers. Express each product or quotient as a rational number in lowest terms. See Objective 2.

21. $\dfrac{3}{4} \cdot \dfrac{20}{9}$

22. $\dfrac{2}{3} \cdot \dfrac{15}{6}$

23. $-\dfrac{5}{6} \cdot \dfrac{18}{5}$

24. $-\dfrac{9}{8} \cdot \dfrac{16}{3}$

25. $\dfrac{5}{8} \cdot \dfrac{2}{15}$

26. $\dfrac{3}{14} \cdot \dfrac{7}{12}$

27. $\dfrac{5}{2} \div \dfrac{25}{4}$

28. $\dfrac{2}{3} \div \dfrac{8}{9}$

29. $\dfrac{\dfrac{6}{5}}{\dfrac{8}{15}}$

30. $\dfrac{\dfrac{12}{7}}{\dfrac{18}{21}}$

31. $\dfrac{\dfrac{9}{2}}{\dfrac{3}{4}}$

32. $\dfrac{\dfrac{10}{7}}{\dfrac{5}{14}}$

In Problems 33–51, add or subtract the rational numbers. Express each sum or difference as a rational number in lowest terms. See Objective 3.

33. $\dfrac{5}{3} + \dfrac{1}{3}$

34. $\dfrac{3}{4} + \dfrac{9}{4}$

35. $\dfrac{11}{6} - \dfrac{1}{6}$

36. $\dfrac{19}{6} - \dfrac{5}{6}$

37. $\dfrac{3}{4} + \dfrac{1}{5}$

38. $\dfrac{-1}{7} + \dfrac{4}{9}$

39. $\dfrac{1}{4} + \dfrac{5}{6}$

40. $\dfrac{5}{8} + \dfrac{5}{12}$

41. $-\dfrac{3}{10} - \dfrac{7}{15}$

42. $\dfrac{7}{16} - \dfrac{9}{20}$

43. $\dfrac{5}{18} - \dfrac{11}{15}$

44. $\dfrac{5}{24} + \dfrac{7}{32}$

45. $-\dfrac{7}{8} + \dfrac{3}{10}$

46. $-\dfrac{7}{12} + \dfrac{2}{15}$

47. $\dfrac{7}{24} - \dfrac{3}{20}$

48. $\dfrac{3}{28} + \dfrac{5}{12}$

49. $-\dfrac{7}{9} - \dfrac{2}{15}$

50. $-\dfrac{5}{18} - \dfrac{1}{45}$

51. $\dfrac{-4}{25} - \dfrac{7}{30}$

Explaining the Concepts

52. Explain how to write a rational number in lowest terms.

53. Explain how to find the least common denominator between two rational numbers.

54. Explain how to add two rational numbers that do not have a common denominator.

5 Rational Expressions and Rational Functions

Can a mathematical formula be used to predict the number of runs a major league baseball team will score in a season? Yes! In fact, his knowledge of the mathematical formula is one of the reasons that Billy Beane, general manager of the Oakland A's, seeks out baseball players who get a lot of walks. See Problem 69 in Section 5.4.

OUTLINE

The Big Picture: Putting It Together

In Chapter 4, we learned how to add, subtract, multiply, and divide polynomials. We then learned how to factor polynomial expressions and use the result (along with the Zero-Product Property) to solve a polynomial equation.

We will do the same thing with *rational expressions*. A rational expression is a polynomial divided by another polynomial. Factoring comes in handy when working with rational expressions. The methods for reducing, adding, subtracting, multiplying, and dividing rational expressions are identical to the methods used to do these operations on rational numbers. The point is this—the algebra of rational expressions can be thought of as a generic arithmetic of rational numbers.

Beginning with this chapter, we introduce a new category of problems called Synthesis Review. The synthesis review problems are created to assist you in seeing the "big picture" of algebra. For example, we might ask you to add various objects (polynomials, rational expressions, and so on). We then ask for you to discuss similarities and differences in performing the operation on the objects.

5.1 Multiplying and Dividing Rational Expressions

OBJECTIVES

1. Determine the Domain of a Rational Expression
2. Simplify Rational Expressions
3. Multiply Rational Expressions
4. Divide Rational Expressions
5. Work with Rational Functions

Preparing for Multiplying and Dividing Rational Expressions

Before getting started, take the following readiness quiz. If you get a problem wrong, go back to the section cited and review the material.

P1. Factor: $2x^2 - 11x - 21$ [Section 4.5, pp. 363–368]

P2. Solve: $q^2 - 16 = 0$ [Section 4.8, pp. 385–387]

P3. Determine the reciprocal of $\dfrac{5}{2}$.   [Section R.3, p. 24]

P4. Explain what *domain* means.   [Section 2.1, pp. 149–151]

If we form the quotient of two polynomials, then we have a **rational expression.** Some examples of rational expressions are

$$\textbf{(a)}\ \frac{x-5}{2x+1} \qquad \textbf{(b)}\ \frac{x^2-7x-18}{x^2-4} \qquad \textbf{(c)}\ \frac{2a^2+5ab+2b^2}{a^2-6ab+8b^2} \qquad \textbf{(d)}\ \frac{1}{x-3}$$

Expressions **(a)**, **(b)**, and **(d)** are rational expressions in one variable, x, while expression **(c)** is a rational expression in two variables, a and b.

Rational expressions are described the same way as rational numbers. In the expression $\dfrac{x-5}{2x+1}$, we call $x-5$ the **numerator** and $2x+1$ the **denominator.** When the numerator and denominator have no common factors (except 1 and -1), we say that the rational expression is expressed in **lowest terms,** or **simplified.**

1 Determine the Domain of a Rational Expression

To find the domain of a rational expression, we determine all values of the variable that cause the denominator to equal 0 and exclude these values from the domain because division by 0 is not defined. Knowing the domain of a rational expression is important because it will play a role in solving rational equations later in this chapter.

EXAMPLE 1 Determining the Domain of a Rational Expression

For each of the following rational expressions, determine the domain.

$$\textbf{(a)}\ \frac{2x}{x+3} \qquad \textbf{(b)}\ \frac{p^2+5p+6}{p^2-4}$$

Solution

(a) We want to find all values of x that cause $x + 3$ to equal 0, so we solve

$$x + 3 = 0$$

Subtract 3 from both sides: $x = -3$

Since -3 causes the denominator, $x + 3$, to equal 0, the domain of $\dfrac{2x}{x+3}$ is $\{x \mid x \neq -3\}$.

(b) We want to find all values of p that cause $p^2 - 4$ to equal 0.

$$p^2 - 4 = 0$$

Factor the difference of two squares: $(p - 2)(p + 2) = 0$

Zero-Product Property: $p - 2 = 0$ or $p + 2 = 0$

$p = 2$ or $p = -2$

The domain of $\dfrac{p^2+5p+6}{p^2-4}$ is $\{p \mid p \neq -2, p \neq 2\}$. ∎

Work Smart

Because we are working with the set of real numbers, the domain of a variable is understood to be all real numbers except those listed. For example, the notation $\{x \mid x \neq -3\}$ means x is any real number except -3.

Preparing for...Answers

P1. $(2x + 3)(x - 7)$ **P2.** $\{-4, 4\}$

P3. $\dfrac{2}{5}$ **P4.** The set of all inputs for which an algebraic expression is defined.

Quick ✔

1. The quotient of two polynomials is called a _____ _____.

2. In the expression $\dfrac{x + 3}{3x - 5}$, we call $x + 3$ the _____, and $3x - 5$ is called the _____.

3. *True or False:* The domain of all rational functions is the set of all real numbers.

In Problems 4 and 5, determine the domain of the rational expression.

4. $\dfrac{x - 4}{x + 6}$

5. $\dfrac{z^2 - 9}{z^2 + 3z - 28}$

2 Simplify Rational Expressions

A rational expression is simplified by completely factoring the numerator and the denominator and dividing out any common factors using the Reduction Property.

$$\frac{ac}{bc} = \frac{a\cancel{c}}{b\cancel{c}} = \frac{a}{b} \qquad \text{if } b \neq 0, c \neq 0$$

We simplify rational expressions in the same way that we write rational numbers in lowest terms. For example, the rational number $\dfrac{12}{20}$ is not written in lowest terms because there is a common factor of 4. We write $\dfrac{12}{20}$ in lowest terms as follows: $\dfrac{12}{20} = \dfrac{4 \cdot 3}{4 \cdot 5} = \dfrac{3}{5}$.

EXAMPLE 2 Simplifying a Rational Expression

Simplify each rational expression:

(a) $\dfrac{x^2 + 2x - 15}{2x^2 - 3x - 9}$

(b) $\dfrac{q^3 - 8}{3q^2 - 6q}$

Solution

(a) Factor the numerator and denominator and divide out common factors using the Reduction Property.

$$\frac{x^2 + 2x - 15}{2x^2 - 3x - 9} = \frac{(x + 5)\cancel{(x - 3)}}{(2x + 3)\cancel{(x - 3)}}$$
$$= \frac{x + 5}{2x + 3} \qquad x \neq -\frac{3}{2}, x \neq 3$$

(b) Factor the numerator and denominator. Then divide out common factors.

$$\frac{q^3 - 8}{3q^2 - 6q} = \frac{\cancel{(q - 2)}(q^2 + 2q + 4)}{3q\cancel{(q - 2)}}$$
$$= \frac{q^2 + 2q + 4}{3q} \qquad q \neq 0, q \neq 2 \qquad ■$$

Work Smart

When we divide out like factors, the quotient is 1. For example,

$$\frac{\cancel{(x + 3)}^{1}}{2x\cancel{(x + 3)}_{1}} = \frac{1}{2x}$$

To keep the original rational expression and the simplified rational expression equivalent, we must restrict from the domain all values of the variable that are not in the domain of the *original* rational expression.

Consider Example 2(a). We include the restriction $x \neq -\dfrac{3}{2}, x \neq 3$ for two reasons:

1. To remind us of the restrictions on the variable x.

2. To keep the rational expressions equal. Without the restriction $x \neq -\dfrac{3}{2}, x \neq 3$, the expression $\dfrac{x^2 + 2x - 15}{2x^2 - 3x - 9}$ is not equal to $\dfrac{x + 5}{2x + 3}$ because in $\dfrac{x^2 + 2x - 15}{2x^2 - 3x - 9}, x$ cannot take on the value 3, while in $\dfrac{x + 5}{2x + 3}, x$ can take on the value 3. By not allowing x to equal 3 in both instances, the expressions remain equal.

The same logic is used to justify the restrictions on q in Example 2**(b)**. For the remainder of the text, we shall not include the restrictions on the variable, but you should be aware that the restrictions are necessary to maintain equality.

Sometimes, we can obtain common factors in the numerator and denominator of a rational expression by factoring -1 out of one of the factors. Consider the expressions $3 - 4x$ and $4x - 3$. If we factor -1 out of $3 - 4x$, we obtain $-1(-3 + 4x)$ or $-1(4x - 3)$ so that we can now divide out the common factor, $4x - 3$.

EXAMPLE 3 Simplifying a Rational Expression

Simplify: $\dfrac{3x^2 + 11x - 4}{1 - 3x}$

Solution

$$\frac{3x^2 + 11x - 4}{1 - 3x} = \frac{(3x - 1)(x + 4)}{1 - 3x}$$

Factor -1 from $1 - 3x$; Divide out common factors: $\quad = \dfrac{\cancel{(3x - 1)}(x + 4)}{-1\cancel{(3x - 1)}}$

$$= \frac{(x + 4)}{-1}$$

$\dfrac{a}{-1} = -a$: $\quad = -(x + 4)$ ∎

Work Smart

A common error for students to make is to divide out terms rather than dividing out factors. **When simplifying, we can only divide out common factors, not common terms!**

WRONG! $\dfrac{x + 1}{x} = \dfrac{\cancel{x} + 1}{\cancel{x}} = 1$ WRONG! $\dfrac{x^2 + x + 2}{x + 2} = \dfrac{x^2 + \cancel{x} + \cancel{2}}{\cancel{x} + \cancel{2}} = x^2$

If you aren't quite sure whether you can simplify, try the computation with actual numbers and see if it works. For example, does $\dfrac{4}{3} = \dfrac{3 + 1}{3} = \dfrac{\cancel{3} + 1}{\cancel{3}} = 1$? NO! So, $\dfrac{x + 1}{x} \neq 1$.

Quick ✔

6. *True or False:* $\dfrac{x^2 + 3x + 5}{x^2 + 7} = \dfrac{3x + 5}{7}$

In Problems 7–9, simplify each rational expression.

7. $\dfrac{x^2 - 7x + 12}{x^2 + 4x - 21}$ **8.** $\dfrac{z^3 - 64}{2z^2 - 3z - 20}$ **9.** $\dfrac{3w^2 + 13w - 10}{2 - 3w}$

3 Multiply Rational Expressions

We show how to multiply rational expressions in the next example.

EXAMPLE 4 How to Multiply Rational Expressions

Multiply $\dfrac{x^2 + 2x - 15}{x + 1} \cdot \dfrac{x^2 + 7x}{x^2 + 4x - 21}$. Simplify the product.

Step-by-Step Solution

Step 1: Completely factor each polynomial in the numerator and denominator.	$\dfrac{x^2 + 2x - 15}{x + 1} \cdot \dfrac{x^2 + 7x}{x^2 + 4x - 21} = \dfrac{(x + 5)(x - 3)}{x + 1} \cdot \dfrac{x(x + 7)}{(x + 7)(x - 3)}$
Step 2: Multiply.	$= \dfrac{(x + 5)(x - 3) \cdot x(x + 7)}{(x + 1) \cdot (x + 7)(x - 3)}$

Step 3: Divide out common factors in the numerator and denominator.

$$= \frac{(x + 5)\cancel{(x - 3)}x\cancel{(x + 7)}}{(x + 1)\cancel{(x + 7)}\cancel{(x - 3)}}$$

$$= \frac{x(x + 5)}{x + 1}$$

The steps for multiplying rational expressions are the same as the steps for multiplying rational numbers.

MULTIPLYING RATIONAL EXPRESSIONS

Step 1: Completely factor each polynomial in the numerator and denominator.

Step 2: Use the fact that if $\dfrac{a}{b}$ and $\dfrac{c}{d}$, $b \neq 0$, $d \neq 0$, are two rational expressions, then

$$\frac{a}{b} \cdot \frac{c}{d} = \frac{ac}{bd}.$$

Step 3: Divide out common factors in the numerator and denominator.

When using the steps given above, always leave your answer in factored form because the factored form is required when solving rational equations (Section 5.4) and rational inequalities (Section 5.5).

Quick ✔ *In Problem 10, multiply and simplify the rational expressions.*

10. $\dfrac{p^2 - 9}{p^2 + 5p + 6} \cdot \dfrac{3p^2 - p - 2}{2p - 6}$

EXAMPLE 5 Multiplying Rational Expressions

Multiply and simplify each of the following rational expressions.

(a) $\dfrac{y^2 + 2y + 1}{3y^2 + y - 2} \cdot \dfrac{2 - 3y}{y^2 + 5y + 4}$

(b) $\dfrac{p^2 + 5pq + 6q^2}{2p^2 + 7pq + 3q^2} \cdot \dfrac{2p + q}{3p + 6q}$

Solution

(a)

Factor the numerator and denominator

$$\dfrac{y^2 + 2y + 1}{3y^2 + y - 2} \cdot \dfrac{2 - 3y}{y^2 + 5y + 4} = \dfrac{(y + 1)(y + 1)}{(3y - 2)(y + 1)} \cdot \dfrac{-1(3y - 2)}{(y + 4)(y + 1)}$$

Multiply: $= \dfrac{(y + 1)(y + 1)(-1)(3y - 2)}{(3y - 2)(y + 1)(y + 4)(y + 1)}$

Divide out common factors: $= \dfrac{\cancel{(y + 1)}\cancel{(y + 1)}(-1)\cancel{(3y - 2)}}{\cancel{(3y - 2)}\cancel{(y + 1)}(y + 4)\cancel{(y + 1)}}$

$$= -\dfrac{1}{y + 4}$$

Work Smart: Study Skills

It is a good idea to use a different symbol for each factor that divides out. Or use colored pencils to highlight the like factors that divide out.

(b)

Factor the numerator and denominator

$$\dfrac{p^2 + 5pq + 6q^2}{2p^2 + 7pq + 3q^2} \cdot \dfrac{2p + q}{3p + 6q} = \dfrac{(p + 2q)(p + 3q)}{(2p + q)(p + 3q)} \cdot \dfrac{2p + q}{3(p + 2q)}$$

Multiply: $= \dfrac{(p + 2q)(p + 3q)(2p + q)}{(2p + q)(p + 3q)(3)(p + 2q)}$

Divide out common factors: $= \dfrac{\cancel{(p + 2q)}\cancel{(p + 3q)}\cancel{(2p + q)}}{\cancel{(2p + q)}\cancel{(p + 3q)}(3)\cancel{(p + 2q)}}$

$$= \dfrac{1}{3}$$

Work Smart:

Did you notice in Example 5(b) that all the factors in the numerator divide out? This means that a factor of 1 remains in the numerator, not 0!

Quick ✔ *In Problems 11 and 12, multiply and simplify the rational expressions.*

11. $\dfrac{2x+8}{2x^2+11x+12} \cdot \dfrac{2x^2-3x-9}{6-2x}$

12. $\dfrac{m^2+2mn+n^2}{2m^2+3mn+n^2} \cdot \dfrac{2m^2-5mn-3n^2}{3n-m}$

4 Divide Rational Expressions

The rule for dividing rational expressions is the same as the rule for dividing rational numbers.

In Words

To divide two rational expressions, multiply the rational expression in the numerator by the reciprocal of the rational expression in the denominator.

DIVIDING RATIONAL EXPRESSIONS

To divide rational expressions, use the fact that if $\dfrac{a}{b}$ and $\dfrac{c}{d}$, $b \neq 0, c \neq 0, d \neq 0$,

are two rational expressions, then $\dfrac{\dfrac{a}{b}}{\dfrac{c}{d}} = \dfrac{a}{b} \cdot \dfrac{d}{c}$. Then follow the steps for multiplying two rational expressions.

EXAMPLE 6 Dividing Rational Expressions

Divide each of the following rational expressions. Simplify the quotient, if possible.

(a) $\dfrac{\dfrac{20x^5}{3y}}{\dfrac{4x^2}{15y^5}}$

(b) $\dfrac{\dfrac{x^2-4x-12}{4x^3-6x^2}}{\dfrac{x^3+8}{2x^3-4x^2+8x}}$

Solution

For parts **(a)** and **(b)**, rewrite the division problem as a multiplication problem by multiplying the numerator by the reciprocal of the denominator.

Work Smart

When you see $\dfrac{\dfrac{20x^5}{3y}}{\dfrac{4x^2}{15y^5}}$, you may find

it helpful to think

$\dfrac{20x^5}{3y} \div \dfrac{4x^2}{15y^5}$

(a) $\dfrac{\dfrac{20x^5}{3y}}{\dfrac{4x^2}{15y^5}} = \dfrac{20x^5}{3y} \cdot \dfrac{15y^5}{4x^2}$

Multiply: $= \dfrac{20 \cdot 15 \cdot x^5 \cdot y^5}{3 \cdot 4 \cdot y \cdot x^2}$

Divide out like factors: $= \dfrac{\overset{5}{\cancel{20}} \cdot \overset{5}{\cancel{15}}}{\underset{1}{\cancel{3}} \cdot \underset{1}{\cancel{4}}} x^{5-2} y^{5-1}$

Simplify: $= 25x^3 y^4$

(b) $\dfrac{\dfrac{x^2-4x-12}{4x^3-6x^2}}{\dfrac{x^3+8}{2x^3-4x^2+8x}} = \dfrac{x^2-4x-12}{4x^3-6x^2} \cdot \dfrac{2x^3-4x^2+8x}{x^3+8}$

Factor the numerator and denominator: $= \dfrac{(x-6)(x+2)}{2x^2(2x-3)} \cdot \dfrac{2x(x^2-2x+4)}{(x+2)(x^2-2x+4)}$

Multiply; divide out common factors: $= \dfrac{(x-6)\cancel{(x+2)} \cdot \cancel{2x}\,\cancel{(x^2-2x+4)}}{\cancel{2}x^{\cancel{2}}(2x-3) \cdot \cancel{(x+2)}\,\cancel{(x^2-2x+4)}}$

Simplify: $= \dfrac{x-6}{x(2x-3)}$ ∎

Quick ✔ *In Problems 13 and 14, divide the rational expressions. Simplify the quotient, if possible.*

13. $\dfrac{\dfrac{12a^4}{5b^2}}{\dfrac{4a^2}{15b^5}}$

14. $\dfrac{\dfrac{m^2 - 5m}{m - 7}}{\dfrac{2m}{m^2 - 6m - 7}}$

5 Work with Rational Functions

Ratios of integers, such as $\dfrac{3}{5}$, are called *rational numbers* and ratios of polynomial expressions are called *rational expressions*. Similarly, ratios of polynomial functions are called *rational functions*.

DEFINITION

A **rational function** is a function of the form

$$R(x) = \frac{p(x)}{q(x)}$$

where p and q are polynomial functions and q is not the zero polynomial. The domain consists of all real numbers except those for which the denominator q is 0.

We want to find the domain of a rational function because the behavior of the graph of a rational function is quite interesting near values excluded from the domain. See Problem 97 for a preview.

EXAMPLE 7 Finding the Domain of a Rational Function

Find the domain of $R(x) = \dfrac{x + 2}{x^2 - 5x - 14}$.

Solution

The domain is the set of all real numbers such that the denominator, $x^2 - 5x - 14$, does not equal zero. We will find the values of x such that $x^2 - 5x - 14 = 0$ and exclude these values from the domain.

$$x^2 - 5x - 14 = 0$$

Factor: $(x - 7)(x + 2) = 0$

Set each factor to 0: $x - 7 = 0$ or $x + 2 = 0$

Solve: $x = 7$ or $x = -2$

The values $x = 7$ and $x = -2$ cause the denominator to equal 0, so the domain of R is $\{x | x \neq 7, x \neq -2\}$.   ■

Quick ✔ *In Problem 15, find the domain of the rational function.*

15. $R(x) = \dfrac{2x}{x^2 + x - 30}$

We can multiply and divide rational functions just as we multiplied and divided polynomial functions. The domain of the product or quotient of two rational functions is the set of all numbers that are in the domains of the functions being multiplied or divided. In addition, for $R(x) = \dfrac{f(x)}{g(x)}$, we exclude values of x such that $g(x) = 0$.

EXAMPLE 8 Multiplying and Dividing Rational Functions

Given that $f(x) = \dfrac{x^2 - 4}{3x^2 + 9x}$, $g(x) = \dfrac{x + 3}{x^2 - 2x - 8}$, and

$h(x) = \dfrac{2x^2 + 7x + 6}{x^2 + 5x}$, find

(a) $R(x) = f(x) \cdot g(x)$ 　　　　(b) $P(x) = \dfrac{f(x)}{h(x)}$

and state the domain of each function.

Solution

(a) $\qquad R(x) = f(x) \cdot g(x) = \dfrac{x^2 - 4}{3x^2 + 9x} \cdot \dfrac{x + 3}{x^2 - 2x - 8}$

Factor the numerator
and denominator: $\qquad = \dfrac{(x + 2)(x - 2)}{3x(x + 3)} \cdot \dfrac{x + 3}{(x - 4)(x + 2)}$

Multiply; divide out common factors: $\qquad = \dfrac{\cancel{(x + 2)}(x - 2)\cancel{(x + 3)}}{3x\cancel{(x + 3)}(x - 4)\cancel{(x + 2)}}$

Simplify: $\qquad = \dfrac{x - 2}{3x(x - 4)}$

The domain of $f(x)$ is $\{x \mid x \neq -3, x \neq 0\}$. The domain of $g(x)$ is $\{x \mid x \neq -2, x \neq 4\}$. Therefore, the domain of $R(x)$ is $\{x \mid x \neq -3, x \neq -2, x \neq 0, x \neq 4\}$.

(b) $\qquad P(x) = \dfrac{f(x)}{h(x)} = \dfrac{\dfrac{x^2 - 4}{3x^2 + 9x}}{\dfrac{2x^2 + 7x + 6}{x^2 + 5x}}$

$\qquad = \dfrac{x^2 - 4}{3x^2 + 9x} \cdot \dfrac{x^2 + 5x}{2x^2 + 7x + 6}$

Factor the numerator
and denominator: $\qquad = \dfrac{(x - 2)(x + 2)}{3x(x + 3)} \cdot \dfrac{x(x + 5)}{(2x + 3)(x + 2)}$

Multiply; divide out common factors: $\qquad = \dfrac{(x - 2)\cancel{(x + 2)}\,\cancel{x}(x + 5)}{3\cancel{x}(x + 3)(2x + 3)\cancel{(x + 2)}}$

Simplify: $\qquad = \dfrac{(x - 2)(x + 5)}{3(x + 3)(2x + 3)}$

Work Smart

In Example 8(b), $3x^2 + 9x$ cannot equal 0. Why? In addition, $2x^2 + 7x + 6$ cannot equal 0. Why? And $x^2 + 5x$ cannot equal 0. Why?

The domain of $f(x)$ is $\{x \mid x \neq -3, x \neq 0\}$. The domain of $h(x)$ is $\{x \mid x \neq -5, x \neq 0\}$. Because the denominator of $P(x)$ cannot equal 0, we must exclude those values of x such that $2x^2 + 7x + 6 = 0$. These values are $x = -2$ and $x = -\dfrac{3}{2}$. Therefore, the domain of $H(x)$ is

$\{x \mid x \neq -5, x \neq -3, x \neq -2, x \neq -\dfrac{3}{2}, x \neq 0\}$. ■

Quick ✔

16. Given that $f(x) = \dfrac{x^2 - 4x - 5}{3x - 5}$, $g(x) = \dfrac{3x^2 + 4x - 15}{x^2 - 2x - 15}$, and

$h(x) = \dfrac{4x^2 + 7x + 3}{9x^2 - 15x}$, find

(a) $R(x) = f(x) \cdot g(x)$ 　　(b) $H(x) = \dfrac{f(x)}{h(x)}$

and state the domain of each function.

5.1 EXERCISES

1–16. *are the* **Quick ✔s** *that follow each* **EXAMPLE**

Building Skills

In Problems 17–26, state the domain of each rational expression. See Objective 1.

17. $\dfrac{3}{x + 5}$

18. $\dfrac{4}{x - 7}$

19. $\dfrac{x - 1}{x^2 - 6x - 16}$

20. $\dfrac{2x + 1}{x^2 + 4x - 45}$

21. $\dfrac{p^2 - 4}{2p^2 + p - 10}$

22. $\dfrac{m^2 + 5m + 6}{3m^2 + 4m - 4}$

23. $\dfrac{x + 1}{x^2 + 1}$

24. $\dfrac{x - 2}{x^2 + 4}$

25. $\dfrac{3x - 2}{(x - 1)^2}$

26. $\dfrac{x + 5}{x^2 + 8x + 16}$

In Problems 27–46, simplify each rational expression. See Objective 2.

27. $\dfrac{2x + 8}{x^2 - 16}$

28. $\dfrac{x^2 - 3x}{x^2 - 9}$

29. $\dfrac{p^2 + 4p + 3}{p + 1}$

30. $\dfrac{a^2 - 2a - 24}{a + 4}$

31. $\dfrac{5x + 25}{x^3 + 5x^2}$

32. $\dfrac{6x - 42}{x^3 - 7x^2}$

33. $\dfrac{q^2 - 3q - 18}{q^2 - 8q + 12}$

34. $\dfrac{w^2 + 5w - 14}{w^2 + 6w - 16}$

35. $\dfrac{2y^2 - 3y - 20}{2y^2 + 15y + 25}$

36. $\dfrac{3n^2 + n - 2}{3n^2 - 20n + 12}$

37. $\dfrac{9 - x^2}{x^2 + 2x - 15}$

38. $\dfrac{25 - k^2}{k^2 + 2k - 35}$

39. $\dfrac{x^3 + 2x^2 - 8x}{2x^4 - 32x^2}$

40. $\dfrac{2z^2 - 10z - 28}{4z^3 - 32z^2 + 28z}$

41. $\dfrac{x^2 - xy - 6y^2}{x^2 - 4y^2}$

42. $\dfrac{a^2 + 5ab + 4b^2}{a^2 + 8ab + 16b^2}$

43. $\dfrac{x^3 - 5x^2 + 3x - 15}{x^2 - 10x + 25}$

44. $\dfrac{v^3 + 3v^2 - 5v - 15}{v^2 + 6v + 9}$

45. $\dfrac{x^3 + 8}{x^2 - 5x - 14}$

46. $\dfrac{27q^3 + 1}{6q^2 - 7q - 3}$

In Problems 47–58, multiply and simplify each rational expression. See Objective 3.

47. $\dfrac{3x}{x^2 - x - 12} \cdot \dfrac{x - 4}{12x^2}$

48. $\dfrac{5x^2}{x + 3} \cdot \dfrac{x^2 + 7x + 12}{20x}$

49. $\dfrac{2x^2 - x - 6}{x^2 + 3x - 4} \cdot \dfrac{x^2 - x - 20}{2x^2 - 7x - 15}$

50. $\dfrac{3x^2 + 14x - 5}{x^2 + x - 30} \cdot \dfrac{x^2 - 2x - 15}{3x^2 + 8x - 3}$

51. $\dfrac{x^2 - 9}{x^2 - 25} \cdot \dfrac{x^2 - 2x - 15}{x^2 + 4x - 21}$

52. $\dfrac{p^2 - 16}{p^2 - 25} \cdot \dfrac{p^2 + 2p - 24}{p^2 + 3p - 4}$

53. $\dfrac{2q^2 - 5q - 3}{3q^2 + 19q + 6} \cdot \dfrac{3q^2 + 7q + 2}{3 - q}$

54. $\dfrac{2y^2 - 5y - 12}{2y^2 - y - 6} \cdot \dfrac{4y^2 - 5y - 6}{4 - y}$

55. $\dfrac{x^2 - 5x + 6}{x^2 + 2x - 8} \cdot (x + 4)$

56. $\dfrac{p^2 - 4p - 5}{p^2 - 5p - 6} \cdot (p - 6)$

57. $\dfrac{m^2 - n^2}{5m - 5n} \cdot \dfrac{10m + 5n}{2m^2 + 3mn + n^2}$

58. $\dfrac{a^2 + 2ab + b^2}{3a + 3b} \cdot \dfrac{b - a}{a^2 - b^2}$

In Problems 59–66, divide each rational expression. Simplify the quotient, if possible. See Objective 4.

59. $\dfrac{\dfrac{x + 3}{2x - 8}}{\dfrac{4x}{9}}$

60. $\dfrac{\dfrac{x - 2}{3x}}{\dfrac{5x - 10}{x}}$

61. $\dfrac{\dfrac{4a}{b^2}}{\dfrac{2a^2}{b}}$

62. $\dfrac{\dfrac{9m^3}{2n^2}}{\dfrac{3m}{8n^4}}$

63. $\dfrac{\dfrac{p^2 - 4p - 5}{2p^2 - 3p - 2}}{\dfrac{p^2 + p}{p^2 + p - 6}}$

64. $\dfrac{\dfrac{y^2 - 9}{2y^2 - y - 15}}{\dfrac{3y^2 + 10y + 3}{2y^2 + y - 10}}$

65. $\dfrac{\dfrac{x^3 - 1}{x^2 - 1}}{\dfrac{3x^2 + 3x + 3}{x^2 + 3x + 1}}$

66. $\dfrac{\dfrac{8x^3 + 1}{2x}}{\dfrac{x^3 + 2x^2 - 15x}{2x^2 - 5x - 3}}$

In Problems 67–76, determine the domain of each rational function. See Objective 5.

67. $R(x) = \dfrac{2}{x - 1}$

68. $R(x) = \dfrac{5}{x + 3}$

69. $R(x) = \dfrac{x - 2}{(2x + 1)(x - 4)}$

70. $R(x) = \dfrac{3x + 2}{(4x - 1)(x + 5)}$

71. $R(x) = \dfrac{x + 9}{x^2 + 6x + 5}$

72. $R(x) = \dfrac{5x - 2}{x^2 - 6x - 16}$

73. $R(x) = \dfrac{x - 2}{2x^2 - 9x + 10}$

74. $R(x) = \dfrac{x + 3}{3x^2 + 7x - 6}$

75. $R(x) = \dfrac{x - 1}{x^2 + 1}$

76. $R(x) = \dfrac{4x}{4x^2 + 1}$

For Problems 77–80, see Objective 5.

77. If $f(x) = \dfrac{x^2 - 2x - 15}{x + 6}$, $g(x) = \dfrac{x^2 + 5x - 6}{2x^2 - 7x - 15}$, and $h(x) = \dfrac{x + 3}{3x^2 + 17x - 6}$, find **(a)** $R(x) = f(x) \cdot g(x)$ and state its domain **(b)** $R(x) = \dfrac{f(x)}{h(x)}$ and state its domain.

78. If $f(x) = \dfrac{x^2 - 7x - 8}{2x - 5}$, $g(x) = \dfrac{2x^2 + 3x - 20}{x^2 - 10x + 16}$, and $h(x) = \dfrac{x^2 - 3x - 40}{x + 9}$, find **(a)** $R(x) = f(x) \cdot g(x)$ and state its domain **(b)** $R(x) = \dfrac{f(x)}{h(x)}$ and state its domain.

79. If $f(x) = \dfrac{3x^2 - x - 10}{x^3 - 1}$, $g(x) = \dfrac{x^2 + 5x - 6}{2x^2 + 3x - 14}$, and $h(x) = \dfrac{3x^2 + 8x + 5}{x^2 - 1}$, find **(a)** $R(x) = (f \cdot g)(x)$ and state its domain **(b)** $R(x) = \left(\dfrac{f}{h}\right)(x)$ and state its domain.

80. If $f(x) = \dfrac{4x^2 - 9x - 9}{x^3 - 8}$, $g(x) = \dfrac{x^2 + 7x - 18}{5x^2 - 14x - 3}$, and $h(x) = \dfrac{x^2 - 6x + 9}{x^2 - 4}$, find **(a)** $R(x) = (f \cdot g)(x)$ and state its domain **(b)** $R(x) = \left(\dfrac{f}{h}\right)(x)$ and state its domain.

Mixed Practice

In Problems 81–88, multiply or divide each rational expression, as indicated. Simplify the product or quotient, if possible.

81. $\dfrac{z^3 + 8}{z^2 - 3z - 10} \cdot \dfrac{z^2 - 2z - 15}{2z^2 - 4z + 8}$

82. $\dfrac{x^3 - 27}{2x^2 + 5x - 25} \cdot \dfrac{x^2 + 2x - 15}{x^3 + 3x^2 + 9x}$

83. $\dfrac{\dfrac{m^2 - 4n^2}{m^3 - n^3}}{\dfrac{2m + 4n}{m^2 + mn + n^2}}$

84. $\dfrac{\dfrac{x^2 + 2xy + y^2}{x^2 + 3xy + 2y^2}}{\dfrac{x^2 - y^2}{x + 2y}}$

85. $\dfrac{4w + 8}{w^2 - 4w} \cdot \dfrac{w^2 - 3w - 4}{w^2 + 3w + 2}$

86. $\dfrac{5m - 5}{m^2 + 6m} \cdot \dfrac{m^2 + 2m - 24}{m^2 + 3m - 4}$

87. $\dfrac{\dfrac{2x - 6}{x^2 + x}}{\dfrac{x^2 - 4x + 3}{x^2}} \cdot \dfrac{x^2 + 3x + 2}{x^2 + x}$

88. $\dfrac{\dfrac{3x + 15}{2x + 4}}{\dfrac{x + 5}{x^2 - 4}} \cdot \dfrac{4x + 8}{3x^2 - 12}$

Applying the Concepts

89. Make up a rational expression that is undefined at $x = 3$.

90. Make up a rational expression that is undefined at $x = -2$.

91. Make up a rational expression that is undefined at $x = -4$ and at $x = 5$.

92. Make up a rational expression that is undefined at $x = -6$ and at $x = 0$.

93. Develop a rational function R that is undefined at $x = -2$ and at $x = 1$ such that $R(-3) = 1$.

94. Develop a rational function R that is undefined at $x = -4$ and at $x = 3$ such that $R(4) = 1$.

95. Gravity In physics, it is established that the acceleration due to gravity g (in meters per second^2) at a height h meters above sea level is given by

$$g(h) = \frac{3.99 \times 10^{14}}{(6.374 \times 10^6 + h)^2}$$

where 6.374×10^6 is the radius of Earth in meters.

(a) What is the acceleration due to gravity at sea level?

(b) What is the acceleration due to gravity in Denver, Colorado, elevation 1600 meters?

(c) What is the acceleration due to gravity on the peak of Mount Everest, elevation 8848 meters?

96. Economics The Gross Domestic Product (GDP) is the total value of all goods and services manufactured within the United States. A model for determining the change in GDP of a government spending plan is given by the function

$$G(s) = \frac{s}{1 - b}$$

where G is the change in Gross Domestic Product, s is the amount spent by the government, and b is the marginal propensity to consume with $0 < b < 1$. The marginal propensity to consume can be thought of as the amount an individual would spend for each additional dollar of income earned. For example, if $b = 0.9$, then individuals will spend $0.90 for each additional dollar earned. If $b = 0.95$, then individuals will spend $0.95 for each additional dollar earned.

(a) Suppose the government spends $100 million on highway infrastructure and the marginal propensity to consume in the United States is $b = 0.9$. What will be the change in GDP?

(b) Suppose the government spends $100 million on highway infrastructure and the marginal propensity to consume in the United States is $b = 0.95$. What will be the change in GDP?

Extending the Concepts

97. Math for the Future Consider the function

$$f(x) = \frac{1}{x - 2}$$

(a) Determine the domain of f.

(b) Fill in the following table. What happens to the values of f as x approaches 2, but remains greater than 2?

x	3	2.5	2.1	2.01	2.001	2.0001
$f(x)$						

(c) Fill in the following table. What happens to the values of f as x approaches 2, but remains less than 2?

x	1	1.5	1.9	1.99	1.999	1.9999
$f(x)$						

(d) Below is the graph of $f(x) = \frac{1}{x - 2}$. What happens to the graph of the function as x approaches 2 for values of x larger than 2? What happens to the graph of the function as x approaches 2 for values of x smaller than 2? Compare your results to the results obtained in parts **(b)** and **(c)**.

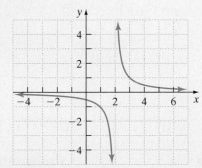

98. Math for the Future Consider the function

$$R(x) = \frac{2x + 1}{x - 2}$$

(a) Fill in the following table. What happens to the values of R as x gets larger in the positive direction?

x	5	10	50	100	1000
$R(x)$					

(b) Fill in the following table. What happens to the values of R as x gets larger in the negative direction?

x	-5	-10	-50	-100	-1000
$R(x)$					

(c) What is the term of highest degree in the numerator? What is the term of highest degree in the denominator? What is the ratio of the coefficients on the terms of highest degree in the numerator and denominator? Compare this result to your results in parts **(a)** and **(b)**.

(d) Below is the graph of $R(x) = \dfrac{2x + 1}{x - 2}$. What happens to the graph of the function as x gets larger? That is, what happens to the graph of the function as x approaches ∞? What happens to the graph of the function as x gets smaller? That is, what happens to the graph of the function as x approaches $-\infty$? Compare your results to the results obtained in parts **(b)** and **(c)**.

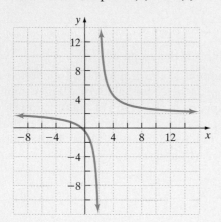

99. Write $\dfrac{x^{-1}}{x + 1}$ as a rational expression.

Explaining the Concepts

100. Define rational expression. Explain how a rational expression is related to a rational number.

101. What does it mean when we say that a rational expression is simplified?

102. Explain why we can only divide out common factors, not common terms.

103. Why is $\dfrac{\sqrt{x}}{x + 1}$ not a rational expression?

104. What is the difference between $f(x) = \dfrac{x^2 - 3x + 2}{x - 1}$ and $g(x) = x - 2$?

Synthesis Review

In Problems 105–110, graph each function.

105. $f(x) = 2x - 3$

106. $g(x) = 3x - 6$

107. $F(x) = -4x + 8$

108. $G(x) = -5x + 10$

109. $h(x) = x^2 - 4$

110. $H(x) = -x^2 + 4$

111. Discuss the methods that you used to graph each function. What methods were the same? What was different?

5.2 Adding and Subtracting Rational Expressions

OBJECTIVES

1. Add or Subtract Rational Expressions with a Common Denominator

2. Find the Least Common Denominator of Two or More Rational Expressions

3. Add or Subtract Rational Expressions with Different Denominators

Preparing for... Answers **P1.** $-\dfrac{11}{24}$

P2. (a) -5 **(b)** $-(x - 2)$ or $2 - x$

Preparing for Adding and Subtracting Rational Expressions

Before getting started, take the following readiness quiz. If you get a problem wrong, go back to the section cited and review the material.

P1. Evaluate: $\dfrac{1}{6} - \dfrac{5}{8}$ [Getting Ready, pp. 407–409]

P2. Determine the additive inverse of **(a)** 5 **(b)** $x - 2$ [Section R.3, p. 21]

In Section 5.1, we learned how to multiply and divide rational expressions. We now learn to add and subtract rational expressions.

1 Add or Subtract Rational Expressions with a Common Denominator

Let's go over an example that illustrates how to add or subtract rational expressions that have a common denominator.

EXAMPLE 1   How to Add or Subtract Rational Expressions

Perform the indicated operation.

(a) $\dfrac{x^2 - 3x + 6}{x + 3} + \dfrac{7x - 3}{x + 3},\ x \neq -3$

(b) $\dfrac{3x - 5}{x + 1} - \dfrac{x + 3}{x + 1},\ x \neq -1$

Step-by-Step Solution

(a) $\dfrac{x^2 - 3x + 6}{x + 3} + \dfrac{7x - 3}{x + 3},\ x \neq -3$. Notice that the rational expressions have a common denominator, $x + 3$.

Step 1: Add the numerators and write the result over the common denominator.	$\dfrac{x^2 - 3x + 6}{x + 3} + \dfrac{7x - 3}{x + 3} = \dfrac{x^2 - 3x + 6 + (7x - 3)}{x + 3}$
	Combine like terms in the numerator: $= \dfrac{x^2 + 4x + 3}{x + 3}$
Step 2: Simplify the rational expression.	Factor the numerator: $= \dfrac{(x + 3)(x + 1)}{x + 3}$
	Divide out like factors: $= x + 1$

(b) $\dfrac{3x - 5}{x + 1} - \dfrac{x + 3}{x + 1},\ x \neq -1$. The rational expressions have a common denominator, $x + 1$.

Step 1: Subtract the numerators and write the result over the common denominator.	$\dfrac{3x - 5}{x + 1} - \dfrac{x + 3}{x + 1} = \dfrac{3x - 5 - (x + 3)}{x + 1}$
	Distribute the -1: $= \dfrac{3x - 5 - x - 3}{x + 1}$
	Combine like terms in the numerator: $= \dfrac{2x - 8}{x + 1}$
Step 2: Simplify the rational expression.	Factor out the common factor: $= \dfrac{2(x - 4)}{x + 1}$

■

The rules for adding and subtracting rational expressions are the same as the rules for adding and subtracting rational numbers.

In Words

To add or subtract rational expressions with the same denominator, we add or subtract the numerators and write the result over the common denominator.

ADDING OR SUBTRACTING RATIONAL EXPRESSIONS

Step 1: If $\dfrac{a}{c}$ and $\dfrac{b}{c}$, $c \neq 0$, are two rational expressions, then $\dfrac{a}{c} + \dfrac{b}{c} = \dfrac{a + b}{c}$ and

$\dfrac{a}{c} - \dfrac{b}{c} = \dfrac{a - b}{c}$.

Step 2: Simplify the result.

Quick ✔ *In Problems 1 and 2, perform the indicated operation. Be sure to simplify the result.*

1. $\dfrac{x^2 - 3x - 1}{x - 2} + \dfrac{x^2 - 2x + 3}{x - 2}$

2. $\dfrac{4x + 3}{x + 5} - \dfrac{x - 6}{x + 5}$

EXAMPLE 2 Adding Rational Expressions with Denominators That Are Additive Inverses

Perform the indicated operation and simplify the result.

$$\frac{3x}{x-2} + \frac{2}{2-x}, x \neq 2$$

Solution

Although the denominators of the two rational expressions are different, we should notice that

$$2 - x = -x + 2 = -1(x - 2)$$

So

$$\frac{3x}{x-2} + \frac{2}{2-x} = \frac{3x}{x-2} + \frac{2}{-1(x-2)}$$

$$\text{Use } \frac{a}{-b} = \frac{-a}{b}: = \frac{3x}{x-2} + \frac{-2}{x-2}$$

$$= \frac{3x-2}{x-2}$$

∎

Quick ✔ *In Problem 3, perform the indicated operation. Be sure to simplify the result.*

3. $\dfrac{4x}{x-5} + \dfrac{3}{5-x}$

⎡2⎤ Find the Least Common Denominator of Two or More Rational Expressions

What if the denominators of the rational expressions to be added or subtracted are not the same? In this case, we must rewrite each rational expression over a *least common denominator*. The **least common denominator (LCD)** is the smallest polynomial that is a multiple of each denominator in the rational expressions to be added or subtracted. The idea is exactly the same as that used to add rational numbers that do not have common denominators. In fact, it would be a great idea to refer back to Example 4 on page 408 in Getting Ready for Chapter 5 prior to reading Example 3.

EXAMPLE 3 How to Find the Least Common Denominator

Find the least common denominator of each expression.

(a) $\dfrac{4}{3x^2y^2}$ and $\dfrac{5}{6xy^3}$ **(b)** $\dfrac{x-1}{x^2+4x+3}$ and $\dfrac{3x-5}{x^3+2x^2+x}$

Step-by-Step Solution

(a) $\dfrac{4}{3x^2y^2}$ and $\dfrac{5}{6xy^3}$

Step 1: *Factor each denominator.* $3x^2y^2$ is factored completely.
$6xy^3 = 2 \cdot 3 \cdot xy^3$

Step 2: List the factors that are common to all denominators. Then list the uncommon factors.

We look at each factor in the list from Step 1.
- 3 is common to each denominator, so it is part of the LCD.
- We list x^2 as part of the LCD because 2 is the highest exponent on the factor x.
- We list y^3 as part of the LCD because 3 is the highest exponent on the factor y.
- The factor that is not common is 2, so it is also part of the LCD.

$$LCD = 2 \cdot 3 \cdot x^2 \cdot y^3$$
$$= 6x^2y^3$$

(b) $\dfrac{x - 1}{x^2 + 4x + 3}$ and $\dfrac{3x - 5}{x^3 + 2x^2 + x}$

Step 1: Factor each denominator.

$$x^2 + 4x + 3 = (x + 3)(x + 1)$$
$$x^3 + 2x^2 + x = x(x^2 + 2x + 1)$$
$$= x(x + 1)^2$$

Step 2: List the factors that are common to all denominators. Then list the uncommon factors.

- We list $(x + 1)^2$ as part of the LCD because 2 is the highest exponent on the common factor $x + 1$.
- The factors that are not common are x and $x + 3$, so they are also part of the LCD.

$$LCD = x(x + 3)(x + 1)^2$$

FINDING THE LEAST COMMON DENOMINATOR

Step 1: Factor each denominator completely. When factoring, write the factored form using powers. For example, write $x^2 + 4x + 4$ as $(x + 2)^2$.

Step 2: List the common factors. If factors are common except for their power, then list the factor with the highest power. Then list the factors that are not common.

Quick ✔

4. The _____ _____ _____ is the smallest polynomial that is a multiple of each denominator in the rational expressions to be added or subtracted.

In Problems 5 and 6, find the least common denominator of each expression.

5. $\dfrac{5}{8x^2y}$ and $\dfrac{1}{12xy^3}$

6. $\dfrac{4x - 3}{x^2 - 5x - 14}$ and $\dfrac{x + 1}{x^2 + 4x + 4}$

⎡3⎤ Add or Subtract Rational Expressions with Different Denominators

Now that we know how to obtain the least common denominator, we can discuss how to add or subtract rational expressions that have unlike denominators.

EXAMPLE 4 How to Add Rational Expressions with Unlike Denominators

Add $\dfrac{3}{8x^2} + \dfrac{1}{12x}$. Simplify the result.

Step-by-Step Solution

Step 1: Find the least common denominator.	$8x^2 = 4 \cdot 2 \quad \cdot x^2$ $12x = 4 \quad \cdot 3 \cdot x$ The LCD is $4 \cdot 2 \cdot 3 \cdot x^2 = 24x^2$.
Step 2: Rewrite each rational expression with the common denominator.	We look at each rational expression in the expression to be added to determine what is "missing" from the denominator that is in the LCD. We then multiply the rational expression by a "disguised" 1 to create an equivalent rational expression with the LCD. For example, in the rational expression $\dfrac{3}{8x^2}$, we need the denominator to be $24x^2$. This can be accomplished by multiplying the denominator by 3. But, whatever we do to the denominator, we must also do to the numerator. Therefore, we also multiply the numerator by 3. Our "disguised" 1 is $\dfrac{3}{3}$. Similarly, we multiply $\dfrac{1}{12x}$ by $\dfrac{2x}{2x}$. Do you see why? $\dfrac{3}{8x^2} = \dfrac{3}{8x^2} \cdot \dfrac{3}{3} = \dfrac{9}{24x^2}$ $\dfrac{1}{12x} = \dfrac{1}{12x} \cdot \dfrac{2x}{2x} = \dfrac{2x}{24x^2}$
Step 3: Add the rational expressions found in Step 2.	$\dfrac{3}{8x^2} + \dfrac{1}{12x} = \dfrac{9}{24x^2} + \dfrac{2x}{24x^2}$ $\dfrac{a}{c} + \dfrac{b}{c} = \dfrac{a+b}{c}: \quad = \dfrac{9 + 2x}{24x^2}$ $= \dfrac{2x + 9}{24x^2}$
Step 4: Simplify the result.	The rational expression is simplified.

So $\dfrac{3}{8x^2} + \dfrac{1}{12x} = \dfrac{2x + 9}{24x^2}$.

> ### ADDING OR SUBTRACTING RATIONAL EXPRESSIONS WITH UNLIKE DENOMINATORS
>
> **Step 1:** Find the least common denominator.
> **Step 2:** Rewrite each rational expression with the common denominator. You will need to multiply out the numerator, but leave the denominator in factored form.
> **Step 3:** Add or subtract the rational expressions found in Step 2.
> **Step 4:** Simplify the result.

Quick ✔ *In Problems 7 and 8, perform the indicated operation and simplify the result.*

7. $\dfrac{3}{10a} + \dfrac{4}{15a^2}$

8. $\dfrac{3}{8y} - \dfrac{13}{24y}$

EXAMPLE 5   Adding Rational Expressions with Unlike Denominators

Perform the indicated operation and simplify the result.

(a) $\dfrac{x-1}{x+3} + \dfrac{x}{x+2}$ **(b)** $\dfrac{x-1}{x^2+2x-8} + \dfrac{x-1}{x^2-16}$

Solution

(a) $\dfrac{x-1}{x+3} + \dfrac{x}{x+2}$

The LCD is $(x+3)(x+2)$.

Multiply $\dfrac{x-1}{x+3}$ by $\dfrac{x+2}{x+2}$; Multiply $\dfrac{x}{x+2}$ by $\dfrac{x+3}{x+3}$

$$\dfrac{x-1}{x+3} + \dfrac{x}{x+2} = \dfrac{x-1}{x+3}\cdot\dfrac{x+2}{x+2} + \dfrac{x}{x+2}\cdot\dfrac{x+3}{x+3}$$

Multiply out the numerator: $= \dfrac{x^2+x-2}{(x+3)(x+2)} + \dfrac{x^2+3x}{(x+3)(x+2)}$

Use $\dfrac{a}{c} + \dfrac{b}{c} = \dfrac{a+b}{c}$: $= \dfrac{x^2+x-2+(x^2+3x)}{(x+3)(x+2)}$

Combine like terms: $= \dfrac{2x^2+4x-2}{(x+3)(x+2)} = \dfrac{2(x^2+2x-1)}{(x+3)(x+2)}$

So $\dfrac{x-1}{x+3} + \dfrac{x}{x+2} = \dfrac{2(x^2+2x-1)}{(x+3)(x+2)}$.

(b) $\dfrac{x-1}{x^2+2x-8} + \dfrac{x-1}{x^2-16}$

First, we factor the denominators to find the LCD.

$$x^2+2x-8 = (x+4)(x-2)$$
$$x^2-16 = (x+4)(x-4)$$
$$\text{LCD} = (x+4)(x-2)(x-4)$$

Multiply $\dfrac{x-1}{(x+4)(x-2)}$ by $\dfrac{x-4}{x-4}$; Multiply $\dfrac{x-1}{(x+4)(x-4)}$ by $\dfrac{x-2}{x-2}$

$$\dfrac{x-1}{x^2+2x-8} + \dfrac{x-1}{x^2-16} = \dfrac{x-1}{(x+4)(x-2)}\cdot\dfrac{x-4}{x-4} + \dfrac{x-1}{(x+4)(x-4)}\cdot\dfrac{x-2}{x-2}$$

Multiply out the numerator: $= \dfrac{x^2-5x+4}{(x+4)(x-2)(x-4)} + \dfrac{x^2-3x+2}{(x+4)(x-2)(x-4)}$

Use $\dfrac{a}{c} + \dfrac{b}{c} = \dfrac{a+b}{c}$: $= \dfrac{x^2-5x+4+(x^2-3x+2)}{(x+4)(x-2)(x-4)}$

Combine like terms: $= \dfrac{2x^2-8x+6}{(x+4)(x-2)(x-4)}$

Factor the numerator: $= \dfrac{2(x-3)(x-1)}{(x+4)(x-2)(x-4)}$

So $\dfrac{x-1}{x^2+2x-8} + \dfrac{x-1}{x^2-16} = \dfrac{2(x-3)(x-1)}{(x+4)(x-2)(x-4)}$.   ∎

Quick ✔

In Problems 9 and 10, perform the indicated operation and simplify the result.

9. $\dfrac{3x}{x-1} + \dfrac{x+5}{x+2}$ **10.** $\dfrac{x-1}{2x^2+7x+6} + \dfrac{x-1}{x^2+6x+8}$

EXAMPLE 6 How to Subtract Rational Expressions with Unlike Denominators

Perform the indicated operation and simplify the result.

$$\frac{2x - 1}{2x^2 - 7x - 4} - \frac{x - 1}{2x^2 + 3x + 1}$$

Step-by-Step Solution

Step 1: Find the least common denominator.

$$2x^2 - 7x - 4 = (2x + 1)(x - 4)$$
$$2x^2 + 3x + 1 = (2x + 1)(x + 1)$$
$$\text{LCD} = (2x + 1)(x - 4)(x + 1)$$

Step 2: Rewrite each rational expression with the common denominator.

Multiply $\dfrac{2x - 1}{(2x + 1)(x - 4)}$ by $\dfrac{x + 1}{x + 1}$; Multiply $\dfrac{x - 1}{(2x + 1)(x + 1)}$ by $\dfrac{x - 4}{x - 4}$

$$\frac{2x - 1}{2x^2 - 7x - 4} - \frac{x - 1}{2x^2 + 3x + 1} = \frac{2x - 1}{(2x + 1)(x - 4)} \cdot \frac{x + 1}{x + 1} - \frac{x - 1}{(2x + 1)(x + 1)} \cdot \frac{x - 4}{x - 4}$$

Multiply out the numerator: $= \dfrac{2x^2 + x - 1}{(2x + 1)(x - 4)(x + 1)} - \dfrac{x^2 - 5x + 4}{(2x + 1)(x - 4)(x + 1)}$

Step 3: Subtract the rational expressions found in Step 2.

Use $\dfrac{a}{c} - \dfrac{b}{c} = \dfrac{a - b}{c}$: $= \dfrac{2x^2 + x - 1 - (x^2 - 5x + 4)}{(2x + 1)(x - 4)(x + 1)}$

Distribute the -1: $= \dfrac{2x^2 + x - 1 - x^2 + 5x - 4}{(2x + 1)(x - 4)(x + 1)}$

Combine like terms: $= \dfrac{x^2 + 6x - 5}{(2x + 1)(x - 4)(x + 1)}$

Step 4: Simplify the rational expression.

The rational expression is simplified.

So $\dfrac{2x - 1}{2x^2 - 7x - 4} - \dfrac{x - 1}{2x^2 + 3x + 1} = \dfrac{x^2 + 6x - 5}{(2x + 1)(x - 4)(x + 1)}.$

Quick ✔ *In Problem 11, perform the indicated operation and simplify the result.*

11. $\dfrac{3x + 4}{2x^2 + x - 6} - \dfrac{x - 1}{x^2 + 4x + 4}$

EXAMPLE 7 Adding and Subtracting Three Rational Expressions

Perform the indicated operations and simplify the result.

$$\frac{6}{x^2 - 9} + \frac{x + 1}{x + 3} - \frac{x - 2}{x - 3}$$

Solution

We factor each denominator.

$$x^2 - 9 = (x + 3)(x - 3)$$
$$x + 3 = x + 3$$
$$x - 3 = x - 3$$

The LCD $= (x + 3)(x - 3)$.

Multiply $\dfrac{x+1}{x+3}$ by $\dfrac{x-3}{x-3}$; Multiply $\dfrac{x-2}{x-3}$ by $\dfrac{x+3}{x+3}$

$$\frac{6}{x^2 - 9} + \frac{x+1}{x+3} - \frac{x-2}{x-3} = \frac{6}{(x+3)(x-3)} + \frac{x+1}{x+3}\cdot\frac{x-3}{x-3} - \frac{x-2}{x-3}\cdot\frac{x+3}{x+3}$$

Multiply out the numerator: $= \dfrac{6}{(x+3)(x-3)} + \dfrac{x^2 - 2x - 3}{(x+3)(x-3)} - \dfrac{x^2 + x - 6}{(x+3)(x-3)}$

Use $\dfrac{a}{c} + \dfrac{b}{c} = \dfrac{a+b}{c}$; $\dfrac{a}{c} - \dfrac{b}{c} = \dfrac{a-b}{c}$: $= \dfrac{6 + x^2 - 2x - 3 - (x^2 + x - 6)}{(x+3)(x-3)}$

Distribute the -1: $= \dfrac{6 + x^2 - 2x - 3 - x^2 - x + 6}{(x+3)(x-3)}$

Combine like terms: $= \dfrac{-3x + 9}{(x+3)(x-3)}$

Factor: $= \dfrac{-3(x-3)}{(x+3)(x-3)}$

Divide out like factors: $= \dfrac{-3}{x+3}$

So $\dfrac{6}{x^2 - 9} + \dfrac{x+1}{x+3} - \dfrac{x-2}{x-3} = \dfrac{-3}{x+3}$. ∎

Quick ✔ *In Problem 12, perform the indicated operations and simplify the result.*

12. $\dfrac{4}{x^2 - 4} - \dfrac{x+3}{x-2} + \dfrac{x+3}{x+2}$

5.2 EXERCISES

MyMathLab   PRACTICE   WATCH   DOWNLOAD   READ   REVIEW

1–12. *are the* **Quick** ✔s *that follow each* **EXAMPLE**

Building Skills

In Problems 13–24, perform the indicated operation and simplify the result. See Objective 1.

13. $\dfrac{3x}{x+1} + \dfrac{5}{x+1}$

14. $\dfrac{5x}{x-3} + \dfrac{2}{x-3}$

15. $\dfrac{2x}{2x+5} - \dfrac{1}{2x+5}$

16. $\dfrac{9x}{6x-5} - \dfrac{2}{6x-5}$

17. $\dfrac{2x}{2x^2 - 7x - 15} + \dfrac{3}{2x^2 - 7x - 15}$

18. $\dfrac{x}{3x^2 + 8x - 3} + \dfrac{3}{3x^2 + 8x - 3}$

19. $\dfrac{2x^2 - 5x + 7}{x^2 - 2x - 15} - \dfrac{x^2 + 3x - 8}{x^2 - 2x - 15}$

20. $\dfrac{3x^2 + 8x - 1}{x^2 - 3x - 28} - \dfrac{2x^2 + 2x - 9}{x^2 - 3x - 28}$

21. $\dfrac{3x}{x-5} + \dfrac{1}{5-x}$

22. $\dfrac{3x}{x-6} + \dfrac{2}{6-x}$

23. $\dfrac{2x^2 - 4x - 1}{x-3} - \dfrac{x^2 - 6x + 4}{3-x}$

24. $\dfrac{x^2 + 2x - 5}{x-4} - \dfrac{x^2 - 5x - 15}{4-x}$

In Problems 25–34, find the least common denominator. See Objective 2.

25. $\dfrac{3}{4x^3}$ and $\dfrac{9}{8x}$

26. $\dfrac{5}{3a^3}$ and $\dfrac{2}{9a^2}$

27. $\dfrac{1}{15xy^2}$ and $\dfrac{7}{18x^3y}$

28. $\dfrac{1}{8a^3b}$ and $\dfrac{5}{12ab^2}$

29. $\dfrac{5x}{x-4}$ and $\dfrac{3}{x+2}$

30. $\dfrac{x-3}{x+2}$ and $\dfrac{x+7}{x-5}$

31. $\dfrac{x-4}{x^2 - x - 12}$ and $\dfrac{2x+1}{x^2 - 9x + 20}$

32. $\dfrac{2m-7}{m^2 + 3m - 18}$ and $\dfrac{5m+1}{m^2 - 7m + 12}$

33. $\dfrac{p+1}{2p^2+3p-2}$ and $\dfrac{4p-1}{p^3+2p^2}$

34. $\dfrac{x-6}{x^2-9}$ and $\dfrac{3x}{x^3-3x^2}$

In Problems 35–60, add or subtract, as indicated, and simplify the result. See Objective 3.

35. $\dfrac{3}{4x^2}+\dfrac{5}{8x}$

36. $\dfrac{2}{9x}+\dfrac{5}{3x^2}$

37. $\dfrac{5}{12a^2b}-\dfrac{4}{15ab^2}$

38. $\dfrac{3}{14mn^3}-\dfrac{2}{21m^2n}$

39. $\dfrac{y+2}{y-5}-\dfrac{y-4}{y+3}$

40. $\dfrac{x+2}{x-3}-\dfrac{x+2}{x+1}$

41. $\dfrac{a+5}{a-2}-\dfrac{5a+18}{a^2-4}$

42. $\dfrac{z+1}{z+3}-\dfrac{z+17}{z^2-z-12}$

43. $\dfrac{3}{(x-2)(x+3)}-\dfrac{5}{(x+3)(x+4)}$

44. $\dfrac{1}{(x-1)(x+3)}+\dfrac{5}{(x+1)(x-1)}$

45. $\dfrac{x-3}{x^2+3x+2}+\dfrac{x-1}{x^2-4}$ **46.** $\dfrac{x-5}{x^2+4x+3}+\dfrac{x-2}{x^2-1}$

47. $\dfrac{w-4}{2w^2+3w+1}-\dfrac{w+3}{2w^2-5w-3}$

48. $\dfrac{y+4}{3y^2-y-2}-\dfrac{1}{3y^2+14y+8}$

49. $\dfrac{x+y}{x^2-6xy+9y^2}+\dfrac{x+2y}{x^2-2xy-3y^2}$

50. $\dfrac{m-2n}{m^2+4mn+4n^2}+\dfrac{m-n}{m^2-mn-6n^2}$

51. $\dfrac{3}{x^2-4x-5}-\dfrac{2}{x^2-6x+5}$

52. $\dfrac{3}{x^2+7x+10}-\dfrac{4}{x^2+6x+5}$

53. $\dfrac{p^2-3p-10}{p^2-16}+\dfrac{p^2-3p-10}{16-p^2}$

54. $\dfrac{y^2+4y+4}{y^2-9}+\dfrac{y^2+4y+4}{9-y^2}$

55. $\dfrac{2}{w+2}-\dfrac{3}{w}+\dfrac{w+10}{w^2-4}$ **56.** $\dfrac{7}{m-3}-\dfrac{5}{m}-\dfrac{2m+6}{m^2-9}$

57. $\dfrac{p-2}{p^2+6p+9}+\dfrac{1}{p+3}-\dfrac{2p+1}{2p^2+p-15}$

58. $\dfrac{x-1}{x^2-16}+\dfrac{1}{x+4}-\dfrac{4x+1}{3x^2-7x-20}$

59. $\dfrac{2}{x}-\dfrac{2}{x-1}+\dfrac{3}{(x-1)^2}$ **60.** $\dfrac{2}{x}-\dfrac{2}{x+2}+\dfrac{2}{(x+2)^2}$

Mixed Practice

In Problems 61–72, perform the indicated operation and simplify the result.

61. $\dfrac{1}{x-3}-\dfrac{x^2+18}{x^3-27}$ **62.** $\dfrac{1}{x+2}+\dfrac{x-10}{x^3+8}$

63. $\dfrac{2x^2-x}{x+3}+\dfrac{3x}{x+3}-\dfrac{x^2+3}{x+3}$

64. $\dfrac{2x^2}{x-1}-\dfrac{x^2-2x}{x-1}+\dfrac{x-4}{x-1}$

65. $6+\dfrac{x-3}{x+3}$ **66.** $3+\dfrac{x+4}{x-4}$

67. $\dfrac{b+3}{b^2+2b-8}-\dfrac{b+2}{b^2-4}$ **68.** $\dfrac{a+3}{a^2-8a+15}+\dfrac{a+3}{a^2-9}$

69. $\dfrac{y-1}{y+4}+\dfrac{y-2}{y+3}-\dfrac{y^2+3y+1}{y^2+7y+12}$

70. $\dfrac{z+3}{z-6}+\dfrac{z-1}{z-2}-\dfrac{6z}{z^2-8z+12}$

71. $\dfrac{x+4}{x^2-5x+6}+\dfrac{x-1}{x^2-2x-3}-\dfrac{2x+1}{x^2-x-2}$

72. $\dfrac{x-1}{x^2+4x-5}+\dfrac{3x-1}{x^2+3x-10}-\dfrac{4x+1}{x^2-3x+2}$

73. Given that $f(x)=\dfrac{3}{x-2}$ and $g(x)=\dfrac{2}{x+1}$,
   (a) find $R(x)=f(x)+g(x)$,
   (b) state the domain of $R(x)$.

74. Given that $f(x)=\dfrac{5}{x+2}$ and $g(x)=\dfrac{3}{x-1}$,
   (a) find $R(x)=f(x)+g(x)$,
   (b) state the domain of $R(x)$.

75. Given that $f(x)=\dfrac{x+1}{x^2-3x-4}$ and
   $g(x)=\dfrac{x+4}{x^2-x-12}$,
   (a) find $R(x)=f(x)+g(x)$,
   (b) state the domain of $R(x)$,
   (c) find $H(x)=f(x)-g(x)$,
   (d) state the domain of $H(x)$.

76. Given that $f(x) = \dfrac{x + 5}{x^2 - 5x + 6}$ and

$g(x) = \dfrac{x + 1}{x^2 - 4x - 12}$,

(a) find $R(x) = f(x) + g(x)$,
(b) state the domain of $R(x)$,
(c) find $H(x) = f(x) - g(x)$,
(d) state the domain of $H(x)$.

Applying the Concepts

△**77. Surface Area of a Box** The volume of a closed box with a square base is 2000 cubic inches. Its surface area S as a function of the length of the base x is given by the function

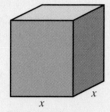

$$S(x) = 2x^2 + \frac{8000}{x}$$

(a) Write S over a common denominator. That is, write S so that the rule is a single rational expression.
(b) Find and interpret $S(10)$.

△**78. Surface Area of a Can** The volume of a cylindrical can is 200 cubic centimeters. Its surface area S as a function of the radius r of the can is given by the function

$$S(r) = 2\pi r^2 + \frac{400}{r}$$

(a) Write S over a common denominator. That is, write S so that the rule is a single rational expression.
(b) Find and interpret $S(4)$. Round your answer to two decimal places.

79. Road Trip Suppose you and a group of your friends decide to go on a road trip to a neighboring university that is 200 miles away. Your average speed for the first 50 miles of the trip is 10 miles an hour slower than the average speed for the remaining 150 miles of the trip. If we let s represent your average speed for the first 50 miles of the trip, the function

$$T(s) = \frac{50}{s} + \frac{150}{s + 10}$$

represents the amount of time T it will take to get to the neighboring university.

(a) Write T over a common denominator. That is, write T so that the rule is a single rational expression.
(b) Find and interpret $T(50)$.

80. Vacation The distance from Chicago, Illinois, to Naples, Florida, is approximately 1200 miles. Atlanta, Georgia, is approximately the midpoint between Chicago and Naples. On a recent trip to Naples, the Sullivan family averaged s miles per hour between Chicago and Atlanta and they averaged 5 miles per hour faster between Atlanta and Naples. The time T of their trip as a function of their average speed s between Chicago and Atlanta is given by the function

$$T(s) = \frac{600}{s} + \frac{600}{s + 5}$$

(a) Write T over a common denominator. That is, write T so that the rule is a single rational expression.
(b) Find and interpret $T(50)$. Round your answer to two decimal places.
(c) Using the result from part **(b)**, compute the average speed of the Sullivans for the entire trip. Are you surprised by the result?

Extending the Concepts

81. Write $x^{-1} + y^{-1}$ as a single rational expression with no negative exponents.

82. Write $\left(\dfrac{a}{b}\right)^{-1} + \left(\dfrac{b}{a}\right)^{-1}$ as a single rational expression with no negative exponents.

Explaining the Concepts

83. Explain how to find the least common denominator when adding or subtracting two rational expressions with unlike denominators.

84. Explain how to add or subtract rational expressions with unlike denominators.

Synthesis Review

In Problems 85–91, multiply the expressions.

85. $4a(a - 3)$

86. $-5z(z + 4)$

87. $(p - 3)(p + 3)$

88. $(3q + 1)(3q - 1)$

89. $(w - 2)(w^2 + 2w + 4)$

90. $(2v + 1)(4v^2 - 2v + 1)$

91. $\dfrac{x^3 - 8}{2x^2 + 5x + 2} \cdot \dfrac{2x^2 - x - 1}{x^2 - 4} \cdot \dfrac{x^2 + 4x + 4}{x - 1}$

5.3 Complex Rational Expressions

OBJECTIVES

[1] Simplify a Complex Rational Expression by Simplifying the Numerator and Denominator Separately

[2] Simplify a Complex Rational Expression Using the Least Common Denominator

Preparing for Complex Rational Expressions

Before getting started, take the following readiness quiz. If you get a problem wrong, go back to the section cited and review the material.

P1. Factor: $6y^2 - 5y - 6$ [Section 4.5, pp. 363–368]

P2. Simplify: $\left(\dfrac{3ab^2}{2a^{-1}b^5}\right)^{-2}$ [Getting Ready, pp. 312–313]

When sums and/or differences of rational expressions occur in the numerator or denominator of a quotient, the quotient is called a **complex rational expression.** The following are examples of complex rational expressions.

In Words

A complex rational expression is simplified when it is of the form *polynomial over polynomial* and the polynomials have no common factors.

$$\frac{3 - \dfrac{1}{x}}{1 + \dfrac{1}{x}} \quad \text{and} \quad \frac{\dfrac{x + 1}{x - 2} - \dfrac{3}{x + 2}}{\dfrac{2x + 3}{x - 2} + 1}$$

To **simplify** a complex rational expression means to write it as a rational expression in simplest form. This can be done using one of two methods: Method I: Simplify the numerator and the denominator separately, or Method II: simplify by using the least common denominator. We'll start by using Method I.

[1] Simplify a Complex Rational Expression by Simplifying the Numerator and Denominator Separately

Let's look at an example that illustrates how to simplify a complex rational expression.

Preparing for...Answers

P1. $(3y + 2)(2y - 3)$ **P2.** $\dfrac{4b^6}{9a^4}$

EXAMPLE 1   How to Simplify a Complex Rational Expression Using Method I

Simplify: $\dfrac{\dfrac{1}{3} + \dfrac{1}{x}}{\dfrac{x + 3}{2}},\ x \neq -3, 0$

Step-by-Step Solution

Notice that x cannot equal -3 because it will cause the denominator, $\dfrac{x + 3}{2}$, to equal zero; x cannot equal 0 because it will cause the expression $\dfrac{1}{x}$ in the numerator to be undefined.

Step 1: Write the numerator of the complex rational expression as a single rational expression.	The least common denominator of $\dfrac{1}{3}$ and $\dfrac{1}{x}$ is $3x$.

$$\frac{1}{3} + \frac{1}{x} = \frac{1}{3} \cdot \frac{x}{x} + \frac{1}{x} \cdot \frac{3}{3}$$

$$= \frac{x}{3x} + \frac{3}{3x}$$

$$\frac{a}{c} + \frac{b}{c} = \frac{a + b}{c} \colon = \frac{x + 3}{3x}$$

Step 2: Write the denominator of the complex rational expression as a single rational expression.	This is already done.
Step 3: Rewrite the complex rational expression using the rational expressions determined in Steps 1 and 2.	$$\dfrac{\frac{1}{3}+\frac{1}{x}}{\frac{x+3}{2}}=\dfrac{\frac{x+3}{3x}}{\frac{x+3}{2}}$$
Step 4: Simplify the rational expression using the techniques for dividing rational expressions from Section 5.1.	Rewrite the division problem as a multiplication problem: $=\dfrac{x+3}{3x}\cdot\dfrac{2}{x+3}$ Divide like factors: $=\dfrac{(x+3)\cdot 2}{3x(x+3)}$ $=\dfrac{2}{3x}$

So $\dfrac{\frac{1}{3}+\frac{1}{x}}{\frac{x+3}{2}}=\dfrac{2}{3x}$.

We summarize the steps to simplify a complex rational expression using Method I.

SIMPLIFYING A COMPLEX RATIONAL EXPRESSION BY SIMPLIFYING THE NUMERATOR AND DENOMINATOR SEPARATELY (METHOD I)

Step 1: Write the numerator of the complex rational expression as a single rational expression.

Step 2: Write the denominator of the complex rational expression as a single rational expression.

Step 3: Rewrite the complex rational expression using the rational expressions determined in Steps 1 and 2.

Step 4: Simplify the rational expression using the techniques for dividing rational expressions from Section 5.1.

Quick ✔

1. When sums and/or differences of rational expressions occur in the numerator or denominator of a quotient (or fraction), the quotient is called a _____ _____ _____.

In Problems 2 and 3, simplify each expression using Method I.

2. $\dfrac{\frac{3}{2}-\frac{1}{3}}{\frac{5}{6}}$

3. $\dfrac{\frac{z}{4}-\frac{4}{z}}{\frac{z+4}{16}}, z\neq 0,-4$

We will not state the domain restrictions for the remaining examples, but you should be aware that the restrictions are needed to maintain equality.

EXAMPLE 2 Simplifying a Complex Rational Expression Using Method I

Simplify: $\dfrac{\dfrac{2x}{x+4} - \dfrac{x-7}{x^2-16}}{x - \dfrac{x^2+4}{x+4}}$

Solution

Write the numerator of the complex rational expression as a single rational expression.

$$LCD = (x-4)(x+4)$$
$$\downarrow$$

$$\frac{2x}{x+4} - \frac{x-7}{x^2-16} = \frac{2x}{x+4} \cdot \frac{x-4}{x-4} - \frac{x-7}{x^2-16}$$

$$= \frac{2x^2-8x}{x^2-16} - \frac{x-7}{x^2-16}$$

Use $\dfrac{a}{c} - \dfrac{b}{c} = \dfrac{a-b}{c}$: $= \dfrac{2x^2-9x+7}{x^2-16}$

Write the denominator of the complex rational expression as a single rational expression.

$$LCD = x+4$$
$$\downarrow$$

$$x - \frac{x^2+4}{x+4} = \frac{x}{1} \cdot \frac{x+4}{x+4} - \frac{x^2+4}{x+4}$$

$$= \frac{x^2+4x}{x+4} - \frac{x^2+4}{x+4}$$

Use $\dfrac{a}{c} - \dfrac{b}{c} = \dfrac{a-b}{c}$: $= \dfrac{4x-4}{x+4}$

Rewrite the complex rational expression using the numerator and denominator just found, and then simplify.

$$\frac{\dfrac{2x}{x+4} - \dfrac{x-7}{x^2-16}}{x - \dfrac{x^2+4}{x+4}} = \frac{\dfrac{2x^2-9x+7}{x^2-16}}{\dfrac{4x-4}{x+4}}$$

Rewrite the division problem
as a multiplication problem: $= \dfrac{2x^2-9x+7}{x^2-16} \cdot \dfrac{x+4}{4x-4}$

Factor and divide out like factors: $= \dfrac{(2x-7)\cancel{(x-1)}\,\cancel{(x+4)}}{(x-4)\cancel{(x+4)} \cdot 4\cancel{(x-1)}}$

$$= \frac{2x-7}{4(x-4)}$$

So $\dfrac{\dfrac{2x}{x+4} - \dfrac{x-7}{x^2-16}}{x - \dfrac{x^2+4}{x+4}} = \dfrac{2x-7}{4(x-4)}$. ∎

Quick ✔

4. Simplify using Method I: $\dfrac{\dfrac{2x}{x+1} - \dfrac{x^2-3}{x^2+3x+2}}{4 + \dfrac{4}{x+2}}$

2   Simplify a Complex Rational Expression Using the Least Common Denominator

We now simplify complex rational expressions using the least common denominator. We will redo Example 1 using this second method so that you can compare the two methods.

EXAMPLE 3   How to Simplify a Complex Rational Expression Using Method II

Simplify: $\dfrac{\dfrac{1}{3} + \dfrac{1}{x}}{\dfrac{x+3}{2}}$

Step-by-Step Solution

Step 1: Find the least common denominator among all the denominators in the complex rational expression.	The denominators of the complex rational expression are 3, x, and 2. The least common denominator is $2 \cdot 3 \cdot x = 6x$.
Step 2: Multiply both the numerator and denominator of the complex rational expression by the least common denominator found in Step 1.	$\dfrac{\dfrac{1}{3} + \dfrac{1}{x}}{\dfrac{x+3}{2}} \cdot \dfrac{6x}{6x} = \dfrac{\left(\dfrac{1}{3} + \dfrac{1}{x}\right) \cdot 6x}{\left(\dfrac{x+3}{2}\right) \cdot 6x}$
	Distribute $6x$ to each term: $= \dfrac{\dfrac{1}{3} \cdot 6x + \dfrac{1}{x} \cdot 6x}{\dfrac{x+3}{2} \cdot 6x}$
Step 3: Simplify the rational expression.	Simplify: $= \dfrac{2x + 6}{3x(x+3)}$
	Factor and divide out like factors: $= \dfrac{2\cancel{(x+3)}}{3x\cancel{(x+3)}} = \dfrac{2}{3x}$

So $\dfrac{\dfrac{1}{3} + \dfrac{1}{x}}{\dfrac{x+3}{2}} = \dfrac{2}{3x}$, the same result as we obtained in Example 1!   ∎

> **SIMPLIFYING A COMPLEX RATIONAL EXPRESSION USING THE LEAST COMMON DENOMINATOR (METHOD II)**
>
> **Step 1:** Find the least common denominator among all the denominators in the complex rational expression.
> **Step 2:** Multiply both the numerator and denominator of the complex rational expression by the least common denominator found in Step 1.
> **Step 3:** Simplify the rational expression.

Quick ✔ *In Problems 5 and 6, simplify each expression using Method II.*

5. $\dfrac{\dfrac{3}{2} - \dfrac{1}{3}}{\dfrac{5}{6}}$

6. $\dfrac{\dfrac{z}{4} - \dfrac{4}{z}}{\dfrac{z+4}{16}}$

EXAMPLE 4 Simplifying Complex Rational Expressions Using Method II

Simplify: $\dfrac{\dfrac{1}{x} + \dfrac{1}{x-2}}{\dfrac{x}{x^2-4} + \dfrac{1}{x-2}}$

Solution

Since $x^2 - 4 = (x-2)(x+2)$, the least common denominator among all denominators is $x(x-2)(x+2)$, so we multiply the numerator and denominator by $x(x-2)(x+2)$.

$$\frac{\dfrac{1}{x} + \dfrac{1}{x-2}}{\dfrac{x}{x^2-4} + \dfrac{1}{x-2}} = \frac{\dfrac{1}{x} + \dfrac{1}{x-2}}{\dfrac{x}{x^2-4} + \dfrac{1}{x-2}} \cdot \frac{x(x-2)(x+2)}{x(x-2)(x+2)}$$

Distribute the LCD
to each term: $= \dfrac{\dfrac{1}{x} \cdot x(x-2)(x+2) + \dfrac{1}{x-2} \cdot x(x-2)(x+2)}{\dfrac{x}{x^2-4} \cdot x(x-2)(x+2) + \dfrac{1}{x-2} \cdot x(x-2)(x+2)}$

Factor and divide
out like factors: $= \dfrac{\dfrac{1}{\cancel{x}} \cdot \cancel{x}(x-2)(x+2) + \dfrac{1}{\cancel{x-2}} \cdot x\cancel{(x-2)}(x+2)}{\dfrac{x}{\cancel{(x-2)}\,\cancel{(x+2)}} \cdot x\cancel{(x-2)}\,\cancel{(x+2)} + \dfrac{1}{\cancel{x-2}} \cdot x\cancel{(x-2)}(x+2)}$

$$= \frac{(x-2)(x+2) + x(x+2)}{x^2 + x(x+2)}$$

Factor out $(x+2)$: $= \dfrac{(x+2)[x-2+x]}{x^2 + x^2 + 2x}$

$$= \frac{(x+2)(2x-2)}{2x^2 + 2x}$$

Factor and divide
out like factors: $= \dfrac{\cancel{2}(x+2)(x-1)}{\cancel{2}x(x+1)}$

$$= \frac{(x+2)(x-1)}{x(x+1)}$$

Quick ✔

7. Simplify using Method II: $\dfrac{\dfrac{x+2}{x+5} - \dfrac{x+2}{x+1}}{\dfrac{2x+1}{x+1} - 1}$

Comparing Methods

We will work through the next example using both methods. As you work through problems in the exercise set, be sure to start developing a sense as to when Method I might be preferred over Method II, and vice versa.

EXAMPLE 5 Comparing Methods I and II

Simplify $\dfrac{x^{-1} + y^{-1}}{x^{-3} + y^{-3}}$ as a rational expression that contains no negative exponents.

Solution

First, we rewrite the expression so that it does not contain any negative exponents.

Work Smart

Remember, $x^{-1} = \dfrac{1}{x}$ and $y^{-1} = \dfrac{1}{y}$

but $x^{-1} + y^{-1} \neq \dfrac{1}{x + y}$

$x^{-1} + y^{-1} = \dfrac{1}{x} + \dfrac{1}{y}$

$$\frac{x^{-1} + y^{-1}}{x^{-3} + y^{-3}} = \frac{\dfrac{1}{x} + \dfrac{1}{y}}{\dfrac{1}{x^3} + \dfrac{1}{y^3}}$$

Method I

We write the numerator of the complex rational expression as a single quotient. The LCD is xy.

$$\frac{1}{x} + \frac{1}{y} = \frac{1}{x} \cdot \frac{y}{y} + \frac{1}{y} \cdot \frac{x}{x}$$

$$= \frac{y}{xy} + \frac{x}{xy}$$

$$= \frac{y + x}{xy}$$

$$= \frac{x + y}{xy}$$

Write the denominator of the complex rational expression as a single quotient. The LCD is $x^3 y^3$.

$$\frac{1}{x^3} + \frac{1}{y^3} = \frac{1}{x^3} \cdot \frac{y^3}{y^3} + \frac{1}{y^3} \cdot \frac{x^3}{x^3}$$

$$= \frac{y^3}{x^3 y^3} + \frac{x^3}{x^3 y^3}$$

$$= \frac{y^3 + x^3}{x^3 y^3}$$

$$= \frac{x^3 + y^3}{x^3 y^3}$$

Now we rewrite the complex rational expression using the numerator and denominator just found and then simplify.

$$\frac{x^{-1} + y^{-1}}{x^{-3} + y^{-3}} = \frac{\dfrac{1}{x} + \dfrac{1}{y}}{\dfrac{1}{x^3} + \dfrac{1}{y^3}}$$

$$= \frac{\dfrac{x + y}{xy}}{\dfrac{x^3 + y^3}{x^3 y^3}}$$

Multiply the rational expression in the numerator by the reciprocal of the rational expression in the denominator:
$$= \frac{x + y}{xy} \cdot \frac{x^3 y^3}{x^3 + y^3}$$

Factor:
$$= \frac{x + y}{xy} \cdot \frac{x^3 y^3}{(x + y)(x^2 - xy + y^2)}$$

Divide out like factors:
$$= \frac{\cancel{x + y}}{\cancel{x}\,\cancel{y}} \cdot \frac{x^{\cancel{3}2} y^{\cancel{3}2}}{\cancel{(x + y)}(x^2 - xy + y^2)}$$

$$= \frac{x^2 y^2}{x^2 - xy + y^2}$$

Method II

The least common denominator of all denominators is x^3y^3. We multiply the numerator and denominator of the complex rational expression by x^3y^3.

$$\frac{\dfrac{1}{x} + \dfrac{1}{y}}{\dfrac{1}{x^3} + \dfrac{1}{y^3}} = \frac{\dfrac{1}{x} + \dfrac{1}{y}}{\dfrac{1}{x^3} + \dfrac{1}{y^3}} \cdot \frac{x^3y^3}{x^3y^3}$$

Distribute the LCD to each term: $= \dfrac{\dfrac{1}{x} \cdot x^3y^3 + \dfrac{1}{y} \cdot x^3y^3}{\dfrac{1}{x^3} \cdot x^3y^3 + \dfrac{1}{y^3} \cdot x^3y^3}$

$$= \frac{x^2y^3 + x^3y^2}{y^3 + x^3}$$

Factor out common factor in numerator:
Factor the sum of two cubes in the denominator: $= \dfrac{x^2y^2(x + y)}{(x + y)(x^2 - xy + y^2)}$

Divide out and simplify: $= \dfrac{x^2y^2}{x^2 - xy + y^2}$

In this particular problem, it seems Method II is more efficient. ∎

> **Quick ✔** *Simplify the expression so that it does not contain any negative exponents. Use both methods and decide which method you prefer for this problem.*
>
> **8.** $\dfrac{3a^{-1} + b^{-1}}{9a^{-2} - b^{-2}}$

5.3 EXERCISES

MyMathLab — PRACTICE · WATCH · DOWNLOAD · READ · REVIEW

1–8. are the Quick ✔*s that follow each* EXAMPLE

Building Skills

In Problems 9–16, simplify the expression using Method I. See Objective 1.

9. $\dfrac{\dfrac{5}{6} + \dfrac{1}{9}}{\dfrac{5}{2} - \dfrac{3}{8}}$

10. $\dfrac{\dfrac{3}{10} - \dfrac{3}{4}}{\dfrac{2}{5} + \dfrac{7}{10}}$

11. $\dfrac{1 + \dfrac{1}{x}}{1 - \dfrac{1}{x}}$

12. $\dfrac{1 + \dfrac{1}{x^2}}{1 - \dfrac{1}{x^2}}$

13. $\dfrac{1 - \dfrac{a}{a - 2}}{2 - \dfrac{a + 2}{a}}$

14. $\dfrac{\dfrac{a}{a + 1} - 1}{\dfrac{a + 3}{a} - 2}$

15. $\dfrac{\dfrac{x + 2}{x - 1} - \dfrac{x + 5}{x + 3}}{x + 11}$

16. $\dfrac{\dfrac{x + 5}{x - 2} - \dfrac{x + 3}{x - 1}}{3x + 1}$

In Problems 17–24, simplify the expression using Method II. See Objective 2.

17. $\dfrac{\dfrac{5}{6} + \dfrac{7}{10}}{\dfrac{1}{5} - 1}$

18. $\dfrac{2 + \dfrac{7}{4}}{\dfrac{3}{8} - 2}$

19. $\dfrac{w - \dfrac{1}{w}}{w + \dfrac{1}{w}}$

20. $\dfrac{\dfrac{7}{w} + \dfrac{9}{x}}{\dfrac{9}{w} - \dfrac{7}{x}}$

21. $\dfrac{\dfrac{x - 1}{x - 4} - \dfrac{x}{x - 2}}{1 - \dfrac{3}{x - 4}}$

22. $\dfrac{\dfrac{x - 4}{x - 1} - \dfrac{x}{x - 3}}{3 + \dfrac{12}{x - 3}}$

23. $\dfrac{\dfrac{z + 2}{z - 2} + \dfrac{z - 2}{z + 2}}{\dfrac{z + 2}{z - 2} - \dfrac{z - 2}{z + 2}}$

24. $\dfrac{\dfrac{m + 3}{m - 3} - \dfrac{m - 3}{m + 3}}{\dfrac{m + 3}{m - 3} + \dfrac{m - 3}{m + 3}}$

Mixed Practice

In Problems 25–44, simplify the complex rational expression using either Method I or Method II.

25. $\dfrac{\dfrac{3}{y} - 1}{\dfrac{9}{y} - y}$

26. $\dfrac{1 - \dfrac{4}{z}}{z - \dfrac{16}{z}}$

27. $\dfrac{\dfrac{4n}{m} - \dfrac{4m}{n}}{\dfrac{2}{m} + \dfrac{2}{n}}$

28. $\dfrac{\dfrac{n^2}{m} - \dfrac{m^2}{n}}{\dfrac{1}{m} - \dfrac{1}{n}}$

29. $\dfrac{2 + \dfrac{3}{x}}{\dfrac{2x^2}{x + 3} - 3}$

30. $\dfrac{1 + \dfrac{5}{x}}{1 + \dfrac{1}{x + 4}}$

31. $\dfrac{\dfrac{x}{3} - \dfrac{3}{x}}{\dfrac{3}{x^2} - \dfrac{1}{3}}$

32. $\dfrac{\dfrac{5}{x} - \dfrac{x}{5}}{\dfrac{1}{5} - \dfrac{5}{x^2}}$

33. $\dfrac{\dfrac{2x + 1}{x - 1} - \dfrac{x - 1}{x - 3}}{x^2 - 3x - 4}$

34. $\dfrac{\dfrac{x + 5}{x - 3} - \dfrac{x}{x + 4}}{3x^2 - 4x - 15}$

35. $\dfrac{\dfrac{x - 4}{x + 4} + \dfrac{x - 4}{x - 2}}{1 - \dfrac{2}{x - 2}}$

36. $\dfrac{\dfrac{x - 3}{x + 3} + \dfrac{x - 3}{x - 4}}{1 + \dfrac{x + 3}{x - 4}}$

37. $\dfrac{\dfrac{b^2}{b^2 - 25} - \dfrac{b}{b + 5}}{\dfrac{b}{b^2 - 25} - \dfrac{1}{b - 5}}$

38. $\dfrac{\dfrac{-6}{x^2 + 5x + 6}}{\dfrac{2}{x + 3} - \dfrac{3}{x + 2}}$

39. $\dfrac{3x^{-1} + 3y^{-1}}{x^{-2} - y^{-2}}$

40. $\dfrac{2x^{-1} + 2y^{-1}}{xy^{-1} - x^{-1}y}$

41. $\dfrac{(m + n)^{-1}}{m^{-1} + n^{-1}}$

42. $\dfrac{(x - y)^{-1}}{x^{-1} - y^{-1}}$

43. $\dfrac{a^{-2}b^{-1} - a^{-1}b^{-2}}{4a^{-2} - 4b^{-2}}$

44. $\dfrac{a^{-3} + 8b^{-3}}{a^{-2} - 4b^{-2}}$

Applying the Concepts

45. Electric Circuits An electrical circuit contains two resistors connected in parallel, as shown in the figure. If the resistance of each is R_1 and R_2 ohms, respectively, then their combined resistance R is given by the formula

$$R = \dfrac{1}{\dfrac{1}{R_1} + \dfrac{1}{R_2}}$$

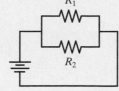

(a) Express R as a simplified rational expression.

(b) Evaluate the rational expression if $R_1 = 4$ ohms and $R_2 = 10$ ohms.

46. Future Value of Money The value of an account V in which P dollars is deposited every year for the next 5 years paying an interest rate i (expressed as a decimal) is given by the formula

$$V = P \cdot \dfrac{1 - \dfrac{1}{(1 + i)^5}}{\dfrac{i}{(1 + i)^5}}$$

(a) Express V as a simplified rational expression.

(b) Determine the value of an account paying 5% when the annual deposit is $1000. Express your answer to the nearest penny.

47. The Lensmaker's Equation The focal length f of a convex lens with index of refraction n is

$$f = \dfrac{1}{(n - 1)\left[\dfrac{1}{R_1} + \dfrac{1}{R_2}\right]}$$

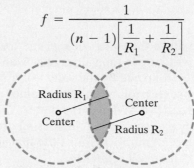

where R_1 and R_2 are the radii of curvature of the front and back surfaces of the lens. See the figure.

(a) Express f as a simplified rational expression.

(b) Determine the focal length of a lens for $n = 1.5$, $R_1 = 0.5$ meter, and $R_2 = 0.3$ meter.

48. Harmonic Mean The harmonic mean is used to determine an average value when data are measured as a rate of change such as 50 miles per hour. The harmonic mean is found using the formula

$$H = \dfrac{n}{\dfrac{1}{x_1} + \dfrac{1}{x_2} + \cdots + \dfrac{1}{x_n}}$$

where $x_1, x_2, \ldots, x_n$ are the n rates of change.

(a) Suppose that a family drove from Chicago, Illinois, to Naples, Florida. The distance each way is about 1200 miles. The trip from Chicago to Naples resulted in an average speed of 48 miles per hour, while the return trip resulted in an average speed of 52 miles per hour. Compute the average speed of the entire trip.

(b) A 300-Kb file is downloaded four separate times resulting in download speeds of 4.3 Kb/s, 4.1 Kb/s, 3.8 Kb/s, and 4.3 Kb/s. Compute the average download time.

Extending the Concepts

49. Fibonacci Strikes Again! Write each of the following expressions in the form $\dfrac{ax + b}{bx + c}$. (*Hint:* Use Method I.)

(a) $1 + \dfrac{1}{1 + \dfrac{1}{x}}$

(b) $1 + \dfrac{1}{1 + \dfrac{1}{1 + \dfrac{1}{x}}}$

(c) $1 + \dfrac{1}{1 + \dfrac{1}{1 + \dfrac{1}{1 + \dfrac{1}{x}}}}$

(d) $1 + \dfrac{1}{1 + \dfrac{1}{1 + \dfrac{1}{1 + \dfrac{1}{1 + \dfrac{1}{x}}}}}$

(e) Write down the values of $a, b,$ and c from part **(a)**. Now write down the values of $a, b,$ and c from part **(b)**, followed by the values of $a, b,$ and c from part **(c)**, followed by the values of $a, b,$ and c from part **(d)**. What is the pattern? Write the sequence of numbers in increasing order. This sequence of numbers forms the first six numbers in the **Fibonacci sequence.**

Math for the Future *In Calculus, you will be asked to simplify the expression $\dfrac{f(x + h) - f(x)}{h}$, which is called the* **difference quotient.** *In Problems 50–53, simplify the difference quotient for the given functions.*

50. $f(x) = \dfrac{1}{x}$

51. $f(x) = \dfrac{1}{x^2}$

52. $f(x) = \dfrac{3}{x^2}$

53. $f(x) = \dfrac{1}{x - 1}$

Explaining the Concepts

54. In your own words, provide a definition for a complex rational expression.

55. Which of the two methods for simplifying complex rational expressions do you prefer? Write a paragraph supporting your opinion.

Synthesis Review

In Problems 56–61, solve each equation.

56. $4x + 3 = 15$

57. $-5a + 2 = 22$

58. $\dfrac{1}{2}w + 3 = 5$

59. $\dfrac{2}{3}x - \dfrac{5}{7}(x + 21) = \dfrac{11}{21}x + \dfrac{4}{7}$

60. $y^2 - 5y = 50$

61. $3p^2 + 19p = 14$

PUTTING THE CONCEPTS TOGETHER (SECTIONS 5.1–5.3)

These problems cover important concepts from Sections 5.1 through 5.3. We designed these problems so that you can review the chapter so far and show your mastery of the concepts. Take time to work these problems before proceeding with the next section. The answers to these problems are located at the back of the text on page AN-31.

1. Determine the domain of the rational function
$$g(x) = \dfrac{3x + 1}{3x^2 - 17x - 6}.$$

In Problems 2 and 3, write each rational expression in lowest terms.

2. $\dfrac{24n - 4n^2}{2n^2 - 9n - 18}$

3. $\dfrac{2p^2 - pq - 10q^2}{3p^2 + 2pq - 8q^2}$

In Problems 4–8, perform the indicated operations.

4. $\dfrac{a^2 - 16}{12a^2 + 48a} \cdot \dfrac{6a^3 - 30a^2}{a^2 + 2a - 24}$

5. $\dfrac{\dfrac{x^2 + x - 2}{3x^2 - 5x - 2}}{\dfrac{3x^2 - 2x - 1}{x^2 - 9x + 14}}$

6. $\dfrac{x^2 - 10}{x^2 - 4} - \dfrac{3x}{x^2 - 4}$

7. $\dfrac{3n}{n^2 - 7n + 10} - \dfrac{2n}{n^2 - 8n + 15}$

8. $\dfrac{3y + 2}{y^2 + 5y - 24} + \dfrac{7}{y^2 + 4y - 32}$

In Problems 9 and 10, use the functions $f(x) = \dfrac{2x + 1}{x^2 - 11x + 28}$,

$g(x) = \dfrac{3x - 12}{4x^2 + 4x + 1}$, *and* $h(x) = \dfrac{3x}{x - 7}$ *to find each*

difference or product.

9. $P(x) = f(x) \cdot g(x)$

10. $D(x) = h(x) - f(x)$

In Problems 11 and 12, simplify each complex rational expression using the method you wish.

11. $\dfrac{\dfrac{1}{m^2} - \dfrac{1}{n^2}}{\dfrac{1}{m} - \dfrac{1}{n}}$

12. $\dfrac{\dfrac{z^2 - 2}{z^2 - 4} + \dfrac{7}{z - 2}}{\dfrac{z^2 + z - 24}{z^2 - 4} - \dfrac{2}{z + 2}}$

5.4 Rational Equations

OBJECTIVES

☐1 Solve Equations Containing Rational Expressions

☐2 Solve Equations Involving Rational Functions

Preparing for Rational Equations

Before getting started, take the following readiness quiz. If you get a problem wrong, go back to the section cited and review the material.

P1. Solve: $\dfrac{2}{3}x + \dfrac{1}{2} = \dfrac{3}{4}$ [Section 1.1, pp. 49–54]

P2. Factor: $3z^2 + 11z - 4$ [Section 4.5, pp. 363–368]

P3. Solve: $6y^2 - y - 12 = 0$ [Section 4.8, pp. 385–388]

P4. Determine which of the following is in the

domain of $\dfrac{x + 4}{x^2 - 5x - 24}$.

(a) $x = -4$ (b) $x = 8$ [Section R.5, pp. 43–44]

P5. If $f(x) = x^2 - 3x - 15$, solve $f(x) = 3$. [Section 4.8, pp. 388–389]

P6. If $g(4) = 3$, what point is on the graph of g? [Section 2.3, pp. 164–167]

☐1 Solve Equations Containing Rational Expressions

Up to this point, we have learned how to solve linear equations (Section 1.1), quadratic equations (Section 4.8), and equations that contain polynomial expressions that can be factored (Section 4.8). We now introduce another type of equation, the *rational equation*. A **rational equation** is an equation that contains a rational expression. Examples of rational equations are

$$\frac{3}{x + 4} = \frac{5}{x - 1} + \frac{1}{x^2 + 3x - 4} \quad \text{and} \quad \frac{x - 5}{x^2 + 4x - 12} = 3$$

Preparing for...Answers **P1.** $\left\{\dfrac{3}{8}\right\}$

P2. $(3z - 1)(z + 4)$ **P3.** $\left\{-\dfrac{4}{3}, \dfrac{3}{2}\right\}$

P4. (a) Yes (b) No **P5.** $\{-3, 6\}$

P6. $(4, 3)$

Remember, the domain of a variable is the set of all values that the variable can take on. Because division by zero is not defined, we exclude from the domain all values of the variable that result in division by zero.

EXAMPLE 1 How to Solve a Rational Equation

Solve: $\dfrac{2x - 1}{x - 3} = \dfrac{2(x + 1)}{x - 2}$

Step-by-Step Solution

Step 1: Determine the domain of the variable in the rational equation.	Because $x = 2$ and $x = 3$ result in division by zero, the domain of x is $$\{x \mid x \neq 2, x \neq 3\}$$
Step 2: Determine the least common denominator (LCD) of all the denominators.	The LCD is $(x - 3)(x - 2)$.

Step 3: Multiply both sides of the equation by the LCD and simplify the expression on each side of the equation.		$$\frac{2x-1}{x-3} = \frac{2(x+1)}{x-2}$$
	Multiply both sides by the LCD, $(x-3)(x-2)$:	$$(x-3)(x-2) \cdot \frac{2x-1}{x-3} = (x-3)(x-2) \cdot \frac{2(x+1)}{x-2}$$
	Divide out like factors:	$(x-2)(2x-1) = 2(x-3)(x+1)$
	FOIL:	$2x^2 - 5x + 2 = 2(x^2 - 2x - 3)$
	Distribute the 2:	$2x^2 - 5x + 2 = 2x^2 - 4x - 6$
Step 4: Solve the resulting equation.	Subtract $2x^2$ from both sides:	$-5x + 2 = -4x - 6$
	Add $4x$ to both sides; subtract 2 from both sides:	$-x = -8$
	Divide both sides by -1:	$x = 8$
Step 5: Verify your solution using the original equation.	Let $x = 8$ in the original equation:	$$\frac{2(8)-1}{8-3} \overset{?}{=} \frac{2(8+1)}{8-2}$$
		$$\frac{16-1}{5} \overset{?}{=} \frac{2(9)}{6}$$
		$$\frac{15}{5} \overset{?}{=} \frac{18}{6}$$
		$3 = 3$ True

The solution checks, so the solution set is $\{8\}$. ∎

We summarize the steps that can be used to solve any rational equation.

SOLVING A RATIONAL EQUATION

Step 1: Determine the domain of the variable in the rational equation.

Step 2: Determine the least common denominator (LCD) of all the denominators.

Step 3: Multiply both sides of the equation by the LCD and simplify the expression on each side of the equation.

Step 4: Solve the resulting equation.

Step 5: Verify your solution using the original equation.

In Words

The purpose of Step 3 is to "clear the fractions" so that we transform the equation into one that we already know how to solve, such as a linear equation.

Quick ✔

1. A _____ _____ is an equation that contains a rational expression.

In Problems 2 and 3, solve each equation. Be sure to verify your results.

2. $\dfrac{x-4}{x^2+4} = \dfrac{3}{3x+2}$

3. $\dfrac{4}{x+2} = \dfrac{7}{x+4}$

EXAMPLE 2 Solving a Rational Equation

Solve: $\dfrac{2}{x} - \dfrac{1}{6} = \dfrac{5}{2x} - \dfrac{1}{3}$

Solution

The domain of the variable is $\{x \,|\, x \neq 0\}$. The LCD of all denominators is $6x$, so we multiply both sides of the equation by $6x$.

$$\frac{2}{x} - \frac{1}{6} = \frac{5}{2x} - \frac{1}{3}$$

$$6x \cdot \left(\frac{2}{x} - \frac{1}{6} \right) = 6x \cdot \left(\frac{5}{2x} - \frac{1}{3} \right)$$

Distribute the 6x: $6x \cdot \dfrac{2}{x} - 6x \cdot \dfrac{1}{6} = 6x \cdot \dfrac{5}{2x} - 6x \cdot \dfrac{1}{3}$

Simplify: $12 - x = 15 - 2x$

Add 2x to both sides: $12 + x = 15$

Subtract 12 from both sides: $x = 3$

Check   Let $x = 3$ in the original equation: $\dfrac{2}{3} - \dfrac{1}{6} \overset{?}{=} \dfrac{5}{2 \cdot 3} - \dfrac{1}{3}$

$\dfrac{4}{6} - \dfrac{1}{6} \overset{?}{=} \dfrac{5}{6} - \dfrac{2}{6}$

$\dfrac{3}{6} = \dfrac{3}{6}$ True

The solution checks, so the solution set is $\{3\}$.   ■

> **Quick ✔** *In Problems 4 and 5, solve each equation. Be sure to verify your results.*
>
> **4.** $\dfrac{5}{x} + \dfrac{1}{4} = \dfrac{3}{2x} - \dfrac{3}{2}$ **5.** $\dfrac{5}{x} + 2 = \dfrac{10}{3x} + 1$

EXAMPLE 3   Solving a Rational Equation

Solve: $\dfrac{3}{p^2 - 4p + 3} + \dfrac{6}{p^2 - 2p - 3} = \dfrac{5}{p^2 - 1}$

Solution

First, we find the domain of the variable, p.

$p^2 - 4p + 3 = (p - 3)(p - 1)$, so $p \neq 3, p \neq 1$ in the first term.

$p^2 - 2p - 3 = (p - 3)(p + 1)$, so $p \neq 3, p \neq -1$ in the second term.

$p^2 - 1 = (p - 1)(p + 1)$, so $p \neq 1, p \neq -1$ in the third term.

The domain of the variable p is $\{p \mid p \neq -1, p \neq 1, p \neq 3\}$. The factored form of each denominator found above allows us to determine that the LCD of all denominators is $(p - 1)(p + 1)(p - 3)$, so we multiply both sides of the equation by $(p - 1)(p + 1)(p - 3)$.

$$\dfrac{3}{p^2 - 4p + 3} + \dfrac{6}{p^2 - 2p - 3} = \dfrac{5}{p^2 - 1}$$

$$(p - 1)(p + 1)(p - 3) \cdot \left(\dfrac{3}{(p - 3)(p - 1)} + \dfrac{6}{(p - 3)(p + 1)} \right) = (p - 1)(p + 1)(p - 3) \cdot \dfrac{5}{(p - 1)(p + 1)}$$

Distribute the LCD and simplify: $3(p + 1) + 6(p - 1) = 5(p - 3)$

Distribute: $3p + 3 + 6p - 6 = 5p - 15$

Combine like terms: $9p - 3 = 5p - 15$

Subtract 5p from both sides; add 3 to both sides: $4p = -12$

Divide both sides by 4: $p = -3$

We leave the check to you. The solution set is $\{-3\}$.   ■

> **Quick ✔**
>
> **6.** Solve: $\dfrac{3}{x^2 + 5x + 4} + \dfrac{2}{x^2 - 3x - 4} = \dfrac{4}{x^2 - 16}$

EXAMPLE 4 Solving a Rational Equation with No Solution

Solve: $\dfrac{3}{y^2 - 5y + 4} + \dfrac{2}{y^2 - 10y + 24} = \dfrac{2}{y^2 - 7y + 6}$

Solution

First, we find the domain of the variable, y.

$y^2 - 5y + 4 = (y - 4)(y - 1)$, so $y \ne 4$, $y \ne 1$ in the first term.

$y^2 - 10y + 24 = (y - 6)(y - 4)$, so $y \ne 6$, $y \ne 4$ in the second term.

$y^2 - 7y + 6 = (y - 6)(y - 1)$, so $y \ne 6$, $y \ne 1$ in the third term.

The domain of the variable y is $\{y | y \ne 1, y \ne 4, y \ne 6\}$. The LCD of all denominators is $(y - 1)(y - 4)(y - 6)$. Multiply both sides of the equation by the LCD.

$$\frac{3}{y^2 - 5y + 4} + \frac{2}{y^2 - 10y + 24} = \frac{2}{y^2 - 7y + 6}$$

$$(y - 1)(y - 4)(y - 6) \cdot \left(\frac{3}{(y - 1)(y - 4)} + \frac{2}{(y - 4)(y - 6)} \right) = (y - 1)(y - 4)(y - 6) \cdot \frac{2}{(y - 6)(y - 1)}$$

Distribute the LCD and simplify: $3(y - 6) + 2(y - 1) = 2(y - 4)$

Distribute: $3y - 18 + 2y - 2 = 2y - 8$

Combine like terms: $5y - 20 = 2y - 8$

Subtract $2y$ from both sides; Add 20 to both sides: $3y = 12$

Divide both sides by 3: $y = 4$

Notice that $y = 4$ is not in the domain of the variable y, so there is no solution to the equation. The solution set is $\{\ \}$ or $\varnothing$. ∎

In Words

The word *extraneous* means "not constituting a vital part."

We call $y = 4$ an *extraneous solution*. **Extraneous solutions** are results that develop through the solution process but do not satisfy the original equation.

Quick ✔

7. _____ are results that develop through the solution process but do not satisfy the original equation.

8. *True or False:* Some rational equations have no solution.

In Problems 9 and 10, solve each equation. Be sure to verify your results.

9. $\dfrac{5}{z^2 + 2z - 3} - \dfrac{3}{z^2 + z - 2} = \dfrac{1}{z^2 + 5z + 6}$ **10.** $\dfrac{5}{x - 4} + \dfrac{3}{x - 2} = \dfrac{11}{x - 4}$

EXAMPLE 5 Solving a Rational Equation That Leads to a Quadratic Equation

Solve: $\dfrac{w + 3}{w - 1} + \dfrac{w + 5}{w} = \dfrac{3w + 1}{w - 1}$

Solution

The domain of the variable w is $\{w | w \ne 0, w \ne 1\}$. The LCD of all denominators is $w(w - 1)$, so we multiply both sides of the equation by $w(w - 1)$.

$$\frac{w + 3}{w - 1} + \frac{w + 5}{w} = \frac{3w + 1}{w - 1}$$

$$w(w - 1) \cdot \left(\frac{w + 3}{w - 1} + \frac{w + 5}{w} \right) = w(w - 1) \cdot \frac{3w + 1}{w - 1}$$

Work Smart
Notice that this equation has a term
with a square in it. So, we know the
equation is a quadratic equation—
this is why we rewrite the equation
with 0 on one side (standard form)
rather than isolating the variable (as
we do in solving linear equations).

Distribute the LCD: $\quad w(w+3) + (w-1)(w+5) = w(3w+1)$
$$w^2 + 3w + w^2 + 5w - w - 5 = 3w^2 + w$$

Combine like terms: $\quad 2w^2 + 7w - 5 = 3w^2 + w$

Put equation in standard form: $\quad 0 = w^2 - 6w + 5$

If $a = b$, then $b = a$: $\quad w^2 - 6w + 5 = 0$

Factor: $\quad (w-5)(w-1) = 0$

Zero-Product Property: $\quad w = 5 \quad \text{or} \quad w = 1$

Since $w = 1$ is not in the domain of the variable, it is an extraneous solution. The only potential solution is 5.

Check Let $w = 5$ in the original equation.

$$\frac{5+3}{5-1} + \frac{5+5}{5} \stackrel{?}{=} \frac{3(5)+1}{5-1}$$

$$\frac{8}{4} + \frac{10}{5} \stackrel{?}{=} \frac{16}{4}$$

$$2 + 2 = 4 \text{ True}$$

The solution set is $\{5\}$. ■

Quick ✓ *In Problems 11 and 12, solve each equation. Be sure to verify your results.*

11. $2 - \dfrac{3}{p+2} = \dfrac{6}{p}$

12. $\dfrac{z+1}{z+4} + \dfrac{z+1}{z-3} = \dfrac{z^2 + z + 16}{z^2 + z - 12}$

⌐2 Solve Equations Involving Rational Functions

Now let's look at a problem involving a rational function that leads to a rational equation.

⌐EXAMPLE 6 Working with Rational Functions

For the function $f(x) = x + \dfrac{4}{x}$, $f(x) = 5$. What point(s) are on the graph of f?

Solution

We wish to solve the equation $x + \dfrac{4}{x} = 5$. The domain of the variable is $\{x | x \neq 0\}$.

The LCD of all denominators is x, so we multiply both sides of the equation by x.

$$x \cdot \left(x + \frac{4}{x}\right) = 5 \cdot x$$

Distribute: $\quad x^2 + 4 = 5x$

Subtract 5x from both sides: $\quad x^2 - 5x + 4 = 0$

Factor: $\quad (x-4)(x-1) = 0$

Zero-Product Property: $\quad x - 4 = 0 \quad \text{or} \quad x - 1 = 0$
$$x = 4 \quad \text{or} \quad x = 1$$

We leave the check to you. We have that $f(1) = 5$, so the point $(1, 5)$ is on the graph of f. We have that $f(4) = 5$ so the point $(4, 5)$ is on the graph of f. ■

Quick ✓

13. For the function $f(x) = 2x - \dfrac{3}{x}$, solve $f(x) = 1$. What point(s) are on the graph of f?

EXAMPLE 7 An Application of Rational Functions: Drug Concentration

The concentration C of a drug in a patient's bloodstream in milligrams per liter t hours after ingestion is modeled by

$$C(t) = \frac{40t}{t^2 + 9}$$

When will the concentration of the drug be 4 milligrams per liter?

Solution

Since we want to know when the concentration of the drug is 4, we wish to solve the equation $C(t) = 4$.

$$\frac{40t}{t^2 + 9} = 4$$

Multiply both sides by $t^2 + 9$: $\quad 40t = 4(t^2 + 9)$

Divide both sides by 4: $\quad 10t = t^2 + 9$

Subtract $10t$ from both sides: $\quad 0 = t^2 - 10t + 9$

Factor: $\quad 0 = (t - 1)(t - 9)$

Zero-Product Property: $\quad t = 1 \quad$ or $\quad t = 9$

The concentration of the drug will be 4 milligrams per liter after 1 hour and after 9 hours. ∎

> **Quick ✔**
>
> **14.** The concentration C of a drug in a patient's bloodstream in milligrams per liter t hours after ingestion is modeled by $C(t) = \frac{50t}{t^2 + 6}$. When will the concentration of the drug be 4 milligrams per liter?

5.4 EXERCISES

PRACTICE   WATCH   DOWNLOAD   READ   REVIEW

1–14. *are the* Quick ✔*s that follow each* EXAMPLE

Building Skills

In Problems 15–40, solve each equation. Be sure to verify your results. See Objective 1.

15. $\dfrac{3}{z} - \dfrac{1}{2z} = -\dfrac{5}{8}$

16. $\dfrac{8}{p} + \dfrac{1}{4p} = \dfrac{11}{8}$

17. $\dfrac{y + 2}{y - 5} = \dfrac{y + 6}{y + 1}$

18. $\dfrac{w - 4}{w + 1} = \dfrac{w - 3}{w + 3}$

19. $\dfrac{x + 8}{x + 4} = \dfrac{x + 2}{x - 2}$

20. $\dfrac{2x + 1}{x + 3} = \dfrac{4(x - 1)}{2x + 3}$

21. $a - \dfrac{5}{a} = 4$

22. $m + \dfrac{8}{m} = 6$

23. $6p - \dfrac{3}{p} = 7$

24. $8b - \dfrac{3}{b} = 2$

25. $\dfrac{5 - p}{p - 5} + 2 = \dfrac{1}{p}$

26. $\dfrac{3 - y}{y - 3} + 2 = \dfrac{2}{y}$

27. $\dfrac{3}{2} + \dfrac{5}{x - 3} = \dfrac{x + 9}{2x - 6}$

28. $\dfrac{4}{3} + \dfrac{7}{x - 4} = \dfrac{x - 1}{3x - 12}$

29. $1 + \dfrac{3}{x + 3} = \dfrac{4}{x - 3}$

30. $\dfrac{5}{x + 2} = 1 - \dfrac{3}{x - 2}$

31. $\dfrac{4}{x - 5} + \dfrac{3}{x - 2} = \dfrac{x + 1}{x^2 - 7x + 10}$

32. $\dfrac{4}{x + 3} + \dfrac{5}{x - 6} = \dfrac{4x + 1}{x^2 - 3x - 18}$

33. $\dfrac{1}{x + 5} = \dfrac{2x}{x^2 - 25} - \dfrac{3}{x - 5}$

34. $\dfrac{3}{x - 4} = \dfrac{5x + 4}{x^2 - 16} - \dfrac{4}{x + 4}$

35. $\dfrac{3}{x - 1} - \dfrac{2}{x + 4} = \dfrac{x^2 + 8x + 6}{x^2 + 3x - 4}$

36. $\dfrac{5}{z - 4} + \dfrac{3}{z - 2} = \dfrac{z^2 - z - 2}{z^2 - 6z + 8}$

37. $\dfrac{7}{y^2 + y - 12} - \dfrac{4y}{y^2 + 7y + 12} = \dfrac{6}{y^2 - 9}$

38. $\dfrac{3}{x^2 - 5x - 6} + \dfrac{3}{x^2 - 7x + 6} = \dfrac{6}{x^2 - 1}$

39. $\dfrac{2x + 3}{x - 3} + \dfrac{x + 6}{x - 4} = \dfrac{x + 6}{x - 3}$

40. $\dfrac{x + 5}{x + 1} + 1 = \dfrac{x - 5}{x - 2}$

In Problems 41–48, answer each question regarding the rational function given. See Objective 2.

41. For the function $f(x) = x + \dfrac{9}{x}$, solve $f(x) = 10$. What point(s) are on the graph of f?

42. For the function $f(x) = x + \dfrac{7}{x}$, solve $f(x) = 8$. What point(s) are on the graph of f?

43. For the function $f(x) = 2x + \dfrac{4}{x}$, solve $f(x) = -9$. What point(s) are on the graph of f?

44. For the function $f(x) = 2x + \dfrac{8}{x}$, solve $f(x) = -10$. What point(s) are on the graph of f?

45. For the function $f(x) = \dfrac{x + 3}{x - 4}$, solve $f(x) = \dfrac{9}{2}$. What point(s) are on the graph of f?

46. For the function $f(x) = \dfrac{x + 5}{x - 3}$, solve $f(x) = \dfrac{1}{5}$. What point(s) are on the graph of f?

47. Let $f(x) = \dfrac{x + 2}{2x + 9}$ and $g(x) = \dfrac{x - 1}{x + 3}$. For what value(s) of x does $f(x) = g(x)$? What are the point(s) of intersection of the graphs of f and g?

48. Let $f(x) = \dfrac{4x + 1}{8x + 5}$ and $g(x) = \dfrac{x - 4}{2x - 7}$. For what value(s) of x does $f(x) = g(x)$? What are the point(s) of intersection of the graphs of f and g?

Mixed Practice

In Problems 49–58, solve each equation. Be sure to verify your results.

49. $\dfrac{4}{z + 4} - \dfrac{3}{4} = \dfrac{5z + 2}{4z + 16}$

50. $\dfrac{2b - 1}{b + 5} - \dfrac{2}{3} = \dfrac{1}{3b + 15}$

51. $x + \dfrac{9}{x} = 6$

52. $p + \dfrac{25}{p} = 10$

53. $\dfrac{2}{z^2 + 2z - 3} + \dfrac{3}{z^2 + 4z + 3} = \dfrac{6}{z^2 - 1}$

54. $\dfrac{3}{a^2 + 3a - 10} + \dfrac{2}{a^2 + 7a + 10} = \dfrac{4}{a^2 - 4}$

55. $\dfrac{4}{x} - \dfrac{5}{2x} = \dfrac{3}{4}$

56. $\dfrac{9}{b} + \dfrac{4}{5b} = \dfrac{7}{10}$

57. $\dfrac{3y + 1}{y - 1} + 3 = \dfrac{y + 2}{y + 1}$

58. $\dfrac{x + 3}{x - 2} + 4 = \dfrac{x + 2}{x + 1}$

Recall, to find the zero of a function f, we solve the equation $f(x) = 0$. The zeros of the function also represent the x-intercepts of the graph of the function. To find the zeros of a rational function R, the function must first be simplified. In Problems 59–64, find the zeros of each rational function and list the x-intercepts of the graph of the function.

59. $R(x) = \dfrac{3x + 1}{x^2 - 4}$

60. $R(x) = \dfrac{2x + 5}{x^2 - 9}$

61. $R(x) = \dfrac{2x^2 + 5x - 12}{3x^2 + 5x + 2}$

62. $R(x) = \dfrac{4x^2 + 7x - 2}{6x^2 + 5x - 4}$

63. $R(x) = \dfrac{x^3 + 3x^2 - 4x - 12}{4x^3 + 12x^2 + x + 3}$

64. $R(x) = \dfrac{x^3 - 2x^2 - 9x + 18}{x^3 - 2x^2 + 4x - 8}$

Applying the Concepts

65. Average Cost Suppose that the average daily cost $\overline{C}$ of manufacturing x bicycles is given by the function

$$\overline{C}(x) = \dfrac{x^2 + 75x + 5000}{x}$$

Determine the level of production for which the average daily cost will be $225.

66. Population When loggers began cutting in a region in the Amazon rain forest, a rare insect species was discovered. To protect the species, government scientists declared the insects endangered and moved them into a protected area. The population P of the insect t months after being transplanted is modeled by

$$P(t) = \frac{200(1 + 0.4t)}{2(1 + 0.01t)}$$

Predict when the population will be 1350 insects. Round your answer to two decimal places.

67. Cost-Benefit Model Environmental scientists often use cost-benefit models to estimate the cost of removing a pollutant from the environment as a function of the percentage of pollutant removed. Suppose a cost-benefit function for the cost C (in millions of dollars) of removing x percent of the pollutants from Maple Lake is given by

$$C(x) = \frac{25x}{100 - x}$$

(a) If the federal government budgets $100 million to clean up the lake, what percent of the pollutants can be removed?

(b) If the federal government budgets $225 million to clean up the lake, what percent of the pollutants can be removed?

68. The Learning Curve Suppose that a student is given 500 vocabulary words to learn. The function

$$P(x) = \frac{0.8x - 0.8}{0.8x + 0.1}$$

models the proportion P of words learned after x hours of studying.

(a) How long would a student need to study to learn 70% (0.7) of the words?

(b) How long would a student need to study to learn 400 words?

69. Runs in Baseball In his book *Moneyball,* author Michael Lewis cites a formula for predicting the number of runs a team will score in a season. According to the formula, the number of runs R a team will score is given by

$$R = \frac{(h + w)t}{b + w}$$

where h is the number of hits, w is the number of walks, t is the total number of bases, and b is the number of official at-bats. Suppose that the Oakland Athletics scored 750 runs in a season, had 1400 hits, 2250 total bases, and 5500 total at-bats. Use the formula to predict the number of walks that the Athletics had.

△**70. Regular Polygons** A regular polygon is a polygon that is both equilateral and equiangular. The measure I of

each interior angle of a regular polygon with n sides is $I = \dfrac{180°(n - 2)}{n}$. Find the number of sides of a regular polygon whose interior angles measure $135°$.

Extending the Concepts

71. Make up a rational equation that has one real solution.

72. Make up a rational equation that has no real solution.

73. Solve: $\left(\dfrac{4}{x + 3}\right)^2 - 5\left(\dfrac{4}{x + 3}\right) + 6 = 0$

74. Solve: $2 + 11a^{-1} = -12a^{-2}$

Explaining the Concepts

75. Explain the role that domain plays in solving a rational equation.

76. Is the solution set to the equation $\dfrac{x - 6}{x - 6} = 1$ the set of all real numbers? Explain.

Synthesis Review

In Problems 77–81, simplify or solve.

77. $\dfrac{2a^6}{(a^3)^2} - \dfrac{5a^2}{a^3} = 3\dfrac{a}{a^3}$

78. $\left(\dfrac{z^{-2}}{2z^{-3}}\right)^{-1} + 3(z - 1)^{-1}$

79. $\dfrac{3}{x - 2} - \dfrac{2x + 1}{x + 1}$

80. $\dfrac{5}{x - 6} + \dfrac{2}{x + 2} = \dfrac{1}{x^2 - 4x - 12}$

81. $\dfrac{x + 1}{2x + 3} - \dfrac{3}{x - 4} = \dfrac{-3}{2x^2 - 5x - 12}$

82. Write a sentence or two explaining the difference between "simplify" and "solve."

The Graphing Calculator

We can use a graphing calculator to approximate solutions to rational equations using the INTERSECT or ZERO (or ROOT) feature of the graphing calculator. We use the ZERO or ROOT feature of the graphing calculator when one side of the equation is 0; we use the INTERSECT feature when neither side of the equation is 0. For example, to solve $\dfrac{x - 4}{x + 1} = 4$, we would graph

$Y_1 = \dfrac{x - 4}{x + 1}$ and $Y_2 = 4$. The x-coordinates of the point(s) of intersection represent the solution set as shown in Figure 1.

Figure 1

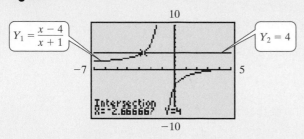

$Y_1 = \dfrac{x-4}{x+1}$

$Y_2 = 4$

Intersection
X=-2.666667 Y=4

When using a graphing calculator to approximate solutions to equations, we will express the solution as a decimal rounded to two decimal places, if necessary. The solution to the equation $\dfrac{x-4}{x+1} = 4$ is $x = -2.67$ rounded to two decimal places.

In Problems 83–88, use a graphing utility to solve the equation by graphing each side of the equation and finding the point(s) of intersection.

83. $\dfrac{x-4}{x+4} = \dfrac{1}{2}$

84. $\dfrac{x-6}{x+1} = \dfrac{2}{3}$

85. $\dfrac{3}{5} + \dfrac{4}{x+6} = \dfrac{x+12}{5x+30}$

86. $\dfrac{4}{3} + \dfrac{7}{x-4} = \dfrac{-7}{3x-12}$

87. $\dfrac{2x^2 + 11x + 12}{x+4} = -5$

88. $\dfrac{3x^2 + 10x + 3}{x+3} = -8$

5.5 Rational Inequalities

OBJECTIVE

1 Solve a Rational Inequality

Preparing for Rational Inequalities

Before getting started, take the following readiness quiz. If you get a problem wrong, go back to the section cited and review the material.

P1. Write $-1 < x \le 8$ in interval notation.   [Section 1.4, pp. 81–84]

P2. Solve: $2x + 3 > 4x - 9$ [Section 1.4, pp. 85–88]

Back in Section 1.4, we solved linear inequalities in one variable such as $2x - 3 > 4x + 5$. We were able to solve these inequalities using methods that were similar to solving linear equations. We also learned to represent the solution set to such an inequality using either set-builder notation or interval notation.

Although the approach to solving inequalities involving rational expressions is not a simple extension of solving rational equations, we will use the skills developed in solving equations to solve rational inequalities.

1 Solve a Rational Inequality

A **rational inequality** is an inequality that contains a rational expression. Examples of rational inequalities include

$$\frac{1}{x} > 1 \qquad \frac{x-1}{x+5} \le 0 \qquad \frac{x^2 + 3x + 2}{x-5} > 0 \qquad \frac{3}{x-5} < \frac{4x}{2x-1} + \frac{1}{x}$$

There are two keys to solving rational inequalities:

1. The quotient of two positive numbers is positive; the quotient of a positive and negative number is negative; and the quotient of two negative numbers is positive.

2. A rational expression may change signs (positive to negative or negative to positive) on either side of a value of the variable that makes the rational expression equal to 0 or for values for which the rational expression is undefined.

Preparing for...Answers **P1.** $(-1, 8]$
P2. $\{x | x < 6\}$ or $(-\infty, 6)$

EXAMPLE 1 How to Solve a Rational Inequality

Solve $\dfrac{x+3}{x-4} \geq 0$. Graph the solution set.

Step-by-Step Solution

Step 1: Write the inequality so that a rational expression is on one side of the inequality and 0 is on the other. Be sure to write the rational expression as a single quotient.	The inequality is already in the form that we need. $$\frac{x+3}{x-4} \geq 0$$
Step 2: Determine the numbers for which the rational expression equals 0 or is undefined.	The rational expression will equal 0 when $x = -3$. The rational expression is undefined when $x = 4$.
Step 3: Use the numbers found in Step 2 to separate the real number line into intervals.	We separate the real number line into the following intervals: $(-\infty, -3) \qquad (-3, 4) \qquad (4, \infty)$ Because the rational expression is undefined at $x = 4$, we plot an open circle at 4.
Step 4: Choose a test point within each interval formed in Step 3 to determine the sign of $x + 3$ and $x - 4$. Then determine the sign of the quotient.	• In the interval $(-\infty, -3)$ we choose a test point of -4. The expression $x + 3$ equals -1 when $x = -4$. The expression $x - 4$ equals -8 when $x = -4$. Since the quotient of two negatives is positive, the expression $\dfrac{x+3}{x-4}$ will be positive when $x = -4$. So the expression $\dfrac{x+3}{x-4}$ will be positive for all x in the interval $(-\infty, -3)$. • In the interval $(-3, 4)$ we choose a test point of 0. For $x = 0$, $x + 3$ is positive, while $x - 4$ is negative, so $\dfrac{x+3}{x-4}$ will be negative when $x = 0$. • In the interval $(4, \infty)$ we choose a test point of 5. For $x = 5$, both $x + 3$ and $x - 4$ are positive, so $\dfrac{x+3}{x-4}$ will be positive. Table 1 shows these results, the sign of $\dfrac{x+3}{x-4}$ in each interval and the value of $\dfrac{x+3}{x-4}$ at $x = -3$ and $x = 4$. We want to know where $\dfrac{x+3}{x-4}$ is greater than or equal to zero. The solution set is $\{x \mid x \leq -3 \text{ or } x > 4\}$ using set-builder notation; the solution is $(-\infty, -3] \cup (4, \infty)$ using interval notation. Notice that -3 is part of the solution set since $x = -3$ causes $\dfrac{x+3}{x-4}$ to equal zero, but 4 is not part of the solution set because it is not in the domain of $\dfrac{x+3}{x-4}$. Figure 2 shows the graph of the solution set.

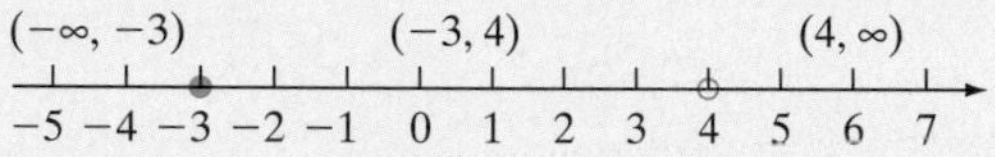

Figure 2

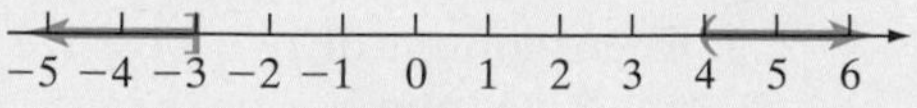

Table 1

Interval	$(-\infty, -3)$	-3	$(-3, 4)$	4	$(4, \infty)$
Test Point	-4	-3	0	4	5
Sign of $x + 3$	Negative	0	Positive	Positive	Positive
Sign of $x - 4$	Negative	Negative	Negative	0	Positive
Sign of $\dfrac{x + 3}{x - 4}$	Positive	0	Negative	Undefined	Positive
Conclusion	$\dfrac{x + 3}{x - 4}$ is positive, so $(-\infty, -3)$ is part of the solution set.	Because the inequality is nonstrict, -3 is part of the solution.	$\dfrac{x + 3}{x - 4}$ is negative, so $(-3, 4)$ is not part of the solution set.	4 cannot be part of the solution set because it causes division by 0.	$\dfrac{x + 3}{x - 4}$ is positive, so $(4, \infty)$ is part of the solution set.

SOLVING RATIONAL INEQUALITIES

Step 1: Write the inequality so that a rational expression is on one side of the inequality and 0 is on the other. Be sure to write the rational expression as a single quotient in factored form.

Step 2: Determine the numbers for which the rational expression equals 0 or is undefined.

Step 3: Use the numbers found in Step 2 to separate the real number line into intervals.

Step 4: Choose a test point within each interval formed in Step 3 to determine the sign of each factor in the numerator and denominator. Then determine the sign of the quotient.

- If the quotient is positive, then the rational expression is positive for all numbers x in the interval.
- If the quotient is negative, then the rational expression is negative for all numbers x in the interval.

Also determine the value of the rational expression at each value found in Step 2. If the inequality is not strict ($\leq$ or $\geq$), include the values of the variable for which the rational expression equals 0 in the solution set, but do not include the values for which the rational expression is undefined!

Quick ✔

1. The inequality $\dfrac{2x - 3}{x + 6} > 1$ is an example of a(n) _____ inequality.

2. Solve $\dfrac{x - 7}{x + 3} \geq 0$. Graph the solution set.

3. Solve $\dfrac{1 - x}{x + 5} > 0$. Graph the solution set.

EXAMPLE 2 Solving a Rational Inequality

Solve $\dfrac{x+3}{x-1} > 2$. Graph the solution set.

Solution

First, we write the inequality so that a rational expression is on one side of the inequality and 0 is on the other.

$$\frac{x+3}{x-1} > 2$$

Subtract 2 from both sides:
$$\frac{x+3}{x-1} - 2 > 0$$

LCD $= x - 1$; multiply -2 by $\dfrac{x-1}{x-1}$:
$$\frac{x+3}{x-1} - 2 \cdot \frac{x-1}{x-1} > 0$$

Write rational expression over common denominator:
$$\frac{x+3-2(x-1)}{x-1} > 0$$

Distribute -2:
$$\frac{x+3-2x+2}{x-1} > 0$$

Combine like terms in numerator:
$$\frac{-x+5}{x-1} > 0$$

We can see that the rational expression will equal 0 when $x = 5$. The rational expression is undefined when $x = 1$. We separate the real number line into the following intervals (Figure 3):

Figure 3

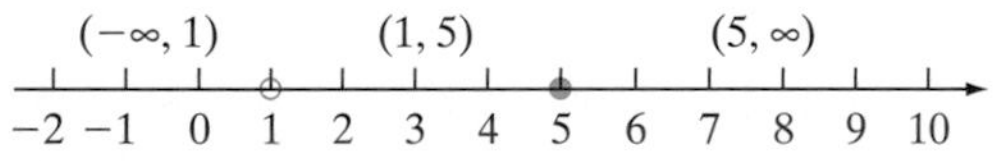

Table 2 shows the sign of $-x + 5$, $x - 1$, and $\dfrac{-x+5}{x-1}$ in each interval. In addition, it shows the value of $\dfrac{-x+5}{x-1}$ at $x = 1$ and $x = 5$.

Table 2					
Interval	$(-\infty, 1)$	1	$(1, 5)$	5	$(5, \infty)$
Test Point	0	1	3	5	6
Sign of $-x + 5$	Positive	Positive	Positive	0	Negative
Sign of $x - 1$	Negative	0	Positive	Positive	Positive
Sign of $\dfrac{-x+5}{x-1}$	Negative	Undefined	Positive	0	Negative
Conclusion	$\dfrac{-x+5}{x-1}$ is negative, so $(-\infty, 1)$ is not part of the solution set.	Because $\dfrac{-x+5}{x-1}$ is undefined at $x = 1$, it is not part of the solution set.	$\dfrac{-x+5}{x-1}$ is positive, so $(1, 5)$ is part of the solution set.	Because the inequality is strict, 5 is not part of the solution set.	$\dfrac{-x+5}{x-1}$ is negative, so $(5, \infty)$ is not part of the solution set.

We want to know the values of x such that $\dfrac{x+3}{x-1}$ is greater than 2. This is equivalent to determining where $\dfrac{-x+5}{x-1}$ is greater than zero. So the solution set is $\{x\,|\,1 < x < 5\}$ using set-builder notation. The solution is $(1, 5)$ using interval notation. Notice that the endpoints of the interval are not part of the solution because the inequality in the original problem is strict. Figure 4 shows the graph of the solution set. ∎

Figure 4

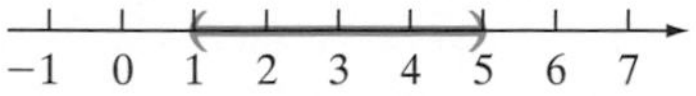

Quick ✔

4. Solve $\dfrac{4x+5}{x+2} < 3$. Graph the solution set.

5.5 EXERCISES

MyMathLab   PRACTICE   WATCH   DOWNLOAD   READ   REVIEW

1–4. *are the* Quick ✔s *that follow each* EXAMPLE

Building Skills

In Problems 5–20, solve each rational inequality. Graph the solution set. See Objective 1.

5. $\dfrac{x-4}{x+1} > 0$

6. $\dfrac{x+5}{x-2} > 0$

7. $\dfrac{x+9}{x-3} < 0$

8. $\dfrac{x+8}{x+2} < 0$

9. $\dfrac{x+10}{x-4} \geq 0$

10. $\dfrac{x+12}{x-2} \geq 0$

11. $\dfrac{(3x+5)(x+8)}{x-2} \leq 0$

12. $\dfrac{(3x-2)(x-6)}{x+1} \geq 0$

13. $\dfrac{x-5}{x+1} < 1$

14. $\dfrac{x+3}{x-4} > 1$

15. $\dfrac{2x-9}{x-3} > 4$

16. $\dfrac{3x+20}{x+6} < 5$

17. $\dfrac{3}{x-4} + \dfrac{1}{x} \geq 0$

18. $\dfrac{2}{x+3} + \dfrac{2}{x} \leq 0$

19. $\dfrac{3}{x-2} \leq \dfrac{4}{x+5}$

20. $\dfrac{1}{x-4} \geq \dfrac{3}{2x+1}$

Mixed Practice

In Problems 21–30, solve each inequality. Graph the solution set.

21. $\dfrac{(2x-1)(x+3)}{x-5} > 0$

22. $\dfrac{(5x-2)(x+4)}{x-5} < 0$

23. $3 - 4(x+1) < 11$

24. $2x + 3(x-2) \geq x + 2$

25. $\dfrac{x+7}{x-8} \leq 0$

26. $\dfrac{x-10}{x+5} \leq 0$

27. $(x-2)(2x+1) \geq 2(x-1)^2$

28. $(x+2)^2 < 3x^2 - 2(x+1)(x-2)$

29. $\dfrac{3x-1}{x+4} \geq 2$

30. $\dfrac{3x-7}{x+2} \leq 2$

In Problems 31–34, for each function, find the values of x that satisfy the given condition.

31. Solve $R(x) \leq 0$ if $R(x) = \dfrac{x-6}{x+1}$.

32. Solve $R(x) \geq 0$ if $R(x) = \dfrac{x+3}{x-8}$.

33. Solve $R(x) < 0$ if $R(x) = \dfrac{2x-5}{x+2}$.

34. Solve $R(x) < 0$ if $R(x) = \dfrac{3x+2}{x-4}$.

Applying the Concepts

35. Average Cost Suppose that the daily cost C of manufacturing x bicycles is given by $C(x) = 80x + 5000$. Then the average daily cost $\overline{C}$ is given by $\overline{C}(x) = \dfrac{80x + 5000}{x}$. How many bicycles must be produced each day in order for the average cost to be no more than \$130?

36. Average Cost See Problem 35. Suppose that the government imposes a \$10 tax on each bicycle manufactured so that the daily cost C of manufacturing x bicycles is now given by $C(x) = 90x + 5000$. Now the average daily cost $\overline{C}$ is given by $\overline{C}(x) = \dfrac{90x + 5000}{x}$. How many bicycles must be produced each day in order for the average cost to be no more than \$130?

Extending the Concepts

37. Write a rational inequality that has $(2, \infty)$ as the solution set.

38. Write a rational inequality that has $(-2, 5]$ as the solution set.

Explaining the Concepts

39. In solving the rational inequality $\dfrac{x - 4}{x + 1} \le 0$, a student determines that the only interval that makes the inequality true is $(-1, 4)$. He states that the solution set is $\{x \mid -1 \le x \le 4\}$. What is wrong with this solution?

40. In Step 2 of the steps for solving a rational inequality, we determine the numbers for which the rational expression equals 0 or is undefined. We then use these numbers to form intervals on the real number line. Explain why this guarantees that there is not a change in the sign of the rational expression within any given interval.

Synthesis Review

In Problems 41–46, find the x-intercepts of the graph of each function.

41. $F(x) = 6x - 12$

42. $G(x) = 5x + 30$

43. $f(x) = 2x^2 + 3x - 14$

44. $h(x) = -3x^2 - 7x + 20$

45. $R(x) = \dfrac{3x - 2}{x + 4}$

46. $R(x) = \dfrac{x^2 + 5x + 6}{x + 2}$

The Graphing Calculator

We can use a graphing calculator to approximate solutions to rational inequalities using the INTERSECT or ZERO (or ROOT) feature of the graphing calculator. We use the ZERO or ROOT feature of the graphing calculator when one side of the inequality is 0; we use the INTERSECT feature when neither side of the inequality is 0. For example, to solve $\dfrac{x - 4}{x + 1} > \dfrac{7}{2}$, we would graph $Y_1 = \dfrac{x - 4}{x + 1}$ and $Y_2 = \dfrac{7}{2}$. To determine the x-values such that the graph of Y_1 is above that of Y_2, we find x-coordinates of the point(s) of intersection. The graph of Y_1 is above that of Y_2 between $x = -3$ and $x = -1$. See Figure 5.

Figure 5

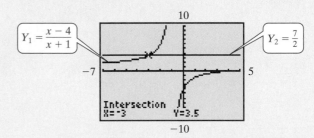

When using a graphing calculator to approximate solutions to inequalities, we typically express the solution as a decimal rounded to two decimal places, if exact answers cannot be found. The solution to the inequality $\dfrac{x - 4}{x + 1} > \dfrac{7}{2}$ is $\{x \mid -3 < x < -1\}$, or $(-3, -1)$ using interval notation.

In Problems 47–50, solve each inequality using a graphing calculator.

47. $\dfrac{x - 5}{x + 1} \le 3$

48. $\dfrac{x + 2}{x - 5} > -2$

49. $\dfrac{2x + 5}{x - 7} > 3$

50. $\dfrac{2x - 1}{x + 5} \le 4$

5.6 Models Involving Rational Expressions

OBJECTIVES

1. Solve for a Variable in a Rational Expression
2. Model and Solve Ratio and Proportion Problems
3. Model and Solve Work Problems
4. Model and Solve Uniform Motion Problems

Preparing for Models Involving Rational Expressions

Before getting started, take the following readiness quiz. If you get a problem wrong, go back to the section cited and review the material.

P1. Solve for y: $4x - 2y = 10$ [Section 1.3, pp. 73–76]

1   Solve for a Variable in a Rational Expression

The expression "solve for the variable" means to get the variable by itself on one side of the equation with all other variables and constants, if any, on the other side. The steps that we follow when solving formulas for a certain variable are identical to those that we followed when solving rational equations.

EXAMPLE 1   Solving for a Variable in a Lens Construction Formula

The formula $\dfrac{1}{f} = \dfrac{1}{p} + \dfrac{1}{q}$ is used in telescope and camera construction, where f is the focal length of the lens. In general, the larger f, the more power the telescope has. The variable p is the distance between the object we wish to see and the lens; the variable q is the distance from the lens to the point of focus (such as the film or your eye). See Figure 6.

Figure 6

(a) Solve the formula for q.

(b) Suppose that a camera has a focal length of 100 mm and the camera is focusing on an object 5000 mm away. What is q, the distance from the lens to the point of focus? Round your answer to the nearest millimeter.

Solution

(a) Our goal is to get q by itself. We follow the same steps that we used to solve a rational equation. First, we note that none of the variables can equal 0. The LCD of all denominators is pqf, so we multiply both sides of the equation by pqf.

$$\frac{1}{f} = \frac{1}{p} + \frac{1}{q}$$

$$pqf \cdot \frac{1}{f} = pqf \cdot \left(\frac{1}{p} + \frac{1}{q}\right)$$

Distribute pqf: $$pqf \cdot \frac{1}{f} = pqf \cdot \frac{1}{p} + pqf \cdot \frac{1}{q}$$

Simplify: $$pq = qf + pf$$

To get all terms involving q on one side, subtract qf from both sides: $$pq - qf = qf + pf - qf$$

$$pq - qf = pf$$

Factor out q: $$q(p - f) = pf$$

Divide both sides by $p - f$: $$q = \frac{pf}{p - f}$$

(b) Substitute $f = 100$ mm and $p = 5000$ mm in $q = \dfrac{pf}{p - f}$.

$$q = \frac{5000 \cdot 100}{5000 - 100}$$

$$\approx 102 \text{ mm}$$

The distance from the lens to the point of focus is approximately 102 mm. ■

Quick ✔

1. The formula $Y = \dfrac{G}{1 - b}$ is used in economics to determine the impact on Gross Domestic Product (GDP) Y by increasing government spending by G dollars if the proportion of additional income that people spend is b.

   (a) Solve the formula for b.

   (b) Find b if the government increased spending by \$100 billion and GDP increased by \$1000 billion.

⌐2 Model and Solve Ratio and Proportion Problems

The problems in this objective focus on the idea of ratio and proportion. The **ratio** of two numbers a and b can be written as

$$a{:}b \qquad \text{or} \qquad \frac{a}{b}$$

When solving algebraic problems, we write ratios as $\dfrac{a}{b}$. A **proportion** is a statement (equation) that two ratios are equal. That is, proportions are equations of the form $\dfrac{a}{b} = \dfrac{c}{d}$. You may be familiar with using proportions to solve problems involving similar

Figure 7

figures, such as triangles, from geometry. Recall, that two figures are **similar** if their angles have the same measure and their corresponding sides are proportional. Figure 7 shows examples of similar figures.

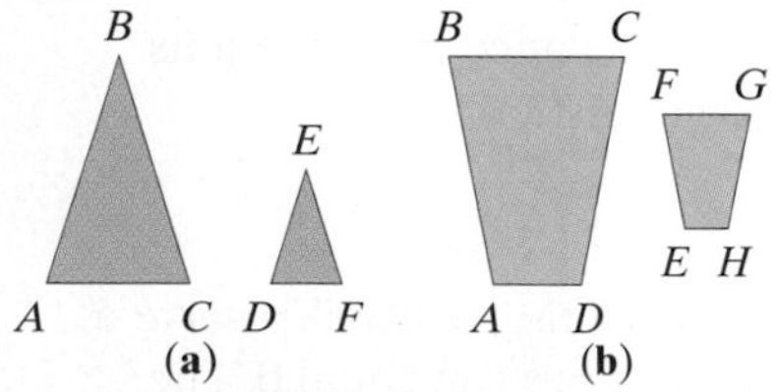

In Figure 7**(a)**, $\triangle ABC$ is similar to $\triangle DEF$ and in Figure 7**(b)**, quadrilateral $ABCD$ is similar to quadrilateral $EFGH$. Because $\triangle ABC$ is similar to $\triangle DEF$, we know that the ratio of AB to AC equals the ratio of DE to DF. That is,

$$\frac{AB}{AC} = \frac{DE}{DF}$$

The principle that the ratios of corresponding sides are equal can be used to find unknown lengths in similar figures.

⌐EXAMPLE 2 Similar Figures

Suppose that you are standing next to a tall building and wish to know the building's height. A light post that is 20 feet tall casts a shadow that is 12 feet long. The shadow from the building is measured to be 660 feet. Determine the height of the building.

Solution

The ratio of the length of the building's shadow to the height of the building equals the ratio of the length of the light post's shadow to the height of the light post because the building and its shadow form a triangle that is similar to the light post and its shadow. See Figure 8.

Figure 8

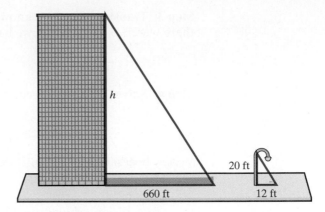

We set up the proportion problem as

$$\frac{660}{h} = \frac{12}{20}$$

and solve the equation. The domain of h is $\{h \mid h > 0\}$ since h represents the height of the building. The LCD of all denominators is $20h$, so we multiply both sides of the equation by $20h$.

$$\frac{660}{h} = \frac{12}{20}$$

$$20h \cdot \frac{660}{h} = 20h \cdot \frac{12}{20}$$

$$13{,}200 = 12h$$

Divide both sides by 12: $\quad 1100 = h$

The height of the building is 1100 feet. ■

Figure 9

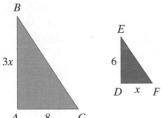

Quick ✔

2. A(n) _____ is a statement (equation) that two ratios are equal. Two figures are _____ if their angles have the same measure and their corresponding sides are proportional.

3. Suppose a man who is 6 feet tall casts a shadow that is 2 feet long. At the same time, a building casts a shadow that is 40 feet long. How tall is the building?

4. Suppose that $\triangle ABC$ is similar to $\triangle DEF$ as shown in Figure 9. Find the length of AB and DF.

Proportion problems also come up in direct translation problems as well.

|EXAMPLE 3 A Proportion Problem

According to the National Vital Statistics Report dated December 5, 2007, the birth rate for unmarried women (15–44 years of age) was 47.5 live births per 1000 population in the United States in 2005. In 2005, there were 1,527,000 births to unmarried women. Determine the population of unmarried women between 15 and 44 years of age in 2005.

Solution

Step 1: Identify This is a direct translation problem involving proportions. We are looking for the population of unmarried women in 2005.

Step 2: Name We let p represent the population of unmarried women in 2005.

Step 3: Translate Since we know that the rate of births was 47.5 per 1000 and that there were 1,527,000 births, we have the model

$$\frac{47.5}{1000} = \frac{1,527,000}{p}$$

Step 4: Solve We now proceed to solve the equation.

$$\frac{47.5}{1000} = \frac{1,527,000}{p}$$

Multiply both sides by the LCD, 1000p: $\quad 1000p \cdot \dfrac{47.5}{1000} = 1000p \cdot \dfrac{1,527,000}{p}$

Divide out common factors: $\qquad\qquad 47.5p = 1,527,000,000$

Divide both sides by 47.5: $\qquad\qquad\quad p = 32,147,368$

Step 5: Check It is always a good idea to make sure your answer is reasonable. According to the U.S. Census Bureau, there were over 60 million women 15–44 years of age in the United States in 2005, so the answer seems reasonable.

Step 6: Answer The population of unmarried women 15–44 years of age in the United States in 2005 was 32,147,368. ∎

Quick ✔

5. According to the American Cancer Society, the incidence rate of melanoma of the skin is 20 per 100,000 population in the United States. There were approximately 62,480 reported cases of melanoma in the United States in 2008. Determine the population of the United States in 2008.

---

3 Model and Solve Work Problems

We are now going to solve work or "constant rate jobs" problems. These problems assume that jobs are performed at a **constant rate.** While this assumption is reasonable for machines, it is not likely to be true for people simply because of the old phrase "too many chefs spoil the broth." Think of it this way—if you continually add more people to paint a room, the time to complete the job may decrease initially, but eventually the painters get in each other's way and the time to completion actually increases. While we could build models that take this into account, we will make the "constant rate" assumption for humans as well in order to keep the mathematics manageable.

The constant rate assumption states that if it takes t units of time to complete a job, then $\dfrac{1}{t}$ of the job is done in 1 unit of time. For example, if it takes 5 hours to paint a room, then $\dfrac{1}{5}$ of the room should be painted in 1 hour.

Work Smart

Remember, when we model we make simplifying assumptions to make the math easier to deal with.

EXAMPLE 4 Working Together on a Job

It's Saturday and Kevin needs to cut and edge the grass. At 9 A.M., Michael asks Kevin to go golfing at 11:00 A.M. Typically, it takes Kevin 3 hours to cut and edge the grass. When Michael cuts and edges the grass, it takes 4 hours. If they worked together, would they be able to finish the lawn and still make the golf date?

Solution

Step 1: Identify We want to know how long it will take for Michael and Kevin to finish the lawn.

Step 2: Name We let t represent the time (in hours) that it takes to finish the lawn working together. Then, in 1 hour they will complete $\dfrac{1}{t}$ of the job.

Step 3: Translate Since we know that Kevin can finish the job in 3 hours, Kevin will finish $\frac{1}{3}$ of the job in 1 hour. We know that Michael can finish the job in 4 hours, so Michael will finish $\frac{1}{4}$ of the job in 1 hour. We set up the model using the following logic:

$$\left(\begin{array}{c}\text{Part done by Kevin}\\\text{in 1 hour}\end{array}\right) + \left(\begin{array}{c}\text{Part done by Michael}\\\text{in 1 hour}\end{array}\right) = \left(\begin{array}{c}\text{Part done together}\\\text{in 1 hour}\end{array}\right)$$

$$\frac{1}{3} \qquad + \qquad \frac{1}{4} \qquad = \qquad \frac{1}{t} \quad \text{The Model}$$

Step 4: Solve We now proceed to solve the equation.

$$\frac{1}{3} + \frac{1}{4} = \frac{1}{t}$$

Multiply both sides by the LCD, $12t$: $12t \cdot \left(\frac{1}{3} + \frac{1}{4}\right) = 12t \cdot \frac{1}{t}$

Distribute: $12t \cdot \frac{1}{3} + 12t \cdot \frac{1}{4} = 12t \cdot \frac{1}{t}$

Divide like factors: $4t + 3t = 12$

Combine like terms: $7t = 12$

Divide both sides by 7: $t = \frac{12}{7} \approx 1.714$

Work Smart

We convert 0.714 hour to minutes by multiplying 0.714 by 60 minutes and obtain 43 minutes.

Step 5: Check It is always a good idea to make sure your answer is reasonable. We expect our answer to be greater than 0 but less than 3 (because it takes Kevin 3 hours working by himself). Our answer of 1.714 hours or 1 hour, 43 minutes seems reasonable.

Step 6: Answer If they start right away, they should finish at 10:43 A.M. As long as they can get to the course in 17 minutes, they can make the tee time. ∎

Quick ✔

6. Juan and Maria have a pool in their backyard. If they use their hose alone to fill the pool, the pool can be filled in 30 hours. Their neighbor has the same-sized pool and was able to fill it in 24 hours. Suppose their neighbor agrees to let them use his hose. How long will it take to fill the pool with both hoses?

EXAMPLE 5 The Kitchen Sink

Suppose that the kitchen sink can be filled in 5 minutes. If the sink is full, it takes 8 minutes to drain the sink when the drain is left partially open. If the sink's drain is accidentally left partially open, how long will it take to fill the sink?

Solution

Step 1: Identify We want to know how long it will take to fill the sink with the drain partially open.

Step 2: Name We let t represent the time (in minutes) that it takes to fill the sink. Then, in 1 minute $\frac{1}{t}$ of the sink will be full.

Step 3: Translate We know that the sink can be filled in 5 minutes when the drain is closed, so after 1 minute, $\frac{1}{5}$ of the sink is full. It takes 8 minutes to drain, so after 1 minute, $\frac{1}{8}$ of the sink is drained. We set up the model using the following logic:

Work Smart
Notice we subtract the portion of sink drained after 1 minute since it is "working against us."

$$\begin{pmatrix} \text{Portion of sink filled} \\ \text{in 1 minute with} \\ \text{closed drain} \end{pmatrix} - \begin{pmatrix} \text{Portion of sink drained} \\ \text{after 1 minute} \end{pmatrix} = \begin{pmatrix} \text{Portion of sink filled} \\ \text{after 1 minute with} \\ \text{open drain} \end{pmatrix}$$

$$\frac{1}{5} \qquad - \qquad \frac{1}{8} \qquad = \qquad \frac{1}{t} \quad \text{The Model}$$

Step 4: Solve We now proceed to solve the equation.

$$\frac{1}{5} - \frac{1}{8} = \frac{1}{t}$$

Multiply both sides by the LCD: $40t$: $\quad 40t \cdot \left(\frac{1}{5} - \frac{1}{8} \right) = 40t \cdot \frac{1}{t}$

Distribute: $\quad 40t \cdot \frac{1}{5} - 40t \cdot \frac{1}{8} = 40t \cdot \frac{1}{t}$

Simplify: $\quad 8t - 5t = 40$

Combine like terms: $\quad 3t = 40$

Divide both sides by 3: $\quad t = \frac{40}{3} \approx 13.3 \text{ minutes}$

Step 5: Check It is always a good idea to make sure your answer is reasonable. We expect our answer to be greater than 5 since this is the time it takes to fill the sink with the drain closed. Our answer of 13.3 minutes or 13 minutes, 20 seconds seems reasonable.

Step 6: Answer It will take 13.3 minutes or 13 minutes, 20 seconds to fill the sink. ■

Quick ✔

7. A children's inflatable pool takes 20 minutes to fill with an electric air pump. It takes 50 minutes to let the air out of the pool. If the pool's valve is accidentally left open, how long will it take to fill the pool?

⌐4⌐ Model and Solve Uniform Motion Problems

We first introduced uniform motion problems back in Section 1.2. Recall that uniform motion problems use the fact that distance equals rate times time, that is, $d = rt$. When modeling uniform motion problems that lead to rational equations, we usually end up using an alternative form of this model, $t = \frac{d}{r}$.

⌐EXAMPLE 6⌐ A Round-Trip Flight

A plane flies 990 miles west (into the wind) and makes the return trip following the same flight path. The effect of the wind on the plane is 20 miles per hour. The round trip takes 10 hours. What is the speed of the plane in still air?

Solution

Step 1: Identify This is a uniform motion problem. We wish to know the speed of the plane in still air.

Step 2: Name Let r represent the speed of the plane in still air.

Step 3: Translate Going west, the plane is flying into the wind. The speed of the plane is its rate in still air less the impact of the wind, so $r - 20$ represents the speed of the plane going west. Similar logic tells us that the speed of the plane going east is $r + 20$. We set up Table 3. Remember, $d = r \cdot t$, so that $t = \dfrac{d}{r}$ or $\dfrac{d}{r} = t$.

Table 3			
	Distance (miles)	Rate (miles per hour)	Time (hours)
West	990	$r - 20$	$\dfrac{990}{r - 20}$
East	990	$r + 20$	$\dfrac{990}{r + 20}$

The round trip takes 10 hours, so that we have the following model:

$$\text{Time going west} + \text{Time going east} = 10$$

$$\frac{990}{r - 20} + \frac{990}{r + 20} = 10 \quad \text{The Model}$$

Step 4: Solve We wish to solve for r:

$$\frac{990}{r - 20} + \frac{990}{r + 20} = 10$$

Multiply both sides by the LCD, $(r - 20)(r + 20)$: $\quad (r - 20)(r + 20)\left(\dfrac{990}{r - 20} + \dfrac{990}{r + 20}\right) = 10(r - 20)(r + 20)$

Distribute: $\quad (r - 20)(r + 20)\dfrac{990}{r - 20} + (r - 20)(r + 20)\dfrac{990}{r + 20} = 10(r - 20)(r + 20)$

Divide out common factors: $\quad 990(r + 20) + 990(r - 20) = 10(r - 20)(r + 20)$

Distribute: $\quad 990r + 19{,}800 + 990r - 19{,}800 = 10(r^2 - 400)$

Combine like terms: $\quad 1980r = 10(r^2 - 400)$

Divide both sides by 10: $\quad 198r = r^2 - 400$

Set equal to 0: $\quad 0 = r^2 - 198r - 400$

Factor: $\quad 0 = (r - 200)(r + 2)$

Zero-Product Property: $\quad r = 200 \text{ or } r = -2$

Step 5: Check We disregard the -2 because the rate of the plane must be positive. So it appears that the plane will travel at a rate of 200 miles per hour in still air. Flying west, the plane travels at 180 miles per hour, so it takes $\dfrac{990 \text{ miles}}{180 \text{ miles per hour}} = 5.5 \text{ hours}$ to fly west. Flying east, the plane travels at 220 miles per hour, so the trip takes $\dfrac{990 \text{ miles}}{220 \text{ miles per hour}} = 4.5 \text{ hours}$. The total trip is $5.5 + 4.5 = 10$ hours. It checks!

Step 6: Answer the Question The plane travels at 200 miles per hour in still air. ∎

Quick ✔

8. A canoe travels on a river whose current is running at 2 miles per hour. After traveling 12 miles upstream, the canoe turns around and makes the 12-mile trip back downstream. The trip up and back takes 8 hours. What is the speed of the canoe in still water?

5.6 EXERCISES

PRACTICE   WATCH   DOWNLOAD   READ   REVIEW

1–8. *are the* Quick ✓s *that follow each* EXAMPLE

Building Skills

In Problems 9–18, solve each formula for the indicated variable. See Objective 1.

9. Chemistry (Gas Laws) Solve $\dfrac{V_1}{V_2} = \dfrac{P_2}{P_1}$ for P_1.

10. Chemistry (Gas Laws) Solve $\dfrac{V_1}{V_2} = \dfrac{P_2}{P_1}$ for V_2.

11. Finance Solve $R = \dfrac{r}{1-t}$ for t.

12. Finance Solve $P = \dfrac{A}{1+r}$ for r.

13. Slope Solve $m = \dfrac{y-y_1}{x-x_1}$ for x.

14. Slope Solve $m = \dfrac{y-y_1}{x-x_1}$ for x_1.

15. Physics Solve $\omega = \dfrac{rmv}{I+mr^2}$ for v.

16. Physics Solve $\omega = \dfrac{rmv}{I+mr^2}$ for I.

17. Physics Solve $V = \dfrac{mv}{M+m}$ for m.

18. Physics Solve $v_2 = \dfrac{2m_1}{m_1+m_2}v_1$ for m_1.

Applying the Concepts

In Problems 19–26, solve the proportion problem. See Objective 2.

△ **19.** Suppose that $\triangle ABC$ is similar to $\triangle DEF$ as shown in the figure. Find the length of AB and DF.

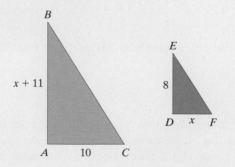

△ **20.** Suppose that $\triangle ABC$ is similar to $\triangle DEF$ as shown in the figure. Find the length of AB and DF.

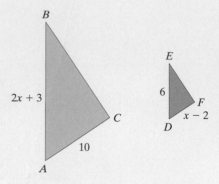

21. Motor Vehicle Death Rates According to the Centers for Disease Control, the death rate as a result of a motor vehicle accident is 15.3 per 100,000 population. In 2005, there were 43,443 fatalities in motor vehicle accidents. What was the population in the United States in 2005?

22. Flight Accidents According to the *Statistical Abstract of the United States,* in 2006, there were 1.32 fatal airplane accidents per 100,000 flight hours. Also, in 2006, there were a total of 303 fatal accidents. How many flight hours were flown in 2006?

23. Road Trip At current prices, Roberta can drive her car 8.2 miles per dollar of gasoline that she buys. Roberta and three of her friends decide to go on a road trip to a neighboring university that is 105 miles away and agree to split the cost evenly. To the nearest cent, how much money will each have to contribute to get to the university and back?

24. Car Payments At current rates, a 60-month term car loan is being offered where the monthly payments are $0.0191 per dollar borrowed. Suppose that Eduardo's car payment is $340 per month. To the nearest dollar, how much did Eduardo borrow?

25. Pascal's Principle Pascal's Principle applied to a hydraulic lever states that the ratio of the force exerted on an input piston F_1 to the area displaced A_1 will equal the ratio of force on the output piston F_2 to the area displaced A_2. See the figure. If a force of 30 pounds is exerted with an area of 12 square feet of water displaced in the right pipe and an area of 5 square feet is displaced in the left pipe, determine the force exerted by the left pipe.

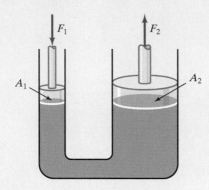

26. **Pascal's Principle** See Problem 25. If a force of 40 pounds is exerted with an area of 15 square feet of water displaced in the right pipe and an area of 8 square feet is displaced in the left pipe, determine the force exerted by the left pipe.

In Problems 27–32, solve the work problem. See Objective 3.

27. **Sharing a Paper Route** Amiri can deliver his newspapers in 80 minutes. It takes Horus 60 minutes to do the same route. How long would it take them to deliver the newspapers if they work together?

28. **Painting a Room** Latoya can paint five 10-foot-by-14-foot rooms by herself in 14 hours. Lisa can paint five 10-foot-by-14-foot rooms by herself in 10 hours. Working together, how long would it take to paint five 10-foot-by-14-foot rooms?

29. **Cutting the Grass** Avery can cut the grass working by himself in 3 hours. When Avery cuts the grass with his younger brother Connor, it takes 2 hours. How long would it take Connor to cut the grass if he worked by himself?

30. **Assembling a Swing Set** Alexandra and Frank can assemble a King Kong swing set working together in 6 hours. One day, when Frank called in sick, Alexandra was able to assemble a King Kong swing set in 10 hours. How long would it take Frank to assemble a King Kong swing set if he worked by himself?

31. **Emptying a Pool** A swimming pool can be emptied in 6 hours using a 10-horsepower pump along with a 6-horsepower pump. The 6-horsepower pump requires 5 hours more than the 10-horsepower pump to empty the pool when working by itself. How long would it take to empty the pool using just the 10-horsepower pump?

32. **Draining a Pond** A pond can be emptied in $3.75 \left(= \dfrac{15}{4} \right)$ hours using a 10-horsepower pump along with a 4-horsepower pump. The 4-horsepower pump requires 4 hours more than the 10-horsepower pump to empty the pond when working by itself. How long would it take to empty the pond using just the 10-horsepower pump?

In Problems 33–42, solve the uniform motion problem. See Objective 4.

33. **Tough Commute** You have a 20-mile commute into work. Since you leave very early, the trip going to work is easier than the trip home. You can travel to work in the same time that it takes for you to make it 16 miles on the trip back home. Your average speed coming home is 7 miles per hour slower than your average speed going to work. What is your average speed going to work?

34. **Riding Your Bicycle** Every weekend, you ride your bicycle on a forest preserve path. The path is 20 miles long and ends at a waterfall, at which point you relax and then make the trip back to the starting point. One weekend, you find that in the same time it takes you to travel to the waterfall, you are only able to return 12 miles. Your average speed going to the waterfall is 4 miles per hour faster than the return trip. What was your average speed going to the waterfall?

35. **Moving Walkway** In order to access the outer part of Terminal 1 at O'Hare International Airport, you must walk quite some distance in a tunnel that travels under part of the airport. To make the walk less difficult, there is a moving walkway that travels at 2 feet per second. Suppose that Hana can travel 152 feet while walking on the walkway in the same amount of time it takes her to travel 72 feet while walking on the pavement without the aid of the moving sidewalk. How fast does Hana walk?

36. **Escalator** When exiting Terminal 1 at O'Hare International Airport, you can either take an escalator up to the main level or you can take traditional stairs. Suppose that the escalator travels 1.5 feet per second. Karli can walk up the 50-foot escalator in the same amount of time it takes her to walk 30 feet up the stairs. How fast does Karli walk up stairs?

37. **Football** Suppose that Jeremy Shockey of the New Orleans Saints can run 100 yards in 12 seconds. Further suppose that Brian Urlacher of the Chicago Bears can run 100 yards in 9 seconds. Suppose that Shockey catches a pass at his own 20-yard line in stride and starts running away from Urlacher, who is at the 15-yard line directly behind Shockey. See the figure. At what yard line will Urlacher catch up to Shockey?

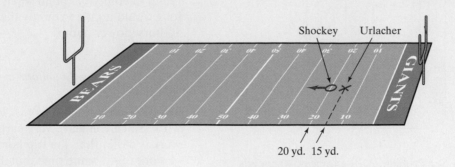

Shockey   Urlacher

20 yd. 15 yd.

---

38. **Running a Race** Roger can run one mile in 8 minutes. Jeff can run one mile in 6 minutes. If Jeff gives Roger a 1-minute head start, how long will it take before Jeff catches up to Roger? How far will each have run?

39. **Uphill/Downhill** A bicyclist rides his bicycle 12 miles up a hill and then comes back down. His speed coming downhill is 8 miles per hour faster than going uphill. The roundtrip takes 2 hours and 15 minutes $\left(= \dfrac{9}{4} \text{ hours} \right)$. What was the speed of the bicyclist going uphill?

40. **Round Trip** A plane flies 600 miles west (into the wind) and makes the return trip following the same flight path. The effect of the jet stream on the plane is 15 miles per hour. The round trip takes 9 hours. What is the speed of the plane in still air?

41. **Scenic Drive** Joe and Nancy live in Morro Bay, California, right off of Highway 1. They decide to take a trip north to Monterey. The first 50 miles of the drive is pretty easy, while the last 68 miles of the drive is filled with curves. They drove at an average of 9 miles per hour faster for the first 50 miles of the trip. The entire trip took 3 hours. How fast were Joe and Nancy driving for the first 50 miles of the trip?

42. **A Race** Dirk and Garret decide to have a 40-mile bicycle race. During the race, Dirk averages 2 miles per hour faster than Garret and beats Garret by $\dfrac{2}{3}$ of an hour. What was Dirk's average speed?

Extending the Concepts

43. **The Olympics** The current world record holder in the 100-meter dash is Maurice Greene, with a time of 9.79 seconds. In the 1984 Olympics, Carl Lewis won the gold medal in the 100-meter dash with a time of 9.99 seconds. If these two athletes ran in the same race repeating their respective times, by how many meters would Greene beat Lewis?

Explaining the Concepts

44. When solving work problems, we assume that each individual works at a constant rate and that there is no gain or loss of efficiency when additional individuals are added to the job. Explain what "no gain or loss of efficiency" means. Do you think this assumption is reasonable? If not, then why do we make the assumption?

Synthesis Review

In Problems 45–50, use the Laws of Exponents to simplify each expression.

45. $(a^3)^5$

46. $a(a^2b^{-3})^3$

47. $(ab)^{-2} \cdot \left(\dfrac{a^3}{b^2} \right)^2$

48. $\left(\dfrac{13a^5b^2}{ab^{-7}} \right)^0$

49. $\left(\dfrac{3m^3n^{-1}}{mn^5} \right)^{-2}$

50. $\left(\dfrac{12pq^{-3}}{3p^4q^{-4}} \right)^2$

CHAPTER 5 Activity: Correct the Quiz

Focus: Performing operations and solving equations and inequalities with rational expressions
Time: 20 minutes
Group size: 2

In this activity you will work as a team to grade the student quiz shown below. One of you will grade the odd questions, and the other will grade the even questions. If an answer is correct, mark it correct. If an answer is wrong, mark it wrong and show the correct answer.

Once all of the quiz questions are graded, explain your results to each other and compute the final score for the quiz. Be prepared to discuss your results with the rest of the class.

Student Quiz	
Name: _Ima Student_	Quiz Score: _____
(1) Multiply: $\dfrac{2x^3 + 54}{5x^2 + 5x - 30} \cdot \dfrac{6x + 12}{3x^2 - 9x + 27}$	Answer: $\dfrac{4(x + 2)}{5(x - 2)}$
(2) Subtract: $\dfrac{xy}{x^2 - y^2} - \dfrac{y}{x + y}$	Answer: $\dfrac{y^2}{x^2 - y^2}$
(3) Solve: $\dfrac{3}{x - 3} + \dfrac{4}{x} = \dfrac{-12}{x^2 - 3x}$	Answer: $\varnothing$
(4) Divide: $\dfrac{x^2 + x - 6}{5x^2 - 7x - 6} \div \dfrac{3x^2 + 13x + 12}{6x^2 + 17x + 12}$	Answer: $\dfrac{2}{5}$
(5) Joe can mow his lawn in 2 hrs. Mike can mow the same lawn in 3 hrs. If they work together, how long will it take them to mow the lawn?	Answer: 1 hr, 12 min
(6) Simplify: $\dfrac{\dfrac{1}{x + 5} - \dfrac{2}{x - 7}}{\dfrac{4}{x - 7} + \dfrac{1}{x + 5}}$	Answer: $\dfrac{x + 17}{5x + 13}$
(7) Add: $\dfrac{x}{x^2 + 10x + 25} + \dfrac{4}{x^2 + 6x + 5}$	Answer: $\dfrac{x^2 + 5x + 20}{(x + 5)(x + 1)}$
(8) Solve: $\dfrac{4x}{x - 3} \geq 5$	Answer: $(3, 15]$

CHAPTER 5 Review

Section 5.1 Multiplying and Dividing Rational Expressions

KEY CONCEPTS	KEY TERMS
• **Multiplying Rational Expressions** If $\dfrac{a}{b}$ and $\dfrac{c}{d}$, $b \neq 0$, $d \neq 0$, are two rational expressions, then $\dfrac{a}{b} \cdot \dfrac{c}{d} = \dfrac{ac}{bd}$. • **Dividing Rational Expressions** If $\dfrac{a}{b}$ and $\dfrac{c}{d}$, $b \neq 0$, $c \neq 0$, $d \neq 0$, are two rational expressions, then $\dfrac{\dfrac{a}{b}}{\dfrac{c}{d}} = \dfrac{a}{b} \cdot \dfrac{d}{c} = \dfrac{ad}{bc}$.	Rational expression Numerator Denominator Lowest terms Simplified Rational function

YOU SHOULD BE ABLE TO...	EXAMPLE	REVIEW EXERCISES
⬜1 Determine the domain of a rational expression (p. 412)	Example 1	1–4
⬜2 Simplify rational expressions (p. 413)	Examples 2 and 3	5–10
⬜3 Multiply rational expressions (p. 414)	Examples 4 and 5	11–16
⬜4 Divide rational expressions (p. 416)	Example 6	17–22
⬜5 Work with rational functions (p. 417)	Examples 7 and 8	23–26

In Problems 1–4, state the domain of each rational expression.

1. $\dfrac{x - 5}{3x - 2}$

2. $\dfrac{a^2 - 16}{a^2 - 3a - 28}$

3. $\dfrac{m - 3}{m^2 + 9}$

4. $\dfrac{n^2 + 7n + 10}{n^2 - 2n - 8}$

In Problems 5–10, simplify each rational expression.

5. $\dfrac{6x + 30}{x^2 - 25}$

6. $\dfrac{4y^2 - 28y}{2y^5 - 14y^4}$

7. $\dfrac{w^2 - 4w - 21}{w^2 + 7w + 12}$

8. $\dfrac{6a^2 - 7ab - 3b^2}{10a^2 - 11ab - 6b^2}$

9. $\dfrac{7 - m}{3m^2 - 20m - 7}$

10. $\dfrac{n^3 - 4n^2 + 3n - 12}{n^2 - 8n + 16}$

16. $\dfrac{m^2 + m - 20}{m^3 - 64} \cdot \dfrac{3m^2 + 12m + 48}{m^2 + 3m - 10}$

17. $\dfrac{\dfrac{4c^2}{3d^4}}{\dfrac{8c}{27d}}$

18. $\dfrac{\dfrac{6z - 24}{7z + 21}}{\dfrac{z - 4}{z^2 - 9}}$

19. $\dfrac{\dfrac{x^2 - 11x + 30}{x^2 - 8x + 15}}{\dfrac{x^2 - 5x - 6}{x^2 + 8x + 7}}$

20. $\dfrac{\dfrac{m^2 + mn - 12n^2}{m^3 - 27n^3}}{\dfrac{m + 5n}{m^2 + 3mn + 9n^2}}$

21. $\dfrac{\dfrac{4p^3 - 4pq^2}{p^2 - 5pq - 24q^2}}{\dfrac{2p^3 + 4p^2q + 2pq^2}{p^2 - 7pq - 8q^2}}$

22. $\dfrac{\dfrac{15a^2 + 11a - 14}{25a^2 - 49}}{\dfrac{27a^3 - 8}{10a^2 + 11a - 35}}$

In Problems 11–22, multiply or divide each rational expression, as indicated. Simplify the product or quotient.

11. $\dfrac{4p^2}{p^2 - 3p - 18} \cdot \dfrac{p + 3}{8p}$

12. $\dfrac{q^2 + 6q}{6q + 12} \cdot \dfrac{4q + 8}{q^2 + q - 30}$

13. $\dfrac{x^3 - 4x^2}{x^2 - 4} \cdot \dfrac{x^2 + 4x - 12}{x^3 + 2x^2}$

14. $\dfrac{y^2 - 3y - 28}{y^3 + 4y^2} \cdot \dfrac{2y^2 + 10y}{y^2 - 12y + 35}$

15. $\dfrac{6a^2 + ab - b^2}{3a^2 + 2ab - b^2} \cdot \dfrac{3a^2 + 4ab + b^2}{4a^2 - b^2}$

In Problems 23–26, use the functions

$f(x) = \dfrac{2x^2 + 3x - 2}{x - 5}$, $g(x) = \dfrac{x^2 - 3x - 10}{2x - 1}$, *and*

$h(x) = \dfrac{2x - 1}{x^2 + 9x + 14}$ *to find each product or quotient. State the domain of each product or quotient.*

23. $P(x) = f(x) \cdot g(x)$

24. $R(x) = g(x) \cdot h(x)$

25. $Q(x) = \dfrac{g(x)}{f(x)}$

26. $T(x) = \dfrac{f(x)}{h(x)}$

Section 5.2 Adding and Subtracting Rational Expressions

KEY CONCEPTS	KEY TERM
• **Adding/Subtracting Rational Expressions** If $\dfrac{a}{c}$ and $\dfrac{b}{c}$, $c \neq 0$, are two rational expressions, then $\dfrac{a}{c} + \dfrac{b}{c} = \dfrac{a+b}{c}$ and $\dfrac{a}{c} - \dfrac{b}{c} = \dfrac{a-b}{c}$. *Note:* If the rational expressions do not have a common denominator, then the least common denominator can be found using the steps on page 425. Then follow the steps listed on page 426 to add or subtract rational expressions with unlike denominators.	Least common denominator

YOU SHOULD BE ABLE TO...	EXAMPLE	REVIEW EXERCISES
1 Add or subtract rational expressions with a common denominator (p. 422)	Examples 1 and 2	27–32
2 Find the least common denominator of two or more rational expressions (p. 424)	Example 3	33–36
3 Add or subtract rational expressions with different denominators (p. 425)	Examples 4 through 7	37–50

In Problems 27–32, perform the indicated operation and simplify the result.

27. $\dfrac{4x}{x-5} + \dfrac{3}{x-5}$

28. $\dfrac{4y}{y-3} - \dfrac{12}{y-3}$

29. $\dfrac{a^2 - 2a - 4}{a^2 - 6a + 8} + \dfrac{4a - 20}{a^2 - 6a + 8}$

30. $\dfrac{3b^2 + 8b - 5}{2b^2 - 5b - 12} - \dfrac{2b^2 + 7b + 15}{2b^2 - 5b - 12}$

31. $\dfrac{5c^2 - 8c}{c-8} + \dfrac{2c^2 + 16c}{8-c}$

32. $\dfrac{2d^2 + d}{d^2 - 1} - \dfrac{d^2 + 1}{d^2 - 1} + \dfrac{d - 2}{d^2 - 1}$

In Problems 33–36, find the least common denominator.

33. $\dfrac{4}{9x^4}$ and $\dfrac{5}{12x^2}$

34. $\dfrac{2y+1}{y-9}$ and $\dfrac{3y}{y+2}$

35. $\dfrac{3p+4}{2p^2 - 3p - 20}$ and $\dfrac{7p^2}{2p^3 + 5p^2}$

36. $\dfrac{q-4}{q^2 + 4q - 5}$ and $\dfrac{q-6}{q^2 + 2q - 15}$

In Problems 37–48, perform the indicated operation and simplify the result.

37. $\dfrac{1}{mn^4} + \dfrac{4}{m^3 n^2}$

38. $\dfrac{3}{2xy^3} - \dfrac{7}{6x^2 y}$

39. $\dfrac{p}{p-q} - \dfrac{q}{p+q}$

40. $\dfrac{x+8}{x^2 - 10x + 21} - \dfrac{x-5}{x^2 - 3x - 28}$

41. $\dfrac{3}{y^2 - 2y + 1} - \dfrac{2}{y^2 + y - 2}$

42. $\dfrac{3a - 5b}{4a^2 - 9b^2} + \dfrac{4}{2a - 3b}$

43. $\dfrac{4x^2 - 10x}{x^2 - 9} + \dfrac{8x - 2x^2}{9 - x^2}$

44. $\dfrac{1}{n+5} - \dfrac{n^2 - 10n}{n^3 + 125}$

45. $\dfrac{m+n}{m+3n} - \dfrac{m-4n}{m-7n} + \dfrac{7mn + n^2}{m^2 - 4mn - 21n^2}$

46. $\dfrac{z^2 + 10z + 3}{z^2 - 9} - \dfrac{2z}{z-3} + \dfrac{z}{z+3}$

47. $\dfrac{y-1}{y-2} - \dfrac{y+1}{y+2} + \dfrac{y-6}{y^2 - 4}$

48. $\dfrac{2a}{a^2 - 16} - \dfrac{1}{a - 4} - \dfrac{1}{a^2 + 2a - 8}$

49. $f(x) = \dfrac{5}{x - 4}$ and $g(x) = \dfrac{x}{x + 2}$

    (a) Find $S(x) = f(x) + g(x)$.

    (b) State the domain of $S(x)$.

50. $f(x) = \dfrac{x + 3}{2x^2 + x - 15}$ and

    $g(x) = \dfrac{x - 7}{4x^2 - 8x - 5}$

    (a) Find $D(x) = f(x) - g(x)$.

    (b) State the domain of $D(x)$.

Section 5.3   Complex Rational Expressions

KEY CONCEPT	KEY TERMS
• There are two methods that can be utilized in simplifying a complex rational expression. The steps for Method I are presented on page 433 while the steps for Method II are presented on page 435.	Complex rational expression Complex fraction Simplify

YOU SHOULD BE ABLE TO...	EXAMPLE	REVIEW EXERCISES
1 Simplify a complex rational expression by simplifying the numerator and denominator separately (p. 432)	Examples 1, 2, and 5	51–54, 59–66
2 Simplify a complex rational expression using the least common denominator (p. 435)	Examples 3 through 5	55–58, 59–66

In Problems 51–54, simplify each complex rational expression by using Method I (that is, by simplifying the numerator and denominator separately).

51. $\dfrac{x - \dfrac{1}{x}}{1 - \dfrac{1}{x}}$

52. $\dfrac{\dfrac{1}{x} - \dfrac{1}{y}}{\dfrac{1}{x^2} - \dfrac{1}{y^2}}$

53. $\dfrac{\dfrac{a}{b} - \dfrac{a - b}{a + b}}{\dfrac{a}{b} + \dfrac{a + b}{a - b}}$

54. $\dfrac{\dfrac{2}{a + 2} - 1}{\dfrac{1}{a + 2} + 1}$

In Problems 55–58, simplify each complex rational expression using Method II (that is, by using the least common denominator).

55. $\dfrac{\dfrac{3}{t} + \dfrac{4}{t^2}}{5 + \dfrac{1}{t^2}}$

56. $\dfrac{\dfrac{1}{a} - \dfrac{1}{b}}{\dfrac{b}{a} - \dfrac{a}{b}}$

57. $\dfrac{\dfrac{1}{z - 1} - \dfrac{1}{z}}{\dfrac{1}{z} - \dfrac{1}{z + 1}}$

58. $\dfrac{1 + \dfrac{x}{x + 1}}{\dfrac{2x + 1}{x - 1}}$

In Problems 59–66, simplify the complex rational expression using either Method I or Method II.

59. $\dfrac{\dfrac{x}{y} + 1}{\dfrac{x}{y} - 1}$

60. $\dfrac{\dfrac{a}{a - b} - \dfrac{b}{a + b}}{\dfrac{b}{a - b} + \dfrac{a}{a + b}}$

61. $\dfrac{\dfrac{1}{x - 2} - \dfrac{x}{x^2 - 4}}{1 - \dfrac{2}{x + 2}}$

62. $\dfrac{z - \dfrac{5z}{z + 5}}{z + \dfrac{5z}{z - 5}}$

63. $\dfrac{\dfrac{m - n}{m + n} + \dfrac{n}{m}}{\dfrac{m}{n} - \dfrac{m - n}{m + n}}$

64. $\dfrac{\dfrac{x + 4}{x - 2} - \dfrac{x - 3}{x + 1}}{5x^2 + 4x - 1}$

65. $\dfrac{3x^{-1} - 3y^{-1}}{(x + y)^{-1}}$

66. $\dfrac{2c^{-1} - (3d)^{-1}}{(6d)^{-1}}$

Section 5.4 Rational Equations

KEY CONCEPT	KEY TERMS
• The steps for solving any rational equation are given on page 442.	Rational equation Extraneous solution

YOU SHOULD BE ABLE TO...	EXAMPLE	REVIEW EXERCISES
1 Solve equations containing rational expressions (p. 441)	Examples 1 through 5	67–78
2 Solve equations involving rational functions (p. 445)	Examples 6 and 7	79, 80

In Problems 67–78, solve each equation. Be sure to verify your results.

67. $\dfrac{2}{z} - \dfrac{1}{3z} = \dfrac{1}{6}$

68. $\dfrac{4}{m-4} = \dfrac{-5}{m+2}$

69. $m - \dfrac{14}{m} = 5$

70. $\dfrac{2}{n+3} = \dfrac{1}{n-3}$

71. $\dfrac{s}{s-1} = 1 + \dfrac{2}{s}$

72. $\dfrac{3}{x^2 - 7x + 10} + 2 = \dfrac{x-4}{x-5}$

73. $\dfrac{1}{k-1} + \dfrac{1}{k+2} = \dfrac{3}{k^2 + k - 2}$

74. $x + \dfrac{3x}{x-3} = \dfrac{9}{x-3}$

75. $\dfrac{2}{a+3} - \dfrac{4}{a^2 - 4} = \dfrac{a+1}{a^2 + 5a + 6}$

76. $\dfrac{2}{z^2 + 2z - 8} = \dfrac{1}{z^2 + 9z + 20} + \dfrac{4}{z^2 + 3z - 10}$

77. $\dfrac{x-3}{x+4} = \dfrac{14}{x^2 + 6x + 8}$

78. $\dfrac{5}{y-5} + 4 = \dfrac{3y-10}{y-5}$

79. For the function $f(x) = \dfrac{6}{x-2}$, solve $f(x) = 2$. What point(s) are on the graph of f?

80. For the function $g(x) = x - \dfrac{21}{x}$, solve $g(x) = 4$. What point(s) are on the graph of g?

Section 5.5 Rational Inequalities

KEY CONCEPT	KEY TERM
• The steps for solving any rational inequality are given on page 451.	Rational inequality

YOU SHOULD BE ABLE TO...	EXAMPLE	REVIEW EXERCISES
1 Solve a rational inequality (p. 449)	Examples 1 and 2	81–90

In Problems 81–88, solve each rational inequality. Graph the solution set.

81. $\dfrac{x-4}{x+2} \geq 0$

82. $\dfrac{y-5}{y+4} < 0$

83. $\dfrac{4}{z^2 - 9} \leq 0$

84. $\dfrac{w^2 + 5w - 14}{w-4} < 0$

85. $\dfrac{m-5}{m^2 + 3m - 10} \geq 0$

86. $\dfrac{4}{n-2} \leq -2$

87. $\dfrac{a+1}{a-2} > 3$

88. $\dfrac{4}{c-2} - \dfrac{3}{c} < 0$

In Problems 89 and 90, for each function, find the values of x that satisfy the given condition.

89. Solve $Q(x) < 0$ if $Q(x) = \dfrac{2x+3}{x-4}$.

90. Solve $R(x) \geq 0$ if $R(x) = \dfrac{x+5}{x+1}$.

Section 5.6 Models Involving Rational Expressions

KEY TERMS

Ratio	Proportion	Similar	Constant rate

YOU SHOULD BE ABLE TO...	EXAMPLE	REVIEW EXERCISES
1 Solve for a variable in a rational expression (p. 455)	Example 1	91–94
2 Model and solve ratio and proportion problems (p. 456)	Examples 2 and 3	95–98
3 Model and solve work problems (p. 458)	Examples 4 and 5	99–102
4 Model and solve uniform motion problems (p. 460)	Example 6	103–106

In Problems 91–94, solve each formula for the indicated variable.

91. Electronics (Capacitance) Solve $\dfrac{1}{C_1} + \dfrac{1}{C_2} = \dfrac{1}{C}$ for C.

92. Chemistry (Ideal Gas Law) Solve $\dfrac{P_1 V_1}{T_1} = \dfrac{P_2 V_2}{T_2}$ for T_2.

93. Physics (Kepler's Third Law) Solve $T = \dfrac{4\pi^2 a^2}{MG}$ for G.

94. Statistics (z-score) Solve $z = \dfrac{x - \mu}{\sigma}$ for x.

In Problems 95–98, solve each proportion problem.

95. Suppose that $\triangle ABC$ is similar to $\triangle DEF$ as shown in the figure. Find the lengths of AB and DF.

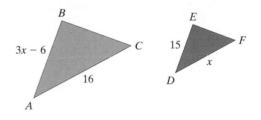

96. At a particular time of day, a pine tree casts a 30-foot shadow. At the exact same time, a nearby 5-foot post casts an 8-foot shadow. Find the height of the tree.

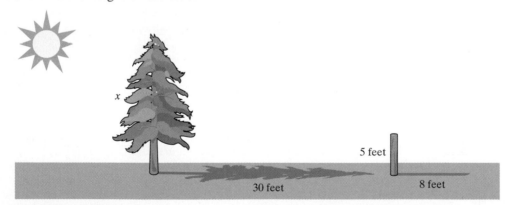

97. According to the nutrition facts on a box of Honey Nut Chex® (SOURCE: *General Mills*), a $\dfrac{3}{4}$-cup serving contains 26 grams of total carbohydrates. How many grams of total carbohydrates are in a 3-cup bowl of the cereal?

98. One day, Jeri earns $48.75 for 5 hours of work. How much will she earn for 8 hours of work?

In Problems 99–102, solve each work problem.

99. Filling a Tank One pipe can fill a tank in 48 minutes. Another pipe can fill the tank in 1 hour and 12 minutes. If both pipes are used, how long will it take to fill the tank?

100. Mowing the Lawn Together, Diane and Craig can mow their lawn in 1 hour and 10 minutes. Working alone, Diane can mow the lawn in 2 hours. How long will it take Craig to mow the lawn when working alone?

101. Carpeting Together, Rick and John can carpet a large room in 12 hours. Alone, Rick can carpet the same size room in 7 hours less time than John. How long would it take Rick to carpet the same size room if working alone? How long would it take John if working alone?

102. Draining a Sink A faucet can fill a sink in 1 minute when the drain is plugged, but when the drain is unplugged, it takes 1 minute and 30 seconds to fill the sink. With the faucet off, how long would it take the drain to empty a full sink?

In Problems 103–106, solve each motion problem.

103. Pleasure Flight In his private plane, Nick can fly 180 miles per hour if the wind is not blowing. One day, Nick took a pleasure flight. He flew 100 miles directly against the wind and then returned (flying with the wind) to his point of origin. If the total time of the flight was 1 hour and 15 minutes, what was the speed of the wind?

104. Boating In his motorboat, Jesse can travel 20 miles downstream in the same amount of time it takes him to travel 10 miles upstream. If the speed of the current is 5 miles per hour, how fast can Jesse's motorboat travel in still water?

105. Running/Walking To stay in shape, Todd first runs 3 miles and then walks 1 mile every morning. Todd's average running speed is 4 times his average walking speed. If Todd spends a total of 35 minutes running and walking each morning, find the average speed at which he walks and the average speed at which he runs.

106. Road Trip Because of heavy traffic, Danielle averaged only 30 miles per hour for the first 20 miles of her trip. If she averaged 50 miles per hour for the entire 100-mile trip, what was her average speed for the last 80 miles?

CHAPTER 5 TEST

Remember to use your Chapter Test Prep Video CD to see fully worked-out solutions to any of these problems you would like to review.

1. Determine the domain of $f(x) = \dfrac{2x + 1}{2x^2 - 13x - 7}$.

In Problems 2 and 3, simplify each rational expression.

2. $\dfrac{2m^2 + 5m - 12}{3m^2 + 11m - 4}$

3. $\dfrac{2b - 3a}{3a^2 + 10ab - 8b^2}$

In Problems 4–7, perform the indicated operations.

4. $\dfrac{4x^2 - 12x}{x^2 - 9} \cdot \dfrac{2x^2 + 11x + 15}{8x^3 - 32x^2}$

5. $\dfrac{\dfrac{y^2 + 2y - 8}{4y^2 - 5y - 6}}{\dfrac{3y^2 - 14y - 5}{4y^2 - 17y - 15}}$

6. $\dfrac{3p^2 + 3pq}{p^2 - q^2} - \dfrac{3p - 2q}{p - q}$

7. $\dfrac{9c + 2}{3c^2 - 2c - 8} + \dfrac{7}{3c^2 + c - 4}$

In Problems 8 and 9, use the functions $f(x) = \dfrac{3x}{x^2 - 4}$,

$g(x) = \dfrac{6}{x^2 + 2x}$, *and* $h(x) = \dfrac{9x^2 - 45x}{x^2 - 2x - 8}$ *to find each sum or quotient. State the domain of each.*

8. $Q(x) = \dfrac{f(x)}{h(x)}$

9. $S(x) = f(x) + g(x)$

In Problems 10 and 11, simplify each complex rational expression using either Method I or Method II.

10. $\dfrac{1 - \dfrac{1}{a}}{1 - \dfrac{1}{a^2}}$

11. $\dfrac{\dfrac{5}{d + 2} - \dfrac{1}{d - 2}}{\dfrac{3}{d + 2} - \dfrac{6}{d - 2}}$

In Problems 12 and 13, solve each rational equation. Be sure to verify the results.

12. $\dfrac{1}{6x} - \dfrac{1}{3} = \dfrac{5}{4x} + \dfrac{3}{4}$

13. $\dfrac{7n}{n + 3} + \dfrac{21}{n - 3} = \dfrac{126}{n^2 - 9}$

14. Solve $\dfrac{x + 5}{x - 2} \geq 3$. Graph the solution set.

15. Electronics (Coulomb's Law) Solve $\dfrac{1}{F} = \dfrac{D^2}{kq_1q_2}$ for k.

16. Printing Documents A particular laser printer can print out a 10-page document in 25 seconds. How long will it take to print out a 48-page document?

17. Cleaning House Linnette can clean the house in 4 hours. Her husband Darrell can do the same job in 6 hours. If the two work together, how long will it take them to clean the house?

18. Kayaking Chuck kayaked 4 miles upstream in the same time it took him to kayak 10 miles downstream. If Chuck can average 7 miles per hour in still water, what was the rate of the current?

CUMULATIVE REVIEW CHAPTERS R–5

1. Evaluate: $\dfrac{4^3 - 6 \cdot 7 + 14}{4 - 1^2}$

2. Simplify: $2x(x - 3) + 4(x - 2) + 15$

3. Evaluate $\dfrac{3x^2 - 4x - 5}{x - 3}$ for $x = -2$.

4. Solve: $7x + 9 = 3x - 23$

5. Solve: $|3x + 7| \le 8$

6. Determine the domain of $h(x) = \dfrac{x - 5}{2x^2 - 7x - 15}$.

7. For $f(x) = x^2 - 5x$, find each of the following.

   (a) $f(-3)$ (b) $f\left(\dfrac{1}{4}\right)$

   (c) $f(x + 2)$

8. Graph the linear equation $4x + 3y = 15$.

9. Find the equation of the line that passes through the points $(-5, 1)$ and $(10, -8)$. Write your answer in either slope-intercept or standard form, whichever you prefer.

10. Find the equation of the line that passes through the point $(3, 5)$ and is perpendicular to the graph of $x + 4y = 20$. Write your answer in either slope-intercept or standard form, whichever you prefer.

11. The recommended dosage D of a prescription drug varies directly with a person's weight w. If the recommended dosage for a 125-pound person is 1500 milligrams, find the recommended dosage for a 180-pound person.

12. Write the system of linear equations that corresponds to the following augmented matrix.
$$\begin{bmatrix} 2 & -3 & | & 7 \\ 5 & 2 & | & 8 \end{bmatrix}$$

13. Perform each row operation on the given augmented matrix. $\begin{bmatrix} 1 & 1 & 0 & | & -3 \\ 0 & 2 & -1 & | & -1 \\ 5 & 0 & 1 & | & 1 \end{bmatrix}$

   (a) $R_3 = -5r_1 + r_3$ followed by

   (b) $R_2 = \dfrac{1}{2}r_2$

14. Solve the following system of equations
$$\begin{cases} x + 4y = -2 \\ 2x - 12y = -9 \end{cases}$$

15. Evaluate: $\begin{vmatrix} 2 & 0 & 4 \\ 1 & -1 & -2 \\ 2 & -2 & 3 \end{vmatrix}$

16. Graph the following system of linear inequlities:
$$\begin{cases} 3x + 2y < 8 \\ x - 4y \ge 12 \end{cases}$$

In Problems 17–20, perform the indicated operation.

17. $(3x^2 - 4xy + 7y^2) + (5x^2 - 9xy + 2y^2)$

18. $(5x^2 - 3x + 12) - (2x^2 - 4x - 15)$

19. $(2x - 3)(x^2 - 4x + 6)$

20. $\dfrac{4x^3 - 7x + 45}{2x + 5}$

In Problems 21–22, factor completely.

21. $x^4 + 5x^3 - 8x - 40$

22. $6x^2 + x - 15$

In Problems 23–24, perform the indicated operations. Be sure to simplify each result.

23. $\dfrac{3x^2 - 2x - 1}{3x^2 - 5x - 2} \cdot \dfrac{x^2 - 9x + 14}{x^2 + x - 2}$

24. $\dfrac{3}{x^2 + x - 6} - \dfrac{2}{x^2 + 2x - 3}$

25. **Grading Tests** Bill can grade a set of test papers in 80 minutes. Karl can grade the same number of test papers in 120 minutes. How long will it take Bill and Karl to grade the test papers if they work together?

Getting Ready for Chapter 6:
Square Roots

In Words

Taking the square root of a number is the "inverse" of squaring a number.

In Words

The notation $b = \sqrt{a}$ means "give me the number b greater than or equal to 0 whose square is a."

In Section R.4, we introduced the concept of exponents. Exponents are used to indicate repeated multiplication. For example, 4^2 means $4 \cdot 4$, so $4^2 = 16$; $(-6)^2$ means $(-6) \cdot (-6)$, so $(-6)^2 = 36$. Now, we will reverse the process of raising a number to the second power and ask questions such as, "What number, or numbers, when squared, give me 16?"

1 Evaluate Square Roots of Perfect Squares

A real number is squared when it is raised to the power 2. The inverse of squaring a number is finding the **square root.** For example, since $5^2 = 25$ and $(-5)^2 = 25$, the square roots of 25 are -5 and 5. The square roots of $\dfrac{16}{49}$ are $-\dfrac{4}{7}$ and $\dfrac{4}{7}$.

If we want only the positive square root of a number, we use the symbol $\sqrt{}$, called a **radical sign,** to denote the **principal square root,** or nonnegative (zero or positive) square root.

> **DEFINITION**
>
> If a is a nonnegative real number, the nonnegative real number b such that $b^2 = a$, is the **principal square root** of a and is denoted by $b = \sqrt{a}$.

For example, if we want the positive square root of 25, we would write $\sqrt{25} = 5$. We read $\sqrt{25} = 5$ as "the principal (or positive) square root of 25 is 5." But what if we want the negative square root of a real number? In that case, we use the expression $-\sqrt{25} = -5$ to obtain the negative square root of 25.

> **PROPERTIES OF SQUARE ROOTS**
>
> - Every positive real number has two square roots, one positive and one negative.
> - The square root of 0 is 0. That is, $\sqrt{0} = 0$.
> - We use the symbol $\sqrt{}$, called a radical, to denote the nonnegative square root of a real number. The nonnegative square root is called the principal square root.
> - The number under the radical is called the **radicand.** For example, the radicand in $\sqrt{25}$ is 25.
> - For any real number c, such that $c \geq 0$, $\left(\sqrt{c}\right)^2 = c$. For example, $\left(\sqrt{4}\right)^2 = 4$ and $\left(\sqrt{8.3}\right)^2 = 8.3$.

To **evaluate** a square root, we ask ourselves, "What is the nonnegative number whose square is equal to the radicand?"

EXAMPLE 1 Evaluating Square Roots

Evaluate each square root.

(a) $\sqrt{36}$ **(b)** $\sqrt{\dfrac{1}{9}}$ **(c)** $\sqrt{0.01}$ **(d)** $\left(\sqrt{2.3}\right)^2$

Solution

(a) Is there a positive number whose square is 36? Because $6^2 = 36$, $\sqrt{36} = 6$.

(b) $\sqrt{\dfrac{1}{9}} = \dfrac{1}{3}$ because $\left(\dfrac{1}{3}\right)^2 = \dfrac{1}{9}$.

(c) $\sqrt{0.01} = 0.1$ because $0.1^2 = 0.01$.

(d) $\left(\sqrt{2.3}\right)^2 = 2.3$ because $\left(\sqrt{c}\right)^2 = c$ when $c \geq 0$.   ■

Figure 1

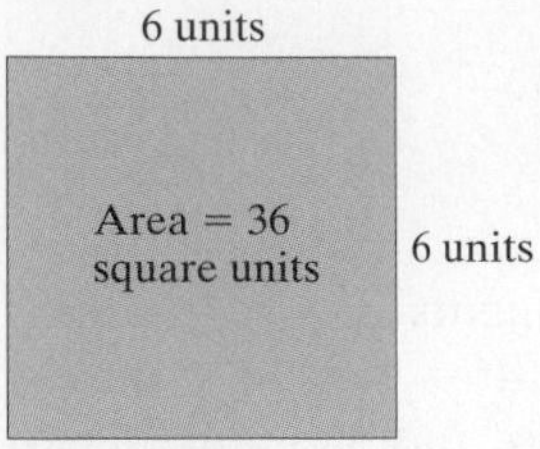

6 units

Area = 36 square units

6 units

A rational number is a **perfect square** if it is the square of a rational number. Examples 1(a), (b), and (c) are square roots of perfect squares since $6^2 = 36$, $\left(\frac{1}{3}\right)^2 = \frac{1}{9}$, and $0.1^2 = 0.01$. We can think of perfect squares geometrically as shown in Figure 1, where we have a square whose area is 36 square units. The square root of the area, $\sqrt{36}$, gives us the length of each side of the square, 6 units.

Quick ✔

1. The symbol $\sqrt{\ }$ is called a _____ ___.

2. If a is a nonnegative real number, the nonnegative number b such that $b^2 = a$ is the _____ _____ ___ of a and is denoted by $b = \sqrt{a}$.

3. The square roots of 16 are __ and __.

In Problems 4–8, evaluate each square root.

4. $\sqrt{81}$ 5. $\sqrt{900}$ 6. $\sqrt{\dfrac{1}{4}}$ 7. $\sqrt{0.16}$ 8. $(\sqrt{13})^2$

EXAMPLE 2 Evaluating an Expression Containing Square Roots

Evaluate each expression:

(a) $-4\sqrt{36}$ (b) $\sqrt{9} + \sqrt{16}$ (c) $\sqrt{9 + 16}$ (d) $\sqrt{64 - 4 \cdot 7 \cdot 1}$

Solution

(a) The expression $-4\sqrt{36}$ is asking us to find -4 times the positive square root of 36. We first find the positive square root of 36 and then multiply this result by -4.

$$-4\sqrt{36} = -4 \cdot 6$$
$$= -24$$

Work Smart

In Examples 2(b) and (c), notice that
$$\sqrt{9} + \sqrt{16} \neq \sqrt{9 + 16}$$
In general,
$$\sqrt{a} + \sqrt{b} \neq \sqrt{a + b}$$
The radical acts like a grouping symbol, so always simplify the radicand before taking the square root.

(b) $\sqrt{9} + \sqrt{16} = 3 + 4$
$$= 7$$

(c) $\sqrt{9 + 16} = \sqrt{25}$
$$= 5$$

(d) $\sqrt{64 - 4 \cdot 7 \cdot 1} = \sqrt{64 - 28}$
$$= \sqrt{36}$$
$$= 6$$ ∎

Quick ✔ *In Problems 9–12, evaluate each expression.*

9. $5\sqrt{9}$ 10. $\sqrt{36 + 64}$ 11. $\sqrt{36} + \sqrt{64}$ 12. $\sqrt{25 - 4 \cdot 3 \cdot (-2)}$

⌐2 Determine Whether a Square Root Is Rational, Irrational, or Not a Real Number

Not all radical expressions will simplify to a rational number. For example, because there is no rational number whose square is 5, $\sqrt{5}$ is not a rational number. In fact, $\sqrt{5}$ is an *irrational* number. Remember, an irrational number is a number that cannot be written as the quotient of two integers.

What if we wanted to evaluate $\sqrt{-16}$? Because any positive real number squared is positive, any negative real number squared is also positive, and 0 squared is 0, there is no real number whose square is -16. We conclude: **Negative real numbers do not have square roots that are real numbers!**

Work Smart

The square roots of negative real numbers are not real.

The following comments regarding square roots are important.

> **MORE PROPERTIES OF SQUARE ROOTS**
> - The square root of a perfect square is a rational number.
> - The square root of a positive rational number that is not a perfect square is an irrational number. For example, $\sqrt{20}$ is an irrational number because 20 is not a perfect square.
> - The square root of a negative real number is not a real number. For example, $\sqrt{-2}$ is not a real number.

When a radical has a radicand that is not a perfect square, we can do one of two things:

1. Write a decimal approximation of the radical.
2. Simplify the radical using properties of radicals, if possible (Section 6.3).

Figure 2

```
√(5)
          2.236067977
```

EXAMPLE 3 Writing a Radical as a Decimal Using a Calculator

Write $\sqrt{5}$ as a decimal rounded to two decimal places.

Solution

Figure 2 shows the results from a TI-84 Plus graphing calculator. From the display, we see that $\sqrt{5} \approx 2.24$. ■

EXAMPLE 4 Determining Whether a Square Root of an Integer Is Rational, Irrational, or Not a Real Number

Determine if each square root is rational, irrational, or not a real number. Then evaluate each real square root. For each square root that is irrational, express the square root as a decimal rounded to two decimal places.

(a) $\sqrt{51}$ **(b)** $\sqrt{169}$ **(c)** $\sqrt{-81}$

Solution

Work Smart

$\sqrt{-81}$ is not a real number, but $-\sqrt{81}$ is a real number because $-\sqrt{81} = -9$. Note the placement of the negative sign!

(a) $\sqrt{51}$ is irrational because 51 is not a perfect square. That is, there is no rational number whose square is 51. Using a calculator, we find $\sqrt{51} \approx 7.14$.
(b) $\sqrt{169}$ is a rational number because $13^2 = 169$. So, $\sqrt{169} = 13$.
(c) $\sqrt{-81}$ is not a real number. There is no real number whose square is -81. ■

> **Quick ✔**
>
> 13. *True or False:* Negative numbers do not have square roots that are real numbers.
>
> *In Problems 14–17, determine whether each square root is rational, irrational, or not a real number. Evaluate each square root that is rational. For each square root that is irrational, approximate the square root rounded to two decimal places.*
>
> **14.** $\sqrt{400}$ **15.** $\sqrt{40}$ **16.** $\sqrt{-25}$ **17.** $-\sqrt{196}$

3 Find Square Roots of Variable Expressions

What is $\sqrt{4^2}$? Because $4^2 = 16$, we have that $\sqrt{4^2} = \sqrt{16} = 4$. Based on this result, we might conclude that $\sqrt{a^2} = a$ for any real number a. Before we jump to this conclusion, let's consider $\sqrt{(-4)^2}$. Our "formula" says that $\sqrt{a^2} = a$, so we would think that $\sqrt{(-4)^2} = -4$, right? Wrong! $\sqrt{(-4)^2} = \sqrt{16} = 4$. So $\sqrt{4^2} = 4$ and $\sqrt{(-4)^2} = 4$.

Regardless of whether the "a" in $\sqrt{a^2}$ is positive or negative, the result ends up being positive. So to say that $\sqrt{a^2} = a$ would not quite be correct. How can we fix our "formula"? In Section R.3, we learned that $|a|$ will be a positive number if a is nonzero. From this, we have the following result:

In Words

The square root of a nonzero number squared will always be positive. The absolute value ensures this.

For any **real number** a,

$$\sqrt{a^2} = |a|$$

The bottom line is this—if you are taking the square root of some variable expression raised to the second power, the result will be the absolute value of the variable expression.

EXAMPLE 5 Evaluating Square Roots

Evaluate each square root.

(a) $\sqrt{7^2}$ (b) $\sqrt{(-15)^2}$ (c) $\sqrt{x^2}$ (d) $\sqrt{(3x-1)^2}$ (e) $\sqrt{x^2 + 6x + 9}$

Solution

(a) $\sqrt{7^2} = 7$

(b) $\sqrt{(-15)^2} = |-15| = 15$

(c) We don't know whether the real number x is positive, negative, or zero. To ensure that the result is positive or zero, we write $\sqrt{x^2} = |x|$.

(d) $\sqrt{(3x-1)^2} = |3x - 1|$

(e) Notice that the radicand is a perfect square trinomial, so that $x^2 + 6x + 9$ factors to $(x+3)^2$. Therefore,

$$\sqrt{x^2 + 6x + 9} = \sqrt{(x+3)^2}$$
$$= |x + 3|$$

Quick ✔

18. $\sqrt{a^2} = $ ___ .

In Problems 19–22, evaluate each square root.

19. $\sqrt{(-14)^2}$ **20.** $\sqrt{z^2}$ **21.** $\sqrt{(2x+3)^2}$ **22.** $\sqrt{p^2 - 12p + 36}$

GETTING READY FOR CHAPTER 6 EXERCISES

MyMathLab *Powered by CourseCompass™ and MathXL®*

 PRACTICE   WATCH   DOWNLOAD   READ   REVIEW

1–22. *are the* Quick ✔s *that follow each* **EXAMPLE**

Building Skills

In Problems 23–32, evaluate each square root. See Objective 1.

23. $\sqrt{1}$ **24.** $\sqrt{9}$

25. $-\sqrt{100}$ **26.** $-\sqrt{144}$

27. $\sqrt{\dfrac{1}{4}}$ **28.** $\sqrt{\dfrac{4}{81}}$

29. $\sqrt{0.36}$ **30.** $\sqrt{0.16}$

31. $\left(\sqrt{1.6}\right)^2$ **32.** $\left(\sqrt{3.7}\right)^2$

In Problems 33–44, tell if the square root is rational, irrational, or not a real number. If the square root is rational, find the exact value; if the square root is irrational, write the approximate value rounded to two decimal places. See Objective 2.

33. $\sqrt{-14}$ **34.** $\sqrt{-50}$

35. $\sqrt{64}$

36. $\sqrt{121}$

37. $\sqrt{\dfrac{1}{16}}$

38. $\sqrt{\dfrac{49}{100}}$

39. $\sqrt{44}$

40. $\sqrt{24}$

41. $\sqrt{50}$

42. $\sqrt{12}$

43. $\sqrt{-16}$

44. $\sqrt{-64}$

In Problems 45–56, simplify each square root. See Objective 3.

45. $\sqrt{8^2}$

46. $\sqrt{5^2}$

47. $\sqrt{(-19)^2}$

48. $\sqrt{(-13)^2}$

49. $\sqrt{r^2}$

50. $\sqrt{w^2}$

51. $\sqrt{(x+4)^2}$

52. $\sqrt{(x-8)^2}$

53. $\sqrt{(4x-3)^2}$

54. $\sqrt{(5x+2)^2}$

55. $\sqrt{4y^2+12y+9}$

56. $\sqrt{9z^2-24z+16}$

Mixed Practice

In Problems 57–74, simplify each expression.

57. $\sqrt{25+144}$

58. $\sqrt{9+16}$

59. $\sqrt{25}+\sqrt{144}$

60. $\sqrt{9}+\sqrt{16}$

61. $\sqrt{-144}$

62. $\sqrt{-36}$

63. $3\sqrt{25}$

64. $-10\sqrt{16}$

65. $5\sqrt{\dfrac{16}{25}}-\sqrt{144}$

66. $2\sqrt{\dfrac{9}{4}}-\sqrt{4}$

67. $\sqrt{8^2-4\cdot1\cdot7}$

68. $\sqrt{9^2-4\cdot1\cdot20}$

69. $\sqrt{(-5)^2-4\cdot2\cdot5}$

70. $\sqrt{(-3)^2-4\cdot3\cdot2}$

71. $\dfrac{-(-1)+\sqrt{(-1)^2-4\cdot6\cdot(-2)}}{2\cdot(-1)}$

72. $\dfrac{-7+\sqrt{7^2-4\cdot2\cdot6}}{2\cdot2}$

73. $\sqrt{(6-1)^2+(15-3)^2}$

74. $\sqrt{(2-(-1))^2+(6-2)^2}$

75. What are the square roots of 36? What is $\sqrt{36}$?

76. What are the square roots of 64? What is $\sqrt{64}$?

Math for the Future: Statistics *For Problems 77 and 78, use the formula* $Z=\dfrac{X-\mu}{\dfrac{\sigma}{\sqrt{n}}}$ *from statistics (a formula used to determine the relative value of one observation to another) to evaluate the expression for the given values. Write the exact value and then write your answer rounded to two decimal places.*

77. $X=120,\ \mu=100,\ \sigma=15,\ n=13$

78. $X=40,\ \mu=50,\ \sigma=10,\ n=5$

Explaining the Concepts

79. Explain why $\sqrt{a^2}=|a|$. Provide examples to support your explanation.

6 Radicals and Rational Exponents

Where would we be without electricity? In 1752, when Ben Franklin first sent his kite into the clouds, the idea of a number whose square is -1 was still being developed by mathematicians. Yet it turns out that this concept is extremely useful in describing alternating electric currents. See Problems 127 and 128 in Section 6.8.

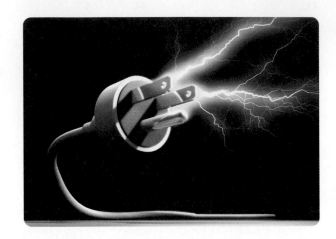

The Big Picture: Putting It Together

In Chapter 4 we simplified polynomial expressions by adding, subtracting, multiplying, and dividing. We also factored polynomials. In Chapter 5 we used the skills learned in Chapter 4 to simplify rational expressions and perform operations on rational expressions.

We now present a similar discussion with radical expressions. We will learn how to add, subtract, multiply, and divide radical expressions. In addition, we will use factoring to simplify radical expressions. Throughout this discussion, keep in mind that radicals perform the "inverse" operation to raising a real number to a positive integer exponent. For example, a square root undoes the "squaring" operation.

6.1 nth Roots and Rational Exponents

OBJECTIVES

1. Evaluate nth Roots
2. Simplify Expressions of the Form $\sqrt[n]{a^n}$
3. Evaluate Expressions of the Form $a^{\frac{1}{n}}$
4. Evaluate Expressions of the Form $a^{\frac{m}{n}}$

Preparing for nth Roots and Rational Exponents

Before getting started, take the following readiness quiz. If you get a problem wrong, go to the section cited and review the material.

P1. Simplify: $\left(\dfrac{x^2 y}{x y^{-2}}\right)^{-3}$ [Getting Ready: Laws of Exponents, pp. 312–313]

P2. Simplify: $\left(\sqrt{7}\right)^2$ [Getting Ready: Square Roots, pp. 473–474]

P3. Evaluate: $\sqrt{64}$ [Getting Ready: Square Roots, pp. 473–474]

P4. Evaluate: $\sqrt{(x+1)^2}$ [Getting Ready: Square Roots, pp. 475–476]

P5. Simplify: **(a)** 3^{-2} **(b)** x^{-4} [Getting Ready: Laws of Exponents, pp. 307–309]

In the Getting Ready: Square Roots, we reviewed skills for evaluating square roots. We now extend this skill to other types of roots.

1 Evaluate nth Roots

A real number is cubed when it is raised to the power 3. The inverse of cubing a number is finding the *cube root*. For example, since $2^3 = 8$, the cube root of 8 is 2; since $(-2)^3 = -8$, the cube root of -8 is -2. In general, we can find *n*th roots of numbers.

In Words

When you see the notation $\sqrt[n]{a} = b$, think to yourself, "Find a number b such that raising that number to the nth power gives me a."

DEFINITION

The **principal nth root of a number** a, symbolized by $\sqrt[n]{a}$, where $n \geq 2$ is an integer, is defined as follows:

$$\sqrt[n]{a} = b \qquad \text{means} \qquad a = b^n$$

- If $n \geq 2$ and even, then a and b must be greater than or equal to 0.
- If $n \geq 3$ and odd, then a and b can be any real number.

Work Smart

If the index is even, then the radicand must be greater than or equal to zero in order for a radical to simplify to a real number. If the index is odd, the radicand can be any real number.

In the notation $\sqrt[n]{a}$, the integer n, $n \geq 2$, is called the **index.** If a radical is written without the index, it is understood that we mean the square root, so $\sqrt{a}$ represents the square root of a. If the index is 3, we call $\sqrt[3]{a}$ the **cube root** of a.

If the index is even, then the radicand must be greater than or equal to 0. If the index is odd, then the radicand can be any real number. Do you know why? Since $\sqrt[n]{a} = b$ means $b^n = a$, if the index n is even, then $b^n \geq 0$ so $a \geq 0$. If we have an odd index n, then b^n can be any real number, so a can be any real number.

Before we evaluate *n*th roots, we list some "perfect" powers of 2, 3, 4, and 5. Having this list will be a great help in finding roots in the examples that follow. Notice in the display that follows that perfect cubes or perfect fifths can be negative, but perfect squares or perfect fourths cannot. Do you know why?

Preparing for...Answers P1. $\dfrac{1}{x^3 y^9}$ **P2.** 7

P3. 8 **P4.** $|x + 1|$ **P5. (a)** $\dfrac{1}{9}$

(b) $\dfrac{1}{x^4}$

Perfect Squares	Perfect Cubes	Perfect Fourths	Perfect Fifths
$1^2 = 1$	$(-2)^3 = -8$	$1^4 = 1$	$(-2)^5 = -32$
$2^2 = 4$	$(-1)^3 = -1$	$2^4 = 16$	$(-1)^5 = -1$
$3^2 = 9$	$1^3 = 1$	$3^4 = 81$	$1^5 = 1$
$4^2 = 16$ and so on	$2^3 = 8$ and so on	$4^4 = 256$ and so on	$2^5 = 32$ and so on

EXAMPLE 1 Evaluating *n*th Roots of Real Numbers

Evaluate:

(a) $\sqrt[3]{1000}$ (b) $\sqrt[4]{16}$ (c) $\sqrt[3]{-8}$ (d) $\sqrt[4]{-81}$

Solution

(a) We are looking for a number whose cube is 1000. Since $10^3 = 1000$, we have $\sqrt[3]{1000} = 10$.

(b) $\sqrt[4]{16} = 2$ since $2^4 = 16$.

(c) $\sqrt[3]{-8} = -2$ since $(-2)^3 = -8$.

(d) Because there is no real number b such that $b^4 = -81$, $\sqrt[4]{-81}$ is not a real number. ∎

Quick ✔

1. In the notation $\sqrt[n]{a}$, the integer $n, n \geq 2$, is called the ____.

In Problems 2–6, evaluate each root.

2. $\sqrt[3]{64}$ 3. $\sqrt[4]{81}$ 4. $\sqrt[3]{-216}$

5. $\sqrt[4]{-32}$ 6. $\sqrt[5]{\dfrac{1}{32}}$

The *n*th roots in Examples 1(a)–(c) were all rational numbers. This is not always the case. Just as we can approximate square roots using a calculator, we can also approximate *n*th roots.

EXAMPLE 2 Approximating an *n*th Root Using a Calculator

(a) Write $\sqrt[3]{25}$ as a decimal rounded to two decimal places.

(b) Write $\sqrt[4]{18}$ as a decimal rounded to two decimal places.

Solution

(a) Because $\sqrt[3]{8} = 2$ and $\sqrt[3]{27} = 3$, we expect $\sqrt[3]{25}$ is between 2 and 3 (closer to 3). Figure 1(a) shows the approximate value of $\sqrt[3]{25}$ obtained from a TI-84 Plus graphing calculator. So $\sqrt[3]{25} \approx 2.92$.

(b) Because $\sqrt[4]{16} = 2$ and $\sqrt[4]{81} = 3$, we expect $\sqrt[4]{18}$ is between 2 and 3 (closer to 2). Figure 1(b) shows the approximate value of $\sqrt[4]{18}$ obtained from a TI-84 Plus graphing calculator. So $\sqrt[4]{18} \approx 2.06$.

Figure 1

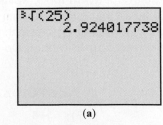

(a)   (b)

Quick ✔ *In Problems 7 and 8, use a calculator to write the approximate value of each radical rounded to two decimal places.*

7. $\sqrt[3]{50}$ 8. $\sqrt[4]{80}$

2 Simplify Expressions of the Form $\sqrt[n]{a^n}$

We have already seen that $\sqrt{a^2} = |a|$. But what about $\sqrt[3]{a^3}$ or $\sqrt[4]{a^4}$? Recall that the definition of the principal *n*th root, $\sqrt[n]{a}$, requires that $a \geq 0$ when *n* is even and *a* can be any real number when *n* is odd.

SIMPLIFYING $\sqrt[n]{a^n}$

If $n \geq 2$ is a positive integer and *a* is a real number, then
$$\sqrt[n]{a^n} = a \quad \text{if } n \geq 3 \text{ is odd}$$
$$\sqrt[n]{a^n} = |a| \quad \text{if } n \geq 2 \text{ is even}$$

EXAMPLE 3 Simplifying Radicals

Simplify:

    (a) $\sqrt[3]{x^3}$ **(b)** $\sqrt[4]{(x-7)^4}$ **(c)** $-\sqrt[6]{(-3)^6}$ **(d)** $\sqrt[3]{-\dfrac{8}{125}}$

Solution

    (a) Because the index, 3, is odd, we have that $\sqrt[3]{x^3} = x$.

    (b) Because the index, 4, is even, we have that $\sqrt[4]{(x-7)^4} = |x - 7|$.

    (c) $-\sqrt[6]{(-3)^6} = -|-3| = -3$

    (d) $\sqrt[3]{-\dfrac{8}{125}} = \sqrt[3]{\dfrac{-8}{125}} = \sqrt[3]{\dfrac{(-2)^3}{5^3}} = \sqrt[3]{\left(\dfrac{-2}{5}\right)^3} = -\dfrac{2}{5}$

Quick ✔ *In Problems 9–13, simplify each radical.*

  9. $\sqrt[4]{5^4}$ **10.** $\sqrt[6]{z^6}$ **11.** $\sqrt[7]{(3x - 2)^7}$

  12. $\sqrt[8]{(-2)^8}$ **13.** $\sqrt[5]{\left(-\dfrac{2}{3}\right)^5}$

---

3 Evaluate Expressions of the Form $a^{\frac{1}{n}}$

In the "Getting Ready: Laws of Exponents," we carefully developed methods for simplifying algebraic expressions that contained integer exponents. This development started with methods for simplifying algebraic expressions containing only positive integer exponents. We then presented a definition for raising a nonzero real number to the power of 0. With this material in hand, we were able to develop rules for simplifying algebraic expressions involving *all* integer exponents. Of course, the world cannot easily be described using only integers, so it is logical that we would want to extend the rules of exponents to rational exponents.

We start by providing a definition for "*a* raised to the power $\dfrac{1}{n}$," where *a* is a real number and *n* is a positive integer. This definition needs to be written so that the laws of exponents apply. For example, we know that $a^2 = a \cdot a$, so

$$\left(5^{\frac{1}{2}}\right)^2 = 5^{\frac{1}{2}} \cdot 5^{\frac{1}{2}}$$
$$a^m \cdot a^n = a^{m+n}: \quad = 5^{\frac{1}{2}+\frac{1}{2}}$$
$$= 5^1$$
$$= 5$$

We also know that $\left(\sqrt{5}\right)^2 = 5$, so it is reasonable to conclude that

$$5^{\frac{1}{2}} = \sqrt{5}$$

Work Smart

Remember, a rational number is a number of the form $\dfrac{p}{q}$, where *p* and *q* are integers and $q \neq 0$.

This suggests the following definition:

> **DEFINITION OF $a^{\frac{1}{n}}$**
>
> If a is a real number and n is an integer with $n \geq 2$, then
> $$a^{\frac{1}{n}} = \sqrt[n]{a}$$
> provided that $\sqrt[n]{a}$ exists.

EXAMPLE 4 Evaluating Expressions Containing Exponents of the Form $\dfrac{1}{n}$

Write each of the following expressions as a radical and simplify, if possible.

(a) $9^{\frac{1}{2}}$ (b) $(-64)^{\frac{1}{3}}$ (c) $-100^{\frac{1}{2}}$ (d) $(-100)^{\frac{1}{2}}$ (e) $z^{\frac{1}{2}}$

Solution

(a) $9^{\frac{1}{2}} = \sqrt{9} = 3$ (b) $(-64)^{\frac{1}{3}} = \sqrt[3]{-64}$ (c) $-100^{\frac{1}{2}} = -1 \cdot 100^{\frac{1}{2}}$
$$= -4 \qquad\qquad = -\sqrt{100}$$
$$= -10$$

(d) $(-100)^{\frac{1}{2}} = \sqrt{-100}$ is not a real number because there is no real number whose square is -100.

(e) $z^{\frac{1}{2}} = \sqrt{z}$

Work Smart

Notice the use of parentheses in Examples 4(c) and (d). In Example 4(c), $-100^{\frac{1}{2}}$ means that we should evaluate $100^{\frac{1}{2}}$ first and then multiply the result by -1. Remember, evaluate exponents before multiplying.

Quick ✔
14. If a is a nonnegative real number and $n \geq 2$ is an integer, then $a^{\frac{1}{n}} = \_\_$.

In Problems 15–19, write each of the following expressions as a radical and simplify, if possible.

15. $25^{\frac{1}{2}}$ **16.** $(-27)^{\frac{1}{3}}$ **17.** $-64^{\frac{1}{2}}$ **18.** $(-64)^{\frac{1}{2}}$ **19.** $b^{\frac{1}{2}}$

EXAMPLE 5 Writing Radicals with Rational Exponents

Rewrite each of the following radicals with a rational exponent.

(a) $\sqrt[4]{7a}$ (b) $\sqrt[5]{\dfrac{xy^3}{4}}$

Solution

(a) The index on the radical is 4, so this becomes the denominator of the rational exponent. Parentheses are necessary because the radicand is $7a$ and the exponent $\dfrac{1}{4}$ is applied to both the 7 and the a.
$$\sqrt[4]{7a} = (7a)^{\frac{1}{4}}$$

(b) The index on the radical is 5, so this becomes the denominator of the rational exponent.
$$\sqrt[5]{\frac{xy^3}{4}} = \left(\frac{xy^3}{4}\right)^{\frac{1}{5}}$$

Quick ✔ *In Problems 20 and 21, rewrite each of the following radicals with a rational exponent.*

20. $\sqrt[5]{8b}$ **21.** $\sqrt[8]{\dfrac{mn^5}{3}}$

4 Evaluate Expressions of the Form $a^{\frac{m}{n}}$

We now look for a definition for $a^{\frac{m}{n}}$, where m and n are integers, $\dfrac{m}{n}$ is expressed in lowest terms, and $n \geq 2$. The definition we provide should obey all the laws of exponents presented earlier. For example,

$$a^{\frac{m}{n}} = a^{m \cdot \frac{1}{n}} = \left(a^m\right)^{\frac{1}{n}} = \sqrt[n]{a^m}$$

and

$$a^{\frac{m}{n}} = a^{\frac{1}{n} \cdot m} = \left(a^{\frac{1}{n}}\right)^m = \left(\sqrt[n]{a}\right)^m$$

This suggests the following definition:

In Words

The expression $a^{\frac{m}{n}} = \sqrt[n]{a^m}$ means that we will raise *a* to the *m*th power first, and then take the *n*th root. The expression $a^{\frac{m}{n}} = \left(\sqrt[n]{a}\right)^m$ means that we will take the *n*th root of *a* first, and then raise to the power of *m*.

> **DEFINITION OF $a^{\frac{m}{n}}$**
>
> If a is a real number, $\dfrac{m}{n}$ is a rational number in lowest terms with $n \geq 2$, then
> $$a^{\frac{m}{n}} = \sqrt[n]{a^m} = \left(\sqrt[n]{a}\right)^m$$
> provided that $\sqrt[n]{a}$ exists.

When simplifying $a^{\frac{m}{n}}$ either $\sqrt[n]{a^m}$ or $\left(\sqrt[n]{a}\right)^m$ may be used. Use the one that makes simplifying the expression easier. Generally, taking the root first, as in $\left(\sqrt[n]{a}\right)^m$, is easier.

EXAMPLE 6   Evaluating Expressions of the Form $a^{\frac{m}{n}}$

Evaluate each of the following expressions, if possible.

(a) $25^{\frac{3}{2}}$ (b) $64^{\frac{2}{3}}$ (c) $-9^{\frac{5}{2}}$ (d) $(-8)^{\frac{4}{3}}$ (e) $(-81)^{\frac{7}{2}}$

Solution

(a) $25^{\frac{3}{2}} = \left(\sqrt{25}\right)^3 = 5^3 = 125$

(b) $64^{\frac{2}{3}} = \left(\sqrt[3]{64}\right)^2 = 4^2 = 16$

(c) $-9^{\frac{5}{2}} = -1 \cdot 9^{\frac{5}{2}} = -1 \cdot \left(\sqrt{9}\right)^5 = -1 \cdot 3^5 = -1 \cdot 243 = -243$

(d) $(-8)^{\frac{4}{3}} = \left(\sqrt[3]{-8}\right)^4 = (-2)^4 = 16$

(e) $(-81)^{\frac{7}{2}}$ is not a real number because $(-81)^{\frac{7}{2}} = \left(\sqrt{-81}\right)^7$ and $\sqrt{-81}$ is not a real number. ∎

Work Smart

When simplifying expressions of the form $a^{\frac{m}{n}}$ it is typically easier to evaluate the radical first.

> **Quick ✔**
>
> **22.** If a is a real number, and $\dfrac{m}{n}$ is a rational number in lowest terms with $n \geq 2$, then $a^{\frac{m}{n}} = $ _____ or _____.
>
> *In Problems 23–27, evaluate each expression, if possible.*
>
> **23.** $16^{\frac{3}{2}}$ **24.** $27^{\frac{2}{3}}$ **25.** $-16^{\frac{3}{4}}$
>
> **26.** $(-64)^{\frac{2}{3}}$ **27.** $(-25)^{\frac{5}{2}}$

The expressions in Examples 6(a)–(d) were all rational numbers. Not all expressions involving rational exponents will simplify to rational numbers.

EXAMPLE 7   Approximating Expressions Involving Rational Exponents

Write $35^{\frac{3}{4}}$ as a decimal rounded to two decimal places.

Solution

Figure 2

```
35^(3/4)
        14.38967659
■
```

Figure 2 shows the results obtained from a TI-84 Plus graphing calculator. So $35^{\frac{3}{4}} \approx 14.39$. ∎

> **Quick ✔** *In Problems 28 and 29, approximate the expression rounded to two decimal places.*
>
> **28.** $50^{\frac{2}{3}}$ **29.** $40^{0.15}$

EXAMPLE 8 Writing Radicals with Rational Exponents

Rewrite each of the following radicals with a rational exponent.

(a) $\sqrt[3]{x^2}$

(b) $\left(\sqrt[5]{10a^2b}\right)^4$

Solution

(a) The index, 3, is the denominator of the rational exponent and the power on the radicand, 2, is the numerator of the rational exponent.

$$\sqrt[3]{x^2} = x^{\frac{2}{3}}$$

(b) The index, 5, is the denominator of the rational exponent and the power, 4, is the numerator of the rational exponent.

$$\left(\sqrt[5]{10a^2b}\right)^4 = (10a^2b)^{\frac{4}{5}}$$

> **Quick** ✔ *In Problems 30 and 31, write each radical with a rational exponent.*
>
> **30.** $\sqrt[8]{a^3}$
>
> **31.** $\left(\sqrt[4]{12ab^3}\right)^9$

If a rational exponent is negative, then we can use the rule for negative rational exponents given below.

> **DEFINITION** NEGATIVE-EXPONENT RULE
>
> If $\dfrac{m}{n}$ is a rational number, and if a is a nonzero real number (that is, if $a \neq 0$), then we define
>
> $$a^{-\frac{m}{n}} = \frac{1}{a^{\frac{m}{n}}} \quad \text{and} \quad \frac{1}{a^{-\frac{m}{n}}} = a^{\frac{m}{n}} \quad \text{if } a \neq 0$$

EXAMPLE 9 Evaluating Expressions with Negative Rational Exponents

Rewrite each of the following with positive exponents, and completely simplify, if possible.

(a) $36^{-\frac{1}{2}}$

(b) $\dfrac{1}{27^{-\frac{2}{3}}}$

(c) $(6a)^{-\frac{5}{4}}$

Solution

(a) $36^{-\frac{1}{2}} = \dfrac{1}{36^{\frac{1}{2}}} = \dfrac{1}{\sqrt{36}} = \dfrac{1}{6}$

(b) Because the negative exponent is in the exponential expression in the denominator, we use $\dfrac{1}{a^{-\frac{m}{n}}} = a^{\frac{m}{n}}$ to simplify:

$$\frac{1}{27^{-\frac{2}{3}}} = 27^{\frac{2}{3}} = \left(\sqrt[3]{27}\right)^2 = 3^2 = 9$$

(c) $(6a)^{-\frac{5}{4}} = \dfrac{1}{(6a)^{\frac{5}{4}}}$

> **Quick** ✔ *In Problems 32–34, rewrite each of the following with positive exponents, and completely simplify, if possible.*
>
> **32.** $81^{-\frac{1}{2}}$
>
> **33.** $\dfrac{1}{8^{-\frac{2}{3}}}$
>
> **34.** $(13x)^{-\frac{3}{2}}$

6.1 EXERCISES

PRACTICE   WATCH   DOWNLOAD   READ   REVIEW

1–34. *are the* Quick ✔*s that follow each* **EXAMPLE**

Building Skills

In Problems 35–44, simplify each radical. See Objective 1.

35. $\sqrt[3]{125}$ **36.** $\sqrt[3]{216}$

37. $\sqrt[3]{-27}$ **38.** $\sqrt[3]{-64}$

39. $-\sqrt[4]{625}$ **40.** $-\sqrt[4]{256}$

41. $\sqrt[3]{-\dfrac{1}{8}}$ **42.** $\sqrt[3]{\dfrac{8}{125}}$

43. $-\sqrt[5]{-243}$ **44.** $-\sqrt[5]{-1024}$

In Problems 45–48, use a calculator to write each expression as a decimal rounded to two decimal places. See Objective 1.

45. $\sqrt[3]{25}$ **46.** $\sqrt[3]{85}$

47. $\sqrt[4]{12}$ **48.** $\sqrt[4]{2}$

In Problems 49–56, simplify each radical. See Objective 2.

49. $\sqrt[3]{5^3}$ **50.** $\sqrt[4]{6^4}$

51. $\sqrt[4]{m^4}$ **52.** $\sqrt[5]{n^5}$

53. $\sqrt[9]{(x-3)^9}$ **54.** $\sqrt[6]{(2x-3)^6}$

55. $-\sqrt[4]{(3p+1)^4}$ **56.** $-\sqrt[3]{(6z-5)^3}$

In Problems 57–70, evaluate each expression, if possible. See Objective 3.

57. $4^{\frac{1}{2}}$ **58.** $16^{\frac{1}{2}}$

59. $-36^{\frac{1}{2}}$ **60.** $-25^{\frac{1}{2}}$

61. $8^{\frac{1}{3}}$ **62.** $27^{\frac{1}{3}}$

63. $-16^{\frac{1}{4}}$ **64.** $-81^{\frac{1}{4}}$

65. $\left(\dfrac{4}{25}\right)^{\frac{1}{2}}$ **66.** $\left(\dfrac{8}{27}\right)^{\frac{1}{3}}$

67. $(-125)^{\frac{1}{3}}$ **68.** $(-216)^{\frac{1}{3}}$

69. $(-4)^{\frac{1}{2}}$ **70.** $(-81)^{\frac{1}{2}}$

In Problems 71–74, rewrite each of the following radicals with a rational exponent. See Objective 3.

71. $\sqrt[3]{3x}$ **72.** $\sqrt[5]{2y}$

73. $\sqrt[4]{\dfrac{x}{3}}$ **74.** $\sqrt{\dfrac{w}{2}}$

In Problems 75–90, evaluate each expression. See Objective 4.

75. $4^{\frac{5}{2}}$ **76.** $25^{\frac{3}{2}}$

77. $-16^{\frac{3}{2}}$ **78.** $-100^{\frac{5}{2}}$

79. $8^{\frac{4}{3}}$ **80.** $27^{\frac{4}{3}}$

81. $(-64)^{\frac{2}{3}}$ **82.** $(-125)^{\frac{2}{3}}$

83. $-(-32)^{\frac{3}{5}}$ **84.** $-(-216)^{\frac{2}{3}}$

85. $144^{-\frac{1}{2}}$ **86.** $121^{-\frac{1}{2}}$

87. $\dfrac{1}{25^{-\frac{3}{2}}}$ **88.** $\dfrac{1}{49^{-\frac{3}{2}}}$

89. $\dfrac{1}{8^{-\frac{5}{3}}}$ **90.** $27^{-\frac{4}{3}}$

In Problems 91–98, rewrite each of the following radicals with a rational exponent. See Objective 4.

91. $\sqrt[4]{x^3}$ **92.** $\sqrt[3]{p^5}$

93. $\left(\sqrt[5]{3x}\right)^2$ **94.** $\left(\sqrt[4]{6z}\right)^3$

95. $\sqrt{\left(\dfrac{5x}{y}\right)^3}$ **96.** $\sqrt[6]{\left(\dfrac{2a}{b}\right)^5}$

97. $\sqrt[3]{(9ab)^4}$ **98.** $\sqrt[4]{(3pq)^7}$

In Problems 99–104, use a calculator to write each expression as a decimal rounded to two decimal places. See Objective 4.

99. $20^{\frac{1}{2}}$ **100.** $5^{\frac{1}{2}}$

101. $4^{\frac{5}{3}}$ **102.** $100^{\frac{3}{4}}$

103. $10^{0.1}$ **104.** $100^{0.25}$

Mixed Practice

In Problems 105–128, evaluate each expression, if possible.

105. $\sqrt[3]{x^3} + 4\sqrt[6]{x^6}$ **106.** $\sqrt[3]{(x-1)^3} + \sqrt[5]{32}$

107. $-16^{\frac{3}{4}} - \sqrt[5]{32}$ **108.** $\dfrac{5\sqrt[4]{x^7}}{\sqrt[3]{x^3}}$

109. $\sqrt[3]{512}$ **110.** $\sqrt[3]{-125}$

111. $9^{\frac{5}{2}}$ **112.** $100^{\frac{3}{2}}$

113. $\sqrt[4]{-16}$ **114.** $\sqrt[4]{-1}$

115. $144^{-\frac{1}{2}} \cdot 3^2$

116. $125^{-\frac{1}{3}}$

117. $\sqrt[3]{0.008}$

118. $\sqrt[4]{0.0081}$

119. $4^{\frac{1}{2}} + 25^{\frac{3}{2}}$

120. $100^{\frac{1}{2}} - 4^{\frac{3}{2}}$

121. $(-25)^{\frac{5}{2}}$

122. $(-125)^{-\frac{1}{3}}$

123. $\sqrt[3]{(3p-5)^3}$

124. $\sqrt[5]{(6b-1)^5}$

125. $-9^{\frac{3}{2}} + \dfrac{1}{27^{-\frac{2}{3}}}$

126. $\dfrac{1}{64^{\frac{1}{2}}} - 4^{-\frac{3}{2}}$

127. $\sqrt[6]{(-2)^6}$

128. $\sqrt[4]{(-10)^4}$

In Problems 129–132, evaluate each function.

129. $f(x) = x^{\frac{3}{2}}$; find $f(4)$

130. $g(x) = x^{-\frac{3}{2}}$; find $g(16)$

131. $F(z) = z^{\frac{4}{3}}$; find $F(-8)$

132. $G(a) = a^{\frac{5}{3}}$; find $G(-8)$

Applying the Concepts

133. What is the cube root of 1000? What is $\sqrt[3]{1000}$?

134. What is the cube root of 729? What is $\sqrt[3]{729}$?

135. Wind Chill According to the National Weather Service, the wind chill temperature is how cold people and animals feel when outside. Wind chill is based on the rate of heat loss from exposed skin caused by wind and cold. The formula for computing wind chill W is

$$W = 35.74 + 0.6215T - 35.75v^{0.16} + 0.4275Tv^{0.16}$$

where T is the air temperature in degrees Fahrenheit and v is the wind speed in miles per hour.

(a) What is the wind chill if it is 30°F and the wind speed is 10 miles per hour?
(b) What is the wind chill if it is 30°F and the wind speed is 20 miles per hour?
(c) What is the wind chill if it is 0°F and the wind speed is 10 miles per hour?

136. Money The annual rate of interest r (expressed as a decimal) required to have A dollars after t years from an initial deposit of P dollars is given by

$$r = \left(\frac{A}{P}\right)^{\frac{1}{t}} - 1$$

(a) If you deposit \$100 in a mutual fund today and have \$144 in the account in 2 years, what was your annual rate of interest earned?
(b) If you deposit \$100 in a mutual fund today and have \$337.50 in 3 years, what was your annual rate of interest earned?

(c) The Rule of 72 states that your money will double in $\dfrac{72}{100r}$ years where r is the rate of interest earned (expressed as a decimal). Suppose that you deposit \$1000 in a mutual fund today and have \$2000 in 8 years. What rate of interest did you earn? Compute $\dfrac{72}{100r}$ for this rate of interest. Is it close?

137. Terminal Velocity Terminal velocity is the maximum speed that a body falling through air can reach due to air resistance. Terminal velocity is given by the formula $v_t = \sqrt{\dfrac{2mg}{C\rho A}}$, where m is the mass of the falling object, g is acceleration due to gravity (≈ 9.81 meters per second^2), C is a drag coefficient with $0.5 \le C \le 1.0$, ρ is the density of air (≈ 1.2 kg/m^3), and A is the cross-sectional area of the object. Suppose that a raindrop whose radius is 1.5 mm falls from the sky. The mass of the raindrop is given by $m = \dfrac{4}{3}\pi r^3 \rho_w$ where r is its radius and $\rho_w = 1000$ kg/m^3. The cross-sectional area of the raindrop is $A = \pi r^2$.

(a) Substitute the formulas for the mass and area of a raindrop into the formula for terminal speed and simplify the expression.
(b) Determine the terminal velocity of a raindrop whose radius is 0.0015 m with $C = 0.6$.

138. Kepler's Law Early in the seventeenth century, Johannes Kepler (1571–1630) discovered that the square of the period T of a planet varies directly with the cube of its mean distance r from the Sun. The period of a planet is the amount of time (in years) for the planet to complete one orbit around the Sun. Kepler's Law can be expressed using rational exponents as $T = kr^{\frac{3}{2}}$, where k is the constant of proportionality.

(a) The period of Mercury is 0.241 years and its mean distance from the Sun is 5.79×10^{10} meters. Use this information to state Kepler's Law (find the value of k).
(b) The mean distance of Mars to the Sun is 2.28×10^{11} m. Use this information along with the result of part **(a)** to find the amount of time it takes Mars to complete one orbit around the Sun.

Explaining the Concepts

139. Explain why $(-9)^{\frac{1}{2}}$ is not a real number, but $-9^{\frac{1}{2}}$ is a real number.

140. In your own words, provide a justification for why $a^{\frac{1}{n}} = \sqrt[n]{a}$.

141. Under what conditions is $a^{\frac{m}{n}}$ a real number?

Synthesis Review

In Problems 142–145, simplify each expression completely.

142. $\left(\dfrac{x^2 y}{y^{-2}}\right)^3$

143. $\dfrac{(x+2)^2(x-1)^4}{(x+2)(x-1)}$

144. $\dfrac{(3a^2 + 5a - 3) - (a^2 - 2a - 9)}{4a^2 + 12a + 9}$

145. $\dfrac{(4z^2 - 7z + 3) + (-3z^2 - z + 9)}{(4z^2 - 2z - 7) + (-3z^2 - z + 9)}$

6.2 Simplify Expressions Using the Laws of Exponents

OBJECTIVES

1̄ Use the Laws of Exponents to Simplify Expressions Involving Rational Exponents

2̄ Use the Laws of Exponents to Simplify Radical Expressions

3̄ Factor Expressions Containing Rational Exponents

Preparing for Simplifying Expressions Using the Laws of Exponents

Before getting started, take the following readiness quiz. If you get a problem wrong, go to the section cited and review the material.

P1. Simplify: z^{-3} [Getting Ready: Laws of Exponents, pp. 307–309]

P2. Simplify: $x^{-2} \cdot x^5$ [Getting Ready: Laws of Exponents, pp. 309–310]

P3. Simplify: $\left(\dfrac{2a^2}{b^{-1}}\right)^3$ [Getting Ready: Laws of Exponents, pp. 312–313]

P4. Evaluate: $\sqrt{64}$ [Getting Ready: Square Roots, pp. 473–474]

1̄ Use the Laws of Exponents to Simplify Expressions Involving Rational Exponents

The Laws of Exponents that were presented in Getting Ready: Laws of Exponents on pages 312–313 applied to integer exponents. These same laws apply to rational exponents as well.

THE LAWS OF EXPONENTS

If a and b are real numbers and if r and s are rational numbers, then assuming the expression is defined,

Zero-Exponent Rule:	$a^0 = 1$	if $a \neq 0$
Negative-Exponent Rule:	$a^{-r} = \dfrac{1}{a^r}$	if $a \neq 0$
Product Rule:	$a^r \cdot a^s = a^{r+s}$	
Quotient Rule:	$\dfrac{a^r}{a^s} = a^{r-s} = \dfrac{1}{a^{s-r}}$	if $a \neq 0$
Power Rule:	$(a^r)^s = a^{r \cdot s}$	
Product to Power Rule:	$(a \cdot b)^r = a^r \cdot b^r$	
Quotient to Power Rule:	$\left(\dfrac{a}{b}\right)^r = \dfrac{a^r}{b^r}$	if $b \neq 0$
Quotient to a Negative Power Rule:	$\left(\dfrac{a}{b}\right)^{-r} = \left(\dfrac{b}{a}\right)^r$	if $a \neq 0, b \neq 0$

Work Smart

We *simplify* expressions (no equal sign) and *solve* equations.

The direction **simplify** shall mean the following:

- All the exponents are positive.
- Each base only occurs once.
- There are no parentheses in the expression.
- There are no powers written to powers.

Preparing for...Answers   **P1.** $\dfrac{1}{z^3}$
P2. x^3 **P3.** $8a^6 b^3$ **P4.** 8

EXAMPLE 1 Simplifying Expressions Involving Rational Exponents

Simplify each of the following:

(a) $27^{\frac{1}{2}} \cdot 27^{\frac{5}{6}}$

(b) $\dfrac{8^{\frac{1}{3}}}{8^{\frac{5}{3}}}$

Solution

(a)
$$a^r \cdot a^s = a^{r+s}$$
$$\downarrow$$
$$27^{\frac{1}{2}} \cdot 27^{\frac{5}{6}} = 27^{\frac{1}{2}+\frac{5}{6}}$$
$$= 27^{\frac{3}{6}+\frac{5}{6}}$$
$$= 27^{\frac{8}{6}}$$
$$= 27^{\frac{4}{3}}$$
$$a^{\frac{m}{n}} = (\sqrt[n]{a})^m: \quad = \left(\sqrt[3]{27}\right)^4$$
$$= 3^4$$
$$= 81$$

(b)
$$\dfrac{a^r}{a^s} = a^{r-s}$$
$$\downarrow$$
$$\dfrac{8^{\frac{1}{3}}}{8^{\frac{5}{3}}} = 8^{\frac{1}{3}-\frac{5}{3}}$$
$$= 8^{-\frac{4}{3}}$$
$$= \dfrac{1}{8^{\frac{4}{3}}}$$
$$a^{\frac{m}{n}} = (\sqrt[n]{a})^m: \quad = \dfrac{1}{\left(\sqrt[3]{8}\right)^4}$$
$$= \dfrac{1}{2^4}$$
$$= \dfrac{1}{16}$$

EXAMPLE 2 Simplifying Expressions Involving Rational Exponents

Simplify each of the following:

(a) $\left(36^{\frac{2}{5}}\right)^{\frac{5}{4}}$

(b) $\left(x^{\frac{1}{2}} \cdot y^{\frac{2}{3}}\right)^{\frac{3}{2}}$

Solution

(a)
$$(a^r)^s = a^{r \cdot s}$$
$$\downarrow$$
$$\left(36^{\frac{2}{5}}\right)^{\frac{5}{4}} = 36^{\frac{2}{5} \cdot \frac{5}{4}}$$
$$= 36^{\frac{10}{20}}$$
$$= 36^{\frac{1}{2}}$$
$$= 6$$

(b)
$$(ab)^r = a^r \cdot b^r$$
$$\downarrow$$
$$\left(x^{\frac{1}{2}} \cdot y^{\frac{2}{3}}\right)^{\frac{3}{2}} = \left(x^{\frac{1}{2}}\right)^{\frac{3}{2}} \cdot \left(y^{\frac{2}{3}}\right)^{\frac{3}{2}}$$
$$= x^{\frac{1}{2} \cdot \frac{3}{2}} \cdot y^{\frac{2}{3} \cdot \frac{3}{2}}$$
$$(a^r)^s = a^{r \cdot s}: \quad = x^{\frac{3}{4}}y$$

Quick ✔

1. If a and b are real numbers and if r and s are rational numbers, then assuming the expression is defined, $(ab)^r = \underline{\quad}$.

2. If a and b are real numbers and if r and s are rational numbers, then assuming the expression is defined, $a^r \cdot a^s = \underline{\quad}$.

In Problems 3–7, simplify each expression.

3. $5^{\frac{3}{4}} \cdot 5^{\frac{1}{6}}$

4. $\dfrac{32^{\frac{6}{5}}}{32^{\frac{3}{5}}}$

5. $\left(100^{\frac{3}{8}}\right)^{\frac{4}{3}}$

6. $\left(a^{\frac{3}{2}} \cdot b^{\frac{5}{4}}\right)^{\frac{2}{3}}$

7. $\dfrac{x^{\frac{1}{2}} \cdot x^{\frac{1}{3}}}{\left(x^{\frac{1}{12}}\right)^2}$

EXAMPLE 3 Simplifying Expressions Involving Rational Exponents

Simplify each of the following:

(a) $\left(x^{\frac{2}{3}}y^{-1}\right) \cdot \left(x^{-1}y^{\frac{1}{2}}\right)^{\frac{2}{3}}$

(b) $\left(\dfrac{9xy^{\frac{4}{3}}}{x^{\frac{5}{6}}y^{-\frac{2}{3}}}\right)^{\frac{1}{2}}$

Solution

(a)

$$\text{Product to Power Rule: } (ab)^r = a^r b^r$$
$$\downarrow$$
$$\left(x^{\frac{2}{3}}y^{-1}\right) \cdot \left(x^{-1}y^{\frac{1}{2}}\right)^{\frac{2}{3}} = x^{\frac{2}{3}}y^{-1}(x^{-1})^{\frac{2}{3}}\left(y^{\frac{1}{2}}\right)^{\frac{2}{3}}$$
$$\text{Power Rule: } (a^r)^s = a^{rs}: \quad = x^{\frac{2}{3}}y^{-1}x^{-\frac{2}{3}}y^{\frac{1}{3}}$$
$$\text{Product Rule: } a^r \cdot a^s = a^{r+s}: \quad = x^{\frac{2}{3}+\left(-\frac{2}{3}\right)}y^{-1+\frac{1}{3}}$$
$$= x^0 y^{-\frac{2}{3}}$$
$$a^0 = 1; \text{ Negative Exponent Rule: } a^{-r} = \frac{1}{a^r}: \quad = \frac{1}{y^{\frac{2}{3}}}$$

(b)

$$\text{Quotient Rule: } \frac{a^r}{a^s} = a^{r-s}$$
$$\downarrow$$
$$\left(\frac{9xy^{\frac{4}{3}}}{x^{\frac{5}{6}}y^{-\frac{2}{3}}}\right)^{\frac{1}{2}} = \left(9x^{1-\frac{5}{6}}y^{\frac{4}{3}-\left(-\frac{2}{3}\right)}\right)^{\frac{1}{2}}$$
$$x^{1-\frac{5}{6}} = x^{\frac{6}{6}-\frac{5}{6}} = x^{\frac{1}{6}};$$
$$y^{\frac{4}{3}-\left(-\frac{2}{3}\right)} = y^{\frac{4}{3}+\frac{2}{3}} = y^{\frac{6}{3}} = y^2: \quad = \left(9x^{\frac{1}{6}}y^2\right)^{\frac{1}{2}}$$
$$\text{Power Rule: } (a^r)^s = a^{rs}: \quad = 9^{\frac{1}{2}} \cdot \left(x^{\frac{1}{6}}\right)^{\frac{1}{2}} \cdot (y^2)^{\frac{1}{2}}$$
$$9^{\frac{1}{2}} = \sqrt{9} = 3; \text{ Power Rule: } (a^r)^s = a^{rs}: \quad = 3x^{\frac{1}{12}}y \quad \blacksquare$$

Quick ✔ *In Problems 8–10, simplify each expression.*

8. $\left(8x^{\frac{3}{4}}y^{-1}\right)^{\frac{2}{3}}$

9. $\left(\dfrac{25x^{\frac{1}{2}}y^{\frac{3}{4}}}{x^{-\frac{3}{4}}y}\right)^{\frac{1}{2}}$

10. $8\left(125a^{\frac{3}{4}}b^{-1}\right)^{\frac{2}{3}}$

❷ Use the Laws of Exponents to Simplify Radical Expressions

Rational exponents can be used to simplify radicals.

EXAMPLE 4 Simplifying Radicals Using Rational Exponents

Use rational exponents to simplify the radicals.

(a) $\sqrt[8]{16^4}$　　　(b) $\sqrt[3]{64x^6y^3}$　　　(c) $\dfrac{\sqrt{x}}{\sqrt[3]{x^2}}$　　　(d) $\sqrt{\sqrt[3]{z}}$

Solution

The idea in all these problems is to rewrite the radical as an expression involving a rational exponent. Then use the Laws of Exponents to simplify the expression. Finally, write the simplified expression as a radical.

(a)

$$\text{Write radical as a rational exponent using } \sqrt[n]{a^m} = a^{\frac{m}{n}}.$$
$$\downarrow$$
$$\sqrt[8]{16^4} = 16^{\frac{4}{8}}$$
$$\text{Simplify the exponent: } = 16^{\frac{1}{2}}$$
$$\text{Write rational exponent as a radical: } = \sqrt{16}$$
$$= 4$$

(b)

$$\sqrt[n]{a} = a^{\frac{1}{n}}$$
$$\downarrow$$
$$\sqrt[3]{64x^6y^3} = (64x^6y^3)^{\frac{1}{3}}$$
$$(ab)^r = a^r \cdot b^r: \quad = 64^{\frac{1}{3}} \cdot (x^6)^{\frac{1}{3}} \cdot (y^3)^{\frac{1}{3}}$$
$$(a^r)^s = a^{rs}: \quad = 64^{\frac{1}{3}} \cdot x^{6 \cdot \frac{1}{3}} \cdot y^{3 \cdot \frac{1}{3}}$$
$$64^{\frac{1}{3}} = \sqrt[3]{64} = 4: \quad = 4x^2y$$

(c)

$$\sqrt{a} = a^{\frac{1}{2}}; \sqrt[n]{a^m} = a^{\frac{m}{n}}$$
$$\downarrow$$
$$\frac{\sqrt{x}}{\sqrt[3]{x^2}} = \frac{x^{\frac{1}{2}}}{x^{\frac{2}{3}}}$$

$$\frac{a^r}{a^s} = a^{r-s}: \quad = x^{\frac{1}{2}-\frac{2}{3}}$$

$$\text{LCD} = 6; \frac{1}{2} - \frac{2}{3} = \frac{3}{6} - \frac{4}{6} = -\frac{1}{6}: \quad = x^{-\frac{1}{6}}$$

$$a^{-r} = \frac{1}{a^r}: \quad = \frac{1}{x^{\frac{1}{6}}}$$

Write rational exponent as a radical: $\quad = \dfrac{1}{\sqrt[6]{x}}$

(d)

Write radicand with a rational exponent.
$$\downarrow$$
$$\sqrt{\sqrt[3]{z}} = \sqrt{z^{\frac{1}{3}}}$$

$$\sqrt{a} = a^{\frac{1}{2}}: \quad = \left(z^{\frac{1}{3}}\right)^{\frac{1}{2}}$$

$$(a^r)^s = a^{rs}: \quad = z^{\frac{1}{3}\cdot\frac{1}{2}}$$

$$= z^{\frac{1}{6}}$$

Write rational exponent as a radical: $\quad = \sqrt[6]{z}$ ■

Quick ✔ *In Problems 11–14, use rational exponents to simplify each radical.*

11. $\sqrt[10]{36^5}$ **12.** $\sqrt[4]{16a^8b^{12}}$

13. $\dfrac{\sqrt[3]{x^2}}{\sqrt[4]{x}}$ **14.** $\sqrt[4]{\sqrt[3]{a^2}}$

---

3 Factor Expressions Containing Rational Exponents

Often, expressions involving rational exponents contain a common factor. When this occurs, we want to factor out the common factor to write the expression in simplified form. The goal of these types of problems is to write the expression as either a single product or a single quotient. We present two examples to illustrate the idea.

EXAMPLE 5 Writing an Expression Containing Rational Exponents as a Single Product

Simplify $9x^{\frac{4}{3}} + 4x^{\frac{1}{3}}(3x + 5)$ by factoring out $x^{\frac{1}{3}}$.

Solution

Clearly, $x^{\frac{1}{3}}$ is a factor of the second term, $4x^{\frac{1}{3}}(3x + 5)$. It is also a factor of the first term, $9x^{\frac{4}{3}}$. We can see this by rewriting $9x^{\frac{4}{3}}$ as $9x^{\frac{3}{3}+\frac{1}{3}} = 9x^{\frac{3}{3}} \cdot x^{\frac{1}{3}} = 9x \cdot x^{\frac{1}{3}}$. Now we proceed to factor out $x^{\frac{1}{3}}$.

$$9x^{\frac{4}{3}} + 4x^{\frac{1}{3}}(3x + 5) = 9x \cdot x^{\frac{1}{3}} + 4x^{\frac{1}{3}}(3x + 5)$$

$$\text{Factor out } x^{1/3}: \quad = x^{\frac{1}{3}}(9x + 4(3x + 5))$$

$$\text{Distribute the 4:} \quad = x^{\frac{1}{3}}(9x + 12x + 20)$$

$$\text{Combine like terms:} \quad = x^{\frac{1}{3}}(21x + 20)$$ ■

Work Smart

When factoring out the greatest common factor, factor out the variable expression raised to the smallest exponent that the expressions have in common. For example,

$3x^5 + 12x^2 = 3x^2(x^3 + 4)$

Quick ✔

15. Simplify $8x^{\frac{3}{2}} + 3x^{\frac{1}{2}}(4x + 3)$ by factoring out $x^{\frac{1}{2}}$.

EXAMPLE 6   Writing an Expression Containing Rational Exponents as a Single Quotient

Simplify $4x^{\frac{1}{2}} + x^{-\frac{1}{2}}(2x + 1)$ by factoring out $x^{-\frac{1}{2}}$.

Solution

Clearly, $x^{-\frac{1}{2}}$ is a factor of the second term, $x^{-\frac{1}{2}}(2x + 1)$. It is also a factor of the first term, $4x^{\frac{1}{2}}$. We can see this by rewriting $4x^{\frac{1}{2}}$ as $4x^{\frac{2}{2}-\frac{1}{2}} = 4x^{\frac{2}{2}} \cdot x^{-\frac{1}{2}} = 4x \cdot x^{-\frac{1}{2}}$. Now we proceed to factor out $x^{-\frac{1}{2}}$.

$$4x^{\frac{1}{2}} + x^{-\frac{1}{2}}(2x + 1) = 4x \cdot x^{-\frac{1}{2}} + x^{-\frac{1}{2}}(2x + 1)$$

Factor out $x^{-1/2}$: $= x^{-\frac{1}{2}}(4x + (2x + 1))$

Combine like terms: $= x^{-\frac{1}{2}}(6x + 1)$

Rewrite without negative exponents: $= \dfrac{6x + 1}{x^{\frac{1}{2}}}$

Quick ✔

16. Simplify $9x^{\frac{1}{3}} + x^{-\frac{2}{3}}(3x + 1)$ by factoring out $x^{-\frac{2}{3}}$.

6.2 EXERCISES

Powered by CourseCompass™ and MathXL®
MyMathLab

| MathXL | | | | |
| PRACTICE | WATCH | DOWNLOAD | READ | REVIEW |

1–16. *are the* Quick ✔*s that follow each* EXAMPLE

Building Skills

In Problems 17–38, simplify each of the following expressions. See Objective 1.

17. $5^{\frac{1}{2}} \cdot 5^{\frac{3}{2}}$

18. $3^{\frac{1}{3}} \cdot 3^{\frac{5}{3}}$

19. $\dfrac{8^{\frac{5}{4}}}{8^{\frac{1}{4}}}$

20. $\dfrac{10^{\frac{7}{5}}}{10^{\frac{2}{5}}}$

21. $2^{\frac{1}{3}} \cdot 2^{-\frac{2}{3}}$

22. $9^{-\frac{5}{4}} \cdot 9^{\frac{1}{3}}$

23. $\dfrac{x^{\frac{1}{4}}}{x^{\frac{5}{6}}}$

24. $\dfrac{y^{\frac{1}{5}}}{y^{\frac{9}{10}}}$

25. $\left(4^{\frac{4}{3}}\right)^{\frac{3}{8}}$

26. $\left(9^{\frac{3}{5}}\right)^{\frac{5}{6}}$

27. $\left(25^{\frac{3}{4}} \cdot 4^{-\frac{3}{4}}\right)^{2}$

28. $\left(36^{-\frac{1}{4}} \cdot 9^{\frac{3}{4}}\right)^{-2}$

29. $\left(x^{\frac{3}{4}} \cdot y^{\frac{3}{3}}\right)^{\frac{2}{3}}$

30. $\left(a^{\frac{5}{4}} \cdot b^{\frac{3}{2}}\right)^{\frac{2}{5}}$

31. $\left(x^{-\frac{1}{3}} \cdot y\right)\left(x^{\frac{1}{2}} \cdot y^{-\frac{4}{3}}\right)$

32. $\left(a^{\frac{4}{3}} \cdot b^{-\frac{1}{2}}\right)\left(a^{-2} \cdot b^{\frac{5}{2}}\right)$

33. $\left(4a^{2}b^{-\frac{3}{2}}\right)^{\frac{1}{2}}$

34. $\left(25p^{\frac{2}{5}}q^{-1}\right)^{\frac{1}{2}}$

35. $\left(\dfrac{x^{\frac{2}{3}}y^{-\frac{1}{3}}}{8x^{\frac{1}{2}}y}\right)^{\frac{1}{3}}$

36. $\left(\dfrac{64m^{\frac{1}{2}}n}{m^{-2}n^{\frac{4}{3}}}\right)^{\frac{1}{2}}$

37. $\left(\dfrac{50x^{\frac{3}{4}}y}{2x^{\frac{1}{2}}}\right)^{\frac{1}{2}} + \left(\dfrac{x^{\frac{1}{2}}y^{\frac{1}{2}}}{9x^{\frac{3}{4}}y^{\frac{3}{2}}}\right)^{-\frac{1}{2}}$ **38.** $\left(\dfrac{27x^{\frac{1}{2}}y^{-1}}{y^{-\frac{2}{3}}x^{-\frac{1}{2}}}\right)^{\frac{1}{3}} - \left(\dfrac{4x^{\frac{1}{3}}y^{\frac{4}{9}}}{x^{-\frac{1}{3}}y^{\frac{2}{3}}}\right)^{\frac{1}{2}}$

In Problems 39–54, use rational exponents to simplify each radical. Assume all variables are positive. See Objective 2.

39. $\sqrt{x^{8}}$

40. $\sqrt[3]{x^{6}}$

41. $\sqrt[12]{8^{4}}$

42. $\sqrt[9]{125^{6}}$

43. $\sqrt[3]{8a^{3}b^{12}}$

44. $\sqrt{25x^{4}y^{6}}$

45.  $\dfrac{\sqrt{x}}{\sqrt[4]{x}}$

46. $\dfrac{\sqrt[3]{y^{2}}}{\sqrt{y}}$

47. $\sqrt{x} \cdot \sqrt[3]{x}$

48. $\sqrt[4]{p^{3}} \cdot \sqrt[3]{p}$

49. $\sqrt{\sqrt[4]{x^{3}}}$

50. $\sqrt[3]{\sqrt{x^{3}}}$

51. $\sqrt{3} \cdot \sqrt[3]{9}$

52. $\sqrt{5} \cdot \sqrt[3]{25}$

53. $\dfrac{\sqrt{6}}{\sqrt[4]{36}}$

54. $\dfrac{\sqrt[4]{49}}{\sqrt{7}}$

For Problems 55–64, see Objective 3.

55. Simplify $2x^{\frac{3}{2}} + 3x^{\frac{1}{2}}(x + 5)$ by factoring out $x^{\frac{1}{2}}$.

56. Simplify $6x^{\frac{4}{3}} + 4x^{\frac{1}{3}}(2x - 3)$ by factoring out $x^{\frac{1}{3}}$.

57. Simplify $5(x + 2)^{\frac{2}{3}}(3x - 2) + 9(x + 2)^{\frac{5}{3}}$ by factoring out $(x + 2)^{\frac{2}{3}}$.

58. Simplify $3(x - 5)^{\frac{1}{2}}(3x + 1) + 6(x - 5)^{\frac{3}{2}}$ by factoring out $(x - 5)^{\frac{1}{2}}$.

59. Simplify $x^{-\frac{1}{2}}(2x + 5) + 4x^{\frac{1}{2}}$ by factoring out $x^{-\frac{1}{2}}$.

60. Simplify $x^{-\frac{2}{3}}(3x + 2) + 9x^{\frac{1}{3}}$ by factoring out $x^{-\frac{2}{3}}$.

61. Simplify $2(x - 4)^{-\frac{1}{3}}(4x - 3) + 12(x - 4)^{\frac{2}{3}}$ by factoring out $2(x - 4)^{-\frac{1}{3}}$.

62. Simplify $4(x + 3)^{\frac{1}{2}} + (x + 3)^{-\frac{1}{2}}(2x + 1)$ by factoring out $(x + 3)^{-\frac{1}{2}}$.

63. Simplify $15x(x^2 + 4)^{\frac{1}{2}} + 5(x^2 + 4)^{\frac{3}{2}}$.

64. Simplify $24x(x^2 - 1)^{\frac{1}{3}} + 9(x^2 - 1)^{\frac{4}{3}}$.

Mixed Practice

In Problems 65–76, simplify each expression.

65. $\sqrt[8]{4^4}$

66. $\sqrt[6]{27^2}$

67. $(-2)^{\frac{1}{2}} \cdot (-2)^{\frac{3}{2}}$

68. $25^{\frac{3}{4}} \cdot 25^{\frac{3}{4}}$

69. $\left(100^{\frac{1}{3}}\right)^{\frac{3}{2}}$

70. $(8^4)^{\frac{5}{12}}$

71. $\left(\sqrt[4]{25}\right)^2$

72. $\left(\sqrt[6]{27}\right)^2$

73. $\sqrt[4]{x^2} - \dfrac{\sqrt[4]{x^6}}{x}$

74. $\sqrt[9]{a^6} - \dfrac{\sqrt[6]{a^5}}{\sqrt[6]{a}}$

75. $\left(4 \cdot 9^{\frac{1}{4}}\right)^{-2}$

76. $\left(4^{-1} \cdot 81^{\frac{1}{2}}\right)^{\frac{1}{2}}$

In Problems 77–82, distribute and simplify.

77. $x^{\frac{1}{2}}\left(x^{\frac{3}{2}} - 2\right)$

78. $x^{\frac{1}{3}}\left(x^{\frac{5}{3}} + 4\right)$

79. $2y^{-\frac{1}{4}}(1 + 3y)$

80. $3a^{-\frac{1}{2}}(2 - a)$

81. $4z^{\frac{3}{2}}\left(z^{\frac{3}{2}} - 8z^{-\frac{3}{2}}\right)$

82. $8p^{\frac{2}{3}}\left(p^{\frac{4}{3}} - 4p^{-\frac{2}{3}}\right)$

Applying the Concepts

83. If $3^x = 25$, what does $3^{\frac{x}{2}}$ equal?

84. If $5^x = 64$, what does $5^{\frac{x}{3}}$ equal?

85. If $7^x = 9$, what does $\sqrt{7^x}$ equal?

86. If $5^x = 27$, what does $\sqrt[3]{5^x}$ equal?

Extending the Concepts

In Problems 87 and 88, simplify the expression using rational exponents.

87. $\sqrt[4]{\sqrt[3]{\sqrt{x}}}$

88. $\sqrt[5]{\sqrt[3]{\sqrt{x^2}}}$

89. Without using a calculator, determine the value of $\left(6^{\sqrt{2}}\right)^{\sqrt{2}}$.

90. Determine the domain of $g(x) = (x - 3)^{\frac{1}{2}}(x - 1)^{-\frac{1}{2}}$.

91. Determine the domain of $f(x) = (x + 3)^{\frac{1}{2}}(x + 1)^{-\frac{1}{2}}$.

Synthesis Review

In Problems 92–95, simplify each expression.

92. $(2x - 1)(x + 4) - (x + 1)(x - 1)$

93. $3a(a - 3) + (a + 3)(a - 2)$

94. $\dfrac{\sqrt{x^2 + 4x + 4}}{x + 2}, x + 2 > 0$

95. $\dfrac{x^2 - 4}{x + 2} \cdot (x + 5) - (x + 4)(x - 1)$

6.3 Simplifying Radical Expressions Using Properties of Radicals

OBJECTIVES

1	Use the Product Property to Multiply Radical Expressions
2	Use the Product Property to Simplify Radical Expressions
3	Use the Quotient Property to Simplify Radical Expressions
4	Multiply Radicals with Unlike Indices

Preparing for Simplifying Radical Expressions

Before getting started, take the following readiness quiz. If you get a problem wrong, go back to the section cited and review the material.

P1. List the perfect squares that are less than 200.

P2. List the perfect cubes that are less than 200.

P3. Simplify: **(a)** $\sqrt{16}$ **(b)** $\sqrt{p^2}$ [Getting Ready: Square Roots, pp. 473–476]

1 Use the Product Property to Multiply Radical Expressions

Perhaps you are noticing a trend at this point. When we introduce a new algebraic expression, we then learn how to multiply, divide, add, and subtract the algebraic expression. Well, here we go again! First, we are going to learn how to multiply radical expressions when they have the same index.

Preparing for...Answers **P1.** 1, 4, 9, 16, 25, 36, 49, 64, 81, 100, 121, 144, 169, 196 **P2.** 1, 8, 27, 64, 125 **P3.** **(a)** 4 **(b)** $|p|$

Consider the following:

$$\sqrt{4 \cdot 25} = \sqrt{100} = 10 \quad \text{and} \quad \sqrt{4} \cdot \sqrt{25} = 2 \cdot 5 = 10$$

This suggests the following result:

In Words
$\sqrt[n]{a} \cdot \sqrt[n]{b} = \sqrt[n]{ab}$ means "the product of the roots equals the root of the product provided the index is the same."

PRODUCT PROPERTY OF RADICALS

If $\sqrt[n]{a}$ and $\sqrt[n]{b}$ are real numbers and $n \geq 2$ is an integer, then

$$\sqrt[n]{a} \cdot \sqrt[n]{b} = \sqrt[n]{ab}$$

We can justify this formula using rational exponents.

$$\sqrt[n]{a} \cdot \sqrt[n]{b} = a^{\frac{1}{n}} \cdot b^{\frac{1}{n}}$$

Product to a Power Rule: $= (a \cdot b)^{\frac{1}{n}}$

$a^{\frac{1}{n}} = \sqrt[n]{a}: \quad = \sqrt[n]{a \cdot b}$

EXAMPLE 1 Using the Product Property to Multiply Radicals

Multiply.

    (a) $\sqrt{5} \cdot \sqrt{3}$ **(b)** $\sqrt[3]{2} \cdot \sqrt[3]{13}$ **(c)** $\sqrt{x-3} \cdot \sqrt{x+3}$ **(d)** $\sqrt[5]{6c} \cdot \sqrt[5]{7c^2}$

Solution

    (a) $\sqrt{5} \cdot \sqrt{3} = \sqrt{5 \cdot 3} = \sqrt{15}$

    (b) $\sqrt[3]{2} \cdot \sqrt[3]{13} = \sqrt[3]{2 \cdot 13} = \sqrt[3]{26}$

Work Smart
In Example 1(c), notice that $\sqrt{x^2 - 9}$ does not equal $\sqrt{x^2} - \sqrt{9}$.

    (c) $\sqrt{x-3} \cdot \sqrt{x+3} = \sqrt{(x-3)(x+3)} = \sqrt{x^2 - 9}$

    (d) $\sqrt[5]{6c} \cdot \sqrt[5]{7c^2} = \sqrt[5]{6c \cdot 7c^2} = \sqrt[5]{42c^3}$

Quick ✔

1. If $\sqrt[n]{a}$ and $\sqrt[n]{b}$ are real numbers and $n \geq 2$ is an integer, then $\sqrt[n]{a} \cdot \sqrt[n]{b} = $ _____.

In Problems 2–5, multiply each radical expression.

2. $\sqrt{11} \cdot \sqrt{7}$ **3.** $\sqrt[4]{6} \cdot \sqrt[4]{7}$ **4.** $\sqrt{x-5} \cdot \sqrt{x+5}$ **5.** $\sqrt[7]{5p} \cdot \sqrt[7]{4p^3}$

2 Use the Product Property to Simplify Radical Expressions

Up until now, we have simplified radicals only when the radicand simplified to a perfect square, such as $\sqrt{81} = 9$ or $\sqrt[3]{\frac{1}{8}} = \frac{1}{2}$. When a radical does not simplify to a rational number, we can do one of two things:

  1. Write a decimal approximation of the radical.

  2. Simplify the radical using properties of radicals, if possible.

We learned how to approximate radicals using a calculator in the Getting Ready: Square Roots and Section 6.1. Now we are going to learn how to use properties of radicals to write the radical in simplified form.

    The advantage of simplifying over writing a decimal approximation is that simplifying maintains an *exact* radical rather than an approximate value.

    Recall that a number that is the square of a rational number is called a perfect square. So $1^2 = 1, 2^2 = 4, 3^2 = 9$, and so on are perfect squares. A number that is the cube of a rational number is called a perfect cube. So $1^3 = 1, 2^3 = 8, 3^3 = 27$, $(-1)^3 = -1, (-2)^3 = -8$, and so on are perfect cubes. In general, if n is the index of a radical, then a^n is a perfect power of the index where a is a rational number.

Work Smart

index $\rightarrow \sqrt[n]{a} \leftarrow$ radicand

We say that a radical expression is **simplified** provided that the radicand does not contain any factors that are perfect powers of the index. For example, $\sqrt{50}$ is not simplified because 25 is a factor of 50 and 25 is a perfect square or $\sqrt[3]{16}$ is not simplified because 8 is a factor of 16 and 8 is a perfect cube; $\sqrt[3]{x^5}$ is not simplified because $x^5 = x^3 \cdot x^2$ and x^3 is a perfect cube.

To simplify radicals that contain perfect square factors, we use the Product Property of Radicals "in reverse." That is, we use $\sqrt[n]{ab} = \sqrt[n]{a} \cdot \sqrt[n]{b}$.

EXAMPLE 2 How to Use the Product Property to Simplify a Radical

Simplify: $\sqrt{18}$

Step-by-Step Solution

Step 1: What is the index on the radical? Since the index is 2, we write each factor of the radicand as the product of two factors, one of which is a perfect square.	The perfect squares are 1, 4, 9, 16, 25, ... Because 9 is a factor of 18 and 9 is a perfect square, we write 18 as $9 \cdot 2$. $\quad \sqrt{18} = \sqrt{9 \cdot 2}$
Step 2: Write the radicand as the product of two radicals, one of which contains a perfect square.	$= \sqrt{9} \cdot \sqrt{2}$
Step 3: Take the square root of each perfect power.	$= 3\sqrt{2}$

We summarize the steps used in Example 2 below.

Work Smart

When performing Step 1 with real numbers, we want to look for the *largest* factor of the radicand that is a perfect power of the index.

SIMPLIFYING A RADICAL EXPRESSION

Step 1: Write each factor of the radicand as the product of two factors, one of which is a perfect power of the index.

Step 2: Write the radicand as the product of two radicals, one of which contains perfect powers of the index using the Product Property of Radicals.

Step 3: Take the nth root of each perfect power.

EXAMPLE 3 Using the Product Property to Simplify a Radical

Simplify each of the following:

(a) $5\sqrt[3]{24}$ (b) $\sqrt{128x^2}$ (c) $\sqrt[4]{20}$

Solution

(a) We are looking for the largest factor of 24 that is a perfect cube. The positive perfect cubes are $1, 8, 27, \ldots$. Because 8 is a factor of 24 and 8 is a perfect cube we write 24 as $8 \cdot 3$.

$$5\sqrt[3]{24} = 5 \cdot \sqrt[3]{8 \cdot 3}$$

$$\sqrt[n]{ab} = \sqrt[n]{a} \cdot \sqrt[n]{b}: \quad = 5 \cdot \sqrt[3]{8} \cdot \sqrt[3]{3}$$

$$= 5 \cdot 2 \cdot \sqrt[3]{3}$$

$$= 10\sqrt[3]{3}$$

(b) Because 64 is a factor of 128 and 64 is a perfect square, we write 128 as $64 \cdot 2$; x^2 is a perfect square.

$$\sqrt{128x^2} = \sqrt{64x^2 \cdot 2}$$
$$\sqrt[n]{ab} = \sqrt[n]{a} \cdot \sqrt[n]{b}: \quad = \sqrt{64x^2} \cdot \sqrt{2}$$
$$\sqrt[n]{ab} = \sqrt[n]{a} \cdot \sqrt[n]{b}: \quad = \sqrt{64} \cdot \sqrt{x^2} \cdot \sqrt{2}$$
$$\sqrt{64} = 8, \sqrt{x^2} = |x|: \quad = 8|x|\sqrt{2}$$

(c) In $\sqrt[4]{20}$, the index is 4. The fourth powers (or perfect fourths) are $1, 16, 81, \ldots$. There are no factors of 20 that are fourth powers, so the radical $\sqrt[4]{20}$ cannot be simplified any further.   ∎

Quick ✔

6. List the first six integers that are perfect squares.

7. List the first six positive integers that are perfect cubes.

In Problems 8–11, simplify each of the radical expressions.

8. $\sqrt{48}$ **9.** $4\sqrt[3]{54}$ **10.** $\sqrt{200a^2}$ **11.** $\sqrt[4]{40}$

EXAMPLE 4   Simplifying an Expression Involving a Square Root

Simplify: $\dfrac{4 - \sqrt{20}}{2}$

Solution

We can simplify this expression using two different approaches.

Method 1:

4 is the largest perfect square factor of 20
$$\downarrow$$
$$\frac{4 - \sqrt{20}}{2} = \frac{4 - \sqrt{4 \cdot 5}}{2}$$

Use $\sqrt{a \cdot b} = \sqrt{a} \cdot \sqrt{b}$: $= \dfrac{4 - \sqrt{4} \cdot \sqrt{5}}{2}$

$$= \frac{4 - 2 \cdot \sqrt{5}}{2}$$

Factor out the 2 in the numerator: $= \dfrac{2(2 - \sqrt{5})}{2}$

Divide out common factor: $= 2 - \sqrt{5}$

Method 2:

4 is the largest perfect square factor of 20
$$\downarrow$$
$$\frac{4 - \sqrt{20}}{2} = \frac{4 - \sqrt{4 \cdot 5}}{2}$$

Use $\sqrt{a \cdot b} = \sqrt{a} \cdot \sqrt{b}$: $= \dfrac{4 - \sqrt{4} \cdot \sqrt{5}}{2}$

$$= \frac{4 - 2 \cdot \sqrt{5}}{2}$$

Use $\dfrac{A + B}{C} = \dfrac{A}{C} + \dfrac{B}{C}$: $= \dfrac{4}{2} - \dfrac{2 \cdot \sqrt{5}}{2}$

Divide out common factor: $= 2 - \sqrt{5}$ ∎

Quick ✔   *In Problems 12 and 13, simplify the expression.*

12. $\dfrac{6 + \sqrt{45}}{3}$ **13.** $\dfrac{-2 + \sqrt{32}}{4}$

Recall how to simplify $\sqrt[n]{a^n}$ from Section 6.1.

SIMPLIFYING $\sqrt[n]{a^n}$

If $n \geq 2$ is a positive integer and a is a real number, then

$$\sqrt[n]{a^n} = a \quad \text{if } n \geq 3 \text{ is odd}$$
$$\sqrt[n]{a^n} = |a| \quad \text{if } n \geq 2 \text{ is even}$$

This means that

$$\sqrt{a^2} = |a| \qquad \sqrt[3]{a^3} = a \qquad \sqrt[4]{a^4} = |a| \qquad \sqrt[5]{a^5} = a \qquad \text{and so on}$$

In order to make our mathematical lives a little easier, periodically, we shall assume that all variables that appear in the radicand are greater than or equal to zero (nonnegative). So

$$\sqrt{a^2} = a \qquad \sqrt[3]{a^3} = a \qquad \sqrt[4]{a^4} = a \qquad \sqrt[5]{a^5} = a \qquad \text{and so on}$$

What if the exponent on the radicand is greater than the index as in $\sqrt{x^3}$ or $\sqrt[3]{x^6}$? We could use the Laws of Exponents along with the rule for simplifying $\sqrt[n]{a^n}$ or we could use rational exponents.

$$\sqrt{x^6} = \sqrt{(x^3)^2} = x^3 \qquad \text{or} \qquad \sqrt{x^6} = x^{\frac{6}{2}} = x^3$$

$$\sqrt[3]{x^{12}} = \sqrt[3]{(x^4)^3} = x^4 \qquad \text{or} \qquad \sqrt[3]{x^{12}} = x^{\frac{12}{3}} = x^4$$

EXAMPLE 5 Simplifying a Radical with a Variable Radicand

Simplify $\sqrt{20x^{10}}$. Assume $x \geq 0$.

Solution

Because 4 is the largest perfect square factor of 20, we write 20 as $4 \cdot 5$.

$$\sqrt{20x^{10}} = \sqrt{4 \cdot 5 \cdot x^{10}}$$
$$= \sqrt{4x^{10}} \cdot \sqrt{5}$$

$\sqrt{4} = 2, \sqrt{x^{10}} = \sqrt{(x^5)^2} = x^5$
or $\sqrt{x^{10}} = x^{\frac{10}{2}} = x^5$: $\qquad = 2x^5\sqrt{5}$ ■

> **Quick ✔**
>
> **14.** Simplify $\sqrt{75a^6}$. Assume $a \geq 0$.

What if the index does not divide evenly into the exponent on the variable in the radicand as in $\sqrt[3]{x^8}$? Under these circumstances, we rewrite the variable expression as the product of two variable expressions where one of the factors has an exponent that is a multiple of the index. For example, we can write

$$\sqrt[3]{x^8} \qquad \text{as} \qquad \sqrt[3]{x^6 \cdot x^2}$$

so that

$$\sqrt[3]{x^8} = \sqrt[3]{x^6 \cdot x^2} = \sqrt[3]{x^6} \cdot \sqrt[3]{x^2} = x^2\sqrt[3]{x^2}$$

EXAMPLE 6 Simplifying Radicals

Simplify:

(a) $\sqrt{80a^3}$ **(b)** $\sqrt[3]{27m^4n^{14}}$

Assume all variables are greater than or equal to zero.

Solution

(a)
$$80 = 16 \cdot 5; \ a^3 = a^2 \cdot a$$

$$\sqrt{80a^3} = \sqrt{16 \cdot 5 \cdot a^2 \cdot a}$$
$$= \sqrt{16a^2 \cdot 5a}$$
$\sqrt[n]{ab} = \sqrt[n]{a} \cdot \sqrt[n]{b}: \qquad = \sqrt{16a^2} \cdot \sqrt{5a}$
$\sqrt{a^2} = a \text{ assuming } a \geq 0: \qquad = 4a\sqrt{5a}$

(b)

$$m^4 = m^3 \cdot m; \quad n^{14} = n^{12} \cdot n^2$$

$$\sqrt[3]{27m^4n^{14}} = \sqrt[3]{27 \cdot m^3 \cdot m \cdot n^{12} \cdot n^2}$$

$$= \sqrt[3]{27 \cdot m^3 \cdot n^{12} \cdot m \cdot n^2}$$

$$\sqrt[n]{ab} = \sqrt[n]{a} \cdot \sqrt[n]{b}: \quad = \sqrt[3]{27m^3n^{12}} \cdot \sqrt[3]{mn^2}$$

$$\sqrt[3]{27} = 3; \ \sqrt[3]{m^3} = m; \ \sqrt[3]{n^{12}} = n^{\frac{12}{3}} = n^4: \quad = 3mn^4\sqrt[3]{mn^2} \qquad ■$$

> **Quick** ✔ *In Problems 15–17, simplify each radical. Assume all variables are greater than or equal to zero.*
> **15.** $\sqrt{18a^5}$ **16.** $\sqrt[3]{128x^6y^{10}}$ **17.** $\sqrt[4]{16a^5b^{11}}$

In this next example, we first multiply radical expressions and then simplify the product.

EXAMPLE 7 Multiplying and Simplifying Radicals

Multiply and simplify:

   (a) $\sqrt{3} \cdot \sqrt{15}$ **(b)** $3\sqrt[3]{4x} \cdot \sqrt[3]{2x^4}$ **(c)** $\sqrt[4]{27a^2b^5} \cdot \sqrt[4]{6a^3b^6}$

Assume all variables are greater than or equal to zero.

Solution

Remember, to multiply two radicals the index must be the same. When we have the same index, we multiply the radicands and then we simplify the product.

   (a) We start by looking to see if the index is the same. The index on both radicals is 2, so we multiply the radicands.

$$\sqrt{3} \cdot \sqrt{15} = \sqrt{3 \cdot 15}$$

$$= \sqrt{45}$$

9 is the largest factor of
45 that is a perfect square: $\quad = \sqrt{9 \cdot 5}$

Product Property of Radicals: $\quad = \sqrt{9} \cdot \sqrt{5}$

$$= 3\sqrt{5}$$

   (b) The index on both radicals is 3, so we multiply the radicands.

$$3\sqrt[3]{4x} \cdot \sqrt[3]{2x^4} = 3\sqrt[3]{4x \cdot 2x^4}$$

$$= 3\sqrt[3]{8x^5}$$

x^3 is a perfect cube; 8 is a perfect cube: $\quad = 3\sqrt[3]{8x^3 \cdot x^2}$

Product Property of Radicals: $\quad = 3\sqrt[3]{8x^3} \cdot \sqrt[3]{x^2}$

$\sqrt[3]{8} = 2; \ \sqrt[3]{x^3} = x: \quad = 3 \cdot 2 \cdot x \cdot \sqrt[3]{x^2}$

$$= 6x\sqrt[3]{x^2}$$

Work Smart

Notice that $27 = 3^3$ and that $6 = 3 \cdot 2$, so that $27 \cdot 6 = 3^3 \cdot 3 \cdot 2 = 3^4 \cdot 2$. This makes finding the perfect power of 4 a lot easier!

   (c) The index on both radicals is 4, so we multiply the radicands.

$$\sqrt[4]{27a^2b^5} \cdot \sqrt[4]{6a^3b^6} = \sqrt[4]{3^3 \cdot a^2b^5 \cdot 3 \cdot 2 \cdot a^3b^6}$$

$$= \sqrt[4]{3^4 \cdot 2 \cdot a^5b^{11}}$$

$$= \sqrt[4]{3^4 \cdot 2 \cdot a^4 \cdot a \cdot b^8 \cdot b^3}$$

Product Property of Radicals: $\quad = \sqrt[4]{3^4a^4b^8} \cdot \sqrt[4]{2ab^3}$

$$= 3ab^2\sqrt[4]{2ab^3} \qquad ■$$

> **Quick** ✔ *In Problems 18–20, multiply and simplify the radicals. Assume all variables are greater than or equal to zero.*
> **18.** $\sqrt{6} \cdot \sqrt{8}$ **19.** $\sqrt[3]{12a^2} \cdot \sqrt[3]{10a^4}$ **20.** $4\sqrt[3]{8a^2b^5} \cdot \sqrt[3]{6a^2b^4}$

3 Use the Quotient Property to Simplify Radical Expressions

Now consider the following:

$$\sqrt{\frac{64}{4}} = \sqrt{\frac{4 \cdot 16}{4}} = \sqrt{16} = 4 \qquad \text{and} \qquad \frac{\sqrt{64}}{\sqrt{4}} = \frac{8}{2} = 4$$

This suggests the following result:

In Words

$$\sqrt[n]{\frac{a}{b}} = \frac{\sqrt[n]{a}}{\sqrt[n]{b}}$$

means "the root of the quotient equals the quotient of the roots" provided that the radicals have the same index.

QUOTIENT PROPERTY OF RADICALS

If $\sqrt[n]{a}$ and $\sqrt[n]{b}$ are real numbers, $b \neq 0$, and $n \geq 2$ is an integer, then

$$\frac{\sqrt[n]{a}}{\sqrt[n]{b}} = \sqrt[n]{\frac{a}{b}}$$

We can justify this formula using rational exponents.

$$\frac{\sqrt[n]{a}}{\sqrt[n]{b}} = \frac{a^{\frac{1}{n}}}{b^{\frac{1}{n}}} = \left(\frac{a}{b}\right)^{\frac{1}{n}} = \sqrt[n]{\frac{a}{b}}$$

EXAMPLE 8 Using the Quotient Property to Simplify Radicals

Simplify:

(a) $\sqrt{\dfrac{18}{25}}$ (b) $\sqrt[3]{\dfrac{6z^3}{125}}$ (c) $\sqrt[4]{\dfrac{10a^2}{81b^4}}, b \neq 0$

Assume all variables are greater than or equal to zero.

Solution

In all three of these problems, you should notice that the expression in the denominator is a perfect power of the index. Therefore, we are going to use the Quotient Rule "in reverse" to simplify the expressions. That is, we use $\sqrt[n]{\dfrac{a}{b}} = \dfrac{\sqrt[n]{a}}{\sqrt[n]{b}}$.

(a) $\sqrt{\dfrac{18}{25}} = \dfrac{\sqrt{18}}{\sqrt{25}}$

$= \dfrac{3\sqrt{2}}{5}$

(b) $\sqrt[3]{\dfrac{6z^3}{125}} = \dfrac{\sqrt[3]{6z^3}}{\sqrt[3]{125}}$

$= \dfrac{z\sqrt[3]{6}}{5}$

(c) $\sqrt[4]{\dfrac{10a^2}{81b^4}} = \dfrac{\sqrt[4]{10a^2}}{\sqrt[4]{81b^4}}$

$= \dfrac{\sqrt[4]{10a^2}}{3b}$ ∎

Quick ✔ *In Problems 21–23, simplify the radicals. Assume all variables are greater than or equal to zero.*

21. $\sqrt{\dfrac{13}{49}}$ 22. $\sqrt[3]{\dfrac{27p^3}{8}}$ 23. $\sqrt[4]{\dfrac{3q^4}{16}}$

EXAMPLE 9 Using the Quotient Property to Simplify Radicals

Simplify:

(a) $\dfrac{\sqrt{24a^3}}{\sqrt{6a}}$ (b) $\dfrac{-2\sqrt[3]{54a}}{\sqrt[3]{2a^4}}$ (c) $\dfrac{\sqrt[3]{-375x^2y}}{\sqrt[3]{3x^{-1}y^7}}$

Assume all variables are greater than zero.

Solution

In these problems, we notice that the radical expression in the denominator cannot be simplified. However, the index on the numerator and denominator of each expression is the same, so we can write each expression as a single radical.

(a) $\dfrac{\sqrt{24a^3}}{\sqrt{6a}} = \sqrt{\dfrac{24a^3}{6a}}$

$= \sqrt{4a^2}$

$= 2a$

(b) $\dfrac{-2\sqrt[3]{54a}}{\sqrt[3]{2a^4}} = -2 \cdot \sqrt[3]{\dfrac{54a}{2a^4}}$

$= -2 \cdot \sqrt[3]{\dfrac{27}{a^3}}$

$= -2 \cdot \dfrac{3}{a}$

$= -\dfrac{6}{a}$

(c) $\dfrac{\sqrt[3]{-375x^2y}}{\sqrt[3]{3x^{-1}y^7}} = \sqrt[3]{\dfrac{-375x^2y}{3x^{-1}y^7}}$

$= \sqrt[3]{-125x^{2-(-1)}y^{1-7}}$

$= \sqrt[3]{-125x^3y^{-6}}$

$= \sqrt[3]{\dfrac{-125x^3}{y^6}}$

$= -\dfrac{5x}{y^2}$

Quick ✔ *In Problems 24–26, simplify the radicals. Assume all variables are greater than zero.*

24. $\dfrac{\sqrt{12a^5}}{\sqrt{3a}}$ **25.** $\dfrac{\sqrt[3]{-24x^2}}{\sqrt[3]{3x^{-1}}}$ **26.** $\dfrac{\sqrt[3]{250a^5b^{-2}}}{\sqrt[3]{2ab}}$

---

4 Multiply Radicals with Unlike Indices

To multiply radicals we use the fact that $\sqrt[n]{a} \cdot \sqrt[n]{b} = \sqrt[n]{ab}$. This rule only works when the index on each radical is the same. What if the index on each radical is different? Can we still simplify the product? The answer is yes! To perform the multiplication we use the fact that $\sqrt[n]{a} = a^{\frac{1}{n}}$.

EXAMPLE 10 Multiplying Radicals with Unlike Indices

Multiply and simplify:

$$\sqrt[4]{8} \cdot \sqrt[3]{5}$$

Solution

Notice that the index is not the same, so $\sqrt[n]{a} \cdot \sqrt[n]{b} = \sqrt[n]{ab}$ cannot be used to find the product. We will use rational exponents along with $\sqrt[n]{a} = a^{\frac{1}{n}}$ instead.

$$\sqrt[4]{8} \cdot \sqrt[3]{5} = 8^{\frac{1}{4}} \cdot 5^{\frac{1}{3}}$$

$$\text{LCD} = 12: \quad = 8^{\frac{3}{12}} \cdot 5^{\frac{4}{12}}$$

$$a^{\frac{r}{s}} = (a^r)^{\frac{1}{s}}: \quad = \left[(8^3)^{\frac{1}{12}} \cdot (5^4)^{\frac{1}{12}}\right]$$

$$a^r \cdot b^r = (ab)^r: \quad = [(8^3)(5^4)]^{\frac{1}{12}}$$

$$= (320{,}000)^{\frac{1}{12}}$$

$$a^{\frac{1}{n}} = \sqrt[n]{a}: \quad = \sqrt[12]{320{,}000}$$

Quick ✔ *In Problems 27 and 28, multiply and simplify.*

27. $\sqrt[4]{5} \cdot \sqrt[3]{3}$ **28.** $\sqrt{10} \cdot \sqrt[3]{12}$

6.3 EXERCISES

PRACTICE · WATCH · DOWNLOAD · READ · REVIEW

1–28. *are the* Quick ✔*s that follow each* EXAMPLE

Building Skills

In Problems 29–36, use the Product Property to multiply. Assume that all variables can be any real number. See Objective 1.

29. $\sqrt[3]{6} \cdot \sqrt[3]{10}$

30. $\sqrt[3]{-5} \cdot \sqrt[3]{7}$

31. $\sqrt{3a} \cdot \sqrt{5b}$

32. $\sqrt[4]{6a^2} \cdot \sqrt[4]{7b^2}$

33. $\sqrt{x-7} \cdot \sqrt{x+7}$

34. $\sqrt{p-5} \cdot \sqrt{p+5}$

35. $\sqrt{\dfrac{5x}{3}} \cdot \sqrt{\dfrac{3}{x}}$

36. $\sqrt[3]{\dfrac{-9x^2}{4}} \cdot \sqrt[3]{\dfrac{4}{3x}}$

In Problems 37–64, simplify each radical using the Product Property. Assume that all variables can be any real number. See Objective 2.

37. $\sqrt{50}$

38. $\sqrt{32}$

39. $\sqrt[3]{54}$

40. $\sqrt[4]{162}$

41. $\sqrt{48x^2}$

42. $\sqrt{20a^2}$

43. $\sqrt[3]{-27x^3}$

44. $\sqrt[3]{-64p^3}$

45. $\sqrt[4]{32m^4}$

46. $\sqrt[4]{48z^4}$

47. $\sqrt{12p^2q}$

48. $\sqrt{45m^2n}$

49. $\sqrt{162m^4}$

50. $\sqrt{98w^8}$

51. $\sqrt{y^{13}}$

52. $\sqrt{s^9}$

53. $\sqrt[3]{c^8}$

54. $\sqrt[5]{x^{12}}$

55. $\sqrt{125p^3q^4}$

56. $\sqrt{243ab^5}$

57. $\sqrt[3]{-16x^9}$

58. $\sqrt[3]{-54q^{12}}$

59. $\sqrt[5]{-16m^8n^2}$

60. $\sqrt{75x^6y}$

61. $\sqrt[4]{(x-y)^5}, x > y$

62. $\sqrt[3]{(a+b)^5}$

63. $\sqrt[3]{8x^3 - 8y^3}$

64. $\sqrt[3]{8a^3 + 8b^3}$

In Problems 65–70, simplify each expression. See Objective 2.

65. $\dfrac{4 + \sqrt{36}}{2}$

66. $\dfrac{5 - \sqrt{100}}{5}$

67. $\dfrac{9 + \sqrt{18}}{3}$

68. $\dfrac{10 - \sqrt{75}}{5}$

69. $\dfrac{7 - \sqrt{98}}{14}$

70. $\dfrac{-6 + \sqrt{108}}{6}$

In Problems 71–88, multiply and simplify. Assume that all variables are greater than or equal to zero. See Objective 2.

71. $\sqrt{5} \cdot \sqrt{5}$

72. $\sqrt{6} \cdot \sqrt{6}$

73. $\sqrt{2} \cdot \sqrt{8}$

74. $\sqrt{3} \cdot \sqrt{12}$

75. $\sqrt[3]{4} \cdot \sqrt[3]{2}$

76. $\sqrt[3]{9} \cdot \sqrt[3]{3}$

77. $\sqrt{5x} \cdot \sqrt{15x}$

78. $\sqrt{6x} \cdot \sqrt{30x}$

79. $\sqrt[3]{4b^2} \cdot \sqrt[3]{6b^2}$

80. $\sqrt[3]{9a} \cdot \sqrt[3]{6a^2}$

81. $2\sqrt{6ab} \cdot 3\sqrt{15ab^3}$

82. $3\sqrt{14pq^3} \cdot 2\sqrt{7pq}$

83. $\sqrt[4]{27p^3q^2} \cdot \sqrt[4]{12p^2q^2}$

84. $\sqrt[3]{16m^2n} \cdot \sqrt[3]{27m^2n}$

85. $\sqrt[5]{-8a^3b^4} \cdot \sqrt[5]{12a^3b}$

86. $\sqrt[5]{-27x^4y^2} \cdot \sqrt[5]{18x^3y^4}$

87. $\sqrt[4]{8(x-y)^2} \cdot \sqrt[4]{6(x-y)^3}, x > y$

88. $\sqrt[3]{9(a+b)^2} \cdot \sqrt[3]{6(a+b)^5}$

In Problems 89–96, simplify each expression. Assume that all variables are greater than zero. See Objective 3.

89. $\sqrt{\dfrac{3}{16}}$

90. $\sqrt{\dfrac{5}{36}}$

91. $\sqrt[4]{\dfrac{5x^4}{16}}$

92. $\sqrt[4]{\dfrac{2a^8}{81}}$

93. $\sqrt{\dfrac{9y^2}{25x^2}}$

94. $\sqrt{\dfrac{4a^4}{81b^2}}$

95. $\sqrt[3]{\dfrac{-27x^9}{64y^{12}}}$

96. $\sqrt[5]{\dfrac{-32a^{15}}{243b^{10}}}$

In Problems 97–110, divide and simplify. Assume that all variables are greater than zero. See Objective 3.

97. $\dfrac{\sqrt{8}}{\sqrt{2}}$

98. $\dfrac{\sqrt{27}}{\sqrt{3}}$

99. $\dfrac{\sqrt[3]{128}}{\sqrt[3]{2}}$

100. $\dfrac{\sqrt[4]{64}}{\sqrt[4]{4}}$

101. $\dfrac{\sqrt{48a^3}}{\sqrt{6a}}$

102. $\dfrac{\sqrt{54y^5}}{\sqrt{3y}}$

103. $\dfrac{\sqrt{24a^5b}}{\sqrt{3ab^3}}$

104. $\dfrac{\sqrt{360m^7n^3}}{\sqrt{5mn^5}}$

105. $\dfrac{\sqrt{512a^7b}}{3\sqrt{2ab^3}}$

106. $\dfrac{\sqrt{375x^2y^7}}{10\sqrt{3y}}$

107. $\dfrac{\sqrt[3]{104a^5}}{\sqrt[3]{4a^{-1}}}$

108. $\dfrac{\sqrt[3]{-128x^8}}{\sqrt[3]{2x^{-1}}}$

109. $\dfrac{\sqrt{90x^3y^{-1}}}{\sqrt{2x^{-3}y}}$

110. $\dfrac{\sqrt{96a^5b^{-3}}}{\sqrt{3a^{-5}b}}$

In Problems 111–118, multiply and simplify. See Objective 4.

111. $\sqrt{3} \cdot \sqrt[3]{4}$

112. $\sqrt{2} \cdot \sqrt[3]{7}$

113. $\sqrt[3]{2} \cdot \sqrt[6]{3}$

114. $\sqrt[4]{3} \cdot \sqrt[8]{5}$

115. $\sqrt{3} \cdot \sqrt[3]{18}$

116. $\sqrt{6} \cdot \sqrt[3]{9}$

117. $\sqrt[4]{9} \cdot \sqrt[6]{12}$

118. $\sqrt[5]{8} \cdot \sqrt[10]{16}$

Mixed Practice

In Problems 119–134, perform the indicated operation and simplify. Assume all variables are greater than zero.

119. $\sqrt[3]{\dfrac{5x}{8}}$

120. $\sqrt[3]{\dfrac{7a^2}{64}}$

121. $\sqrt[3]{5a} \cdot \sqrt[3]{9a}$

122. $\sqrt[5]{8b^2} \cdot \sqrt[5]{3b}$

123. $\sqrt{72a^4}$

124. $\sqrt{24b^6}$

125. $\sqrt[3]{6a^2b} \cdot \sqrt[3]{9ab}$

126. $\sqrt[4]{8x^3y^2} \cdot \sqrt[4]{4x^2y^3}$

127. $\dfrac{\sqrt[3]{-32a}}{\sqrt[3]{2a^4}}$

128. $\dfrac{\sqrt[3]{-250p^2}}{\sqrt[3]{2p^5}}$

129. $-5\sqrt[3]{32m^3}$

130. $-7\sqrt[3]{250p^3}$

131. $\sqrt[3]{81a^4b^7}$

132. $\sqrt[5]{32p^7q^{11}}$

133. $\sqrt[3]{12} \cdot \sqrt[3]{18}$

134. $\sqrt[4]{8} \cdot \sqrt[4]{18}$

Applying the Concepts

△**135. Length of a Line Segment** The length of the line segment joining the points $(2, 5)$ and $(-1, -1)$ is given by

$$\sqrt{(5 - (-1))^2 + (2 - (-1))^2}$$

(a) Plot the points in the Cartesian plane and draw a line segment connecting the points.
(b) Express the length of the line segment as a radical in simplified form.

△**136. Length of a Line Segment** The length of the line segment joining the points $(4, 2)$ and $(-2, 4)$ is given by

$$\sqrt{(4 - 2)^2 + (-2 - 4)^2}$$

(a) Plot the points in the Cartesian plane and draw a line segment connecting the points.
(b) Express the length of the line segment as a radical in simplified form.

137. Revenue Growth Suppose that the annual revenue R (in millions of dollars) of a company after t years of operating is modeled by the function

$$R(t) = \sqrt[3]{\dfrac{t}{2}}$$

(a) Predict the revenue of the company after 8 years of operation.
(b) Predict the revenue of the company after 27 years of operation.

△**138. Sphere** The radius r of a sphere whose volume is V is given by

$$r = \sqrt[3]{\dfrac{3V}{4\pi}}$$

(a) Write the radius of a sphere whose volume is 9 cubic centimeters as a radical in simplified form.
(b) Write the radius of a sphere whose volume is 32π cubic meters as a radical in simplified form.

Extending the Concepts

139. Suppose that $f(x) = \sqrt{2x}$ and $g(x) = \sqrt{8x^3}$.
(a) Find $(f \cdot g)(x)$.
(b) Evaluate $(f \cdot g)(3)$.

In Problems 140–143, evaluate the formula

$$x = \dfrac{-b \pm \sqrt{b^2 - 4ac}}{2a}$$

for the given values of a, b, and c. Note that the symbol $\pm$ is shorthand notation to indicate that there are two solutions. One solution is obtained when you add the quantity after the $\pm$ symbol, and another is obtained when you subtract. This formula can be used to solve any equation of the form $ax^2 + bx + c = 0$.

140. $a = 1, b = 4, c = 1$

141. $a = 1, b = 6, c = 3$

142. $a = 2, b = 1, c = -1$

143. $a = 3, b = 4, c = -1$

Explaining the Concepts

144. Explain how you would simplify $\sqrt[3]{16a^5}$.

145. In order to use the Product Property to multiply radicals, what must be true about the index in each radical?

Synthesis Review

In Problems 146–149, solve the following.

146. $4x + 3 = 13$

147. $2|7x - 1| + 4 = 16$

148. $\dfrac{3}{5}x + 2 \leq 28$

149. $\dfrac{5}{2}|x + 1| + 1 \leq 11$

150. How are the solutions in Problems 146 and 148 similar? How are the solutions in Problems 147 and 149 similar?

The Graphing Calculator

151. Exploration To understand the circumstances under which absolute value symbols are required when simplifying radicals, do the following.

(a) Graph $Y_1 = \sqrt{x^2}$ and $Y_2 = x$. Do you think that $\sqrt{x^2} = x$? Now graph $Y_1 = \sqrt{x^2}$ and $Y_2 = |x|$. Do you think that $\sqrt{x^2} = |x|$?
(b) Graph $Y_1 = \sqrt[3]{x^3}$ and $Y_2 = x$. Do you think that $\sqrt[3]{x^3} = x$? Now graph $Y_1 = \sqrt[3]{x^3}$ and $Y_2 = |x|$. Do you think that $\sqrt[3]{x^3} = |x|$?
(c) Graph $Y_1 = \sqrt[4]{x^4}$ and $Y_2 = x$. Do you think that $\sqrt[4]{x^4} = x$? Now graph $Y_1 = \sqrt[4]{x^4}$ and $Y_2 = |x|$. Do you think that $\sqrt[4]{x^4} = |x|$?
(d) In your own words, make a generalization about $\sqrt[n]{x^n}$.

6.4 Adding, Subtracting, and Multiplying Radical Expressions

Preparing for Adding, Subtracting, and Multiplying Radical Expressions
Before getting started, take the following readiness quiz. If you get a problem wrong, go back to the section cited and review the material.

P1. Add: $4y^3 - 2y^2 + 8y - 1 + (-2y^3 + 7y^2 - 3y + 9)$ [Section 4.1, pp. 323–324]

P2. Subtract: $5z^2 + 6 - (3z^2 - 8z - 3)$ [Section 4.1, pp. 324–325]

P3. Multiply: $(4x + 3)(x - 5)$ [Section 4.2, pp. 333–334]

P4. Multiply: $(2y - 3)(2y + 3)$ [Section 4.2, pp. 335–336]

1 Add or Subtract Radical Expressions

Recall, a radical expression is an algebraic expression that contains a radical. Two radicals are **like radicals** if each radical has the same index and the same radicand. For example,

$$4\sqrt[3]{x - 4} \quad \text{and} \quad 10\sqrt[3]{x - 4}$$

are like radicals because each has the same index, 3, and the same radicand, $x - 4$.

To add or subtract radical expressions, we combine like radicals using the Distributive Property as follows:

$$\text{Factor out } \sqrt[3]{x - 4}$$
$$\downarrow$$
$$4\sqrt[3]{x - 4} + 10\sqrt[3]{x - 4} = (4 + 10)\sqrt[3]{x - 4}$$
$$4 + 10 = 14: \ = 14\sqrt[3]{x - 4}$$

EXAMPLE 1 Adding and Subtracting Radical Expressions

Add or subtract, as indicated. Assume all variables are greater than or equal to zero.

(a) $5\sqrt{2x} + 9\sqrt{2x}$

(b) $3\sqrt[3]{10} + 7\sqrt[3]{10} - 5\sqrt[3]{10}$

Solution

(a) Both radicals have the same index, 2, and the same radicand, $2x$.

$$5\sqrt{2x} + 9\sqrt{2x} = (5 + 9)\sqrt{2x}$$
$$5 + 9 = 14: \ = 14\sqrt{2x}$$

(b) All three radicals have the same index, 3, and the same radicand, 10.

$$3\sqrt[3]{10} + 7\sqrt[3]{10} - 5\sqrt[3]{10} = (3 + 7 - 5)\sqrt[3]{10}$$
$$3 + 7 - 5 = 5: \ = 5\sqrt[3]{10}$$

Work Smart

Remember that to add or subtract radicals both the index and the radicand must be the same.

Preparing for...Answers
P1. $2y^3 + 5y^2 + 5y + 8$ **P2.** $2z^2 + 8z + 9$
P3. $4x^2 - 17x - 15$ **P4.** $4y^2 - 9$

Quick ✔

1. Two radicals are _____ if each radical has the same index and the same radicand.

In Problems 2 and 3, add or subtract, as indicated.

2. $9\sqrt{13y} + 4\sqrt{13y}$

3. $\sqrt[4]{5} + 9\sqrt[4]{5} - 3\sqrt[4]{5}$

Sometimes we have to simplify the radical so that the radicands are the same before adding or subtracting.

EXAMPLE 2 Adding and Subtracting Radical Expressions

Add or subtract, as indicated. Assume all variables are greater than or equal to zero.

(a) $3\sqrt{12} + 7\sqrt{3}$ **(b)** $3x\sqrt{20x} - 7\sqrt{5x^3}$ **(c)** $3\sqrt{5} + 7\sqrt{13}$

Solution

(a) The index on each radical is the same, but the radicands are different. However, we can simplify the radicals to make the radicands the same.

$$\sqrt{12} = \sqrt{4} \cdot \sqrt{3}$$

$$3\sqrt{12} + 7\sqrt{3} = 3\sqrt{4} \cdot \sqrt{3} + 7\sqrt{3}$$

$\sqrt{4} = 2$: $= 3 \cdot 2\sqrt{3} + 7\sqrt{3}$

$= 6\sqrt{3} + 7\sqrt{3}$

Factor out $\sqrt{3}$: $= (6 + 7)\sqrt{3}$

$= 13\sqrt{3}$

(b) The index on each radical is the same, but the radicands are different. However, we can simplify the radicals to make the radicands the same.

$$\sqrt{20x} = \sqrt{4} \cdot \sqrt{5x}; \ \sqrt{5x^3} = \sqrt{x^2} \cdot \sqrt{5x}$$

$$3x\sqrt{20x} - 7\sqrt{5x^3} = 3x \cdot \sqrt{4} \cdot \sqrt{5x} - 7 \cdot \sqrt{x^2} \cdot \sqrt{5x}$$

Simplify radicals: $= 3x \cdot 2 \cdot \sqrt{5x} - 7 \cdot x \cdot \sqrt{5x}$

Multiply: $= 6x\sqrt{5x} - 7x\sqrt{5x}$

Factor out $\sqrt{5x}$: $= (6x - 7x)\sqrt{5x}$

$= -x\sqrt{5x}$

(c) For $3\sqrt{5} + 7\sqrt{13}$ the index on each radical is the same, but the radicands are different and we cannot simplify the radicals.   ■

Quick ✔ *In Problems 4–6, add or subtract, as indicated. Assume all variables are greater than or equal to zero.*

4. $4\sqrt{18} - 3\sqrt{8}$ **5.** $-5x\sqrt[3]{54x} + 7\sqrt[3]{2x^4}$ **6.** $7\sqrt{10} - 6\sqrt{3}$

EXAMPLE 3 Adding or Subtracting Radical Expressions

Add or subtract, as indicated. Assume all variables are greater than or equal to zero.

(a) $\sqrt[3]{16x^4} - 7x\sqrt[3]{-2x} + \sqrt[3]{54x}$ **(b)** $3\sqrt[4]{m^4n} - 5m\sqrt[8]{n^2}$

Solution

(a) The index on each radical is the same, but the radicands are different. However, we can simplify the radicals to make the radicands the same.

$$\sqrt[3]{16x^4} = \sqrt[3]{8x^3}\cdot\sqrt[3]{2x}; \sqrt[3]{-2x} = \sqrt[3]{-1}\cdot\sqrt[3]{2x}; \sqrt[3]{54x} = \sqrt[3]{27}\cdot\sqrt[3]{2x}$$

$$\sqrt[3]{16x^4} - 7x\sqrt[3]{-2x} + \sqrt[3]{54x} = \sqrt[3]{8x^3}\cdot\sqrt[3]{2x} - 7x\sqrt[3]{-1}\cdot\sqrt[3]{2x} + \sqrt[3]{27}\cdot\sqrt[3]{2x}$$

$$\sqrt[3]{8x^3} = 2x; \sqrt[3]{-1} = -1; \sqrt[3]{27} = 3: \quad = 2x\sqrt[3]{2x} - 7x(-1)\sqrt[3]{2x} + 3\sqrt[3]{2x}$$

$$-7x(-1) = 7x: \quad = 2x\sqrt[3]{2x} + 7x\sqrt[3]{2x} + 3\sqrt[3]{2x}$$

Factor out $\sqrt[3]{2x}:\quad = (2x + 7x + 3)\sqrt[3]{2x}$

Simplify: $\quad = (9x + 3)\sqrt[3]{2x}$

Factor out 3: $\quad = 3(3x + 1)\sqrt[3]{2x}$

Work Smart: Study Skills

Contrast adding radicals with multiplying radicals:

Add: $3\sqrt{5} + 8\sqrt{5} = (3 + 8)\sqrt{5}$
$$= 11\sqrt{5}$$

Multiply:
$3\sqrt{5}\cdot 8\sqrt{5} = 3\cdot 8\cdot\sqrt{5}\cdot\sqrt{5}$
$$= 24\sqrt{25}$$
$$= 24\cdot 5$$
$$= 120$$

Ask yourself these questions:

How must the radicals be "like" to be added?

How must the radicals be "like" to be multiplied?

(b) Here, the index on the radical and the radicand are different. We start by dealing with the index using rational exponents.

$$\sqrt[n]{a^m} = a^{\frac{m}{n}}$$

$$3\sqrt[4]{m^4n} - 5m\sqrt[8]{n^2} = 3\sqrt[4]{m^4n} - 5m\cdot n^{\frac{2}{8}}$$

Reduce rational exponent: $\quad = 3\sqrt[4]{m^4n} - 5m\cdot n^{\frac{1}{4}}$

Rewrite as radical: $\quad = 3\sqrt[4]{m^4n} - 5m\cdot\sqrt[4]{n}$

Now the index is the same, but the radicands are different. We can deal with this issue as well.

$$\sqrt[4]{m^4n} = \sqrt[4]{m^4}\cdot\sqrt[4]{n}:\quad = 3\sqrt[4]{m^4}\cdot\sqrt[4]{n} - 5m\cdot\sqrt[4]{n}$$

Simplify: $\quad = 3m\cdot\sqrt[4]{n} - 5m\cdot\sqrt[4]{n}$

Factor out $\sqrt[4]{n}:\quad = (3m - 5m)\cdot\sqrt[4]{n}$

Simplify: $\quad = -2m\sqrt[4]{n}$ ∎

Quick ✔ *In Problems 7 and 8, add or subtract, as indicated. Assume all variables are greater than or equal to zero.*

7. $\sqrt[3]{8z^4} - 2z\sqrt[3]{-27z} + \sqrt[3]{125z}$

8. $\sqrt{25m} - 3\sqrt[4]{m^2}$

⎡2⎤ Multiply Radical Expressions

We have already multiplied radical expressions in which a single radical was multiplied by a second single radical. Now we concentrate on multiplying radical expressions involving more than one radical. These expressions are multiplied in the same way that we multiplied polynomials.

⎡EXAMPLE 4⎤ Multiplying Radical Expressions

Multiply and simplify:

   (a) $\sqrt{5}(3 - 4\sqrt{5})$ **(b)** $\sqrt[3]{2}(3 + \sqrt[3]{4})$ **(c)** $(3 + 2\sqrt{7})(2 - 3\sqrt{7})$

Solution

(a) We use the Distributive Property and multiply each term in the parentheses by $\sqrt{5}$.

$$\sqrt{5}(3 - 4\sqrt{5}) = \sqrt{5}\cdot 3 - \sqrt{5}\cdot 4\sqrt{5}$$

Multiply radicals: $\quad = 3\sqrt{5} - 4\cdot\sqrt{25}$

$\sqrt{25} = 5:\quad = 3\sqrt{5} - 4\cdot 5$

Simplify: $\quad = 3\sqrt{5} - 20$

(b) We use the Distributive Property and multiply each term in parentheses by $\sqrt[3]{2}$.

$$\sqrt[3]{2}\left(3 + \sqrt[3]{4}\right) = \sqrt[3]{2}\cdot 3 + \sqrt[3]{2}\cdot\sqrt[3]{4}$$

Multiply radicals: $= 3\sqrt[3]{2} + \sqrt[3]{8}$

$\sqrt[3]{8} = 2$: $= 3\sqrt[3]{2} + 2$

Work Smart

$-36 - 5\sqrt{7} \neq -41\sqrt{7}$

Do you know why?

(c) We treat this just like the product of two binomials and use the FOIL method to multiply.

$$\left(3 + 2\sqrt{7}\right)\left(2 - 3\sqrt{7}\right) = 3\cdot 2 - 3\cdot 3\sqrt{7} + 2\sqrt{7}\cdot 2 - 2\sqrt{7}\cdot 3\sqrt{7}$$

Multiply: $= 6 - 9\sqrt{7} + 4\sqrt{7} - 6\sqrt{49}$

$\sqrt{49} = 7$: $= 6 - 9\sqrt{7} + 4\sqrt{7} - 6\cdot 7$

$= 6 - 9\sqrt{7} + 4\sqrt{7} - 42$

Simplify: $= -36 - 5\sqrt{7}$ ∎

Quick ✔ *In Problems 9–11, multiply and simplify.*

9. $\sqrt{6}\left(3 - 5\sqrt{6}\right)$ **10.** $\sqrt[3]{12}\left(3 - \sqrt[3]{2}\right)$ **11.** $\left(2 - 7\sqrt{3}\right)\left(5 + 4\sqrt{3}\right)$

We can use our special products formulas (Section 4.2) to multiply radicals as well. In particular, we are going to use the formulas for perfect squares, $(A + B)^2 = A^2 + 2AB + B^2$ and $(A - B)^2 = A^2 - 2AB + B^2$, as well as the formula for the difference of two squares, $(A + B)(A - B) = A^2 - B^2$.

EXAMPLE 5 Multiplying Radical Expressions Involving Special Products

Multiply and simplify.

(a) $\left(2\sqrt{3} + \sqrt{5}\right)^2$ **(b)** $\left(3 + \sqrt{7}\right)\left(3 - \sqrt{7}\right)$

Solution $(A + B)^2 = A^2 + 2 A B + B^2$

(a) $\left(2\sqrt{3} + \sqrt{5}\right)^2 = \left(2\sqrt{3}\right)^2 + 2\cdot 2\sqrt{3}\cdot\sqrt{5} + \left(\sqrt{5}\right)^2$

Multiply: $= 4\sqrt{9} + 4\sqrt{15} + \sqrt{25}$

Simplify: $= 4\cdot 3 + 4\sqrt{15} + 5$

Combine like terms: $= 17 + 4\sqrt{15}$

Work Smart

Notice in Example 5(a),

$\left(2\sqrt{3} + \sqrt{5}\right)^2 \neq \left(2\sqrt{3}\right)^2 + \left(\sqrt{5}\right)^2$

(b) We should notice that $\left(3 + \sqrt{7}\right)\left(3 - \sqrt{7}\right)$ is in the form $(A + B)(A - B)$, so that

$(A + B)(A - B) = A^2 - B^2$

$\left(3 + \sqrt{7}\right)\left(3 - \sqrt{7}\right) = 3^2 - \left(\sqrt{7}\right)^2$

$= 9 - 7$

$= 2$ ∎

Notice that the product found in Example 5(b) is an integer. That is, there are no radicals in the product. Radical expressions such as $3 + \sqrt{7}$ and $3 - \sqrt{7}$ are called **conjugates** of each other. When we multiply radical expressions involving square roots that are conjugates, the result will never contain a radical. This result plays a huge role in the next section.

Quick ✔

12. The radical expressions $4 + \sqrt{5}$ and $4 - \sqrt{5}$ are examples of _____.

13. *True or False:* The conjugate of $-5 + \sqrt{2}$ is $5 - \sqrt{2}$.

In Problems 14–16, multiply and simplify.

14. $\left(5\sqrt{2} + \sqrt{3}\right)^2$ **15.** $\left(\sqrt{7} - 3\sqrt{2}\right)^2$ **16.** $\left(\sqrt{3} + \sqrt{2}\right)\left(\sqrt{3} - \sqrt{2}\right)$

6.4 EXERCISES

PRACTICE   WATCH   DOWNLOAD   READ   REVIEW

1–16. *are the* Quick ✔s *that follow each* EXAMPLE

Building Skills

In Problems 17–24, add or subtract as indicated. Assume all variables are greater than or equal to zero. See Objective 1.

17. $3\sqrt{2} + 7\sqrt{2}$

18. $6\sqrt{3} + 8\sqrt{3}$

19. $5\sqrt[3]{x} - 3\sqrt[3]{x}$

20. $12\sqrt[4]{z} - 5\sqrt[4]{z}$

21. $8\sqrt{5x} - 3\sqrt{5x} + 9\sqrt{5x}$

22. $4\sqrt[3]{3y} + 8\sqrt[3]{3y} - 10\sqrt[3]{3y}$

23. $4\sqrt[3]{5} - 3\sqrt{5} + 7\sqrt[3]{5} - 8\sqrt{5}$

24. $12\sqrt{7} + 5\sqrt[4]{7} - 5\sqrt{7} + 6\sqrt[4]{7}$

In Problems 25–46, add or subtract as indicated. Assume all variables are greater than or equal to zero. See Objective 1.

25. $\sqrt{8} + 6\sqrt{2}$

26. $6\sqrt{3} + \sqrt{12}$

27. $\sqrt[3]{24} - 4\sqrt[3]{3}$

28. $\sqrt[3]{32} - 5\sqrt[3]{4}$

29. $\sqrt[3]{54} - 7\sqrt[3]{128}$

30. $7\sqrt[4]{48} - 4\sqrt[4]{243}$

31. $5\sqrt{54x} - 3\sqrt{24x}$

32. $2\sqrt{48z} - \sqrt{75z}$

33. $2\sqrt{8} + 3\sqrt{10}$

34. $4\sqrt{12} + 2\sqrt{20}$

35. $\sqrt{12x^3} + 5x\sqrt{108x}$

36. $3\sqrt{63z^3} + 2z\sqrt{28z}$

37. $\sqrt{12x^2} + 3x\sqrt{2} - 2\sqrt{98x^2}$

38. $\sqrt{48y^2} - 4y\sqrt{12} + \sqrt{108y^2}$

39. $\sqrt[3]{-54x^3} + 3x\sqrt[3]{16} - 2\sqrt[3]{128}$

40. $2\sqrt[3]{-5x^3} + 4x\sqrt[3]{40} - \sqrt[3]{135}$

41. $\sqrt{9x - 9} + \sqrt{4x - 4}$

42. $\sqrt{4x + 12} - \sqrt{9x + 27}$

43. $\sqrt{16x} - \sqrt[6]{x^3}$

44. $\sqrt{25x} - \sqrt[4]{x^2}$

45. $\sqrt[3]{27x} + 2\sqrt[9]{x^3}$

46. $\sqrt[4]{16y} + \sqrt[8]{y^2}$

In Problems 47–80, multiply and simplify. Assume all variables are greater than or equal to zero. See Objective 2.

47. $\sqrt{3}(2 - 3\sqrt{2})$

48. $\sqrt{5}(5 + 3\sqrt{3})$

49. $\sqrt{3}(\sqrt{2} + \sqrt{6})$

50. $\sqrt{2}(\sqrt{5} - 2\sqrt{10})$

51. $\sqrt[3]{4}(\sqrt[3]{3} - \sqrt[3]{6})$

52. $\sqrt[3]{6}(\sqrt[3]{2} + \sqrt[3]{12})$

53. $\sqrt{2x}(3 - \sqrt{10x})$

54. $\sqrt{5x}(6 + \sqrt{15x})$

55. $(3 + \sqrt{2})(4 + \sqrt{3})$

56. $(5 + \sqrt{5})(3 + \sqrt{6})$

57. $(6 + \sqrt{3})(2 - \sqrt{7})$

58. $(7 - \sqrt{3})(6 + \sqrt{5})$

59. $(4 - 2\sqrt{7})(3 + 3\sqrt{7})$ **60.** $(9 + 5\sqrt{10})(1 - 3\sqrt{10})$

61. $(\sqrt{2} + 3\sqrt{6})(\sqrt{3} - 2\sqrt{2})$

62. $(2\sqrt{3} + \sqrt{10})(\sqrt{5} - 2\sqrt{2})$

63. $(2\sqrt{5} + \sqrt{3})(4\sqrt{5} - 3\sqrt{3})$

64. $(\sqrt{6} - 2\sqrt{2})(2\sqrt{6} + 3\sqrt{2})$

65. $(1 + \sqrt{3})^2$

66. $(2 - \sqrt{3})^2$

67. $(\sqrt{2} - \sqrt{5})^2$

68. $(\sqrt{7} - \sqrt{3})^2$

69. $(\sqrt{x} - \sqrt{2})^2$

70. $(\sqrt{z} + \sqrt{5})^2$

71. $(\sqrt{2} - 1)(\sqrt{2} + 1)$

72. $(\sqrt{3} - 1)(\sqrt{3} + 1)$

73. $(3 - 2\sqrt{5})(3 + 2\sqrt{5})$

74. $(6 + 3\sqrt{2})(6 - 3\sqrt{2})$

75. $(\sqrt{2x} + \sqrt{3y})(\sqrt{2x} - \sqrt{3y})$

76. $(\sqrt{5a} + \sqrt{7b})(\sqrt{5a} - \sqrt{7b})$

77. $(\sqrt[3]{x} + 4)(\sqrt[3]{x} - 3)$

78. $(\sqrt[3]{y} - 6)(\sqrt[3]{y} + 3)$

79. $(\sqrt[3]{2a} - 5)(\sqrt[3]{2a} + 5)$

80. $(\sqrt[3]{4p} - 1)(\sqrt[3]{4p} + 3)$

Mixed Practice

In Problems 81–100, perform the indicated operation and simplify.
Assume all variables are greater than or equal to zero.

81. $\sqrt{5}\left(\sqrt{3} + \sqrt{10}\right)$

82. $\sqrt{7}\left(\sqrt{14} + \sqrt{3}\right)$

83. $\sqrt{28x^5} - x\sqrt{7x^3} + 5\sqrt{175x^5}$

84. $\sqrt{180a^5} + a^2\sqrt{20} - a\sqrt{80a^3}$

85. $\left(2\sqrt{3} + 5\right)\left(2\sqrt{3} - 5\right)$

86. $\left(4\sqrt{2} - 2\right)\left(4\sqrt{2} + 2\right)$

87. $\sqrt[3]{7}\left(2 + \sqrt[3]{4}\right)$

88. $\sqrt[3]{9}\left(5 + 2\sqrt[3]{2}\right)$

89. $\left(2\sqrt{2} + 5\right)\left(4\sqrt{2} - 4\right)$

90. $\left(5\sqrt{5} - 3\right)\left(3\sqrt{5} - 4\right)$

91. $4\sqrt{18} + 2\sqrt{32}$

92. $5\sqrt{20} + 2\sqrt{80}$

93. $\left(\sqrt{5} - \sqrt{3}\right)^2$

94. $\left(\sqrt{2} - \sqrt{7}\right)^2$

95. $3\sqrt[3]{5x^3y} + \sqrt[3]{40y}$

96. $5\sqrt[3]{3m^3n} + \sqrt[3]{81n}$

97. $\left(\sqrt{2x} - \sqrt{7y}\right)\left(\sqrt{2x} + \sqrt{7y}\right)$

98. $\left(\sqrt{3a} - \sqrt{4b}\right)\left(\sqrt{3a} + \sqrt{4b}\right)$

99. $-\dfrac{3}{5}\cdot\left(-\dfrac{\sqrt{5}}{5}\right) - \dfrac{4}{5}\cdot\left(-\dfrac{2\sqrt{5}}{5}\right)$

100. $\dfrac{4}{5}\cdot\left(-\dfrac{\sqrt{5}}{5}\right) + \left(-\dfrac{3}{5}\right)\cdot\left(-\dfrac{2\sqrt{5}}{5}\right)$

101. Suppose that $f(x) = \sqrt{3x}$ and $g(x) = \sqrt{12x}$; find

    (a) $(f + g)(x)$ **(b)** $(f + g)(4)$
    (c) $(f \cdot g)(x)$

102. Suppose that $f(x) = \sqrt{4x - 4}$ and
    $g(x) = \sqrt{25x - 25}$; find

    (a) $(f + g)(x)$ **(b)** $(f + g)(10)$
    (c) $(f \cdot g)(x)$

103. Show that $-2 + \sqrt{5}$ is a solution to the equation
$x^2 + 4x - 1 = 0$. Show that $-2 - \sqrt{5}$ is also a
solution.

104. Show that $3 + \sqrt{7}$ is a solution to the equation
$x^2 - 6x + 2 = 0$. Show that $3 - \sqrt{7}$ is also a solution.

Applying the Concepts

In Problems 105 and 106, find the perimeter and area of the figures
shown. Express your answer as a radical in simplified form.

105.   **106.**

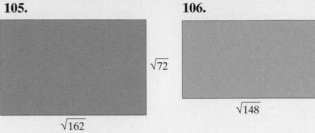

*Problems 107 and 108, use **Heron's Formula** for finding the area*
of a triangle whose sides are known. Heron's Formula states that
the area A of a triangle with sides a, b, and c is

$$A = \sqrt{s(s - a)(s - b)(s - c)}$$

where

$$s = \frac{1}{2}(a + b + c)$$

Find the area of the shaded region by computing the difference in
the areas of each triangle. That is, compute "area of larger triangle
minus area of smaller triangle." Write your answer as a radical in
simplified form.

107.   **108.**

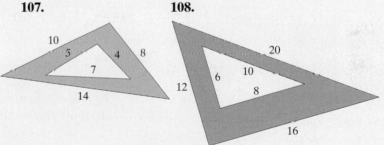

Explaining the Concepts

109. Explain how to add or subtract radicals.

110. Multiply $\left(\sqrt{a} - \sqrt{b}\right)\left(\sqrt{a} + \sqrt{b}\right)$ and provide a
general result regarding the product of conjugates
involving square roots.

Synthesis Review

In Problems 111–116, multiply each of the following.

111. $(3a^3b)(4a^2b^4)$ **112.** $(3p - 1)(2p + 3)$

113. $(3y + 2)(2y - 1)$ **114.** $(m - 4)(m + 4)$

115. $(5w + 2)(5w - 2)$ **116.** $\left(\sqrt{x} + 2\right)\left(\sqrt{x} - 2\right)$

6.5 Rationalizing Radical Expressions

OBJECTIVES

1 Rationalize a Denominator Containing One Term

2 Rationalize a Denominator Containing Two Terms

In Words

We call the process "rationalizing the denominator" because we are making the denominator a rational number (no radicals).

Preparing for Rationalizing Radical Expressions

Before getting started, take the following readiness quiz. If you get a problem wrong, go back to the section cited and review the material.

P1. What would we need to multiply 12 by in order to make it the smallest perfect square that is a multiple of 12?

P2. Simplify: $\sqrt{25x^2}, x > 0$ [Section 6.3, pp. 493–495]

When radical expressions appear in the denominator of a quotient, it is customary to rewrite the quotient so that the denominator does not contain any radicals. The process is referred to as **rationalizing the denominator.** In this section, we shall concentrate on rationalizing denominators that contain a single term and denominators that contain two terms.

1 Rationalize a Denominator Containing One Term

To rationalize a denominator containing a single square root, we multiply the numerator and denominator of the quotient by a square root so that the radicand in the denominator becomes a perfect square. For example, if the denominator of a quotient contains $\sqrt{5}$, we would multiply the numerator and denominator by $\sqrt{5}$ because $5 \cdot 5 = 25$, which is a perfect square. If the denominator of a quotient contains $\sqrt{8}$, we would multiply the numerator and denominator by $\sqrt{2}$ because $8 \cdot 2 = 16$, which is a perfect square.

EXAMPLE 1 Rationalizing a Denominator Containing a Square Root

Rationalize the denominator of each expression:

(a) $\dfrac{1}{\sqrt{7}}$ (b) $\dfrac{\sqrt{5}}{\sqrt{12}}$ (c) $\dfrac{2}{3\sqrt{2x}}, x > 0$

Solution

(a) We have $\sqrt{7}$ in the denominator. So, we ask ourselves, "What can I multiply 7 by and obtain a perfect square?" Because $7 \cdot 7 = 49$ and 49 is a perfect square, we multiply the numerator and denominator by $\sqrt{7}$.

$$\frac{1}{\sqrt{7}} = \frac{1}{\sqrt{7}} \cdot \frac{\sqrt{7}}{\sqrt{7}}$$

Multiply numerators;
multiply denominators: $= \dfrac{\sqrt{7}}{\sqrt{49}}$

$\sqrt{49} = 7$: $= \dfrac{\sqrt{7}}{7}$

Work Smart

Remember that $a = 1 \cdot a$ and that 1 can take many forms. In Example 1(a), $1 = \dfrac{\sqrt{7}}{\sqrt{7}}$.

Work Smart

An alternative approach to Example 1(b) would be to simplify $\sqrt{12}$ first, as follows:

$$\frac{\sqrt{5}}{\sqrt{12}} = \frac{\sqrt{5}}{\sqrt{4 \cdot 3}}$$

$$= \frac{\sqrt{5}}{2\sqrt{3}}$$

$$= \frac{\sqrt{5}}{2\sqrt{3}} \cdot \frac{\sqrt{3}}{\sqrt{3}}$$

$$= \frac{\sqrt{15}}{6}$$

(b) We have $\sqrt{12}$ in the denominator. Again, we ask, "What can I multiply 12 by and obtain a perfect square?" Certainly, multiplying 12 by itself would result in a perfect square, but is this the best choice? No, you want to find the smallest integer that makes the radicand a perfect square. So, multiply 12 by 3 to obtain 36, a perfect square.

$$\frac{\sqrt{5}}{\sqrt{12}} = \frac{\sqrt{5}}{\sqrt{12}} \cdot \frac{\sqrt{3}}{\sqrt{3}}$$

Multiply numerators;
multiply denominators: $= \dfrac{\sqrt{15}}{\sqrt{36}}$

$\sqrt{36} = 6$: $= \dfrac{\sqrt{15}}{6}$

Preparing for...Answers **P1.** 3   **P2.** $5x$

(c)

$$\frac{2}{3\sqrt{2x}} = \frac{2}{3\sqrt{2x}} \cdot \frac{\sqrt{2x}}{\sqrt{2x}}$$

Multiply numerators;
multiply denominators: $= \dfrac{2\sqrt{2x}}{3\sqrt{4x^2}}$

$\sqrt{4x^2} = 2x$ since $x > 0$: $= \dfrac{2\sqrt{2x}}{3 \cdot 2x}$

Divide out common factor, 2: $= \dfrac{\sqrt{2x}}{3x}$ ∎

Quick ✔

1. Rewriting a quotient to remove radicals from the denominator is called _____ __ _____ .

2. To rationalize the denominator of $\dfrac{\sqrt{5}}{\sqrt{11}}$, we would multiply the numerator and denominator by ____ .

In Problems 3–5, rationalize each denominator.

3. $\dfrac{1}{\sqrt{3}}$ **4.** $\dfrac{\sqrt{5}}{\sqrt{8}}$ **5.** $\dfrac{5}{\sqrt{10x}}$

In general, to rationalize a denominator when the denominator contains a single radical, we multiply the numerator and denominator of the quotient by a radical so that the product in the denominator has a radicand that is a perfect power of the index n. So, if the denominator contains a radical whose index is 3, we multiply the numerator and denominator by a cube root so that the radicand in the denominator becomes a perfect cube. For example, if the denominator of a quotient contains $\sqrt[3]{4}$, we would multiply the numerator and denominator of the quotient by $\sqrt[3]{2}$ because $4 \cdot 2 = 8$ and 8 is a perfect cube.

EXAMPLE 2   Rationalizing a Denominator Containing Cube Roots and Fourth Roots

Rationalize the denominator of each expression:

(a) $\dfrac{1}{\sqrt[3]{6}}$ **(b)** $\sqrt[3]{\dfrac{5}{18}}$ **(c)** $\dfrac{6}{\sqrt[4]{4z^3}}$

Assume all variables represent positive real numbers.

Solution

(a) We have $\sqrt[3]{6}$ in the denominator. We want the radicand in the denominator to be a perfect cube (since the index is 3), so we multiply the numerator and denominator by $\sqrt[3]{6^2} = \sqrt[3]{36}$ since $6 \cdot 36 = 216$ and 216 is a perfect cube.

$$\frac{1}{\sqrt[3]{6}} = \frac{1}{\sqrt[3]{6}} \cdot \frac{\sqrt[3]{6^2}}{\sqrt[3]{6^2}}$$

Multiply numerators;
multiply denominators: $= \dfrac{\sqrt[3]{36}}{\sqrt[3]{6^3}}$

$\sqrt[3]{6^3} = 6$: $= \dfrac{\sqrt[3]{36}}{6}$

(b) First, we use the Quotient Property $\left(\sqrt[n]{\dfrac{a}{b}} = \dfrac{\sqrt[n]{a}}{\sqrt[n]{b}} \right)$ to rewrite the radical as the quotient of two radicals.

$$\sqrt[3]{\frac{5}{18}} = \frac{\sqrt[3]{5}}{\sqrt[3]{18}}$$

Work Smart

The radicand in $\sqrt[3]{6}$ is 6. Think of 6 as 6^1. To make it a perfect cube, 6^3, we need to multiply by 6^2 or 36. Then $6 \cdot 36 = 6^1 \cdot 6^2 = 6^3$. The cube root of 6^3 or 216 is 6.

What do we need to multiply $\sqrt[3]{18}$ by in order to make it a perfect cube? We will write 18 as $9 \cdot 2 = 3^2 \cdot 2^1$. Therefore, if we multiply $18 = 3^2 \cdot 2^1$ by $3^1 \cdot 2^2 = 12$, we will have a perfect cube as the radicand in the denominator.

$$\sqrt[3]{\frac{5}{18}} = \frac{\sqrt[3]{5}}{\sqrt[3]{18}} = \frac{\sqrt[3]{5}}{\sqrt[3]{3^2 \cdot 2}} \cdot \frac{\sqrt[3]{3 \cdot 2^2}}{\sqrt[3]{3 \cdot 2^2}}$$

Multiply numerators; multiply denominators:
$$= \frac{\sqrt[3]{60}}{\sqrt[3]{3^3 \cdot 2^3}}$$

$$= \frac{\sqrt[3]{60}}{6}$$

(c) We rewrite the denominator as $\sqrt[4]{2^2 \cdot z^3}$. To make the radicand a perfect power of 4, we need to multiply $\sqrt[4]{2^2 \cdot z^3}$ by $\sqrt[4]{2^2 \cdot z} = \sqrt[4]{4z}$ to obtain $\sqrt[4]{2^4 z^4}$ in the denominator.

$$\frac{6}{\sqrt[4]{4z^3}} = \frac{6}{\sqrt[4]{2^2 \cdot z^3}} \cdot \frac{\sqrt[4]{2^2 \cdot z}}{\sqrt[4]{2^2 \cdot z}}$$

Multiply numerators; multiply denominators:
$$= \frac{6\sqrt[4]{4z}}{\sqrt[4]{2^4 \cdot z^4}}$$

$$= \frac{6\sqrt[4]{4z}}{2z}$$

Simplify:
$$= \frac{3\sqrt[4]{4z}}{z}$$ ∎

> **Quick ✔** *In Problems 6–8, rationalize each denominator. Assume all variables are positive.*
>
> **6.** $\dfrac{4}{\sqrt[3]{3}}$ **7.** $\sqrt[3]{\dfrac{3}{20}}$ **8.** $\dfrac{3}{\sqrt[4]{p}}$

2 Rationalize a Denominator Containing Two Terms

To rationalize a denominator containing two terms involving square roots, we use the fact that

$$(A + B)(A - B) = A^2 - B^2$$

and multiply both the numerator and denominator of the quotient by the conjugate of the denominator. For example, if the quotient is $\dfrac{3}{\sqrt{3} + 2}$, we would multiply both the numerator and the denominator by the conjugate of $\sqrt{3} + 2$, which is $\sqrt{3} - 2$. We know from the last section that the product $\left(\sqrt{3} + 2\right)\left(\sqrt{3} - 2\right)$ will not contain a radical.

EXAMPLE 3 Rationalizing a Denominator Containing Two Terms

Rationalize the denominator: $\dfrac{\sqrt{2}}{\sqrt{6} + 2}$

Solution

We see that $\sqrt{6} + 2$ is in the denominator of the quotient, so we multiply the numerator and denominator by the conjugate of $\sqrt{6} + 2$, $\sqrt{6} - 2$.

$$\frac{\sqrt{2}}{\sqrt{6} + 2} = \frac{\sqrt{2}}{\sqrt{6} + 2} \cdot \frac{\sqrt{6} - 2}{\sqrt{6} - 2}$$

Multiply the numerators and denominators:
$$= \frac{\sqrt{2}\left(\sqrt{6} - 2\right)}{\left(\sqrt{6} + 2\right)\left(\sqrt{6} - 2\right)}$$

$$\begin{array}{ll} \text{Distribute in the numerator;} & = \dfrac{\sqrt{12} - 2\sqrt{2}}{\left(\sqrt{6}\right)^2 - 2^2} \\ (A + B)(A - B) = A^2 - B^2 \text{ in the denominator:} & \end{array}$$

$$\sqrt{12} = 2\sqrt{3}: \quad = \dfrac{2\sqrt{3} - 2\sqrt{2}}{6 - 4}$$

$$\text{Factor out common factor of 2 in numerator:} \quad = \dfrac{2\left(\sqrt{3} - \sqrt{2}\right)}{2}$$

$$\text{Divide out the 2s:} \quad = \sqrt{3} - \sqrt{2} \qquad \blacksquare$$

Quick ✔

9. To rationalize the denominator of $\dfrac{4 - \sqrt{3}}{-2 + \sqrt{7}}$, we would multiply the numerator and denominator by _____ .

In Problems 10 and 11, rationalize the denominator.

10. $\dfrac{4}{\sqrt{3} + 1}$

11. $\dfrac{\sqrt{2}}{\sqrt{6} - \sqrt{2}}$

EXAMPLE 4   Rationalizing a Denominator Containing Two Terms

Rationalize the denominator: $\dfrac{\sqrt{6} - 3}{\sqrt{10} - \sqrt{6}}$

Solution

We see that $\sqrt{10} - \sqrt{6}$ is in the denominator of the quotient, so we multiply the numerator and denominator by the conjugate of the denominator, $\sqrt{10} + \sqrt{6}$.

$$\dfrac{\sqrt{6} - 3}{\sqrt{10} - \sqrt{6}} = \dfrac{\sqrt{6} - 3}{\sqrt{10} - \sqrt{6}} \cdot \dfrac{\sqrt{10} + \sqrt{6}}{\sqrt{10} + \sqrt{6}}$$

$$\begin{array}{ll} \text{Multiply the numerators} & = \dfrac{\left(\sqrt{6} - 3\right)\left(\sqrt{10} + \sqrt{6}\right)}{\left(\sqrt{10} - \sqrt{6}\right)\left(\sqrt{10} + \sqrt{6}\right)} \\ \text{and denominators:} & \end{array}$$

$$\begin{array}{ll} \text{FOIL the numerator;} & = \dfrac{\sqrt{60} + \sqrt{36} - 3\sqrt{10} - 3\sqrt{6}}{\left(\sqrt{10}\right)^2 - \left(\sqrt{6}\right)^2} \\ (A + B)(A - B) = A^2 - B^2 \text{ in the denominator:} & \end{array}$$

$$\text{Simplify radicals:} \quad = \dfrac{2\sqrt{15} + 6 - 3\sqrt{10} - 3\sqrt{6}}{10 - 6}$$

$$= \dfrac{2\sqrt{15} + 6 - 3\sqrt{10} - 3\sqrt{6}}{4} \qquad \blacksquare$$

Quick ✔ *In Problem 12, rationalize the denominator.*

12. $\dfrac{\sqrt{5} + 4}{\sqrt{5} - \sqrt{2}}$

6.5 EXERCISES

PRACTICE   WATCH   DOWNLOAD   READ   REVIEW

1–12. *are the* Quick ✔s *that follow each* EXAMPLE

Building Skills

In Problems 13–36, rationalize each denominator. Assume all variables are positive. See Objective 1.

13. $\dfrac{1}{\sqrt{2}}$

14. $\dfrac{2}{\sqrt{3}}$

15. $-\dfrac{6}{5\sqrt{3}}$

16. $-\dfrac{3}{2\sqrt{3}}$

17. $\dfrac{3}{\sqrt{12}}$

18. $\dfrac{5}{\sqrt{20}}$

19. $\dfrac{\sqrt{2}}{\sqrt{6}}$

20. $\dfrac{\sqrt{3}}{\sqrt{11}}$

21. $\sqrt{\dfrac{2}{p}}$

22. $\sqrt{\dfrac{5}{z}}$

23. $\dfrac{\sqrt{8}}{\sqrt{y^3}}$

24. $\dfrac{\sqrt{32}}{\sqrt{a^5}}$

59. $\dfrac{\sqrt{10}}{2} - \dfrac{1}{\sqrt{2}}$

60. $\dfrac{\sqrt{5}}{2} + \dfrac{3}{\sqrt{5}}$

25. $\dfrac{2}{\sqrt[3]{2}}$

26. $\dfrac{5}{\sqrt[3]{3}}$

27. $\sqrt[3]{\dfrac{7}{q}}$

61. $\sqrt{\dfrac{1}{3}} + \sqrt{12} + \sqrt{75}$

62. $\sqrt{\dfrac{2}{5}} + \sqrt{20} - \sqrt{45}$

28. $\sqrt[3]{\dfrac{-4}{p}}$

29. $\sqrt[3]{\dfrac{-3}{50}}$

30. $\sqrt[3]{\dfrac{-5}{72}}$

63. $\dfrac{3}{\sqrt{18}} - \sqrt{\dfrac{1}{2}}$

64. $\sqrt{\dfrac{4}{3}} + \dfrac{4}{\sqrt{48}}$

31. $\dfrac{2}{\sqrt[3]{20y}}$

32. $\dfrac{8}{\sqrt[3]{36z^2}}$

33. $\dfrac{-4}{\sqrt[4]{3x^3}}$

In Problems 65–76, simplify each expression so that the denominator does not contain a radical. Work smart because in some of the problems, it will be easier if you divide the radicands before attempting to rationalize the denominator.

34. $\dfrac{6}{\sqrt[4]{9b^2}}$

35. $\dfrac{12}{\sqrt[5]{m^3n^2}}$

36. $\dfrac{-3}{\sqrt[5]{ab^3}}$

65. $\dfrac{\sqrt{3}}{\sqrt{12}}$

66. $\dfrac{\sqrt{2}}{\sqrt{18}}$

67. $\dfrac{3}{\sqrt{72}}$

In Problems 37–56, rationalize each denominator. Assume all variables are positive. See Objective 2.

68. $\dfrac{7}{\sqrt{98}}$

69. $\sqrt{\dfrac{4}{3}}$

70. $\sqrt{\dfrac{9}{5}}$

37. $\dfrac{4}{\sqrt{6} - 2}$

38. $\dfrac{6}{\sqrt{7} - 2}$

39. $\dfrac{5}{\sqrt{5} + 2}$

71. $\dfrac{\sqrt{3} - 3}{\sqrt{3} + 3}$

72. $\dfrac{\sqrt{2} - 5}{\sqrt{2} + 5}$

73. $\dfrac{2}{\sqrt{5} + 2}$

40. $\dfrac{10}{\sqrt{10} + 3}$

41. $\dfrac{8}{\sqrt{7} - \sqrt{3}}$

42. $\dfrac{12}{\sqrt{11} - \sqrt{7}}$

74. $\dfrac{5}{\sqrt{6} + 4}$

75. $\dfrac{\sqrt{8}}{\sqrt{2}}$

76. $\dfrac{\sqrt{75}}{\sqrt{3}}$

43. $\dfrac{\sqrt{2}}{\sqrt{10} - \sqrt{6}}$

44. $\dfrac{\sqrt{3}}{\sqrt{15} - \sqrt{6}}$

45. $\dfrac{\sqrt{p}}{\sqrt{p} + \sqrt{q}}$

In Problems 77–82, find the reciprocal of the given number. Be sure to rationalize the denominator.

77. $\sqrt{3}$

78. $\sqrt{7}$

79. $\sqrt[3]{12}$

46. $\dfrac{\sqrt{a}}{\sqrt{a} + \sqrt{b}}$

47. $\dfrac{18}{2\sqrt{3} + 3\sqrt{2}}$

48. $\dfrac{15}{3\sqrt{5} + 4\sqrt{3}}$

80. $\sqrt[3]{18}$

81. $\sqrt{3} + 5$

82. $7 - \sqrt{2}$

49. $\dfrac{\sqrt{7} + 3}{\sqrt{7} - 3}$

50. $\dfrac{\sqrt{5} + 3}{\sqrt{5} - 3}$

51. $\dfrac{\sqrt{3} - 4\sqrt{2}}{2\sqrt{3} + 5\sqrt{2}}$

Applying the Concepts

Problems 83 and 84 contain expressions that are seen in a course in Trigonometry. Simplify each expression completely.

52. $\dfrac{3\sqrt{6} + 5\sqrt{7}}{2\sqrt{6} - 3\sqrt{7}}$

53. $\dfrac{\sqrt{p} + 2}{\sqrt{p} - 2}$

54. $\dfrac{\sqrt{x} - 4}{\sqrt{x} + 4}$

83. $\dfrac{1}{\sqrt{2}} \cdot \dfrac{\sqrt{3}}{2} - \dfrac{1}{\sqrt{2}} \cdot \dfrac{1}{2}$

55. $\dfrac{\sqrt{2} - 3}{\sqrt{8} - \sqrt{2}}$

56. $\dfrac{2\sqrt{3} + 3}{\sqrt{12} - \sqrt{3}}$

84. $-\sqrt{\dfrac{2}{3}} \cdot \left(-\dfrac{2}{\sqrt{5}}\right) + \dfrac{1}{\sqrt{3}} \cdot \dfrac{1}{\sqrt{5}}$

Mixed Practice

In Problems 57–64, perform the indicated operation and simplify.

Sometimes we are asked to rationalize a numerator. In Problems 85–88, rationalize each expression by multiplying the numerator and denominator by the conjugate of the numerator.

57. $\sqrt{3} + \dfrac{1}{\sqrt{3}}$

58. $\sqrt{5} - \dfrac{1}{\sqrt{5}}$

85. $\dfrac{\sqrt{2} + 1}{3}$

86. $\dfrac{\sqrt{3} + 2}{2}$

87. $\dfrac{\sqrt{x} - \sqrt{h}}{\sqrt{x}}$

88. $\dfrac{\sqrt{a} - \sqrt{b}}{\sqrt{2}}$

Extending the Concepts

89. When two quantities a and b are positive, we can verify that $a = b$, by showing that $a^2 = b^2$. Verify that $\dfrac{\sqrt{6} + \sqrt{2}}{4} = \dfrac{\sqrt{2} + \sqrt{3}}{2}$ by squaring each side.

90. Rationalize the denominator: $\dfrac{2}{\sqrt{2} + \sqrt{3} - \sqrt{9}}$

91. **Math for the Future: Calculus** Sometimes, rather than rationalizing the denominator, we need to **rationalize the numerator.** This problem comes up in Calculus.

Consider the rational expression $\dfrac{\sqrt{x + h} - \sqrt{x}}{h}$.

(a) Rationalize the numerator by multiplying the numerator and denominator by $\sqrt{x + h} + \sqrt{x}$. Be sure to completely simplify the expression.

(b) Evaluate the expression found in part **(a)** at $h = 0$.

(c) The expression found in part **(b)** represents the formula for the slope of the line tangent to the function $f(x) = \sqrt{x}$ at any value of $x \geq 0$. Find the slope of the line tangent to the function $f(x) = \sqrt{x}$ at $x = 4$.

(d) If $f(x) = \sqrt{x}$, what is $f(4)$? What point is on the graph of $f(x) = \sqrt{x}$?

(e) Find the equation of the line tangent to $f(x) = \sqrt{x}$ at $x = 4$ using the slope found in part **(c)** and the point found in part **(d).**

(f) Graph the function $f(x) = \sqrt{x}$ and the equation of the tangent line on the same Cartesian plane.

Explaining the Concepts

92. Explain why it is necessary to multiply the numerator and denominator by the conjugate of the denominator when rationalizing a denominator containing two terms.

93. Explain why removing irrational numbers from the denominator is called "rationalization."

Synthesis Review

In Problems 94–97, graph each of the following functions using point plotting.

94. $f(x) = 5x - 3$

95. $g(x) = -3x + 9$

96. $G(x) = x^2$

97. $F(x) = x^3$

PUTTING THE CONCEPTS TOGETHER (Sections 6.1–6.5)

These problems cover important concepts from Sections 6.1 through 6.5. We designed these problems so that you can review the chapter so far and show your mastery of the concepts. Take time to work these problems before proceeding with the next section. The answers to these problems are located at the back of the text on page AN-35.

1. Evaluate: $-25^{\frac{1}{2}}$

2. Evaluate: $(-64)^{-\frac{2}{3}}$

3. Write the expression $\sqrt[4]{3x^3}$ with a rational exponent.

4. Write the expression $7z^{\frac{4}{5}}$ as a radical expression.

5. Simplify using rational exponents: $\sqrt[3]{\sqrt{64x^3}}$

6. Distribute and simplify: $c^{\frac{1}{2}}(c^{\frac{3}{2}} + c^{\frac{5}{2}})$

In Problems 7–9, use Laws of Exponents to simplify each expression. Assume all variables in the radicand are greater than or equal to zero. Express answers with positive exponents.

7. $(a^{\frac{2}{3}}b^{-\frac{1}{3}})(a^{\frac{4}{3}}b^{-\frac{5}{3}})$

8. $\dfrac{x^{\frac{3}{4}}}{x^{\frac{1}{8}}}$

9. $(x^{\frac{3}{4}}y^{-\frac{1}{8}})^8$

In Problems 10–19, perform the indicated operation and simplify. Assume all variables in the radicand are greater than or equal to zero.

10. $\sqrt{15a} \cdot \sqrt{2b}$

11. $\sqrt{10m^3n^2} \cdot \sqrt{20mn}$

12. $\sqrt[3]{\dfrac{-32xy^4}{4x^{-2}y}}$

13. $2\sqrt{108} - 3\sqrt{75} + \sqrt{48}$

14. $-5b\sqrt{8b} + 7\sqrt{18b^3}$

15. $\sqrt[3]{16y^4} - y\sqrt[3]{2y}$

16. $(3\sqrt{x})(4\sqrt{x})$

17. $3\sqrt{x} + 4\sqrt{x}$

18. $(2 - 3\sqrt{2})(10 + \sqrt{2})$

19. $(4\sqrt{2} - 3)^2$

In Problems 20 and 21, rationalize the denominator.

20. $\dfrac{3}{2\sqrt{32}}$

21. $\dfrac{4}{\sqrt{3} - 8}$

6.6 Functions Involving Radicals

OBJECTIVES

1. Evaluate Functions Whose Rule Is a Radical Expression
2. Find the Domain of a Function Whose Rule Contains a Radical
3. Graph Functions Involving Square Roots
4. Graph Functions Involving Cube Roots

Preparing for Functions Involving Radicals

Before getting started, take the following readiness quiz. If you get a problem wrong, go back to the section cited and review the material.

P1. Simplify: $\sqrt{121}$ [Getting Ready: Square Roots, pp. 473–474]

P2. Simplify: $\sqrt{p^2}$ [Getting Ready: Square Roots, pp. 475–476]

P3. Given $f(x) = x^2 - 4$, find $f(3)$.   [Section 2.2, pp. 158–159]

P4. Solve: $-2x + 3 \geq 0$ [Section 1.4, pp. 85–88]

P5. Graph $f(x) = x^2 + 1$ using point plotting.   [Section 2.3, pp. 164–165]

1 Evaluate Functions Whose Rule Is a Radical Expression

We can evaluate functions whose rule contains a radical by substituting the value of the independent variable into the rule, just as we did in Section 2.2.

EXAMPLE 1 Evaluating Functions for Which the Rule Is a Radical Expression

For the functions $f(x) = \sqrt{x + 2}$ and $g(x) = \sqrt[3]{3x + 1}$, find

(a) $f(7)$ (b) $f(10)$ (c) $g(-3)$

Solution

(a) $f(x) = \sqrt{x + 2}$
$f(7) = \sqrt{7 + 2}$
$= \sqrt{9}$
$= 3$

(b) $f(x) = \sqrt{x + 2}$
$f(10) = \sqrt{10 + 2}$
$= \sqrt{12}$
$= 2\sqrt{3}$

(c) $g(x) = \sqrt[3]{3x + 1}$
$g(-3) = \sqrt[3]{3(-3) + 1}$
$= \sqrt[3]{-8}$
$= -2$ ∎

Quick ✔ *In Problems 1 and 2, find the values for each function.*

1. $f(x) = \sqrt{3x + 7}$
  (a) $f(3)$ (b) $f(7)$

2. $g(x) = \sqrt[3]{2x + 7}$
  (a) $g(-4)$ (b) $g(10)$

2 Find the Domain of a Function Whose Rule Contains a Radical

Recall the definition of the principal nth root of a number a, $\sqrt[n]{a}$. This definition states that $\sqrt[n]{a} = b$ means $a = b^n$. From this definition we learned that for $n \geq 2$ and even, the radicand, a, must be greater than or equal to 0. For $n \geq 3$ and odd, the radicand, a, can be any real number. This leads to a procedure for finding the domain of a function whose rule contains a radical.

Preparing for...Answers **P1.** 11
P2. $|p|$ **P3.** 5
P4. $\left\{x \mid x \leq \dfrac{3}{2}\right\}$ or $\left(-\infty, \dfrac{3}{2}\right]$
P5.

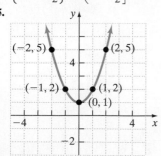

FINDING THE DOMAIN OF A FUNCTION FOR WHICH THE RULE CONTAINS A RADICAL

- If the index on a radical is even, then the radicand must be greater than or equal to zero.
- If the index on a radical is odd, then the radicand can be any real number.

EXAMPLE 2 Finding the Domain of a Radical Function

Find the domain of each of the following functions:

(a) $f(x) = \sqrt{x - 5}$ **(b)** $G(x) = \sqrt[3]{2x + 1}$ **(c)** $h(t) = \sqrt[4]{5 - 2t}$

Solution

(a) First, we take a look at the rule given in the function and interpret it. The function $f(x) = \sqrt{x - 5}$ tells us to take the square root of $x - 5$. We can only take square roots of numbers greater than or equal to zero, so the radicand, $x - 5$, must be greater than or equal to zero. This requires that

$$x - 5 \geq 0$$

Add 5 to both sides: $x \geq 5$

The domain of f is $\{x | x \geq 5\}$ or the interval $[5, \infty)$.

(b) The function $G(x) = \sqrt[3]{2x + 1}$ tells us to take the cube root of $2x + 1$. We can take the cube root of any real number, so the domain of G is any real number.

(c) The function $h(t) = \sqrt[4]{5 - 2t}$ tells us to take the fourth root of $5 - 2t$. We can only take fourth roots of numbers greater than or equal to zero, so the radicand, $5 - 2t$, must be greater than or equal to zero. This requires that

$$5 - 2t \geq 0$$

Subtract 5 from both sides: $-2t \geq -5$

Divide both sides by -2 (Don't forget to change the direction of the inequality!): $t \leq \dfrac{5}{2}$

The domain of h is $\left\{ t | t \leq \dfrac{5}{2} \right\}$ or the interval $\left(-\infty, \dfrac{5}{2} \right]$.   ∎

Quick ✔

3. If the index on a radical expression is ____ , then the radicand must be greater than or equal to zero. If the index on a radical expression is ___ , then the radicand can be any real number.

In Problems 4–6, find the domain of each function.

4. $H(x) = \sqrt{x + 6}$ **5.** $g(t) = \sqrt[5]{3t - 1}$ **6.** $F(m) = \sqrt[4]{6 - 3m}$

3 Graph Functions Involving Square Roots

The **square root function** is given by $f(x) = \sqrt{x}$. The domain of the square root function is $\{x | x \geq 0\}$ or using interval notation $[0, \infty)$. We can obtain the graph of $f(x) = \sqrt{x}$ by determining some ordered pairs (x, y) such that $y = \sqrt{x}$. We then plot the ordered pairs in the xy-plane and connect the points. To make life easy, we choose values of x that are perfect squares $(0, 1, 4, 9,$ and so on). Table 1 shows some points on the graph of $f(x) = \sqrt{x}$. Figure 3 shows the graph of $f(x) = \sqrt{x}$. From the graph of $f(x) = \sqrt{x}$ given in Figure 3, we can see that the range of $f(x) = \sqrt{x}$ is $[0, \infty)$.

Table 1		
x	$f(x) = \sqrt{x}$	(x, y) or $(x, f(x))$
0	$f(0) = 0$	$(0, 0)$
1	$f(1) = 1$	$(1, 1)$
4	$f(4) = 2$	$(4, 2)$
9	$f(9) = 3$	$(9, 3)$
16	$f(16) = 4$	$(16, 4)$

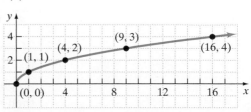

Figure 3
$f(x) = \sqrt{x}$

The point-plotting method can be used to graph a variety of functions involving square roots.

EXAMPLE 3 Graphing a Function Involving a Square Root

For the function $f(x) = \sqrt{x - 2}$,

(a) Find the domain.

(b) Graph the function using point plotting.

(c) Based on the graph, determine the range.

Solution

(a) The function $f(x) = \sqrt{x - 2}$ tells us to take the square root of $x - 2$. We can only take square roots of numbers greater than or equal to zero, so the radicand, $x - 2$, must be greater than or equal to zero. This requires that

$$x - 2 \geq 0$$

Add 2 to both sides: $x \geq 2$

The domain of f is $\{x | x \geq 2\}$ or the interval $[2, \infty)$.

(b) We choose values of x that are greater than or equal 2. Again, to make life easy, we choose values of x that will make the radicand a perfect square. See Table 2. Figure 4 shows the graph of $f(x) = \sqrt{x - 2}$.

Table 2		
x	$f(x) = \sqrt{x - 2}$	(x, y) or $(x, f(x))$
2	$f(2) = 0$	$(2, 0)$
3	$f(3) = 1$	$(3, 1)$
6	$f(6) = 2$	$(6, 2)$
11	$f(11) = 3$	$(11, 3)$
18	$f(18) = 4$	$(18, 4)$

Figure 4

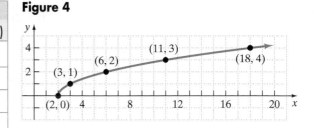

(c) From the graph of $f(x) = \sqrt{x - 2}$ given in Figure 4, we can see that the range of $f(x) = \sqrt{x - 2}$ is $[0, \infty)$.

Quick ✔

7. For the function $f(x) = \sqrt{x + 3}$,

(a) Find the domain.

(b) Graph the function using point plotting.

(c) Based on the graph, determine the range.

4 Graph Functions Involving Cube Roots

The **cube root function** is given by $f(x) = \sqrt[3]{x}$. The domain of the cube root function is $\{x | x \text{ is any real number}\}$ or using interval notation $(-\infty, \infty)$. We can obtain the graph of $f(x) = \sqrt[3]{x}$ by determining some ordered pairs (x, y) such that $y = \sqrt[3]{x}$. We then plot the ordered pairs in the xy-plane and connect the points. To make life easy, we choose values of x that are perfect cubes ($-8, -1, 0, 1, 8$, and so on). See Table 3. Figure 5 shows the graph of $f(x) = \sqrt[3]{x}$.

Table 3

x	$f(x) = \sqrt[3]{x}$	(x, y) or $(x, f(x))$
-8	$f(-8) = -2$	$(-8, -2)$
-1	$f(-1) = -1$	$(-1, -1)$
0	$f(0) = 0$	$(0, 0)$
1	$f(1) = 1$	$(1, 1)$
8	$f(8) = 2$	$(8, 2)$

Figure 5
$f(x) = \sqrt[3]{x}$

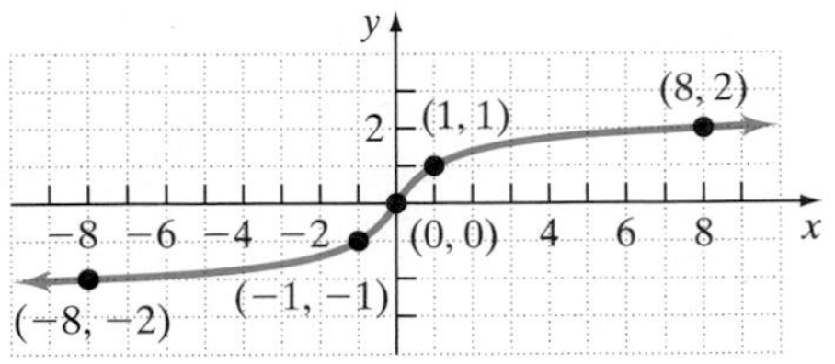

From the graph of $f(x) = \sqrt[3]{x}$ given in Figure 5, we can see that the range of $f(x) = \sqrt[3]{x}$ is $(-\infty, \infty)$.

The point-plotting method can be used to graph a variety of functions involving cube roots.

EXAMPLE 4   Graphing a Function Involving a Cube Root

For the function $g(x) = \sqrt[3]{x} + 2$,

(a) Find the domain.

(b) Graph the function using point plotting.

(c) Based on the graph, determine the range.

Solution

(a) The function $g(x) = \sqrt[3]{x} + 2$ tells us to take the cube root of x and then add 2. We can take the cube root of any real number, so the domain of g is $\{x \mid x \text{ is any real number}\}$ or the interval $(-\infty, \infty)$.

(b) We choose values of x that make the radicand a perfect cube. See Table 4. Figure 6 shows the graph of $g(x) = \sqrt[3]{x} + 2$.

Table 4

x	$g(x) = \sqrt[3]{x} + 2$	(x, y) or $(x, g(x))$
-8	$g(-8) = \sqrt[3]{-8} + 2 = 0$	$(-8, 0)$
-1	$g(-1) = 1$	$(-1, 1)$
0	$g(0) = 2$	$(0, 2)$
1	$g(1) = 3$	$(1, 3)$
8	$g(8) = 4$	$(8, 4)$

Figure 6

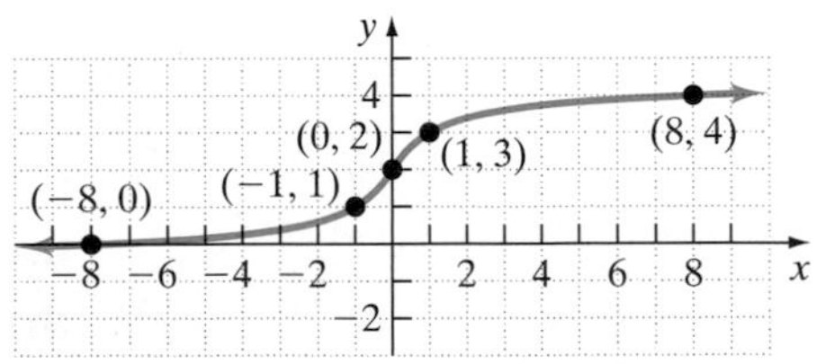

(c) From the graph of $g(x) = \sqrt[3]{x} + 2$ given in Figure 6 we can see that the range of $g(x) = \sqrt[3]{x} + 2$ is $(-\infty, \infty)$. ∎

Quick ✔

8. For the function $G(x) = \sqrt[3]{x} - 1$,

(a) Find the domain.

(b) Graph the function using point plotting.

(c) Based on the graph, determine the range.

6.6 EXERCISES

PRACTICE   WATCH   DOWNLOAD   READ   REVIEW

1–8. *are the* Quick ✔s *that follow each* EXAMPLE

Building Skills

In Problems 9–20, evaluate each radical function at the indicated values. See Objective 1.

9. $f(x) = \sqrt{x + 6}$
  (a) $f(3)$
  (b) $f(8)$
  (c) $f(-2)$

10. $f(x) = \sqrt{x + 10}$
  (a) $f(6)$
  (b) $f(2)$
  (c) $f(-6)$

11. $g(x) = -\sqrt{2x + 3}$
  (a) $g(11)$
  (b) $g(-1)$
  (c) $g\left(\dfrac{1}{8}\right)$

12. $g(x) = -\sqrt{4x + 5}$
  (a) $g(1)$
  (b) $g(10)$
  (c) $g\left(\dfrac{1}{8}\right)$

13. $G(m) = 2\sqrt{5m - 1}$
  (a) $G(1)$
  (b) $G(5)$
  (c) $G\left(\dfrac{1}{2}\right)$

14. $G(p) = 3\sqrt{4p + 1}$
  (a) $G(2)$
  (b) $G(11)$
  (c) $G\left(\dfrac{1}{8}\right)$

15. $H(z) = \sqrt[3]{z + 4}$
  (a) $H(4)$
  (b) $H(-12)$
  (c) $H(-20)$

16. $G(t) = \sqrt[3]{t - 6}$
  (a) $G(7)$
  (b) $G(-21)$
  (c) $G(22)$

17. $f(x) = \sqrt{\dfrac{x - 2}{x + 2}}$
  (a) $f(7)$
  (b) $f(6)$
  (c) $f(10)$

18. $f(x) = \sqrt{\dfrac{x - 4}{x + 4}}$
  (a) $f(5)$
  (b) $f(8)$
  (c) $f(12)$

19. $g(z) = \sqrt[3]{\dfrac{2z}{z - 4}}$
  (a) $g(-4)$
  (b) $g(8)$
  (c) $g(12)$

20. $H(z) = \sqrt[3]{\dfrac{3z}{z + 5}}$
  (a) $H(3)$
  (b) $H(4)$
  (c) $H(-1)$

In Problems 21–36, find the domain of the radical function. See Objective 2.

21. $f(x) = \sqrt{x - 7}$

22. $f(x) = \sqrt{x + 4}$

23. $g(x) = \sqrt{2x + 7}$

24. $g(x) = \sqrt{3x + 7}$

25. $F(x) = \sqrt{4 - 3x}$

26. $G(x) = \sqrt{5 - 2x}$

27. $H(z) = \sqrt[3]{2z + 1}$

28. $G(z) = \sqrt[3]{5z - 3}$

29. $W(p) = \sqrt[4]{7p - 2}$

30. $C(y) = \sqrt[4]{3y - 2}$

31. $g(x) = \sqrt[5]{x - 3}$

32. $g(x) = \sqrt[5]{x + 9}$

33. $f(x) = \sqrt{\dfrac{3}{x + 5}}$

34. $f(x) = \sqrt{\dfrac{3}{x - 3}}$

35. $H(x) = \sqrt{\dfrac{x + 3}{x - 3}}$

36. $H(x) = \sqrt{\dfrac{x - 5}{x}}$

In Problems 37–52, (a) determine the domain of the function; (b) graph the function using point plotting; and (c) based on the graph, determine the range of the function. See Objective 3.

37. $f(x) = \sqrt{x - 4}$

38. $f(x) = \sqrt{x - 1}$

39. $g(x) = \sqrt{x + 2}$

40. $g(x) = \sqrt{x + 5}$

41. $G(x) = \sqrt{2 - x}$

42. $F(x) = \sqrt{4 - x}$

43. $f(x) = \sqrt{x} + 3$

44. $f(x) = \sqrt{x} + 1$

45. $g(x) = \sqrt{x} - 4$

46. $g(x) = \sqrt{x} - 2$

47. $H(x) = 2\sqrt{x}$

48. $h(x) = 3\sqrt{x}$

49. $f(x) = \dfrac{1}{2}\sqrt{x}$

50. $g(x) = \dfrac{1}{4}\sqrt{x}$

51. $G(x) = -\sqrt{x}$

52. $F(x) = \sqrt{-x}$

In Problems 53–58, (a) determine the domain of the function;
(b) graph the function using point-plotting; and (c) based
on the graph, determine the range of the function. See
Objective 4.

53. $h(x) = \sqrt[3]{x} + 2$ **54.** $g(x) = \sqrt[3]{x} - 4$

55. $f(x) = \sqrt[3]{x} - 3$ **56.** $H(x) = \sqrt[3]{x} + 3$

57. $G(x) = 2\sqrt[3]{x}$ **58.** $F(x) = 3\sqrt[3]{x}$

Applying the Concepts

59. Distance to a Point on a Graph Suppose that
$P = (x, y)$ is a point on the graph of $y = x^2 - 4$. The
distance from P to $(0, 1)$ is given by the function

$$d(x) = \sqrt{x^4 - 9x^2 + 25}$$

See the figure.

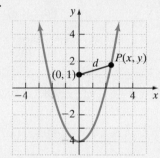

(a) What is the distance from $P = (0, -4)$ to $(0, 1)$?
That is, what is $d(0)$?

(b) What is the distance from $P = (1, -3)$ to $(0, 1)$?
That is, what is $d(1)$?

(c) What is the distance from $P = (5, 21)$ to $(0, 1)$?
That is, what is $d(5)$?

60. Distance to a Point on a Graph Suppose that
$P = (x, y)$ is a point on the graph of $y = x^2 - 2$. The
distance from P to $(0, 2)$ is given by the function

$$d(x) = \sqrt{x^4 - 7x^2 + 16}$$

See the figure.

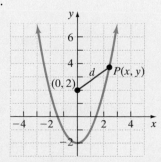

(a) What is the distance from $P = (0, -2)$ to $(0, 2)$?
That is, what is $d(0)$?

(b) What is the distance from $P = (1, -1)$ to $(0, 2)$?
That is, what is $d(1)$?

(c) What is the distance from $P = (4, 14)$ to $(0, 2)$?
That is, what is $d(4)$?

△**61. Area** A rectangle is inscribed in a semicircle of radius
3 as shown in the figure. Let $P = (x, y)$ be the point
in Quadrant I that is a vertex of the rectangle and is
on the circle.

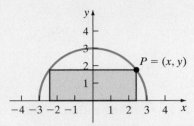

The area A of the rectangle as a function of x is
given by

$$A(x) = 2x\sqrt{9 - x^2}$$

(a) What is the area of the rectangle whose vertex is
at $\left(1, 2\sqrt{2}\right)$?

(b) What is the area of the rectangle whose vertex is
at $\left(2, \sqrt{5}\right)$?

(c) What is the area of the rectangle whose vertex is
at $\left(\sqrt{2}, \sqrt{7}\right)$?

△**62. Area** A rectangle is inscribed in a semicircle of radius
4 as shown in the figure. Let $P = (x, y)$ be the point
in Quadrant I that is a vertex of the rectangle and is
on the circle.

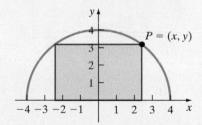

The area A of the rectangle as a function of x is
given by

$$A(x) = 2x\sqrt{16 - x^2}$$

(a) What is the area of the rectangle whose vertex is
at $\left(1, \sqrt{15}\right)$?

(b) What is the area of the rectangle whose vertex is
at $\left(2, 2\sqrt{3}\right)$?

(c) What is the area of the rectangle whose vertex is
at $\left(2\sqrt{2}, 2\sqrt{2}\right)$?

Extending the Concepts

63. Use the results of Problems 37–40 to make a generalization about how to obtain the graph of
$g(x) = \sqrt{x} + c$ from the graph of $f(x) = \sqrt{x}$.

64. Use the results of Problems 43–46 to make a generalization about how to obtain the graph of
$g(x) = \sqrt{x} + c$ from the graph of $f(x) = \sqrt{x}$.

Synthesis Review

In Problems 65–69, add each of the following.

65. $\dfrac{1}{3} + \dfrac{1}{2}$

66. $\dfrac{1}{5} + \dfrac{3}{4}$

67. $\dfrac{1}{x} + \dfrac{3}{x + 1}$

68. $\dfrac{5}{x - 3} + \dfrac{2}{x + 1}$

69. $\dfrac{4}{x - 1} + \dfrac{3}{x + 1}$

70. Explain how adding rational numbers that do not have denominators with any common factors is similar to adding rational expressions that do not have denominators with any common factors.

The Graphing Calculator

The graphing calculator can graph square root and cube root functions. The figure below shows the graph of $f(x) = \sqrt{x} - 2$ using a TI-84 Plus graphing calculator. Note how the graph shown only exists for $x \geq 2$. Graphing functions is useful in verifying the domain that we found algebraically.

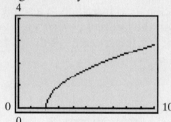

In Problems 71–92, graph the function using a graphing calculator. Compare the graphs obtained on the calculator to the hand-drawn graphs in Problems 37–58.

71. $f(x) = \sqrt{x - 4}$

72. $f(x) = \sqrt{x - 1}$

73. $g(x) = \sqrt{x + 2}$

74. $g(x) = \sqrt{x + 5}$

75. $G(x) = \sqrt{2 - x}$

76. $F(x) = \sqrt{4 - x}$

77. $f(x) = \sqrt{x} + 3$

78. $f(x) = \sqrt{x} + 1$

79. $g(x) = \sqrt{x} - 4$

80. $g(x) = \sqrt{x} - 2$

81. $H(x) = 2\sqrt{x}$

82. $h(x) = 3\sqrt{x}$

83. $f(x) = \dfrac{1}{2}\sqrt{x}$

84. $g(x) = \dfrac{1}{4}\sqrt{x}$

85. $G(x) = -\sqrt{x}$

86. $F(x) = \sqrt{-x}$

87. $h(x) = \sqrt[3]{x + 2}$

88. $g(x) = \sqrt[3]{x - 4}$

89. $f(x) = \sqrt[3]{x} - 3$

90. $H(x) = \sqrt[3]{x} + 3$

91. $G(x) = 2\sqrt[3]{x}$

92. $F(x) = 3\sqrt[3]{x}$

6.7 Radical Equations and Their Applications

OBJECTIVES

1. Solve Radical Equations Containing One Radical
2. Solve Radical Equations Containing Two Radicals
3. Solve for a Variable in a Radical Equation

Preparing for Radical Equations and Their Applications

Before getting started, take the following readiness quiz. If you get a problem wrong, go back to the section cited and review the material.

P1. Solve: $3x - 5 = 0$ [Section 1.1, pp. 49–51]

P2. Solve: $2p^2 + 4p - 6 = 0$ [Section 4.8, pp. 384–387]

P3. Simplify: $\left(\sqrt[3]{x - 5}\right)^3$ [Section 6.1, p. 481]

When the variable in an equation occurs in a radicand, the equation is called a **radical equation.** Examples of radical equations are

$$\sqrt{3x + 1} = 5 \qquad \sqrt[3]{x - 5} - 5 = 12 \qquad \sqrt{x - 2} - \sqrt{2x + 5} = 2$$

In this section, we are going to solve radical equations involving one or two radicals. We start with radical equations containing one radical.

Preparing for...Answers **P1.** $\left\{\dfrac{5}{3}\right\}$
P2. $\{-3, 1\}$ **P3.** $x - 5$

1 Solve Radical Equations Containing One Radical

Example 1 illustrates how to solve a radical equation.

EXAMPLE 1   How to Solve a Radical Equation Containing One Radical

Solve: $\sqrt{2x - 3} - 5 = 0$

Step-by-Step Solution

Step 1: Isolate the radical.	Add 5 to both sides:	$\sqrt{2x - 3} - 5 = 0$ $\sqrt{2x - 3} = 5$
Step 2: Raise both sides to the power of the index.	The index is 2, so we square both sides:	$\left(\sqrt{2x - 3}\right)^2 = 5^2$ $2x - 3 = 25$
Step 3: Solve the equation that results.	Add 3 to both sides: Divide both sides by 2:	$2x - 3 + 3 = 25 + 3$ $2x = 28$ $\dfrac{2x}{2} = \dfrac{28}{2}$ $x = 14$
Step 4: Check	Let $x = 14$ in the original equation:	$\sqrt{2x - 3} - 5 = 0$ $\sqrt{2 \cdot 14 - 3} - 5 \stackrel{?}{=} 0$ $\sqrt{28 - 3} - 5 \stackrel{?}{=} 0$ $5 - 5 = 0$ True

The solution set is $\{14\}$.   ■

Below we summarize the steps to solve a radical equation that contains a single radical.

> **SOLVING A RADICAL EQUATION CONTAINING ONE RADICAL**
>
> **Step 1:** Isolate the radical. That is, get the radical by itself on one side of the equation and everything else on the other side.
>
> **Step 2:** Raise both sides of the equation to the power of the index. This will eliminate the radical from the equation.
>
> **Step 3:** Solve the equation that results.
>
> **Step 4:** Check your answer. When solving radical equations containing an even index, apparent solutions that are not solutions to the original equation creep in. These solutions are called **extraneous solutions.**

Quick ✔

1. When the variable in an equation occurs in a radical, the equation is called a

   _____ _____ .

2. When an apparent solution is not a solution of the original equation, we say the apparent solution is an _____ solution.

3. *True or False:* The first step in solving $x + \sqrt{x - 3} = 5$ is to square both sides of the equations.

4. Solve: $\sqrt{3x + 1} - 4 = 0$

EXAMPLE 2 Solving a Radical Equation Containing One Radical

Solve:

(a) $\sqrt{3x + 10} + 2 = 4$ **(b)** $\sqrt{5x - 1} + 7 = 5$

Solution

(a)

$$\sqrt{3x + 10} + 2 = 4$$

Subtract 2 from both sides: $\sqrt{3x + 10} + 2 - 2 = 4 - 2$

$$\sqrt{3x + 10} = 2$$

The index is 2, so we square both sides: $\left(\sqrt{3x + 10}\right)^2 = 2^2$

$$3x + 10 = 4$$

Subtract 10 from both sides: $3x + 10 - 10 = 4 - 10$

$$3x = -6$$

Divide both sides by 3: $\dfrac{3x}{3} = \dfrac{-6}{3}$

$$x = -2$$

Work Smart

Just because the apparent solution is negative does not automatically make it extraneous. Determine if the apparent solution makes the radicand negative.

Check

$$\sqrt{3x + 10} + 2 = 4$$

Let $x = -2$ in the original equation: $\sqrt{3 \cdot (-2) + 10} + 2 \overset{?}{=} 4$

$$\sqrt{-6 + 10} + 2 \overset{?}{=} 4$$

$$\sqrt{4} + 2 \overset{?}{=} 4$$

$$2 + 2 \overset{?}{=} 4$$

$$4 = 4 \quad \text{True}$$

The solution set is $\{-2\}$.

(b)

$$\sqrt{5x - 1} + 7 = 5$$

Subtract 7 from both sides: $\sqrt{5x - 1} + 7 - 7 = 5 - 7$

$$\sqrt{5x - 1} = -2$$

The equation has no real solution because the principal square root of a number cannot be less than 0. Put another way, there is no real number whose square root is -2, so the equation has no real solution. The solution set is $\varnothing$ or $\{\ \}$. ∎

Quick ✔

5. Solve: $\sqrt{2x + 35} - 2 = 3$ **6.** Solve: $\sqrt{2x + 3} + 8 = 6$

EXAMPLE 3 Solving a Radical Equation Containing One Radical

Solve: $\sqrt{x + 5} = x - 1$

Solution

Work Smart

$(x - 1)^2 = x^2 - 2x + 1$

Do not write

$(x - 1)^2 = x^2 + 1$

$$\sqrt{x + 5} = x - 1$$

The index is 2, so we square both sides: $\left(\sqrt{x + 5}\right)^2 = (x - 1)^2$

$$x + 5 = x^2 - 2x + 1$$

Subtract x and 5 from both sides: $x + 5 - x - 5 = x^2 - 2x + 1 - x - 5$

$$0 = x^2 - 3x - 4$$

Factor: $0 = (x - 4)(x + 1)$

Zero-Product Property: $x - 4 = 0$ or $x + 1 = 0$

$$x = 4 \text{ or} \qquad x = -1$$

Check
$$\sqrt{x + 5} = x - 1$$

$x = 4$: $\sqrt{4 + 5} \overset{?}{=} 4 - 1$ $x = -1$: $\sqrt{-1 + 5} \overset{?}{=} -1 - 1$

$\sqrt{9} \overset{?}{=} 3$ $\sqrt{4} \overset{?}{=} -2$

$3 = 3$ True $2 = -2$ False

The apparent solution $x = -1$ does not check, so it is an extraneous solution. The solution set is $\{4\}$.

Quick ✔

7. Solve: $\sqrt{2x + 1} = x - 1$

EXAMPLE 4   Solving a Radical Equation Containing One Radical

Solve: $\sqrt[3]{3x - 12} + 4 = 1$

Solution

$$\sqrt[3]{3x - 12} + 4 = 1$$

Subtract 4 from both sides: $\sqrt[3]{3x - 12} + 4 - 4 = 1 - 4$

$$\sqrt[3]{3x - 12} = -3$$

The index is 3, so we cube both sides: $\left(\sqrt[3]{3x - 12}\right)^3 = (-3)^3$

$$3x - 12 = -27$$

Add 12 to both sides: $3x - 12 + 12 = -27 + 12$

$$3x = -15$$

Divide both sides by 3: $x = -5$

Check

$$\sqrt[3]{3x - 12} + 4 = 1$$

Let $x = -5$ in the original equation: $\sqrt[3]{3 \cdot (-5) - 12} + 4 \overset{?}{=} 1$

$$\sqrt[3]{-15 - 12} + 4 \overset{?}{=} 1$$

$$\sqrt[3]{-27} + 4 \overset{?}{=} 1$$

$$-3 + 4 \overset{?}{=} 1$$

$$1 = 1 \qquad\qquad \text{True}$$

The solution set is $\{-5\}$.

Quick ✔

8. Solve: $\sqrt[3]{3x + 1} - 4 = -6$

Sometimes, rather than an equation containing radicals, it will contain rational exponents. When solving these problems, we can rewrite the equation with a radical or we use the fact that $(a^r)^s = a^{r \cdot s}$.

EXAMPLE 5   Solving an Equation Containing a Rational Exponent

Solve: $(5x - 1)^{\frac{1}{2}} + 3 = 10$

Solution

$$(5x - 1)^{\frac{1}{2}} + 3 = 10$$

Subtract 3 from both sides: $(5x - 1)^{\frac{1}{2}} = 7$

Square both sides: $\left((5x - 1)^{\frac{1}{2}}\right)^2 = 7^2$

Use $(a^r)^s = a^{r \cdot s}$: $(5x - 1)^{\frac{1}{2} \cdot 2} = 49$

$$5x - 1 = 49$$

Add 1 to both sides: $5x = 50$

Divide both sides by 5: $x = 10$

Check

$$(5x - 1)^{\frac{1}{2}} + 3 = 10$$

Let $x = 10$ in the original equation: $(5 \cdot 10 - 1)^{\frac{1}{2}} + 3 \stackrel{?}{=} 10$

$$(49)^{\frac{1}{2}} + 3 \stackrel{?}{=} 10$$

$$7 + 3 = 10$$

$$10 = 10 \quad \text{True}$$

The solution set is $\{10\}$.

> **Quick ✔**
>
> **9.** Solve: $(2x - 3)^{\frac{1}{3}} - 7 = -4$

⌐2 Solve Radical Equations Containing Two Radicals

Example 6 illustrates how to solve a radical equation containing two radicals.

⌐EXAMPLE 6 How to Solve a Radical Equation Containing Two Radicals

Solve: $\sqrt[3]{p^2 - 4p - 4} = \sqrt[3]{-3p + 2}$

Step-by-Step-Solution

Step 1: Isolate one of the radicals.	The radical on the left side of the equation is isolated: $\sqrt[3]{p^2 - 4p - 4} = \sqrt[3]{-3p + 2}$
Step 2: Raise both sides to the power of the index.	The index is 3, so we cube both sides: $\left(\sqrt[3]{p^2 - 4p - 4}\right)^3 = \left(\sqrt[3]{-3p + 2}\right)^3$ $p^2 - 4p - 4 = -3p + 2$
Step 3: Because there is no radical, we solve the equation that results.	Add $3p$ to both sides; subtract 2 from both sides: $p^2 - 4p - 4 + 3p - 2 = -3p + 2 + 3p - 2$ Combine like terms: $p^2 - p - 6 = 0$ Factor: $(p - 3)(p + 2) = 0$ Zero-Product Property: $p - 3 = 0 \quad \text{or} \quad p + 2 = 0$ $p = 3 \quad \text{or} \quad p = -2$
Step 4: Check	$\sqrt[3]{p^2 - 4p - 4} = \sqrt[3]{-3p + 2}$ $p = -2$: $\sqrt[3]{(-2)^2 - 4(-2) - 4} \stackrel{?}{=} \sqrt[3]{-3(-2) + 2}$ $\sqrt[3]{4 + 8 - 4} \stackrel{?}{=} \sqrt[3]{6 + 2}$ $\sqrt[3]{8} = \sqrt[3]{8} \quad \text{True}$ $p = 3$: $\sqrt[3]{(3)^2 - 4(3) - 4} \stackrel{?}{=} \sqrt[3]{-3(3) + 2}$ $\sqrt[3]{9 - 12 - 4} \stackrel{?}{=} \sqrt[3]{-9 + 2}$ $\sqrt[3]{-7} = \sqrt[3]{-7} \quad \text{True}$

Both apparent solutions check. The solution set is $\{-2, 3\}$.

When a radical equation contains two radicals, the following steps should be used to solve the equation for the variable.

> **SOLVING A RADICAL EQUATION CONTAINING TWO RADICALS**
>
> **Step 1:** Isolate one of the radicals. That is, get one of the radicals by itself on one side of the equation and everything else on the other side.
>
> **Step 2:** Raise both sides of the equation to the power of the index. This will eliminate one radical or both radicals from the equation.
>
> **Step 3:** If a radical remains in the equation, then follow the steps for solving a radical equation containing one radical. Otherwise, solve the equation that results.
>
> **Step 4:** Check your answer. When solving radical equations, apparent solutions that, in fact, are not solutions to the original equation may creep in. Remember, these solutions are called extraneous solutions.

Quick ✔

10. Solve: $\sqrt[3]{m^2 + 4m + 4} = \sqrt[3]{2m + 7}$

|EXAMPLE 7 Solving a Radical Equation Containing Two Radicals

Solve: $\sqrt{3x + 6} - \sqrt{x + 6} = 2$

Solution

$$\sqrt{3x + 6} - \sqrt{x + 6} = 2$$

Add $\sqrt{x + 6}$ to both sides: $\sqrt{3x + 6} = 2 + \sqrt{x + 6}$

Square both sides: $\left(\sqrt{3x + 6}\right)^2 = \left(2 + \sqrt{x + 6}\right)^2$

Use $(A + B)^2 = A^2 + 2AB + B^2$: $3x + 6 = 4 + 4\sqrt{x + 6} + \left(\sqrt{x + 6}\right)^2$

$\left(\sqrt{x + 6}\right)^2 = x + 6$: $3x + 6 = 4 + 4\sqrt{x + 6} + x + 6$

Isolate the radical: $2x - 4 = 4\sqrt{x + 6}$

Factor out 2: $2(x - 2) = 4\sqrt{x + 6}$

Divide both sides by 2: $x - 2 = 2\sqrt{x + 6}$

Square both sides: $(x - 2)^2 = \left(2\sqrt{x + 6}\right)^2$

$$x^2 - 4x + 4 = 4(x + 6)$$

Distribute: $x^2 - 4x + 4 = 4x + 24$

Subtract 4x and 24 from both sides: $x^2 - 8x - 20 = 0$

Factor: $(x - 10)(x + 2) = 0$

Zero-Product Property: $x - 10 = 0 \quad \text{or} \quad x + 2 = 0$

$$x = 10 \quad \text{or} \qquad x = -2$$

Work Smart

When there is more than one radical, it is best to isolate the radical with the more complicated radicand.

Work Smart

$(2 + \sqrt{x + 6})^2 \neq 2^2 + (\sqrt{x + 6})^2$

Remember,

$(A + B)^2 = (A + B)(A + B)$
$\qquad\quad = A^2 + 2AB + B^2$

Check $x = -2$: $\sqrt{3 \cdot (-2) + 6} - \sqrt{-2 + 6} \overset{?}{=} 2$ $x = 10$: $\sqrt{3 \cdot 10 + 6} - \sqrt{10 + 6} \overset{?}{=} 2$

$\sqrt{0} - \sqrt{4} \overset{?}{=} 2$ $\sqrt{36} - \sqrt{16} \overset{?}{=} 2$

$0 - 2 \overset{?}{=} 2$ $6 - 4 \overset{?}{=} 2$

$-2 = 2 \quad \text{False}$ $2 = 2 \quad \text{True}$

The apparent solution $x = -2$ does not check, so it is an extraneous solution. The solution set is $\{10\}$. ∎

Quick ✔

11. Solve: $\sqrt{2x + 1} - \sqrt{x + 4} = 1$

⌈3⌉ Solve for a Variable in a Radical Equation

In many situations, you will be required to solve for a variable in a formula. For instance, in Example 8, we are assessing how much error there is in an estimate based upon a statistical study. This commonly used formula from statistics contains a radical.

⌈EXAMPLE 8⌉ Solving for a Variable

A formula from statistics for finding the margin of error in estimating a population mean is given by

$$E = z \cdot \frac{\sigma}{\sqrt{n}}$$

where E represents the margin of error, σ represents a measure of variability, and z is a measure of relative position.

    (a) Solve this equation for n, the sample size.

    (b) Find n when $\sigma = 12$, $z = 2$, and $E = 3$.

Solution

In Words
The symbol σ is pronounced "sigma."

(a)
$$E = z \cdot \frac{\sigma}{\sqrt{n}}$$

Multiply both sides by $\sqrt{n}$: $\sqrt{n} \cdot E = z\sigma$

Divide both sides by E: $\sqrt{n} = \dfrac{z\sigma}{E}$

Square both sides: $n = \left(\dfrac{z\sigma}{E}\right)^2$

(b) $n = \left(\dfrac{z\sigma}{E}\right)^2 = \left(\dfrac{2 \cdot 12}{3}\right)^2$

$$= 64$$

We need the sample size to be $n = 64$ for E to equal 3.   ■

Quick ✔

12. The period of a pendulum is the time it takes to complete one trip back and forth. The period T, in seconds, of a pendulum of length L, in feet, may be approximated using the formula $T = 2\pi\sqrt{\dfrac{L}{32}}$.

    (a) Solve the equation for L.

    (b) Determine the length of a pendulum whose period is 2π seconds.

6.7 EXERCISES

PRACTICE   WATCH   DOWNLOAD   READ   REVIEW

1–12. *are the* Quick ✔s *that follow each* EXAMPLE

Building Skills

In Problems 13–44, solve each equation. See Objective 1.

13. $\sqrt{x} = 4$ **14.** $\sqrt{p} = 6$

15. $\sqrt{x - 3} = 2$ **16.** $\sqrt{y - 5} = 3$

17. $\sqrt{2t + 3} = 5$ **18.** $\sqrt{3w - 2} = 4$

◉**19.** $\sqrt{4x + 3} = -2$ **20.** $\sqrt{6p - 5} = -5$

21. $\sqrt[3]{4t} = 2$ **22.** $\sqrt[3]{9w} = 3$

23. $\sqrt[3]{5q + 4} = 4$ **24.** $\sqrt[3]{7m + 20} = 5$

25. $\sqrt{y} + 3 = 8$ **26.** $\sqrt{q} - 5 = 2$

27. $\sqrt{x + 5} - 3 = 1$ **28.** $\sqrt{x - 4} + 4 = 7$

29. $\sqrt{2x + 9} + 5 = 6$ **30.** $\sqrt{4x + 21} + 2 = 5$

31. $3\sqrt{x} + 5 = 8$ **32.** $4\sqrt{t} - 2 = 10$

33. $\sqrt{4 - x} - 3 = 0$ **34.** $\sqrt{6 - w} - 3 = 1$

35. $\sqrt{p} = 2p$

36. $\sqrt{q} = 3q$

37. $\sqrt{x + 6} = x$

38. $\sqrt{2p + 8} = p$

39. $\sqrt{w} = 6 - w$

40. $\sqrt{m} = 12 - m$

41. $\sqrt{17 - 2x} + 1 = x$

42. $\sqrt{1 - 4x} - 5 = x$

43. $\sqrt{w^2 - 11} + 5 = w + 4$

44. $\sqrt{z^2 - z - 7} + 3 = z + 2$

In Problems 45–58, solve each equation. See Objective 2.

45. $\sqrt{x + 9} = \sqrt{2x + 5}$

46. $\sqrt{3x + 1} = \sqrt{2x + 7}$

47. $\sqrt[3]{4x - 3} = \sqrt[3]{2x - 9}$

48. $\sqrt[3]{3y - 2} = \sqrt[3]{5y + 8}$

49. $\sqrt{2w^2 - 3w - 4} = \sqrt{w^2 + 6w + 6}$

50. $\sqrt{2x^2 + 7x - 10} = \sqrt{x^2 + 4x + 8}$

51. $\sqrt{3w + 4} = 2 + \sqrt{w}$

52. $\sqrt{3y - 2} = 2 + \sqrt{y}$

53. $\sqrt{x + 1} - \sqrt{x - 2} = 1$

54. $\sqrt{2x - 1} - \sqrt{x - 1} = 1$

55. $\sqrt{2x + 6} - \sqrt{x - 1} = 2$

56. $\sqrt{2x + 6} - \sqrt{x - 6} = 3$

57. $\sqrt{2x + 5} - \sqrt{x - 1} = 2$

58. $\sqrt{4x + 1} - \sqrt{2x + 1} = 2$

In Problems 59–64, solve each equation.

59. $(2x + 3)^{\frac{1}{2}} = 3$

60. $(4x + 1)^{\frac{1}{2}} = 5$

61. $(6x - 1)^{\frac{1}{4}} = (2x + 15)^{\frac{1}{4}}$

62. $(6p + 3)^{\frac{1}{5}} = (4p - 9)^{\frac{1}{5}}$

63. $(x + 3)^{\frac{1}{2}} - (x - 5)^{\frac{1}{2}} = 2$

64. $(3x + 1)^{\frac{1}{2}} - (x - 1)^{\frac{1}{2}} = 2$

For Problems 65–70, see Objective 3.

65. Finance Solve $A = P\sqrt{1 + r}$ for r.

66. Centripetal Acceleration Solve $v = \sqrt{ar}$ for a.

67. Volume of a Sphere Solve $r = \sqrt[3]{\dfrac{3V}{4\pi}}$ for V.

68. Surface Area of a Sphere Solve $r = \sqrt{\dfrac{S}{4\pi}}$ for S.

69. Coulomb's Law Solve $r = \sqrt{\dfrac{4F\pi\varepsilon_0}{q_1 q_2}}$ for F.

70. Potential Energy Solve $V = \sqrt{\dfrac{2U}{C}}$ for U.

Mixed Practice

In Problems 71–86, solve each equation.

71. $\sqrt{5p - 3} + 7 = 3$

72. $\sqrt{3b - 2} + 8 = 5$

73. $\sqrt{x + 12} = x$

74. $\sqrt{x + 20} = x$

75. $\sqrt{2p + 12} = 4$

76. $\sqrt{3a - 5} = 2$

77. $\sqrt[4]{x + 7} = 2$

78. $\sqrt[5]{x + 23} = 2$

79. $(3x + 1)^{\frac{1}{3}} + 2 = 0$

80. $(5x - 2)^{\frac{1}{3}} + 3 = 0$

81. $\sqrt{10 - x} - x = 10$

82. $\sqrt{9 - x} - x = 11$

83. $\sqrt{2x + 5} = \sqrt{3x - 4}$

84. $\sqrt{4c - 5} = \sqrt{3c + 1}$

85. $\sqrt{x - 1} + \sqrt{x + 4} = 5$

86. $\sqrt{x - 3} + \sqrt{x + 4} = 7$

87. Solve $\sqrt{x^2} = x + 4$ using the techniques of this section. Now solve $\sqrt{x^2} = x + 4$ using the fact that $\sqrt{x^2} = |x|$. Which approach do you like better?

88. Solve $\sqrt{p^2} = 3p + 4$ using the techniques of this section. Now solve $\sqrt{p^2} = 3p + 4$ using the fact that $\sqrt{p^2} = |p|$. Which approach do you like better?

89. Suppose that $f(x) = \sqrt{x - 2}$.

  (a) Solve $f(x) = 0$. What point is on the graph of f?
  (b) Solve $f(x) = 1$. What point is on the graph of f?
  (c) Solve $f(x) = 2$. What point is on the graph of f?
  (d) Use the information obtained in parts **(a)–(c)** to graph $f(x) = \sqrt{x - 2}$.
  (e) Use the graph and the concept of the range of a function to explain why the equation $f(x) = -1$ has no solution.

90. Suppose that $g(x) = \sqrt{x + 3}$.

  (a) Solve $g(x) = 0$. What point is on the graph of g?
  (b) Solve $g(x) = 1$. What point is on the graph of g?
  (c) Solve $g(x) = 2$. What point is on the graph of g?
  (d) Use the information obtained in parts **(a)–(c)** to graph $g(x) = \sqrt{x + 3}$.
  (e) Use the graph and the concept of the range of a function to explain why the equation $g(x) = -1$ has no solution.

Applying the Concepts

△**91. Finding a y-Coordinate** The solutions to the equation

$$\sqrt{4^2 + (y - 2)^2} = 5$$

represent the y-coordinates such that the distance from the point $(3, 2)$ to $(-1, y)$ in the Cartesian plane is 5 units.

  (a) Solve the equation for y.
  (b) Plot the points in the Cartesian plane and label the lengths of the sides of the figure formed.

△ **92. Finding an x-Coordinate** The solutions to the equation

$$\sqrt{x^2 + 4^2} = 5$$

represent the x-coordinates such that the distance from the point $(0, 3)$ to $(x, -1)$ in the Cartesian plane is 5 units.

(a) Solve the equation for x.

(b) Plot the points in the Cartesian plane and label the lengths of the sides of the figure formed.

93. Revenue Growth Suppose that the annual revenue R (in millions of dollars) of a company after t years of operating is modeled by the function

$$R(t) = \sqrt[3]{\frac{t}{2}}$$

(a) After how many years can the company expect to have annual revenue of $1 million?

(b) After how many years can the company expect to have annual revenue of $2 million?

△ **94. Sphere** The radius r of a sphere whose volume is V is given by

$$r = \sqrt[3]{\frac{3V}{4\pi}}$$

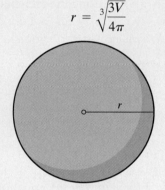

(a) Find the volume of a sphere whose radius is 3 meters.

(b) Find the volume of a sphere whose radius is 2 meters.

95. Birth Rates A plural birth is a live birth to twins, triplets, and so forth. The function $R(t) = 26 \cdot \sqrt[10]{t}$ models the plural birth rate R (live births per 1,000 live births), where t is the number of years since 1995.

(a) Use the model to predict the year in which the plural birth rate will be 39.

(b) Use the model to predict the year in which the plural birth rate will be 36.

96. Money The annual rate of interest r (expressed as a decimal) required to have A dollars after t years from an initial deposit of P dollars is given by

$$r = \sqrt[t]{\frac{A}{P}} - 1$$

(a) Suppose that you deposit $1,000 in an account that pays 5% annual interest so that $r = 0.05$. How much will you have after $t = 2$ years?

(b) Suppose that you deposit $1,000 in an account that pays 5% annual interest so that $r = 0.05$. How much will you have after $t = 3$ years?

Extending the Concepts

97. Solve: $\sqrt{3\sqrt{x + 1}} = \sqrt{2x + 3}$

98. Solve: $\sqrt[3]{2\sqrt{x - 2}} = \sqrt[3]{x - 1}$

Explaining the Concepts

99. Why is it always necessary to check solutions when solving radical equations?

100. How can you tell by inspection that the equation $\sqrt{x - 2} + 5 = 0$ will have no real solution?

101. Using the concept of domain explain why radical equations with an even index may have extraneous solutions, but radical equations with an odd index will not have extraneous solutions.

102. Which step in the process of solving a radical equation leads to the possibility of extraneous solutions?

Synthesis Review

In Problems 103–106, identify which of the numbers in the set

$$\left\{0, -4, 12, \frac{2}{3}, 1.\overline{56}, \sqrt{2^3}, \pi, \sqrt{-5}, \sqrt[3]{-4}\right\}$$

are ...

103. Integers

104. Rational numbers

105. Irrational numbers

106. Real numbers

107. State the difference between a rational number and an irrational number. Why is $\sqrt{-1}$ not real?

The Graphing Calculator

A graphing calculator can be used to verify solutions obtained algebraically. To solve $\sqrt{2x - 3} = 5$ presented in Example 1, we graph $Y_1 = \sqrt{2x - 3}$ and $Y_2 = 5$ and determine the x-coordinate of the point of intersection.

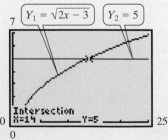

The x-coordinate of the point of intersection is 14, so the solution set is $\{14\}$.

108. Verify your solution to Problem 17 by graphing $Y_1 = \sqrt{2x + 3}$ and $Y_2 = 5$ and then finding the x-coordinate of their point of intersection.

109. Verify your solution to Problem 18 by graphing $Y_1 = \sqrt{3x - 2}$ and $Y_2 = 4$ and then finding the x-coordinate of their point of intersection.

110. When you solved Problem 19 algebraically, you should have determined that the equation has <u>no real</u> solution. Verify this result by graphing $Y_1 = \sqrt{4x + 3}$ and $Y_2 = -2$. Explain what the algebraic solution means graphically.

111. When you solved Problem 20 algebraically, you should have determined that the equation has <u>no real</u> solution. Verify this result by graphing $Y_1 = \sqrt{6x - 5}$ and $Y_2 = -5$. Explain what the algebraic solution means graphically.

6.8 The Complex Number System

OBJECTIVES

1. Evaluate the Square Root of Negative Real Numbers
2. Add or Subtract Complex Numbers
3. Multiply Complex Numbers
4. Divide Complex Numbers
5. Evaluate the Powers of i

Preparing for The Complex Number System

Before getting started, take the following readiness quiz. If you get a problem wrong, go back to the section cited and review the material.

P1. List the numbers in the set $\left\{ 8, -\dfrac{1}{3}, -23, 0, \sqrt{2}, 1.\overline{26}, -\dfrac{12}{3}, \sqrt{-5} \right\}$ that are

    (a) Natural numbers   **(b)** Whole numbers

    (c) Integers   **(d)** Rational numbers

    (e) Irrational numbers   **(f)** Real numbers   [Section R.2, pp. 11–14]

P2. Distribute: $3x(4x - 3)$ [Section 4.2, p. 333]

P3. Multiply: $(z + 4)(3z - 2)$ [Section 4.2, pp. 333–334]

P4. Multiply: $(2y + 5)(2y - 5)$ [Section 4.2, pp. 335–336]

If you look back at Section R.2, where we introduced the various number systems, you should notice that each time we encounter a situation where a number system can't handle a problem, we expand the number system. For example, if we only considered the whole numbers, we could not describe a negative balance in a checking account, so we introduced integers. If the world could only be described by integers, then we could not talk about parts of a whole as in ½ a pizza or ¾ of a dollar, so we introduced rational numbers. If we only considered rational numbers, then we wouldn't be able to find a number whose square is 2, so we introduced the irrational numbers, so that $\left(\sqrt{2} \right)^2 = 2$. By combining the rational numbers with the irrational numbers, we created the real number system. The real number system is usually sufficient for solving most problems in mathematics, but not for all problems.

For example, suppose we wanted to determine a number whose square is -1. We know that when we square any real number, the result is never negative. We call this property of real numbers, the *Nonnegativity Property*.

NONNEGATIVITY PROPERTY OF REAL NUMBERS

For any real number a, $a^2 \geq 0$.

Because the square of any real number is never negative, there is no real number x for which

$$x^2 = -1$$

To remedy this situation, we introduce a new number.

DEFINITION

The **imaginary unit,** denoted by i, is the number whose square is -1. That is,

$$i^2 = -1$$

If we take the square root of both sides of $i^2 = -1$, we find that

$$i = \sqrt{-1}$$

In looking at the development of the real number system, each new number system contained the earlier number system as a subset. By introducing the number i, we now have a new number system called the **complex number system.**

Preparing for...Answers **P1. (a)** 8
(b) $8, 0$ **(c)** $8, -23, 0, -12/3$
(d) $8, -1/3, -23, 0, 1.\overline{26}, -12/3$
(e) $\sqrt{2}$
(f) $8, -\dfrac{1}{3}, -23, 0, \sqrt{2}, 1.\overline{26}, -\dfrac{12}{3}$
P2. $12x^2 - 9x$ **P3.** $3z^2 + 10z - 8$
P4. $4y^2 - 25$

DEFINITION

Complex numbers are numbers of the form $a + bi$, where a and b are real numbers. The real number a is called the **real part** of the number $a + bi$; the real number b is called the **imaginary part** of $a + bi$.

In Words

The real number system is a subset of the complex number system. This means that all real numbers are, more generally, complex numbers.

For example, the complex number $6 + 2i$ has the real part 6 and the imaginary part 2. The complex number $4 - 3i = 4 + (-3)i$ has the real part 4 and the imaginary part -3.

When a complex number is written in the form $a + bi$, where a and b are real numbers, we say that it is in **standard form.** The complex number $a + 0i$ is typically written as a. This serves as a reminder that the real number system is a subset of the complex number system. The complex number $0 + bi$ is usually written as bi. Any number of the form bi is called a **pure imaginary number.** Figure 7 shows the relation between the number systems.

Figure 7
The Complex Number System

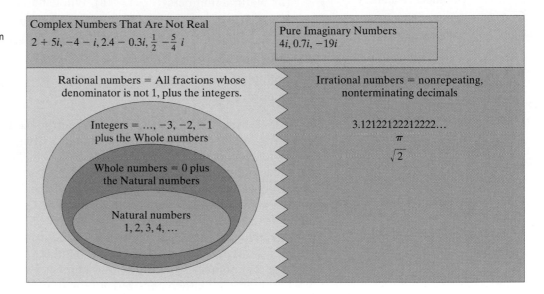

1 Evaluate the Square Root of Negative Real Numbers

First, we define square roots of negative numbers.

DEFINITION SQUARE ROOTS OF NEGATIVE NUMBERS

If N is a positive real number, we define the **principal square root of $-N$,** denoted by $\sqrt{-N}$, as

$$\sqrt{-N} = \sqrt{N}i$$

where $i = \sqrt{-1}$.

EXAMPLE 1 Evaluating the Square Root of a Negative Number

Write each of the following as a pure imaginary number.

(a) $\sqrt{-16}$ (b) $\sqrt{-3}$ (c) $\sqrt{-18}$

Work Smart

When writing complex numbers whose imaginary part is a radical as in $\sqrt{3}i$ be sure that the "i" is not written under the radical.

Solution

(a) $\sqrt{-16} = \sqrt{16}i$
$\qquad\quad\ = 4i$

(b) $\sqrt{-3} = \sqrt{3}i$

(c) $\sqrt{-18} = \sqrt{18}i$
$\qquad\quad\ = 3\sqrt{2}i$ ∎

Quick ✔

1. The _____ ___, denoted by i, is the number whose square is -1.
2. Any number of the form bi is called a ____ _____ _____.
3. If N is a positive real number, we define the principal square root of $-N$, denoted by $\sqrt{-N}$, as $\sqrt{-N} =$ ___.
4. *True or False:* All real numbers are complex numbers.

In Problems 5–7, write each radical as a pure imaginary number.

5. $\sqrt{-36}$ 6. $\sqrt{-5}$ 7. $\sqrt{-12}$

EXAMPLE 2 Writing Complex Numbers in Standard Form

Write each of the following in standard form.

(a) $2 - \sqrt{-25}$ (b) $3 + \sqrt{-50}$ (c) $\dfrac{4 - \sqrt{-12}}{2}$

Solution

The standard form of a complex number is $a + bi$.

(a)
$$2 - \sqrt{-25} = 2 - \sqrt{25}i$$
$$= 2 - 5i$$

(b)
$$3 + \sqrt{-50} = 3 + \sqrt{50}i$$
$\sqrt{50} - \sqrt{25} \cdot \sqrt{2} = 5\sqrt{2}:$ $= 3 + 5\sqrt{2}i$

(c)
$$\frac{4 - \sqrt{-12}}{2} = \frac{4 - \sqrt{12}i}{2}$$
$\sqrt{12} = \sqrt{4} \cdot \sqrt{3} = 2\sqrt{3}:$ $= \dfrac{4 - 2\sqrt{3}i}{2}$

Factor out 2: $= \dfrac{2\left(2 - \sqrt{3}i\right)}{2}$

Divide out the 2's: $= 2 - \sqrt{3}i$ ∎

Quick ✔ *In Problems 8–10, write each expression in the standard form of a complex number, $a + bi$.*

8. $4 + \sqrt{-100}$ 9. $-2 - \sqrt{-8}$ 10. $\dfrac{6 - \sqrt{-72}}{3}$

2 Add or Subtract Complex Numbers

Throughout your math career, whenever you were introduced to a new number system, you learned how to perform the four binary operations of addition, subtraction, multiplication, and division using this number system. Therefore, we will now show how to add and subtract complex numbers. Then we will discuss multiplying and dividing complex numbers.

Two complex numbers are added by adding the real parts and then adding the imaginary parts.

SUM OF COMPLEX NUMBERS

$$(a + bi) + (c + di) = (a + c) + (b + d)i$$

In Words
To add two complex numbers, add the real parts, then add the imaginary parts. To subtract two complex numbers, subtract the real parts, then subtract the imaginary parts.

To subtract two complex numbers, we use this rule:

DIFFERENCE OF COMPLEX NUMBERS

$$(a + bi) - (c + di) = (a - c) + (b - d)i$$

EXAMPLE 3 Adding Complex Numbers

Add:

  (a) $(4 - 3i) + (-2 + 5i)$

  (b) $(4 + \sqrt{-25}) + (6 - \sqrt{-16})$

Solution

Work Smart
Adding or subtracting complex numbers is just like combining like terms. For example,
$(4 - 3x) + (-2 + 5x)$
$= 4 + (-2) - 3x + 5x$
$= 2 + 2x$
so
$(4 - 3i) + (-2 + 5i)$
$= 4 + (-2) - 3i + 5i$
$= 2 + 2i$

  (a) $(4 - 3i) + (-2 + 5i) = [4 + (-2)] + (-3 + 5)i$

$$= 2 + 2i$$

$$\sqrt{-25} = 5i; \quad \sqrt{-16} = 4i$$
$$\downarrow \qquad\qquad \downarrow$$

  (b) $(4 + \sqrt{-25}) + (6 - \sqrt{-16}) = (4 + 5i) + (6 - 4i)$

$$= (4 + 6) + (5 - 4)i$$

$$= 10 + 1i$$

$$= 10 + i \qquad \blacksquare$$

EXAMPLE 4 Subtracting Complex Numbers

Subtract:

  (a) $(-3 + 7i) - (5 - 4i)$ (b) $(3 + \sqrt{-12}) - (-2 - \sqrt{-27})$

Solution

  (a) $(-3 + 7i) - (5 - 4i) = (-3 - 5) + (7 - (-4))i$

$$= -8 + 11i$$

$$\sqrt{-12} = 2\sqrt{3}i; \quad \sqrt{-27} = 3\sqrt{3}i$$
$$\downarrow \qquad\qquad \downarrow$$

  (b) $(3 + \sqrt{-12}) - (-2 - \sqrt{-27}) = (3 + 2\sqrt{3}i) - (-2 - 3\sqrt{3}i)$

Distribute the minus: $= 3 + 2\sqrt{3}i + 2 + 3\sqrt{3}i$

$$= [3 + 2] + [2\sqrt{3} + 3\sqrt{3}]i$$

$$= 5 + 5\sqrt{3}i \qquad \blacksquare$$

Quick ✔ *In Problems 11–13, add or subtract as indicated.*

11. $(4 + 6i) + (-3 + 5i)$ **12.** $(4 - 2i) - (-2 + 7i)$

13. $(4 - \sqrt{-4}) + (-7 + \sqrt{-9})$

3 Multiply Complex Numbers

We multiply complex numbers using the Distributive Property. The methods are almost the same methods that we used to multiply polynomials.

EXAMPLE 5 Multiplying Complex Numbers

Multiply:

(a) $4i(3 - 6i)$ (b) $(-2 + 4i)(3 - i)$

Solution

(a) We distribute the $4i$ to each term in the parentheses.

$$4i(3 - 6i) = 4i \cdot 3 - 4i \cdot 6i$$
$$= 12i - 24i^2$$
$$i^2 = -1: \quad = 12i - 24 \cdot (-1)$$
$$= 24 + 12i$$

(b)
$$(-2 + 4i)(3 - i) = -2 \cdot 3 - 2 \cdot (-i) + 4i \cdot 3 + 4i \cdot (-i)$$
$$= -6 + 2i + 12i - 4i^2$$
$$\text{Combine like terms; } i^2 = -1: \quad = -6 + 14i - 4(-1)$$
$$= -6 + 14i + 4$$
$$= -2 + 14i$$

Quick ✔ *In Problems 14 and 15, multiply.*

14. $3i(5 - 4i)$ **15.** $(-2 + 5i)(4 - 2i)$

Look back at the Product Property for Radicals on page 493. You should notice that the property only applies when $\sqrt[n]{a}$ and $\sqrt[n]{b}$ are real numbers. This means that

$$\sqrt{a} \cdot \sqrt{b} \neq \sqrt{ab} \quad \text{if } a < 0 \text{ and } b < 0$$

So how do we perform this multiplication? Well, we first need to write the radical as a complex number using the fact that $\sqrt{-N} = \sqrt{N}i$ and then perform the multiplication.

EXAMPLE 6 Multiplying Square Roots of Negative Numbers

Multiply:

(a) $\sqrt{-25} \cdot \sqrt{-4}$ (b) $(2 + \sqrt{-16})(1 - \sqrt{-4})$

Solution

(a) We cannot use the Product Property of Radicals to multiply these radicals because $\sqrt{-25}$ and $\sqrt{-4}$ are not real numbers. Therefore, we express the radicals as pure imaginary numbers and then multiply.

$$\sqrt{-25} \cdot \sqrt{-4} = 5i \cdot 2i$$
$$= 10i^2$$
$$i^2 = -1: \quad = -10$$

Work Smart

$\sqrt{-25} \cdot \sqrt{-4} \neq \sqrt{(-25)(-4)}$ because the Product Property of Radicals only applies when the radical is a real number.

(b) First, we rewrite each expression in parentheses as a complex number in standard form.

$$(2 + \sqrt{-16})(1 - \sqrt{-4}) = (2 + 4i)(1 - 2i)$$
$$\text{FOIL:} \quad = 2 \cdot 1 + 2 \cdot (-2i) + 4i \cdot 1 + 4i \cdot (-2i)$$
$$= 2 - 4i + 4i - 8i^2$$
$$\text{Combine like terms; } i^2 = -1: \quad = 2 - 8(-1)$$
$$= 2 + 8$$
$$= 10$$

Quick ✔ *In Problems 16 and 17, multiply.*

16. $\sqrt{-9} \cdot \sqrt{-36}$ **17.** $(2 + \sqrt{-36})(4 - \sqrt{-25})$

Complex Conjugates

We now introduce a special product that involves the *conjugate* of a complex number.

In Words

To find the complex conjugate of $a + bi$ or $a - bi$, simply change the sign from "+" to "−" or "−" to "+" between the "a" and "b" in the complex number.

COMPLEX CONJUGATE

If $a + bi$ is a complex number, then its **conjugate** is defined as $a - bi$.

For example,

Complex Number	Conjugate
$4 + 7i$	$4 - 7i$
$-10 - 3i$	$-10 + 3i$

Notice what happens when we multiply a complex number and its conjugate.

EXAMPLE 7 Multiplying a Complex Number by Its Conjugate

Find the product of $4 + 3i$ and its conjugate, $4 - 3i$.

Solution

$$
\begin{aligned}
(4 + 3i)(4 - 3i) &= 4 \cdot 4 + 4 \cdot (-3i) + 3i \cdot 4 + 3i \cdot (-3i) \\
&= 16 - 12i + 12i - 9i^2 \\
&= 16 - 9(-1) \\
&= 16 + 9 \\
&= 25
\end{aligned}
$$

Wow! The product of the complex number $4 + 3i$ and its conjugate $4 - 3i$ is 25—a real number! In fact, the result of Example 7 is true in general.

PRODUCT OF A COMPLEX NUMBER AND ITS CONJUGATE

The product of a complex number and its conjugate is a nonnegative real number. That is,

$$(a + bi)(a - bi) = a^2 + b^2$$

Perhaps you noticed that multiplying a complex number and its conjugate is akin to multiplying $(a + b)(a - b) = a^2 - b^2$.

Quick ✔

18. The complex conjugate of $-3 + 5i$ is _____.

In Problems 19 and 20, multiply.

19. $(3 - 8i)(3 + 8i)$ **20.** $(-2 + 5i)(-2 - 5i)$

4 Divide Complex Numbers

Now that we understand the product of a complex number and its conjugate we can proceed to divide complex numbers. As you read through the next example, notice how the approach is similar to rationalizing a denominator. (See Examples 3 and 4 in Section 6.5.)

EXAMPLE 8   How to Divide Complex Numbers

Divide: $\dfrac{-3 + i}{5 + 3i}$

Step-by-Step Solution

Step 1: Write the numerator and denominator in standard form, $a + bi$.	The numerator and denominator are already in standard form.

Step 2: Multiply the numerator and denominator by the complex conjugate of the denominator.	The complex conjugate of $5 + 3i$ is $5 - 3i$: $\dfrac{-3 + i}{5 + 3i} = \dfrac{-3 + i}{5 + 3i} \cdot \dfrac{5 - 3i}{5 - 3i}$
	$= \dfrac{(-3 + i)(5 - 3i)}{(5 + 3i)(5 - 3i)}$

Step 3: Simplify by writing the quotient in standard form, $a + bi$.	Multiply numerator and denominator; $(a + bi)(a - bi) = a^2 + b^2$: $= \dfrac{-3 \cdot 5 - 3 \cdot (-3i) + i \cdot 5 + i \cdot (-3i)}{5^2 + 3^2}$
	$= \dfrac{-15 + 9i + 5i - 3i^2}{25 + 9}$
	Combine like terms; $i^2 = -1$: $= \dfrac{-15 + 14i + 3}{34}$
	$= \dfrac{12 + 14i}{34}$
	Divide 34 into each term in the numerator to write in standard form: $= \dfrac{-12}{34} + \dfrac{14}{34}i$
	Write each fraction in lowest terms: $= -\dfrac{6}{17} + \dfrac{7}{17}i$

We summarize the steps used in Example 8 below.

> **DIVIDING COMPLEX NUMBERS**
>
> **Step 1:** Write the numerator and denominator in standard form, $a + bi$.
>
> **Step 2:** Multiply the numerator and denominator by the complex conjugate of the denominator.
>
> **Step 3:** Simplify by writing the quotient in standard form, $a + bi$.

EXAMPLE 9   Dividing Complex Numbers

Divide: $\dfrac{3 + 4i}{2i}$

Solution

Work Smart

We could also have multiplied the numerator and denominator in Example 9 by i. Do you know why? Try it yourself! Which approach do you prefer?

$$\frac{3 + 4i}{2i} = \frac{3 + 4i}{0 + 2i}$$

The complex conjugate of $0 + 2i$ is $0 - 2i$: $= \dfrac{3 + 4i}{0 + 2i} \cdot \dfrac{0 - 2i}{0 - 2i}$

The 0s are not necessary: $= \dfrac{3 + 4i}{2i} \cdot \dfrac{-2i}{-2i}$

$$\text{Multiply numerator; multiply denominator:} \quad = \frac{(3 + 4i)(-2i)}{(2i)(-2i)}$$

$$\text{Distribute in numerator:} \quad = \frac{-6i - 8i^2}{-4i^2}$$

$$i^2 = -1: \quad = \frac{-6i + 8}{4}$$

$$\begin{array}{c}\text{Divide 4 into each term in the numerator} \\ \text{to write in standard form:}\end{array} \quad = \frac{8}{4} - \frac{6}{4}i$$

$$\text{Reduce each fraction to lowest terms:} \quad = 2 - \frac{3}{2}i \qquad \blacksquare$$

Look back to Example 5(b), where we found $(-2 + 4i)(3 - i) = -2 + 14i$. Now find $\dfrac{-2 + 14i}{3 - i}$. What result do you expect? Verify that $\dfrac{-2 + 14i}{3 - i} = -2 + 4i$. Remember, we can always check that $\dfrac{A}{B} = C$, by verifying that $A = B \cdot C$.

> **Quick** ✔ *In Problems 21 and 22, divide.*
>
> **21.** $\dfrac{-4 + i}{3i}$ **22.** $\dfrac{4 + 3i}{1 - 3i}$

⌐5 Evaluate the Powers of *i*

The **powers of *i*** follow a pattern.

$$i^1 = i \qquad\qquad i^2 = -1 \qquad\qquad i^3 = i^2 \cdot i^1 = -1 \cdot i = -i \qquad i^4 = i^2 \cdot i^2 = (-1)(-1) = 1$$
$$i^5 = i^4 \cdot i = 1 \cdot i = i \quad i^6 = i^4 \cdot i^2 = 1 \cdot (-1) = -1 \quad i^7 = i^4 \cdot i^3 = 1 \cdot (-i) = -i \quad i^8 = i^4 \cdot i^4 = 1 \cdot 1 = 1$$
$$i^9 = i^8 \cdot i = 1 \cdot i = i \quad i^{10} = i^8 \cdot i^2 = 1 \cdot (-1) = -1 \quad i^{11} = i^8 \cdot i^3 = 1 \cdot (-i) = -i \quad i^{12} = (i^4)^3 = (1)^3 = 1$$

Do you see the pattern? In the first column, the expressions all simplify to i; in the second column, the expressions all simplify to -1; in the third column, the expressions all simplify to $-i$; in the fourth column, the expressions all simplify to 1. That is, the powers of i repeat with every fourth power. Figure 8 shows the pattern.

Figure 8

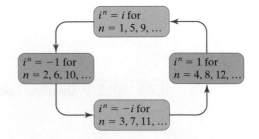

For this reason any power of i can be expressed in terms of $1, -1, i,$ or $-i$. The following steps can be used to simplify any power of i.

SIMPLIFYING THE POWERS OF *i*

Step 1: Divide the exponent of i by 4. Rewrite i^n as $(i^4)^q \cdot i^r$, where q is the quotient and r is the remainder of the division.

Step 2: Simplify the product in Step 1 to i^r since $i^4 = 1$.

EXAMPLE 10 Simplifying Powers of i

Simplify:

(a) i^{34}

(b) i^{101}

Solution

(a) We divide 34 by 4 and obtain a quotient of $q = 8$ and a remainder of $r = 2$. So

$$i^{34} = (i^4)^8 \cdot i^2$$
$$= (1)^8 \cdot (-1)$$
$$= -1$$

(b) We divide 101 by 4 and obtain a quotient of $q = 25$ and a remainder of $r = 1$. So

$$i^{101} = (i^4)^{25} \cdot i^1$$
$$= (1)^{25} \cdot i$$
$$= i$$ ∎

Work Smart

An alternative approach to Example 10:

(a) $i^{34} = (i^2)^{17} = (-1)^{17} = -1$

(b) $i^{101} = i^{100} \cdot i^1 = (i^2)^{50} \cdot i$
$$= (-1)^{50} \cdot i$$
$$= 1 \cdot i$$
$$= i$$

> **Quick** ✔ *In Problems 23 and 24, simplify the power of i.*
> **23.** i^{43}
> **24.** i^{98}

6.8 EXERCISES

MyMathLab *Powered by CourseCompass™ and MathXL*

Math XL — PRACTICE   WATCH   DOWNLOAD   READ   REVIEW

1–24. are the **Quick** ✔s *that follow each* **EXAMPLE**

Building Skills

In Problems 25–34, write each expression as a pure imaginary number. See Objective 1.

25. $\sqrt{-4}$ **26.** $\sqrt{-25}$ **27.** $-\sqrt{-81}$

28. $-\sqrt{-100}$ **29.** $\sqrt{-45}$ **30.** $\sqrt{-48}$

31. $\sqrt{-300}$ **32.** $\sqrt{-162}$ **33.** $\sqrt{-7}$

34. $\sqrt{-13}$

In Problems 35–42, write each expression as a complex number in standard form. See Objective 1.

35. $5 + \sqrt{-49}$ **36.** $4 - \sqrt{-36}$

37. $-2 - \sqrt{-28}$ **38.** $10 + \sqrt{-32}$

39. $\dfrac{4 + \sqrt{-4}}{2}$ **40.** $\dfrac{10 - \sqrt{-25}}{5}$

41. $\dfrac{4 + \sqrt{-8}}{12}$ **42.** $\dfrac{15 - \sqrt{-50}}{5}$

In Problems 43–50, add or subtract as indicated. See Objective 2.

43. $(4 + 5i) + (2 - 7i)$ **44.** $(-6 + 2i) + (3 + 12i)$

45. $(4 + i) - (8 - 5i)$ **46.** $(-7 + 3i) - (-3 + 2i)$

47. $\left(4 - \sqrt{-4}\right) - \left(2 + \sqrt{-9}\right)$

48. $\left(-4 + \sqrt{-25}\right) + \left(1 - \sqrt{-16}\right)$

49. $\left(-2 + \sqrt{-18}\right) + \left(5 - \sqrt{-50}\right)$

50. $\left(-10 + \sqrt{-20}\right) - \left(-6 + \sqrt{-45}\right)$

In Problems 51–74, multiply. See Objective 3.

51. $6i(2 - 4i)$ **52.** $3i(-2 - 6i)$

53. $-\dfrac{1}{2}i(4 - 10i)$ **54.** $\dfrac{1}{3}i(12 + 15i)$

55. $(2 + i)(4 + 3i)$ **56.** $(3 - i)(1 + 2i)$

57. $(-3 - 5i)(2 + 4i)$ **58.** $(5 - 2i)(-1 + 2i)$

59. $(2 - 3i)(4 + 6i)$ **60.** $(6 + 8i)(-3 + 4i)$

61. $\left(3 - \sqrt{2}i\right)\left(-2 + \sqrt{2}i\right)$ **62.** $\left(1 + \sqrt{3}i\right)\left(-4 - \sqrt{3}i\right)$

63. $\left(\dfrac{1}{2} - \dfrac{1}{4}i\right)\left(\dfrac{2}{3} + \dfrac{3}{4}i\right)$ **64.** $\left(-\dfrac{2}{3} + \dfrac{4}{3}i\right)\left(\dfrac{1}{2} - \dfrac{3}{2}i\right)$

65. $(3 + 2i)^2$ **66.** $(2 + 5i)^2$

67. $(-4 - 5i)^2$ **68.** $(2 - 7i)^2$

69. $\sqrt{-9} \cdot \sqrt{-4}$

70. $\sqrt{-36} \cdot \sqrt{-4}$

71. $\sqrt{-8} \cdot \sqrt{-10}$

72. $\sqrt{-12} \cdot \sqrt{-15}$

73. $\left(2 + \sqrt{-81}\right)\left(-3 - \sqrt{-100}\right)$

74. $\left(1 - \sqrt{-64}\right)\left(-2 + \sqrt{-49}\right)$

In Problems 75–80, (a) find the conjugate of the complex number, and (b) multiply the complex number by its conjugate. See Objective 3.

75. $3 + 5i$

76. $5 + 2i$

77. $2 - 7i$

78. $9 - i$

79. $-7 + 2i$

80. $-1 - 4i$

In Problems 81–94, divide. See Objective 4.

81. $\dfrac{1 + i}{3i}$

82. $\dfrac{2 - i}{2i}$

83. $\dfrac{-5 + 2i}{5i}$

84. $\dfrac{-4 + 5i}{6i}$

85. $\dfrac{3}{2 + i}$

86. $\dfrac{2}{4 + i}$

87. $\dfrac{-2}{-3 - 7i}$

88. $\dfrac{-4}{-5 - 3i}$

89. $\dfrac{2 + 3i}{3 - 2i}$

90. $\dfrac{2 + 5i}{5 - 2i}$

91. $\dfrac{4 + 2i}{1 - i}$

92. $\dfrac{-6 + 2i}{1 + i}$

93. $\dfrac{4 - 2i}{1 + 3i}$

94. $\dfrac{5 - 3i}{2 + 4i}$

In Problems 95–102, simplify. See Objective 5.

95. i^{53}

96. i^{72}

97. i^{43}

98. i^{110}

99. i^{153}

100. i^{131}

101. i^{-45}

102. i^{-26}

Mixed Practice

In Problems 103–116, perform the indicated operation.

103. $(-4 - i)(4 + i)$

104. $(-5 + 2i)(5 - 2i)$

105. $(3 + 2i)^2$

106. $(-3 + 2i)^2$

107. $\dfrac{-3 + 2i}{3i}$

108. $\dfrac{5 - 3i}{4i}$

109. $\dfrac{-4 + i}{-5 - 3i}$

110. $\dfrac{-4 + 6i}{-5 - i}$

111. $(10 - 3i) + (2 + 3i)$

112. $(-4 + 5i) + (4 - 2i)$

113. $5i^{37}(-4 + 3i)$

114. $2i^{57}(3 - 4i)$

115. $\sqrt{-10} \cdot \sqrt{-15}$

116. $\sqrt{-8} \cdot \sqrt{-12}$

In Problems 117–122, find the reciprocal of the complex number. Write each number in standard form.

117. $5i$

118. $7i$

119. $2 - i$

120. $3 - 5i$

121. $-4 + 5i$

122. $-6 + 2i$

123. Suppose that $f(x) = x^2$; find **(a)** $f(i)$ **(b)** $f(1 + i)$.

124. Suppose that $f(x) = x^2 + x$; find **(a)** $f(i)$ **(b)** $f(1 + i)$.

125. Suppose that $f(x) = x^2 + 2x + 2$; find **(a)** $f(3i)$ **(b)** $f(1 - i)$.

126. Suppose that $f(x) = x^2 + x - 1$; find **(a)** $f(2i)$ **(b)** $f(2 + i)$.

Applying the Concepts

127. Impedance (Series Circuit) The total impedance, Z, of an ac circuit containing components in series is equivalent to the sum of the individual impedances. Impedance is measured in ohms (Ω) and is expressed as an imaginary number of the form $Z = R + i \cdot X$. Here, R represents resistance and X represents reactance.
  (a) If the impedance in one part of a series circuit is $7 + 3i$ ohms and the impedance of the remainder of the circuit is $3 - 4i$ ohms, find the total impedance of the circuit.
  (b) What is the total resistance of the circuit?
  (c) What is the total reactance of the circuit?

128. Impedance (Parallel Circuit) The total impedance, Z, of an ac circuit consisting of two parallel pathways is given by the formula $\dfrac{1}{Z} = \dfrac{1}{Z_1} + \dfrac{1}{Z_2}$, where Z_1 and Z_2 are the impedances of each pathway. If the impedances of the individual pathways are $Z_1 = 5$ ohms and $Z_2 = 1 - 2i$ ohms, find the total impedance of the circuit.

Extending the Concepts

129. For the function $f(x) = x^2 + 4x + 5$, find
  (a) $f(-2 + i)$ **(b)** $f(-2 - i)$.

130. For the function $f(x) = x^2 - 2x + 2$, find
  (a) $f(1 + i)$ **(b)** $f(1 - i)$.

131. For the function $f(x) = x^3 + 1$, find **(a)** $f(-1)$
  (b) $f\left(\dfrac{1}{2} + \dfrac{\sqrt{3}}{2}i\right)$ **(c)** $f\left(\dfrac{1}{2} - \dfrac{\sqrt{3}}{2}i\right)$.

132. For the function $f(x) = x^3 - 1$, find **(a)** $f(1)$

(b) $f\left(-\dfrac{1}{2} + \dfrac{\sqrt{3}}{2}i\right)$ **(c)** $f\left(-\dfrac{1}{2} - \dfrac{\sqrt{3}}{2}i\right)$.

133. Any complex number z such that $f(z) = 0$ is called a **complex zero** of f. Look at the complex zeros in Problems 129–132. Conjecture a general result regarding the complex zeros of polynomials that have real coefficients.

134. The Complex Plane We are able to plot real numbers on a real number line. We are able to plot ordered pairs (x, y) in a Cartesian plane. Can we plot complex numbers? Yes! A complex number $x + yi$ can be interpreted geometrically as the point (x, y) in the xy-plane. Each point in the plane corresponds to a complex number, and conversely, each complex number corresponds to a point in the plane (just like ordered pairs). In the **complex plane**, the x-axis is called the **real axis** and the y-axis is called the **imaginary axis.**

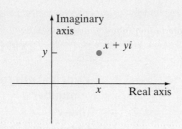

(a) Plot the complex number $4 + 2i$ in the complex plane.

(b) Plot the complex number $-2 + 6i$ in the complex plane.

(c) Plot the complex number $-5i$ in the complex plane.

(d) Plot the complex number -4 in the complex plane.

Explaining the Concepts

135. Explain the relation between the natural numbers, whole numbers, integers, rational numbers, real numbers, and complex number system.

136. Explain why the product of a complex number and its conjugate is a nonnegative real number. That is, explain why $(a + bi)(a - bi) = a^2 + b^2$.

137. How is multiplying two complex numbers related to multiplying two binomials?

138. How is the method used to rationalize denominators related to the method used to write the quotient of two complex numbers in standard form?

Synthesis Review

139. Expand: $(x + 2)^3$

140. Expand: $(y - 4)^2$

141. Evaluate: $(3 + i)^3$

142. Evaluate: $(4 - 3i)^2$

143. How is raising a complex number to a positive integer power related to raising a binomial to a positive integer power?

The Graphing Calculator

Graphing calculators have the ability to add, subtract, multiply, and divide complex numbers. First, put the calculator into complex mode as shown in Figure 9(a). Figure 9(b) shows the results of Examples 3(a) and 3(b). Figure 9(c) shows the results of Examples 5(b) and 8.

Figure 9

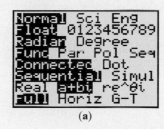   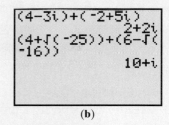

(a)   (b)

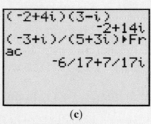

(c)

In Problems 144–151, use a graphing calculator to simplify each expression. Write your answers in standard form, $a + bi$.

144. $(1.3 - 4.3i) + (-5.3 + 0.7i)$

145. $(-3.4 + 1.9i) - (6.5 - 5.3i)$

146. $(0.3 - 5.2i)(1.2 + 3.9i)$

147. $(-4.3 + 0.2i)(7.2 - 0.5i)$

148. $\dfrac{4}{3 - 8i}$ **149.** $\dfrac{1 - 7i}{-4 + i}$

150. $3i^6 + (5 - 0.3i)(3 + 2i)$

151. $-6i^{14} + 5i^6 - (2 + i)(3 + 11i)$

CHAPTER 6 Activity: Which One Does Not Belong?

Focus: Simplifying Radicals and Rational Exponents
Time: 15–25 minutes
Group Size: 2–4
5–10 Minutes: Individually, evaluate each row below. Decide which item does not belong and why. Be creative with your reasons!

10–15 Minutes: Discuss each row and make a list of each member's response. Is there any example that everyone agrees with?

	A	B	C	D
1	$16^{\frac{3}{2}}$	$-16^{\frac{3}{2}}$	$-16^{\frac{2}{3}}$	$-16^{-\frac{2}{3}}$
2	$\sqrt[2]{(a-b)^3},\ a > b$	$\sqrt[2]{a^3 - b^3}$	$\sqrt[2]{(a-b)^3},\ a < b$	$\sqrt[2]{a-b},\ a > b$
3	The range of $f(x) = x^2$	The range of $f(x) = \sqrt[3]{x}$	The range of $f(x) = |x|$	The range of $f(x) = x^3$
4	i^{212}	i^0	i^{-108}	i^1

CHAPTER 6 Review

Section 6.1   nth Roots and Rational Exponents

KEY CONCEPTS	KEY TERMS
• **Simplifying** $\sqrt[n]{a^n}$ If $n \geq 2$ is a positive integer and a is a real number, then $\sqrt[n]{a^n} = a$ if $n \geq 3$ is odd $\sqrt[n]{a^n} = |a|$ if $n \geq 2$ is even • If a is a real number and $n \geq 2$ is an integer, then $a^{\frac{1}{n}} = \sqrt[n]{a}$ provided that $\sqrt[n]{a}$ exists. • If a is a real number, $\dfrac{m}{n}$ is a rational number in lowest terms with $n \geq 2$, the $a^{\frac{m}{n}} = \sqrt[n]{a^m} = \left(\sqrt[n]{a}\right)^m$ provided that $\sqrt[n]{a}$ exists. • If $\dfrac{m}{n}$ is a rational number and if a is a nonzero real number, then $a^{-\frac{m}{n}} = \dfrac{1}{a^{\frac{m}{n}}}$ or $\dfrac{1}{a^{-\frac{m}{n}}} = a^{\frac{m}{n}}$.	Principal nth root of a number a Index Cube root

YOU SHOULD BE ABLE TO...	EXAMPLE	REVIEW EXERCISES
1 Evaluate nth roots (p. 479)	Examples 1 and 2	1–5, 19, 20
2 Simplify expressions of the form $\sqrt[n]{a^n}$ (p. 481)	Example 3	6–8
3 Evaluate expressions of the form $a^{\frac{1}{n}}$ (p. 481)	Examples 4 and 5	9–12, 17, 21
4 Evaluate expressions of the form $a^{\frac{m}{n}}$ (p. 482)	Examples 6 through 9	13–16, 18, 22–24

In Problems 1–8, simplify each radical.

1. $\sqrt[3]{343}$

2. $\sqrt[3]{-125}$

3. $\sqrt[3]{\dfrac{8}{27}}$

4. $\sqrt[4]{81}$

5. $-\sqrt[5]{-243}$

6. $\sqrt[3]{10^3}$

7. $\sqrt[5]{z^5}$

8. $\sqrt[4]{(5p-3)^4}$

In Problems 9–16, evaluate each of the following expressions.

9. $81^{\frac{1}{2}}$

10. $(-256)^{\frac{1}{4}}$

11. $-4^{\frac{1}{2}}$

12. $729^{\frac{1}{3}}$

13. $16^{\frac{7}{4}}$

14. $-(-27)^{\frac{2}{3}}$

15. $-121^{\frac{3}{2}}$

16. $\dfrac{1}{36^{-\frac{1}{2}}}$

In Problems 17–20, use a calculator to write each expression rounded to two decimal places.

17. $(-65)^{\frac{1}{3}}$

18. $4^{\frac{3}{5}}$

19. $\sqrt[3]{100}$

20. $\sqrt[4]{10}$

In Problems 21–24, rewrite each of the following radicals with a rational exponent.

21. $\sqrt[3]{5a}$

22. $\sqrt[5]{p^7}$

23. $\left(\sqrt[4]{10z}\right)^3$

24. $\sqrt[6]{(2ab)^5}$

Section 6.2 Simplify Expressions Using the Laws of Exponents

KEY CONCEPTS		KEY TERM
• **If a and b are real numbers and if r and s are rational numbers, then assuming the expression is defined.**		Simplify

Zero-Exponent Rule:	$a^0 = 1$	if $a \neq 0$
Negative-Exponent Rule:	$a^{-r} = \dfrac{1}{a^r}$	if $a \neq 0$
Product Rule:	$a^r \cdot a^s = a^{r+s}$	
Quotient Rule:	$\dfrac{a^r}{a^s} = a^{r-s} = \dfrac{1}{a^{s-r}}$	if $a \neq 0$
Power Rule:	$(a^r)^s = a^{r \cdot s}$	
Product to Power Rule:	$(a \cdot b)^r = a^r \cdot b^r$	
Quotient to Power Rule:	$\left(\dfrac{a}{b}\right)^r = \dfrac{a^r}{b^r}$	if $b \neq 0$
Quotient to a Negative Power Rule:	$\left(\dfrac{a}{b}\right)^{-r} = \left(\dfrac{b}{a}\right)^r$	if $a \neq 0, b \neq 0$

YOU SHOULD BE ABLE TO...	EXAMPLE	REVIEW EXERCISES
1 Use the Laws of Exponents to simplify expressions involving rational exponents (p. 487)	Examples 1 through 3	25–30
2 Use the Laws of Exponents to simplify radical expressions (p. 489)	Example 4	31–34
3 Factor expressions containing rational exponents (p. 490)	Examples 5 and 6	35, 36

In Problems 25–36, simplify the expression.

25. $4^{\frac{2}{3}} \cdot 4^{\frac{7}{3}}$

26. $\dfrac{k^{\frac{1}{2}}}{k^{\frac{3}{4}}}$

27. $\left(p^{\frac{4}{3}} \cdot q^4\right)^{\frac{3}{2}}$

28. $\left(32a^{-\frac{3}{2}} \cdot b^{\frac{1}{4}}\right)^{\frac{1}{5}}$

29. $5m^{-\frac{2}{3}}\left(2m + m^{-\frac{1}{3}}\right)$

30. $\left(\dfrac{16x^{\frac{1}{3}}}{x^{-\frac{1}{3}}}\right)^{-\frac{1}{2}} + \left(\dfrac{x^{-\frac{3}{2}}}{64x^{-\frac{1}{2}}}\right)^{\frac{1}{3}}$

31. $\sqrt[8]{x^6}$

32. $\sqrt{121x^4 y^{10}}$

33. $\sqrt[3]{m^2} \cdot \sqrt{m^3}$

34. $\dfrac{\sqrt[3]{c}}{\sqrt[6]{c^4}}$

35. $2(3m - 1)^{\frac{1}{4}} + (m - 7)(3m - 1)^{\frac{5}{4}}$

36. $3(x^2 - 5)^{\frac{1}{3}} - 4x(x^2 - 5)^{-\frac{2}{3}}$

Section 6.3 Simplifying Radical Expressions

KEY CONCEPTS	KEY TERM

• **Product Property of Radicals**
  If $\sqrt[n]{a}$ and $\sqrt[n]{b}$ are real numbers and $n \geq 2$ is an integer, then $\sqrt[n]{a} \cdot \sqrt[n]{b} = \sqrt[n]{ab}$.
• **Quotient Property of Radicals**
  If $\sqrt[n]{a}$ and $\sqrt[n]{b}$ are real numbers, $b \neq 0$ and $n \geq 2$ is an integer, then $\dfrac{\sqrt[n]{a}}{\sqrt[n]{b}} = \sqrt[n]{\dfrac{a}{b}}$.
	Simplify

YOU SHOULD BE ABLE TO...	EXAMPLE	REVIEW EXERCISES
1 Use the Product Property to multiply radical expressions (p. 492)	Example 1	37, 38, 49–52
2 Use the Product Property to simplify radical expressions (p. 493)	Examples 2 through 7	39–52
3 Use the Quotient Property to simplify radical expressions (p. 498)	Examples 8 and 9	53–60
4 Multiply radicals with unlike indices (p. 499)	Example 10	61, 62

In Problems 37 and 38, use the Product Property to multiply. Assume that all variables can be any real number.

37. $\sqrt{15} \cdot \sqrt{7}$ **38.** $\sqrt[4]{2ab^2} \cdot \sqrt[4]{6a^2b}$

In Problems 39–44, simplify each radical using the Product Property. Assume that all variables can be any real number.

39. $\sqrt{80}$ **40.** $\sqrt[3]{-500}$

41. $\sqrt[3]{162m^6n^4}$ **42.** $\sqrt[4]{50p^8q^4}$

43. $2\sqrt{16x^6y}$ **44.** $\sqrt{(2x+1)^3}$

In Problems 45–48, simplify each radical using the Product Property. Assume that all variables are greater than or equal to zero.

45. $\sqrt{w^3z^2}$ **46.** $\sqrt{45x^4yz^3}$

47. $\sqrt[3]{16a^{12}b^5}$ **48.** $\sqrt{4x^2 + 8x + 4}$

In Problems 49–52, multiply and simplify. Assume that all variables are greater than or equal to zero.

49. $\sqrt{15} \cdot \sqrt{18}$ **50.** $\sqrt[3]{20} \cdot \sqrt[3]{30}$

51. $\sqrt[3]{-3x^4y^7} \cdot \sqrt[3]{24x^3y^2}$ **52.** $3\sqrt{4xy^2} \cdot 5\sqrt{3x^2y}$

In Problems 53–60, simplify. Assume that all variables are greater than zero.

53. $\sqrt{\dfrac{121}{25}}$ **54.** $\sqrt{\dfrac{5a^4}{64b^2}}$

55. $\sqrt[3]{\dfrac{54k^2}{9k^5}}$ **56.** $\sqrt[3]{\dfrac{-160w^{11}}{343w^{-4}}}$

57. $\dfrac{\sqrt{12h^3}}{\sqrt{3h}}$ **58.** $\dfrac{\sqrt{50a^3b^3}}{\sqrt{8a^5b^{-3}}}$

59. $\dfrac{\sqrt[3]{-8x^7y}}{\sqrt[3]{27xy^4}}$ **60.** $\dfrac{\sqrt[4]{48m^2n^7}}{\sqrt[4]{3m^6n}}$

In Problems 61 and 62, multiply and simplify.

61. $\sqrt{5} \cdot \sqrt[3]{2}$ **62.** $\sqrt[4]{8} \cdot \sqrt[6]{4}$

Section 6.4 Adding, Subtracting, and Multiplying Radical Expressions

KEY CONCEPTS	KEY TERM
• To add or subtract radicals, the index and the radicand must be the same. • When we multiply radicals, the index on each radical must be the same. Then we multiply the radicands.	Like radicals

YOU SHOULD BE ABLE TO...	EXAMPLE	REVIEW EXERCISES
1 Add or subtract radical expressions (p. 502)	Examples 1 through 3	63–72
2 Multiply radical expressions (p. 504)	Examples 4 and 5	73–82

In Problems 63–72, add or subtract as indicated. Assume all variables are positive or zero.

63. $2\sqrt[4]{x} + 6\sqrt[4]{x}$

64. $7\sqrt[3]{4y} + 2\sqrt[3]{4y} - 3\sqrt[3]{4y}$

65. $5\sqrt{2} - 2\sqrt{12}$

66. $\sqrt{18} + 2\sqrt{50}$

67. $\sqrt[3]{-16z} + \sqrt[3]{54z}$

68. $7\sqrt[3]{8x^2} - \sqrt[3]{-27x^2}$

69. $\sqrt{16a} + \sqrt[6]{729a^3}$

70. $\sqrt{27x^2} - x\sqrt{48} + 2\sqrt{75x^2}$

71. $5\sqrt[3]{4m^5y^2} - \sqrt[6]{16m^{10}y^4}$

72. $\sqrt{y^3 - 4y^2} - 2\sqrt{y - 4} + \sqrt[4]{y^2 - 8y + 16}$

In Problems 73–82, multiply and simplify.

73. $\sqrt{3}\left(\sqrt{5} - \sqrt{15}\right)$

74. $\sqrt[3]{5}\left(3 + \sqrt[3]{4}\right)$

75. $\left(3 + \sqrt{5}\right)\left(4 - \sqrt{5}\right)$

76. $\left(7 + \sqrt{3}\right)\left(6 + \sqrt{2}\right)$

77. $\left(1 - 3\sqrt{5}\right)\left(1 + 3\sqrt{5}\right)$

78. $\left(\sqrt[3]{x} + 1\right)\left(9\sqrt[3]{x} - 4\right)$

79. $\left(\sqrt{x} - \sqrt{5}\right)^2$

80. $\left(11\sqrt{2} + \sqrt{5}\right)^2$

81. $\left(\sqrt{2a} - b\right)\left(\sqrt{2a} + b\right)$

82. $\left(\sqrt[3]{6s} + 2\right)\left(\sqrt[3]{6s} - 7\right)$

Section 6.5 Rationalizing Radical Expressions

KEY CONCEPTS	KEY TERM
• To rationalize the denominator when the denominator contains a single radical, multiply the numerator and denominator by a radical such that the radicand in the denominator is a perfect power of the index, n. • To rationalize a denominator containing two terms, use the fact that $(A + B)(A - B) = A^2 - B^2$.	Rationalizing the denominator

YOU SHOULD BE ABLE TO...	EXAMPLE	REVIEW EXERCISES
1 Rationalize a denominator containing one term (p. 508)	Examples 1 and 2	83–90, 99
2 Rationalize a denominator containing two terms (p. 510)	Examples 3 and 4	91–98, 100

In Problems 83–98, rationalize the denominator.

83. $\dfrac{2}{\sqrt{6}}$

84. $\dfrac{6}{\sqrt{3}}$

85. $\dfrac{\sqrt{48}}{\sqrt{p^3}}$

86. $\dfrac{5}{\sqrt{2a}}$

87. $\dfrac{-2}{\sqrt{6y^3}}$

88. $\dfrac{3}{\sqrt[3]{5}}$

89. $\sqrt[3]{\dfrac{-4}{45}}$

90. $\dfrac{27}{\sqrt[5]{8p^3q^4}}$

91. $\dfrac{6}{7 - \sqrt{6}}$

92. $\dfrac{3}{\sqrt{3} - 9}$

93. $\dfrac{\sqrt{3}}{3 + \sqrt{2}}$

94. $\dfrac{\sqrt{k}}{\sqrt{k} - \sqrt{m}}$

95. $\dfrac{\sqrt{10} + 2}{\sqrt{10} - 2}$

96. $\dfrac{3 - \sqrt{y}}{3 + \sqrt{y}}$

97. $\dfrac{4}{2\sqrt{3} + 5\sqrt{2}}$

98. $\dfrac{\sqrt{5} - \sqrt{6}}{\sqrt{10} + \sqrt{3}}$

99. Simplify: $\dfrac{\sqrt{7}}{3} + \dfrac{6}{\sqrt{7}}$

100. Find the reciprocal: $4 - \sqrt{7}$

Section 6.6 Functions Involving Radicals	
KEY CONCEPT	**KEY TERMS**

• **Finding the Domain of a Function Whose Rule Contains a Radical Expression**
  1. If the index on a radical expression is even, then the radicand must be greater than or equal to zero.
  2. If the index on a radical expression is odd, then the radicand can be any real number.
	Square root function
	Cube root function

YOU SHOULD BE ABLE TO...	EXAMPLE	REVIEW EXERCISES
1 Evaluate functions whose rule is a radical expression (p. 514)	Example 1	101–104
2 Find the domain of a function whose rule contains a radical (p. 514)	Example 2	105–110, 111(a), 112(a), 113(a), 114(a)
3 Graph functions involving square roots (p. 515)	Example 3	111–113
4 Graph functions involving cube roots (p. 516)	Example 4	114

In Problems 101–104, evaluate each radical function at the indicated values.

101. $f(x) = \sqrt{x + 4}$
 (a) $f(-3)$
 (b) $f(0)$
 (c) $f(5)$

102. $g(x) = \sqrt{3x - 2}$
 (a) $g\left(\dfrac{2}{3}\right)$
 (b) $g(2)$
 (c) $g(6)$

103. $H(t) = \sqrt[3]{t + 3}$
 (a) $H(-2)$
 (b) $H(-4)$
 (c) $H(5)$

104. $G(z) = \sqrt{\dfrac{z - 1}{z + 2}}$
 (a) $G(1)$
 (b) $G(-3)$
 (c) $G(2)$

In Problems 105–110, find the domain of the radical function.

105. $f(x) = \sqrt{3x - 5}$ **106.** $g(x) = \sqrt[3]{2x - 7}$

107. $h(x) = \sqrt[4]{6x + 1}$ **108.** $F(x) = \sqrt[5]{2x - 9}$

109. $G(x) = \sqrt{\dfrac{4}{x - 2}}$ **110.** $H(x) = \sqrt{\dfrac{x - 3}{x}}$

In Problems 111–114, (a) determine the domain of the function; (b) graph the function using point-plotting; and (c) based on the graph, determine the range of the function.

111. $f(x) = \dfrac{1}{2}\sqrt{1 - x}$ **112.** $g(x) = \sqrt{x + 1} - 2$

113. $h(x) = -\sqrt{x + 3}$ **114.** $F(x) = \sqrt[3]{x + 1}$

Section 6.7 Radical Equations and Their Applications		
KEY TERMS		
Radical equation	Extraneous solution	

YOU SHOULD BE ABLE TO...	EXAMPLE	REVIEW EXERCISES
1 Solve radical equations containing one radical (p. 520)	Examples 1 through 5	115–124, 129, 130
2 Solve radical equations containing two radicals (p. 524)	Examples 6 and 7	125–128
3 Solve for a variable in a radical equation (p. 526)	Example 8	131, 132

In Problems 115–130, solve each equation.

115. $\sqrt{m} = 13$ **116.** $\sqrt[3]{3t + 1} = -2$

117. $\sqrt[4]{3x - 8} = 3$ **118.** $\sqrt{2x + 5} + 4 = 2$

119. $\sqrt{4 - k} - 3 = 0$ **120.** $3\sqrt{t} - 4 = 11$

121. $2\sqrt[3]{m} + 5 = -11$ **122.** $\sqrt{q + 2} = q$

123. $\sqrt{w + 11} + 3 = w + 2$

124. $\sqrt{p^2 - 2p + 9} = p + 1$

125. $\sqrt{a + 10} = \sqrt{2a - 1}$

126. $\sqrt{5x + 9} = \sqrt{7x - 3}$

127. $\sqrt{c - 8} + \sqrt{c} = 4$

128. $\sqrt{x + 2} - \sqrt{x + 9} = 7$

129. $(4x - 3)^{1/3} - 3 = 0$

130. $(x^2 - 9)^{1/4} = 2$

131. Height of a Cone Solve $r = \sqrt{\dfrac{3V}{\pi h}}$ for h.

132. Ball Slide Speed Factor Solve $f_s = \sqrt[3]{\dfrac{30}{v}}$ for v.

Section 6.8   The Complex Number System

KEY CONCEPTS	KEY TERMS
• **Nonnegativity Property of Real Numbers** For any real number a, $a^2 \geq 0$ • **Imaginary Unit** The imaginary unit, denoted by i, is the number whose square is -1. That is, $i^2 = -1$. • **Complex numbers** Complex numbers are numbers of the form $a + bi$, where a and b are real numbers. The real number a is called the real part of the number $a + bi$; the real number b is called the imaginary part of $a + bi$. • **Square Roots of Negative Numbers** If N is a positive real number, the principal square root of $-N$, denoted by $\sqrt{-N}$, is $\sqrt{-N} = \sqrt{N}i$, where $i = \sqrt{-1}$. • **Sum of Complex Numbers** $(a + bi) + (c + di) = (a + c) + (b + d)i$ • **Difference of Complex Numbers** $(a + bi) - (c + di) = (a - c) + (b - d)i$ • **Complex Conjugate** If $a + bi$ is a complex number, then its conjugate is $a - bi$. • **Product of a Complex Number and Its Conjugate** $(a + bi)(a - bi) = a^2 + b^2$	Imaginary unit Complex number system Complex number Real part Imaginary part Standard form Pure imaginary number Principal square root Conjugate Powers of i

YOU SHOULD BE ABLE TO...	EXAMPLE	REVIEW EXERCISES
1 Evaluate the square root of negative real numbers (p. 530)	Examples 1 and 2	133–136
2 Add or subtract complex numbers (p. 531)	Examples 3 and 4	137–140
3 Multiply complex numbers (p. 532)	Examples 5 through 7	141–146
4 Divide complex numbers (p. 534)	Examples 8 and 9	147–150
5 Evaluate the powers of i (p. 536)	Example 10	151–152

In Problems 133 and 134, write each expression as a pure imaginary number.

133. $\sqrt{-29}$

134. $\sqrt{-54}$

In Problems 135 and 136, write each expression as a complex number in standard form.

135. $14 - \sqrt{-162}$

136. $\dfrac{6 + \sqrt{-45}}{3}$

In Problems 137–150, perform the indicated operation.

137. $(3 - 7i) + (-2 + 5i)$

138. $(4 + 2i) - (9 - 8i)$

139. $\left(8 - \sqrt{-45}\right) - \left(3 + \sqrt{-80}\right)$

140. $\left(1 + \sqrt{-9}\right) + \left(-6 + \sqrt{-16}\right)$

141. $(4 - 5i)(3 + 7i)$

142. $\left(\dfrac{1}{2} + \dfrac{2}{3}i\right)(4 - 9i)$

143. $\sqrt{-3} \cdot \sqrt{-27}$

144. $\left(1 + \sqrt{-36}\right)\left(-5 - \sqrt{-144}\right)$

145. $(1 + 12i)(1 - 12i)$

146. $(7 + 2i)(5 + 4i)$

147. $\dfrac{4}{3 + 5i}$

148. $\dfrac{-3}{7 - 2i}$

149. $\dfrac{2 - 3i}{5 + 2i}$

150. $\dfrac{4 + 3i}{1 - i}$

In Problems 151 and 152, simplify.

151. i^{59}

152. i^{173}

CHAPTER 6 TEST

Remember to use your Chapter Test Prep Video CD to see fully worked-out solutions to any of these problems you would like to review.

1. Evaluate: $49^{-\frac{1}{2}}$

In Problems 2 and 3, simplify using rational exponents.

2. $\sqrt[3]{8x^{\frac{1}{2}}y^3} \cdot \sqrt{9xy^{\frac{1}{2}}}$

3. $\sqrt[5]{(2a^4b^3)^7}$

In Problems 4–9, perform the indicated operation and simplify. Assume all variables in the radicand are greater than or equal to zero.

4. $\sqrt{3m} \cdot \sqrt{13n}$

5. $\sqrt{32x^7y^4}$

6. $\dfrac{\sqrt{9a^3b^{-3}}}{\sqrt{4ab}}$

7. $\sqrt{5x^3} + 2\sqrt{45x}$

8. $\sqrt{9a^2b} - \sqrt[4]{16a^4b^2}$

9. $\left(11 + 2\sqrt{x}\right)\left(3 - \sqrt{x}\right)$

In Problems 10 and 11, rationalize the denominator.

10. $\dfrac{-2}{3\sqrt{72}}$

11. $\dfrac{\sqrt{5}}{\sqrt{5} + 2}$

12. For $f(x) = \sqrt{-2x + 3}$, find the following:

   (a) $f(1)$ **(b)** $f(-3)$

13. Determine the domain of the function $g(x) = \sqrt{-3x + 5}$.

14. For $f(x) = \sqrt{x} - 3$, do the following:

   (a) Determine the domain of the function.

   (b) Graph the function using point plotting.

   (c) From the graph, determine the range of the function.

In Problems 15–17, solve the given equations.

15. $\sqrt{x + 3} = 4$

16. $\sqrt{x + 13} - 4 = x - 3$

17. $\sqrt{x - 1} + \sqrt{x + 2} = 3$

In Problems 18–20, perform the indicated operation.

18. $(13 + 2i) + (4 - 15i)$

19. $(4 - 7i)(2 + 3i)$

20. $\dfrac{7 - i}{12 + 11i}$

7 Quadratic Equations and Functions

One of the more unusual sports is found in Millsboro, Delaware—Punkin Chunkin. Participants catapult or fire pumkins to see who can toss them the farthest (and most accurately). Interestingly, this bizarre ritual is an application of a quadratic function at work. See Problems 79–82 in Section 7.5.

OUTLINE

The Big Picture: Putting It Together

In Part I of Chapter 1, we reviewed solving linear equations and inequalities in one variable. In Part II of Chapter 1, we completed our discussion of "everything linear" by covering linear equations and inequalities in two variables.

This chapter is dedicated to completing our discussion of "everything quadratic" that began in Section 4.8, when we solved quadratic equations $ax^2 + bx + c = 0$, where the expression $ax^2 + bx + c$ was factorable. Remember, if the expression $ax^2 + bx + c$ was not factorable, we did not have a method for solving the equation. The missing piece for solving this type of quadratic equation was the idea of a radical. Having learned how to work with radicals in Chapter 6, we now have the tools necessary to expand our understanding of solving all quadratic equations $ax^2 + bx + c = 0$, regardless of whether the expression $ax^2 + bx + c$ is factorable. The theme of the chapter will be to solve quadratic equations, graph quadratic functions, and solve quadratic inequalities.

7.1 Solving Quadratic Equations by Completing the Square

OBJECTIVES

1. Solve Quadratic Equations Using the Square Root Property
2. Complete the Square in One Variable
3. Solve Quadratic Equations by Completing the Square
4. Solve Problems Using the Pythagorean Theorem

Preparing for Solving Quadratic Equations by Completing the Square

Before getting started, take the following readiness quiz. If you get a problem wrong, go back to the section cited and review the material.

P1. Multiply: $(2p + 3)^2$ [Section 4.2, pp. 336–337]

P2. Factor: $y^2 - 8y + 16$ [Section 4.6, pp. 371–372]

P3. Solve: $x^2 + 5x - 14 = 0$ [Section 4.8, pp. 384–387]

P4. Solve: $x^2 - 16 = 0$ [Section 4.8, pp. 384–387]

P5. Simplify: **(a)** $\sqrt{36}$ **(b)** $\sqrt{45}$ **(c)** $\sqrt{-12}$ [Getting Ready, pp. 473–474; Section 6.3, pp. 492–495; Section 6.8, pp. 530–531]

P6. Find the complex conjugate of $-3 + 2i$.   [Section 6.8, p. 534]

P7. Simplify: $\sqrt{x^2}$ [Getting Ready, pp. 475–476]

P8. Define: $|x|$ [Section R.3, p. 22]

1   Solve Quadratic Equations Using the Square Root Property

Suppose that we want to solve the quadratic equation

$$x^2 = p$$

where p is any real number. In words, this equation is saying, "give me all numbers whose square is p." So, if $p = 16$, then we would have the equation

$$x^2 = 16$$

which means we want "all numbers whose square is 16." There are two numbers whose square is 16, -4 and 4, so the solution set to the equation $x^2 = 16$ is $\{-4, 4\}$.

In general, suppose we want to solve an equation of the form $x^2 = p$. One approach we could take is to take the square root of both sides of the equation.

$$x^2 = p$$

Take the square root of both sides: $\sqrt{x^2} = \sqrt{p}$

$\sqrt{x^2} = |x|$: $|x| = \sqrt{p}$

$|x| = -x$ if $x < 0$; $|x| = x$ if $x \geq 0$: $-x = \sqrt{p}$ or $x = \sqrt{p}$

Solve for x: $x = -\sqrt{p}$ or $x = \sqrt{p}$

This gives us the following result.

THE SQUARE ROOT PROPERTY

If $x^2 = p$, then $x = \sqrt{p}$ or $x = -\sqrt{p}$.

Work Smart

The Square Root Property is useful for solving equations of the form "some unknown squared equals a real number." To solve this equation, we take the square root of both sides of the equation, but don't forget the ± symbol to obtain the positive and negative square root.

When using the Square Root Property to solve an equation such as $x^2 = p$, we usually abbreviate the solutions as $x = \pm\sqrt{p}$, read "x equals plus or minus the square root of p." For example, the two solutions of the equation

$$x^2 = 16$$

are

$$x = \pm\sqrt{16}$$

and since $\sqrt{16} = 4$, we have

$$x = \pm 4$$

Let's look at an example that discusses how to solve a quadratic equation using the Square Root Property.

Preparing for...Answers
P1. $4p^2 + 12p + 9$ **P2.** $(y - 4)^2$
P3. $\{-7, 2\}$ **P4.** $\{-4, 4\}$ **P5. (a)** 6
(b) $3\sqrt{5}$ **(c)** $2\sqrt{3}i$ **P6.** $-3 - 2i$
P7. $|x|$ **P8.** $|x| = -x$ if $x < 0$
            $|x| = x$ if $x \geq 0$

EXAMPLE 1 How to Solve a Quadratic Equation Using the Square Root Property

Solve: $p^2 - 9 = 0$

Step-by-Step Solution

Step 1: Isolate the expression containing the square term.

$$p^2 - 9 = 0$$
Add 9 to both sides: $\quad p^2 = 9$

Step 2: Use the Square Root Property. Don't forget the $\pm$ symbol.

$$p = \pm\sqrt{9}$$
Simplify the radical: $\quad = \pm 3$

Step 3: Isolate the variable, if necessary.

The variable is already isolated.

Step 4: Verify your solution(s).

$p = -3$: $\quad (-3)^2 - 9 \overset{?}{=} 0 \qquad p = 3$: $\quad 3^2 - 9 \overset{?}{=} 0$

$\quad 9 - 9 = 0$ True $\qquad\qquad 9 - 9 = 0$ True

The solution set is $\{-3, 3\}$. ∎

We summarize the steps used to solve a quadratic equation using the Square Root Property.

SOLVING A QUADRATIC EQUATION USING THE SQUARE ROOT PROPERTY

Step 1: Isolate the expression containing the squared term.

Step 2: Use the Square Root Property, which states if $x^2 = p$, then $x = \pm\sqrt{p}$. Don't forget the $\pm$ symbol.

Step 3: Isolate the variable, if necessary.

Step 4: Verify your solution(s).

You could also solve the equation in Example 1 by factoring the difference of two squares:

$$p^2 - 9 = 0$$
$$(p - 3)(p + 3) = 0$$
Zero-Product Property: $\quad p - 3 = 0 \quad$ or $\quad p + 3 = 0$
$$p = 3 \quad \text{or} \quad p = -3$$

Work Smart

As our mathematical knowledge develops, we will find there is more than one way to solve a problem.

So there is more than one way to obtain the solution! However, factoring only works nicely when solving equations of the form $x^2 = p$ when p is a perfect square. It doesn't work nicely when p is not a perfect square as Example 2 illustrates.

EXAMPLE 2 Solving a Quadratic Equation Using the Square Root Property

Solve: $3x^2 - 60 = 0$

Solution

$$3x^2 - 60 = 0$$
Add 60 to both sides of the equation: $\quad 3x^2 = 60$
Divide both sides by 3: $\quad x^2 = 20$
Use the Square Root Property: $\quad x = \pm\sqrt{20}$
Simplify the radical: $\quad = \pm 2\sqrt{5}$

Check

$$x = -2\sqrt{5}: \quad 3(-2\sqrt{5})^2 - 60 \stackrel{?}{=} 0 \qquad x = 2\sqrt{5}: \quad 3(2\sqrt{5})^2 - 60 \stackrel{?}{=} 0$$

$$(ab)^2 = a^2b^2: \quad 3(-2)^2(\sqrt{5})^2 - 60 \stackrel{?}{=} 0 \qquad\qquad 3 \cdot (2)^2(\sqrt{5})^2 - 60 \stackrel{?}{=} 0$$

$$3 \cdot 4 \cdot 5 - 60 \stackrel{?}{=} 0 \qquad\qquad 3 \cdot 4 \cdot 5 - 60 \stackrel{?}{=} 0$$

$$60 - 60 = 0 \quad \text{True} \qquad\qquad 60 - 60 = 0 \quad \text{True}$$

The solution set is $\left\{-2\sqrt{5}, 2\sqrt{5}\right\}$. ∎

Quick ✔

1. If $x^2 = p$, then $x =$ _____ or $x =$ _____.

In Problems 2–4, solve the quadratic equation using the Square Root Property.

2. $p^2 = 48$ **3.** $3b^2 = 75$ **4.** $s^2 - 81 = 0$

There is no reason that the solution to a quadratic equation must be real. The next example illustrates a solution to a quadratic equation that is a nonreal complex number.

EXAMPLE 3 Solving a Quadratic Equation Using the Square Root Property

Solve: $y^2 + 14 = 2$

Solution

$$y^2 + 14 = 2$$

Subtract 14 from both sides of the equation: $y^2 = -12$

Use the Square Root Property: $y = \pm\sqrt{-12}$

Simplify the radical: $= \pm 2\sqrt{3}i$

Check

$$y = -2\sqrt{3}i: \quad (-2\sqrt{3}i)^2 + 14 \stackrel{?}{=} 2 \qquad y = 2\sqrt{3}i: \quad (2\sqrt{3}i)^2 + 14 \stackrel{?}{=} 2$$

$$(-2\sqrt{3})^2 i^2 + 14 \stackrel{?}{=} 2 \qquad\qquad (2\sqrt{3})^2 i^2 + 14 \stackrel{?}{=} 2$$

$$i^2 = -1: \quad 4 \cdot 3 \cdot (-1) + 14 \stackrel{?}{=} 2 \qquad\qquad 4 \cdot 3 \cdot (-1) + 14 \stackrel{?}{=} 2$$

$$-12 + 14 \stackrel{?}{=} 2 \qquad\qquad -12 + 14 \stackrel{?}{=} 2$$

$$2 = 2 \quad \text{True} \qquad\qquad 2 = 2 \quad \text{True}$$

The solution set is $\left\{-2\sqrt{3}i, 2\sqrt{3}i\right\}$. ∎

Quick ✔ *In Problems 5 and 6, solve the quadratic equation using the Square Root Property.*

5. $d^2 = -72$ **6.** $3q^2 + 27 = 0$

EXAMPLE 4 Solving Quadratic Equations Using the Square Root Property

Solve:

    (a) $(x - 2)^2 = 25$ **(b)** $(y + 5)^2 + 24 = 0$

Solution

    (a)
$$(x - 2)^2 = 25$$

Use the Square Root Property: $x - 2 = \pm\sqrt{25}$

Simplify the radical: $x - 2 = \pm 5$

Add 2 to each side: $x = 2 \pm 5$

2 ± 5 means $2 - 5$ or $2 + 5$: $\quad x = 2 - 5 \quad \text{or} \quad x = 2 + 5$

$$= -3 \qquad\qquad = 7$$

Check

$$x = -3: \quad (-3 - 2)^2 \overset{?}{=} 25 \qquad\qquad x = 7: \quad (7 - 2)^2 \overset{?}{=} 25$$

$$(-5)^2 \overset{?}{=} 25 \qquad\qquad 5^2 \overset{?}{=} 25$$

$$25 = 25 \quad \text{True} \qquad\qquad 25 = 25 \quad \text{True}$$

The solution set is $\{-3, 7\}$.

(b)
$$\qquad\qquad (y + 5)^2 + 24 = 0$$

Subtract 24 from both sides of the equation: $\quad (y + 5)^2 = -24$

Use the Square Root Property: $\qquad y + 5 = \pm\sqrt{-24}$

$\sqrt{-24} = \sqrt{24}\cdot\sqrt{-1} = \sqrt{4\cdot 6}i = 2\sqrt{6}i$: $\qquad y + 5 = \pm 2\sqrt{6}i$

Subtract 5 from each side: $\qquad\qquad y = -5 \pm 2\sqrt{6}i$

$$y = -5 - 2\sqrt{6}i \quad \text{or} \quad y = -5 + 2\sqrt{6}i$$

Check

$$y = -5 - 2\sqrt{6}i: \qquad\qquad y = -5 + 2\sqrt{6}i:$$

$$\left(-5 - 2\sqrt{6}i + 5\right)^2 + 24 \overset{?}{=} 0 \qquad \left(-5 + 2\sqrt{6}i + 5\right)^2 + 24 \overset{?}{=} 0$$

$$\left(-2\sqrt{6}i\right)^2 + 24 \overset{?}{=} 0 \qquad\qquad \left(2\sqrt{6}i\right)^2 + 24 \overset{?}{=} 0$$

$$4\cdot 6\cdot i^2 + 24 \overset{?}{=} 0 \qquad\qquad 4\cdot 6\cdot i^2 + 24 \overset{?}{=} 0$$

$$-24 + 24 = 0 \quad \text{True} \qquad\qquad -24 + 24 = 0 \quad \text{True}$$

The solution set is $\left\{-5 - 2\sqrt{6}i, -5 + 2\sqrt{6}i\right\}$. ∎

Quick ✔ *In Problems 7 and 8, solve the quadratic equation using the Square Root Property.*

7. $(y + 3)^2 = 100$ **8.** $(q - 5)^2 + 20 = 4$

⎡2⎤ Complete the Square in One Variable

We now introduce the method of **completing the square.** The idea behind completing the square in one variable is to "adjust" the left side of a quadratic equation of the form $x^2 + bx + c = 0$ in order to make it a perfect square trinomial. Recall that perfect square trinomials are trinomials of the form

$$A^2 + 2AB + B^2 = (A + B)^2$$

or

$$A^2 - 2AB + B^2 = (A - B)^2$$

For example, $x^2 + 6x + 9$ is a perfect square trinomial because $x^2 + 6x + 9 = (x + 3)^2$. Or $p^2 - 12p + 36$ is a perfect square trinomial because $p^2 - 12p + 36 = (p - 6)^2$.

We "adjust" $x^2 + bx + c$ by adding a number to make it a perfect square trinomial. For example, to make $x^2 + 6x$ a perfect square we would add 9. But where does this 9 come from? If we divide the coefficient on the first-degree term, 6, by 2, and then square the result, we obtain 9. This approach works in general.

Work Smart

To complete the square, the coefficient of x^2 must be 1.

> **OBTAINING A PERFECT SQUARE TRINOMIAL**
>
> Identify the coefficient of the first-degree term. Multiply this coefficient by $\frac{1}{2}$ and then square the result. That is, determine the value of b in $x^2 + bx + c$ and compute $\left(\frac{1}{2}b\right)^2$.

EXAMPLE 5 Obtaining a Perfect Square Trinomial

Determine the number that must be added to each expression in order to make it a perfect square trinomial. Then factor the expression.

Start	Add	Result	Factored Form
$y^2 + 8y$	$\left(\frac{1}{2} \cdot 8\right)^2 = 16$	$y^2 + 8y + 16$	$(y + 4)^2$
$x^2 + 12x$	$\left(\frac{1}{2} \cdot 12\right)^2 = 36$	$x^2 + 12x + 36$	$(x + 6)^2$
$a^2 - 20a$	$\left(\frac{1}{2} \cdot (-20)\right)^2 = 100$	$a^2 - 20a + 100$	$(a - 10)^2$
$p^2 - 5p$	$\left(\frac{1}{2} \cdot (-5)\right)^2 = \frac{25}{4}$	$p^2 - 5p + \frac{25}{4}$	$\left(p - \frac{5}{2}\right)^2$

Work Smart

It is common to write the value $\left(\frac{1}{2}b\right)^2$ as a fraction, not a decimal.

Did you notice in the factored form that the perfect square trinomial always factors so that

$$x^2 + bx + \left(\frac{b}{2}\right)^2 = \left(x + \frac{b}{2}\right)^2 \quad \text{or} \quad x^2 - bx + \left(\frac{b}{2}\right)^2 = \left(x - \frac{b}{2}\right)^2$$

That is, the perfect square trinomial will always factor as $\left(x \pm \frac{b}{2}\right)^2$, where we use the $+$ if the coefficient of the first-degree term is positive and we use the $-$ if the coefficient of the first-degree term is negative. The $\frac{b}{2}$ represents $\frac{1}{2}$ the value of the coefficient of the first-degree term.

> **Quick ✔** *In Problems 9 and 10, determine the number that must be added to the expression to make it a perfect square trinomial. Then factor the expression.*
>
> **9.** $p^2 + 14p$ **10.** $w^2 + 3w$

Figure 1

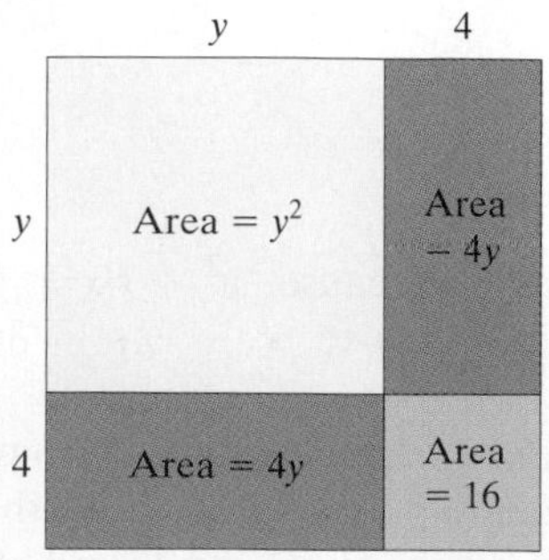

Are you wondering why we call making an expression a perfect square trinomial "completing the square"? Consider the expression $y^2 + 8y$ given in Example 5. We can geometrically represent this algebraic expression as shown in Figure 1. The yellow area is y^2 and each orange area is $4y$ (for a total area of $8y$). But what is the area of the green region in order to make the square complete? The dimensions of the green region must be 4 by 4, so the area of the green region is 16. The area of the entire square region, $(y + 4)^2$, equals the sum of the area of the regions that make up the square: $y^2 + 4y + 4y + 16 = y^2 + 8y + 16$.

⌐3⌐ Solve Quadratic Equations by Completing the Square

Until now, we have only been able to solve quadratic equations of the form $ax^2 + bx + c = 0$ when $ax^2 + bx + c$ was factorable. This raises the question, "Is there a method to solve $ax^2 + bx + c = 0$ when $ax^2 + bx + c$ is not factorable?" The answer is yes! We begin by presenting a method for solving quadratic equations of the form $x^2 + bx + c = 0$. That is, the coefficient of the square term is 1.

EXAMPLE 6   How to Solve a Quadratic Equation by Completing the Square

Solve: $x^2 + 6x + 1 = 0$

Step-by-Step Solution

Step 1: Rewrite $x^2 + bx + c = 0$ as $x^2 + bx = -c$ by subtracting the constant from both sides of the equation.	Subtract 1 from both sides:	$x^2 + 6x + 1 = 0$ $x^2 + 6x = -1$
Step 2: Complete the square in the expression $x^2 + bx$ by making it a perfect square trinomial.	$\left(\dfrac{1}{2}\cdot 6\right)^2 = 9$; Add 9 to both sides:	$x^2 + 6x + 9 = -1 + 9$ $x^2 + 6x + 9 = 8$
Step 3: Factor the perfect square trinomial on the left side of the equation.	$x^2 + 6x + 9 = (x + 3)^2$:	$(x + 3)^2 = 8$
Step 4: Solve the equation using the Square Root Property.	$\sqrt{8} = 2\sqrt{2}$: Subtract 3 from both sides: $a \pm b$ means $a - b$ or $a + b$:	$x + 3 = \pm\sqrt{8}$ $x + 3 = \pm 2\sqrt{2}$ $x = -3 \pm 2\sqrt{2}$ $x = -3 - 2\sqrt{2}$ or $x = -3 + 2\sqrt{2}$

Step 5: Verify your solution(s).

$$x^2 + 6x + 1 = 0$$

$x = -3 - 2\sqrt{2}$:

$$\left(-3 - 2\sqrt{2}\right)^2 + 6\left(-3 - 2\sqrt{2}\right) + 1 \stackrel{?}{=} 0$$

$$9 + 12\sqrt{2} + 8 - 18 - 12\sqrt{2} + 1 \stackrel{?}{=} 0$$

$$0 = 0 \quad \text{True}$$

$x = -3 + 2\sqrt{2}$:

$$\left(-3 + 2\sqrt{2}\right)^2 + 6\left(-3 + 2\sqrt{2}\right) + 1 \stackrel{?}{=} 0$$

$$9 - 12\sqrt{2} + 8 - 18 + 12\sqrt{2} + 1 \stackrel{?}{=} 0$$

$$0 = 0 \quad \text{True}$$

The solution set is $\left\{-3 - 2\sqrt{2}, -3 + 2\sqrt{2}\right\}$.

The following is a summary of the steps used to solve a quadratic equation by completing the square.

SOLVING A QUADRATIC EQUATION BY COMPLETING THE SQUARE

Step 1: Rewrite $x^2 + bx + c = 0$ as $x^2 + bx = -c$ by subtracting the constant from both sides of the equation.

Step 2: Complete the square in the expression $x^2 + bx$ by making it a perfect square trinomial. Don't forget, whatever you add to the left side of the equation must also be added to the right side.

Step 3: Factor the perfect square trinomial on the left side of the equation.

Step 4: Solve the equation using the Square Root Property.

Step 5: Verify your solutions.

Quick ✔ *In Problems 11 and 12, solve the equation by completing the square.*

11. $b^2 + 2b - 8 = 0$ **12.** $z^2 - 8z + 9 = 0$

Work Smart

If the coefficient of the square term is not 1, we must divide each side of the equation by the coefficient of the square term so that it becomes 1 before using the method of completing the square.

Up to this point we have only looked at quadratic equations where the coefficient of the square term is 1. When the coefficient of the square term is not 1, we multiply or divide both sides of the equation by a nonzero constant so this coefficient becomes 1. The next example demonstrates this method.

EXAMPLE 7 Solving a Quadratic Equation by Completing the Square When the Coefficient of the Square Term Is Not 1

Solve: $2x^2 + 4x + 3 = 0$

Solution

First, we notice that the coefficient of the square term is 2, so we divide both sides of the equation by 2 in order to make the coefficient of the square term equal to 1.

$$2x^2 + 4x + 3 = 0$$

Divide both sides of the equation by 2: $\quad \dfrac{2x^2 + 4x + 3}{2} = \dfrac{0}{2}$

Simplify: $\quad x^2 + 2x + \dfrac{3}{2} = 0$

Now we are ready to solve the equation by completing the square.

Subtract $\dfrac{3}{2}$ from both sides: $\qquad x^2 + 2x = -\dfrac{3}{2}$

$\left(\dfrac{1}{2} \cdot 2\right)^2 = 1$; Add 1 to both sides: $\quad x^2 + 2x + 1 = -\dfrac{3}{2} + 1$

Simplify: $\quad x^2 + 2x + 1 = -\dfrac{1}{2}$

Factor expression on left: $\qquad (x + 1)^2 = -\dfrac{1}{2}$

Use Square Root Property: $\qquad x + 1 = \pm\sqrt{-\dfrac{1}{2}}$

$\sqrt{-N} = \sqrt{N}\,i \qquad x + 1 = \pm\sqrt{\dfrac{1}{2}}\,i$

$\sqrt{\dfrac{1}{2}} = \dfrac{\sqrt{1}}{\sqrt{2}} = \dfrac{\sqrt{1}}{\sqrt{2}} \cdot \dfrac{\sqrt{2}}{\sqrt{2}} = \dfrac{\sqrt{2}}{2}: \qquad x + 1 = \pm\dfrac{\sqrt{2}}{2}\,i$

Subtract 1 from both sides: $\qquad x = -1 \pm \dfrac{\sqrt{2}}{2}\,i$

$a \pm b$ means $a - b$ or $a + b$: $\qquad x = -1 - \dfrac{\sqrt{2}}{2}\,i \quad$ or $\quad x = -1 + \dfrac{\sqrt{2}}{2}\,i$

Work Smart

Notice the solutions in Example 7 are complex conjugates of each other.

We leave it to you to verify the solutions. The solution set is

$$\left\{-1 - \dfrac{\sqrt{2}}{2}\,i,\ -1 + \dfrac{\sqrt{2}}{2}\,i\right\}.$$
∎

Quick ✔ *In Problems 13 and 14, solve the quadratic equation by completing the square.*

13. $2q^2 + 6q - 1 = 0$

14. $3m^2 + 2m + 7 = 0$

Figure 2

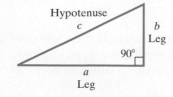

Hypotenuse c

b Leg

$90°$

a Leg

⌐4⌐ Solve Problems Using the Pythagorean Theorem

The Pythagorean Theorem is a statement about *right triangles*. A **right triangle** is one that contains a **right angle**, that is, an angle of 90°. The side of the triangle opposite the 90° angle is called the **hypotenuse;** the remaining two sides are called **legs**. In Figure 2 we use c to represent the length of the hypotenuse and a and b to represent the lengths of the legs. Notice the use of the symbol ⌐ to show the 90° angle.

We now state the Pythagorean Theorem.

THE PYTHAGOREAN THEOREM

In a right triangle, the square of the length of the hypotenuse is equal to the sum of the squares of the lengths of the legs. That is, in the right triangle shown in Figure 2,

$$c^2 = a^2 + b^2$$

EXAMPLE 8 Finding the Hypotenuse of a Right Triangle

In a right triangle, one leg is of length 5 inches and the other is of length 12 inches. What is the length of the hypotenuse?

Solution

Since the triangle is a right triangle, we use the Pythagorean Theorem with $a = 5$ and $b = 12$ to find the length c of the hypotenuse.

$$c^2 = a^2 + b^2$$
$$c^2 = 5^2 + 12^2$$
$$= 25 + 144$$
$$= 169$$

We now use the Square Root Property to find c, the length of the hypotenuse.

$$c = \sqrt{169} = 13$$

The length of the hypotenuse is 13 inches. Notice that we only find the positive square root of 169 since c represents the length of a side of a triangle and a negative length does not make sense. ∎

Quick ✔

15. The side of a right triangle opposite the 90° angle is called the _____ ; the remaining two sides are called _____ .

16. *True or False:* The Pythagorean Theorem states that for any triangle, the length of the hypotenuse is equal to the sum of the squares of the lengths of the legs.

In Problem 17, the lengths of the legs of a right triangle are given. Find the length of the hypotenuse.

17. $a = 3, b = 4$

EXAMPLE 9 How Far Can You See?

The Currituck Lighthouse is located in Corolla, North Carolina. As part of North Carolina's Outer Banks, the lighthouse was completed in 1875. It stands 162 feet tall with the observation deck located 158 feet above the ground. See Figure 3.

Figure 3

The website for the Currituck Lighthouse states that if a person were standing on the observation deck, he or she could see approximately 18 miles. See Figure 4. Assuming that the radius of the Earth is 3960 miles, verify this claim.

Figure 4

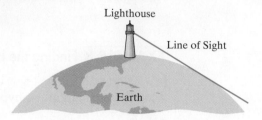

Lighthouse

Line of Sight

Earth

Solution

Step 1: Identify We want to know how far a person can see from the lighthouse.

Step 2: Name We will call this unknown distance, d.

Step 3: Translate To help with the translation, we draw a picture. From the center of Earth, draw two lines: one through the lighthouse and the other to the farthest point a person can see from the lighthouse. See Figure 5.

Figure 5

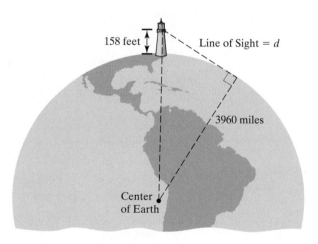

158 feet

Line of Sight = d

3960 miles

Center of Earth

The line of sight and the two lines drawn from the center of Earth form a right triangle. So the angle where the line of sight touches the horizon measures 90°. From the Pythagorean Theorem, we know that

$$\text{Hypotenuse}^2 = \text{Leg}^2 + \text{Leg}^2$$

The length of the hypotenuse is 3960 miles plus 158 feet. We can't add 3960 miles to 158 feet without first converting the height of the tower to miles. Since 158 feet $=$ 158 feet $\cdot \dfrac{1 \text{ mile}}{5280 \text{ feet}} = \dfrac{158}{5280}$ mile, we have that the hypotenuse is $\left(3960 + \dfrac{158}{5280}\right)$ miles. One of the legs is 3960 miles. The length of the other leg is our unknown, d. So we have

$$3960^2 + d^2 = \left(3960 + \frac{158}{5280}\right)^2 \quad \text{The Model}$$

Step 4: Solve

$$3960^2 + d^2 = \left(3960 + \frac{158}{5280}\right)^2$$

Subtract 3960^2 from both sides: $\quad d^2 = \left(3960 + \dfrac{158}{5280}\right)^2 - 3960^2$

Use a calculator: $\quad d^2 \approx 237.000895$

Square Root Property: $\quad d \approx \sqrt{237.000895}$

$$\approx 15.39 \text{ miles}$$

Step 5: Check Our answer is less than the distance given on the website.

Step 6: Answer The distance given on the Currituck Lighthouse website appears to overstate the actual distance a person could see. Someone standing on the observation deck of the lighthouse could see about 15.39 miles.

■

> **Quick ✔**
>
> **18.** The USS *Constitution* (aka *Old Ironsides*) is perhaps the most famous ship from United States Naval history. The mainmast of the *Constitution* is 220 feet high. Suppose that a sailor climbs the mainmast to a height of 200 feet in order to look for enemy vessels. How far could the sailor see? Assume the radius of the Earth is 3960 miles.

7.1 EXERCISES

PRACTICE   WATCH   DOWNLOAD   READ   REVIEW

1–18. are the **Quick ✔***s that follow each* **EXAMPLE**

Building Skills

In Problems 19–44, solve each equation using the Square Root Property. See Objective 1.

19. $y^2 = 100$

20. $x^2 = 81$

21. $p^2 = 50$

22. $z^2 = 48$

23. $m^2 = -25$

24. $n^2 = -49$

25. $w^2 = \dfrac{5}{4}$

26. $z^2 = \dfrac{8}{9}$

27. $x^2 + 5 = 13$

28. $w^2 - 6 - 14$

29. $3z^2 = 48$

30. $4y^2 = 100$

31. $3x^2 = 8$

32. $5y^2 = 32$

33. $2p^2 + 23 = 15$

34. $-3x^2 - 5 = 22$

35. $(d - 1)^2 = -18$

36. $(z + 4)^2 = -24$

37. $3(q + 5)^2 - 1 = 8$

38. $5(x - 3)^2 + 2 = 27$

39. $(3q + 1)^2 = 9$

40. $(2p + 3)^2 = 16$

41. $\left(x - \dfrac{2}{3}\right)^2 = \dfrac{5}{9}$

42. $\left(y + \dfrac{3}{2}\right)^2 = \dfrac{3}{4}$

43. $x^2 + 8x + 16 = 81$

44. $q^2 - 6q + 9 = 16$

In Problems 45–52, complete the square in each expression. Then factor the perfect square trinomial. See Objective 2.

45. $x^2 + 10x$

46. $y^2 + 16y$

47. $z^2 - 18z$

48. $p^2 - 4p$

49. $y^2 + 7y$

50. $x^2 + x$

51. $w^2 + \dfrac{1}{2}w$

52. $z^2 - \dfrac{1}{3}z$

In Problems 53–72, solve each quadratic equation by completing the square. See Objective 3.

53. $x^2 + 4x = 12$

54. $y^2 + 3y = 18$

55. $x^2 - 4x + 1 = 0$

56. $p^2 - 6p + 4 = 0$

57. $a^2 - 4a + 5 = 0$

58. $m^2 - 2m + 5 = 0$

59. $b^2 + 5b - 2 = 0$

60. $q^2 + 7q + 7 = 0$

61. $m^2 = 8m + 3$

62. $n^2 = 10n + 5$

63. $p^2 - p + 3 = 0$

64. $z^2 - 3z + 5 = 0$

65. $2y^2 - 5y - 12 = 0$

66. $3a^2 - 4a - 4 = 0$

67. $3y^2 - 6y + 2 = 0$

68. $2y^2 - 2y - 1 = 0$

69. $2z^2 - 5z + 1 = 0$ **70.** $2x^2 - 7x + 2 = 0$

71. $2x^2 + 4x + 5 = 0$ **72.** $2z^2 + 6z + 5 = 0$

In Problems 73–82, the lengths of the legs of a right triangle are given. Find the hypotenuse. Give exact answers and decimal approximations rounded to two decimal places. See Objective 4.

73. $a = 6, b = 8$ **74.** $a = 7, b = 24$

75. $a = 12, b = 16$ **76.** $a = 15, b = 8$

77. $a = 5, b = 5$ **78.** $a = 3, b = 3$

79. $a = 1, b = \sqrt{3}$ **80.** $a = 2, b = \sqrt{5}$

81. $a = 6, b = 10$ **82.** $a = 8, b = 10$

In Problems 83–86, use the right triangle shown below and find the missing length. Give exact answers and decimal approximations rounded to two decimal places. See Objective 4.

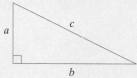

83. $a = 4, c = 8$ **84.** $a = 4, c = 10$

85. $b = 8, c = 12$ **86.** $b = 2, c = 10$

Mixed Practice

87. Given that $f(x) = (x - 3)^2$, find all x such that $f(x) - 36$. What points are on the graph of f?

88. Given that $f(x) = (x - 5)^2$, find all x such that $f(x) = 49$. What points are on the graph of f?

89. Given that $g(x) = (x + 2)^2$, find all x such that $g(x) = 18$. What points are on the graph of g?

90. Given that $h(x) = (x + 1)^2$, find all x such that $h(x) = 32$. What points are on the graph of h?

Applying the Concepts

In Problems 91 and 92, find the exact length of the diagonal in each figure.

91.

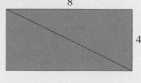

92.

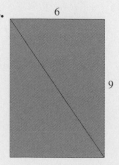

In Problems 93–100, express your answer as a decimal rounded to three decimal places.

93. Golf A golfer hits an errant tee shot that lands in the rough. The golfer finds that the ball is exactly 30 yards to the right of the 100-yard marker, which indicates the distance to the center of the green as shown in the figure. How far is the ball from the center of the green?

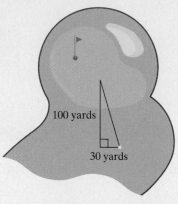

94. Baseball Jermaine Dye plays right field for the Chicago White Sox. He catches a fly ball 40 feet from the right field foul line, as indicated in the figure. How far is it to home plate?

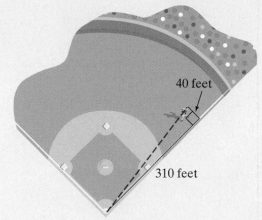

95. Guy Wire A guy wire is a wire used to support telephone poles. Suppose that a guy wire is located 30 feet up a telephone pole and is anchored to the ground 10 feet from the base of the pole. How long is the guy wire?

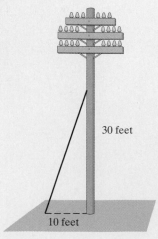

96. Guy Wire A guy wire is used to support an antenna on a rooftop. The wire is located 40 feet up on the antenna and anchored to the roof 8 feet from the base of the antenna. What is the length of the guy wire?

97. Ladder Bob needs to wash the windows on his house. He has a 25-foot ladder and places the base of the ladder 10 feet from the wall on the house.

   (a) How far up the wall will the ladder reach?

   (b) If his windows are 20 feet above the ground, what is the farthest distance the base of the ladder can be from the wall?

98. Fire Truck Ladder A fire truck has a 75-foot ladder. If the truck can safely park 20 feet from a building, how far up the building can the ladder reach assuming that the top of the base of the ladder is resting on top of the truck and the truck is 10 feet tall?

99. Gravity The distance s that an object falls (in feet) after t seconds, ignoring air resistance, is given by the equation $s = 16t^2$.

   (a) How long does it take an object to fall 16 feet?

   (b) How long does it take an object to fall 48 feet?

   (c) How long does it take an object to fall 64 feet?

△**100. Equilateral Triangles** An equilateral triangle is one whose sides are all the same length. The area A of an equilateral triangle whose sides are each length x is given by $A = \dfrac{\sqrt{3}}{4}x^2$.

   (a) What is the length of each side of an equilateral triangle whose area is $\dfrac{8\sqrt{3}}{9}$ square feet?

   (b) What is the length of each side of an equilateral triangle whose area is $\dfrac{25\sqrt{3}}{4}$ square meters?

Problems 101 and 102 are based on the following discussion. If P dollars are invested today at an annual interest rate r compounded once a year, then the value of the account A after 2 years is given by the formula $A = P(1 + r)^2$.

101. Value of Money Find the rate of interest required to turn an investment of $1000 into $1200 after 2 years. Express your answer as a percent rounded to two decimal places.

102. Value of Money Find the rate of interest required to turn an investment of $5000 into $6200 after 2 years. Express your answer as a percent rounded to two decimal places.

Extending the Concepts

*If you look carefully at the Pythagorean Theorem, it states, "If we have a right triangle, then $c^2 = a^2 + b^2$, where c is the length of the hypotenuse." In this theorem "a right triangle" represents the hypothesis, while "$c^2 = a^2 + b^2$" represents the conclusion. The **converse** of a theorem interchanges the hypothesis and conclusion. The converse of the Pythagorean Theorem is true.*

CONVERSE OF THE PYTHAGOREAN THEOREM

In a triangle, if the square of the length of one side equals the sum of the squares of the lengths of the other two sides, then the triangle is a right triangle. The 90° angle is opposite the longest side.

In Problems 103–106, the lengths of the sides of a triangle are given. Determine if the triangle is a right triangle. If it is, identify the hypotenuse.

103. 8, 15, 17   **104.** 4, 6, 8

105. 14, 18, 20   **106.** 20, 48, 52

107. Pythagorean Triples Suppose that m and n are positive integers with $m > n$. If $a = m^2 - n^2$, $b = 2mn$, and $c = m^2 + n^2$, show that a, b, and c are the lengths of the sides of a right triangle using the Converse of the Pythagorean Theorem. We call any numbers a, b, and c found from the above formulas **Pythagorean Triples.**

108. Solve $ax^2 + bx + c = 0$ for x by completing the square.

Synthesis Review

In Problems 109–112, solve each equation.

109. $a^2 - 5a - 36 = 0$ **110.** $p^2 + 4p = 32$

111. $|4q + 1| = 3$ **112.** $\left|\dfrac{3}{4}w - \dfrac{2}{3}\right| = \dfrac{5}{2}$

113. In Problems 109–112, you are asked to solve quadratic and absolute value equations. In solving both types of equations, we reduce the equation to a simpler equation. What is the simpler equation?

7.2 Solving Quadratic Equations by the Quadratic Formula

OBJECTIVES

1. Solve Quadratic Equations Using the Quadratic Formula
2. Use the Discriminant to Determine the Nature of Solutions in a Quadratic Equation
3. Model and Solve Problems Involving Quadratic Equations

Preparing for Solving Quadratic Equations by the Quadratic Formula
Before getting started, take the following readiness quiz. If you get a problem wrong, go back to the section cited and review the material.

P1. Simplify: **(a)** $\sqrt{54}$ **(b)** $\sqrt{121}$

[Getting Ready, pp. 473–474; Section 6.3, pp. 492–495]

P2. Simplify: **(a)** $\sqrt{-9}$ **(b)** $\sqrt{-72}$

[Section 6.8, pp. 530–531]

P3. Simplify: $\dfrac{3 + \sqrt{18}}{6}$

[Section 6.3, pp. 492–495]

At this stage of the course, we know three methods for solving quadratic equations: (1) factoring, (2) the Square Root Property, and (3) completing the square. Why do we need three methods? Well, each method provides the "quickest" route to the solution when used appropriately. For example, if the quadratic expression is easy to factor, the method of factoring will get you to the solution faster than the other two. If the equation is in the form $x^2 = p$, using the Square Root Property is fastest. If the quadratic expression is not factorable, we have no choice but to complete the square. But the method of completing the square is tedious. So you may be asking yourself if there is an alternative to this method. The answer is yes!

1 Solve Quadratic Equations Using the Quadratic Formula

We can use the method of completing the square to obtain a general formula for solving the quadratic equation

$$ax^2 + bx + c = 0 \qquad a \neq 0$$

To complete the square, we first must get the constant c on the right-hand side of the equation.

$$ax^2 + bx = -c \qquad a \neq 0$$

Since $a \neq 0$, we can divide both sides of the equation by a to get

$$x^2 + \frac{b}{a}x = -\frac{c}{a}$$

Now that the coefficient of x^2 is 1, we complete the square on the left side by adding the square of $\frac{1}{2}$ of the coefficient of x to both sides of the equation. That is, we add

$$\left(\frac{1}{2} \cdot \frac{b}{a}\right)^2 = \frac{b^2}{4a^2}$$

to both sides of the equation. We now have

$$x^2 + \frac{b}{a}x + \frac{b^2}{4a^2} = -\frac{c}{a} + \frac{b^2}{4a^2}$$

or

$$x^2 + \frac{b}{a}x + \frac{b^2}{4a^2} = \frac{b^2}{4a^2} - \frac{c}{a}$$

We combine like terms on the right-hand side by writing the right-hand side over a common denominator. The least common denominator on the right-hand side is $4a^2$. So we multiply $-\dfrac{c}{a}$ by $\dfrac{4a}{4a}$:

$$x^2 + \frac{b}{a}x + \frac{b^2}{4a^2} = \frac{b^2}{4a^2} - \frac{c}{a} \cdot \frac{4a}{4a}$$

$$x^2 + \frac{b}{a}x + \frac{b^2}{4a^2} = \frac{b^2}{4a^2} - \frac{4ac}{4a^2}$$

$$x^2 + \frac{b}{a}x + \frac{b^2}{4a^2} = \frac{b^2 - 4ac}{4a^2}$$

Preparing for...Answers **P1. (a)** $3\sqrt{6}$
(b) 11 **P2. (a)** $3i$ **(b)** $6\sqrt{2}i$
P3. $\dfrac{1}{2} + \dfrac{\sqrt{2}}{2}$ or $\dfrac{1 + \sqrt{2}}{2}$

Work Smart

To factor any perfect square trinomial of the form $x^2 + bx + c$, we write $\left(x + \dfrac{b}{2}\right)^2$.

The expression on the left-hand side is a perfect square trinomial. We factor the left-hand side and obtain

$$\left(x + \frac{b}{2a}\right)^2 = \frac{b^2 - 4ac}{4a^2}$$

At this point we will assume that $a > 0$ (you'll see why in a little while). This assumption does not compromise the results because if $a < 0$, we could multiply both sides of the equation $ax^2 + bx + c = 0$ by -1 to make it positive. With this assumption, we use the Square Root Property and get

$$x + \frac{b}{2a} = \pm\sqrt{\frac{b^2 - 4ac}{4a^2}}$$

$$\sqrt{\frac{a}{b}} = \frac{\sqrt{a}}{\sqrt{b}}: \quad x + \frac{b}{2a} = \pm\frac{\sqrt{b^2 - 4ac}}{\sqrt{4a^2}}$$

$$\sqrt{4a^2} = 2a \text{ since } a > 0: \quad x + \frac{b}{2a} = \pm\frac{\sqrt{b^2 - 4ac}}{2a}$$

Subtract $\dfrac{b}{2a}$ from both sides: $\quad x = -\dfrac{b}{2a} \pm \dfrac{\sqrt{b^2 - 4ac}}{2a}$

Write over a common denominator: $\quad x = \dfrac{-b \pm \sqrt{b^2 - 4ac}}{2a}$

In Words

The quadratic formula says that the solution(s) to the equation $ax^2 + bx + c = 0$ is (are) "the opposite of b plus or minus the square root of b squared minus $4ac$ all over $2a$."

This gives us the *quadratic formula.*

Work Smart: Study Skill

When solving homework problems always write the quadratic formula as part of the solution so you "accidentally" memorize the formula.

THE QUADRATIC FORMULA

The solution(s) to the quadratic equation $ax^2 + bx + c = 0, a \neq 0$, are given by the **quadratic formula**

$$x = \frac{-b \pm \sqrt{b^2 - 4ac}}{2a}$$

EXAMPLE 1 How to Solve a Quadratic Equation Using the Quadratic Formula

Solve: $12x^2 + 5x - 3 = 0$

Step-by-Step Solution

Step 1: Write the equation in standard form $ax^2 + bx + c = 0$ and identify the values of a, b, and c.

$a = 12$ $b = 5$ $c = -3$

$$12x^2 + 5x - 3 = 0$$

Step 2: Substitute the values of a, b, and c into the quadratic formula.

$$x = \frac{-b \pm \sqrt{b^2 - 4ac}}{2a}$$

$$x = \frac{-5 \pm \sqrt{5^2 - 4(12)(-3)}}{2(12)}$$

(continued)

Step 3: Simplify the expression found in Step 2.

$$= \frac{-5 \pm \sqrt{25 + 144}}{24}$$

$$= \frac{-5 \pm \sqrt{169}}{24}$$

$\sqrt{169} = 13:$ $\quad = \frac{-5 \pm 13}{24}$

$a \pm b$ means $a - b$ or $a + b$: $\quad x = \frac{-5 - 13}{24} \quad$ or $\quad x = \frac{-5 + 13}{24}$

$$= \frac{-18}{24} \quad \text{or} \quad = \frac{8}{24}$$

Reduce: $\quad = -\frac{3}{4} \quad$ or $\quad = \frac{1}{3}$

Step 4: Check

$$12x^2 + 5x - 3 = 0$$

$x = -\frac{3}{4}:$ $12\left(-\frac{3}{4}\right)^2 + 5\left(-\frac{3}{4}\right) - 3 \stackrel{?}{=} 0$

$12 \cdot \frac{9}{16} - \frac{15}{4} - 3 \stackrel{?}{=} 0$

$\frac{27}{4} - \frac{15}{4} - 3 \stackrel{?}{=} 0$

$\frac{12}{4} - 3 \stackrel{?}{=} 0$

$0 = 0$ True

$x = \frac{1}{3}:$ $12\left(\frac{1}{3}\right)^2 + 5\left(\frac{1}{3}\right) - 3 \stackrel{?}{=} 0$

$12 \cdot \frac{1}{9} + \frac{5}{3} - 3 \stackrel{?}{=} 0$

$\frac{4}{3} + \frac{5}{3} - 3 \stackrel{?}{=} 0$

$\frac{9}{3} - 3 \stackrel{?}{=} 0$

$0 = 0$ True

The solution set is $\left\{-\frac{3}{4}, \frac{1}{3}\right\}$. ∎

Work Smart

If $b^2 - 4ac$ is a perfect square, then the quadratic equation can be solved by factoring. In Example 1, $b^2 - 4ac = 169$, a perfect square.

$$12x^2 + 5x - 3 = 0$$

$$(4x + 3)(3x - 1) = 0$$

$$4x + 3 = 0 \quad \text{or} \quad 3x - 1 = 0$$

$$x = -\frac{3}{4} \quad \text{or} \quad x = \frac{1}{3}$$

Notice that the solutions to the equation in Example 1 are rational numbers and the expression $b^2 - 4ac$ under the radical in the quadratic formula, 169, is a perfect square. This leads to a generalization. Whenever the expression $b^2 - 4ac$ is a perfect square, then the quadratic equation will have rational solutions and the quadratic equation can be solved by factoring (provided the coefficients of the quadratic equation are rational numbers).

We summarize the steps used to solve a quadratic equation using the quadratic formula.

SOLVING A QUADRATIC EQUATION USING THE QUADRATIC FORMULA

Step 1: Write the equation in standard form $ax^2 + bx + c = 0$ and identify the values of a, b, and c.

Step 2: Substitute the values of a, b, and c into the quadratic formula.

Step 3: Simplify the expression found in Step 2.

Step 4: Verify your solution(s).

Quick ✔

1. The solution(s) to the quadratic equation $ax^2 + bx + c = 0$, $a \neq 0$, are given by the quadratic formula $x = $ _____ .

In Problems 2 and 3, solve each equation using the quadratic formula.

2. $2x^2 - 3x - 9 = 0$

3. $2x^2 + 7x = 4$

EXAMPLE 2 Solving a Quadratic Equation Using the Quadratic Formula

Solve: $3p^2 = 6p - 1$

Solution

First, we must write the equation in standard form to identify a, b, and c.

$$3p^2 = 6p - 1$$

Subtract $6p$ from both sides;
Add 1 to both sides:
$$3p^2 - 6p + 1 = 0$$

The variable in the equation is p,
so write "$p =$":
$$p = \frac{-b \pm \sqrt{b^2 - 4ac}}{2a}$$

$a = 3$, $b = -6$, $c = 1$:
$$p = \frac{-(-6) \pm \sqrt{(-6)^2 - 4(3)(1)}}{2(3)}$$

$$= \frac{6 \pm \sqrt{36 - 12}}{6}$$

$$= \frac{6 \pm \sqrt{24}}{6}$$

$\sqrt{24} = \sqrt{4 \cdot 6} = 2\sqrt{6}$:
$$= \frac{6 \pm 2\sqrt{6}}{6}$$

$\dfrac{a + b}{c} = \dfrac{a}{c} + \dfrac{b}{c}$:
$$= \frac{6}{6} \pm \frac{2\sqrt{6}}{6}$$

Simplify:
$$= 1 \pm \frac{\sqrt{6}}{3}$$

$a \pm b$ means $a - b$ or $a + b$:
$$p = 1 - \frac{\sqrt{6}}{3} \quad \text{or} \quad p = 1 + \frac{\sqrt{6}}{3}$$

Work Smart

We could also simplify $\dfrac{6 \pm 2\sqrt{6}}{6}$ by factoring:

$$\frac{6 \pm 2\sqrt{6}}{6} = \frac{2(3 \pm \sqrt{6})}{6}$$

$$= \frac{3 \pm \sqrt{6}}{3}$$

This is equivalent to $1 \pm \dfrac{\sqrt{6}}{3}$.
Ask your instructor which form of the solution is preferred, if any.

We leave it to you to verify the solutions. The solution set is $\left\{ 1 - \dfrac{\sqrt{6}}{3}, 1 + \dfrac{\sqrt{6}}{3} \right\}$. ∎

Notice in Example 2 that the value of $b^2 - 4ac$ is positive, but not a perfect square. There are two solutions to the quadratic equation and they are irrational.

Quick ✔

4. Solve: $4z^2 + 1 = 8z$

EXAMPLE 3 Solving a Rational Equation That Leads to a Quadratic Equation

Solve: $9m + \dfrac{4}{m} = 12$

Solution

We first note that m cannot equal 0. To clear the equation of rational expressions, we multiply both sides of the equation by the LCD, m.

$$m\left(9m + \frac{4}{m} \right) = 12 \cdot m$$

Distribute the m:
$$9m^2 + 4 = 12m$$

Subtract $12m$ from both sides:
$$9m^2 - 12m + 4 = 0$$

$$m = \frac{-b \pm \sqrt{b^2 - 4ac}}{2a}$$

Work Smart
Notice that the entire expression $-b \pm \sqrt{b^2 - 4ac}$ is in the numerator of the quadratic formula.

$a = 9, b = -12, c = 4$:

$$m = \frac{-(-12) \pm \sqrt{(-12)^2 - 4(9)(4)}}{2(9)}$$

$$= \frac{12 \pm \sqrt{144 - 144}}{18}$$

$$= \frac{12 \pm \sqrt{0}}{18}$$

$$= \frac{12}{18} = \frac{2}{3}$$

We leave it to you to verify the solution. The solution set is $\left\{\frac{2}{3}\right\}$. ∎

In Example 3, we had one solution rather than two (as in Examples 1 and 2). In fact, the solution of $\frac{2}{3}$ is called a **repeated root** because it actually occurs twice! To see why, we solve the equation given in Example 3 by factoring.

$$9m^2 + 4 = 12m$$

Subtract $12m$ from both sides: $\quad 9m^2 - 12m + 4 = 0$

$$(3m - 2)(3m - 2) = 0$$

Zero-Product Property: $\qquad 3m - 2 = 0 \quad \text{or} \quad 3m - 2 = 0$

$$m = \frac{2}{3} \quad \text{or} \qquad m = \frac{2}{3}$$

So we obtain two identical solutions because the expression $9m^2 - 12m + 4$ is a perfect square trinomial. We know that the equation $9m^2 - 12m + 4 = 0$ has a repeated root because the value $b^2 - 4ac$ equals 0. We will have more to say about this soon.

Quick ✔ *In Problems 5 and 6, solve each equation.*

5. $4w + \dfrac{25}{w} = 20$

6. $2x = 8 - \dfrac{3}{x}$

EXAMPLE 4 Solving a Quadratic Equation Using the Quadratic Formula

Solve: $y^2 - 4y + 13 = 0$

Solution

$$y^2 - 4y + 13 = 0$$
$$1y^2 - 4y + 13 = 0$$

$$y = \frac{-b \pm \sqrt{b^2 - 4ac}}{2a}$$

$a = 1, b = -4, c = 13$:

$$y = \frac{-(-4) \pm \sqrt{(-4)^2 - 4(1)(13)}}{2(1)}$$

$$= \frac{4 \pm \sqrt{16 - 52}}{2}$$

$\sqrt{-36} = 6i$:

$$= \frac{4 \pm \sqrt{-36}}{2} = \frac{4 \pm 6i}{2}$$

$\dfrac{a + b}{c} = \dfrac{a}{c} + \dfrac{b}{c}$:

$$= \frac{4}{2} \pm \frac{6}{2}i = 2 \pm 3i$$

$a \pm b$ means $a - b$ or $a + b$:

$$x = 2 - 3i \quad \text{or} \quad x = 2 + 3i$$

We leave it to you to verify the solution. The solution set is $\{2 - 3i, 2 + 3i\}$. ∎

Notice in Example 4 that the value of $b^2 - 4ac$ is negative and the equation has two complex solutions that are not real.

Quick ✔

7. Solve: $z^2 + 2z + 26 = 0$

---

2 Use the Discriminant to Determine the Nature of Solutions in a Quadratic Equation

In the quadratic formula $x = \dfrac{-b \pm \sqrt{b^2 - 4ac}}{2a}$, the quantity $b^2 - 4ac$ is called the **discriminant** of the quadratic equation, because its value tells us the number of solutions and the type of solution to expect from the quadratic formula.

THE DISCRIMINANT AND THE NATURE OF THE SOLUTION OF A QUADRATIC EQUATION

For a quadratic equation $ax^2 + bx + c = 0$, the discriminant $b^2 - 4ac$ can be used to describe the nature of the solution as shown:

Discriminant	Number of Solutions	Type of Solution	Example
Positive and a perfect square	2	Rational	1
Positive and not a perfect square	2	Irrational	2
Zero	1 (repeated root)	Rational	3
Negative	2	Complex, nonreal	4

Work Smart

The rules in the box to the right only apply if the coefficients of the quadratic equation are rational numbers.

If you look back at the results of Example 4, you should notice that the solutions are complex conjugates of each other. In general, for any quadratic equation of the form $ax^2 + bx + c = 0$, where a, b, and c are real numbers and $b^2 - 4ac < 0$, the equation will have two complex solutions that are not real and are complex conjugates of each other.

This result is a consequence of the quadratic formula. Suppose that $b^2 - 4ac = -N < 0$. Then, by the quadratic formula, the solutions are

$$x = \frac{-b + \sqrt{b^2 - 4ac}}{2a} = \frac{-b + \sqrt{-N}}{2a}$$

$$= \frac{-b + \sqrt{N}i}{2a} = \frac{-b}{2a} + \frac{\sqrt{N}}{2a}i$$

and

$$x = \frac{-b - \sqrt{b^2 - 4ac}}{2a} = \frac{-b - \sqrt{-N}}{2a}$$

$$= \frac{-b - \sqrt{N}i}{2a} = \frac{-b}{2a} - \frac{\sqrt{N}}{2a}i$$

which are conjugates of each other.

⌐EXAMPLE 5 Determining the Nature of the Solutions of a Quadratic Equation

For each quadratic equation, determine the discriminant. Use the value of the discriminant to determine whether the quadratic equation has two unequal rational solutions, two irrational solutions, one repeated real solution, or two complex solutions that are not real.

(a) $x^2 - 5x + 2 = 0$ **(b)** $9y^2 + 6y + 1 = 0$ **(c)** $3p^2 - p = -5$

Solution

(a) We compare $x^2 - 5x + 2 = 0$ to the standard form $ax^2 + bx + c = 0$.

$$x^2 - 5x + 2 = 0$$

$$\boxed{a = 1} \quad \boxed{b = -5} \quad \boxed{c = 2}$$

We have that $a = 1$, $b = -5$, and $c = 2$. Substituting these values into the formula for the discriminant, $b^2 - 4ac$, we obtain

$$b^2 - 4ac = (-5)^2 - 4(1)(2) = 25 - 8 = 17$$

Because $b^2 - 4ac = 17$ and 17 is positive, but not a perfect square, the quadratic equation will have two irrational solutions.

(b) For the quadratic equation $9y^2 + 6y + 1 = 0$, we have that $a = 9$, $b = 6$, and $c = 1$. Substituting these values into the formula for the discriminant, $b^2 - 4ac$, we obtain

$$b^2 - 4ac = 6^2 - 4(9)(1) = 36 - 36 = 0$$

Because $b^2 - 4ac = 0$, the quadratic equation will have one repeated real solution.

(c) Is the quadratic equation $3p^2 - p = -5$ in standard form? No! We add 5 to both sides of the equation and write the equation as $3p^2 - p + 5 = 0$. So we have that $a = 3$, $b = -1$, and $c = 5$. Substituting these values into the formula for the discriminant, $b^2 - 4ac$, we obtain

$$b^2 - 4ac = (-1)^2 - 4(3)(5) = 1 - 60 = -59$$

Because $b^2 - 4ac = -59 < 0$, the quadratic equation will have two complex solutions that are not real. The solutions will be complex conjugates of each other. ∎

Quick ✔

8. In the quadratic formula, the quantity $b^2 - 4ac$ is called the _____ of the quadratic equation.

9. If the discriminant of a quadratic equation is _____, then the quadratic equation has two complex solutions that are not real.

10. *True or False:* If the discriminant of a quadratic equation is zero, then the equation has no solution.

11. *True or False:* When solving a quadratic equation in which the solutions are complex numbers that are not real, the solutions will be complex conjugates of each other.

In Problems 12–14, use the value of the discriminant to determine whether the quadratic equation has two unequal rational solutions, two unequal irrational solutions, one repeated real solution, or two complex solutions that are not real.

12. $2z^2 + 5z + 4 = 0$ **13.** $4y^2 + 12y = -9$ **14.** $2x^2 - 4x + 1 = 0$

Which Method Should I Use?

We have now introduced four methods for solving quadratic equations:

1. Factoring

2. Square Root Property

3. Completing the Square

4. The Quadratic Formula

You are probably asking yourself, "Which method should I use?" and "Does it matter which method I use?" The answer to the second question is that it does not matter which method you use, but one method may be more efficient than the others. Table 1 contains guidelines to help you solve any quadratic equation. Notice how the value of the discriminant can be used to guide us in choosing the most efficient method.

Table 1		
Form of the Quadratic Equation	**Method**	**Example**
$x^2 = p$, where p is any real number	Square Root Property	$x^2 = 45$ Square Root Property: $\quad x = \pm\sqrt{45}$ $= \pm 3\sqrt{5}$
$ax^2 + c = 0$	Square Root Property	$3p^2 + 12 = 0$ Subtract 12 from both sides: $\quad 3p^2 = -12$ Divide both sides by 3: $\quad p^2 = -4$ Square Root Property: $\quad p = \pm\sqrt{-4}$ $= \pm 2i$
$ax^2 + bx + c = 0$, where $b^2 - 4ac$ is a perfect square. That is, $b^2 - 4ac$ is 1, 4, 9, 16, 25, …	Factoring or the Quadratic Formula	$a = 2, b = 1, c = -10: \quad 2m^2 + m - 10 = 0$ $b^2 - 4ac = 1^2 - 4(2)(-10) = 1 + 80 = 81$ 81 is a perfect square, so we can use factoring: $2m^2 + m - 10 = 0$ $(2m + 5)(m - 2) = 0$ $2m + 5 = 0 \quad$ or $\quad m - 2 = 0$ $m = -\dfrac{5}{2} \quad$ or $\quad m = 2$
$ax^2 + bx + c = 0$, where $b^2 - 4ac$ is not a perfect square.	Quadratic Formula or Completing the Square	$a = 2, b = 4, c = -1: \quad 2x^2 + 4x - 1 = 0$ $b^2 - 4ac = 4^2 - 4(2)(-1) = 16 + 8 = 24$ 24 is not a perfect square, so we use the quadratic formula (since it's easier than completing the square): $x = \dfrac{-b \pm \sqrt{b^2 - 4ac}}{2a}$ $= \dfrac{-4 \pm \sqrt{24}}{2(2)}$ $= \dfrac{-4 \pm 2\sqrt{6}}{4}$ $= -1 \pm \dfrac{\sqrt{6}}{2}$ $x = -1 - \dfrac{\sqrt{6}}{2}$ or $x = -1 + \dfrac{\sqrt{6}}{2}$

Notice if the value of the discriminant is a perfect square, we can either factor or use the quadratic formula to solve the equation. We should factor if the quadratic expression is easy to factor, otherwise use the quadratic formula.

You may have noticed that we did not recommend completing the square as one of the methods to use in solving a quadratic equation. This is because the quadratic formula was developed by completing the square of $ax^2 + bx + c = 0$. Besides, completing the square is a cumbersome task, whereas the quadratic formula is fairly straightforward to use. We did not waste your time by discussing completing the square, however, because it was needed to present a discussion of the quadratic formula. In addition, completing the square is a skill that you will need later in this course and in future math courses.

Quick ✔

15. *True or False:* If the discriminant of a quadratic equation is a perfect square, then the equation can be solved by factoring.

In Problems 16–18, solve each quadratic equation using any appropriate method.

16. $5n^2 - 45 = 0$ **17.** $-2y^2 + 5y - 6 = 0$ **18.** $3w^2 + 2w = 5$

⌐3¬ Model and Solve Problems Involving Quadratic Equations

Many applied problems require solving quadratic equations. In the example below, we use a quadratic equation to determine the number of units that a company must sell in order to earn a certain amount of revenue. As always, we shall employ the problem-solving strategy first presented in Section 1.2.

EXAMPLE 6 Revenue

The revenue R received by a company selling x specialty T-shirts per week is given by the function $R(x) = -0.005x^2 + 30x$.

(a) How many T-shirts must be sold in order for revenue to be $25,000 per week?

(b) How many T-shirts must be sold in order for revenue to be $45,000 per week?

Solution

(a) **Step 1: Identify** Here, we are looking to determine the number of T-shirts x required so that $R = \$25,000$.

Step 2: Name We know that x represents the number of T-shirts sold.

Step 3: Translate We need to solve the equation $R(x) = 25,000$.

$$R(x) = 25,000$$
$$-0.005x^2 + 30x = 25,000$$
$$-0.005x^2 + 30x - 25,000 = 0$$

Step 4: Solve $a = -0.005, b - 30, c = -25,000$

$$b^2 - 4ac = 30^2 - 4(-0.005)(-25,000)$$
$$= 400$$

Because 400 is a perfect square, we can solve the equation by factoring or using the quadratic formula. It is not obvious how to factor $-0.005x^2 + 30x - 25000$, so we will use the quadratic formula to solve the equation.

$$b^2 - 4ac = 400$$
$$\downarrow$$
$$x = \frac{-30 \pm \sqrt{400}}{2(-0.005)}$$
$$= \frac{-30 \pm 20}{-0.01}$$

$$x = \frac{-30 - 20}{-0.01} = 5000 \quad \text{or} \quad x = \frac{-30 + 20}{-0.01} = 1000$$

Step 5: Check If 1000 T-shirts are sold, then revenue is $R(1000) = -0.005(1000)^2 + 30(1000) = \$25,000$. If 5000 T-shirts are sold, then revenue is $R(5000) = -0.005(5000)^2 + 30(5000) = \$25,000$.

Step 6: Answer The company needs to sell either 1000 or 5000 T-shirts each week to earn \$25,000 in revenue.

(b) **Step 1: Identify** Here, we are looking to determine the number of T-shirts x required so that $R = \$45,000$. That is, we wish to solve the equation $R(x) = 45,000$.

Step 2: Name We know that x represents the number of T-shirts sold.

Step 3: Translate We need to solve the equation $R(x) = 45,000$.

$$R(x) = 45,000$$
$$-0.005x^2 + 30x = 45,000$$
$$-0.005x^2 + 30x - 45,000 = 0$$

Step 4: Solve $a = -0.005, b = 30, c = -45,000$
$$b^2 - 4ac = 30^2 - 4(-0.005)(-45,000) = 0$$

Because the discriminant is 0, the quadratic equation will have a single real solution. In addition, because the discriminant is 0, we can solve the equation by factoring or using the quadratic formula. It is not obvious how to factor $-0.005x^2 + 30x - 45,000$, so we will use the quadratic formula to solve the equation.

$$x = \frac{-30 \pm \sqrt{0}}{2(-0.005)} \qquad b^2 - 4ac = 0$$
$$= \frac{-30 \pm 0}{-0.01}$$
$$= \frac{-30}{-0.01} = 3000$$

Step 5: Check If 3000 T-shirts are sold, then revenue is $R(3000) = -0.005(3000)^2 + 30(3000) = \$45,000$.

Step 6: Answer The company needs to sell 3,000 T-shirts each week to earn \$45,000 in revenue. ▪

Quick ✔

19. The revenue R received by a video store renting x DVDs per day is given by the function $R(x) = -0.005x^2 + 4x$.

  (a) How many DVDs must be rented in order for revenue to be \$600 per day?

  (b) How many DVDs must be rented in order for revenue to be \$800 per day?

EXAMPLE 7 Designing a Window

A window designer wishes to design a window so that the diagonal is 20 feet. In addition, the length of the window needs to be 4 feet more than the height. What are the dimensions of the window?

Solution

Step 1: Identify We wish to know the dimensions of the window. That is, we want to know the length and height of the window.

Step 2: Name Let h represent the height of the window so that $h + 4$ is the length (since the length is 4 feet more than the height).

Figure 6

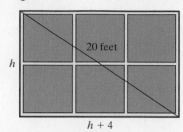

Step 3: Translate Figure 6 illustrates the situation. From the figure, we can see that the three sides form a right triangle. We can express the relation among the three sides using the Pythagorean Theorem.

$$\text{leg}^2 + \text{leg}^2 = \text{hypotenuse}^2: \qquad h^2 + (h+4)^2 = 20^2$$
$$(A+B)^2 = A^2 + 2AB + B^2: \quad h^2 + h^2 + 8h + 16 = 400$$
$$\text{Combine like terms:} \qquad 2h^2 + 8h + 16 = 400$$
$$\text{Subtract 400 from both sides:} \qquad 2h^2 + 8h - 384 = 0$$
$$\text{Divide both sides by 2:} \qquad h^2 + 4h - 192 = 0$$

Step 4: Solve In the model, we have that $a = 1, b = 4, c = -192$. The discriminant is $b^2 - 4ac = 4^2 - 4(1)(-192) = 784$ and $784 = 28^2$. So we can solve the equation by factoring.

$$h^2 + 4h - 192 = 0$$
$$(h + 16)(h - 12) = 0$$
$$h + 16 = 0 \quad \text{or} \quad h - 12 = 0$$
$$h = -16 \quad \text{or} \qquad h = 12$$

Step 5: Check We disregard the solution $h = -16$ because h represents the height of the window. We see if a window whose dimensions are 12 feet by $12 + 4 = 16$ feet has a diagonal that is 20 feet by verifying that $12^2 + 16^2 = 20^2$.

$$12^2 + 16^2 \overset{?}{=} 20^2$$
$$144 + 256 \overset{?}{=} 400$$
$$400 = 400$$

Step 6: Answer The dimensions of the window are 12 feet by 16 feet. ∎

Quick ✔

20. A rectangular plot of land is designed so that its length is 14 meters more than its width. The diagonal of the land is known to be 34 meters. What are the dimensions of the land?

7.2 EXERCISES

PRACTICE   WATCH   DOWNLOAD   READ   REVIEW

1–20. *are the* Quick ✔*s that follow each* EXAMPLE

Building Skills

In Problems 21–38, solve each equation using the quadratic formula. See Objective 1.

21. $x^2 - 4x - 12 = 0$

22. $p^2 - 4p - 32 = 0$

23. $6y^2 - y - 15 = 0$

24. $10x^2 + x - 2 = 0$

25. $4m^2 - 8m + 1 = 0$

26. $2q^2 - 4q + 1 = 0$

27. $3w - 6 = \dfrac{1}{w}$

28. $x + \dfrac{1}{x} = 3$

29. $3p^2 = -2p + 4$

30. $5w^2 = -3w + 1$

31. $x^2 - 2x + 7 = 0$

32. $y^2 - 4y + 5 = 0$

33. $2z^2 + 7 = 2z$

34. $2z^2 + 7 = 4z$

35. $4x^2 = 2x + 1$

36. $6p^2 - 4p + 1$

37. $1 = 3q^2 + 4q$

38. $1 = 5w^2 + 6w$

In Problems 39–48, determine the discriminant of each quadratic equation. Use the value of the discriminant to determine whether the quadratic equation has two rational solutions, two irrational solutions, one repeated real solution, or two complex solutions that are not real. See Objective 2.

39. $x^2 - 5x + 1 = 0$

40. $p^2 + 4p - 2 = 0$

41. $3z^2 + 2z + 5 = 0$

42. $2y^2 - 3y + 5 = 0$

43. $9q^2 - 6q + 1 = 0$

44. $16x^2 + 24x + 9 = 0$

45. $3w^2 = 4w - 2$

46. $6x^2 - x = -4$

47. $6x = 2x^2 - 1$

48. $10w^2 = 3$

Mixed Practice

In Problems 49–74, solve each equation.

49. $w^2 - 5w + 5 = 0$

50. $q^2 - 7q + 7 = 0$

51. $3x^2 + 5x = 8$

52. $4p^2 + 5p = 9$

53. $2x^2 = 3x + 35$

54. $3x^2 + 5x = 2$

55. $q^2 + 2q + 8 = 0$

56. $w^2 + 4w + 9 = 0$

57. $2z^2 = 2(z + 3)^2$

58. $3z^2 = 3(z + 1)(z - 2)$

59. $7q - 2 = \dfrac{4}{q}$

60. $5m - 4 = \dfrac{5}{m}$

61. $5a^2 - 80 = 0$

62. $4p^2 - 100 = 0$

63. $8n^2 + 1 = 4n$

64. $4q^2 + 1 = 2q$

65. $27x^2 + 36x + 12 = 0$

66. $8p^2 - 40p + 50 = 0$

67. $\dfrac{1}{3}x^2 + \dfrac{2}{9}x - 1 = 0$

68. $\dfrac{1}{2}x^2 + \dfrac{3}{4}x - 1 = 0$

69. $(x - 5)(x + 1) = 4$

70. $(a - 3)(a + 1) = 2$

71. $\dfrac{x - 2}{x + 2} = x - 3$

72. $\dfrac{x - 5}{x + 3} = x - 3$

73. $\dfrac{x - 4}{x^2 + 2} = 2$

74. $\dfrac{x - 1}{x^2 + 4} = 1$

75. Suppose that $f(x) = x^2 + 4x - 21$.
 (a) Solve $f(x) = 0$ for x.
 (b) Solve $f(x) = -21$ for x. What points are on the graph of f?

76. Suppose that $f(x) = x^2 + 2x - 8$.
 (a) Solve $f(x) = 0$ for x.
 (b) Solve $f(x) = -8$ for x. What points are on the graph of f?

77. Suppose that $H(x) = -2x^2 - 4x + 1$.
 (a) Solve $H(x) = 0$ for x.
 (b) Solve $H(x) = 2$ for x.

78. Suppose that $g(x) = 3x^2 + x - 1$.
 (a) Solve $g(x) = 0$ for x.
 (b) Solve $g(x) = 4$ for x.

79. What are the zeros of $G(x) = 3x^2 + 2x - 2$?

80. What are the zeros of $F(x) = x^2 + 3x - 3$?

Applying the Concepts

In Problems 81–84, use the Pythagorean Theorem to determine the value of x and the measurements of each side of the right triangle.

81.

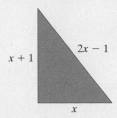

82.

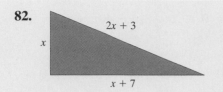

$2x + 3$

x

$x + 7$

83.

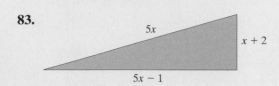

$5x$

$x + 2$

$5x - 1$

84.

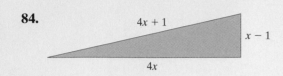

$4x + 1$

$x - 1$

$4x$

△ **85. Area** The area of a rectangle is 40 square inches. The width of the rectangle is 4 inches more than the length. What are the dimensions of the rectangle?

△ **86. Area** The area of a rectangle is 60 square inches. The width of the rectangle is 6 inches more than the length. What are the dimensions of the rectangle?

△ **87. Area** The area of a triangle is 25 square inches. The height of the triangle is 3 inches less than the base. What are the base and height of the triangle?

△ **88. Area** The area of a triangle is 35 square inches. The height of the triangle is 2 inches less than the base. What are the base and height of the triangle?

89. Revenue The revenue R received by a company selling x pairs of sunglasses per week is given by the function $R(x) = -0.1x^2 + 70x$.

(a) Find and interpret the values of $R(17)$ and $R(25)$.
(b) How many pairs of sunglasses must be sold in order for revenue to be $10,000 per week?
(c) How many pairs of sunglasses must be sold in order for revenue to be $12,250 per week?

90. Revenue The revenue R received by a company selling x "all-day passes" to a small amusement park per day is given by the function $R(x) = -0.02x^2 + 24x$.

(a) Find and interpret the values of $R(300)$ and $R(800)$.
(b) How many tickets must be sold in order for revenue to be $4000 per day?
(c) How many tickets must be sold in order for revenue to be $7200 per day?

91. Projectile Motion The height s of a ball after t seconds when thrown straight up with an initial speed of 70 feet per second from an initial height of 5 feet can be modeled by the function

$$s(t) = -16t^2 + 70t + 5$$

(a) When will the height of the ball be 40 feet? Round your answer to the nearest tenth of a second.
(b) When will the height of the ball be 70 feet? Round your answer to the nearest tenth of a second.
(c) Will the ball ever reach a height of 150 feet? How does the result of the equation tell you this?

92. Projectile Motion The height s of a toy rocket after t seconds when fired straight up with an initial speed of 150 feet per second from an initial height of 2 feet can be modeled by the function

$$s(t) = -16t^2 + 150t + 2$$

(a) When will the height of the rocket be 200 feet? Round your answer to the nearest tenth of a second.
(b) When will the height of the rocket be 300 feet? Round your answer to the nearest tenth of a second.
(c) Will the rocket ever reach a height of 500 feet?

△ **93. Similar Triangles** Consult the figure. Suppose that $\triangle ABC \sim \triangle DEC$. The length of $\overline{BC}$ is 24 inches and the length of $\overline{DE}$ is 6 inches. If the length of $\overline{AB}$ equals the length of $\overline{CE}$, which we call x, find x.

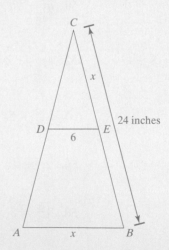

94. Number Sense Three times the square of a number equals the sum of two times the number and 5. Find the number(s).

95. Life Cycle Hypothesis The Life Cycle Hypothesis from Economics was presented by Franco Modigliani in 1954. One of its components states that income is a function of age. The function $I(a) = -55a^2 + 5119a - 54,448$

represents the relation between average annual income I and age a.

(a) For what age does average income I equal $40,000? Round your answer to the nearest year.

(b) For what age does average income I equal $50,000? Round your answer to the nearest year.

96. Population The function $P(a) = 0.015a^2 - 4.962a + 290.580$ represents the population (in millions) of Americans in 2001, P, that are a years of age or older.

(SOURCE: *United States Census Bureau*)

(a) For what age range was the population 200 million in 2001? Round your answer to the nearest year.

(b) For what age range was the population 50 million in 2001? Round your answer to the nearest year.

97. Upstream and Back Zene decides to canoe 4 miles upstream on a river to a waterfall and then canoe back. The total trip (excluding the time spent at the waterfall) takes 6 hours. Zene knows she can canoe at an average speed of 5 miles per hour in still water. What is the speed of the current?

98. Round Trip A Cessna aircraft flies 200 miles due west into the jet stream and flies back home on the same route. The total time of the trip (excluding the time on the ground) takes 4 hours. The Cessna aircraft can fly 120 miles per hour in still air. What is the net effect of the jet stream on the aircraft?

99. Work Robert and Susan have a newspaper route. When they work the route together, it takes 2 hours to deliver all the newspapers. One morning Robert told Susan he was too sick to deliver the papers. Susan doesn't remember how long it takes for her to deliver the newspapers working alone, but she does remember that Robert can finish the route one hour sooner than Susan can when working alone. How long will it take Susan to finish the route?

100. Work Demitrius needs to fill up his pool. When he rents a water tanker to fill the pool with the help of the hose from his house, it takes 5 hours to fill the pool. One year, money is tight and he can't afford to rent the water tanker to fill the pool. He doesn't remember how long it takes for his house hose to fill the pool, but does remember that the tanker hose filling the pool alone can finish the job in 8 fewer hours than using his house hose alone. How long will it take Demitrius to fill his pool using only his house hose?

Extending the Concepts

101. Show that the sum of the solutions to a quadratic equation is $-\dfrac{b}{a}$.

102. Show that the product of the solutions to a quadratic equation is $\dfrac{c}{a}$.

103. Show that the real solutions of the equation $ax^2 + bx + c = 0$ are the negatives of the real solutions of the equation $ax^2 - bx + c = 0$. Assume that $b^2 - 4ac \geq 0$.

104. Show that the real solutions of the equation $ax^2 + bx + c = 0$ are the reciprocals of the real solutions of the equation $cx^2 + bx + a = 0$. Assume that $b^2 - 4ac \geq 0$.

Explaining the Concepts

105. Explain the circumstances for which you would use factoring to solve a quadratic equation.

106. Explain the circumstances for which you would use the Square Root Property to solve a quadratic equation.

Synthesis Review

107. (a) Graph $f(x) = x^2 + 3x + 2$ by plotting points.

(b) Solve the equation $x^2 + 3x + 2 = 0$.

(c) Compare the solutions to the equation in part **(b)** to the x-intercepts of the graph drawn in part **(a)**. What do you notice?

108. (a) Graph $f(x) = x^2 - x - 6$ by plotting points.

(b) Solve the equation $x^2 - x - 6 = 0$.

(c) Compare the solutions to the equation in part **(b)** to the x-intercepts of the graph drawn in part **(a)**. What do you notice?

109. (a) Graph $g(x) = x^2 - 2x + 1$ by plotting points.

(b) Solve the equation $x^2 - 2x + 1 = 0$.

(c) Compare the solutions to the equation in part **(b)** to the x-intercepts of the graph drawn in part **(a)**. What do you notice?

110. (a) Graph $g(x) = x^2 + 4x + 4$ by plotting points.

(b) Solve the equation $x^2 + 4x + 4 = 0$.

(c) Compare the solutions to the equation in part **(b)** to the x-intercepts of the graph drawn in part **(a)**. What do you notice?

The Graphing Calculator

In Problems 111–114, the graph of the quadratic function f is given. For each function determine the discriminant of the equation $f(x) = 0$ in order to determine the nature of the solutions of the equation $f(x) = 0$. Compare the nature of solutions based on the discriminant to the graph of the function.

111. $f(x) = x^2 - 7x + 3$

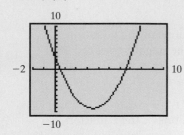

112. $f(x) = -x^2 - 3x + 1$

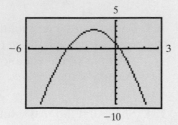

113. $f(x) = -x^2 - 3x - 4$

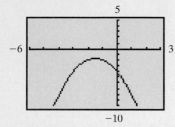

114. $f(x) = x^2 - 6x + 9$

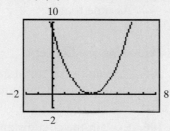

115. (a) Solve the equation $x^2 - 5x - 24 = 0$ algebraically.
  (b) Graph $Y_1 = x^2 - 5x - 24$. Compare the x-intercepts of the graph to the solutions found in part **(a)**.

116. (a) Solve the equation $x^2 - 4x - 45 = 0$ algebraically.
  (b) Graph $Y_1 = x^2 - 4x - 45$. Compare the x-intercepts of the graph to the solutions found in part **(a)**.

117. (a) Solve the equation $x^2 - 6x + 9 = 0$ algebraically.
  (b) Graph $Y_1 = x^2 - 6x + 9$. Compare the x-intercepts of the graph to the solutions found in part **(a)**.

118. (a) Solve the equation $x^2 + 10x + 25 = 0$ algebraically.
  (b) Graph $Y_1 = x^2 + 10x + 25$. Compare the x-intercepts of the graph to the solutions found in part **(a)**.

119. (a) Solve the equation $x^2 + 5x + 8 = 0$ algebraically.
  (b) Graph $Y_1 = x^2 + 5x + 8$. How does the result of part **(a)** relate to the graph?

120. (a) Solve the equation $x^2 + 2x + 5 = 0$ algebraically.
  (b) Graph $Y_1 = x^2 + 2x + 5$. How does the result of part **(a)** relate to the graph?

7.3 Solving Equations Quadratic in Form

OBJECTIVE

1 Solve Equations That Are Quadratic in Form

Preparing for Solving Equations Quadratic in Form

Before getting started, take the following readiness quiz. If you get a problem wrong, go back to the section cited and review the material.

P1. Factor: $x^4 - 5x^2 - 6$ [Section 4.5, p. 368]

P2. Factor: $2(p + 3)^2 + 3(p + 3) - 5$ [Section 4.5, p. 368]

P3. Simplify: **(a)** $(x^2)^2$ **(b)** $(p^{-1})^2$ [Getting Ready: Integer Exponents, pp. 310–311]

1 Solve Equations That Are Quadratic in Form

Consider the equation $x^4 - 4x^2 - 12 = 0$. While this equation is not in the form of a quadratic equation, $ax^2 + bx + c = 0$, we can write the equation as $(x^2)^2 - 4x^2 - 12 = 0$. Then, if we let $u = x^2$ in the equation, we obtain $u^2 - 4u - 12 = 0$, which is of the form $ax^2 + bx + c = 0$. Now we can solve $u^2 - 4u - 12 = 0$ for u by factoring. Then, using the fact that $u = x^2$, we find x, which was our goal in the first place.

In general, if a substitution u transforms an equation into one of the form

$$au^2 + bu + c = 0$$

then the original equation is called an **equation quadratic in form.**

Preparing for...Answers
P1. $(x^2 - 6)(x^2 + 1)$
P2. $(2p + 11)(p + 2)$
P3. (a) x^4 **(b)** $p^{-2} = \dfrac{1}{p^2}$

The difficulty in solving equations that are quadratic in form is that it is often hard to determine that the equation is, in fact, quadratic in form. Table 2 shows some equations that are quadratic in form and the appropriate substitution.

Table 2		
Original Equation	Substitution	Equation with Substitution
$2x^4 - 3x^2 + 5 = 0$ $2(x^2)^2 - 3x^2 + 5 = 0$	$u = x^2$	$2u^2 - 3u + 5 = 0$
$3(z - 5)^2 + 4(z - 5) + 1 = 0$	$u = z - 5$	$3u^2 + 4u + 1 = 0$
$-2y + 5\sqrt{y} - 2 = 0$ $-2(\sqrt{y})^2 + 5\sqrt{y} - 2 = 0$	$u = \sqrt{y}$	$-2u^2 + 5u - 2 = 0$

EXAMPLE 1 How to Solve Equations That Are Quadratic in Form

Solve: $x^4 + x^2 - 12 = 0$

Step-by-Step Solution

Step 1: Determine the appropriate substitution and write the equation in the form $au^2 + bu + c = 0$.

$$x^4 + x^2 - 12 = 0$$
$$(x^2)^2 + x^2 - 12 = 0$$
Let $x^2 = u$: $\quad u^2 + u - 12 = 0$

Step 2: Solve the equation $au^2 + bu + c = 0$.

$$(u + 4)(u - 3) = 0$$
$$u + 4 = 0 \quad \text{or} \quad u - 3 = 0$$
$$u = -4 \quad \text{or} \quad u = 3$$

Step 3: Solve for the variable in the original equation using the value of u found in Step 2.

We want to know x, so replace u with x^2: $\quad x^2 = -4 \quad$ or $\quad x^2 = 3$

Square Root Property: $\quad x = \pm\sqrt{-4} \quad$ or $\quad x = \pm\sqrt{3}$
$$= \pm 2i$$

Step 4: Verify your solutions.

$x = 2i$:
$$(2i)^4 + (2i)^2 - 12 \stackrel{?}{=} 0$$
$$2^4 i^4 + 2^2 i^2 - 12 \stackrel{?}{=} 0$$
$$16(1) + 4(-1) - 12 \stackrel{?}{=} 0$$
$$16 - 4 - 12 \stackrel{?}{=} 0$$
$$0 = 0 \quad \text{True}$$

$x = -2i$:
$$(-2i)^4 + (-2i)^2 - 12 \stackrel{?}{=} 0$$
$$(-2)^4 i^4 + (-2)^2 i^2 - 12 \stackrel{?}{=} 0$$
$$16(1) + 4(-1) - 12 \stackrel{?}{=} 0$$
$$16 - 4 - 12 \stackrel{?}{=} 0$$
$$0 = 0 \quad \text{True}$$

$x = \sqrt{3}$:
$$(\sqrt{3})^4 + (\sqrt{3})^2 - 12 \stackrel{?}{=} 0$$
$$\sqrt{3}^4 + \sqrt{3}^2 - 12 \stackrel{?}{=} 0$$
$$\sqrt{81} + 3 - 12 \stackrel{?}{=} 0$$
$$9 + 3 - 12 \stackrel{?}{=} 0$$
$$0 = 0 \quad \text{True}$$

$x = -\sqrt{3}$:
$$(-\sqrt{3})^4 + (-\sqrt{3})^2 - 12 \stackrel{?}{=} 0$$
$$(-1)^4 \sqrt{3}^4 + (-1)^2 \sqrt{3}^2 - 12 \stackrel{?}{=} 0$$
$$\sqrt{81} + 3 - 12 \stackrel{?}{=} 0$$
$$9 + 3 - 12 \stackrel{?}{=} 0$$
$$0 = 0 \quad \text{True}$$

The solution set is $\left\{2i, -2i, \sqrt{3}, -\sqrt{3}\right\}$. ∎

We summarize the steps used to solve an equation that is quadratic in form.

SOLVING EQUATIONS QUADRATIC IN FORM

Step 1: Determine the appropriate substitution and write the equation in the form $au^2 + bu + c = 0$.

Step 2: Solve the equation $au^2 + bu + c = 0$.

Step 3: Solve for the variable in the original equation using the value of u found in Step 2.

Step 4: Verify your solutions.

Quick ✔

1. If a substitution u transforms an equation into one of the form $au^2 + bu + c = 0$, then the original equation is called an equation _____ __ ____.

2. For the equation $2(3x + 1)^2 - 5(3x + 1) + 2 = 0$, an appropriate substitution would be $u = $ _____.

3. *True or False:* The equation $3\left(\dfrac{x}{x - 2}\right)^2 - \dfrac{5x}{x - 2} + 3 = 0$ is quadratic in form.

4. What is the appropriate choice for u when solving the equation $2 \cdot \dfrac{1}{x^2} - 6 \cdot \dfrac{1}{x} + 3 = 0$?

In Problems 5 and 6, solve each equation.

5. $x^4 - 13x^2 + 36 = 0$ 6. $p^4 - 7p^2 = 18$

⌐EXAMPLE 2⌐ Solving Equations That Are Quadratic in Form

Solve: $(z^2 - 5)^2 - 3(z^2 - 5) - 4 = 0$

Solution

$$(z^2 - 5)^2 - 3(z^2 - 5) - 4 = 0$$

Let $u = z^2 - 5$: $u^2 - 3u - 4 = 0$

$$(u - 4)(u + 1) = 0$$

$$u - 4 = 0 \quad \text{or} \quad u + 1 = 0$$

$$u = 4 \quad \text{or} \quad u = -1$$

Replace u with $z^2 - 5$ and solve for z: $z^2 - 5 = 4 \quad \text{or} \quad z^2 - 5 = -1$

$$z^2 = 9 \quad \text{or} \quad z^2 = 4$$

Square Root Property: $z = \pm 3 \quad \text{or} \quad z = \pm 2$

Check

$$z = -3:$$
$$((-3)^2 - 5)^2 - 3((-3)^2 - 5) - 4 \overset{?}{=} 0$$
$$(9 - 5)^2 - 3(9 - 5) - 4 \overset{?}{=} 0$$
$$4^2 - 3(4) - 4 \overset{?}{=} 0$$
$$16 - 12 - 4 \overset{?}{=} 0$$
$$0 = 0 \quad \text{True}$$

$$z = 3:$$
$$((3)^2 - 5)^2 - 3((3)^2 - 5) - 4 \overset{?}{=} 0$$
$$(9 - 5)^2 - 3(9 - 5) - 4 \overset{?}{=} 0$$
$$4^2 - 3(4) - 4 \overset{?}{=} 0$$
$$16 - 12 - 4 \overset{?}{=} 0$$
$$0 = 0 \quad \text{True}$$

$$z = -2:$$
$$((-2)^2 - 5)^2 - 3((-2)^2 - 5) - 4 \overset{?}{=} 0$$
$$(4 - 5)^2 - 3(4 - 5) - 4 \overset{?}{=} 0$$
$$(-1)^2 - 3(-1) - 4 \overset{?}{=} 0$$
$$1 + 3 - 4 \overset{?}{=} 0$$
$$0 = 0 \quad \text{True}$$

$$z = 2:$$
$$((2)^2 - 5)^2 - 3((2)^2 - 5) - 4 \overset{?}{=} 0$$
$$(4 - 5)^2 - 3(4 - 5) - 4 \overset{?}{=} 0$$
$$(-1)^2 - 3(-1) - 4 \overset{?}{=} 0$$
$$1 + 3 - 4 \overset{?}{=} 0$$
$$0 = 0 \quad \text{True}$$

The solution set is $\{-3, -2, 2, 3\}$.   ∎

> **Quick ✔** *In Problems 7 and 8, solve each equation.*
>
> **7.** $(p^2 - 2)^2 - 9(p^2 - 2) + 14 = 0$ **8.** $2(2z^2 - 1)^2 + 5(2z^2 - 1) - 3 = 0$

When we raise both sides of an equation to an even power (such as squaring both sides of the equation), there is a possibility that we will introduce extraneous solutions to the equation. Under these circumstances, it is imperative that we verify our solutions.

EXAMPLE 3 Solving Equations That Are Quadratic in Form

Solve: $3x - 5\sqrt{x} - 2 = 0$

Solution

$$3x - 5\sqrt{x} - 2 = 0$$
$$3(\sqrt{x})^2 - 5\sqrt{x} - 2 = 0$$

Let $u = \sqrt{x}$:
$$3u^2 - 5u - 2 = 0$$
$$(3u + 1)(u - 2) = 0$$
$$3u + 1 = 0 \quad \text{or} \quad u - 2 = 0$$
$$3u = -1 \quad \text{or} \quad u = 2$$
$$u = -\frac{1}{3}$$

Replace u with $\sqrt{x}$ and solve for x:
$$\sqrt{x} = -\frac{1}{3} \quad \text{or} \quad \sqrt{x} = 2$$

Square both sides:
$$x = \frac{1}{9} \quad \text{or} \quad x = 4$$

Check

$$x = \frac{1}{9}: \quad 3 \cdot \frac{1}{9} - 5\sqrt{\frac{1}{9}} - 2 = 0$$
$$\frac{1}{3} - 5 \cdot \frac{1}{3} - 2 = 0$$
$$\frac{1}{3} - \frac{5}{3} + \frac{6}{3} = 0$$
$$\frac{2}{3} = 0 \quad \text{False}$$

$$x = 4: \quad 3 \cdot 4 - 5\sqrt{4} - 2 = 0$$
$$12 - 5 \cdot 2 - 2 = 0$$
$$12 - 10 - 2 = 0$$
$$0 = 0 \quad \text{True}$$

The apparent solution $x = \frac{1}{9}$ is extraneous. The solution set is $\{4\}$.   ∎

We could also have solved the equation in Example 3 using the methods introduced in Section 6.7 by isolating the radical and squaring both sides.

> **Quick ✔** *In Problems 9 and 10, solve the equation.*
>
> **9.** $3w - 14\sqrt{w} + 8 = 0$ **10.** $2q - 9\sqrt{q} - 5 = 0$

EXAMPLE 4 Solving Equations That Are Quadratic in Form

Solve: $4x^{-2} + 13x^{-1} - 12 = 0$

Solution

$$4x^{-2} + 13x^{-1} - 12 = 0$$
$$4(x^{-1})^2 + 13x^{-1} - 12 = 0$$

Let $u = x^{-1}$: $\qquad 4u^2 + 13u - 12 = 0$

Factor: $\qquad (4u - 3)(u + 4) = 0$

$$4u - 3 = 0 \quad \text{or} \quad u + 4 = 0$$
$$4u = 3 \quad \text{or} \qquad u = -4$$
$$u = \frac{3}{4}$$

Replace u with x^{-1} and solve for x: $\qquad x^{-1} = \frac{3}{4} \quad \text{or} \quad x^{-1} = -4$

$x^{-1} = \frac{1}{x}$: $\qquad\qquad \dfrac{1}{x} = \dfrac{3}{4} \quad \text{or} \quad \dfrac{1}{x} = -4$

Take the reciprocal of both sides
of the equation: $\qquad\qquad x = \dfrac{4}{3} \quad \text{or} \quad x = \dfrac{1}{-4} = -\dfrac{1}{4}$

Check $\qquad x = \dfrac{4}{3}$: $\qquad\qquad\qquad\qquad\qquad x = -\dfrac{1}{4}$:

$$4\left(\frac{4}{3}\right)^{-2} + 13 \cdot \left(\frac{4}{3}\right)^{-1} - 12 \stackrel{?}{=} 0 \qquad 4\left(-\frac{1}{4}\right)^{-2} + 13 \cdot \left(-\frac{1}{4}\right)^{-1} - 12 \stackrel{?}{=} 0$$

$$4\left(\frac{3}{4}\right)^2 + 13 \cdot \frac{3}{4} - 12 \stackrel{?}{=} 0 \qquad\qquad 4(-4)^2 + 13 \cdot (-4) - 12 \stackrel{?}{=} 0$$

$$4 \cdot \frac{9}{16} + \frac{39}{4} - 12 \stackrel{?}{=} 0 \qquad\qquad\qquad 4 \cdot 16 - 52 - 12 \stackrel{?}{=} 0$$

$$\frac{9}{4} + \frac{39}{4} - \frac{48}{4} \stackrel{?}{=} 0 \qquad\qquad\qquad 64 - 52 - 12 \stackrel{?}{=} 0$$

$$\qquad\qquad\qquad\qquad\qquad\qquad\qquad\qquad 0 = 0 \;\; \text{True}$$

$$0 = 0 \;\; \text{True}$$

The solution set is $\left\{-\dfrac{1}{4}, \dfrac{4}{3}\right\}$. ∎

> **Quick ✔** *In Problem 11, solve the equation.*
>
> **11.** $5x^{-2} + 12x^{-1} + 4 = 0$

EXAMPLE 5 Solving Equations That Are Quadratic in Form

Solve: $a^{\frac{2}{3}} + 3a^{\frac{1}{3}} - 28 = 0$

Solution

$$a^{\frac{2}{3}} + 3a^{\frac{1}{3}} - 28 = 0$$
$$\left(a^{\frac{1}{3}}\right)^2 + 3a^{\frac{1}{3}} - 28 = 0$$

Let $u = a^{\frac{1}{3}}$: $\qquad u^2 + 3u - 28 = 0$

$$(u + 7)(u - 4) = 0$$
$$u + 7 = 0 \qquad \text{or} \quad u - 4 = 0$$
$$u = -7 \qquad \text{or} \qquad u = 4$$

Replace u with $a^{\frac{1}{3}}$ and solve for a: $\qquad a^{\frac{1}{3}} = -7 \qquad \text{or} \qquad a^{\frac{1}{3}} = 4$

Cube both sides of the equation: $\qquad \left(a^{\frac{1}{3}}\right)^3 = (-7)^3 \quad \text{or} \quad \left(a^{\frac{1}{3}}\right)^3 = 4^3$

$$a = -343 \qquad \text{or} \qquad a = 64$$

Check　　　$a = -343$:

$$(-343)^{\frac{2}{3}} + 3(-343)^{\frac{1}{3}} - 28 = 0$$

$$\left(\sqrt[3]{-343}\right)^2 + 3 \cdot \sqrt[3]{-343} - 28 \stackrel{?}{=} 0$$

$$(-7)^2 + 3 \cdot (-7) - 28 \stackrel{?}{=} 0$$

$$49 - 21 - 28 \stackrel{?}{=} 0$$

$$0 = 0 \quad \text{True}$$

$a = 64$:

$$(64)^{\frac{2}{3}} + 3(64)^{\frac{1}{3}} - 28 = 0$$

$$\left(\sqrt[3]{64}\right)^2 + 3 \cdot \sqrt[3]{64} - 28 \stackrel{?}{=} 0$$

$$4^2 + 3 \cdot 4 - 28 \stackrel{?}{=} 0$$

$$16 + 12 - 28 \stackrel{?}{=} 0$$

$$0 = 0 \quad \text{True}$$

The solution set is $\{-343, 64\}$. ∎

> **Quick** ✔ *In Problem 12, solve the equation.*
>
> **12.** $p^{\frac{2}{3}} - 4p^{\frac{1}{3}} - 5 = 0$

7.3 EXERCISES

Powered by CourseCompass™ and MathXL®
MyMathLab

PRACTICE WATCH DOWNLOAD READ REVIEW

1–12. *are the* **Quick** ✔*s that follow each* **EXAMPLE**

Building Skills

In Problems 13–48, solve each equation. See Objective 1.

13. $x^4 - 5x^2 + 4 = 0$　　　**14.** $x^4 - 10x^2 + 9 = 0$

15. $q^4 + 13q^2 + 36 = 0$　　　**16.** $z^4 + 10z^2 + 9 = 0$

17. $4a^4 - 17a^2 + 4 = 0$　　　**18.** $4b^4 - 5b^2 + 1 = 0$

19. $p^4 + 6 = 5p^2$　　　**20.** $q^4 + 15 = 8q^2$

21. $(x - 3)^2 - 6(x - 3) - 7 = 0$

22. $(x + 2)^2 - 3(x + 2) - 10 = 0$

23. $(x^2 - 1)^2 - 11(x^2 - 1) + 24 = 0$

24. $(p^2 - 2)^2 - 8(p^2 - 2) + 12 = 0$

25. $(y^2 + 2)^2 + 7(y^2 + 2) + 10 = 0$

26. $(q^2 + 4)^2 + 3(q^2 + 4) - 4 = 0$

27. $x - 3\sqrt{x} - 4 = 0$　　　**28.** $x - 5\sqrt{x} - 6 = 0$

29. $w + 5\sqrt{w} + 6 = 0$　　　**30.** $z + 7\sqrt{z} + 6 = 0$

31. $2x + 5\sqrt{x} = 3$　　　**32.** $3x = 11\sqrt{x} + 4$

33. $x^{-2} + 3x^{-1} = 28$　　　**34.** $q^{-2} + 2q^{-1} = 15$

35. $10z^{-2} + 11z^{-1} = 6$　　　**36.** $10a^{-2} + 23a^{-1} = 5$

37. $x^{\frac{2}{3}} + 3x^{\frac{1}{3}} - 4 = 0$　　　**38.** $y^{\frac{2}{3}} - 2y^{\frac{1}{3}} - 3 = 0$

39. $z^{\frac{2}{3}} - z^{\frac{1}{3}} = 2$　　　**40.** $w^{\frac{2}{3}} + 2w^{\frac{1}{3}} = 3$

41. $a + a^{\frac{1}{2}} = 30$　　　**42.** $b + 3b^{\frac{1}{2}} = 28$

43. $\dfrac{1}{x^2} - \dfrac{5}{x} + 6 = 0$

44. $\dfrac{1}{x^2} - \dfrac{7}{x} + 12 = 0$

45. $\left(\dfrac{1}{x + 2}\right)^2 + \dfrac{4}{x + 2} = 5$

46. $\left(\dfrac{1}{x + 2}\right)^2 + \dfrac{6}{x + 2} = 7$

47. $p^6 - 28p^3 + 27 = 0$

48. $y^6 - 7y^3 - 8 = 0$

Mixed Practice

In Problems 49–62, solve each equation.

49. $8a^{-2} + 2a^{-1} = 1$

50. $6b^{-2} - b^{-1} = 1$

51. $z^4 = 4z^2 + 32$

52. $x^4 + 3x^2 = 4$

53. $x^{\frac{1}{2}} + x^{\frac{1}{4}} - 6 = 0$

54. $c^{\frac{1}{2}} + c^{\frac{1}{4}} - 12 = 0$

55. $w^4 - 5w^2 - 36 = 0$

56. $p^4 - 15p^2 - 16 = 0$

57. $\left(\dfrac{1}{x+3}\right)^2 + \dfrac{2}{x+3} = 3$

58. $\left(\dfrac{1}{x-1}\right)^2 + \dfrac{7}{x-1} = 8$

59. $x - 7\sqrt{x} + 12 = 0$

60. $x - 8\sqrt{x} + 12 = 0$

61. $2(x-1)^2 - 7(x-1) = 4$

62. $3(y-2)^2 - 4(y-2) = 4$

63. Suppose that $f(x) = x^4 + 7x^2 + 12$. Find the values of x such that
   (a) $f(x) = 12$ **(b)** $f(x) = 6$

64. Suppose that $f(x) = x^4 + 5x^2 + 3$. Find the values of x such that
   (a) $f(x) = 3$ **(b)** $f(x) = 17$

65. Suppose that $g(x) = 2x^4 - 6x^2 - 5$. Find the values of x such that
   (a) $g(x) = -5$ **(b)** $g(x) = 15$

66. Suppose that $h(x) = 3x^4 - 9x^2 - 8$. Find the values of x such that
   (a) $h(x) = -8$ **(b)** $h(x) = 22$

67. Suppose that $F(x) = x^{-2} - 5x^{-1}$. Find the values of x such that
   (a) $F(x) = 6$ **(b)** $F(x) = 14$

68. Suppose that $f(x) = x^{-2} - 3x^{-1}$. Find the values of x such that
   (a) $f(x) = 4$ **(b)** $f(x) = 18$

In Problems 69–74, find the zeros of the function. (Hint: Remember, r is a zero if f(r) = 0.)

69. $f(x) = x^4 + 9x^2 + 14$

70. $f(x) = x^4 - 13x^2 + 42$

71. $g(t) = 6t - 25\sqrt{t} - 9$

72. $h(p) = 8p - 18\sqrt{p} - 35$

73. $s(d) = \dfrac{1}{(d+3)^2} - \dfrac{4}{d+3} + 3$

74. $f(a) = \dfrac{1}{(a-2)^2} + \dfrac{3}{a-2} - 4$

Applying the Concepts

75. **(a)** Solve $x^2 - 5x + 6 = 0$.
   (b) Solve $(x-3)^2 - 5(x-3) + 6 = 0$. Compare the solutions to part (a).
   (c) Solve $(x+2)^2 - 5(x+2) + 6 = 0$. Compare the solutions to part (a).
   (d) Solve $(x-5)^2 - 5(x-5) + 6 = 0$. Compare the solutions to part (a).
   (e) Conjecture a generalization for the solution of $(x-a)^2 - 5(x-a) + 6 = 0$.

76. **(a)** Solve $x^2 + 3x - 18 = 0$.
   (b) Solve $(x-1)^2 + 3(x-1) - 18 = 0$. Compare the solutions to part (a).
   (c) Solve $(x+5)^2 + 3(x+5) - 18 = 0$. Compare the solutions to part (a).
   (d) Solve $(x-3)^2 + 3(x-3) - 18 = 0$. Compare the solutions to part (a).
   (e) Conjecture a generalization for the solution of $(x-a)^2 + 3(x-a) - 18 = 0$.

77. For the function $f(x) = 2x^2 - 3x + 1$,
   (a) Solve $f(x) = 0$.
   (b) Solve $f(x - 2) = 0$. Compare the solutions to part **(a)**.
   (c) Solve $f(x - 5) = 0$. Compare the solutions to part **(a)**.
   (d) Conjecture a generalization for the zeros of $f(x - a)$.

78. For the function $f(x) = 3x^2 - 5x - 2$,
   (a) Solve $f(x) = 0$.
   (b) Solve $f(x - 1) = 0$. Compare the solutions to part **(a)**.
   (c) Solve $f(x - 4) = 0$. Compare the solutions to part **(a)**.
   (d) Conjecture a generalization for the zeros of $f(x - a)$.

79. Revenue The function
$$R(x) = \frac{(x - 1990)^2}{2} + \frac{3(x - 1990)}{2} + 3000$$
models the revenue R (in thousands of dollars) of a start-up computer consulting firm in year x, where $x \geq 1990$.
   (a) Determine and interpret $R(1990)$.
   (b) Solve and interpret $R(x) = 3065$.
   (c) According to the model, in what year can the firm expect to receive $3350 thousand in revenue?

80. Revenue The function
$$R(x) = \frac{(x - 2000)^2}{3} + \frac{5(x - 2000)}{3} + 2000$$
models the revenue R (in thousands of dollars) of a start-up computer software firm in year x, where $x \geq 2000$.
   (a) Determine and interpret $R(2000)$.
   (b) Solve and interpret $R(x) = 2250$.
   (c) According to the model, in what year can the firm expect to receive $2350 thousand in revenue?

Extending the Concepts

All of the problems given in this section resulted in equations quadratic in form that could be factored after the appropriate substitution. However, this is not a necessary requirement to solving equations quadratic in form. In Problems 81–84, determine the appropriate substitution, and then use the quadratic formula to find the value of u. Finally, determine the value of the variable in the equation.

81. $x^4 + 5x^2 + 2 = 0$

82. $x^4 + 7x^2 + 4 = 0$

83. $2(x - 2)^2 + 8(x - 2) - 1 = 0$

84. $3(x + 1)^2 + 6(x + 1) - 1 = 0$

Explaining the Concepts

85. The equation $x - 5\sqrt{x} - 6 = 0$ can be solved either by using the methods of this section or by isolating the radical and squaring both sides. Solve it both ways and explain which approach you prefer.

86. Explain the steps required to solve an equation quadratic in form. Be sure to include an explanation as to how to identify the appropriate substitution.

87. Under what circumstances might extraneous solutions occur when solving equations quadratic in form?

Synthesis Review

In Problems 88–91, add or subtract the expressions.

88. $(4x^2 - 3x - 1) + (-3x^2 + x + 5)$

89. $(3p^{-2} - 4p^{-1} + 8) - (2p^{-2} - 8p^{-1} - 1)$

90. $3\sqrt{2x} - \sqrt{8x} + \sqrt{50x}$

91. $\sqrt[3]{16a} + \sqrt[3]{54a} - \sqrt[3]{128a^4}$

92. Write a sentence or two that discusses how to add or subtract algebraic expressions, in general.

The Graphing Calculator

In Problems 93–98, use a graphing calculator to find the real solutions to the equations using either the ZERO or INTERSECT feature. Round your answers to two decimal places, if necessary.

93. $x^4 + 5x^2 - 14 = 0$ **94.** $x^4 - 4x^2 - 12 = 0$

95. $2(x - 2)^2 = 5(x - 2) + 1$

96. $3(x + 3)^2 = 2(x + 3) + 6$

97. $x - 5\sqrt{x} = -3$ **98.** $x + 4\sqrt{x} = 5$

99. (a) Graph $Y_1 = x^2 - 5x - 6$. Find the x-intercepts of the graph.
(b) Graph $Y_1 = (x + 2)^2 - 5(x + 2) - 6$. Find the x-intercepts of the graph.
(c) Graph $Y_1 = (x + 5)^2 - 5(x + 5) - 6$. Find the x-intercepts of the graph.
(d) Make a generalization based upon the results of parts **(a)**, **(b)**, and **(c)**.

100. (a) Graph $Y_1 = x^2 + 4x + 3$. Find the x-intercepts of the graph.
(b) Graph $Y_1 = (x - 3)^2 + 4(x - 3) + 3$. Find the x-intercepts of the graph.
(c) Graph $Y_1 = (x - 6)^2 + 4(x - 6) + 3$. Find the x-intercepts of the graph.
(d) Make a generalization based upon the results of parts **(a)**, **(b)**, and **(c)**.

PUTTING THE CONCEPTS TOGETHER (SECTIONS 7.1–7.3)

These problems cover important concepts from Sections 7.1 through 7.3. We designed these problems so that you can review the chapter so far and show your mastery of the concepts. Take time to work these problems before proceeding with the next section. The answers to these problems are located at the back of the text on page AN-40.

In Problems 1–3, complete the square in the given expression. Then factor the perfect square trinomial.

1. $z^2 + 10z$

2. $x^2 + 7x$

3. $n^2 - \dfrac{1}{4}n$

In Problems 4–6, solve each quadratic equation using the stated method.

4. $(2x - 3)^2 - 5 = -1$; square root property

5. $x^2 + 8x + 4 = 0$; completing the square

6. $x(x - 6) = -7$; quadratic formula

In Problems 7–10, solve each equation using the method you prefer.

7. $49x^2 - 80 = 0$

8. $p^2 - 8p + 6 = 0$

9. $3y^2 + 6y + 4 = 0$

10. $\dfrac{1}{4}n^2 + n = \dfrac{1}{6}$

In Problems 11–13, determine the discriminant of each quadratic equation. Use the value of the discriminant to determine whether the equation has two rational solutions, two irrational solutions, one repeated real solution, or two complex solutions that are not real.

11. $9x^2 + 12x + 4 = 0$

12. $3x^2 + 6x - 2 = 0$

13. $2x^2 + 6x + 5 = 0$

14. Find the missing length in the right triangle shown below.

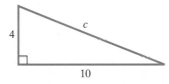

In Problems 15 and 16, solve each equation.

15. $2m + 7\sqrt{m} - 15 = 0$

16. $p^{-2} - 3p^{-1} - 18 = 0$

17. Revenue The revenue R received by a company selling x microwave ovens per day is given by the function $R(x) = -0.4x^2 + 140x$. How many microwave ovens must be sold in order for revenue to be $12,000 per day?

18. Airplane Ride An airplane flies 300 miles into the wind and then flies home against the wind. The total time of the trip (excluding time on the ground) is 5 hours. If the plane can fly 140 miles per hour in still air, what was the speed of the wind? Round your answer to the nearest tenth.

7.4 Graphing Quadratic Functions Using Transformations

OBJECTIVES

1. Graph Quadratic Functions of the Form $f(x) = x^2 + k$
2. Graph Quadratic Functions of the Form $f(x) = (x - h)^2$
3. Graph Quadratic Functions of the Form $f(x) = ax^2$
4. Graph Quadratic Functions of the Form $f(x) = ax^2 + bx + c$
5. Find a Quadratic Function from Its Graph

Preparing for Graphing Quadratic Functions Using Transformations

Before getting started, take the following readiness quiz. If you get a problem wrong, go back to the section cited and review the material.

P1. Graph $y = x^2$ using point plotting. [Section 1.5, p. 98]

P2. Use the point-plotting method to graph $y = x^2 - 3$. [Section 1.5, pp. 97–99]

P3. What is the domain of $f(x) = 2x^2 + 5x + 1$? [Section 2.3, pp. 163–164]

We begin with a definition.

DEFINITION

A **quadratic function** is a function of the form

$$f(x) = ax^2 + bx + c$$

where $a, b,$ and c are real numbers and $a \neq 0$. The domain of a quadratic function consists of all real numbers.

Many situations can be modeled using quadratic functions. For example, we saw in Example 8 of Section 2.2 that Franco Modigliani used the quadratic function $I(a) = -55a^2 + 5119a - 54{,}448$ to model the relation between average annual income, I, and age, a.

A second situation in which a quadratic function appears involves the motion of a projectile. If we ignore the effect of air resistance on a projectile, the height H of the projectile as a function of horizontal distance traveled, x, can be modeled using a quadratic function. See Figure 7.

Figure 7

The goal of this and the next section is to learn methods that will allow us to obtain the graph of a quadratic function. Back in Section 1.5 we learned how to graph virtually any type of equation using point plotting. However, we also discovered that this method is inefficient and could lead to incomplete graphs. Remember, a graph is complete if it shows all of the "interesting features" of the graph. Some of the interesting features that must be included are the intercepts and the high and low points of the graph. We will present two methods that can be used to graph quadratic functions that are superior to the point-plotting method. The first method utilizes a technique called *transformations*. This will be the subject of this section. The second method uses properties of quadratic functions, and is discussed in the next section.

1 Graph Quadratic Functions of the Form *f*(x) = x² + k

We begin by looking at the graph of any quadratic function of the form $f(x) = x^2 + k$ such as $f(x) = x^2 + 3$ or $f(x) = x^2 - 4$.

In Example 4 from Section 1.5, we graphed the equation $y = x^2$. For convenience, we provide the graph of $y = f(x) = x^2$ in Figure 8.

Preparing for...Answers

P1.

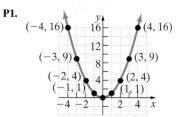

P2.

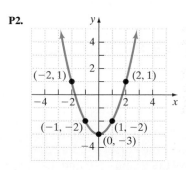

P3. The set of all real numbers

Figure 8

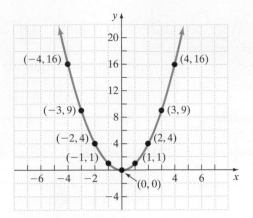

Work Smart

Consider the quadratic function $f(x) = ax^2 + bx + c$, where $a = 1$, $b = 0$, and c is any real number. This is a function of the form $f(x) = x^2 + k$.

What effect does adding a real number k to the function $f(x) = x^2$ have on its graph? Let's see!

EXAMPLE 1 Graphing a Quadratic Function of the Form $f(x) = x^2 + k$

On the same Cartesian plane, graph $g(x) = x^2$ and $f(x) = x^2 + 3$.

Solution

We begin by obtaining some points on the graphs of g and f. For example, when $x = 0$, then $y = g(0) = 0$ and $y = f(0) = 0^2 + 3 = 3$. When $x = 1$, then $y = g(1) = 1$ and $y = f(1) = 1^2 + 3 = 4$. Table 3 lists these points along with a few others. Notice that the y-coordinates on the graph of $f(x) = x^2 + 3$ are exactly 3 units larger than the corresponding y-coordinates on the graph of $g(x) = x^2$. Figure 9 shows the graphs of f and g.

		Table 3			
x	$g(x) = x^2$	$(x, g(x))$	$f(x) = x^2 + 3$	$(x, f(x))$	
-2	$(-2)^2 = 4$	$(-2, 4)$	$(-2)^2 + 3 = 7$	$(-2, 7)$	
-1	$(-1)^2 = 1$	$(-1, 1)$	$(-1)^2 + 3 = 4$	$(-1, 4)$	
0	0	$(0, 0)$	3	$(0, 3)$	
1	1	$(1, 1)$	4	$(1, 4)$	
2	4	$(2, 4)$	7	$(2, 7)$	

Figure 9

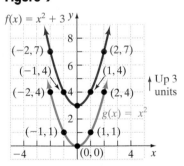

We conclude that the graph of f is identical to the graph of g except that it is shifted vertically up 3 units. ∎

Let's look at another example.

EXAMPLE 2 Graphing a Quadratic Function of the Form $f(x) = x^2 + k$

On the same Cartesian plane, graph $g(x) = x^2$ and $f(x) = x^2 - 4$.

Solution

Table 4 lists some points on the graphs of g and f. Notice that the y-coordinates on the graph of $f(x) = x^2 - 4$ are exactly 4 units smaller than the corresponding y-coordinates on the graph of $g(x) = x^2$. Figure 10 shows the graphs of f and g.

	Table 4				
x	$g(x) = x^2$	$(x, g(x))$	$f(x) = x^2 - 4$	$(x, f(x))$	
-2	$(-2)^2 = 4$	$(-2, 4)$	$(-2)^2 - 4 = 0$	$(-2, 0)$	
-1	$(-1)^2 = 1$	$(-1, 1)$	$(-1)^2 - 4 = -3$	$(-1, -3)$	
0	0	$(0, 0)$	-4	$(0, -4)$	
1	1	$(1, 1)$	-3	$(1, -3)$	
2	4	$(2, 4)$	0	$(2, 0)$	

Figure 10

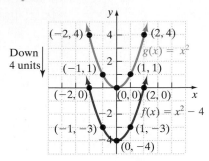

We conclude that the graph of g is identical to the graph of f except that it is shifted vertically down 4 units. ∎

Based on the results of Examples 1 and 2, we are led to the following conclusion.

GRAPHING A FUNCTION OF THE FORM $f(x) = x^2 + k$ OR $f(x) = x^2 - k$

To obtain the graph of $f(x) = x^2 + k$, $k > 0$, from the graph of $y = x^2$, shift the graph of $y = x^2$ vertically up k units. To obtain the graph of $f(x) = x^2 - k$, $k > 0$, from the graph of $y = x^2$ shift the graph of $y = x^2$ vertically down k units.

Quick ✔

1. A _____ _____ is a function of the form $f(x) = ax^2 + bx + c$ where a, b, and c are real numbers and $a \neq 0$.

2. To graph $f(x) = x^2 + k$, $k > 0$, from using the graph of $y - x^2$, shift the graph of $y = x^2$ vertically____ k units. To graph $f(x) = x^2 - k$, $k > 0$, from the graph of $y = x^2$ shift the graph of $y = x^2$ vertically _____ k units.

In Problems 3 and 4, use the graph of $g(x) = x^2$ to graph the quadratic function. Show at least 3 points on the graph.

3. $f(x) = x^2 + 5$ 4. $f(x) = x^2 - 2$

---

2   Graph Quadratic Functions of the Form $f(x) = (x - h)^2$

We now look at the graph of any quadratic function of the form $f(x) = (x - h)^2$ such as $f(x) = (x + 3)^2$ or $f(x) = (x - 2)^2$. Our goal in the next example is to determine the effect subtracting a real positive number h from x has on the graph of the function $f(x) = x^2$.

EXAMPLE 3   Graphing a Quadratic Function of the Form $f(x) = (x - h)^2$

On the same Cartesian plane, graph $g(x) = x^2$ and $f(x) = (x - 2)^2$.

Work Smart

Because we are subtracting 2 from each x-value in the function $f(x) = (x - 2)^2$, the x-values must be bigger by 2 to obtain the same y-value that was obtained in the graph of $g(x) = x^2$.

Solution

Again, we use the point-plotting method. Table 5 lists some points on the graphs of g and f. Notice when $g(x) = 0$, $x = 0$, and when $f(x) = 0$, $x = 2$. Also, when $g(x) = 4$, $x = -2$ or 2, and when $f(x) = 4$, $x = 0$ or 4. We conclude that the graph of f is identical to that of g, except that f is shifted 2 units to the right of g. See Figure 11.

		Table 5		
x	$g(x) = x^2$	$(x, g(x))$	$f(x) = (x - 2)^2$	$(x, f(x))$
-2	$(-2)^2 = 4$	$(-2, 4)$	$(-2 - 2)^2 = 16$	$(-2, 16)$
-1	$(-1)^2 = 1$	$(-1, 1)$	$(-1 - 2)^2 = 9$	$(-1, 9)$
0	0	$(0, 0)$	4	$(0, 4)$
1	1	$(1, 1)$	1	$(1, 1)$
2	4	$(2, 4)$	0	$(2, 0)$
3	9	$(3, 9)$	1	$(3, 1)$
4	16	$(4, 16)$	4	$(4, 4)$

Figure 11

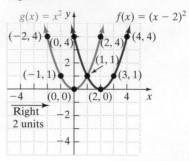

What if we add a positive number h to x?

EXAMPLE 4 Graphing a Quadratic Function of the Form $f(x) = (x + h)^2$

On the same Cartesian plane, graph $g(x) = x^2$ and $f(x) = (x + 3)^2$.

Solution

Table 6 lists some points on the graphs of g and f. Notice that when $g(x) = 0$, then $x = 0$, and when $f(x) = 0$, then $x = -3$. Also, when $g(x) = 4$, then $x = -2$ or 2, and when $f(x) = 4$, then $x = -5$ or -1. We conclude that the graph of f is identical to that of g, except that f is shifted 3 units to the left of g. See Figure 12.

		Table 6		
x	$g(x) = x^2$	$(x, g(x))$	$f(x) = (x + 3)^2$	$(x, f(x))$
-5	$(-5)^2 = 25$	$(-5, 25)$	$(-5 + 3)^2 = 4$	$(-5, 4)$
-4	$(-4)^2 = 16$	$(-4, 16)$	$(-4 + 3)^2 = 1$	$(-4, 1)$
-3	$(-3)^2 = 9$	$(-3, 9)$	$(-3 + 3)^2 = 0$	$(-3, 0)$
-2	4	$(-2, 4)$	1	$(-2, 1)$
-1	1	$(-1, 1)$	4	$(-1, 4)$
0	0	$(0, 0)$	9	$(0, 9)$
1	1	$(1, 1)$	16	$(1, 16)$
2	4	$(2, 4)$	25	$(2, 25)$

Figure 12

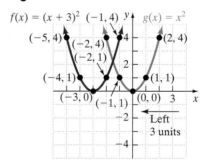

Based upon the results of Examples 3 and 4, we are led to the following conclusion.

Work Smart

Because we are adding 3 to each x-value in the function $f(x) = (x + 3)^2$, the x-values must be smaller by 3 to obtain the same y-value that was obtained in the graph of $g(x) = x^2$.

GRAPHING A FUNCTION OF THE FORM $f(x) = (x - h)^2$ OR $f(x) = (x + h)^2$

To obtain the graph of $f(x) = (x - h)^2$, $h > 0$, from the graph of $y = x^2$, shift the graph of $y = x^2$ horizontally to the right h units. To obtain the graph of $f(x) = (x + h)^2$, $h > 0$, from the graph of $y = x^2$, shift the graph of $y = x^2$ horizontally to the left h units.

Quick ✔

5. *True or False:* To obtain the graph of $f(x) = (x + 12)^2$ from the graph of $y = x^2$, shift the graph of $y = x^2$ horizontally to the right 12 units.

In Problems 6 and 7, use the graph of $y = x^2$ to graph the quadratic function. Show at least 3 points on the graph.

6. $f(x) = (x + 5)^2$ **7.** $f(x) = (x - 1)^2$

Let's do an example where we combine a horizontal shift with a vertical shift.

EXAMPLE 5   Combining Horizontal and Vertical Shifts

Graph the function $f(x) = (x + 2)^2 - 3$.

Solution

We will graph f in steps. We begin with the graph of $y = x^2$ as shown in Figure 13(a).
We shift the graph of $y = x^2$ horizontally 2 units to the left to get the graph of
$y = (x + 2)^2$. See Figure 13(b). Then, we shift the graph of $y = (x + 2)^2$ vertically
down 3 units to get the graph of $y = (x + 2)^2 - 3$. See Figure 13(c). Notice that we
keep track of key points plotted on each graph.

Figure 13

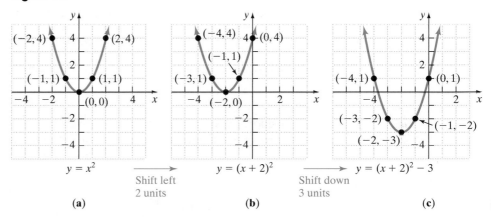

Note: The order in which we obtain the graph does not matter. In Example 5, we
could just as easily have shifted down 3 units first and then shifted left 2 units. ■

> Quick ✔ *In Problems 8 and 9, graph each quadratic function using horizontal and
> vertical shifts. Show at least 3 points on the graph.*
>
> **8.** $f(x) = (x - 3)^2 + 2$ **9.** $f(x) = (x + 1)^2 - 4$

3   Graph Quadratic Functions of the Form $f(x) = ax^2$

In the examples presented thus far, the coefficient of the square term has been equal
to 1. We now discuss the impact that the value of a has on the graph of
$f(x) = ax^2 + bx + c$. To make the discussion a little easier, we will only consider
quadratic functions of the form $f(x) = ax^2, a \neq 0$.

First, let's consider situations in which the value of a is positive. Table 7 on the next
page shows points on the graphs of $f(x) = x^2$, $g(x) = \frac{1}{2}x^2$, and $h(x) = 2x^2$. Figure 14
shows the graphs of $f(x) = x^2$, $g(x) = \frac{1}{2}x^2$, and $h(x) = 2x^2$. Notice that the
y-coordinates on the graph of g are exactly $\frac{1}{2}$ of the values of the y-coordinates on
the graph of f. The y-coordinates on the graph of h are exactly 2 times the values of
the y-coordinates on the graph of f. Put another way, the larger the value of a, the
"taller" the graph is, and the smaller the value of a, the "shorter" the graph is.
Also, notice that all three graphs open "up."

	Table 7		
x	$f(x) = x^2$	$g(x) = \dfrac{1}{2}x^2$	$h(x) = 2x^2$
-2	$(-2)^2 = 4$	$\dfrac{1}{2}(-2)^2 = 2$	$2(-2)^2 = 8$
-1	$(-1)^2 = 1$	$\dfrac{1}{2}(-1)^2 = \dfrac{1}{2}$	$2(-1)^2 = 2$
0	0	0	0
1	1	$\dfrac{1}{2}$	2
2	4	2	8

Figure 14
$f(x) = ax^2$. Since $a > 0$, the graphs open up.

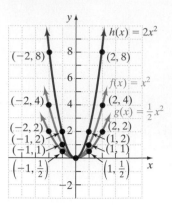

Now let's consider what happens when a is negative. Table 8 shows points on the graphs of $f(x) = -x^2$, $g(x) = -\dfrac{1}{2}x^2$, and $h(x) = -2x^2$. Figure 15 shows the graphs of $f(x) = -x^2$, $g(x) = -\dfrac{1}{2}x^2$, and $h(x) = -2x^2$. Notice that the y-coordinates on the graph of g are exactly $\dfrac{1}{2}$ times the values of the y-coordinates on the graph of f. The y-coordinates on the graph of h are exactly 2 times the values of the y-coordinates on the graph of f. Put another way, the larger the value of $|a|$, the "taller" the graph is, and the smaller the value of $|a|$, the "shorter" the graph is. Also, notice that all three graphs open "down."

	Table 8		
x	$f(x) = -x^2$	$g(x) = -\dfrac{1}{2}x^2$	$h(x) = -2x^2$
-2	$-(-2)^2 = -4$	$-\dfrac{1}{2}(-2)^2 = -2$	$-2(-2)^2 = -8$
-1	$-(-1)^2 = -1$	$-\dfrac{1}{2}(-1)^2 = -\dfrac{1}{2}$	$-2(-1)^2 = -2$
0	0	0	0
1	-1	$-\dfrac{1}{2}$	-2
2	-4	-2	-8

Figure 15
$f(x) = ax^2$. Since $a < 0$, the graphs open down.

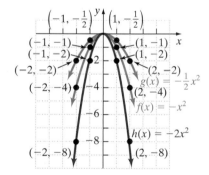

We summarize these conclusions below.

PROPERTIES OF THE GRAPH OF $f(x) = ax^2$

- If $a > 0$, the graph of $f(x) = ax^2$ will open upward. In addition, if $0 < a < 1$ (a is between 0 and 1), the graph will be "shorter" than that of $y = x^2$. If $a > 1$, the graph will be "taller" than that of $y = x^2$.
- If $a < 0$, the graph of $f(x) = ax^2$ will open downward. In addition, if $0 < |a| < 1$, the graph will be "shorter" than that of $y = x^2$. If $|a| > 1$, the graph will be "taller" than that of $y = x^2$.
- When $|a| > 1$, we say that the graph is **vertically stretched** by a factor of $|a|$. When $0 < |a| < 1$, we say that the graph is **vertically compressed** by a factor of $|a|$.

> ### GRAPHING A FUNCTION OF THE FORM $f(x) = ax^2$
>
> To obtain the graph of $f(x) = ax^2$ from the graph of $y = x^2$, multiply each y-coordinate on the graph of $y = x^2$ by a.

EXAMPLE 6   Graphing a Quadratic Function of the Form $f(x) = ax^2$

Use the graph of $y = x^2$ to obtain the graph of $f(x) = -2x^2$.

Solution

To obtain the graph of $f(x) = -2x^2$ from the graph of $y = x^2$, we multiply each y-coordinate on the graph of $y = x^2$ by -2 (the value of a). See Figure 16.

Figure 16

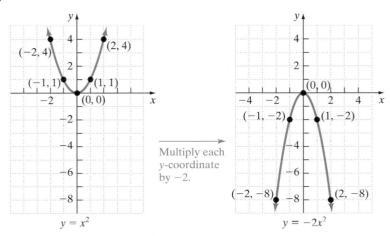

$y = x^2$ $y = -2x^2$

Multiply each y-coordinate by -2.

Quick ✔

10. When obtaining the graph of $f(x) = ax^2$ from the graph of $y = x^2$, we multiply each ___-coordinate on the graph of $y = x^2$ by___. If $|a| > 1$, we say that the graph is _____ _____ by a factor of $|a|$. If $0 < |a| < 1$, we say that the graph is _____ _____ by a factor of $|a|$.

In Problems 11 and 12, use the graph of $y = x^2$ to graph each quadratic function. Label at least 3 points on the graph.

11. $f(x) = 3x^2$ **12.** $f(x) = -\dfrac{1}{4}x^2$

4   Graph Quadratic Functions of the Form $f(x) = ax^2 + bx + c$

The graphs obtained in Examples 1–6 are typical of graphs of all quadratic functions. We call the graph of a quadratic function a **parabola** (pronounced puh-ráb-ō-luh). Refer to Figure 17, where two parabolas are shown.

The parabola in Figure 17(a) **opens up** (since $a > 0$) and has a lowest point; the parabola in Figure 17(b) **opens down** (since $a < 0$) and has a highest point. The lowest or highest point of a parabola is called the **vertex**. The vertical line passing through the vertex in each parabola in Figure 17 is called the **axis of symmetry** of the parabola. If we were to take the portion of the parabola to the right of the vertex and fold it over the axis of symmetry, it would lie directly on top of the portion of the parabola to the left of the vertex. Therefore, we say that the parabola is symmetric about its axis of symmetry. It is important to note that the axis of symmetry is not part of the graph of

Figure 17

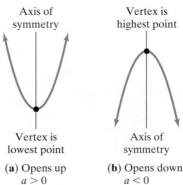

Axis of symmetry

Vertex is highest point

Vertex is lowest point

Axis of symmetry

(a) Opens up
$a > 0$

(b) Opens down
$a < 0$

Work Smart

The axis of symmetry is useful in graphing a quadratic function by hand.

the quadratic function, but it will be useful when graphing quadratic functions using the methods we present in the next section.

Our goal right now is to combine the techniques learned from Examples 1–6 to graph any quadratic function. The techniques of shifting horizontally, shifting vertically, stretching, and compressing are collectively referred to as **transformations.** To graph any quadratic function of the form $f(x) = ax^2 + bx + c$ using transformations, we use the following steps.

Work Smart

Although order does not matter, we recommend when graphing parabolas using transformations to obtain the graph that results from the vertical compression or stretch first, followed by the horizontal shift, followed by the vertical shift.

STEPS FOR GRAPHING QUADRATIC FUNCTIONS USING TRANSFORMATIONS

Step 1: Write the function $f(x) = ax^2 + bx + c$ as $f(x) = a(x - h)^2 + k$ by completing the square in x.

Step 2: Graph the function $f(x) = a(x - h)^2 + k$ using transformations.

Notice that we must first write the quadratic function $f(x) = ax^2 + bx + c$ as $f(x) = a(x - h)^2 + k$. This is necessary so we can determine the horizontal and vertical shifts.

EXAMPLE 7 How to Graph a Quadratic Function of the Form $f(x) = ax^2 + bx + c$ Using Transformations

Graph $f(x) = x^2 + 4x + 3$ using transformations. Identify the vertex and axis of symmetry of the parabola. Based on the graph, determine the domain and range of the quadratic function.

Step-by-Step Solution

Step 1: Write the function $f(x) = ax^2 + bx + c$ as $f(x) = a(x - h)^2 + k$ by completing the square in x.

Group the terms involving x:

Complete the square in x by taking $\frac{1}{2}$ the coefficient on x and squaring the result: $\left(\frac{1}{2} \cdot 4\right)^2 = 4$.

Because we added 4, we must also subtract 4 (so that we don't change the function):

Factor the perfect square trinomial in parentheses:

$$f(x) = x^2 + 4x + 3$$
$$= (x^2 + 4x) + 3$$

$$= (x^2 + 4x + 4) + 3 - 4$$
$$= (x^2 + 4x + 4) - 1$$
$$= (x + 2)^2 - 1$$

Step 2: Graph the function $f(x) = a(x - h)^2 + k$ using transformations.

The graph of $f(x) = (x + 2)^2 - 1$ is the graph of $y = x^2$ shifted 2 units left and 1 unit down. See Figure 18.

Figure 18

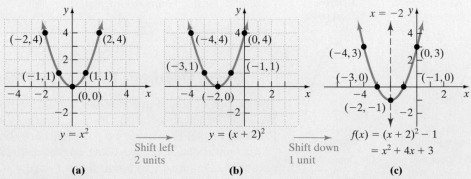

From the graph in Figure 18(c), we can see that the vertex of the parabola is $(-2, -1)$. In addition, because the parabola opens up (because $a = 1 > 0$), the vertex is the lowest point on the graph. The axis of symmetry is the line $x = -2$. The domain is the set of all real numbers, or using interval notation $(-\infty, \infty)$. The range is $\{y | y \geq -1\}$, or using interval notation $[-1, \infty)$.

EXAMPLE 8 Graphing a Quadratic Function of the Form $f(x) = ax^2 + bx + c$ Using Transformations

Graph $f(x) = -2x^2 + 4x + 1$ using transformations. Identify the vertex and axis of symmetry of the parabola. Based on the graph, determine the domain and range of the quadratic function.

Solution

Write the function $f(x) = ax^2 + bx + c$ as $f(x) = a(x - h)^2 + k$ by completing the square in x.

$$f(x) = -2x^2 + 4x + 1$$

Group the terms involving x: $= (-2x^2 + 4x) + 1$

Factor out the coefficient of the
square term, -2, from the parentheses: $= -2(x^2 - 2x) + 1$

Complete the square in x by taking $\frac{1}{2}$ the coefficient of x and squaring the result: $\left(\frac{1}{2} \cdot -2\right)^2 = 1$. We add 1 inside the parentheses. Because everything in the parentheses is multiplied by -2, we really added -2, so we must add 2 to offset this: $= -2(x^2 - 2x + 1) + 1 + 2$

Factor the perfect square trinomial in parentheses: $= -2(x - 1)^2 + 3$

Now, graph the function $f(x) = a(x - h)^2 + k$ using transformations. Since $a = -2$, the parabola opens down and is stretched by a factor of 2. Since $h = 1$ the parabola shifts 1 unit to the right; since $k = 3$, the parabola shifts 3 units up. See Figure 19.

Figure 19

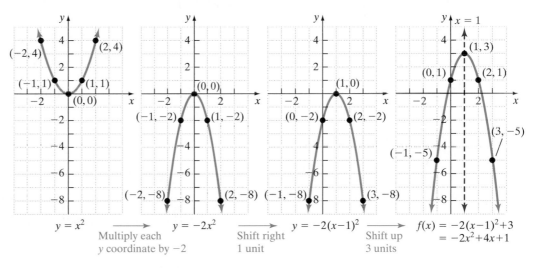

$y = x^2$ — Multiply each y coordinate by -2 → $y = -2x^2$ — Shift right 1 unit → $y = -2(x-1)^2$ — Shift up 3 units → $f(x) = -2(x-1)^2 + 3$ $= -2x^2 + 4x + 1$

The vertex of the parabola is $(1, 3)$. In addition, because the parabola opens down (because $a = -2 < 0$), the vertex is the highest point on the graph. The axis of symmetry is the line $x = 1$. The domain is the set of all real numbers, or using interval notation $(-\infty, \infty)$. The range is $\{y | y \le 3\}$, or using interval notation $(-\infty, 3]$. ∎

Work Smart: Study Skills

Be sure you know what $y = a(x - h)^2 + k$ represents in reference to the graph of $y = x^2$:

- $|a|$ represents the vertical stretch or compression factor: how tall or short the graph appears.
- The sign of a determines whether the parabola opens up or down.
- h represents the number of units the graph is shifted horizontally.
- k represents the number of units the graph is shifted vertically.

For example, $y = 4(x + 2)^2 - 3$ means that the graph of $y = x^2$ is stretched vertically by a factor of 4, is shifted 2 units horizontally to the left, and is shifted vertically down 3 units. The vertex of $y = 4(x + 2)^2 - 3$ is at $(-2, -3)$ and represents the low point of the graph since $a > 0$.

Quick ✔

13. *True or False:* The graph of $f(x) = -3x^2 + x + 6$ opens down.

In Problems 14 and 15, graph each quadratic function using transformations. Be sure to label at least 3 points on the graph. Based on the graph, determine the domain and range of each function.

14. $f(x) = -3(x + 2)^2 + 1$ **15.** $f(x) = 2x^2 - 8x + 5$

⌜5⌝ Find a Quadratic Function from Its Graph

If we are given the vertex, (h, k), and one additional point on the graph of a quadratic function, we can find the quadratic function $f(x) = a(x - h)^2 + k$ that results in the given graph.

⌜**EXAMPLE 9** Finding the Quadratic Function Given Its Vertex
               and One Other Point

Determine the quadratic function whose graph is given in Figure 20. Write the function in the form $f(x) = a(x - h)^2 + k$.

Figure 20

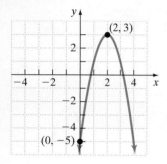

Solution

The vertex is $(2, 3)$, so $h = 2$ and $k = 3$. Substitute these values into $f(x) = a(x - h)^2 + k$.

$$f(x) = a(x - h)^2 + k$$
$$h = 2, k = 3: \quad = a(x - 2)^2 + 3$$

To determine the value of a, we use the fact that $f(0) = -5$ (the y-intercept).

$$f(x) = a(x - 2)^2 + 3$$
$$x = 0, y = f(0) = -5: \quad -5 = a(0 - 2)^2 + 3$$
$$-5 = a(4) + 3$$
$$-5 = 4a + 3$$
$$\text{Subtract 3 from both sides:} \quad -8 = 4a$$
$$a = -2$$

The quadratic function whose graph is shown in Figure 20 is $f(x) = -2(x - 2)^2 + 3$. ∎

Quick ✔ *In Problem 16, find the quadratic function whose graph is given. Write the function in the form $f(x) = a(x - h)^2 + k$.*

16.

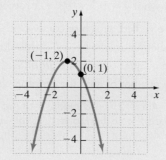

7.4 EXERCISES

 MyMathLab

Math XL PRACTICE   WATCH   DOWNLOAD   READ   REVIEW

1–16. *are the* Quick ✔s *that follow each* **EXAMPLE**

Building Skills

17. Match each quadratic function to its graph.

(I) $f(x) = x^2 + 3$ **(II)** $f(x) = (x + 3)^2$

(III) $f(x) = x^2 - 3$ **(IV)** $f(x) = (x - 3)^2$

(A)   **(B)**

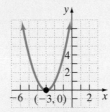   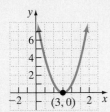

(C)   **(D)**

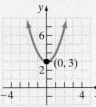

18. Match each quadratic function to its graph.

(I) $f(x) = (x - 2)^2 - 4$ **(II)** $f(x) = -(x - 2)^2 + 4$

(III) $f(x) = -(x + 2)^2 + 4$ **(IV)** $f(x) = 2(x - 2)^2 - 4$

(A)   **(B)**

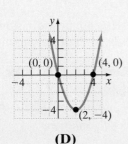

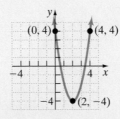

(C)   **(D)**

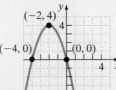   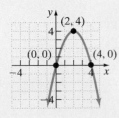

In Problems 19–26, verbally explain how to obtain the graph of the given quadratic function from the graph of $y = x^2$. For example, to obtain the graph of $f(x) = (x - 3)^2 - 6$ from the graph of

$y = x^2$, *we take the graph of $y = x^2$ and shift it 3 units to the right and 6 units down.*

19. $f(x) = (x + 10)^2$ **20.** $G(x) = (x - 9)^2$

21. $F(x) = x^2 + 12$ **22.** $g(x) = x^2 - 8$

23. $H(x) = 2(x - 5)^2$ **24.** $h(x) = 4(x + 7)^2$

25. $f(x) = -3(x + 5)^2 + 8$ **26.** $F(x) = -\dfrac{1}{2}(x - 3)^2 - 5$

In Problems 27–30, use the graph of $y = x^2$ to graph the quadratic function. See Objective 1.

27. $f(x) = x^2 + 1$ **28.** $h(x) = x^2 + 6$

29. $f(x) = x^2 - 1$ **30.** $g(x) = x^2 - 7$

In Problems 31–34, use the graph of $y = x^2$ to graph each quadratic function. See Objective 2.

31. $F(x) = (x - 3)^2$ **32.** $F(x) = (x - 2)^2$

33. $h(x) = (x + 2)^2$ **34.** $f(x) = (x + 4)^2$

In Problems 35–40, use the graph of $y = x^2$ to graph each quadratic function. See Objective 3.

35. $g(x) = 4x^2$ **36.** $G(x) = 5x^2$

37. $H(x) = \dfrac{1}{3}x^2$ **38.** $h(x) = \dfrac{3}{2}x^2$

39. $p(x) = -x^2$ **40.** $P(x) = -3x^2$

In Problems 41–54, use the graph of $y = x^2$ to graph each quadratic function. See Objective 4.

41. $f(x) = (x - 1)^2 - 3$ **42.** $g(x) = (x + 2)^2 - 1$

43. $F(x) = (x + 3)^2 + 1$ **44.** $G(x) = (x - 4)^2 + 2$

45. $h(x) = -(x + 3)^2 + 2$ **46.** $H(x) = -(x - 3)^2 + 5$

47. $G(x) = 2(x + 1)^2 - 2$ **48.** $F(x) = 3(x - 2)^2 - 1$

49. $H(x) = -\dfrac{1}{2}(x + 5)^2 + 3$ **50.** $f(x) = -\dfrac{1}{2}(x + 6)^2 + 2$

51. $f(x) = x^2 + 2x - 4$ **52.** $f(x) = x^2 + 4x - 1$

53. $g(x) = x^2 - 4x + 8$ **54.** $G(x) = x^2 - 2x + 7$

In Problems 55–60, determine the quadratic function whose graph is given. See Objective 5.

55.   **56.**

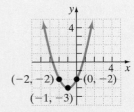   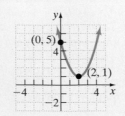

57.

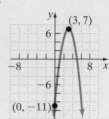

58.

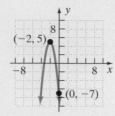

59.

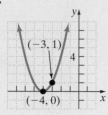

60.

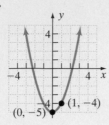

82. Opens up; vertex at $(4, -2)$

83. Opens down; vertex at $(5, -1)$

84. Opens down; vertex at $(-4, -7)$

85. Opens up; vertically stretched by a factor of 4; vertex at $(9, -6)$.

86. Opens up; vertically compressed by a factor of $\frac{1}{2}$; vertex at $(-5, 0)$.

87. Opens down; vertically compressed by a factor of $\frac{1}{3}$; vertex at $(0, 6)$.

88. Opens down; vertically stretched by a factor of 5; vertex at $(5, 8)$.

Mixed Practice

In Problems 61–78, write each function in the form $f(x) = a(x - h)^2 + k$. *Then graph each quadratic function using transformations. Determine the vertex and axis of symmetry. Based on the graph, determine the domain and range of the quadratic function.*

61. $f(x) = x^2 + 6x - 16$ **62.** $f(x) = x^2 + 4x + 5$

63. $F(x) = x^2 + x - 12$ **64.** $h(x) = x^2 - 7x + 10$

65. $H(x) = 2x^2 - 4x - 1$ **66.** $g(x) = 2x^2 + 4x - 3$

67. $P(x) = 3x^2 + 12x + 13$ **68.** $f(x) = 3x^2 + 18x + 25$

69. $F(x) = -x^2 - 10x - 21$ **70.** $g(x) = -x^2 - 8x - 14$

71. $g(x) = -x^2 + 6x - 1$

72. $f(x) = -x^2 + 10x - 17$

73. $H(x) = -2x^2 + 8x - 4$

74. $h(x) = -2x^2 + 12x - 17$

75. $f(x) = \frac{1}{3}x^2 - 2x + 4$

76. $f(x) = \frac{1}{2}x^2 + 2x - 1$

77. $G(x) = -12x^2 - 12x + 1$

78. $h(x) = -4x^2 + 4x$

Applying the Concepts

In Problems 79–88, write a quadratic function in the form $f(x) = a(x - h)^2 + k$ *with the properties given.*

79. Opens up; vertex at $(3, 0)$.

80. Opens up; vertex at $(0, 2)$.

81. Opens up; vertex at $(-3, 1)$

Explaining the Concepts

89. What is the lowest or highest point on a parabola called? How do we know whether this point is a high point or a low point?

90. Why does the graph of a quadratic function open up if $a > 0$ and down if $a < 0$?

91. Can a quadratic function have a range of $(-\infty, \infty)$? Justify your answer.

92. Can the graph of a quadratic function have more than one y-intercept? Justify your answer.

Synthesis Review

In Problems 93–95, divide.

93. $\dfrac{349}{12}$

94. $\dfrac{4x^2 + 19x - 1}{x + 5}$

95. $\dfrac{2x^4 - 11x^3 + 13x^2 - 8x}{2x - 1}$

96. Explain how division of real numbers is related to division of polynomials.

The Graphing Calculator

In Problems 97–104, graph each quadratic function. Determine the vertex and axis of symmetry. Based on the graph, determine the range of the function.

97. $f(x) = x^2 + 1.3$ **98.** $f(x) = x^2 - 3.5$

99. $g(x) = (x - 2.5)^2$ **100.** $G(x) = (x + 4.5)^2$

101. $h(x) = 2.3(x - 1.4)^2 + 0.5$

102. $H(x) = 1.2(x + 0.4)^2 - 1.3$

103. $F(x) = -3.4(x - 2.8)^2 + 5.9$

104. $f(x) = 0.3(x + 3.8)^2 - 8.9$

7.5 Graphing Quadratic Functions Using Properties

OBJECTIVES

1. Graph Quadratic Functions of the Form $f(x) = ax^2 + bx + c$
2. Find the Maximum or Minimum Value of a Quadratic Function
3. Model and Solve Optimization Problems Involving Quadratic Functions

Preparing for Graphing Quadratic Functions Using Properties

Before getting started, take the following readiness quiz. If you get a problem wrong, go back to the section cited and review the material.

P1. Find the intercepts of the graph of $2x + 5y = 20$. [Section 1.6, pp. 106–108]

P2. Solve: $2x^2 - 3x - 20 = 0$ [Section 4.8, pp. 384–387]

P3. Find the zeros of $f(x) = x^2 - 3x - 4$. [Section 4.8, p. 389]

In Section 7.4, we graphed quadratic functions using a method called transformations. We now introduce a second method for graphing quadratic equations that utilizes the properties of a quadratic function such as its intercepts, axis of symmetry, and vertex.

1 Graph Quadratic Functions of the Form $f(x) = ax^2 + bx + c$

We saw in Section 7.4 that a quadratic function $f(x) = ax^2 + bx + c$ can be written in the form $f(x) = a(x - h)^2 + k$ by completing the square in x. We also learned that the value of a determines whether the graph of the quadratic function (the parabola) opens up or down. In addition, we know that the point with coordinates (h, k) is the vertex of the quadratic function.

We can obtain a formula for the vertex of a parabola by completing the square in $f(x) = ax^2 + bx + c, a \neq 0$, as follows:

$$f(x) = ax^2 + bx + c$$

Group terms involving x: $$= (ax^2 + bx) + c$$

Factor out a: $$= a\left(x^2 + \frac{b}{a}x\right) + c$$

Complete the square in x by taking $\frac{1}{2}$ the coefficient of x and squaring the result: $\left(\frac{1}{2} \cdot \frac{b}{a}\right)^2 = \frac{b^2}{4a^2}$. Because we add $\frac{b^2}{4a^2}$ inside the parentheses, we subtract

$a \cdot \frac{b^2}{4a^2} = \frac{b^2}{4a}$ outside the parentheses: $$= a\left(x^2 + \frac{b}{a}x + \frac{b^2}{4a^2}\right) + c - \frac{b^2}{4a}$$

Factor the perfect square trinomial; multiply c by $\frac{4a}{4a}$ to get a common denominator: $$= a\left(x + \frac{b}{2a}\right)^2 + c \cdot \frac{4a}{4a} - \frac{b^2}{4a}$$

Write expression in the form $f(x) = a(x - h)^2 + k$: $$= a\left(x - \left(-\frac{b}{2a}\right)\right)^2 + \frac{4ac - b^2}{4a}$$

If we compare $f(x) = a\left(x - \left(-\frac{b}{2a}\right)\right)^2 + \frac{4ac - b^2}{4a}$ to $f(x) = a(x - h)^2 + k$, we come to the following conclusion:

Work Smart

Another formula for the vertex is

$$\left(-\frac{b}{2a}, \frac{-D}{4a}\right)$$

where $D = b^2 - 4ac$, the discriminant.

Preparing for...Answers

P1. $(0, 4), (10, 0)$ **P2.** $\left\{-\frac{5}{2}, 4\right\}$

P3. -1 and 4

THE VERTEX OF A PARABOLA

Any quadratic function $f(x) = ax^2 + bx + c, a \neq 0$, will have vertex

$$\left(-\frac{b}{2a}, \frac{4ac - b^2}{4a}\right)$$

Because the y-coordinate on the graph of any function can be found by evaluating the function at the corresponding x-coordinate, we can restate the coordinates of the vertex as

$$\left(-\frac{b}{2a}, f\left(-\frac{b}{2a}\right)\right)$$

For example, in Example 7 on page 590 from Section 7.4, we learned that $f(x) = x^2 + 4x + 3 = (x + 2)^2 - 1$ has a vertex of $(-2, -1)$. In $f(x) = x^2 + 4x + 3$, $a = 1$, $b = 4$, and $c = 3$, so the x-coordinate of the vertex is given by $x = -\dfrac{b}{2a} = \dfrac{-4}{2(1)} = -2$. The y-coordinate of the vertex is $f(-2) = (-2)^2 + 4(-2) + 3 = -1$.

Because the axis of symmetry intersects the vertex, we have that the axis of symmetry for any parabola is $x = -\dfrac{b}{2a}$. In addition, we know that the parabola will open up if $a > 0$ and down if $a < 0$. Using this information along with the intercepts of the graph of the quadratic function, we can obtain a complete graph.

The y-intercept is the value of the quadratic function $f(x) = ax^2 + bx + c$ at $x = 0$, that is, $f(0) = c$.

The x-intercepts, if there are any, are found by solving the quadratic equation

$$f(x) = ax^2 + bx + c = 0$$

As we learned in Section 7.2, this equation has two, one, or no real solutions, depending on the value of the discriminant $b^2 - 4ac$. We use the value of the discriminant to determine the number of x-intercepts the graph of the quadratic function will have.

THE x-INTERCEPTS OF THE GRAPH OF A QUADRATIC FUNCTION

1. If the discriminant $b^2 - 4ac > 0$, the graph of $f(x) = ax^2 + bx + c$ has two different x-intercepts. The graph will cross the x-axis at the solutions to the equation $ax^2 + bx + c = 0$.

2. If the discriminant $b^2 - 4ac = 0$, the graph of $f(x) = ax^2 + bx + c$ has one x-intercept. The graph will touch the x-axis at the solution to the equation $ax^2 + bx + c = 0$.

3. If the discriminant $b^2 - 4ac < 0$, the graph of $f(x) = ax^2 + bx + c$ has no x-intercepts. The graph will not cross or touch the x-axis.

Figure 21 illustrates these possibilities for parabolas that open up.

Figure 21

$f(x) = ax^2 + bx + c, a > 0$

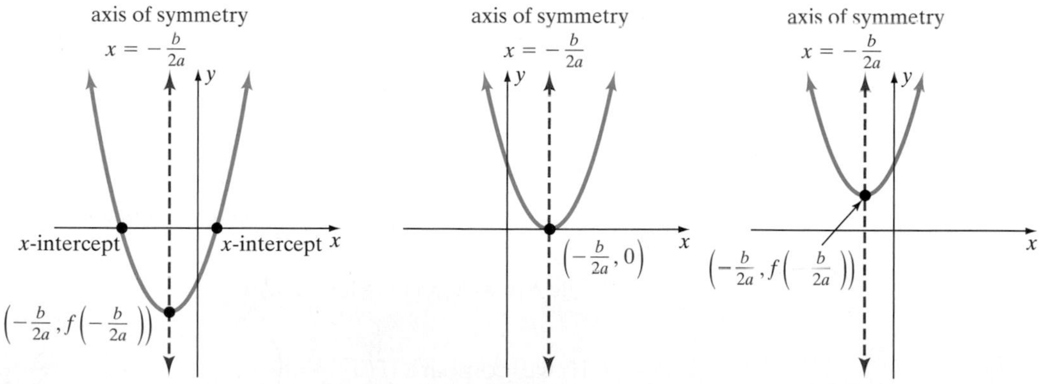

Case 1: $b^2 - 4ac > 0$ Case 2: $b^2 - 4ac = 0$ Case 3: $b^2 - 4ac < 0$

EXAMPLE 1 How to Graph a Quadratic Function Using Its Properties

Graph $f(x) = x^2 + 2x - 15$ using its properties.

Step-by-Step Solution

We compare $f(x) = x^2 + 2x - 15$ to $f(x) = ax^2 + bx + c$ and see that $a = 1$, $b = 2$, and $c = -15$.

| Step1: Determine whether the parabola opens up or down. | The parabola opens up because $a = 1 > 0$. |

Step 2: Determine the vertex and axis of symmetry.

The x-coordinate of the vertex is

$$x = -\frac{b}{2a} = -\frac{2}{2(1)} = -1.$$

The y-coordinate of the vertex is

$$f\left(-\frac{b}{2a}\right) = f(-1)$$

$$= (-1)^2 + 2(-1) - 15$$

$$= 1 - 2 - 15$$

$$= -16$$

The vertex is $(-1, -16)$.
The axis of symmetry is the line

$$x = -\frac{b}{2a} = -1$$

Step 3: Determine the y-intercept, f(0).

$$f(0) = 0^2 + 2(0) - 15$$

$$= -15$$

Step 4: Find the discriminant, $b^2 - 4ac$, to determine the number of the x-intercepts. Then determine the x-intercepts, if any.

We have that $a = 1$, $b = 2$, and $c = -15$, so $b^2 - 4ac = (2)^2 - 4(1)(-15) = 64 > 0$. Because the value of the discriminant is positive, the parabola will have two different x-intercepts. We find the x-intercepts by solving

$$f(x) = 0$$

$$x^2 + 2x - 15 = 0$$

Factor: $(x + 5)(x - 3) = 0$

Zero-Product Property: $x + 5 = 0$ or $x - 3 = 0$

$$x = -5 \quad \text{or} \quad x = 3$$

Step 5: Plot the vertex, y-intercept, and x-intercepts. Use the axis of symmetry to find an additional point. Draw the graph of the quadratic function.

Use the axis of symmetry to find the additional point $(-2, -15)$ by recognizing the y-intercept, $(0, -15)$, is 1 unit to the right of the axis of symmetry, therefore, there must be a point 1 unit to the left of the axis of symmetry. Plot the points and draw the graph. See Figure 22.

Figure 22

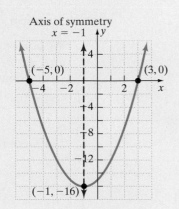

The following steps summarize how to graph any quadratic function using its properties.

GRAPHING A QUADRATIC FUNCTION USING ITS PROPERTIES

To graph any quadratic function of the form $f(x) = ax^2 + bx + c, a \neq 0$, we use the following steps:

Step 1: Determine whether the parabola opens up or down.

Step 2: Determine the vertex and axis of symmetry.

Step 3: Determine the y-intercept, $f(0)$.

Step 4: Determine the discriminant, $b^2 - 4ac$.

- If $b^2 - 4ac > 0$, then the parabola has two x-intercepts, which are found by solving $f(x) = 0$ $(ax^2 + bx + c = 0)$.
- If $b^2 - 4ac = 0$, the vertex is the x-intercept.
- If $b^2 - 4ac < 0$, there are no x-intercepts.

Step 5: Plot the vertex, y-intercept, and x-intercept(s), if any. Use the axis of symmetry to find an additional point. Draw the graph of the quadratic function.

Quick ✔

1. Any quadratic function $f(x) = ax^2 + bx + c, a \neq 0$, will have a vertex whose x-coordinate is $x =$ ____ .

2. The graph of $f(x) = ax^2 + bx + c$ will have two different x-intercepts if $b^2 - 4ac$ ___ 0.

3. How many x-intercepts does the graph of $f(x) = -2x^2 - 3x + 6$ have?

4. What is the vertex of $f(x) = x^2 + 4x - 3$?

5. Graph $f(x) = x^2 - 4x - 12$ using its properties.

In Example 1, the function was factorable, so the x-intercepts were rational numbers. When the quadratic function cannot be factored, we can use the quadratic formula to find the x-intercepts. For the purpose of graphing the quadratic function, we will approximate the x-intercepts rounded to two decimal places.

EXAMPLE 2 Graphing a Quadratic Function Using Its Properties

Graph $f(x) = -2x^2 + 12x - 5$ using its properties.

Solution

We compare $f(x) = -2x^2 + 12x - 5$ to $f(x) = ax^2 + bx + c$ and see that $a = -2, b = 12$, and $c = -5$. The parabola opens down because $a = -2 < 0$. The x-coordinate of the vertex is

$$x = -\frac{b}{2a} = -\frac{12}{2(-2)} = 3$$

The y-coordinate of the vertex is

$$f\left(-\frac{b}{2a}\right) = f(3)$$
$$= -2(3)^2 + 12(3) - 5$$
$$= -18 + 36 - 5$$
$$= 13$$

The vertex is $(3, 13)$. The axis of symmetry is the line

$$x = -\frac{b}{2a} = 3$$

The y-intercept is $f(0) = -2(0)^2 + 12(0) - 5 = -5$. Now we find the discriminant, $b^2 - 4ac$ to determine the number of the x-intercepts. We have that $a = -2$, $b = 12$, and $c = -5$, so $b^2 - 4ac = (12)^2 - 4(-2)(-5) = 104 > 0$. The parabola will have two different x-intercepts. We find the x-intercepts by solving

$$f(x) = 0$$
$$-2x^2 + 12x - 5 = 0$$

The equation cannot be solved by factoring (since $b^2 - 4ac$ is not a perfect square), so we use the quadratic formula:

Figure 23

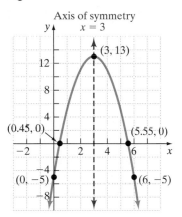

Axis of symmetry
$x = 3$

$(3, 13)$

$(0.45, 0)$
$(5.55, 0)$
$(0, -5)$
$(6, -5)$

$$x = \frac{-b \pm \sqrt{b^2 - 4ac}}{2a}$$

$a = -2, b = 12, b^2 - 4ac = 104:$
$$= \frac{-12 \pm \sqrt{104}}{2(-2)}$$

$\sqrt{104} = \sqrt{4 \cdot 26} = 2\sqrt{26}:$
$$= \frac{-12 \pm 2\sqrt{26}}{-4}$$

Divide -4 into each term in
the numerator and simplify: $x = 3 \pm \dfrac{\sqrt{26}}{-2}$ Exact solution

We evaluate $3 \pm \dfrac{\sqrt{26}}{-2}$ and find the x-intercepts are approximately 0.45 and 5.55.

We use the axis of symmetry to find the additional point $(6, -5)$. (The y-intercept, $(0, -5)$ is 3 units to the left of the axis of symmetry, therefore, there must be a point 3 units to the right of the axis of symmetry.) Next, we plot the vertex, intercepts, and additional point. Draw the graph of the quadratic function. See Figure 23.   ◾

Work Smart

Notice that the vertex in Example 2 lies in quadrant I (above the x-axis) and the graph opens down. This tells us the graph must have two x-intercepts.

Quick ✔

6. Graph $f(x) = -3x^2 + 12x - 7$ using its properties.

EXAMPLE 3   Graphing a Quadratic Function Using Its Properties

Graph $g(x) = x^2 - 8x + 16$ using its properties.

Solution

We compare $g(x) = x^2 - 8x + 16$ to $g(x) = ax^2 + bx + c$ and see that $a = 1$, $b = -8$, and $c = 16$. The parabola opens up because $a = 1 > 0$. The x-coordinate of the vertex is

$$x = -\frac{b}{2a} = -\frac{-8}{2(1)} = 4$$

The y-coordinate of the vertex is

$$f\left(-\frac{b}{2a}\right) = f(4)$$
$$= 4^2 - 8(4) + 16$$
$$= 16 - 32 + 16$$
$$= 0$$

The vertex is $(4, 0)$. The axis of symmetry is the line

$$x = -\frac{b}{2a} = 4$$

Figure 24

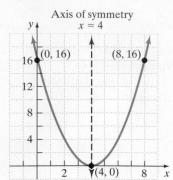

Axis of symmetry
$x = 4$

The y-intercept is $f(0) = 0^2 - 8(0) + 16 = 16$. We have that $a = 1, b = -8$, and $c = 16$, so $b^2 - 4ac = (-8)^2 - 4(1)(16) = 0$. The parabola will have one x-intercept, at the vertex. We verify this by solving

$$f(x) = 0$$
$$x^2 - 8x + 16 = 0$$
$$\text{Factor:} \quad (x - 4)^2 = 0$$
$$x = 4$$

We use the axis of symmetry to find the additional point $(8, 16)$. Now we graph the parabola. See Figure 24. ∎

Quick ✔

7. Graph $f(x) = x^2 + 6x + 9$ using its properties.

EXAMPLE 4 Graphing a Quadratic Function Using Its Properties

Graph $F(x) = 2x^2 + 6x + 5$ using its properties.

Solution

We compare $F(x) = 2x^2 + 6x + 5$ to $F(x) = ax^2 + bx + c$ and see that $a = 2$, $b = 6$, and $c = 5$. The parabola opens up because $a = 2 > 0$. The x-coordinate of the vertex is

$$x = -\frac{b}{2a} = -\frac{6}{2(2)} = -\frac{3}{2}$$

The y-coordinate of the vertex is

$$f\left(-\frac{b}{2a}\right) - f\left(-\frac{3}{2}\right)$$
$$= 2\left(-\frac{3}{2}\right)^2 + 6\left(-\frac{3}{2}\right) + 5$$
$$= 2\left(\frac{9}{4}\right) - 9 + 5$$
$$= \frac{1}{2}$$

Work Smart

Notice that the vertex lies in quadrant II (above the x-axis) and the graph opens up. This tells us the graph will have no x-intercepts.

The vertex is $\left(-\frac{3}{2}, \frac{1}{2}\right)$. The axis of symmetry is the line

$$x = -\frac{b}{2a} = -\frac{3}{2}$$

Figure 25

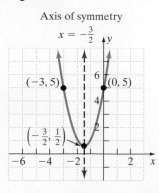

Axis of symmetry
$x = -\frac{3}{2}$

The y-intercept is $f(0) = 2(0)^2 + 6(0) + 5 = 5$. Because the parabola opens up and the vertex is in the second quadrant, we expect that the parabola will have no x-intercepts. We verify this by computing the discriminant with $a = 2, b = 6$, and $c = 5$:

$$b^2 - 4ac = 6^2 - 4(2)(5) = -4 < 0$$

The parabola will have no x-intercepts. Use the axis of symmetry to find the additional point $(-3, 5)$. Now we graph the parabola. See Figure 25. ∎

Figure 26

Vertex is highest point; y-coordinate is maximum value

Vertex is lowest point; y-coordinate is minimum value

(a) Opens up
$a > 0$

(b) Opens down
$a < 0$

Work Smart

The vertex is not the maximum or minimum value—the y-coordinate of the vertex is the maximum or minimum value of the function.

Quick ✔

8. Graph $G(x) = -3x^2 + 9x - 8$ using its properties.

2   Find the Maximum or Minimum Value of a Quadratic Function

Recall, the graph of a quadratic function $f(x) = ax^2 + bx + c$ is a parabola with vertex at $\left(-\dfrac{b}{2a}, f\left(-\dfrac{b}{2a}\right)\right)$. The vertex will be the highest point on the graph if $a < 0$ and the lowest point on the graph if $a > 0$. If the vertex is the highest point $(a < 0)$, then $f\left(-\dfrac{b}{2a}\right)$, the y-coordinate of the vertex, is the **maximum value** of f. If the vertex is the lowest point $(a > 0)$, then $f\left(-\dfrac{b}{2a}\right)$ is the **minimum value** of f. See Figure 26.

This property of the graph of a quadratic function allows us to answer questions involving *optimization*. **Optimization** is the process whereby we find the maximum or minimum value(s) of a function. In the case of quadratic functions, the maximum $(a < 0)$ or minimum $(a > 0)$ is found through the vertex.

EXAMPLE 5 Finding the Maximum or Minimum Value of a Quadratic Function

Determine whether the quadratic function

$$f(x) = 3x^2 + 12x - 7$$

has a maximum or minimum value. Then find the maximum or minimum value of the function.

Solution

If we compare $f(x) = 3x^2 + 12x - 7$ to $f(x) = ax^2 + bx + c$, we find that $a = 3, b = 12$, and $c = -7$. Because $a = 3 > 0$, we know that the graph of the quadratic function will open up, so the function will have a minimum value. The minimum value of the function occurs at

$$x = -\frac{b}{2a} = -\frac{12}{2(3)} = -2$$

The minimum value of the function is

$$f\left(-\frac{b}{2a}\right) = f(-2) = 3(-2)^2 + 12(-2) - 7$$
$$= 3(4) - 24 - 7$$
$$= -19$$

So the minimum value of the function is -19 and occurs at $x = -2$. ∎

Quick ✔

9. *True or False:* For the quadratic function $f(x) = ax^2 + bx + c$, if $a < 0$ then $f\left(-\dfrac{b}{2a}\right)$ is the maximum value of f.

In Problems 10 and 11, determine whether the quadratic function has a maximum or minimum value, then find the maximum or minimum value of the function.

10. $f(x) = 2x^2 - 8x + 1$ 11. $G(x) = -x^2 + 10x + 8$

As we stated at the beginning of Section 7.4, many applications can be modeled using a quadratic function. Once a quadratic model has been determined, we can use properties of quadratic functions to answer interesting questions regarding the model.

EXAMPLE 6 Maximizing Revenue

Suppose that the marketing department of Dell Computer has found that, when a certain model of computer is sold at a price of p dollars, the daily revenue R (in dollars) as a function of the price p is

$$R(p) = -\frac{1}{4}p^2 + 400p$$

(a) For what price will the revenue be maximized?

(b) What is the maximum daily revenue?

Solution

(a) We notice that the revenue function is a quadratic function whose graph opens down because $a = -\frac{1}{4} < 0$. Therefore, the function will have a maximum at

$$p = -\frac{b}{2a} = -\frac{400}{2 \cdot \left(-\dfrac{1}{4}\right)} = -\frac{400}{-\dfrac{1}{2}} = 800$$

Revenue will be maximized when the price is $p = \$800$.

(b) The maximum daily revenue is found by letting $p = \$800$ in the revenue function.

$$R(800) = -\frac{1}{4} \cdot (800)^2 + 400 \cdot 800$$

$$= \$160,000$$

The maximum daily revenue is $160,000. See Figure 27 for an illustration.

Figure 27

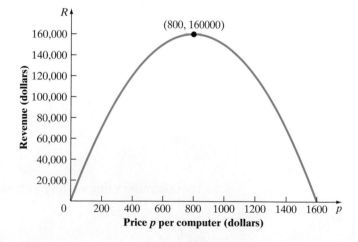

Quick ✔

12. Suppose that the marketing department of Texas Instruments has found that, when a certain model of calculator is sold at a price of p dollars, the daily revenue R (in dollars) as a function of the price p is $R(p) = -0.5p^2 + 75p$.

(a) For what price will the daily revenue be maximized?

(b) What is the maximum daily revenue?

⌐3 Model and Solve Optimization Problems Involving Quadratic Functions

We now discuss models based on verbal descriptions that result in quadratic functions. As always, we shall use the problem-solving strategy introduced in Section 1.2.

⌐EXAMPLE 7 Maximizing the Area Enclosed by a Fence

A farmer has 3000 feet of fence to enclose a rectangular field. What is the maximum area that can be enclosed by the fence? What are the dimensions of the rectangle that encloses the most area?

Solution

Step 1: Identify We wish to determine the dimensions of a rectangle that maximize the area.

Step 2: Name We let w represent the width of the rectangle and l represent the length.

Step 3: Translate Figure 28 illustrates the situation.

Figure 28

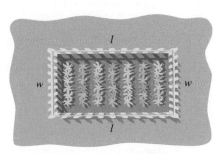

We know that the amount of fence available is 3000 feet. This means that the perimeter of the rectangle will be 3000 feet. Since the perimeter of a rectangle is $2l + 2w$ we have that

$$2l + 2w = 3000$$

The area A of the rectangle is

$$A = lw$$

The equation $A = lw$ represents the area of the rectangle in terms of two variables, l and w. To express A in terms of only one variable, we solve the equation $2l + 2w = 3000$ for l and then substitute for l in the area formula $A = lw$.

$$2l + 2w = 3000$$

Subtract $2w$ from both sides: $2l = 3000 - 2w$

Divide both sides by 2: $l = \dfrac{3000 - 2w}{2}$

Simplify: $l = 1500 - w$

Now let $l = 1500 - w$ in the formula $A = lw$.

$$A = (1500 - w)w$$
$$= -w^2 + 1500w$$

Now, A is a quadratic function of w.

$$A(w) = -w^2 + 1500w \quad \text{The Model}$$

Step 4: Solve We wish to find the dimensions that result in a maximum area enclosed by the fence. The model we developed in Step 3 is a quadratic function that opens down (because $a = -1 < 0$), so the vertex is a maximum point on the graph of A. The maximum value occurs at

$$w = -\frac{b}{2a} = -\frac{1500}{2(-1)} = 750$$

Work Smart

We could just as easily have solved $2l + 2w = 3000$ for w. We ultimately would obtain the same solution.

The maximum value of A is

$$A\left(-\frac{b}{2a}\right) = A(750) = -750^2 + 1500(750)$$
$$= 562{,}500 \text{ square feet}$$

We know that $l = 1500 - w$, so if the width is 750 feet, then the length will be $l = 1500 - 750 = 750$ feet.

Step 5: Check With a length and width of 750 feet, the perimeter is $2(750) + 2(750) = 3000$ feet. The area is $(750 \text{ feet})(750 \text{ feet}) = 562{,}500$ square feet. Everything checks!

Step 6: Answer The largest area that can be enclosed by 3000 feet of fence has an area of 562,500 square feet. Its dimensions are 750 feet by 750 feet. ∎

Quick ✔

13. Roberta has 1000 yards of fence to enclose a rectangular field. What is the maximum area that can be enclosed by the fence? What are the dimensions of the rectangle that encloses the most area?

EXAMPLE 8 Pricing a Charter

Chicago Tours offers boat charters along the Chicago coastline on Lake Michigan. Normally, a ticket costs $20 per person, but for any group, Chicago Tours will lower the price of a ticket by $0.10 per person for each person in excess of 30. Determine the group size that will maximize revenue. What is the maximum revenue that can be earned from a group sale?

Solution

Step 1: Identify This is a direct translation problem involving revenue. Remember, revenue is price times quantity.

Step 2: Name We let x represent the number in the group in excess of 30.

Step 3: Translate Revenue is price times quantity. If 30 individuals make up a group, the revenue to Chicago Tours will be $20(30)$. If 31 individuals make up a group, revenue will be $19.90(31)$. If 32 individuals make up the group, revenue will be $19.80(32)$. In general, if x individuals in excess of 30 make up a group, revenue will be $(20 - 0.1x)(x + 30)$. So the revenue R for a group that has $x + 30$ people in it is given by

$$R(x) = (20 - 0.1x)(x + 30)$$
$$\text{FOIL:} \quad = 20x + 600 - 0.1x^2 - 3x$$
$$\text{This is the model:} \quad = -0.1x^2 + 17x + 600$$

Step 4: Solve We wish to know the revenue-maximizing number of individuals in a group. The function R is a quadratic function with a graph that opens down (because $a = -0.1 < 0$), so we know that the vertex is a maximum point. The value of x that results in a maximum is given by

$$x = -\frac{b}{2a} = -\frac{17}{2(-0.1)}$$
$$= 85$$

The maximum revenue is

$$R(85) = -0.1(85)^2 + 17(85) + 600$$
$$= \$1322.50$$

Step 5: Check Remember that x represents the number of passengers in excess of 30. Therefore, $30 + 85 = 115$ tickets should be sold to maximize revenue. The cost per ticket would be $\$20 - 0.1(85) = \$20 - \$8.50 = \$11.50$. Multiplying the cost per ticket by the number of passengers we obtain $\$11.50(115) = \$1322.50$. We have the right answer!

Step 6: Answer A group sale of 115 passengers will maximize revenue. The maximum revenue would be $\$1322.50$.

Quick ✔

14. A compact disk manufacturer charges $100 for each box of CDs ordered. However, it reduces the price by $1 per box for each box in excess of 30 boxes, but less than 90 boxes. Determine the number of boxes of CDs that should be sold to maximize revenue. What is the maximum revenue?

7.5 EXERCISES

PRACTICE   WATCH   DOWNLOAD   READ   REVIEW

1–14. are the Quick ✔s that follow each EXAMPLE

Building Skills

In Problems 15–22, (a) find the vertex of each parabola, (b) use the discriminant to determine the number of x-intercepts the graph will have. Then determine the x-intercepts. See Objective 1.

15. $f(x) = x^2 - 6x - 16$ **16.** $g(x) = x^2 + 4x - 12$

17. $G(x) = -2x^2 + 4x - 5$ **18.** $H(x) = x^2 - 4x + 5$

19. $h(x) = 4x^2 + 4x + 1$ **20.** $f(x) = x^2 - 6x + 9$

21. $F(x) = 4x^2 - x - 1$ **22.** $P(x) = -2x^2 + 3x + 1$

In Problems 23–62, graph each quadratic function using its properties by following Steps 1–5 on page 598. Based on the graph, determine the domain and range of the quadratic function. See Objective 1.

23. $f(x) = x^2 - 4x - 5$ **24.** $f(x) = x^2 - 2x - 8$

25. $G(x) = x^2 + 12x + 32$ **26.** $g(x) = x^2 - 12x + 27$

27. $F(x) = -x^2 + 2x + 8$ **28.** $g(x) = -x^2 + 2x + 15$

29. $H(x) = x^2 - 4x + 4$ **30.** $h(x) = x^2 + 6x + 9$

31. $g(x) = x^2 + 2x + 5$ **32.** $f(x) = x^2 - 4x + 7$

33. $h(x) = -x^2 - 10x - 25$ **34.** $P(x) = -x^2 - 12x - 36$

35. $p(x) = -x^2 + 2x - 5$ **36.** $f(x) = -x^2 + 4x - 6$

37. $F(x) = 4x^2 - 4x - 3$ **38.** $f(x) = 4x^2 - 8x - 21$

39. $G(x) = -9x^2 + 18x + 7$ **40.** $g(x) = -9x^2 - 36x - 20$

41. $H(x) = 4x^2 - 4x + 1$ **42.** $h(x) = 9x^2 + 12x + 4$

43. $f(x) = -16x^2 - 24x - 9$ **44.** $F(x) = -4x^2 - 20x - 25$

45. $f(x) = 2x^2 + 8x + 11$ **46.** $F(x) = 3x^2 + 6x + 7$

47. $P(x) = -4x^2 + 6x - 3$ **48.** $p(x) = -2x^2 + 6x + 5$

49. $h(x) = x^2 + 5x + 3$ **50.** $H(x) = x^2 + 3x + 1$

51. $G(x) = -3x^2 + 8x + 2$ **52.** $F(x) = -2x^2 + 6x + 1$

53. $f(x) = 5x^2 - 5x + 2$ **54.** $F(x) = 4x^2 + 4x - 1$

55. $H(x) = -3x^2 + 6x$ **56.** $h(x) = -4x^2 + 8x$

57. $f(x) = x^2 - \dfrac{5}{2}x - \dfrac{3}{2}$ **58.** $g(x) = x^2 + \dfrac{5}{2}x - 6$

59. $G(x) = \dfrac{1}{2}x^2 + 2x - 6$ **60.** $H(x) = \dfrac{1}{4}x^2 + x - 8$

61. $F(x) = -\dfrac{1}{4}x^2 + x + 15$ **62.** $G(x) = -\dfrac{1}{2}x^2 - 8x - 24$

In Problems 63–74, determine whether the quadratic function has a maximum or minimum value. Then find the maximum or minimum value. See Objective 2.

63. $f(x) = x^2 + 8x + 13$ **64.** $f(x) = x^2 - 6x + 3$

65. $G(x) = -x^2 - 10x + 3$ **66.** $g(x) = -x^2 + 4x + 12$

67. $F(x) = -2x^2 + 12x + 5$ **68.** $H(x) = -3x^2 + 12x - 1$

69. $h(x) = 4x^2 + 16x - 3$ **70.** $G(x) = 5x^2 + 10x - 1$

71. $f(x) = 2x^2 - 5x + 1$ **72.** $F(x) = 3x^2 + 4x - 3$

73. $H(x) = -3x^2 + 4x + 1$ **74.** $h(x) = -4x^2 - 6x + 1$

Applying the Concepts

75. Revenue Function Suppose that the marketing department of Panasonic has found that, when a certain model of DVD player is sold at a price of p dollars, the daily revenue R (in dollars) as a function of the price p is $R(p) = -2.5p^2 + 600p$.
  (a) For what price will the daily revenue be maximized?
  (b) What is the maximum daily revenue?

76. Revenue Function Suppose that the marketing department of Samsung has found that, when a certain model of cellular telephone is sold at a price of p dollars, the daily revenue R (in dollars) as a function of the price p is $R(p) = -5p^2 + 600p$.
  (a) For what price will the daily revenue be maximized?
  (b) What is the maximum daily revenue?

77. Marginal Cost The marginal cost of a product can be thought of as the cost of producing one additional unit of output. For example, if the marginal cost of producing the fiftieth unit of a product is $6.30, then it costs $6.30 to increase production from 49 to 50 units of output. Suppose that the marginal cost C (in dollars) to produce x digital cameras is given by $C(x) = 0.05x^2 - 6x + 215$. How many digital cameras should be produced to minimize marginal cost? What is the minimum marginal cost?

78. Marginal Cost (See Problem 77.) The marginal cost C (in dollars) of manufacturing x portable CD players is given by $C(x) = 0.05x^2 - 9x + 435$. How many portable CD players should be manufactured to minimize marginal cost? What is the minimum marginal cost?

79. Punkin Chunkin Suppose that an air cannon in the Punkin Chunkin contest whose muzzle is 10 feet above the ground fires a pumpkin at an angle of 45° to the horizontal with a muzzle velocity of 335 feet per second. The

model $s(t) = -16t^2 + 240t + 10$ can be used to estimate the height s of a pumpkin after t seconds.
  (a) Determine the time at which the pumpkin is at a maximum height.
  (b) Determine the maximum height of the pumpkin.
  (c) After how long will the pumpkin strike the ground?

80. Punkin Chunkin Suppose that a catapult in the Punkin Chunkin contest releases a pumpkin 8 feet above the ground at an angle of 45° to the horizontal with an initial speed of 220 feet per second. The model $s(t) = -16t^2 + 155t + 8$ can be used to estimate the height s of a pumpkin after t seconds.
  (a) Determine the time at which the pumpkin is at a maximum height.
  (b) Determine the maximum height of the pumpkin.
  (c) After how long will the pumpkin strike the ground?

81. Punkin Chunkin Suppose that an air cannon in the Punkin Chunkin contest whose muzzle is 10 feet above the ground fires a pumpkin at an angle of 45° to the horizontal with a muzzle velocity of 335 feet per second. The model $h(x) = \dfrac{-32}{335^2}x^2 + x + 10$ can be used to estimate the height h of the pumpkin after it has traveled x feet.
  (a) How far from the cannon will the pumpkin reach a maximum height?
  (b) What is the maximum height of the pumpkin?
  (c) How far will the pumpkin travel before it strikes the ground?
  (d) Compare your answer in part **(b)** of this problem with the answer found in part **(b)** of Problem 79. Why might the answers differ?

82. Punkin Chunkin Suppose that a catapult in the Punkin Chunkin contest releases a pumpkin 8 feet above the ground at an angle of 45° to the horizontal with an initial speed of 220 feet per second. The model $h(x) = \dfrac{-32}{220^2}x^2 + x + 8$ can be used to estimate the height h of the pumpkin after it has traveled x feet.
  (a) How far from the cannon will the pumpkin reach a maximum height?
  (b) What is the maximum height of the pumpkin?
  (c) How far will the pumpkin travel before it strikes the ground?
  (d) Compare your answer in part **(b)** of this problem with the answer found in part **(b)** of Problem 80. Why might the answers differ?

83. Life Cycle Hypothesis The Life Cycle Hypothesis from Economics was presented by Franco Modigliani in 1954. One of its components states that income is a function of age. The function $I(a) = -55a^2 + 5119a - 54{,}448$ represents the relation between average annual income I and age a.

   (a) According to the model, at what age will average income be a maximum?

   (b) According to the model, what is the maximum average income?

84. Advanced Degrees The function $P(x) = -0.006x^2 + 0.65x - 6.043$ models the percentage of the United States population whose age is x that have earned an advanced degree (more than a bachelor's degree) as of March 2006. (SOURCE: *Based on data obtained from the U.S. Census Bureau*)

   (a) To the nearest tenth of a year, what is the age for which the highest percentage of Americans have earned an advanced degree?

   (b) According to the model, what is the percentage of Americans who have earned an advanced degree at the age found in part **(a)**?

85. Fun with Numbers The sum of two numbers is 36. Find the numbers such that their product is a maximum.

86. Fun with Numbers The sum of two numbers is 50. Find the numbers such that their product is a maximum.

87. Fun with Numbers The difference of two numbers is 18. Find the numbers such that their product is a minimum.

88. Fun with Numbers The difference of two numbers is 10. Find the numbers such that their product is a minimum.

89. Enclosing a Rectangular Field Maurice has 500 yards of fencing and wishes to enclose a rectangular area. What is the maximum area that can be enclosed by the fence? What are the dimensions of the area enclosed?

90. Enclosing a Rectangular Field Maude has 800 yards of fencing and wishes to enclose a rectangular area. What is the maximum area that can be enclosed by the fence? What are the dimensions of the area enclosed?

91. Maximizing an Enclosed Area A farmer with 2000 meters of fencing wants to enclose a rectangular plot that borders a river. If the farmer does not fence the side along the river, what is the largest area that can be enclosed? What are the dimensions of the enclosed area? See the figure.

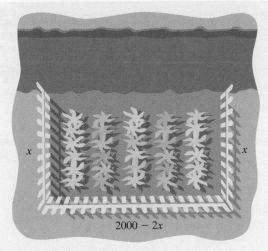

$2000 - 2x$

92. Maximizing an Enclosed Area A farmer with 8000 meters of fencing wants to enclose a rectangular plot and then divide it into two plots with a fence parallel to one of the sides. See the figure. What is the largest area that can be enclosed? What are the lengths of the sides of each part of the enclosed area?

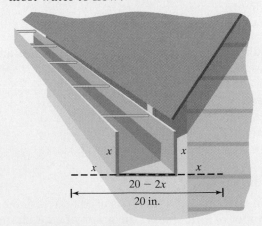

93. Constructing Rain Gutters A rain gutter is to be made of aluminum sheets that are 20 inches wide by turning up the edges 90°. What depth will provide maximum cross-sectional area and hence allow the most water to flow?

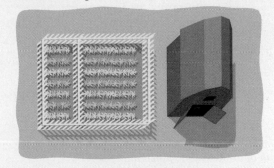

94. Maximizing the Volume of a Box A box with a rectangular base is to be constructed such that the perimeter of the base of the box is to be 40 inches. The height of the box must be 15 inches. Find the dimensions of the box such that the volume is maximized. What is the maximum volume?

95. Revenue Function Weekly demand for jeans at a department store obeys the demand equation

$$x = -p + 110$$

where x is the quantity demanded and p is the price (in dollars).

(a) Express the revenue R as a function of p. (*Hint:* $R = xp$)

(b) What price p maximizes revenue? What is the maximum revenue?

(c) How many pairs of jeans will be sold at the revenue-maximizing price?

96. Revenue Function Demand for hot dogs at a baseball game obeys the demand equation

$$x = -800p + 8000$$

where x is the quantity demanded and p is the price (in dollars).

(a) Express the revenue R as a function of p. (*Hint:* $R = xp$)

(b) What price p maximizes revenue? What is the maximum revenue?

(c) How many hot dogs will be sold at the revenue-maximizing price?

Extending the Concepts

Answer Problems 97 and 98 using the following information: A quadratic function of the form $f(x) = ax^2 + bx + c$ with $b^2 - 4ac > 0$ may also be written in the form $f(x) = a(x - r_1)(x - r_2)$, where r_1 and r_2 are the x-intercepts of the graph of the quadratic function.

97. (a) Find a quadratic function whose x-intercepts are 2 and 6 with $a = 1$; $a = 2$, and $a = -2$.

(b) How does the value of a affect the intercepts?

(c) How does the value of a affect the axis of symmetry?

(d) How does the value of a affect the vertex?

98. (a) Find a quadratic function whose x-intercepts are -1 and 5 with $a = 1$; $a = 2$, and $a = -2$.

(b) How does the value of a affect the intercepts?

(c) How does the value of a affect the axis of symmetry?

(d) How does the value of a affect the vertex?

Explaining the Concepts

99. Explain how the discriminant is used to determine the number of x-intercepts the graph of a quadratic function will have.

100. Provide two methods for finding the vertex of any quadratic function $f(x) = ax^2 + bx + c$.

101. Refer to Example 6 on page 602. Notice that if the price charged for the computer is $0 or $1600, the revenue is $0. It is easy to explain why revenue

would be $0 if the price charged is $0, but how can revenue be $0 if the price charged is $1600?

Synthesis Review

In Problems 102–105, graph each function using point-plotting.

102. $f(x) = -2x + 12$

103. $G(x) = \dfrac{1}{4}x - 2$

104. $f(x) = x^2 - 5$

105. $f(x) = (x + 2)^2 + 4$

106. For each function in Problems 102–105, explain an alternative method for graphing the function. Which method do you prefer? Why?

The Graphing Calculator

Graphing calculators have a maximum and a minimum feature that allows us to determine the coordinates of the vertex of a parabola. For example, to find the vertex of $f(x) = x^2 + 2x - 15$ using a TI-84 graphing calculator, we use the MINIMUM feature. See Figure 29. The vertex is $(-1, -16)$.

Figure 29

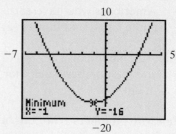

In Problems 107–114, use a graphing calculator to graph each quadratic function. Using the MAXIMUM or MINIMUM feature on the calculator, determine the vertex. If necessary, round your answers to two decimal places.

107. $f(x) = x^2 - 7x + 3$

108. $f(x) = x^2 + 3x + 8$

109. $G(x) = -2x^2 + 14x + 13$

110. $g(x) = -4x^2 - x + 11$

111. $F(x) = 5x^2 + 3x - 20$

112. $F(x) = 3x^2 + 2x - 21$

113. $H(x) = \dfrac{1}{2}x^2 - \dfrac{2}{3}x + 5$

114. $h(x) = \dfrac{3}{4}x^2 + \dfrac{4}{3}x - 1$

115. On the same screen, graph the family of parabolas $f(x) = x^2 + 2x + c$ for $c = -3$, $c = 0$, and $c = 1$. Describe the role that c plays in the graph for this family of functions.

116. On the same screen, graph the family of parabolas $f(x) = x^2 + bx + 1$ for $b = -4$, $b = 0$, and $b = 4$. Describe the role that b plays in the graph for this family of functions.

CHAPTER 7 Activity: Presidential Decision Making

Focus: Developing quadratic equations.
Time: 30–35 minutes
Group size: 2–4

1. Your boss, Huntington Corporation's President, Gerald Cain, is very concerned about his approval rating with his employees. Last year, January 1, he made some policy changes and he saw his approval rating drop. In fact, his approval rating was 48% just before he made some policy changes. One month later, his rating was at 41%, two months later it was at 40%, and at three months it began to climb and was 45%. He discovered that the following function described his approval rating for that year where x is the month:

$$R(x) = 3x^2 - 10x + 48$$

   (a) As a group, use the above function to find when President Cain's approval rating will return to the original rating.
   (b) If his approval rating continues to climb, when will he reach a 68% approval rating?

2. On January 1 of this year, President Cain surveyed his employees again and found that 68% of them approved of his leadership skills. At this time, President Cain decided to become very strict with his employees and began a series of new policies. He noticed that his approval rating began to steadily slip and reached an all-time low of 38% on March 30 (3 months later). President Cain is not worried because he knows from last year that this drop in popularity will bottom out and eventually rise. He believes his popularity can be modeled by a quadratic function and needs your help. He has more bad news to deliver but does not want to begin the next round of policy changes until his approval rating is back to approximately 50%.

   (a) As a group, write a quadratic function that would model President Cain's approval rating.
   (b) As a group, develop different ways to advise President Cain what date to begin his policy changes. Use graphs and computations to prove your point.

CHAPTER 7 Review

Section 7.1 Solving Quadratic Equations by Completing the Square

KEY CONCEPTS	KEY TERMS
• **Square Root Property** If $x^2 = p$, then $x = \sqrt{p}$ or $x = -\sqrt{p}$. • **Pythagorean Theorem** In a right triangle, the square of the length of the hypotenuse is equal to the sum of the squares of the lengths of the legs. That is, $\text{leg}^2 + \text{leg}^2 = \text{hypotenuse}^2$.	Completing the square Right triangle Right angle Hypotenuse Legs

YOU SHOULD BE ABLE TO...	EXAMPLE	REVIEW EXERCISES
1 Solve quadratic equations using the Square Root Property (p. 548)	Examples 1 through 4	1–10
2 Complete the square in one variable (p. 551)	Example 5	11–16
3 Solve quadratic equations by completing the square (p. 552)	Examples 6 and 7	17–26
4 Solve problems using the Pythagorean Theorem (p. 554)	Examples 8 and 9	27–36

In Problems 1–10, solve each equation using the Square Root Property.

1. $m^2 = 169$

2. $n^2 = 75$

3. $a^2 = -16$

4. $b^2 = \dfrac{8}{9}$

5. $(x - 8)^2 = 81$

6. $(y - 2)^2 - 62 = 88$

7. $(3z + 5)^2 = 100$

8. $7p^2 = 18$

9. $3q^2 + 251 = 11$

10. $\left(x + \dfrac{3}{4}\right)^2 = \dfrac{13}{16}$

In Problems 11–16, complete the square in each expression. Then factor the perfect square trinomial.

11. $a^2 + 30a$

12. $b^2 - 14b$

13. $c^2 - 11c$

14. $d^2 + 9d$

15. $m^2 - \dfrac{1}{4}m$

16. $n^2 + \dfrac{6}{7}n$

In Problems 17–26, solve each quadratic equation by completing the square.

17. $x^2 - 10x + 16 = 0$

18. $y^2 - 3y - 28 = 0$

19. $z^2 - 6z - 3 = 0$

20. $a^2 - 5a - 7 = 0$

21. $b^2 + b + 7 = 0$

22. $c^2 - 6c + 17 = 0$

23. $2d^2 - 7d + 3 = 0$

24. $2w^2 + 2w + 5 = 0$

25. $3x^2 - 9x + 8 = 0$

26. $3x^2 + 4x - 2 = 0$

In Problems 27–32, the lengths of the legs of a right triangle are given. Find the hypotenuse.

27. $a = 9, b = 12$

28. $a = 8, b = 8$

29. $a = 3, b = 6$

30. $a = 10, b = 24$

31. $a = 5, b = \sqrt{11}$

32. $a = 6, b = \sqrt{13}$

In Problems 33–35, use the right triangle shown below and find the missing length.

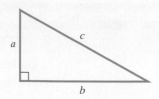

33. $a = 9, c = 12$ **34.** $b = 5, c = 10$

35. $b = 6, c = 17$

36. Baseball Diamond A baseball diamond is really a square that is 90 feet long on each side. (See the figure.) What is the distance between home plate and

second base? Round your answer to the nearest tenth of a foot.

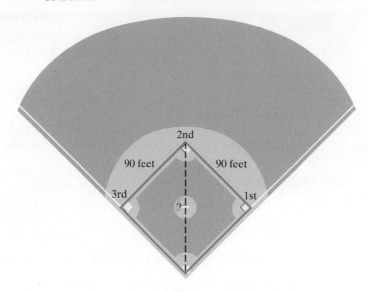

Section 7.2 Solving Quadratic Equations by the Quadratic Formula

KEY CONCEPTS	KEY TERM
	Discriminant

- **The Quadratic Formula**
  The solutions to the equation $ax^2 + bx + c = 0, a \neq 0$, are given by
  $$x = \frac{-b \pm \sqrt{b^2 - 4ac}}{2a}$$

- **Discriminant**
  For the quadratic equation $ax^2 + bx + c = 0, a \neq 0$:
  - If $b^2 - 4ac > 0$, the equation has two unequal real solutions.
    - If $b^2 - 4ac$ is a perfect square, the equation has two rational solutions.
    - If $b^2 - 4ac$ is not a perfect square, the equation has two irrational solutions.
  - If $b^2 - 4ac = 0$, the equation has a repeated real solution.
  - If $b^2 - 4ac < 0$, the equation has two complex solutions that are not real.

YOU SHOULD BE ABLE TO...	EXAMPLE	REVIEW EXERCISES
1 Solve quadratic equations using the quadratic formula (p. 560)	Examples 1 through 4	37–46
2 Use the discriminant to determine the nature of solutions in a quadratic equation (p. 565)	Example 5	47–52
3 Model and solve problems involving quadratic equations (p. 568)	Examples 6 and 7	63–68

In Problems 37–46, solve each equation using the quadratic formula.

37. $x^2 - x - 20 = 0$ **38.** $4y^2 = 8y + 21$

39. $3p^2 + 8p = -3$ **40.** $2q^2 - 3 = 4q$

41. $3w^2 + w = -3$ **42.** $9z^2 + 16 = 24z$

43. $m^2 - 4m + 2 = 0$ **44.** $5n^2 + 4n + 1 = 0$

45. $5x + 13 = -x^2$ **46.** $-2y^2 = 6y + 7$

In Problems 47–52, determine the discriminant of each quadratic equation. Use the value of the discriminant to determine whether the quadratic equation has two rational solutions, two irrational solutions, one repeated real solution, or two complex solutions that are not real.

47. $p^2 - 5p - 8 = 0$ **48.** $m^2 + 8m + 16 = 0$

49. $3n^2 + n = -4$ **50.** $7w^2 + 3 = 8w$

51. $4x^2 + 49 = 28x$ **52.** $11z - 12 = 2z^2$

In Problems 53–62, solve each equation using any appropriate method.

53. $x^2 + 8x - 9 = 0$ **54.** $6p^2 + 13p = 5$

55. $n^2 + 13 = -4n$ **56.** $5y^2 - 60 = 0$

57. $\frac{1}{4}q^2 - \frac{1}{2}q - \frac{3}{8} = 0$ **58.** $\frac{1}{8}m^2 + m + \frac{5}{2} = 0$

59. $(w - 8)(w + 6) = -33$ **60.** $(x - 3)(x + 1) = -2$

61. $9z^2 = 16$ **62.** $\frac{1 - 2x}{x^2 + 5} = 1$

63. Pythagorean Theorem Use the Pythagorean Theorem to determine the value of x for the given measurements of the right triangle shown below.

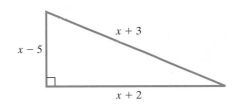

64. Area The area of a rectangle is 108 square centimeters. The width of the rectangle is 3 inches less than the length. What are the dimensions of the rectangle?

65. Revenue The revenue R received by a company selling x cellular phones per week is given by the function $R(x) = -0.2x^2 + 180x$.
   (a) How many cellular phones must be sold in order for revenue to be $36,000 per week?
   (b) How many cellular phones must be sold in order for revenue to be $40,500 per week?

66. Projectile Motion The height s of a ball after t seconds when thrown straight up with an initial speed of 50 feet per second from an initial height of 180 feet can be modeled by the function $s(t) = -16t^2 + 50t + 180$.
   (a) When will the height of the ball be 200 feet? Round your answer to the nearest tenth of a second.
   (b) When will the height of the ball be 100 feet? Round your answer to the nearest tenth of a second.
   (c) Will the ball ever reach a height of 300 feet? How does the result of the equation tell you this?

67. Pleasure Boat Ride A pleasure boat carries passengers 10 miles upstream and then returns to the starting point. The total time of the trip (excluding the time on the ground) takes 2 hours. If the speed of the current is 3 miles per hour, find the speed of the boat in still water. Round your answer to the nearest tenth of a mile per hour.

68. Work Together, Tom and Beth can wash their car in 30 minutes. By himself, Tom can wash the car in 14 minutes less time than Beth can by herself. How long will it take Beth to wash the car by herself? Round your answer to the nearest tenth of a minute.

Section 7.3 Solving Equations Quadratic in Form

KEY TERM

Equation quadratic in form

YOU SHOULD BE ABLE TO...	EXAMPLE	REVIEW EXERCISES
⫾ Solve equations that are quadratic in form (p. 574)	Examples 1 through 5	69–80

In Problems 69–78, solve each equation.

69. $x^4 + 7x^2 - 144 = 0$ **70.** $4w^4 + 5w^2 - 6 = 0$

71. $3(a + 4)^2 - 11(a + 4) + 6 = 0$

72. $(q^2 - 11)^2 - 2(q^2 - 11) - 15 = 0$

73. $y - 13\sqrt{y} + 36 = 0$ **74.** $5z + 2\sqrt{z} - 3 = 0$

75. $p^{-2} - 4p^{-1} - 21 = 0$ **76.** $2b^{\frac{2}{3}} + 13b^{\frac{1}{3}} - 7 = 0$

77. $m^{\frac{1}{2}} + 2m^{\frac{1}{4}} - 8 = 0$ **78.** $\left(\dfrac{1}{x + 5}\right)^2 + \dfrac{3}{x + 5} = 28$

In Problems 79 and 80, find the zeros of the function.

79. $f(x) = 4x - 20\sqrt{x} + 21$ **80.** $g(x) = x^4 - 17x^2 + 60$

Section 7.4   Graphing Quadratic Functions Using Transformations

KEY CONCEPTS

- **Graphing a Function of the Form $f(x) = x^2 + k$ or $f(x) = x^2 - k$**
  To obtain the graph of $f(x) = x^2 + k$, $k > 0$, from the graph of $y = x^2$, shift the graph of $y = x^2$ vertically up k units. To obtain the graph of $f(x) = x^2 - k$, $k > 0$, from the graph of $y = x^2$ shift the graph of $y = x^2$ vertically down k units.

- **Graphing a Function of the Form $f(x) = (x - h)^2$ or $f(x) = (x + h)^2$**
  To obtain the graph of $f(x) = (x - h)^2$, $h > 0$, from the graph of $y = x^2$, shift the graph of $y = x^2$ horizontally to the right h units. To obtain the graph of $f(x) = (x + h)^2$, $h > 0$, from the graph of $y = x^2$ shift the graph of $y = x^2$ horizontally left h units.

- **Graphing a Function of the Form $f(x) = ax^2$**
  To obtain the graph of $f(x) = ax^2$ from the graph of $y = x^2$, multiply each y-coordinate on the graph of $y = x^2$ by a.

KEY TERMS

Quadratic function
Vertically stretched
Vertically compressed
Parabola
Opens up
Opens down
Vertex
Axis of symmetry
Transformations

YOU SHOULD BE ABLE TO...	EXAMPLE	REVIEW EXERCISES
1 Graph quadratic functions of the form $f(x) = x^2 + k$ (p. 583)	Examples 1 and 2	81–82; 87–90
2 Graph quadratic functions of the form $f(x) = (x - h)^2$ (p. 585)	Examples 3 through 5	83–84; 87–90
3 Graph quadratic functions of the form $f(x) = ax^2$ (p. 587)	Example 6	85–86; 89–90
4 Graph quadratic functions of the form $f(x) = ax^2 + bx + c$ (p. 589)	Examples 7 and 8	91–96
5 Find a quadratic function from its graph (p. 592)	Example 9	97–100

In Problems 81–90, use the graph of $y = x^2$ to graph the quadratic function.

81. $f(x) = x^2 + 4$ **82.** $g(x) = x^2 - 5$

83. $h(x) = (x + 1)^2$ **84.** $F(x) = (x - 4)^2$

85. $G(x) = -4x^2$ **86.** $H(x) = \dfrac{1}{5}x^2$

87. $p(x) = (x - 4)^2 - 3$ **88.** $P(x) = (x + 4)^2 + 2$

89. $f(x) = -(x - 1)^2 + 4$ **90.** $F(x) = \dfrac{1}{2}(x + 2)^2 - 1$

In Problems 91–96, graph each quadratic function using transformations. Determine the vertex and axis of symmetry. Based on the graph determine the domain and range of each function.

91. $g(x) = x^2 - 6x + 10$ **92.** $G(x) = x^2 + 8x + 11$

93. $h(x) = 2x^2 - 4x - 3$ **94.** $H(x) = -x^2 - 6x - 10$

95. $p(x) = -3x^2 + 12x - 8$ **96.** $P(x) = \dfrac{1}{2}x^2 - 2x + 5$

In Problems 97–100, determine the quadratic function whose graph is given.

97.

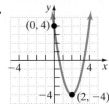

98.

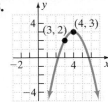

99.

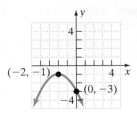

100.

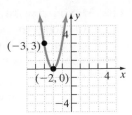

Section 7.5 Graphing Quadratic Functions Using Properties

KEY CONCEPTS	KEY TERMS

• **Vertex of a Parabola**
 Any quadratic function of the form $f(x) = ax^2 + bx + c, a \neq 0$, will have vertex $$\left(-\frac{b}{2a}, f\left(-\frac{b}{2a}\right)\right)$$
 • **The x-Intercepts of the Graph of a Quadratic Function**
   1. If $b^2 - 4ac > 0$, the graph of $f(x) = ax^2 + bx + c$ has two different x-intercepts.
   2. If $b^2 - 4ac = 0$, the graph of $f(x) = ax^2 + bx + c$ has one x-intercept.
   3. If $b^2 - 4ac < 0$, the graph of $f(x) = ax^2 + bx + c$ has no x-intercepts.
	Maximum value
	 Minimum value
	 Optimization

YOU SHOULD BE ABLE TO...	EXAMPLE	REVIEW EXERCISES
⃞1 Graph quadratic functions of the form $f(x) = ax^2 + bx + c$ (p. 595)	Examples 1 through 4	101–108
⃞2 Find the maximum or minimum value of a quadratic function (p. 601)	Examples 5 and 6	109–112
⃞3 Model and solve optimization problems involving quadratic functions (p. 603)	Examples 7 and 8	113–118

In Problems 101–108, graph each quadratic function using its properties by following Steps 1–5 on page 598. Based on the graph, determine the domain and range of each function.

101. $f(x) = x^2 + 2x - 8$ **102.** $F(x) = 2x^2 - 5x + 3$

103. $g(x) = -x^2 + 6x - 7$ **104.** $G(x) = -2x^2 + 4x + 3$

105. $h(x) = 4x^2 - 12x + 9$ **106.** $H(x) = \frac{1}{3}x^2 + 2x + 3$

107. $p(x) = \frac{1}{4}x^2 + 3x + 10$ **108.** $P(x) = -x^2 + 4x - 9$

In Problems 109–112, determine whether the quadratic function has a maximum or minimum value. Then find the maximum or minimum value.

109. $f(x) = -2x^2 + 16x - 10$

110. $g(x) = 6x^2 - 3x - 1$

111. $h(x) = -4x^2 + 8x + 3$

112. $F(x) = -\frac{1}{3}x^2 + 4x - 7$

113. Revenue Suppose that the marketing department of Zenith has found that, when a certain model of television is sold for a price of p dollars, the daily revenue R (in dollars) as a function of the price p is
$$R(p) = -\frac{1}{3}p^2 + 150p.$$

  (a) For what price will the daily revenue be maximized?

  (b) What is this maximum daily revenue?

114. Electrical Power In a 120-volt electrical circuit having a resistance of 16 ohms, the available power P (in watts) is given by the function $P(I) = -16I^2 + 120I$, where I represents the current (in amperes).

  (a) What current will produce the maximum power in the circuit?

  (b) What is this maximum power?

115. Fun with Numbers The sum of two numbers is 24. Find the numbers such that their product is a maximum.

116. Maximizing an Enclosed Area Becky has 15 yards of fencing to make a rectangular kennel for her dog. She will build the kennel next to her garage, so she only needs to enclose three sides. (See the figure.)

(a) What dimensions maximize the area of the kennel?

(b) What is this maximum area?

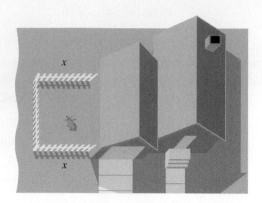

117. Kicking a Football Ted kicks a football at a 45° angle to the horizontal with an initial velocity of 80 feet per second. The model $h(x) = -0.005x^2 + x$ can be used to estimate the height h of the ball after it has traveled x feet.

(a) How far from Ted will the ball reach a maximum height?

(b) What is the maximum height of the ball?

(c) How far will the ball travel before it strikes the ground?

118. Revenue Monthly demand for automobiles at a certain dealership obeys the demand equation $x = -0.002p + 60$, where x is the quantity and p is the price (in dollars).

(a) Express the revenue R as a function of p. (*Hint:* $R = xp$)

(b) What price p maximizes revenue? What is the maximum revenue?

(c) How many automobiles will be sold at the revenue-maximizing price?

CHAPTER 7 TEST

Remember to use your Chapter Test Prep Video CD to see fully worked-out solutions to any of these problems you would like to review.

In Problems 1 and 2, complete the square in the given expression. Then factor the perfect square trinomial.

1. $x^2 - 3x$

2. $m^2 + \dfrac{2}{5}m$

In Problems 3–6, solve each equation using any appropriate method you prefer.

3. $9\left(x + \dfrac{4}{3}\right)^2 = 1$

4. $m^2 - 6m + 4 = 0$

5. $2w^2 - 4w + 3 = 0$

6. $\dfrac{1}{2}z^2 - \dfrac{3}{2}z = -\dfrac{7}{6}$

7. Determine the discriminant of $2x^2 + 5x = 4$. Use the value of the discriminant to determine whether the quadratic equation has two rational solutions, two irrational solutions, one repeated real solution, or two complex solutions that are not real.

8. Find the missing length in the right triangle shown below.

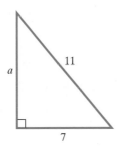

In Problems 9 and 10, solve each equation.

9. $x^4 - 5x^2 - 36 = 0$

10. $6y^{\frac{1}{2}} + 13y^{\frac{1}{4}} - 5 = 0$

In Problems 11 and 12, graph each quadratic function by determining the vertex, intercepts, and axis of symmetry. Based on the graph, determine the domain and range of the quadratic function.

11. $f(x) = (x + 2)^2 - 5$

12. $g(x) = -2x^2 - 8x - 3$

13. Determine the quadratic function whose graph is given.

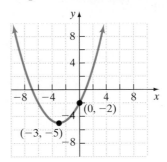

14. Determine whether the quadratic function

$$h(x) = -\dfrac{1}{4}x^2 + x + 5 \text{ has a maximum or minimum}$$

value. Then find the maximum or minimum value.

In Problems 15 and 16, solve each inequality. Graph the solution set.

15. $2m^2 + m - 15 > 0$

16. $z^2 + 6z - 1 \leq 0$

17. Projectile Motion The height s of a rock after t seconds when propelled straight up with an initial speed of 80 feet per second from an initial height of 20 feet can be modeled by the function $s(t) = -16t^2 + 80t + 20$. When will the height of the rock be 50 feet? Round your answer to the nearest tenth of a second.

18. Work Together, Lex and Rupert can roof a house in 16 hours. By himself, Rex can roof the house in 4 hours less time than Rupert can by himself. How long will it take Rupert to roof the house by himself? Round your answer to the nearest tenth of an hour.

19. Revenue A small company has found that, when their product is sold for a price of p dollars, the weekly revenue (in dollars) as a function of price p is $R(p) = -0.25p^2 + 170p$.

(a) For what price will the weekly revenue be maximized?

(b) What is this maximum weekly revenue?

20. Maximizing Volume A box with a rectangular base is to be constructed such that the perimeter of the base of the box is to be 50 inches. The height of the box must be 12 inches.

(a) Find the dimensions that maximize the volume of the box.

(b) What is this maximum volume?

CUMULATIVE REVIEW Chapters R–7

1. Evaluate: $\dfrac{2^4 - 5 \cdot 7 + 3}{1 - 3^2}$

2. Simplify: $2(3c + 1) - (c - 9) - 2c$

3. Solve: $p - 5 = 3(p - 2) - 9$

4. Solve: $5 + 2|x + 1| > 9$

5. Determine the domain of $h(x) = \dfrac{x^2 - 16}{x^2 + x - 12}$.

6. Graph the linear equation: $3x - 4y = 8$

7. Find the equation of the line that passes through the point $(5, -1)$ and is parallel to the graph of $2x + 5y = -15$. Write your answer in either slope-intercept or standard form, whichever you prefer.

8. Solve the following system of equations:
$$\begin{cases} 5x + 2y = 0 \\ 2x - y = -9 \end{cases}$$

9. Evaluate: $\begin{vmatrix} 4 & 1 & 0 \\ 1 & 2 & -1 \\ 3 & -2 & 1 \end{vmatrix}$

10. Graph the following system of linear inequalities:
$$\begin{cases} 2x + 3y < -3 \\ 2x + y > -5 \end{cases}$$

In Problems 11 and 12, add, subtract, multiply, or divide as indicated.

11. $(a^3 - 9a^2 + 11) + (7a^2 - 5a - 8)$

12. $\dfrac{8x^4 + 12x^2 + 17x - 18}{2x^2 - x + 5}$

In Problems 13–14, factor completely.

13. $8m^3 + 27n^3$ **14.** $7y^2 + 23y - 20$

In Problems 15 and 25, perform the indicated operations. Be sure to express the final answer in lowest terms.

15. $\dfrac{\dfrac{2w^2 - 11w + 12}{w^2 - 16}}{\dfrac{2w^2 - 7w + 6}{w^2 + 9w + 20}}$

16. $\dfrac{3}{k^2 - 5k + 4} - \dfrac{2}{k^2 + 4k - 5}$

17. Solve: $\dfrac{1}{2n} - \dfrac{1}{6} = \dfrac{5}{4n} + \dfrac{1}{3}$

18. Solve the inequality and graph the solution set:
$$\dfrac{x - 4}{x + 5} \geq 0$$

19. Plane Speeds Two private planes take off from the same airport at the same time and travel in opposite directions. One plane travels 16 miles per hour faster than the other. After two hours, the planes are 536 miles apart. Find the speed of each plane.

20. Add: $\sqrt{48} + \sqrt{75} - 2\sqrt{3}$

21. Rationalize the denominator: $\dfrac{5}{\sqrt[3]{16}}$

22. Solve: $\sqrt{a - 12} + \sqrt{a} = 6$

23. Pythagorean Theorem Use the Pythagorean Theorem to determine the value of x for the given measurements of the right triangle shown below.

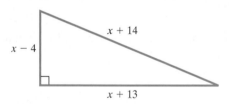

24. Solve: $x^2 + 20 = 8x$

25. Graph: $f(x) = -2x^2 + 4x + 3$

Answers to Selected Exercises

Chapter R Real Numbers and Algebraic Expressions

Section R.1 Success in Mathematics   Answers will vary.

Section R.2 Sets and Classification of Numbers   **1.** set   **2.** set-builder: $\{x \mid x$ is a digit less than 5$\}$; roster: $\{0, 1, 2, 3, 4\}$ **3.** set-builder: $\{x \mid x$ is a digit greater than or equal to 6$\}$; roster: $\{6, 7, 8, 9\}$ **4.** True   **5.** subset   **6.** False   **7.** True   **8.** False   **9.** False   **10.** True   **11.** True   **12.** False   **13.** True   **14.** rational   **15.** irrational numbers   **16.** False   **17.** False   **18.** True   **19.** True   **20.** $10, \dfrac{12}{4}$ **21.** $10, \dfrac{0}{3}, \dfrac{12}{4}$ **22.** $-9, 10, \dfrac{0}{3}, \dfrac{12}{4}$ **23.** $\dfrac{7}{3}, -9, 10, 4.\overline{56}, \dfrac{0}{3}, -\dfrac{4}{7}, \dfrac{12}{4}$ **24.** π and $5.73773777737777\ldots$ **25.** All except $\sqrt{-4}$ **26. (a)** 5.694 **(b)** 5.694   **27. (a)** -4.93 **(b)** -4.94 **28.**

29. $<$ **30.** $<$ **31.** $>$ **32.** $>$ **33.** $=$ **34.** $>$ **35.** $\{0, 1, 2, 3, 4, 5\}$ **37.** $\{-2, -1, 0, 1, 2, 3, 4\}$ **39.** $\varnothing$ or $\{\ \}$ **41.** True   **43.** False   **45.** True   **47.** True   **49.** $\notin$ **51.** $\in$ **53. (a)** 4 **(b)** $-5, 4$ **(c)** $-5, 4, \dfrac{4}{3}, -\dfrac{7}{5}, 5.\overline{1}$ **(d)** π **(e)** $-5, 4, \dfrac{4}{3}, -\dfrac{7}{5}, 5.\overline{1}, \pi$ **55. (a)** 100 **(b)** $100, -64$ **(c)** $100, -5.423, \dfrac{8}{7}, -64$ **(d)** $\sqrt{2} + 4$ **(e)** $100, -5.423, \dfrac{8}{7}, \sqrt{2} + 4, -64$ **57. (a)** 19.9348 **(b)** 19.9348   **59. (a)** 0.0 **(b)** 0.1   **61.**

63. $<$ **65.** $=$ **67.** $>$ **69.** -282 feet   **71.** $-\$4.06$ **73.** -6 **75.** Answers will vary.   **77.** Answers will vary.   **79.** No, if a number is rational, it cannot be irrational and vice-versa because a number cannot have a terminating or non-terminating/repeating decimal while simultaneously having a non-terminating/non-repeating decimal. No; every real number is either a rational or irrational number.   **81.** A set is a well-defined collection of objects. The collection must be well-defined so that it is easy to determine whether an object is in the set or not.   **83.** If $A \subseteq B$, then all elements in A are also in B. Plus, A could equal B. If $A \subset B$, then all elements in A are also in B, but $A \neq B$.   **85.** If the digit *after* the specified final digit is 4 or less, then truncating and rounding will yield the same decimal approximation.   **87.** 1.143; 1.142

Section R.3 Operations on Signed Numbers; Properties of Real Numbers   **1.** factors   **2.** False   **3.** 6   **4.** 10   **5.** 12   **6.** -11 **7.** -6.6 **8.** -2.2 **9.** 0   **10.** -5 **11.** $-\dfrac{4}{5}$ **12.** 12   **13.** $\dfrac{5}{3}$ **14.** 0   **15.** 4   **16.** -9 **17.** -11 **18.** 9.1   **19.** -5.1 **20.** -16.1 **21.** True   **22.** -48 **23.** -60 **24.** 56   **25.** 105   **26.** 5.13   **27.** opposite; reciprocal   **28.** $\dfrac{1}{10}$ **29.** $-\dfrac{1}{8}$ **30.** $\dfrac{5}{2}$ **31.** -5 **32.** $\dfrac{6}{5}$ **33.** $\dfrac{9}{2}$ **34.** $\dfrac{5}{3}$ **35.** $-\dfrac{6}{5}$ **36.** $-\dfrac{5}{6}$ **37.** $\dfrac{4}{5}$ **38.** $\dfrac{1}{2}$ **39.** 8   **40.** $\dfrac{5}{11}$ **41.** $-\dfrac{1}{3}$ **42.** $\dfrac{11}{7}$ **43.** 1   **44.** LCD = 60; $\dfrac{3}{20} = \dfrac{9}{60}, \dfrac{2}{15} = \dfrac{8}{60}$ **45.** LCD – 90, $\dfrac{5}{18}, \dfrac{25}{90}, -\dfrac{1}{45} - -\dfrac{2}{90}$ **46.** $\dfrac{17}{60}$ **47.** $\dfrac{1}{6}$ **48.** $\dfrac{59}{150}$ **49.** $\dfrac{3}{10}$ **50.** $ab + ac$ **51.** $5x + 15$ **52.** $-6x - 6$ **53.** $-4z + 32$ **54.** $2x + 3$ **55.** $\dfrac{2}{3}$ **57.** $\dfrac{8}{3}$ **59.** -9 **61.** 7   **63.** -2.5 **65.** -32 **67.** 84   **69.** -36.55 **71.** $\dfrac{z}{5}$ **73.** $\dfrac{6}{5}$ **75.** $\dfrac{5}{3}$ **77.** $-\dfrac{3}{7}$ **79.** $\dfrac{2}{3}$ **81.** $\dfrac{5}{4}$ **83.** $\dfrac{1}{6}$ **85.** $\dfrac{11}{12}$ **87.** $2x + 8$ **89.** $-3z + 6$ **91.** $3x - 30$ **93.** $6x - 9$ **95.** 3   **97.** $\dfrac{101}{70}$ **99.** $\dfrac{4}{3}$ **101.** 3.3   **103.** -32 **105.** $\dfrac{13}{10}$ **107.** $\dfrac{17}{15}$ **109.** $-\dfrac{139}{32}$ **111.** $\dfrac{1}{9}$ **113.** Commutative Property of Addition   **115.** Multiplicative Inverse Property   **117.** Reduction Property   **119.** Associative Property of Addition   **121.** The difference in age of the oldest and youngest president at the time of inauguration is 27 years.   **123.** The Bears gained a total of 9 yards in the first 3 plays. Since 9 is less than 10, they did not obtain a first down.   **125.** The difference between the highest and lowest elevation is 20,602 feet.   **127.** Consider $3 \cdot 6$. This means to add 6 to itself three times. Since the sum of three positive numbers is positive, the product will be positive. Consider $3 \cdot (-6)$. This means to add -6 to itself three times. Since the sum of three negative numbers is negative, the product will be negative.   **129.** $d(P, Q) = 14$

131. $d(P, Q) = 10.4$

133. $d(P, Q) = \dfrac{68}{15}$

135. (a) $a \cdot 0 = 0$ **(b)** $a \cdot (b + (-b)) = 0$ **(c)** $ab + a(-b) = 0$ **(d)** $ab < 0$ since the product of a negative and a positive is negative; $a(-b)$ must be positive so that $ab + a(-b) = 0$.   **137.** Zero does not have a multiplicative inverse because division by zero is not defined.   **139.** The Reduction Property only applies to dividing out factors.   **141.** No. For example, $4 - (5 - 3) \neq (4 - 5) - 3$ **143.** No. For example, $16 \div (8 \div 2) \neq (16 \div 8) \div 2$ **145.** -3.8 **147.** -19.2 **149.** $\dfrac{1}{30}$ **151.** 14.4   **153.** $\dfrac{9}{2}$

Section R.4 Order of Operations   **1.** base; exponent; power   **2.** False   **3.** 64   **4.** 49   **5.** -1000 **6.** $\dfrac{8}{27}$ **7.** -64 **8.** 125   **9.** 16   **10.** 36   **11.** 32   **12.** 48   **13.** 40   **14.** 26   **15.** $\dfrac{10}{13}$ **16.** 18   **17.** 50   **18.** $\dfrac{4}{5}$ **19.** parentheses; exponents; multiplication; division; addition; subtraction   **20.** 16   **21.** 48   **22.** $\dfrac{6}{7}$ **23.** 14   **24.** 7   **25.** 42   **26.** -9 **27.** 20   **28.** -18 **29.** 5   **30.** -15 **31.** 81   **33.** -625 **35.** 8   **37.** $-\dfrac{4}{9}$ **39.** 7   **41.** 15   **43.** 12   **45.** -28 **47.** 3   **49.** 14   **51.** -2 **53.** 60   **55.** 180   **57.** 9   **59.** 8   **61.** $\dfrac{5}{2}$ **63.** 2   **65.** $\dfrac{6}{5}$ **67.** $\dfrac{2}{3}$ **69.** $-\dfrac{7}{4}$ **71.** $\dfrac{3}{2}$ **73.** $\dfrac{53}{14}$ **75.** $3 \cdot (7 - 2) = 15$ **77.** $3 + 5 \cdot (6 - 3) = 18$

79. The surface area of the cylinder is about 534.07 square inches.   **81.** After 3 seconds, the height of the ball is 6 feet.   **83.** 100   **85.** We cannot use the Reduction Property across addition.   **87.** Answers will vary. One suggestion: $5 \cdot 2^3$ is equivalent to $5 \cdot 2 \cdot 2 \cdot 2$, which equals 40. Since $5 \cdot 2^3 = 5 \cdot 8 = 40$, we can see that we evaluate exponents before multiplication.   **89.** $\frac{16}{45}$ **91.** $\frac{17}{13}$ **93.** -212.96 **95.** -534.53

Section R.5 Algebraic Expressions

1. variable   **2.** constant   **3.** $3 + 11$ **4.** $6 \cdot 7$ **5.** $\frac{y}{4}$ **6.** $3 - z$ **7.** $2(x - 3)$ **8.** $5 + \frac{z}{2}$ **9.** -7 **10.** 41   **11.** 1   **12.** 3   **13.** 10,700 Yen; 107,000 Yen; 1,070,000 Yen   **14.** 0°C, 30°C, 100°C   **15.** term   **16.** $-5x$ **17.** $11x^2$ **18.** $-8x + 3$ **19.** $-4x + 8y$ **20.** $15y - 1$ **21.** $2.3x^2 + 0.9$ **22.** $-6z + 3$ **23.** $4x - 6$ **24.** $-5y + 11$ **25.** $-3z + 10$ **26.** $-6x + 4$ **27.** 1   **28.** $\frac{25x + 25}{6} = \frac{25(x + 1)}{6}$ **29.** The set of all allowed values of the variable.   **30.** (a) Yes (b) Yes (c) No (d) Yes   **31.** (a) Yes (b) Yes (c) Yes (d) No   **32.** (a) No (b) Yes (c) Yes (d) No   **33.** $5 + x$ **35.** $4z$ **37.** $y - 7$ **39.** $2(t + 4)$ **41.** $5x - 3$ **43.** $\frac{y}{3} + 6x$ **45.** 11   **47.** -9 **49.** -21 **51.** $\frac{3}{8}$ **53.** $\frac{6}{7}$ **55.** 29   **57.** 1   **59.** $\frac{3}{2}$ **61.** x **63.** $-6z + 3$ **65.** $-z - 5$ **67.** $\frac{11}{12}x$ **69.** $4x^2 - 3x$ **71.** $1.6x$ **73.** $-3x + 1$ **75.** $-14x + 7$ **77.** $-z + 10$ **79.** $4x - 3$ **81.** $12v - 11$ **83.** $2x + \frac{9}{10}$ **85.** $\frac{13}{36}x$ **87.** $14.46x - 15.49$ **89.** $-11.08x - 5.44$ **91.** (a) No (b) Yes (c) Yes (d) Yes   **93.** (a) Yes (b) Yes (c) Yes (d) Yes   **95.** (a) No (b) Yes (c) Yes (d) No   **97.** 1 in.³; 8 in.³; 27 in.³; 64 in.³   **99.** (a) 0 ft; 59 ft; 86 ft; 81 ft; 44 ft   (b) The ball begins on the ground. When it is hit, it rises in the air (for somewhere around 2 seconds) and then begins to fall back towards the ground.   **101.** Let $x =$ Bob's age in years; Tony's age $= x + 5$; when Bob is 13 years old, Tony is 18 years old.   **103.** Let $p =$ the original price in dollars; discounted price $= \frac{1}{2}p$; when the original price is $900, the discount price is $450.   **105.** $\frac{4}{3}$ **107.** Answers will vary. One possible answer is, *"Twice a number z decreased by 5."*   **109.** Answers will vary. One possible answer is, *"Twice the difference of a number z and 5."*   **111.** Answers will vary. One possible answer is, *"One-half the sum of a number z and 3."*   **113.** A variable is a letter used to represent any number from a set of numbers; a constant is either a fixed number, or a letter that represents a fixed number.   **115.** Like terms are terms that have the same variable or variables along with the same exponents on the variables. We use the Distributive Property "in reverse" to combine like terms as in $3x + 4x = (3 + 4)x = 7x$.   **117.** (a) 3 (b) 15   **119.** (a) 63 (b) 35   **121.** (a) $-\frac{7}{5}$ (b) $\frac{23}{65}$ **123.** (a) 67 (b) 32   **125.** The calculator displays an error message because $x = 5$ makes the denominator equal to 0.

Chapter 1 Linear Equations and Inequalities

Section 1.1 Linear Equations in One Variable

1. linear; sides   **2.** solutions   **3.** $x = 1$ **4.** $x = -7$ **5.** $z = -1$ **6.** To find all solutions of the equation   **7.** For real numbers $a, b,$ and c if $a = b$, then $a + c = b + c$. In words, whatever you add to one side of an equation, you must add to the other side as well.   **8.** For real numbers $a, b,$ and c, where $c \neq 0$, if $a = b$, then $ac = bc$. In words, whenever you multiply one side of an equation by a nonzero expression, you must also multiply the other side by the same non zero expression.   **9.** {3}   **10.** {−2}   **11.** {1/5}   **12.** {2}   **13.** {−1}   **14.** {3/2}   **15.** {4}   **16.** {−4}   **17.** {3/4}   **18.** {1/2}   **19.** {2}   **20.** {−5}   **21.** {−4}   **22.** {−3/5}   **23.** {−3}   **24.** {10}   **25.** {32}   **26.** 1. Conditional equation: an equation that is true for some values of the variable and false for other values of the variable. 2. Contradiction: an equation that is false for every value of the variable. 3. Identity: an equation that is satisfied for every choice of the variable for which both sides of the equation are defined.   **27.** $\varnothing$ or { }; Contradiction   **28.** $\{x | x$ is any real number$\}$; Identity   **29.** {0}; Conditional   **30.** $\{z | z$ is any real number$\}$; Identity   **31.** $x = 2$ **33.** $m = 1$ **35.** $x = 5$ **37.** {2}   **39.** {2}   **41.** $\left\{ -\frac{1}{4} \right\}$ **43.** {9}   **45.** {−9}   **47.** $\left\{ -\frac{2}{3} \right\}$ **49.** {−4}   **51.** {2}   **53.** $\left\{ -\frac{3}{5} \right\}$ **55.** {3}   **57.** {−5}   **59.** { } or $\varnothing$; contradiction   **61.** { } or $\varnothing$; contradiction   **63.** $\{y | y$ is any real number$\}$ or $\mathbb{R}$; identity   **65.** {−3}; conditional   **67.** { } or $\varnothing$; contradiction   **69.** $\left\{ \frac{5}{2} \right\}$; conditional   **71.** $\{z | z$ is any real number$\}$ or $\mathbb{R}$; identity   **73.** $\left\{ -\frac{7}{2} \right\}$; conditional   **75.** $\left\{ \frac{1}{7} \right\}$; conditional   **77.** $\left\{ \frac{7}{2} \right\}$; conditional   **79.** $\{p | p$ is any real number$\}$ or $\mathbb{R}$; identity   **81.** { } or $\varnothing$; contradiction   **83.** {−14}; conditional   **85.** {−3}; conditional   **87.** {−1.6}; conditional   **89.** {2}; conditional   **91.** $a = -4$ **93.** $a = 3$ **95.** $x = -\frac{1}{2}$ **97.** $x = \frac{3}{4}$ **99.** $x = 1$ **101.** The card's annual interest rate is 0.15 or 15%   **103.** You earned $27,525 in 2008.   **105.** $4(x + 1) - 2$ is an algebraic expression and $4(x + 1) = 2$ is an equation. An algebraic expression is any combination of variables, grouping symbols, and mathematical operations, but does not contain an equal sign. An equation is a statement made up of two algebraic expressions that are equal.   **107.** Answers will vary.

Section 1.2 An Introduction to Problem Solving

1. $x + 7 = 12$ **2.** $3y = 21$ **3.** $2(3 + x) = 5x$ **4.** $x - 10 = x/2$ **5.** $y - 3 = 5y$ **6.** 18, 20, 22   **7.** 25, 26, 27   **8.** $15 per hour   **9.** $12 per hour   **10.** 150 miles   **11.** 240 minutes   **12.** 40   **13.** 160   **14.** 75%   **15.** $30   **16.** $1.20   **17.** Interest; principal   **18.** $32.50   **19.** $10.50; $1,410.50   **20.** $67,500 in Aaa-rated bonds; $22,500 in B-rated bonds   **21.** $5,000 in CD; $20,000 in Corporate Bond   **22.** 6 pounds of Tea A and 4 pounds of Tea B   **23.** 10 pounds of cashews; 20 pounds of peanuts   **24.** uniform motion   **25.** After 4 hours; 240 miles   **26.** After 5 hours; 450 miles   **27.** 10   **29.** 40   **31.** 37.5%   **33.** $x + 12 = 20$; 8   **35.** $2(y + 3) = 16$; 5   **37.** $w - 22 = 3w$; −11   **39.** $4x = 2x + 14$; 7   **41.** $0.8x = x + 5$; −25   **43.** 13 and 26   **45.** 24, 25, and 26   **47.** Kendra needs an 83 on her final exam to have an average of 80.   **49.** Jacob would need to print 2500 pages for the cost to be the same for the two printers.   **51.** Connor: $400,000; Olivia: $300,000; Avery: $100,000.   **53.** The final bill will be $616.37.   **55.** The dealer's cost is about $22,434.78.   **57.** The flash drives originally cost $41.50.   **59.** The Nissan Altima weighs 3320 pounds, the Mazda 6s weighs 3340 pounds, and the Honda Accord EX weighs 3390 pounds.   **61.** Adam will get $8500 and Krissy will get $11,500.   **63.** You should invest $15,000 in stocks and $9000 in bonds.   **65.** The interest charge after one month will be $29.17.   **67.** The bank loaned $225,000 at 6% interest.   **69.** Pedro should invest $9375 in the 5% bond and $15,625 in the 9% stock fund. **71.** $50 - x$ pounds of coffee B **73.** Bobby has 15 dimes and 32 quarters saved. **75.** 36 grams of pure gold should be mixed with 36 grams of 12-karat gold. **77.** The race consists of running for 12 miles and biking for 50 miles. **79.** The slow car is traveling at 60 mph while the faster car travels at 70 mph. **81.** The boats will be 155 miles apart after 2.5 hours. **83.** One person is walking at a rate of 4 miles per hour and the other is walking at a rate of 6 miles per hour. **85.** Written answers will vary. The average speed of the trip to Florida and back is roughly 54.55 miles per hour. **87.** Answers will vary. **89.** The train is 0.3 mile or 1584 feet long. **91.** Mathematical modeling is the process of developing an equation or inequality to find a solution to a problem. Just like there is more than one way to solve a problem, there is typically more than one way to develop a mathematical model. **93.** Direct translation, mixture, geometry, uniform motion, work problems. Two types of mixture problems are finance/investment types and dry mixtures.

Section 1.3 Using Formulas to Solve Problems

1. formula **2.** $A = \pi r^2$ **3.** $V = \pi r^2 h$ **4.** $C = 175x + 7000$ **5.** $s = \frac{1}{2} gt^2$

6. $A = \pi r^2$ **7.** $P = 2l + 2w$ **8. (a)** $h = \frac{2A}{b}$ **(b)** 5 inches **9. (a)** $b = \frac{P - 2a}{2}$ **(b)** 10 cm **10.** $P = \frac{I}{rt}$ **11.** $y = \frac{C - Ax}{B}$

12. $h = \frac{4x - 3}{2x - 3}$ **13.** $n = \frac{S + d}{a + d}$ **14.** width: 40 feet; length: 50 feet **15.** height: 72 inches; width: 40 inches **16.** 4.00 inches

17. $F = m \cdot a$ **19.** $V = \frac{4}{3}\pi r^3$ **21.** $r = \frac{d}{t}$ **23.** $m = \frac{y - y_1}{x - x_1}$ **25.** $x = \mu + \sigma Z$ **27.** $m_1 = \frac{r^2 F}{G m_2}$ **29.** $P = \frac{A}{1 + rt}$

31. $F = \frac{9}{5} C + 32$ **33.** $y = -2x + 13$ **35.** $y = 3x - 5$ **37.** $y = -\frac{4}{3}x + \frac{13}{3}$ **39.** $y = -3x + 12$ **41. (a)** $h = \frac{V}{\pi r^2}$ **(b)** The height of

the cylinder is 8 inches. **43. (a)** $A = \frac{206.3 - M}{0.711}$ **(b)** An individual whose maximum heart rate is 160 should be about 65 years old.

45. (a) $P = \frac{A}{(1 + r)^t}$ **(b)** Roughly $4109.64 should be deposited today to have $5000 in 5 years in an account that pays 4% annual interest.

47. The smaller angle measures 75° and its supplement measures 105°. **49.** The smaller angle measures 20° and its complement measures 70°. **51.** The window is 5 feet long and 8 feet wide. **53.** The area of the circle is 25π square inches (roughly 78.54 square inches). **55.** The first angle measures 40°, the second measures 55°, and the third measures 85°. **57. (a)** The patio is 17.5 ft wide and 22.5 ft long. **(b)** You would need to purchase 131.25 cubic feet of cement. **59. (a)** The deck has an area of 84π square feet (roughly 264 square feet). **(b)** It would require roughly 97.39 feet of fencing to encircle the pool. **(c)** The fence would cost about $2434.73. **61.** No, the area would increase by a factor of 4. If the length of a side of a cube is doubled, the volume increases by a factor of 8.

Section 1.4 Linear Inequalities in One Variable

1. closed interval **2.** left endpoint; right endpoint

3. $[-3, 2]$ 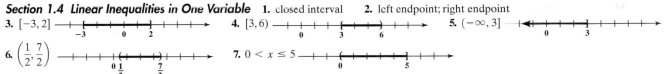 **4.** $[3, 6)$ **5.** $(-\infty, 3]$

6. $\left(\frac{1}{2}, \frac{7}{2}\right)$ **7.** $0 < x \le 5$

8. $-6 < x < 0$ **9.** $x > 5$ **10.** $x \le \frac{8}{3}$

11. $9 < 12$; Addition Property of Inequalities **12.** $x > -9$; Addition Property of Inequalities **13.** $1 < 4$; Multiplication Property of Inequalities **14.** $2 > -3$; Multiplication Property of Inequalities **15.** $x < 6$; Multiplication Property of Inequalities

16. $\{x|x > 2\}; (2, \infty)$ **17.** $\{x|x \le 6\}; (-\infty, 6]$

18. $\{x|x < 4\}; (-\infty, 4)$ **19.** $\{x|x \ge -6\}; [-6, \infty)$

20. $\{x|x > -3\}; (-3, \infty)$ **21.** $\{x|x \ge -2\}; [-2, \infty)$

22. $\left\{x|x > \frac{5}{2}\right\}; \left(\frac{5}{2}, \infty\right)$ **23.** $\{x|x < 4\}; (-\infty, 4)$

24. $\left\{x|x \le -\frac{7}{3}\right\}; \left(-\infty, -\frac{7}{3}\right]$ **25.** $\{x|x \ge 4\}; [4, \infty)$

26. $\{x|x \ge 3\}; [3, \infty)$ **27.** $\{x|x < \frac{1}{2}\}; (-\infty, \frac{1}{2})$

28. $\{x|x > -17\}; (-17, \infty)$ **29.** Any balance over $500 **30.** For any more than 24 boxes, revenue exceeds cost.

31. $[2, 10]$;  **33.** $[-4, 0)$; **35.** $[6, \infty)$;

37. $\left(-\infty, \frac{3}{2}\right)$; **39.** $1 < x < 8$;

41. $-5 < x \le 1$; **43.** $x < 5$; **45.** $x \ge 3$;

47. $<$; Addition Property of Inequalities **49.** $>$; Multiplication Property of Inequalities **51.** $\le$; Addition Property of Inequalities **53.** $\le$; Multiplication Property of Inequalities **55.** $\{x|x \le 6\}; (-\infty, 6]$

57. $\{x|x < 4\}; (-\infty, 4)$ **59.** $\{x|x > -3\}; (-3, \infty)$

61. $\{x|x > 6\}; (6, \infty)$ **63.** $\{x|x > 3\}; (3, \infty)$

65. $\{x|x < -4\}; (-\infty, -4)$ **67.** $\{x|x \le -1\}; (-\infty, -1]$

69. $\{x|x > -2\}; (-2, \infty)$ **71.** $\{x|x < 17\}; (-\infty, 17)$

73. $\{x|x \leq 4\}; (-\infty, 4]$

75. $\{x|x \leq -30\}; (-\infty, -30]$

77. $\left\{x\middle|x < \frac{1}{3}\right\}; \left(-\infty, \frac{1}{3}\right)$

79. $\left\{x\middle|x < -\frac{11}{4}\right\}; \left(-\infty, -\frac{11}{4}\right)$

81. $\left\{x\middle|x < -\frac{16}{15}\right\}; \left(-\infty, -\frac{16}{15}\right)$

83. $\left\{x\middle|x \leq \frac{15}{2}\right\}; \left(-\infty, \frac{15}{2}\right]$

85. $\left\{x\middle|x \geq \frac{21}{16}\right\}; \left[\frac{21}{16}, \infty\right)$

87. $\left\{x\middle|x > \frac{1}{10}\right\}; \left(\frac{1}{10}, \infty\right)$

89. $\{x|x < 3\}; (-\infty, 3)$

91. $\left\{x\middle|x < \frac{9}{2}\right\}; \left(-\infty, \frac{9}{2}\right)$

93. $\{y|y > -15\}; (-15, \infty)$

95. $\{a|a \geq 7\}; [7, \infty)$

97. $\left\{x\middle|x > -\frac{1}{3}\right\}; \left(-\frac{1}{3}, \infty\right)$

99. $\{x|x \leq -14\}; (-\infty, -14]$

101. $\left\{x\middle|x < \frac{3}{2}\right\}; \left(-\infty, \frac{3}{2}\right)$

103. $\{x|x \geq -3\}; [-3, \infty)$

105. $\left\{x\middle|x \geq -\frac{3}{4}\right\}; \left[-\frac{3}{4}, \infty\right)$ **107.** $\{x|x \geq 4\}; [4, \infty)$ **109.** $\{z|z \leq 3\}; (-\infty, 3]$ **111.** Jackie must earn at least 182 points on the final exam to earn an A in Mr. Ruffatto's class.   **113.** You can order no more than 3 hamburgers to keep the fat content to no more than 69 grams.   **115.** The plane can carry up to 18,836 pounds of luggage and cargo.   **117.** The monthly benefit will exceed $1000 in 2012.   **119.** Susan will need to sell at least $5,500,000 in computer systems to earn $100,000.   **121.** Supply will exceed demand when the price is greater than $40.   **123.** All real numbers are solutions; $\mathbb{R}$ **125.** When we multiply both sides of an inequality by a negative number. Or, if the sides of the inequality are interchanged.   **127.** The inequality $4 < x > 7$ means $x > 4$ and $x > 7$, which is equivalent to $x > 7$.

Putting the Concepts Together (Sections 1.1–1.4)   **1. (a)** $x = -3$ is not a solution.   **(b)** $x = 1$ is a solution.   **2.** $\{-5\}$ **3.** $\{0\}$ **4.** identity

5. $x - 3 = \frac{1}{2}x + 2$ **6.** $\frac{x}{2} < x + 5$ **7.** The chemist needs to mix 4 liters of the 20% solution with 12 liters of the 40% solution.   **8.** After 3.4 hours, the two cars will be 255 miles apart.   **9.** $y = \frac{3}{2}x - 2$ **10.** $r = \frac{A - P}{Pt}$ **11. (a)** $h = \frac{V}{\pi r^2}$ **(b)** 6 in.   **12. (a)** Interval: $(-3, \infty)$

Graph: **(b)** Interval: $(2, 5]$ Graph: **13. (a)** Inequality: $x \leq -1.5$

Graph: **(b)** Inequality: $-3 < x \leq 1$ Graph:

14. $[6, \infty)$ **15.** $(-\infty, 1)$

16. $(-\infty, 5]$ **17.** Logan can invite at most 9 children to the party.

Section 1.5 Rectangular Coordinates and Graphs of Equations   **1.** origin   **2.** True

3. *A*: Quadrant I;   **4.** *A*: Quadrant II;   **5.** True   **6. (a)** No **(b)** Yes **(c)** Yes
   B: Quadrant IV;   *B*: *x*-axis;   **7. (a)** Yes **(b)** No **(c)** Yes
   C: *y*-axis;   *C*: Quadrant IV;
   D: Quadrant III   *D*: Quadrant I

8.   **9.**   **10.**   **11.**   **12.**   **13.** intercepts   **14.** False
15. Intercepts: $(-5, 0)$, $(0, -0.9)$, $(1, 0)$, $(6.7, 0)$; *x*-intercepts: $-5, 1, 6.7$; *y*-intercept: -0.9

16. (a) $200 thousand   **(b)** $350 thousand   **(c)** The capacity of the refinery is 700 thousand gallons of gasoline per hour.   **(d)** The intercept is $(0, 100)$. The cost of $100 thousand for producing 0 gallons of gasoline can be thought of as fixed costs.   **17.** *A*: $(2, 3)$; I   *B*: $(-5, 2)$; II   *C*: $(0, -2)$; *y*-axis   *D*: $(-4, -3)$; III   *E*: $(3, -4)$; IV   *F*: $(4, 0)$; *x*-axis

19. *A*: quadrant I;   **21. (a)** yes **(b)** no **(c)** yes **(d)** yes   **23. (a)** yes **(b)** no **(c)** no **(d)** yes
   B: quadrant III;   **25. (a)** no **(b)** yes **(c)** yes **(d)** yes
   C: *x*-axis;
   D: quadrant IV;   **27.** $y = 4x$ **29.** $y = -\frac{1}{2}x$ **31.** $y = x + 3$ **33.** $y = -3x + 1$ **35.** $y = \frac{1}{2}x - 4$
   E: *y*-axis;
   F: quadrant II

37. $2x + y = 7$ **39.** $y = -x^2$ **41.** $y = 2x^2 - 8$ **43.** $y = |x|$ **45.** $y = |x - 1|$ **47.** $y = x^3$ **49.** $y = x^3 + 1$

    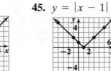

51. $x^2 - y = 4$ **53.** $x = y^2 - 1$ **55.** $(-2, 0)$ and $(0, 3)$; x-intercept: -2; y-intercept: 3 **57.** $(-2, 0)$, $(1, 0)$, and $(0, -4)$;

     x-intercepts: $-2, 1$; y-intercept: -4 **59.** $a = \dfrac{7}{4}$ **61.** $b = 4$

63. (a) 400 ft^2 **(b)** $25 \text{ feet}; 625 \text{ ft}^2$ **(c)** The x-intercepts are $x = 0$ and $x = 50$. These values form the bounds for the width of the opening. The y-intercept is $y = 0$. The area of the opening will be 0 ft^2 when the width is 0 feet.   **65. (a)** $\$100; \$100$ **(b)** $\$1600$ **(c)** $(0, 100)$; The monthly cost will be $\$100$ if no minutes are used.

67. Vertical line with an x-intercept of 4.   **69.** Answers will vary. One possible graph is shown.   **71.** Answers will vary. One possibility: $y = 0$
73. A complete graph is one that shows enough of the graph so that anyone who is looking at it will "see" the rest of it as an obvious continuation of what is shown. A complete graph should show all the interesting features of the graph, such as intercepts and high/low points.
75. The point-plotting method of graphing an equation requires one to choose certain values of one variable and use the equation to find the corresponding values of the other variable. These points are then plotted and connected in a smooth curve.

77. $y = 3x - 9$ **79.** $y = -x^2 + 8$ **81.** $y + 2x^2 = 13$ **83.** $y = x^3 - 6x + 1$

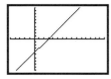 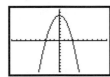 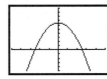 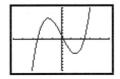

Section 1.6 Linear Equations in Two Variables   **1.** linear equation   **2.** line

3.   **4.**   **5.**   **6.** True   **7.**   **8.**   **9.**

10.   **11.**   **12.**   **13.** undefined   **14.** $\dfrac{2}{5}$ **15.** False   **16.** True   **17.** 3; For every 1-unit increase in x, y will increase by 3 units.   **18.** $-\dfrac{7}{4}$; For every 4-unit increase in x, y will decrease by 7 units.   **19.** 0; For every 1-unit increase in x, there is no change in y; Horizontal line   **20.** Undefined; Vertical line   **21.** True

22. L_1: $m = \dfrac{1}{5}$; L_2: m is undefined; L_3: $m = -1$; L_4: $m = 0$

23. (a)   **(b)** $\$1120$ per bicycle. For each bicycle sold, total revenue increased by $\$1120$ when between 0 and 25 bicycles were sold.   **(c)** $\$120$ per bicycle. For each bicycle sold, total revenue increased by $\$120$ per bicycle when between 102 and 150 bicycles were sold.   **(d)** No, because the average rate of change (slope) is not constant.

24. (a)   **(b)**   **(c)**   **25.** $y - 5 = 2(x - 3)$ **26.** $y - 3 = -4(x + 2)$

27. $y + 4 = \dfrac{1}{3}(x - 3)$ **28.** $y = -2$ **29.** $m = 3$; y-intercept: -2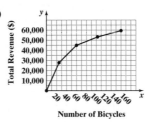

30. $m = -3$; y-intercept: 4   **31.** $m = \dfrac{3}{2}$; y-intercept: $-\dfrac{7}{2}$ **32.** $m = -\dfrac{7}{3}$; y-intercept: 0

33. $y = 2x + 1$

34. $y = -\frac{1}{2}x + 3$

35. $y = 6$

36. $x = 3$

37.   **39.** 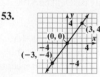 **41.** 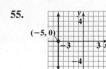 **43.**   **45.**   **47.** 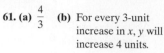 **49.**

51. 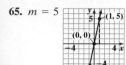 **53.**  **55.** 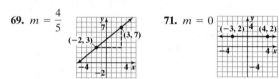 **57.** 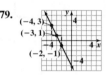 **59.**

61. (a) $\frac{4}{3}$ **(b)** For every 3-unit increase in x, y will increase 4 units.

63. (a) $-\frac{8}{3}$ **(b)** For every 3-unit increase in x, y will decrease by 8 units. For every 3-unit decrease in x, y will increase by 8 units.

65. $m = 5$ **67.** $m = -3$ **69.** $m = \frac{4}{5}$ **71.** $m = 0$

73. m is undefined   **75.** $m = \frac{2}{21}$ $\left(\frac{1}{2}, \frac{5}{3}\right)$ $\left(\frac{9}{4}, \frac{11}{6}\right)$ **77.**   **79.**

81.   **83.**   **85.** 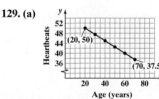 **87.** Answers will vary. One possibility: $(0, 8)$, $(2, 13)$, and $(4, 18)$

89. $y = -\frac{4}{9}x - \frac{7}{9}$ **91.** $y = 3$ **93.** $y = 2x$ **95.** $y = -3x - 2$

97. $y = \frac{4}{3}x - 2$ **99.** $y = -\frac{5}{4}x + \frac{3}{2}$ **101.** $x = 6$ **103.** $y = \frac{7}{5}x$

105. $y = 5x - 13$ **107.** $y - \frac{3}{7}x + \frac{1}{7}$ **109.** $x = -1$ **111.** $y = \frac{5}{2}x + \frac{1}{2}$ **113.** $y = 4$

115. The slope is 2 and the y-intercept is -1.

117. The slope is -4 and the y-intercept is 0.

119. The slope is -2 and the y-intercept is 3.

121. The slope is -2 and the y-intercept is 4.

123. The slope is $\frac{1}{4}$ and the y-intercept is $-\frac{1}{2}$.

125. The slope is undefined and there is no y-intercept.

127. $y = 0$

128. $x = 0$

129. (a)

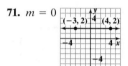

(b) -0.25 heartbeats per year; Between ages 20 and 30, the maximum number of heartbeats decreases at a rate of 0.25 heartbeats per year. **(c)** -0.25 heartbeats per year; Between ages 50 and 60, the maximum number of heartbeats decreases at a rate of 0.25 heartbeats per year. **(d)** Yes. The maximum number of heartbeats appears to be linearly related to age. The average rate of change (slope) is constant for the data provided.

131. (a)

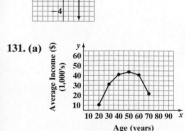

(b) $2069.20 per year; Between ages 20 and 30, the average individual's income increases at a rate of $2069.20 per year. **(c)** -297.30 per year; Between ages 50 and 60, the average individual's income decreases at a rate of $297.30 per year. **(d)** No. The average income is not linearly related to age. The average rate of change (slope) is not constant.

133. $C = \frac{5}{9}(F - 32)$; $60°F$ is equivalent to $15.6°C$ **135. (c)**

137. Horizontal line: $y = b$; Vertical line: $x = a$; Point-slope: $y - y_1 = m(x - x_1)$; Slope-intercept: $y = mx + b$; Standard: $Ax + By = C$
139. Horizontal line of the form $y = b$, where b does not equal 0.   **141.** No. All lines must travel through either the x-axis or y-axis or both.
143. For positive slopes, the larger the slope, the steeper the line.   **145.** Answers may vary.   Answers may vary.

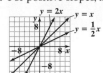   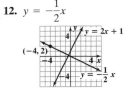   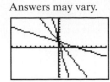

Section 1.7 Parallel and Perpendicular Lines   **1.** slope; y-intercepts   **2.** Not parallel   **3.** Parallel   **4.** Not parallel

5. $y = 3x - 7$ **6.** $y = -\dfrac{3}{2}x + 1$ **7.** -1 **8.** $\dfrac{1}{3}$ **12.** $y = -\dfrac{1}{2}x$

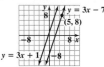      **9.** Perpendicular
                                            10. Not perpendicular
                                            11. Perpendicular

13. $y = -\dfrac{4}{3}x - 8$ **14.** $y = 2$ **15. (a)** $m = 5$ **(b)** $m = 1/5$ **17. (a)** $m = -5/6$ **(b)** $m = 6/5$ **19.** Parallel

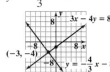   **21.** Neither   **23.** Perpendicular   **25.** Parallel   **27.** $y = \dfrac{3}{2}x - 3$ **29.** $y = \dfrac{1}{2}x + 2$
                                            31. $y = 2$

33. $y = 2x - 5$ **35.** $y = \dfrac{1}{2}x + 2$ **37.** $y = -3$ **39.** $y = 3$ **41.** $y = 3x + 2$

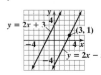   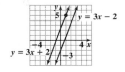

43. $y = \dfrac{3}{4}x + 4$ **45.** $y = -\dfrac{5}{2}x - 8$ **47.** $m_1 - \dfrac{3}{5}; m_2 - \dfrac{5}{3};$ **49.** $m_1 - \dfrac{7}{3}, m_2 - \dfrac{7}{3},$ **51.** $m_1 - -2, m_2 - 2,$
                                                                        Perpendicular   Parallel   Neither

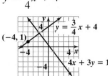   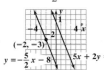   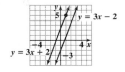

53. (a)   **(b)** Slope of $\overline{AB} = \dfrac{2}{3}$;   **55. (a)**   **(b)** Slope of $\overline{AB} = \dfrac{1}{5}$;

        Slope of $\overline{BC} = -\dfrac{3}{2}$ Slope of $\overline{BC} = 3$;

Because the slopes are negative reciprocals,   Slope of $\overline{CD} = \dfrac{1}{5}$;
segments $\overline{AB}$ and $\overline{BC}$ are perpendicular.
Thus, triangle ABC is a right triangle.   Slope of $\overline{DA} = 3$

Because the slopes of $\overline{AB}$ and $\overline{CD}$ are equal, $\overline{AB}$ and $\overline{CD}$ are parallel.
Becausee the slopes of $\overline{BC}$ and $\overline{DA}$ are equal, $\overline{BC}$ and $\overline{DA}$ are parallel.
Thus, quadrilateral $ABCD$ is a parallelogram.

57. $A = -1$ **59.** (c)   **61.** No. If the two non-vertical lines have the same x-intercept but different y-intercepts, then their slopes cannot be equal. Therefore, they cannot be parallel lines.

Section 1.8 Linear Inequalities in Two Variables   **1.** half-planes   **2. (a)** No   **(b)** Yes   **(c)** Yes   **(d)** Yes   **3.** False   **4.** True

5. $y = -2x + 3$ **6.**   **7.**   **8. (a)** $430x + 330y \leq 800$ **(b)** Yes   **(c)** No
                                            9. (a) yes   **(b)** no   **(c)** yes
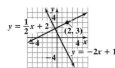   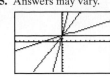   **11. (a)** yes   **(b)** no   **(c)** yes

13.  **15.** $x = -2$ 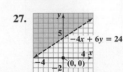 **17.** 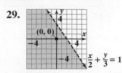 **19.** 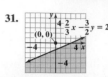 **21.** 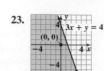 **23.**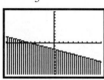

25. 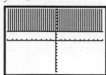 **27.** 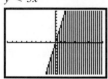 **29.** 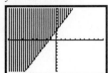 **31.**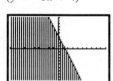

33. (a) Let x = the number of Filet-o-Fish. Let y = the number of orders of fries. $45x + 40y \le 150$ **(b)** yes **(c)** no   **35. (a)** Let x = the number of Switch A assemblies. Let y = the number of Switch B assemblies. $2x + 1.5y \le 80$ **(b)** no **(c)** no   **37.** $y > 2x - 2$ **39.** $y \le -x + 1$

41. Consider the inequality $Ax + By > C$. The equation $Ax + By = C$ separates the Cartesian plane into two half-planes. Any ordered pair (x, y) that makes $Ax + By$ equal to C lies on this line. Any other point will lie in one of the two half-planes. If a point on one side of the line does not satisfy the inequality, then none of the points satisfy the inequality. For this reason, if a point does not satisfy the inequality, then we shade the opposite side.

43. $y > 3$

45. $y < 5x$

47. $y > 2x + 3$

49. $y \le \dfrac{1}{2}x - 5$

51. $3x + y \le 4$
$(y \le -3x + 4)$

53. $y \le -\dfrac{2}{5}x - 2$

Chapter 1 Review **1.** $x = 5$ is a solution to the equation. $x = 6$ is not a solution to the equation.   **2.** $x = -2$ is a solution to the equation. $x = -1$ is a solution to the equation.   **3.** $y = -2$ is not a solution to the equation. $y = 0$ is a solution to the equation.   **4.** $w = -14$ is not a solution to the equation. $w = 7$ is not a solution to the equation.   **5.** conditional; $\{3\}$ **6.** conditional; $\{4\}$ **7.** conditional; $\{3\}$
8. conditional; $\{-8\}$ **9.** identity; $\{x \mid x$ is any real number$\}$ **10.** contradiction; $\{\ \}$ or $\varnothing$ **11.** contradiction; $\{\ \}$ or $\varnothing$ **12.** conditional; $\{-2\}$
13. conditional; $\{-47\}$ **14.** identity; $\{w \mid w$ is any real number$\}$ **15.** $x = -\dfrac{3}{2}$ must be excluded from the domain.   **16.** $x = \dfrac{1}{2}$ must be excluded from the domain.   **17.** Her Missouri taxable income was $43,250.   **18.** The regular club price for a DVD is $21.95.
19. $3x + 7 = 22$ **20.** $x - 3 = \dfrac{x}{2}$ **21.** $0.2x = x - 12$ **22.** $6x = 2x - 4$ **23.** Payton is 5 years old and Shawn is 13 years old.
24. The five odd integers are $21, 23, 25, 27$, and 29.   **25.** Logan needs to get a score of 76.5 on the final exam to have an average of 80.   **26.** After 1 month, Cherie will accrue about $16.64 in interest.   **27.** The original price of the sleeping bag was $135.00.   **28.** The federal minimum wage was $5.85 (per hour).   **29.** The store should mix 4 pounds of chocolate covered blueberries with 8 pounds of chocolate covered strawberries.   **30.** The store should mix 7.5 pounds of baseball gumballs with 2.5 pounds of soccer gumballs.   **31.** Angie should invest $4800 at 8% and $3200 at 18%.
32. About 2.14 quarts would need to be drained and replaced with pure antifreeze.   **33.** Josh drove 90 miles at 60 miles per hour and 210 miles at 70 miles per hour.   **34.** The F14 is traveling at a speed of 1220 miles per hour and the F15 is traveling at a speed of 1420 miles per hour.
35. $x = \dfrac{k}{y}$ **36.** $C = \dfrac{5}{9}(F - 32)$ **37.** $W = \dfrac{P - 2L}{2}$ **38.** $m_2 = \dfrac{\rho - m_1 v_1}{v_2}$ **39.** $T = \dfrac{PV}{nR}$ **40.** $W = \dfrac{S - 2LH}{2L + 2H}$ **41.** $y = -\dfrac{3}{4}x + \dfrac{1}{2}$
42. $y = \dfrac{5}{4}x + \dfrac{5}{2}$ **43.** $y = 4x - 5$ **44.** $y = -\dfrac{6}{5}x + 24$ **45.** The melting point of platinum is 1772°C.   **46.** The angles measure $70°, 70°$, and $40°$.
47. The window measures 15 feet by 23 feet.   **48. (a)** $x = 25C - 73.75$ **(b)** Debbie can talk for 426 minutes in one month and not spend more than $20 on long distance.   **49.** The patio will be $\dfrac{10}{27}$ of a foot thick (i.e. about 4.44 inches).   **50. (a)** $r = \dfrac{A - \pi Rs}{\pi s}$ **(b)** The radius of the top of the frustum is 2 feet.   **51. (a)** $x = \dfrac{C - 7.48}{0.08674}$ **(b)** Approximately 2289 kwh were used.   **52.** The angle measures 60°.
53. $(2, 7]$ **54.** $(-2, \infty)$ **55.** $x \le 4$
56. $-1 \le x < 3$ **57.** $a = 7$ and $b = 15$ **58.** $a = -1$ and $b = 5$ **59.** Solution set: $\{x \mid x \le -4\}$
Interval: $(-\infty, -4]$ Graph: **60.** Solution set: $\left\{x \mid x < -\dfrac{1}{3}\right\}$ Interval: $\left(-\infty, -\dfrac{1}{3}\right)$
Graph: **61.** Solution set: $\left\{h \mid h \ge -\dfrac{2}{3}\right\}$ Interval: $\left[-\dfrac{2}{3}, \infty\right)$ Graph:

62. Solution set: $\{x|x > 2\}$ Interval: $(2, \infty)$ Graph: **63.** Solution set: $\{p|p > 2\}$ Interval: $(2, \infty)$

Graph: **64.** Solution set: $\{x|x \text{ is any real number}\}$ Interval: $(-\infty, \infty)$

Graph: **65.** $\{\ \}$ or $\varnothing$ **66.** Solution set: $\{x|x > 4.2\}$ Interval: $(4.2, \infty)$

Graph: 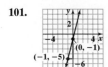 **67.** Solution set: $\{w|w > 1\}$ Interval: $(1, \infty)$ Graph: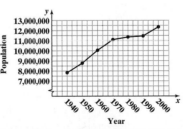

68. Solution set: $\{y|y < -120\}$ Interval: $(-\infty, -120)$ Graph: 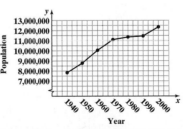 **69.** To stay within budget, no more

than 60 people can attend the banquet. **70.** To stay within budget, you can drive an average of 216 miles per day. **71.** The band must sell more
than 125 candy bars to make a profit. **72.** You can purchase up to 5 DVDs and still be within budget.

73. A: quadrant IV; **74.** A: x-axis; B: quadrant I; **75. (a)** yes **(b)** no **78.** $2x + y = 3$
B: quadrant III; C: quadrant III; D: quadrant II; **(c)** no **(d)** yes
C: y-axis; D: quadrant II; E: quadrant IV; **76. (a)** no **(b)** yes
E: x-axis; F: quadrant I F: y-axis **(c)** yes **(d)** no
  77. $y = x + 2$ **79.** $y = -x^2 + 4$

80. $y = |x + 2| - 1$ **81.** $y = x^3 + 2$ **82.** $x = y^2 + 1$ **83.** $(-3, 0), (0, -1), (0, 3)$ **85.** **86.**
x-intercept: -3;
y-intercepts: $-1, 3$
84. (a) $40
(b) About $500

87. **88.** **89.** **90.** **91.** **92.**

93. **94.** **95.** **96. (a)** $m = \dfrac{5}{4}$ **(b)** For every 4-unit increase in x, y will increase by 5 units.

97. (a) $m = -\dfrac{1}{4}$ **(b)** For every 4-unit increase in x, y will decrease by 1 unit.
For every 4-unit decrease in x, y will increase by 1 unit.

98. $m = -2$ **99.** $m = \dfrac{3}{2}$ **100. (a)**

(b) 81,493.5 people per year; Between 1940 and 1950, the population of Illinois increased at an average rate of 81,493.5 people per year. **(c)** 319.3 people per
year; Between 1980 and 1990, the population of Illinois increased at an average rate of 319.3 people per year. **(d)** 98,869.1 people per year; Between 1990
and 2000, the population of Illinois increased at an average rate of 98,869.1 people per year. **(e)** No. The average rate of change (slope) is not constant.

101. **102.** **103.** **104.** **105.** $y = -\dfrac{1}{2}x + 2$ or $x + 2y = 4$

  106. $y = 3x$ or $3x - y = 0$

  107. $y = -x + 5$ or $x + y = 5$

108. $y = \dfrac{3}{5}x + 2$ or $3x - 5y = -10$ **109.** $y = -\dfrac{1}{3}x + 4$ or $x + 3y = 12$ **110.** $y = 3$ **111.** $y = 2x - 9$ or $2x - y = 9$

112. $y = -\dfrac{1}{3}x + \dfrac{5}{3}$ or $x + 3y = 5$

113. The slope is 4 and the y-intercept is -6.

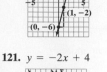

114. The slope is $-\frac{2}{3}$ and the y-intercept is 4.

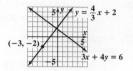

115. $-\frac{3}{8}$ **116.** $\frac{8}{3}$ **117.** Perpendicular

118. Neither **119.** Parallel

120. Perpendicular

121. $y = -2x + 4$

122. $y = \frac{5}{2}x - 7$

123. $x = 1$

124. $y = -\frac{1}{3}x + 4$

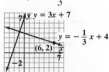

125. $y = \frac{4}{3}x + 2$

126. $y = -4$

127. (a) yes
(b) yes
(c) no
128. (a) no
(b) yes
(c) no

129.

130.

131.

132.

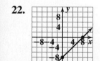

133.

134. $x = -8$

135. (a) Let x = the number of movie tickets. Let y = the number of music CDs. $7.50x + 15y \le 60$
(b) no **(c)** yes
136. (a) Let x = the number of candy bars. Let y = the number of candles. $0.50x + 2y \ge 1000$ **(b)** no **(c)** yes

Chapter 1 Test **1. (a)** $x = 6$ is a solution to the equation. **(b)** $x = -2$ is not a solution to the equation.
2. (a) Interval: $(-4, \infty)$ **(b)** Interval: $(3, 7]$ **3.** $3x - 8 = x + 4$

4. $\frac{2}{3}x + 2(x - 5) > 7$ **5.** $\{2\}$ This is a conditional equation. **6.** contradiction; $\{\ \}$ or $\varnothing$

7. $\{x | x \ge 3\}; [3, \infty)$ **8.** $\left\{x | x > -\frac{1}{5}\right\}; \left(-\frac{1}{5}, \infty\right)$

9. $\left\{x | x \ge \frac{1}{2}\right\}; \left[\frac{1}{2}, \infty\right)$ **10.** $y = -\frac{7}{4}x + \frac{3}{4}$ **11.** Glen's weekly sales must be at least \$4375 for him to earn

at least \$750. **12.** There were 14 children at Payton's party. **13.** The sandbox has a width of 4 feet and a length of 6 feet. **14.** The chemist needs to mix 8 liters of the 10% solution with 4 liters of the 40% solution. **15.** It will take contestant B two hours to catch up to contestant A.

16. A: quadrant IV;
B: y-axis;
C: x-axis;
D: quadrant I;
E: quadrant III;
F: quadrant II

17. (a) no **(b)** yes **(c)** yes
18. $y = 4x - 1$

19. $y = 4x^2$

20. $(-3, 0), (0, 1), (0, 3)$
x-intercept: -3;
y-intercepts: 1, 3

21. (a) At 6 seconds the car is traveling 30 miles per hour. **(b)** $(0, 0)$: At the start of the trip, the car is not moving. $(32, 0)$: After 32 seconds, the speed of the car is 0 miles per hour.

22.

23.

24.

25.

26.

27. $m = -\frac{4}{3}$
For every 3-unit increase in x, y will decrease by 4 units. For every 3-unit decrease in x, y will increase by 4 units.

28.

29. Perpendicular **30.** $y = 4x + 13$ or $4x - y = -13$ **31.** $y = -\frac{2}{3}x + 5$ or $2x + 3y = 15$

32. $y = \frac{1}{5}x - 3$ or $x - 5y = 15$ **33.** $y = -\frac{1}{3}x + 4$ or $x + 3y = 12$ **34. (a)** no **(b)** no **(c)** yes

35.

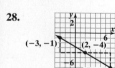

36.

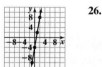

37. (a)

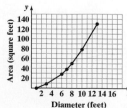

(b) 3.14 square feet per foot; Between diameters of 1 foot and 3 feet, the area of the circle increases at a rate of 3.14 square feet per foot. **(c)** Approximately 18.06 square feet per foot; Between diameters of 10 feet and 13 feet, the area of the circle increases at a rate of approximately 18.06 square feet per foot. **(d)** No. The average rate of change (slope) is not constant.

Cumulative Review Chapters R–1 **1. (a) (i)** 27.235 **(ii)** 27.236 **(b) (i)** 1.0 **(ii)** 1.1 **2.** 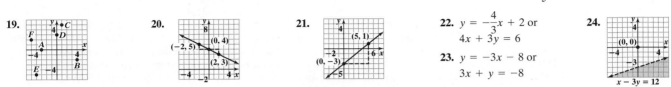 **3.** −14

4. −6 **5.** 6 **6.** 81 **7.** 74 **8.** $\frac{11}{12}$ **9.** 9 **10.** $5a^2 - 4a - 13$ **11. (a)** No **(b)** Yes **12.** $-5x + 18$

13. $x = 3$ is not a solution to the equation. **14.** $\{4\}$ **15.** $\left\{\frac{13}{2}\right\}$ **16.** $y = \frac{2}{5}x - \frac{6}{5}$

17. $\{x \mid x \geq 7\}$; $[7, \infty)$ (number line) **18.** $\{x \mid x \leq 5\}$ or $(-\infty, 5]$ (number line)

19. **20.** (graph with points $(-2, 5)$, $(0, 4)$, $(2, 3)$) **21.** (graph with points $(5, 1)$, $(0, -3)$) **22.** $y = -\frac{4}{3}x + 2$ or $4x + 3y = 6$ **23.** $y = -3x - 8$ or $3x + y = -8$ **24.** (graph with $(0,0)$, $x - 3y = 12$)

25. Shawn needs to score at least 91 on the final exam to earn an A (assuming the maximum score on the exam is 100).
26. A person 62 inches tall would be considered obese if they weighed 160 pounds or more. **27.** The angles measure 55° and 125°.
28. The cylinder should be about 5.96 inches tall. **29.** The three consecutive even integers are 24, 26, and 28.

Chapter 2 Relations, Functions, and More Inequalities

Section 2.1 Relations **1.** corresponds; depends **2.** {(Max, November 8), (Alesia, January 20), (Trent, March 3), (Yolanda, November 8), (Wanda, July 6), (Elvis, January 8)} **3.** 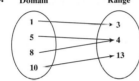 **4.** domain; range **5.** Domain: {Max, Alesia, Trent, Yolanda, Wanda, Elvis}; Range: {January 20, March 3, July 6, November 8, January 8} **6.** Domain: {1, 5, 8, 10}; Range: {3, 4, 13} **7.** Domain: {−2, −1, 2, 3, 4}; Range: {−3, −2, 0, 2, 3} **8.** True **9.** False **10.** Domain: $\{x \mid -2 \leq x \leq 4\}$ or $[-2, 4]$; Range: $\{y \mid -2 \leq y \leq 2\}$ or $[-2, 2]$ **11.** Domain: $\{x \mid x$ is a real number$\}$ or $(-\infty, \infty)$; Range: $\{y \mid y$ is a real number$\}$ or $(-\infty, \infty)$

12. (graph) **13.** (graph) **14.** (graph)

Domain: $\{x \mid x$ is a real number$\}$ or $(-\infty, \infty)$
Range: $\{y \mid y$ is a real number$\}$ or $(-\infty, \infty)$

Domain: $\{x \mid x$ is a real number$\}$ or $(-\infty, \infty)$
Range: $\{y \mid y > -8\}$ or $[-8, \infty)$

Domain: $\{x \mid x \geq 1\}$ or $[1, \infty)$
Range: $\{y \mid y$ is a real number$\}$ or $(-\infty, \infty)$

15. {(*USA Today*, 2.5), (*Wall Street Journal*, 2.1), (*New York Times*, 1.7), (*Los Angeles Times*, 1.2), (*Washington Post*, 1.0)}; Domain: {*USA Today, Wall Street Journal, New York Times, Los Angeles Times, Washington Post*}; Range: {1.0, 1.2, 1.7, 2.1, 2.5} **17.** {(Less than 9th Grade, $16321), (9th–12th Grade – no diploma, $20934), (High School Graduate, $30134), (Associate's Degree, $41934), (Bachelor's Degree or Higher, $58114)}; Domain: {Less than 9th Grade, 9th–12th Grade – no diploma, High School Graduate, Associate's Degree, Bachelor's Degree or Higher}; Range: {$16321, $20934, $30134, $41934, $58114}

19. 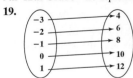 **21.** 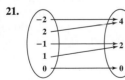 **23.** 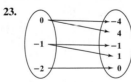 **25.** Domain: {−3, −2, 0, 2, 3}; Range: {−3, −1, 2, 3} **27.** Domain: $\{x \mid -4 \leq x \leq 4\}$ or $[-4, 4]$; Range: $\{y \mid -2 \leq y \leq 2\}$ or $[-2, 2]$ **29.** Domain: $\{x \mid -1 \leq x \leq 3\}$ or $[-1, 3]$; Range: $\{y \mid 0 \leq y \leq 4\}$ or $[0, 4]$ **31.** Domain: $\{x \mid x$ is a real number$\}$ or $(-\infty, \infty)$; Range: $\{y \mid y \geq -3\}$ or $[-3, \infty)$

Domain: {−3, −2, −1, 0, 1}
Range: {4, 6, 8, 10, 12}

Domain: {−2, −1, 0, 1, 2}
Range: {0, 2, 4}

Domain: {−2, −1, 0}
Range: {−4, −1, 0, 1, 4}

33. Domain: $\{x \mid x$ is a real number$\}$ or $(-\infty, \infty)$; Range: $\{y \mid y$ is a real number$\}$ or $(-\infty, \infty)$ **35.** Domain: $\{x \mid x$ is a real number$\}$ or $(-\infty, \infty)$; Range: $\{y \mid y$ is a real number$\}$ or $(-\infty, \infty)$ **37.** Domain: $\{x \mid x$ is a real number$\}$ or $(-\infty, \infty)$; Range: $\{y \mid y$ is a real number$\}$ or $(-\infty, \infty)$ **39.** Domain: $\{x \mid x$ is a real number$\}$ or $(-\infty, \infty)$; Range: $\{y \mid y \leq 0\}$ or $(-\infty, 0]$ **41.** Domain: $\{x \mid x$ is a real number$\}$ or $(-\infty, \infty)$; Range: $\{y \mid y \geq -8\}$ or $[-8, \infty)$ **43.** Domain: $\{x \mid x$ is a real number$\}$ or $(-\infty, \infty)$; Range: $\{y \mid y \geq 0\}$ or $[0, \infty)$ **45.** Domain: $\{x \mid x$ is a real number$\}$ or $(-\infty, \infty)$; Range: $\{y \mid y \geq 0\}$ or $[0, \infty)$ **47.** Domain: $\{x \mid x$ is a real number$\}$ or $(-\infty, \infty)$; Range: $\{y \mid y$ is a real number$\}$ or $(-\infty, \infty)$ **49.** Domain: $\{x \mid x$ is a real number$\}$ or $(-\infty, \infty)$; Range: $\{y \mid y$ is a real number$\}$ or $(-\infty, \infty)$ **51.** Domain: $\{x \mid x$ is a real number$\}$ or $(-\infty, \infty)$; Range: $\{y \mid y \geq -4\}$ or $[-4, \infty)$ **53.** Domain: $\{x \mid x \geq -1\}$ or $[-1, \infty)$; Range: $\{y \mid y$ is a real number$\}$ or $(-\infty, \infty)$ **55. (a)** Domain: $\{x \mid 0 \leq x \leq 50\}$ or $[0, 50]$; Range: $\{y \mid 0 \leq y \leq 625\}$ or $[0, 625]$ **(b)** Width can be no more than $\frac{1}{2}$ the perimeter. **57. (a)** Domain: $\{m \mid 0 \leq m \leq 15,120\}$ or $[0, 15120]$; Range: $\{C \mid 100 \leq C \leq 3380\}$ or $[100, 3380]$ **(b)** $21 \cdot 12 \cdot 60 = 15,120$ minutes **59.** Actual graphs will vary but all should be horizontal lines. **61.** A relation is a correspondence between two sets called the domain and range. The domain is the set of all inputs and the range is the set of all outputs.

Section 2.2 An Introduction to Functions **1.** function **2.** false **3.** Function; Domain: {Max, Alesia, Trent, Yolanda, Wanda, Elvis}; Range: {January 20, March 3, July 6, November 8, January 8} **4.** Not a function **5.** Function; Domain: {−3, −2, −1, 0, 1}; Range: {0, 1, 2, 3}

6. Not a function   **7.** Function   **8.** Not a function   **9.** Function   **10.** True   **11.** Function   **12.** Not a function   **13.** dependent; independent; argument   **14.** 14   **15.** −13   **16.** $3x − 4$ **17.** $3x − 6$ **18. (a)** Independent variable: t; dependent variable: A
(b) $A(30) \approx 706.86$ square miles. After 30 days, the area contaminated with oil will be a circle covering about 706.86 square miles.
19. Function. Domain: {Virginia, Nevada, New Mexico, Tennessee, Texas}; Range: {3, 9, 11, 32}   **21.** Not a function. Domain: {150, 174, 180}; Range: {118, 130, 140}   **23.** Function. Domain: {0, 1, 2, 3}; Range: {3, 4, 5, 6}   **25.** Function. Domain: {−3, 1, 4, 7}; Range: {5}
27. Not a function. Domain: {−10, −5, 0}; Range: {1, 2, 3, 4}   **29.** Function   **31.** Function   **33.** Not a function   **35.** Function
37. Not a function   **39.** Function   **41.** Not a function   **43.** Function   **45.** Function   **47. (a)** $f(0) = 3$ **(b)** $f(3) = 9$ **(c)** $f(−2) = −1$
(d) $f(−x) = −2x + 3$ **(e)** $−f(x) = −2x − 3$ **(f)** $f(x + 2) = 2x + 7$ **(g)** $f(2x) = 4x + 3$ **(h)** $f(x + h) = 2x + 2h + 3$
49. (a) $f(0) = 2$ **(b)** $f(3) = −13$ **(c)** $f(−2) = 12$ **(d)** $f(−x) = 5x + 2$ **(e)** $−f(x) = 5x − 2$ **(f)** $f(x + 2) = −5x − 8$
(g) $f(2x) = −10x + 2$ **(h)** $f(x + h) = −5x − 5h + 2$ **51.** $f(2) = 7$ **53.** $s(−2) = 16$ **55.** $F(−3) = 5$ **57.** $F(4) = −6$
59. $C = −6$ **61.** $A = 5$ **63.** $A(r) = \pi r^2$; 50.27 in.²   **65.** $G(h) = 15h$; $375   **67. (a)** The dependent variable is the population, P, and the independent variable is the age, a.   **(b)** $P(20) = 223{,}091$ thousand; The population of Americans that were 20 years of age or older in 2007 was roughly 223 million.   **(c)** $P(0) = 321{,}783$ thousand; $P(0)$ represents the entire population of the U.S. since every member of the population is at least 0 years of age. The population of the U.S. in 2007 was roughly 322 million.   **69. (a)** The dependent variable is revenue, R, and the independent variable is price, p.   **(b)** $R(50) = 7500$; Selling PDAs for $50 will yield a daily revenue of $7500 for the company.   **(c)** $R(120) = 9600$; Selling PDAs for $120 will yield a daily revenue of $9600 for the company.   **71. (a)(i)** −5   **(ii)** 1   **(iii)** 1   **(b)(i)** 13   **(ii)** 4   **(iii)** 4   **73.** Answers will vary.   **75.** A function is a relation between two sets, the domain and the range. The domain is the set of all inputs to the function and the range is the set of all outputs. In a function, each input in the domain corresponds to one output in the range.   **77.** The four forms of a function are map, ordered pairs, equation, and graph.   **79.** $f(2) = 7$ **81.** $F(−3) = 5$ **83.** $H(7) = 5$ **85.** $F(4) = −6$

Section 2.3 Functions and Their Graphs

1. domain   **2.** $\{x \mid x$ is a real number$\}$; $(−\infty, \infty)$ **3.** $\{x \mid x \neq 3\}$ **4.** $\{r \mid r > 0\}$; $(0, \infty)$
5. 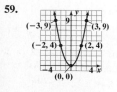   **6.**   **7.**   **8. (a)** Domain: $\{x \mid x$ is a real number$\}$; $(−\infty, \infty)$; Range: $\{y \mid y \leq 2\}$; $(−\infty, 2]$
(b) $(−2, 0), (0, 2), (2, 0)$; x-intercepts: −2 and 2; y-intercept: 2   **9.** $f(3) = 8$; $(−2, 4)$
10. (a) $f(−3) = −15$; $f(1) = −3$ **(b)** Domain: $\{x \mid x$ is a real number$\}$ or $(−\infty, \infty)$
(c) Range: $\{y \mid y$ is a real number$\}$ or $(−\infty, \infty)$ **(d)** $(−2, 0), (0, 0), (2, 0)$; x-intercepts: −2, 0, and 2; y-intercept: 0   **(e)** {3}

11. (a) No   **(b)** $f(3) = −2$; $(3, −2)$ is on the graph   **(c)** $x = 5$; $(5, −8)$ is on the graph   **12.** yes   **13.** no   **14.** yes   **15.** −2 and 2
16. 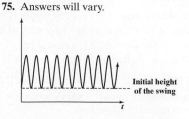   **17.** $\{x \mid x$ is a real number$\}$ or $(−\infty, \infty)$ **19.** $\{z \mid z \neq 5\}$ **21.** $\{x \mid x$ is a real number$\}$ or $(−\infty, \infty)$

23. $\left\{ x \mid x \neq −\dfrac{1}{3} \right\}$ **25.** $f(x) = 4x − 6$ **27.** $h(x) = x^2 − 2$ **29.** $G(x) = |x − 1|$ **31.** $g(x) = x^3$

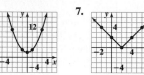 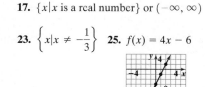 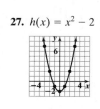 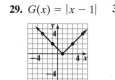

33. (a) Domain: $\{x \mid x$ is a real number$\}$ or $(−\infty, \infty)$; Range: $\{y \mid y$ is a real number$\}$ or $(−\infty, \infty)$ **(b)** $(0, 2)$ and $(1, 0)$ **(c)** 1
35. (a) Domain: $\{x \mid x$ is a real number$\}$ or $(−\infty, \infty)$; Range: $\{y \mid y \geq −2.25\}$ or $[−2.25, \infty)$ **(b)** $(−2, 0), (4, 0)$, and $(0, −2)$ **(c)** −2, 4
37. (a) Domain: $\{x \mid x$ is a real number$\}$ or $(−\infty, \infty)$; Range: $\{y \mid y$ is a real number$\}$ or $(−\infty, \infty)$ **(b)** $(−3, 0), (−1, 0), (2, 0)$, and $(0, −3)$
(c) −3, −1, 2   **39. (a)** Domain: $\{x \mid x$ is a real number$\}$ or $(−\infty, \infty)$; Range: $\{y \mid y \geq 0\}$ or $[0, \infty)$ **(b)** $(−3, 0), (3, 0)$, and $(0, 9)$ **(c)** −3, 3
41. (a) Domain: $\{x \mid x \leq 4\}$ or $(−\infty, 4]$; Range: $\{y \mid y < 3\}$ or $(−\infty, 3]$ **(b)** $(−2, 0)$ and $(0, 2)$ **(c)** −2   **43. (a)** $f(−7) = −2$ **(b)** $f(−3) = 3$
(c) $f(6) = 2$ **(d)** negative   **(e)** $\{−6, −1, 4\}$ **(f)** $\{x \mid −7 \leq x \leq 6\}$ or $[−7, 6]$ **(g)** $\{y \mid −2 \leq y \leq 3\}$ or $[−2, 3]$ **(h)** −6, −1, and 4   **(i)** −1
(j) $\{−7, 2\}$ **(k)** $x = −3$ **(l)** −6, −1, 4   **45. (a)** $F(−2) = 3$ **(b)** $F(3) = −6$ **(c)** $x = −1$ **(d)** −4   **(e)** 2   **47. (a)** no   **(b)** $f(3) = 3$; $(3, 3)$
(c) 4; $(4, 7)$ **(d)** no   **49. (a)** yes   **(b)** $g(6) = 1$; $(6, 1)$ **(c)** −12; $(−12, 10)$ **(d)** yes   **51. (c)**   **53. (e)**   **55. (b)**   **57. (f)**

59.   **61.** 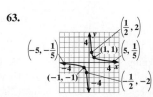   **63.**   **65.** $\{r \mid r > 0\}$ or $(0, \infty)$ **67.** $\{h \mid 0 \leq h \leq 60\}$ or $[0, 60]$
69. $\{p \mid 0 \leq p \leq 120\}$ or $[0, 120]$
71. (a) III   **(b)** I   **(c)** IV   **(d)** V   **(e)** II

73.   **75.** Answers will vary.   **77.** The person's weight increases until age 30, then oscillates back and forth between 158 pounds and 178 pounds, then slowly levels off at about 150 pounds.

79. Answers will vary. One possibility.

81. A function cannot have more than one output for a given input. So, there cannot be two outputs for the input 0.   **83.** The range of a function is the set of all outputs of the elements in the domain.

Putting the Concepts Together (Sections 2.1–2.3) **1.** The relation is a function because each element in the domain corresponds to one element in the range. $\{(-2, -1), (-1, 0), (0, 1), (1, 2), (2, 3)\}$ **2. (a)** Function **(b)** Not a function **3.** Yes; Domain: $\{-4, -1, 0, 3, 6\}$; Range: $\{-3, -2, 2, 6\}$ **4.** The graph passes the vertical line test. $f(5) = -6$ **5.** 4 **6. (a)** -17 **(b)** -34 **(c)** $-5x + 20$ **(d)** $-5x + 23$ **7. (a)** $\{h|h$ is any real number$\}$ or $(-\infty, \infty)$ **(b)** $\left\{w|w \neq -\dfrac{1}{3}\right\}$

8.
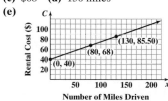
Domain: $\{x|x$ is any real number$\}$ or $(-\infty, \infty)$. Range: $\{y|y \geq -2\}$ or $[-2, \infty)$.
9. (a) $h(2.5) = 80$; After 2.5 seconds, the height of the ball is 80 feet. **(b)** $\{t|0 \leq t \leq 3.8\}$ or $[0, 3.8]$ **(c)** $\{h|0 \leq h \leq 105\}$ or $[0, 105]$ **(d)** 1.25 seconds **10. (a)** no **(b)** -12; $(-2, -12)$ **(c)** -4; $(-4, -22)$ **(d)** yes

Section 2.4 Linear Functions and Models
1. slope; y-intercept **2.** line **3.** False **4.** -2; 3

5. 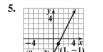 **6.**   **7.**   **8.**   **9.** 5 **10.** -8 **11.** 12
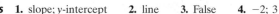

12. (a) $\{x|x \geq 0\}$; $[0, \infty)$ **(b)** \$40
(c) \$68 **(d)** 130 miles
(e)
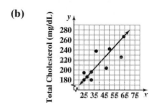
Number of Miles Driven
(f) You may drive between 0 and 250 miles.

13. (a) $C(x) = 81x + 2000$
(b) \$2405 **(c)** 10 bicycles
(d)
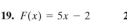
Number of Bicycles

14. (a) $C(x) = 0.18x + 250$
(b) $[0, \infty)$ **(c)** \$307.60
(d) 180 miles
(e)

Number of Miles Driven

15.
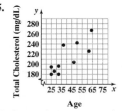
Age
(b) As age increases, total cholesterol also increases.

16. nonlinear **17.** linear, positive slope **18. (a)** Answers will vary. Using $(25, 180)$ and $(65, 269)$: $y = f(x) = 2.225x + 124.375$

(b)
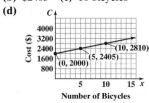
Age

(c) 211 mg/dL **(d)** Each year, a male's total cholesterol increases by 2.225 mg/dL; No

19. $F(x) = 5x - 2$ **21.** $G(x) = -3x + 7$ **23.** $H(x) = -2$ **25.** $f(x) = \dfrac{1}{2}x - 4$
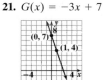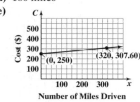

27. $F(x) = -\dfrac{5}{2}x + 5$ **29.** $G(x) = -\dfrac{3}{2}x$ **31.** -5 **33.** 8 **35.** 6 **37.** 9 **39.** nonlinear **41.** linear; positive slope
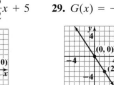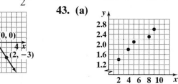

43. (a)
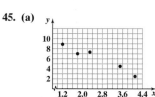
(b) Answers will vary. Using the points $(4, 1.8)$ and $(9, 2.6)$, the equation is $y = 0.16x + 1.16$.

(c)
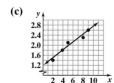

45. (a)

(b) Answers will vary. Using the points $(1.2, 8.4)$ and $(4.1, 2.4)$, the equation is $y = -2.1x + 10.92$.

(c)
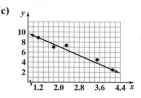

47. (a) 3 **(b)** 2 **(c)** $-2/3$ **(d)** $\{1\}$; $(1, 5)$ **(e)** $\{x|x \leq -1\}$; $(-\infty, -1]$ **(f)**

49. (a) $\{3\}$; -2; $(3, -2)$; $(3, -2)$ **51.** $f(x) = 2x + 2$; $f(-2) = -2$
(b) $\{x|x > 3\}$; $(3, \infty)$
(c)
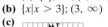

53. $h(x) = -\dfrac{7}{4}x + \dfrac{49}{4}$; $h\left(\dfrac{1}{2}\right) = \dfrac{91}{8}$

55. (a) 3 **(b)** -1 **(c)** 2
(d) $(0, -2)$; $(2, 0)$; x-intercept: 2; y-intercept: -2
(e) $f(x) = x - 2$

57. (a) $\{x|8025 \leq x \leq 32550\}$; $[8025, 32550]$ **(b)** \$2598.75
(c) Independent variable: adjusted gross income; dependent variable: tax bill **(d)**
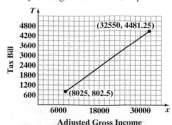
Adjusted Gross Income
(e) \$25,025

59. (a) $\{m|m \geq 0\}$ or $[0, \infty)$
(b) 2; The base fare is $2.00 before any distance is driven.
(c) $9.50.
(d)

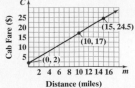

(e) A person can travel 7.5 miles in a cab for $13.25.
(f) A person can ride between 0 miles and 25 miles.

61. (a) The independent variable is age; the dependent variable is insurance cost.
(b) $\{a|15 \leq a \leq 90\}$ or $[15, 90]$
(c) $566.50
(d)

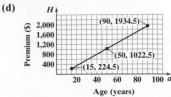

(e) 48 years

63. (a) $B(m) = 0.05m + 5.95$
(b) The independent variable is minutes; the dependent variable is bill.
(c) $\{m|m \geq 0\}$ or $[0, \infty)$ **(d)** $20.95
(e) 240 minutes
(f)

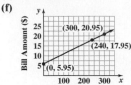

(g) You can talk between 0 minutes and 250 minutes.

65. (a) $V(x) = -900x + 2700$
(b) $\{x|0 \leq x \leq 3\}$ or $[0, 3]$
(c) $1800 **(d)** The V-intercept is 2700 and the x-intercept is 3.
(e) After two years
(f)

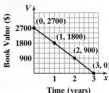

67. (a) $C(x) = 8350x - 2302$
(b) $4127.50
(c) The cost of diamonds increases at a rate of $8350 per carat.
(d) 0.91 carat

71. (a)

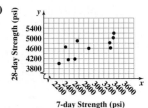

(b) Linear
(c) Answers will vary. Using the points $(2300, 4070)$ and $(3390, 5220)$, the equation is $y = 1.06x + 1632$.

69. (a) $C(x) = 1.086x - 1075.865$
(b) $9503.9 billion
(c) If personal disposable income increases by $1, personal consumption expenditures increase by $1.09.
(d) $9757 billion
(d)

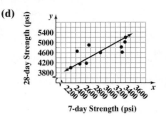

(e) 4812 psi
(f) If the 7-day strength is increased by 1 psi, then the 28-day strength will increase by 1.06 psi.

73. (a) No
(b)

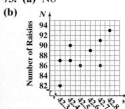

(d)

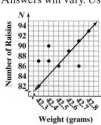

(c) Answers will vary. Using the points $(42.3, 82)$ and $(42.8, 93)$, the equation is $N = 22w - 848.6$.
(e) $N(w) = 22w - 848.6$ **(f)** approximately 86 raisins **(g)** If the weight increases by one gram, then the number of raisins increases by 22 raisins.

75. (a)

(d)

$x = 3$: slope $= 4$; $y = 4x - 5$; $x = 2$: slope $= 2$; $y = 2x - 3$; $x = 1.5$: slope $= 1$; $y = x - 2$; $x = 1.1$: slope $= 0.2$; $y = 0.2x - 1.2$
(e) As x approaches 1, the slope gets closer to 0.

(b) 6 **(c)** $y = 6x - 7$

77. (a)

(b) $y = 0.676x + 2675.562$

79. (a)

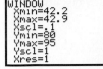 

(b) $y = 11.449x - 399.123$

Section 2.5 Compound Inequalities **1.** intersection **2.** and; or **3.** True **4.** False **5.** $\{1, 3, 5\}$ **6.** $\{2, 4, 6\}$ **7.** $\{1, 2, 3, 4, 5, 6, 7\}$
8. $\{1, 2, 3, 4, 5, 6, 8\}$ **9.** $\varnothing$ or $\{\ \}$ **10.** $\{1, 2, 3, 4, 5, 6, 7, 8\}$ **11.** $\{x|2 < x < 7\}$; $(2, 7)$ [number line]
12. $\{x|x \leq -3 \text{ or } x > 2\}$; $(-\infty, -3] \cup (2, \infty)$ [number line] **13.** $\{x|x \geq 2\}$; $[2, \infty)$ [number line]
14. $\{x|-3 < x < 3\}$; $(-3, 3)$ [number line] **15.** $\{x|1 < x < 3\}$; $(1, 3)$ [number line] **16.** $\{\ \}$ or $\varnothing$
17. $\{1\}$ [number line] **18.** $\{x|-1 < x < 3\}$; $(-1, 3)$ [number line]

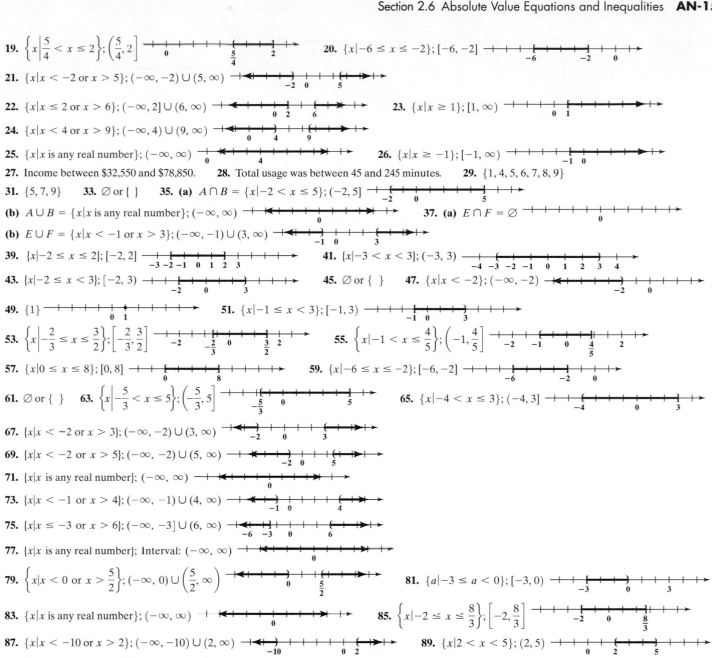

19. $\left\{x \left| \dfrac{5}{4} < x \le 2\right.\right\}; \left(\dfrac{5}{4}, 2\right]$

20. $\{x| -6 \le x \le -2\}; [-6, -2]$

21. $\{x| x < -2 \text{ or } x > 5\}; (-\infty, -2) \cup (5, \infty)$

22. $\{x| x \le 2 \text{ or } x > 6\}; (-\infty, 2] \cup (6, \infty)$

23. $\{x| x \ge 1\}; [1, \infty)$

24. $\{x| x < 4 \text{ or } x > 9\}; (-\infty, 4) \cup (9, \infty)$

25. $\{x| x \text{ is any real number}\}; (-\infty, \infty)$

26. $\{x| x \ge -1\}; [-1, \infty)$

27. Income between \$32,550 and \$78,850.   **28.** Total usage was between 45 and 245 minutes.   **29.** $\{1, 4, 5, 6, 7, 8, 9\}$

31. $\{5, 7, 9\}$ **33.** $\varnothing$ or $\{\ \}$ **35.** (a) $A \cap B = \{x| -2 < x \le 5\}; (-2, 5]$

(b) $A \cup B = \{x| x \text{ is any real number}\}; (-\infty, \infty)$ **37.** (a) $E \cap F = \varnothing$

(b) $E \cup F = \{x| x < -1 \text{ or } x > 3\}; (-\infty, -1) \cup (3, \infty)$

39. $\{x| -2 \le x \le 2\}; [-2, 2]$ **41.** $\{x| -3 < x < 3\}; (-3, 3)$

43. $\{x| -2 \le x < 3\}; [-2, 3)$ **45.** $\varnothing$ or $\{\ \}$ **47.** $\{x| x < -2\}; (-\infty, -2)$

49. $\{1\}$ **51.** $\{x| -1 \le x < 3\}; [-1, 3)$

53. $\left\{x \left| -\dfrac{2}{3} \le x \le \dfrac{3}{2}\right.\right\}; \left[-\dfrac{2}{3}, \dfrac{3}{2}\right]$ **55.** $\left\{x \left| -1 < x \le \dfrac{4}{5}\right.\right\}; \left(-1, \dfrac{4}{5}\right]$

57. $\{x| 0 \le x \le 8\}; [0, 8]$ **59.** $\{x| -6 \le x \le -2\}; [-6, -2]$

61. $\varnothing$ or $\{\ \}$ **63.** $\left\{x \left| -\dfrac{5}{3} < x \le 5\right.\right\}; \left(-\dfrac{5}{3}, 5\right]$ **65.** $\{x| -4 < x \le 3\}; (-4, 3]$

67. $\{x| x < -2 \text{ or } x > 3\}; (-\infty, -2) \cup (3, \infty)$

69. $\{x| x < -2 \text{ or } x > 5\}; (-\infty, -2) \cup (5, \infty)$

71. $\{x| x \text{ is any real number}\}; (-\infty, \infty)$

73. $\{x| x < -1 \text{ or } x > 4\}; (-\infty, -1) \cup (4, \infty)$

75. $\{x| x \le -3 \text{ or } x > 6\}; (-\infty, -3] \cup (6, \infty)$

77. $\{x| x \text{ is any real number}\};$ Interval: $(-\infty, \infty)$

79. $\left\{x \left| x < 0 \text{ or } x > \dfrac{5}{2}\right.\right\}; (-\infty, 0) \cup \left(\dfrac{5}{2}, \infty\right)$ **81.** $\{a| -3 \le a < 0\}; [-3, 0)$

83. $\{x| x \text{ is any real number}\}; (-\infty, \infty)$ **85.** $\left\{x \left| -2 \le x \le \dfrac{8}{3}\right.\right\}; \left[-2, \dfrac{8}{3}\right]$

87. $\{x| x < -10 \text{ or } x > 2\}; (-\infty, -10) \cup (2, \infty)$ **89.** $\{x| 2 < x < 5\}; (2, 5)$

91. $\left\{x \left| x \le -3 \text{ or } x > \dfrac{15}{4}\right.\right\}; (-\infty, -3] \cup \left(\dfrac{15}{4}, \infty\right)$

93. $\left\{x \left| -5 < x \le \dfrac{1}{2}\right.\right\}; \left(-5, \dfrac{1}{2}\right]$ **95.** $a = 1$ and $b = 8$ **97.** $a = 12$ and $b = 30$ **99.** $a = -1$ and $b = 23$

101. $90 < x < 140$ **103.** Joanna needs to score at least a 77 on the final. That is, $77 \le x \le 100$ (assuming 100 is the max score, otherwise $77 \le x \le 104$).
105. The amount withheld ranges between \$95.65 and \$120.65, inclusive.   **107.** The gas usage ranged from 150 to 165 therms.
109. Step 1:   **Step 2:**   **Step 3:**

$$a < b \qquad a < b$$
$$a + a < a + b \qquad a + b < b + b \qquad \text{Since } a < \dfrac{a+b}{2} \text{ and } \dfrac{a+b}{2} < b, \text{ it follows that } a < \dfrac{a+b}{2} < b.$$
$$2a < a + b \qquad a + b < 2b$$
$$\dfrac{2a}{2} < \dfrac{a+b}{2} \qquad \dfrac{a+b}{2} < \dfrac{2b}{2}$$
$$a < \dfrac{a+b}{2} \qquad \dfrac{a+b}{2} < b$$

111. $\{\ \}$ or $\varnothing$ **113.** This is a contradiction. There is no solution. If, during simplification, the variable terms all cancel out and a contradiction results, then there is no solution to the inequality.   **115.** If $x < 2$ then $x - 2 < 2 - 2 \Rightarrow x - 2 < 0$. When multiplying both sides of the inequality by $x - 2$ in the second step, the direction of the inequality must switch.

Section 2.6 Absolute Value Equations and Inequalities

1. $\{-7, 7\}$ **2.** $\{-1, 1\}$ **3.** $a; -a$ **4.** $\{-2, 5\}$ **5.** $\left\{-\dfrac{5}{3}, 3\right\}$ **6.** $\left\{-1, \dfrac{9}{5}\right\}$

7. $\{-5, 1\}$ **8.** True   **9.** $\{\ \}$ or $\varnothing$ **10.** $\{\ \}$ or $\varnothing$ **11.** $\{-1\}$ **12.** $\left\{-8, -\dfrac{2}{3}\right\}$ **13.** $\{-2, 3\}$ **14.** $\{-3, 0\}$ **15.** $\{2\}$

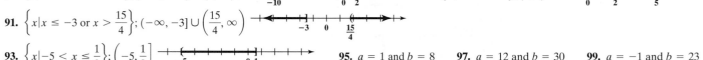

16. $-a < u < a$ **17.** $<$ **18.** $\{x|-5 \le x \le 5\}; [-5, 5]$

19. $\left\{x\left|-\dfrac{3}{2} < x < \dfrac{3}{2}\right\}; \left(-\dfrac{3}{2}, \dfrac{3}{2}\right)\right.$ **20.** $\{x|-8 < x < 2\}; (-8, 2)$

21. $\{x|-2 \le x \le 5\}; [-2, 5]$ **22.** $\{\ \}$ or $\varnothing$

23. $\{x|-2 < x < 2\}; (-2, 2)$ **24.** $\{x|-1 \le x \le 7\}; [-1, 7]$

25. $\{x|-2 \le x \le 1\}; [-2, 1]$ **26.** $\left\{x\left|-\dfrac{7}{3} < x < 3\right\}; \left(-\dfrac{7}{3}, 3\right)\right.$

27. $u < -a; u > a$ **28.** False **29.** $\{x|x \le -6 \text{ or } x \ge 6\}; (-\infty, -6] \cup [6, \infty)$

30. $\left\{x\left|x < -\dfrac{5}{2} \text{ or } x > \dfrac{5}{2}\right\}; \left(-\infty, -\dfrac{5}{2}\right) \cup \left(\dfrac{5}{2}, \infty\right)\right.$

31. $\{x|x < -7 \text{ or } x > 1\}; (-\infty, -7) \cup (1, \infty)$

32. $\left\{x\left|x \le -\dfrac{1}{2} \text{ or } x \ge 2\right\}; \left(-\infty, -\dfrac{1}{2}\right] \cup [2, \infty)\right.$

33. $\left\{x\left|x < -\dfrac{5}{3} \text{ or } x > 3\right\}; \left(-\infty, -\dfrac{5}{3}\right) \cup (3, \infty)\right.$

34. $\left\{x\left|x \ne -\dfrac{5}{2}\right\}; \left(-\infty, -\dfrac{5}{2}\right) \cup \left(-\dfrac{5}{2}, \infty\right)\right.$

35. $\{x|x \text{ is any real number}\}; (-\infty, \infty)$

36. $\{x|x \text{ is any real number}\}; (-\infty, \infty)$ **37.** The acceptable belt width is between 127/32 inches and 129/32 inches.

38. The percentage of Americans that stated they have been shot at is between 7.3% and 10.7%, inclusive. **39.** $\{-10, 10\}$ **41.** $\{-1, 7\}$

43. $\left\{-1, \dfrac{13}{3}\right\}$ **45.** $\{-5, 5\}$ **47.** $\left\{-\dfrac{11}{2}, \dfrac{5}{2}\right\}$ **49.** $\{-4, 10\}$ **51.** $\{0\}$ **53.** $\left\{-\dfrac{7}{3}, 3\right\}$ **55.** $\left\{-7, \dfrac{3}{5}\right\}$ **57.** $\{1, 3\}$ **59.** $\{2\}$

61. $\{x|-9 < x < 9\}; (-9, 9)$ **63.** $\{x|-3 \le x \le 11\}; [-3, 11]$

65. $\left\{x\left|-3 < x < \dfrac{7}{3}\right\}; \left(-3, \dfrac{7}{3}\right)\right.$ **67.** $\varnothing$ or $\{\ \}$ **69.** $\{x|0 < x < 6\}; (0, 6)$

71. $\left\{x\left|-1 < x < \dfrac{9}{5}\right\}; \left(-1, \dfrac{9}{5}\right)\right.$ **73.** $\{x|1.995 < x < 2.005\}; (1.995, 2.005)$

75. $\{y|y < 3 \text{ or } y > 7\}; (-\infty, 3) \cup (7, \infty)$

77. $\left\{x\left|x \le -2 \text{ or } x \ge \dfrac{1}{2}\right\}; (-\infty, -2] \cup \left[\dfrac{1}{2}, \infty\right)\right.$

79. $\{y|y \text{ is any real number}\}; (-\infty, \infty)$

81. $\left\{x\left|x < -2 \text{ or } x > \dfrac{4}{5}\right\}; (-\infty, -2) \cup \left(\dfrac{4}{5}, \infty\right)\right.$

83. $\{x|x < 0 \text{ or } x > 1\}; (-\infty, 0) \cup (1, \infty)$

85. $\{x|x \le -2 \text{ or } x \ge 3\}; (-\infty, -2] \cup [3, \infty)$ **87.** (a) $\{-5, 5\}$ (b) $\{x|-5 \le x \le 5\}; [-5, 5]$

(c) $\{x|x < -5 \text{ or } x > 5\}; (-\infty, -5) \cup (5, \infty)$ **89.** (a) $\{-5, 1\}$ (b) $\{x|-5 < x < 1\}; (-5, 1)$ (c) $\{x|x \le -5 \text{ or } x \ge 1\}; (-\infty, -5] \cup [1, \infty)$

91. $\{x|x < -5 \text{ or } x > 5\}; (-\infty, -5) \cup (5, \infty)$ **93.** $\{-4, -1\}$ **95.** $\{-5, 5\}$

97. $\left\{x\left|-2 \le x \le \dfrac{6}{5}\right\}; \left[-2, \dfrac{6}{5}\right]\right.$ **99.** $\varnothing$ or $\{\ \}$

101. $\left\{x\left|x \le -\dfrac{7}{3} \text{ or } x \ge 1\right\}; \left(-\infty, -\dfrac{7}{3}\right] \cup [1, \infty)\right.$

103. $\left\{x\left|x < 0 \text{ or } x > \dfrac{4}{3}\right\}; (-\infty, 0) \cup \left(\dfrac{4}{3}, \infty\right)\right.$ **105.** $\{-1, 1\}$ **107.** $\varnothing$ or $\{\ \}$ **109.** $\left\{-8, \dfrac{4}{7}\right\}$

111. $|5 - x| < 3$ $\{x|2 < x < 8\}; (2, 8)$ **113.** $|2x - (-6)| > 3$ $\left\{x\left|x < -\dfrac{9}{2} \text{ or } x > -\dfrac{3}{2}\right\}; \left(-\infty, -\dfrac{9}{2}\right) \cup \left(-\dfrac{3}{2}, \infty\right)\right.$

115. The acceptable rod lengths are between 5.6995 inches and 5.7005 inches, inclusive. **117.** An unusual IQ score would be less than 70.6 or greater than 129.4. **119.** $\left\{-\dfrac{5}{2}\right\}$ **121.** {2} **123.** $\varnothing$ or { } **125.** $\{x \mid x \le -5\}; (-\infty, -5]$ **127.** The absolute value, when isolated, is equal to a negative number which is not possible. **129.** The absolute value, when isolated, is less than -3. Since absolute values are always nonnegative, this is not possible.

Section 2.7 Variation **1.** Variation **2.** $y = kx$

3. (a) $C(g) = 4.2g$
(b) $19.32
(c)

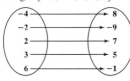

4. $y = \dfrac{k}{x}$ **5. (a)** $V(l) = \dfrac{15{,}000}{l}$ **(b)** 300 oscillations per second **6.** combined variation **7.** 1750 joules

8. 1.44 ohms **9. (a)** $k = 6$ **(b)** $y = 6x$ **(c)** $y = 42$ **11. (a)** $k = \dfrac{3}{7}$ **(b)** $y = \dfrac{3}{7}x$ **(c)** $y = 12$

13. (a) $k = \dfrac{1}{2}$ **(b)** $y = \dfrac{1}{2}x$ **(c)** $y = 15$ **15. (a)** $k = 20$ **(b)** $y = \dfrac{20}{x}$ **(c)** $y = 4$ **17. (a)** $k = 21$

(b) $y = \dfrac{21}{x}$ **(c)** $y = \dfrac{3}{4}$ **19. (a)** $k = \dfrac{1}{4}$ **(b)** $y = \dfrac{1}{4}xz$ **(c)** $y = 27$ **21. (a)** $k = \dfrac{13}{10}$ **(b)** $Q = \dfrac{13x}{10y}$

(c) $Q = \dfrac{117}{40}$

23. (a) $p(b) = 0.0058358b.$
(b) $817.01
(c)

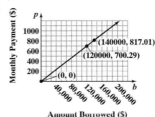

25. (a) $C(w) = 5.6w$
(b) $19.60
(c)

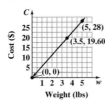

27. 96 feet per second **29. (a)** $D(p) = \dfrac{375}{p}$ **(b)** 125 bags of candy

31. 450 cc **33.** 119.8 pounds

35. 2250 newtons

37. 1.4007×10^{-7} newtons **39.** 360 pounds **41. (a)** 314.16
(b) approximately 942.48 meters per minute; approximately 15.708 meters per second **(c)** $k \approx 0.056$ **(d)** approximately 7.86 newtons

Chapter 2 Review **1.** {(Cent, 2.500), (Nickel, 5.000), (Dime, 2.268), (Quarter, 5.670), (Half Dollar, 11.340), (Dollar, 8.100)}
Domain: {Cent, Nickel, Dime, Quarter, Half Dollar, Dollar}; Range: {2.268, 2.500, 5.000, 5.670, 8.100, 11.340} **2.** {(70, $6.99), (90, $9.99), (120, $9.99),
(128, $12.99), (446, $49.99)}; Domain: {70, 90, 120, 128, 446}; Range: {$6.99, $9.99, $12.99, $49.99}

3. Domain: $\{-4, -2, 2, 3, 6\}$
Range: $\{-9, -1, 5, 7, 8\}$

4. Domain: $\{-2, 1, 3, 5\}$
Range: $\{1, 4, 7, 8\}$

5. Domain: $\{x \mid x$ is a real number$\}$ or $(-\infty, \infty)$
Range: $\{y \mid y$ is a real number$\}$ or $(-\infty, \infty)$
6. Domain: $\{x \mid -6 \le x \le 4\}$ or $[-6, 4]$
Range: $\{y \mid -4 \le y \le 6\}$ or $[-4, 6]$
7. Domain: $\{2\}$; Range: $\{y \mid y$ is a real number$\}$ or $(-\infty, \infty)$
8. Domain: $\{x \mid x \ge -1\}$ or $[-1, \infty)$; Range: $\{y \mid y \ge -2\}$ or $[-2, \infty)$

9. $y = x + 2$
Domain: $\{x \mid x$ is a real number$\}$ or $(-\infty, \infty)$
Range: $\{y \mid y$ is a real number$\}$ or $(-\infty, \infty)$

10. $2x + y = 3$
Domain: $\{x \mid x$ is a real number$\}$ or $(-\infty, \infty)$
Range: $\{y \mid y$ is a real number$\}$ or $(-\infty, \infty)$

11. $y = -x^2 + 4$
Domain: $\{x \mid x$ is a real number$\}$ or
$(-\infty, \infty)$; Range: $\{y \mid y \le 4\}$ or $(-\infty, 4]$

12. $y = |x + 2| - 1$
Domain: $\{x \mid x$ is a real number$\}$ or $(-\infty, \infty)$
Range: $\{y \mid y \ge -1\}$ or $[-1, \infty)$

13. $y = x^3 + 2$
Domain: $\{x \mid x$ is a real number$\}$ or $(-\infty, \infty)$
Range: $\{y \mid y$ is a real number$\}$ or $(-\infty, \infty)$

14. $x = y^2 + 1$
Domain: $\{x \mid x \ge 1\}$ or $[1, \infty)$
Range: $\{y \mid y$ is a real number$\}$ or $(-\infty, \infty)$

15. (a) Domain: $\{x \mid 0 \le x \le 44.64\}$ or $[0, 44.64]$; Range: $\{y \mid 40 \le y \le 2122\}$ or $[40, 2122]$ **(b)** Answers may vary. **16.** Domain: $\{t \mid 0 < t \le 4\}$ or $[0, 4]$;
Range: $\{y \mid 0 \le y \le 121\}$ or $[0, 121]$ **17. (a)** Not a function. Domain: $\{-1, 5, 7, 9\}$; Range: $\{-2, 0, 2, 3, 4\}$ **(b)** Function.
Domain: {Camel, Macaw, Deer, Fox, Tiger, Crocodile}; Range: {14, 22, 35, 45, 50} **18. (a)** Function; Domain: $\{-3, -2, 2, 4, 5\}$; Range: $\{-1, 3, 4, 7\}$
(b) Not a function; Domain: {Red, Blue, Green, Black}; Range: {Camry, Taurus, Windstar, Durango} **19.** Function **20.** Not a function
21. Not a function **22.** Function **23.** Not a function **24.** Function **25.** Function **26.** Not a function **27. (a)** $f(-2) = -5$ **(b)** $f(3) = 10$

28. (a) $g(0) = -\dfrac{1}{3}$ **(b)** $g(2) = -5$ **29. (a)** $F(5) = -3$ **(b)** $F(-x) = 2x + 7$ **30. (a)** $G(7) = 15$ **(b)** $G(x + h) = 2x + 2h + 1$

31. (a) The dependent variable is the population, P, and the independent variable is the number of years after 1900, t. **(b)** $P(110) = 1142.532$; The population of Orange County will be roughly 1,142,532 in 2010. **(c)** $P(-70) = 2934.252$; The population of Orange County was roughly 2,934,252 in 1830. This is not reasonable. (The population of the entire Florida territory was roughly 35,000 in 1830.) **32. (a)** The dependent variable is percent of the population with an advanced degree, P, and the independent variable is age, a. **(b)** $P(30) = 7.9$; According to the model, 7.9% of 30-year-olds have an advanced degree. **33.** $\{x | x \text{ is a real number}\}$ or $(-\infty, \infty)$ **34.** $\left\{ w | w \neq -\dfrac{5}{2} \right\}$ **35.** $\{t | t \neq 5\}$ **36.** $\{t | t \text{ is a real number}\}$ or $(-\infty, \infty)$

37. $f(x) = 2x - 5$ **38.** $g(x) = x^2 - 3x + 2$ **39.** $h(x) = (x - 1)^3 - 3$ **40.** $f(x) = |x + 1| - 4$

  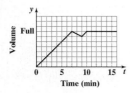

41. (a) Domain: $\{x | x \text{ is a real number}\}$ or $(-\infty, \infty)$; Range: $\{y | y \text{ is a real number}\}$ or $(-\infty, \infty)$ **(b)** $(0, 2)$ and $(4, 0)$
42. (a) Domain: $\{x | x \text{ is a real number}\}$ or $(-\infty, \infty)$; Range: $\{y | y \geq -3\}$ or $[-3, \infty)$ **(b)** $(-2, 0), (2, 0), (0, -3)$

43. (a) Domain: $\{x | x \text{ is a real number}\}$ or $(-\infty, \infty)$; Range: $\{y | y \text{ is a real number}\}$ or $(-\infty, \infty)$ **(b)** $(0, 0)$ and $(2, 0)$
44. (a) Domain: $\{x | x \geq -3\}$ or $[-3, \infty)$; Range: $\{y | y \geq 1\}$ or $[1, \infty)$ **(b)** $(0, 3)$ **45. (a)** 4 **(b)** 1 **(c)** -1 and 3

46. (a) **(b)**

47. (a) yes
(b) $h(-2) = -11; (-2, -11)$
(c) $x = \dfrac{11}{2}; \left(\dfrac{11}{2}, 4 \right)$

48. (a) no
(b) $g(3) = \dfrac{29}{5}; \left(3, \dfrac{29}{5} \right)$
(c) $x = -10; (-10, -2)$

49.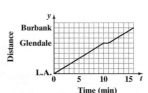

50.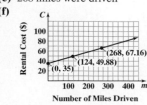

51. Zero: 3

52. Zero: $\dfrac{15}{4}$

53. Zero: -3

54. Zero: 4

55. (a) $\{x | x \geq 0\}$ or $[0, \infty)$
(b) \$21.45
(c)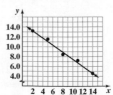
(d) 1000 minutes

56. (a) The independent variable is years; the dependent variable is value.
(b) $\{x | 0 \leq x \leq 5\}$ or $[0, 5]$
(c) \$1800 **(d)** \$1080
(e)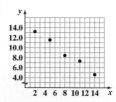
(f) After 5 years

57. (a) $E(x) = 1.94x + 12.6$ **(b)** 35.88% **(c)** Electronically filed tax returns are increasing at a rate of 1.94% per year. **(d)** 2014
58. (a) $H(x) = -x + 220$ **(b)** 175 beats per minute
(c) The maximum recommended heart rate for men under stress decreases at a rate of 1 beat per minute per year. **(d)** 52 years

59. (a) $C(m) = 0.12m + 35$
(b) The independent variable is m; the dependent variable is C.
(c) $\{m | m \geq 0\}$ or $[0, \infty)$
(d) \$49.88
(e) 268 miles were driven
(f)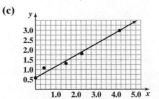

60. (a) $B(x) = 3.50x + 33.99$
(b) The independent variable is x; the dependent variable is B.
(c) $\{x | x \geq 0\}$ or $[0, \infty)$
(d) \$51.49
(e) 7 pay-per-view movies
(f)

61. (a)

(b) Answers will vary. Using the points $(2, 13.3)$ and $(14, 4.6)$, the equation is $y = -0.725x + 14.75$.
(c)

62. (a)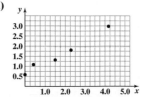

(b) Answers will vary. Using the points $(0, 0.6)$ and $(4.2, 3.0)$, the equation is $y = \dfrac{4}{7}x + 0.6$.
(c)

63. (a)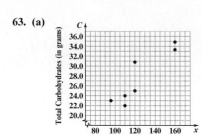

(b) Approximately linear.
(c) Answers will vary. Using the points $(96, 23.2)$ and $(160, 33.3)$, the equation is $y = 0.158x + 8.032$.

(d)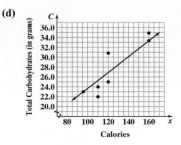

(e) 30.2 grams
(f) In a one-cup serving of cereal, total carbohydrates will increase by 0.158 grams for each one-calorie increase.

64. (a)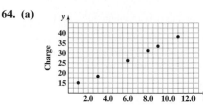

(b) Linear with positive slope
(c) Answers will vary. Using $(3, 18.60)$ and $(9, 33.42)$, $y = 2.47x + 11.19$

(d)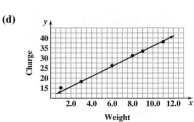

(e) $23.54
(f) If the weight increases by 1 pound, the shipping charge increases $2.47.

65. $\{-1, 0, 1, 2, 3, 4, 6, 8\}$ **66.** $\{2, 4\}$ **67.** $\{1, 2, 3, 4\}$ **68.** $\{1, 2, 3, 4, 6, 8\}$ **69. (a)** $\{x | 2 < x \le 4\}; (2, 4]$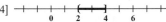

(b) $\{x | x$ is any real number$\}; (-\infty, \infty)$

70. (a) $\{\ \}$ or $\varnothing$ **(b)** $\{x | x < -2$ or $x > 3\}; (-\infty, -2) \cup [3, \infty)$

71. $\{x | -1 < x < 4\}; (-1, 4)$ Graph:

72. $\{x | -5 < x < -1\}; (-5, -1)$ Graph:

73. $\{x | x < -2$ or $x > 2\}; (-\infty, -2) \cup (2, \infty)$ Graph:

74. $\{x | x \le 0$ or $x \ge 4\}; (-\infty, 0] \cup [4, \infty)$ Graph:

75. $\{\ \}$ or $\varnothing$ **76.** $\{x | -2 \le x < 4\}; [-2, 4)$ Graph:

77. $\{x | x \le -2$ or $x > 3\}; (-\infty, -2] \cup (3, \infty)$ Graph:

78. $\{x | x$ is any real number$\}; (-\infty, \infty)$ Graph:

79. $\{x | x < -10$ or $x > 6\}; (-\infty, -10) \cup (6, \infty)$ Graph:

80. $\left\{x \left| -\dfrac{3}{2} \le x < \dfrac{5}{8}\right.\right\}; \left[-\dfrac{3}{2}, \dfrac{5}{8}\right)$ Graph: **81.** $70 \le x \le 75$

82. The electric usage varied from roughly 756.7 kilowatt hours up to roughly 1953.1 kilowatt hours. (recall, x is the number *above* 300).   **83.** $\{-4, 4\}$

84. $\left\{\dfrac{1}{3}, 3\right\}$ **85.** $\{-5, 13\}$ **86.** $\{-3, -1\}$ **87.** $\{\ \}$ or $\varnothing$ **88.** $\left\{-\dfrac{1}{2}, 2\right\}$ **89.** $\{x | -2 < x < 2\}; (-2, 2)$

90. $\left\{x \left| x \le -\dfrac{7}{2}\right.$ or $x \ge \dfrac{7}{2}\right\}; \left(-\infty, -\dfrac{7}{2}\right] \cup \left[\dfrac{7}{2}, \infty\right)$

91. $\{x | -5 \le x \le 1\}; [-5, 1]$ **92.** $\left\{x \left| x \le \dfrac{1}{2}\right.$ or $x \ge 1\right\}; \left(-\infty, \dfrac{1}{2}\right] \cup [1, \infty)$

93. $\{x | x$ is a real number$\}; (-\infty, \infty)$ **94.** $\{\ \}$ or $\varnothing$

95. $\{x | 4.99 \le x \le 5.01\}; [4.99, 5.01]$

96. $\left\{x \left| x < -\dfrac{1}{2}\right.$ or $x > \dfrac{7}{2}\right\}; \left(-\infty, -\dfrac{1}{2}\right) \cup \left(\dfrac{7}{2}, \infty\right)$

97. The acceptable diameters of the bearing are between 0.502 inch and 0.504 inch, inclusive.   **98.** Tensile strengths below 36.08 lb/in.^{2} or above 43.92 lb/in.^{2} would be considered unusual.   **99. (a)** $k = 5$ **(b)** $y = 5x$ **(c)** 50   **100. (a)** $k = -6$ **(b)** $y = -6x$ **(c)** -48 **101. (a)** $k = 60$

(b) $y = \dfrac{60}{x}$ **(c)** 12   **102. (a)** $k = \dfrac{3}{4}$ **(b)** $y = \dfrac{3}{4}xz$ **(c)** 42   **103. (a)** $k = 72$ **(b)** $s = \dfrac{72}{t^2}$ **(c)** 8   **104. (a)** $k = \dfrac{8}{5}$ **(b)** $w = \dfrac{8x}{5z}$ **(c)** $\dfrac{9}{10}$

105. 6 inches   **106.** $352.19   **107.** 1200 kilohertz   **108.** 12 ohms   **109.** 704 cubic cm   **110.** 375 cubic inches

Chapter 2 Test

1. Domain: $\{-4, 2, 5, 7\}$
Range: $\{-7, -2, -1, 3, 8, 12\}$

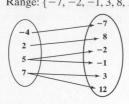

2. Domain: $\left\{x \mid -\dfrac{5\pi}{2} \le x \le \dfrac{5\pi}{2}\right\}$ or $\left[-\dfrac{5\pi}{2}, \dfrac{5\pi}{2}\right]$
Range: $\{y \mid 1 \le y \le 5\}$ or $[1, 5]$

3. $y = x^2 - 3$ Domain: $\{x \mid x \text{ is a real number}\}$ or $(-\infty, \infty)$; Range: $\{y \mid y \ge -3\}$ or $[-3, \infty)$

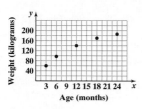

4. Function. Domain: $\{-5, -3, 0, 2\}$; Range: $\{3, 7\}$ **5.** Not a function. Domain: $\{x \mid x \le 3\}$ or $(-\infty, 3]$; Range: $\{y \mid y \text{ is a real number}\}$ or $(-\infty, \infty)$
6. No **7.** $f(x + h) = -3x - 3h + 11$ **8. (a)** $g(-2) = 5$ **(b)** $g(0) = -1$ **(c)** $g(3) = 20$

9. $f(x) = x^2 + 3$

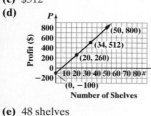

10. (a) The dependent variable is the ticket price, P, and the independent variable is the number of years after $1989, x$.
(b) $P(20) = 6.83$; According to the model, the average ticket price in 2009 $(x = 20)$ was \$6.83. **(c)** 2014

11. $\{x \mid x \ne -2\}$ **12. (a)** yes **(b)** $h(3) = -3; (3, -3)$ **(c)** $x = -3; (-3, 27)$ **(d)** $\dfrac{12}{5}$

13. (a) The car stops accelerating when the speed stops increasing. Thus, the car stops accelerating after 6 seconds.
(b) The car has a constant speed when the graph is horizontal. Thus, the car maintains a constant speed for 18 seconds.

14. (a) $P(x) = 18x - 100$
(b) $\{x \mid x \ge 0\}$ or $[0, \infty)$
(c) \$512
(d)

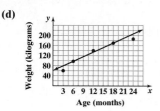

(e) 48 shelves

15. (a)

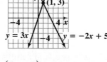

(b) Approximately linear.
(c) Answers will vary. Using the points $(6, 95)$ and $(18, 170)$, the equation is $y = 6.25x + 57.5$.

(d)

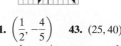

(e) 113.75 kilograms
(f) A Shetland pony's weight will increase by 6.25 kilograms for each one-month increase in age.

16. $\{-4, -1\}$ **17.** $\{x \mid -2 \le x < 6\}; [-2, 6)$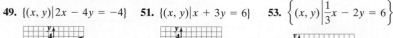

18. $\left\{x \mid x < -\dfrac{3}{2} \text{ or } x > 4\right\}; \left(-\infty, -\dfrac{3}{2}\right) \cup (4, \infty)$ **19.** $\{x \mid 2 < x < 8\}; (2, 8)$

20. $\{x \mid x \le -2 \text{ or } x \ge 3\}; (-\infty, -2] \cup [3, \infty)$ **21.** 20 pounds **22.** 792 cm^2

Chapter 3 Systems of Linear Equations and Inequalities

Section 3.1 Systems of Linear Equations in Two Variables
1. system of linear equations **2. (a)** no **(b)** yes **(c)** no **3.** inconsistent
4. consistent; dependent **5.** False **6.** True **7.** $(3, 1)$ **8.** $(-2, 3)$ **9.** $(-4, 7)$ **10.** $(-6, 10)$ **11.** $\left(\dfrac{1}{2}, \dfrac{7}{3}\right)$ **12.** $(-5, -6)$
13. $(3, 6)$ **14.** $\varnothing$ or $\{\ \}$; inconsistent **15.** $\{(x, y) \mid -3x + 2y = 8\}$ **16.** $(-5, 2)$ **17. (a)** no **(b)** yes **25.** $(1, 3)$
19. (a) yes **(b)** yes
21. consistent; independent
23. inconsistent

27. $(3, -4)$ **29.** $(6, -2)$ **31.** $(-2, -3)$ **33.** $\left(\dfrac{1}{2}, -\dfrac{1}{4}\right)$ **35.** $(2500, 7500)$ **37.** $(-8, 3)$ **39.** $(11, -8)$ **41.** $\left(\dfrac{1}{2}, -\dfrac{4}{5}\right)$ **43.** $(25, 40)$

45. $\varnothing$ or $\{\ \}$ **47.** $\varnothing$ or $\{\ \}$ **49.** $\{(x, y) \mid 2x - 4y = -4\}$ **51.** $\{(x, y) \mid x + 3y = 6\}$ **53.** $\left\{(x, y) \mid \dfrac{1}{3}x - 2y = 6\right\}$

55. $(-9, 3)$ **57.** $\{(x, y) \mid x = 5y - 3\}$ **59.** $\left(\dfrac{39}{11}, -\dfrac{30}{11}\right)$ **61.** $\varnothing$ or $\{\ \}$ **63.** $y = -2x - 5; y = -\dfrac{5}{3}x + \dfrac{1}{3}$; exactly one solution
65. $y = \dfrac{3}{2}x + 1; y = \dfrac{3}{2}x + 1$; infinite number of solutions **67. (a)** $y = -\dfrac{1}{2}x + \dfrac{5}{2}; y = x + 1$ **(b)** $(1, 2)$ **69. (c)** and (f) **71.** $A = \dfrac{7}{6}$ and $B = -\dfrac{1}{2}$

73. Answers will vary. One possibility follows: $\begin{cases} x + y = 3 \\ x - y = -5 \end{cases}$

75. $(1, 2)$ 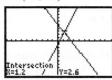   **77.** $(6, -1)$ 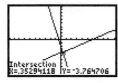   **79.** Yes, Typically, we use substitution when one of the equations is solved for one of the variables or if the coefficient on one of the variables is one (which makes it easy to solve for that variable). Otherwise, we use elimination.   **81.** $(3, -2)$

83. $(1.2, 2.6)$
85. $(4, 13)$
87. $\{(x, y) | 4x - 3y = 1\}$

89. approximately $(0.35, -3.76)$

Section 3.2 Problem Solving: Systems of Two Linear Equations Containing Two Unknowns
1. 15 and -7 **2.** Cheeseburger: $1.60: shake: $1.85   **3.** Width: 60 yards: length: 120 yards   **4.** $x = 15, y = 30$ **5.** $96,000 in Aaa-rated bonds: $24,000 in B-rated bonds.
6. 10 pounds of cashews; 20 pounds of peanuts   **7.** Airspeed: 350 mph; wind resistance: 50 mph

8. (a) $R(x) = 230x$ **(b)** $C(x) = 160x + 2100$ **9.** 8 and 10   **11.** The first number is 12 and the second number is 23.   **13.** $60; $35
(c)

(d) 30 trees; $6900

15. 40 meters by 20 meters   **17.** $x = 4$ and $y = 14$ **19.** Invest $22,500 in stocks and $13,500 in bonds.   **21.** 60 pounds of Arabica beans and 40 pounds of African Robusta beans   **23.** Jonathon and Samantha can row 8 miles per hour in still water.   **25.** The Lincoln traveled 400 miles and the Infiniti traveled 500 miles. The time for both trips was 10 hours.

27. (a)
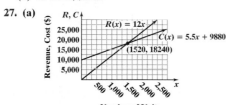

(b) $(1520, 18240)$

29. 15 cm, 15 cm, and 5 cm   **31.** $250,000   **33.** 12 and 19   **35.** Kevin can run 10 feet per second in the sand on level ground.   **37.** $x - 4$ and $y = 8$ **39.** Mix 50 mg of Liquid A with 60 mg of Liquid B.   **41.** A McDonald's hamburger has 280 calories and a medium Coke has 210 calories   **43.** Mix 60 g of the 10% alloy with 40 g of the 25% alloy

45. (a)
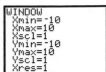

(h) $3; 7000 hot dogs

47. (a)
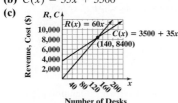

(b) approximately 2020; approximately 34%

49. (a) Let m represent the number of minutes, let A represent the cost of plan A, and let B represent the cost of plan B.
$$\begin{cases} A(m) = 0.05m + 8.95 \\ B(m) = 0.07m + 5.95 \end{cases}$$

(b)
(graph)

(c) 150 minutes; $16.45

51. (a) $R(x) = 60x$
(b) $C(x) = 35x + 3500$
(c)
(graph)

(d) 140 desks: The cost and revenue will both be $8400.

53. (a) and **(b)** Let x represent the number of years since 1968.
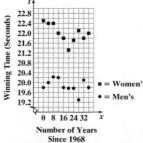

(c) Answers may vary. Using the points $(4, 20.00)$ and $(36, 19.79)$, the equation is $y = -0.0065625x + 20.02625$. See graph in part **(d)**.

(d) Answers may vary. Using the points $(0, 22.50)$ and $(32, 21.84)$, the equation is $y = -0.020625x + 22.50$.

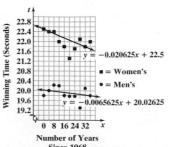

(e) In the year 2144: approximately 18.87 seconds.
(f) Answers will vary.

Section 3.3 Systems of Linear Equations in Three Variables

1. inconsistent; consistent; dependent **2.** solution **3.** False **4.** True

5. (a) no **(b)** yes **6.** $(-3, 1, -1)$ **7.** $\left(-\dfrac{5}{2}, \dfrac{5}{4}, \dfrac{1}{2}\right)$ **8.** $\varnothing$ or { }; the system is inconsistent **9.** $\{(x, y, z)|\, x = -z + 1, y = 2z - 1,\ z \text{ is any}$

real number} **10.** The company can manufacture fourteen 21-inch, eleven 24-inch, and 5 rider lawn mowers. **11. (a)** no **(b)** yes

13. $(3, -2, 4)$ **15.** $(3, -4, -2)$ **17.** $\left(\dfrac{1}{3}, -\dfrac{2}{3}, 2\right)$ **19.** $(3, -3, 1)$ **21.** $\varnothing$ or { } **23.** $\{(x, y, z)|\, x = 3z - 10, y = -4z + 14,\ z \text{ is any real number}\}$

25. $\{(x, y, z)|\, x = -3z + 5, y = -6z + 11,\ z \text{ is any real number}\}$ **27.** $\left(0, 2, \dfrac{3}{2}\right)$ **29.** $\varnothing$ or { } **31.** $(-5, 0, 3)$ **33.** $\left(-\dfrac{7}{2}, -\dfrac{7}{2}, \dfrac{3}{2}\right)$

35. $\{(x, y, z)|\, x = 5z - 5, y = -2z + 3,\ z \text{ is any real number}\}$ **37.** $\left(\dfrac{11}{2}, 0, -\dfrac{1}{2}\right)$ **39.** $\left\{(x, y, z)|\,x = \dfrac{1}{3}z + \dfrac{2}{3}, y = -\dfrac{4}{3}z + \dfrac{7}{3},\ z \text{ is any real number}\right\}$

41. Answers will vary. One possibility follows. $\begin{cases} x + y + z = 4 \\ x - y + z = 6 \\ x + y - z = -2 \end{cases}$ **43. (a)** $a - b + c = -6;\ 4a + 2b + c = 3$ **(b)** $a = -2, b = 5, c = 1;$ $f(x) = -2x^2 + 5x + 1$ **45.** $i_1 = 1, i_2 = 4,$ and $i_3 = 3$ **47.** There are 1490 box seats, 970 reserved seats, and 1640 lawn seats in the stadium. **49.** Nancy needs 1 serving of Chex® cereal, 2 servings of 2% milk, and 1.5 servings of orange juice.

51. $12,000 in Treasury bills, $8000 in municipal bonds, and $5000 in corporate bonds. **53.** $\overline{AM} = 4, \overline{BN} = 2,$ and $\overline{OC} = 10$ **55.** $(10, -4, 6)$
57. $(-2, 1, 0, 4)$ **59.** To create a system of two equations and two unknowns, something we already know how to solve.

Putting the Concepts Together (Sections 3.1–3.3)

1. $(-3, 5)$

2. $(3, -2)$

3. $(5, -1)$ **4.** $\left(\dfrac{4}{5}, -\dfrac{7}{5}\right)$ **5.** $(-10, 6)$ **6.** $\{(x, y)|\, 8x - 4y = 12\}$ **7.** $(-1, -3, 5)$ **8.** $\varnothing$ or { }

9. 450 adult tickets and 375 youth tickets **10.** 290 orchestra seats, 380 mezzanine seats, and 530 balcony seats

Section 3.4 Using Matrices to Solve Systems

1. matrix **2.** augmented **3.** 4; 3 **4.** False **5.** $\begin{bmatrix} 3 & -1 & | & -10 \\ -5 & 2 & | & 0 \end{bmatrix}$

6. $\begin{bmatrix} 1 & 2 & -2 & | & 11 \\ -1 & 0 & -2 & | & 4 \\ 4 & -1 & 1 & | & 3 \end{bmatrix}$ **7.** $\begin{cases} x - 3y = 7 \\ -2x + 5y = -3 \end{cases}$ **8.** $\begin{cases} x - 3y + 2z = 4 \\ 3x \quad - z = -1 \\ -x + 4y \quad = 0 \end{cases}$ **9.** $\begin{bmatrix} 1 & -2 & | & 5 \\ 0 & -3 & | & 9 \end{bmatrix}$ **10.** $R_1 = -5r_2 + r_1;$ $\begin{bmatrix} 1 & 0 & | & 3 \\ 0 & 1 & | & 2 \end{bmatrix}$

11. True **12.** $(6, -2)$ **13.** $(3, -2, 1)$ **14.** $\left(\dfrac{7}{2}, \dfrac{2}{3}, 4\right)$ **15.** $\{(x, y)|\, 2x + 5y = -6\}$

16. $\{(x, y, z)|\, x = -z + 5, y = 4z + 3,\ z \text{ is any real number}\}$ **17.** $\varnothing$ or { } **18.** $\varnothing$ or { } **19.** $\begin{bmatrix} 1 & -3 & | & 2 \\ 2 & 5 & | & 1 \end{bmatrix}$ **21.** $\begin{bmatrix} 1 & 1 & 1 & | & 3 \\ 2 & -1 & 3 & | & 1 \\ -4 & 2 & -5 & | & -3 \end{bmatrix}$

23. $\begin{bmatrix} -1 & 1 & | & 2 \\ 5 & 1 & | & -5 \end{bmatrix}$ **25.** $\begin{bmatrix} 1 & 0 & 1 & | & 2 \\ 2 & 1 & 0 & | & 13 \\ 1 & -1 & 4 & | & -4 \end{bmatrix}$ **27.** $\begin{cases} 2x + 5y = 3 \\ -4x + y = 10 \end{cases}$ **29.** $\begin{cases} x + 5y - 3z = 2 \\ 3y - z = -5 \\ 4x \quad + 8z = 6 \end{cases}$ **31.** $\begin{cases} x - 2y + 9z = 2 \\ y - 5z = 8 \\ z = \dfrac{4}{3} \end{cases}$

33. (a) $\begin{bmatrix} 1 & -3 & | & 2 \\ 0 & -1 & | & 5 \end{bmatrix}$ **(b)** $\begin{bmatrix} 1 & -3 & | & 2 \\ 0 & 1 & | & -5 \end{bmatrix}$ **35. (a)** $\begin{bmatrix} 1 & 1 & -1 & | & 4 \\ 0 & 3 & 5 & | & -11 \\ -1 & -3 & 2 & | & 1 \end{bmatrix}$ **(b)** $\begin{bmatrix} 1 & 1 & -1 & | & 4 \\ 0 & 3 & 5 & | & -11 \\ 0 & -2 & 1 & | & 5 \end{bmatrix}$ **37. (a)** $\begin{bmatrix} 1 & 1 & 1 & | & 4 \\ 0 & 1 & 5 & | & 5 \\ 0 & -4 & 2 & | & 8 \end{bmatrix}$

(b) $\begin{bmatrix} 1 & 1 & 1 & | & 4 \\ 0 & 1 & 5 & | & 5 \\ 0 & -2 & 1 & | & 4 \end{bmatrix}$ **39.** $(8, -5)$ **41.** $(-2, 5, 0)$ **43.** $\left(\dfrac{3}{4}, -\dfrac{3}{5}, \dfrac{1}{2}\right)$ **45.** $\{(x, y)|\, x - 3y = 3\}$ **47.** $\varnothing$ or { }

49. $\left\{(x, y, z)|x = \dfrac{3}{4}z + 1, y = \dfrac{5}{4}z + 3,\ z \text{ is any real number}\right\}$ **51.** $\begin{cases} x + 4y = -5 \quad (1) \\ y = -2 \quad (2) \end{cases}$ consistent and independent; $(3, -2)$

53. $\begin{cases} x + 3y - 2z = 6 \quad (1) \\ y + 5z = -2 \quad (2) \\ 0 = 4 \quad (3) \end{cases}$ inconsistent; $\varnothing$ or { } **55.** $\begin{cases} x - 2y - z = 3 \quad (1) \\ y - 2z = -8 \quad (2) \\ z = 5 \quad (3) \end{cases}$ consistent and independent; $(12, 2, 5)$ **57.** $(3, -5)$

59. $\varnothing$ or { } **61.** $\left(\dfrac{1}{2}, -\dfrac{5}{4}\right)$ **63.** $\{(x, y)|4x - y = 8\}$ **65.** $(3, -4, 1)$ **67.** $(4, 0, -5)$

69. $\{(x, y, z)|\, x = -2z - 0.2, y = -z - 1.4,\ z \text{ is any real number}\}$ **71.** $\varnothing$ or { } **73.** $\left(\dfrac{3}{10}, \dfrac{1}{10}, -\dfrac{1}{2}\right)$ **75.** $\left(\dfrac{5}{3}, \dfrac{2}{5}, -\dfrac{1}{2}\right)$ **77.** $(-2, 1, -5)$

79. (a) $a + b + c = 0;\ 4a + 2b + c = 3$ **(b)** $a = 2, b = -3, c = 1; f(x) = 2x^2 - 3x + 1$ **81.** $8000 in Treasury bills, $7000 in municipal

bonds, and $5000 in corporate bonds **83.** $(-3, 7)$ **85.** $(2, 5, -4)$ **87.** Answers will vary. **89.** Multiply each entry in row 2 by $\dfrac{1}{5}$: $R_2 = \dfrac{1}{5}r_2$.

91. $(5, -3)$ **93.** $(4, -2, 7)$

Section 3.5 Determinants and Cramer's Rule

1. $ad - bc$ **2.** Square **3.** 18 **4.** -9 **5.** $(-3, 5)$ **6.** Dependent or inconsistent

7. -91 **8.** $(-1, 4, 1)$ **9.** Consistent and dependent **10.** Inconsistent **11.** 10 **13.** -2 **15.** $(-8, 4)$ **17.** $(3, -1)$ **19.** $\left(-\dfrac{1}{6}, \dfrac{3}{8}\right)$

21. $\left(\dfrac{3}{4}, -\dfrac{7}{4}\right)$ **23.** -9 **25.** -163 **27.** 0 **29.** $(-2, 1, -1)$ **31.** $(3, -1, 2)$ **33.** Infinitely many solutions **35.** $\varnothing$ or $\{\ \}$

37. $(12, -6, 3)$ **39.** $\left(\dfrac{7}{5}, -\dfrac{5}{3}, \dfrac{11}{3}\right)$ **41.** $x = 5$ **43.** $x = -2$

45. (a)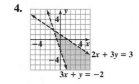

47. (a) 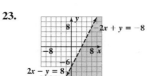 **(b)**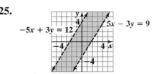

49. (a) $x + 2y = 7$ **(b)** $x + 2y = 7$
51. 14; -14: answers may vary.
53. $(-8, 4)$
55. $(3, -1)$
57. $(-2, 1, -1)$

(b) The area of triangle ABC is 10 square units.

The area of triangle ABC is 4.5 square units.

(c) The area of triangle ADC is 4.5 square units.
(d) 9 square units

Section 3.6 Systems of Linear Inequalities
1. satisfies **2. (a)** no **(b)** yes **(c)** no

3.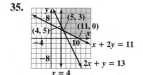

4.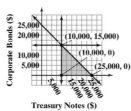

5. False
6.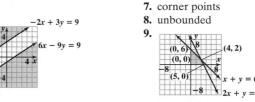

7. corner points
8. unbounded
9.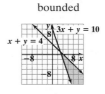
bounded

10. $\begin{cases} x + y \le 25{,}000 \\ x \quad\quad\ \ge 10{,}000 \\ \quad\ y \le 15{,}000 \\ \quad\ y \ge 0 \end{cases}$ where x is amount in Treasury notes and y is amount in corporate bonds

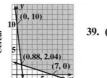

11. (a) no **(b)** yes
13. (a) no **(b)** no
15. (a) no **(b)** yes

17.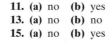

19.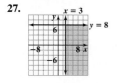

21.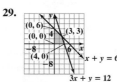

23.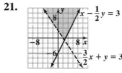

25.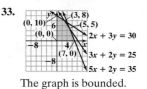

27.

29.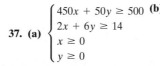
The graph is bounded.

31.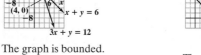
The graph is unbounded.

33.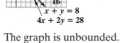
The graph is bounded.

35.
The graph is unbounded.

37. (a) $\begin{cases} 450x + 50y \ge 500 \\ 2x + 6y \ge 14 \\ x \ge 0 \\ y \ge 0 \end{cases}$ **(b)**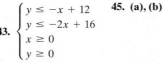

39. (a) $\begin{cases} x + y \le 25{,}000 \\ 0.05x + 0.08y \ge 1{,}400 \\ x \ge 5{,}000 \\ y \le 15{,}000 \\ y \ge 0 \end{cases}$ **(b)**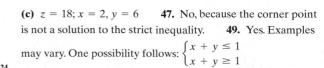

(c) $z = 18$; $x = 2$, $y = 6$ **47.** No, because the corner point is not a solution to the strict inequality. **49.** Yes. Examples may vary. One possibility follows: $\begin{cases} x + y \le 1 \\ x + y \ge 1 \end{cases}$

41. $\begin{cases} y \ge x + 4 \\ y \ge -2x + 10 \end{cases}$ **43.** $\begin{cases} y \le -x + 12 \\ y \le -2x + 16 \\ x \ge 0 \\ y \ge 0 \end{cases}$ **45. (a), (b)**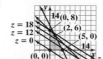

51.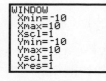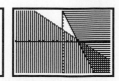

53.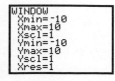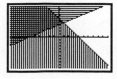

55. The inequalities $x \geq 0$ and $y \geq 0$ restrict the graph to the first quadrant.

  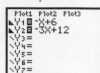

Chapter 3 Review **1. (a)** no **(b)** yes **2. (a)** yes **(b)** no **3. (a)** yes **(b)** no **4. (a)** no **(b)** yes **5.** $(4, 2)$ **6.** $(2, -1)$

7. $(2, -5)$ **8.** $(3, -1)$ **9.** $\varnothing$ or $\{\ \}$ **10.** $(-3, -2)$

 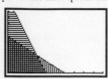 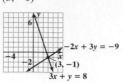 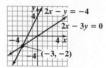

11. $(8, 0)$ **12.** $\left\{(x, y) \mid y = -\dfrac{3}{4}x + 2\right\}$ **13.** $(2, -3)$ **14.** $(-3, -5)$ **15.** $(4, -1)$ **16.** $(2, 2)$ **17.** $\{(x, y) \mid 2x - 4y = 8\}$

18. $(-5, -1)$ **19.** $(0, -4)$ **20.** $(-2, -4)$ **21.** $(1, -1)$ **22.** $\left(\dfrac{1}{2}, \dfrac{3}{4}\right)$ **23.** $\varnothing$ or $\{\ \}$ **24.** $(-7, 4)$ **25.** 35 and 21 **26.** 31 males and 42 females **27.** 300 calories in a slice of pepperoni pizza and 340 calories in a slice of Italian sausage pizza **28.** 21 inches by 13 inches **29.** angle $x = 30°$ and angle $y = 60°$ **30.** $x = 15$ and $y = 5$ **31.** 28 nickels and 12 quarters **32.** 8 liters of the 25%-hydrochloric-acid solution and 4 liters of the 40%-hydrochloric-acid solution **33.** $7000 in stocks and $3000 in bonds **34.** The plane's speed is 136 miles per hour and the wind's speed is 24 miles per hour. **35.** $\dfrac{5}{6}$ hour, or 50 minutes; $66\dfrac{2}{3}$ miles **36.** The speed of the boat in still water is 25 miles per hour and the speed of the current is 5 miles per hour.

37. (a)

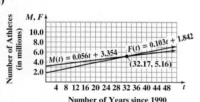

(b) approximately 2022

38. (a) $R(x) = 15x$ **(b)** $C(x) = 2.50x + 1200$

(c)

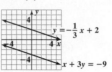 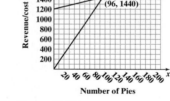

(d) 96 pies; $1440

39. $(4, -2, 1)$
40. $(-1, 3, -2)$
41. $(5, -3, 4)$
42. $\{\ \}$ or $\varnothing$

43. $\left\{(x, y, z) \mid x = \dfrac{1}{2}z + 4, y = \dfrac{1}{2}z - 6, z \text{ is any real number}\right\}$ **44.** $\left(-\dfrac{2}{3}, \dfrac{1}{2}, \dfrac{3}{4}\right)$ **45.** $(1, 0, -6)$ **46.** $(-3, 4, 2)$ **47.** angle $x = 21°$, angle $y = 53°$, and angle $z = 106°$ **48.** A cheeseburger contains 360 calories, a medium order of fries contains 400 calories, and a medium Coke contains 280 calories.

49. $\begin{bmatrix} 3 & 1 & | & 7 \\ 2 & 5 & | & 9 \end{bmatrix}$ **50.** $\begin{bmatrix} 1 & -5 & | & 14 \\ -1 & 1 & | & -3 \end{bmatrix}$ **51.** $\begin{bmatrix} 5 & -1 & 4 & | & 6 \\ -3 & 0 & -3 & | & -1 \\ 1 & -2 & 0 & | & 0 \end{bmatrix}$ **52.** $\begin{bmatrix} 8 & -1 & 3 & | & 14 \\ -3 & 5 & -6 & | & -18 \\ 7 & -4 & 5 & | & 21 \end{bmatrix}$ **53.** $\begin{cases} x + 2y = 12 \\ 3y = 15 \end{cases}$

54. $\begin{cases} 3x - 4y = -5 \\ -x + 2y = 7 \end{cases}$ **55.** $\begin{cases} x + 3y + 4z = 20 \\ y - 2z = -16 \\ z = 7 \end{cases}$ **56.** $\begin{cases} -3x + 7y + 9z = 1 \\ 4x + 10y + 7z = 5 \\ 2x - 5y - 6z = -8 \end{cases}$ **57. (a)** $\begin{bmatrix} 1 & -5 & | & 22 \\ 0 & -1 & | & 4 \end{bmatrix}$ **(b)** $\begin{bmatrix} 1 & -5 & | & 22 \\ 0 & 1 & | & -4 \end{bmatrix}$

58. (a) $\begin{bmatrix} 1 & -4 & | & 7 \\ 0 & 5 & | & -15 \end{bmatrix}$ **(b)** $\begin{bmatrix} 1 & -4 & | & 7 \\ 0 & 1 & | & -3 \end{bmatrix}$ **59. (a)** $\begin{bmatrix} -1 & 2 & 1 & | & 1 \\ 0 & 3 & 5 & | & -1 \\ -1 & 5 & 6 & | & 2 \end{bmatrix}$ **(b)** $\begin{bmatrix} -1 & 2 & 1 & | & 1 \\ 0 & 3 & 5 & | & -1 \\ 0 & 3 & 5 & | & 1 \end{bmatrix}$ **60. (a)** $\begin{bmatrix} 1 & 3 & 4 & | & 4 \\ 0 & 1 & 2 & | & -3 \\ 0 & -4 & -7 & | & 7 \end{bmatrix}$

(b) $\begin{bmatrix} 1 & 3 & 4 & | & 4 \\ 0 & 1 & 2 & | & -3 \\ 0 & 0 & 1 & | & -5 \end{bmatrix}$ **61.** $(7, -3)$ **62.** $\left(\dfrac{1}{2}, 5\right)$ **63.** $(-4, 1)$ **64.** $\varnothing$ or $\{\ \}$ **65.** $\{(x, y) \mid 4x - 2y = 6\}$ **66.** $\left(\dfrac{5}{2}, \dfrac{3}{8}\right)$ **67.** $(-5, 1, 4)$

68. $\varnothing$ or $\{\ \}$ **69.** $\left\{(x, y, z) \mid x = -\dfrac{5}{6}z + 1, y = \dfrac{4}{3}z + 1, z \text{ is any real number}\right\}$ **70.** $(-3, 1, 3)$ **71.** 10 **72.** 0 **73.** -2 **74.** 9

75. 111 **76.** 0 **77.** -31 **78.** 78 **79.** $(5, -3)$ **80.** $\left(-4, \dfrac{1}{3}\right)$ **81.** $(-1, 2)$ **82.** $\left(\dfrac{7}{3}, \dfrac{1}{3}\right)$ **83.** $\varnothing$ or $\{\ \}$ **84.** $\left(\dfrac{3}{10}, \dfrac{12}{5}\right)$

85. $(5, -2, 1)$ **86.** $(1, 7, -5)$ **87.** $(1, 2, -2)$ **88.** $\left(-\dfrac{1}{8}, 2, \dfrac{1}{2}\right)$ **89.** $\{(x, y, z) \mid x = -9z - 17, y = -13z - 24, z \text{ is any real number}\}$ **90.** $(2, -5, -9)$ **91. (a)** yes **(b)** no **92. (a)** no **(b)** yes **93. (a)** no **(b)** yes **94. (a)** no **(b)** yes

95.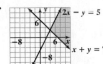

96.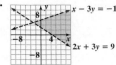

97.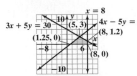

98.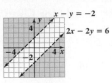

99.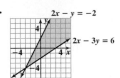

100.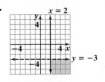

101.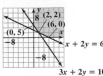

The graph is bounded.

102.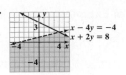

The graph is unbounded.

103. (a) $\begin{cases} x + y \le 4000 \\ 0.06x + 0.08y \ge 275 \\ x \ge 500 \\ y \le 2500 \\ y \ge 0 \end{cases}$ **(b)**

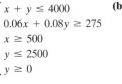

104. (a) $\begin{cases} 6x + 4y \le 144 \\ x \ge y + 4 \\ x \ge 0 \\ y \ge 0 \end{cases}$ **(b)**

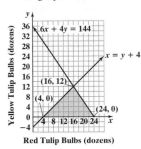

Chapter 3 Test **1.** $(-2, -4)$ **2.** $(1, -4)$ **3.** $\left(\dfrac{2}{3}, -\dfrac{5}{3}\right)$ **4.** $\varnothing$ or $\{\ \}$ **5.** $(-6, 8)$ **6.** $\{(x, y, z)\,|\, x = z + 5, y = 2z + 2,$

z is any real number$\}$ **7.** $(5, 1, -3)$ **8. (a)** $\begin{bmatrix} 1 & -3 & | & -2 \\ 0 & 2 & | & 12 \end{bmatrix}$ **(b)** $\begin{bmatrix} 1 & -3 & | & -2 \\ 0 & 1 & | & 6 \end{bmatrix}$ **9. (a)** $\begin{bmatrix} 1 & -2 & 1 & | & -2 \\ 0 & 1 & -1 & | & 7 \\ 0 & -4 & 5 & | & -32 \end{bmatrix}$ **(b)** $\begin{bmatrix} 1 & -2 & 1 & | & -2 \\ 0 & 1 & -1 & | & 7 \\ 0 & 0 & 1 & | & -4 \end{bmatrix}$

10. $\begin{bmatrix} 1 & -5 & | & 2 \\ 2 & 1 & | & 4 \end{bmatrix}; (2, 0)$ **11.** $\begin{bmatrix} 1 & 2 & 1 & | & 3 \\ 0 & 4 & 3 & | & 5 \\ 2 & 3 & 0 & | & 1 \end{bmatrix}; (2, -1, 3)$ **12.** -4 **13.** 14 **14.** $\left(-\dfrac{7}{4}, \dfrac{1}{4}\right)$ **15.** $(-5, 4, -1)$

16.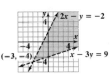

17.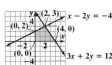

18. 32 twenty-five-ton bins and 18 twenty-ton bins

19. angle $x = 30°$, angle $y = 70°$, and angle $z = 80°$

20. (a) $\begin{cases} 12x + 18y \le 180 \\ x + y \le 13 \\ x \ge 0 \\ y \ge 0 \end{cases}$ **(b)**

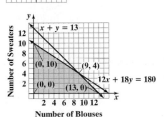

Cumulative Review Chapters R–3

1. (a) 11 **(b)** $-13, 0, 11$ **(c)** $-13, -\dfrac{7}{8}, 0, 2.7, 11$ **(d)** $\dfrac{\pi}{2}, 4\sqrt{2}$ **(e)** $-13, -\dfrac{7}{8}, 0, \dfrac{\pi}{2}, 2.7, 4\sqrt{2}, 11$ **2.** $2(x + 4) = 3x - 6$ **3.** -8

4. 3 **5.** $3x^2 - 11x - 27$ **6.** $\{-15, 1\}$ **7.** $\{x\,|\,x \le -9\}$ or $(-\infty, -9]$ **8.** $\{x\,|\,x < 2$ or $x > 5\}; (-\infty, 2)\cup(5, \infty)$ **9. (a)** $\{0, 6, 12\}$

(b) $\{0, 2, 3, 4, 6, 8, 9, 10, 12, 15\}$ **10.** **11.** 6 **12. (a)** Function **(b)** Function **(c)** Not a function **13.** $\left\{ x\,\middle|\,x \ne \dfrac{1}{2} \right\}$

14. (a) 25 **(b)** -3 **(c)** $3x^2 - 4x - 7$

15. **16.** Parallel **17.** $y = -\dfrac{5}{3}x + 4; 5x + 3y = 12$ **18.** 196.7 g **19. (a)** Independent: year; Dependent: population

(b) $\{x\,|\,0 \le x \le 30\}$ or $[0, 30]$ **(c)** The population in the year 2015 is predicted to be 4,955,688 **(d)** 5,096,775

20. (a) $C(x) = 0.08x + 4.95$ **(b)** $\{x\,|\,x \ge 0\}$ **(c)** $\$56.55$ **(d)** 1575 minutes **21.** $(-8, 5)$ **22.** $\left(\dfrac{2}{3}, -\dfrac{1}{2}, -1\right)$ **23.** -2

24. -13

25.

Getting Ready for Chapter 4: Laws of Exponents and Scientific Notation

1. base; power; exponent **2.** a^{m+n} **3.** 125 **4.** -243 **5.** y^7 **6.** $-10x^7$ **7.** $-6y^5$ **8.** True **9.** 25 **10.** y^2 **11.** $\frac{8}{5}a$ **12.** $-\frac{3}{2}b^2$

13. $1; 0$ **14.** $\frac{1}{a^n}; 0$ **15.** $\frac{1}{125}$ **16.** $\frac{5}{z^7}$ **17.** x^4 **18.** $5y^3$ **19.** -1 **20.** 1 **21.** $\frac{9}{16}$ **22.** -64 **23.** $\frac{x^2}{9}$ **24.** 20 **25.** $\frac{1}{36}$

26. 100 **27.** $\frac{20x^3}{y}$ **28.** $\frac{2}{3}ab^4$ **29.** $-\frac{3}{2}b^8$ **30.** $\frac{10t^5}{3s^3}$ **31.** 64 **32.** 1 **33.** 4096 **34.** a^{15} **35.** $\frac{1}{z^{18}}$ **36.** s^{21} **37.** $125y^3$

38. 1 **39.** $81x^8$ **40.** $\frac{1}{16a^6}$ **41.** $\frac{z^4}{81}$ **42.** $\frac{32}{x^5}$ **43.** $\frac{x^8}{y^{12}}$ **44.** $\frac{27}{a^6b^{12}}$ **45.** $\frac{3x^3y^4}{4}$ **46.** $\frac{3b^5}{4a}$ **47.** $\frac{x^6}{y^{10}}$ **48.** 5.32×10^2

49. -1.23×10^6 **50.** 3.4×10^{-2} **51.** -8.45×10^{-5} **52.** 500 **53.** 910,000 **54.** 0.00018 **55.** 0.000001 **56.** 6×10^8 **57.** 8×10^{-11}
58. 2.4×10^4 **59.** 2×10^2 **60.** 2×10^{-3} **61.** 5×10^3 **62.** 3.75×10^{-13} **63.** 240,000,000,000 **64.** 0.003 **65.** 750

66. 0.000000000003 **67.** -25 **69.** $-\frac{1}{25}$ **71.** -1 **73.** $\frac{81}{16}$ **75.** $-\frac{1}{27}$ **77.** -64 **79.** 288 **81.** 1 (assuming $x \neq 0$) **83.** $-10t^5$

85. $\frac{5x^2}{y}$ **87.** $4x^2y$ **89.** $\frac{3b^3}{2a}$ **91.** $\frac{1}{x^8}$ **93.** $27x^6y^3$ **95.** $\frac{64}{z^3}$ **97.** $\frac{a^6}{9}$ **99.** $\frac{1}{16a^8b^{12}}$ **101.** $\frac{2x^5}{3y^3}$ **103.** $\frac{b^4}{25a^{12}}$ **105.** 1 **107.** $-x^2y^4z$

109. $\frac{9y^8z}{x^5}$ **111.** $\frac{3b^{16}}{2a^9}$ **113.** -1.484×10^{-6} **115.** 6.4×10^{19} **117.** 6.25×10^{-3} **119.** 8×10^6 **121.** 1 **123.** 12,000,000,000,000

125. 0.04 **127.** 4,000,000 **129.** x^6 cubic units **131.** 1.276×10^{-5} meter **133.** 1.276×10^7 meters **135.** 0.000000001 meters
137. 40,000,000,000,000,000,000 possible states **139.** \$46,000 **141. (a)** 70.3 people per square mile; On average, each square mile of land contained about 70 people. **(b)** 85.3 people per square mile; On average, each square mile of land contained about 85 people. **(c)** about 15 people per square mile; on average, the number of people living on each square mile of land increased by 15, thereby making living space more crowded.

143. 2^{x+1} **145.** 3^{10x+3} **147.** 625 **149.** $\frac{1}{2401}$ **151.** No, your friend is incorrect. He added exponents instead of multiplying.

153. Explanations will vary. Essentially, if a were to equal zero, we would end up with division by 0, which is not defined. For example, $0^{-2} = \frac{1}{0^2} = \frac{1}{0}$, which is undefined. If $m + n$ equals 0, we end up with 0^0, which is indeterminate. **155.** Explanations will vary. If a or b equals 0 when n is negative, we would end up with division by 0, which is not defined. If a or b equals 0 when n is zero, we end up with 0^0, which is indeterminate.

157. Explanations will vary. One possibility: $\frac{x^5}{x^2} = \frac{x \cdot x \cdot x \cdot x \cdot x}{x \cdot x} = x^3 = x^{5-2}$ **159.** Explanations will vary. One possibility:
$(xy)^3 = (xy)(xy)(xy) = x \cdot x \cdot x \cdot y \cdot y \cdot y = x^3y^3$ **161.** Explanations will vary. Basically, using scientific notation allows us to use the Laws of Exponents to perform the multiplication or division.

Chapter 4 Polynomials and Polynomial Functions

Section 4.1 Adding and Subtracting Polynomials
1. non-negative integers **2.** Monomial; 8; 5 **3.** Not a monomial
4. Monomial; 12; 0 **5.** Not a monomial **6.** Monomial; Coefficient: 3, Degree: 7 **7.** Monomial; Coefficient: -2, Degree: 4 **8.** Not a monomial
9. Monomial; Coefficient: -1, Degree: 2 **10.** Polynomial; 3 **11.** Not a polynomial **12.** Not a polynomial **13.** Polynomial; 2
14. Polynomial; 4 **15.** $6x^2 + 2x - 2$ **16.** $3w^4 - 2w^3 - 7w^2 + w - 5$ **17.** $5x^2y + 7x^2y^2 - 4xy^2$ **18.** $x^3 - 16x^2 + 7x + 2$
19. $11y^3 - 5y^2 - 3y - 7$ **20.** $11x^2y - 3x^2y^2 - 10xy^2$ **21. (a)** 1 **(b)** -1 **(c)** 34 **22. (a)** In 2006, there were 394,248 first time births to women 25 years of age. **(b)** In 2006, there were 88,818 first time births to women 40 years of age. **23. (a)** $2x^2 + 4x - 5$ **(b)** $4x^2 - 6x + 7$
(c) 1 **(d)** 35 **24. (a)** $4x - 1250$ **(b)** \$1950. If the company manufactures and sells 800 calculators, its profit will be \$1950. **25.** Coefficient: 3;
Degree: 2 **27.** Coefficient: -8; Degree: 5 **29.** Coefficient: $\frac{4}{3}$; Degree: 6 **31.** Coefficient: 2; Degree: 0 **33.** The exponent in the first term is not an integer that is greater than or equal to 0. **35.** There is a variable in the denominator. The expression cannot be written in the standard form for a polynomial. **37.** Yes; $5x^2 - 9x + 1$; 2; trinomial **39.** No **41.** No **43.** Yes; $\frac{5}{8}$; 0; monomial **45.** Yes; $2y^2 - 8y + 5$; 2; trinomial

47. No **49.** Yes; $2xy^4 + 3x^2y^2 + 4$; 5; trinomial **51.** No **53.** $13z^3$ **55.** $4x^2 + 3x - 2$ **57.** $8p^3 - p^2 - 4p - 1$ **59.** $2x^2 + 4x + 3$
61. $3s^2t^3 - 4st^2 - 5t - 1$ **63.** $-4x^2 - 2x + 1$ **65.** $3y^3 - y^2 - 2y + 8$ **67.** $\frac{3}{4}x^2 + \frac{5}{4}x + 1$ **69.** $8x^2y^2 - 7x^2y - 3xy^2$

71. $x^2y + 11xy^2 + 2xy$ **73. (a)** 1 **(b)** -3 **(c)** 22 **75. (a)** 3 **(b)** 5 **(c)** -30 **77. (a)** 3 **(b)** 3 **(c)** 63 **79. (a)** $-3x + 6$ **(b)** $7x + 4$
(c) 0 **(d)** 11 **81. (a)** $3x^2 - 5x + 6$ **(b)** $-x^2 - 5x$ **(c)** 8 **(d)** -6 **83. (a)** $2x^3 + 6x^2 + 12x - 6$ **(b)** $6x^2 + 12x + 10$ **(c)** 58 **(d)** 28
85. $x^3 + x^2 - 7x + 4$ **87.** $-2b^3 + 6b^2 - 4b + 4$ **89. (a)** 4 square units **(b)** 4 square units **(c)** Since the rectangular region is in quadrant I and has one corner at the origin, the coordinates of the vertex give us the length and width of the rectangle. Since the area of a rectangle can be found by multiplying the length and width, we can just multiply the coordinates together to get the area of the region. **91. (a)** The average price per square foot of a home in 1992 was \$55.14. **(b)** We predict the average price per square foot of a home in 2012 will be \$151.70.
93. (a) $P(x) = -0.05x^3 + 0.8x^2 + 155x - 500$ **(b)** \$1836.25 **(c)** P(100) = $-27,000$; If 100 cell phones are sold, there would be a loss of \$27,000.
95. $a = 2$ **97. (a)** 3 **(b)** -2 **(c)** -1 **(d)** 1 **99.** $S(x) = T(x) - F(x)$ **101.** 1 **103.** A polynomial is the sum or difference of monomials. Monomial: $4x^2$; Binomial: $-5y^3 + 8y$; Trinomial: $2z^5 - 8z^3 + 10z$. Linear polynomials are of the form $ax + b$, where a, b are constants.
105. When we add two polynomials, we add the coefficients of the monomials. Therefore, the highest degree term of the polynomials being added will be the degree of the polynomial.

107. (a)–(c)

```
Plot1 Plot2 Plot3
\Y1■4X²-7X+1
\Y2=
\Y3=
\Y4=
\Y5=
\Y6=
\Y7=
```

```
Y1(4)
           37
Y1(-2)
           31
Y1(6)
          103
```

$f(4) = 37$ $f(-2) = 31$ $f(6) = 103$

109. (a)–(c)

```
Plot1 Plot2 Plot3
\Y1■2X^3-5X²+X+5
\Y2=
\Y3=
\Y4=
\Y5=
\Y6=
```

```
Y1(4)
           57
Y1(-2)
          -33
Y1(6)
          263
```

$f(4) = 57$ $f(-2) = -33$ $f(6) = 263$

Section 4.2 Multiplying Polynomials   1. $6x^7$ 2. $-21a^4b^6$ 3. $\frac{5}{4}x^5$ 4. $-3x - 6$ 5. $5x^3 + 15x^2 + 10x$ 6. $6x^3y - 10x^2y^2 + 4xy^3$

7. $y^4 + \frac{1}{6}y^3 + 4y^2$ 8. First, Outer, Inner, Last   9. $x^2 + 5x + 4$ 10. $6v^2 + v - 15$ 11. $2a^2 + 9ab - 5b^2$ 12. $2y^3 + 5y^2 - 2y - 15$

13. $2z^4 - 5z^3 + 7z^2 - 16z + 12$ 14. False   15. $A^2 - B^2$ 16. $25y^2 - 4$ 17. $49y^2 - 4z^6$ 18. False   19. $z^2 - 16z + 64$

20. $36p^2 + 60p + 25$ 21. $16a^2 - 24ab + 9b^2$ 22. $f(x) \cdot g(x)$ 23. (a) 77   (b) $5x^3 + 12x^2 - 4x - 3$ (c) 77   24. (a) $x^2 - 8x + 15$

(b) $2xh + h^2 - 2h$ 25. $-15x^3y^5$ 27. $\frac{5}{3}y^4z^5$ 29. $5x^3 + 20x^2 + 10x$ 31. $-12a^4b - 8a^3b^2 + 4a^2b^3$ 33. $\frac{1}{2}a^3b^2 - \frac{3}{4}a^2b^4 + 4a^2b^2$

35. $0.48x^4 - 0.32x^3 + 0.6x^2$ 37. $x^2 + 8x + 15$ 39. $a^2 + 2a - 15$ 41. $12a^2 + 5a - 3$ 43. $-6x^2 - 19x + 7$ 45. $-10x^2 - 7x + 12$

47. $\frac{1}{3}x^2 - \frac{5}{3}x - 8$ 49. $4a^2 - 17ab - 15b^2$ 51. $x^3 + 5x^2 + 6x + 2$ 53. $6a^3 - a^2 - 17a + 10$ 55. $20z^3 + 27z^2 + 17z + 6$

57. $x^4 - 7x^3 + 14x^2 - 13x + 21$ 59. $2y^3 + 13y^2 + 17y - 12$ 61. $2w^4 + w^3 - 3w^2 - w + 1$ 63. $3x^3 + x^2y + 2xy^2 + 4y^3$

65. $8a^3b - 4a^2b^2 + 2ab^3 + 20a^2 - 10ab + 5b^2$ 67. $x^2 - 36$ 69. $a^2 + 16a + 64$ 71. $9y^2 - 6y + 1$ 73. $25a^2 - 9b^2$

75. $64z^2 + 16yz + y^2$ 77. $100x^2 - 20xy + y^2$ 79. $a^6 - 4b^2$ 81. $9x^2 - y^2 - 2y - 1$ 83. $4a^2 + 4ab - 12a + b^2 - 6b + 9$

85. (a) $x^2 + 3x - 4$ (b) 14   87. (a) $8x^2 + 14x - 15$ (b) 99   89. (a) $x^3 + 3x^2 - 13x + 6$ (b) 21   91. (a) $x^2 + 4x + 5$

(b) $2xh + h^2$ 93. (a) $x^2 + 9x + 12$ (b) $2xh + 5h + h^2$ 95. (a) $3x^2 + 11x + 11$ (b) $6xh - h + 3h^2$ 97. $5a^3b - 10a^2b^2 + 5ab^3$

99. $25y^2 - 1$ 101. $24z^2 + z - 3$ 103. $7m^2 - 6mn - 7n^2$ 105. $x^3 + 27$ 107. $4x^2 - 2x + \frac{1}{4}$ 109. $p^3 + 6p^2 + 12p + 8$

111. $21x^2 - 29xy + 13x + 10y^2 - 9y + 2$ 113. $3p^2 + 5p - 12$ 115. $x^4 - x^3 - 19x^2 + 3x + 84$ 117. $x^2 + 6x$ 119. $4x^2 + 29x + 30$

121. $4x^2 + 11x + 6$ 123. (a) $A_1 = a^2; A_2 = ab; A_3 = ab; A_4 = b^2$ (b) $a^2 + 2ab + b^2$ (c) The length of the region is $a + b$ and the width is also $a + b$. The area of the region would be $A = (a + b)(a + b) = (a + b)^2$. The result from part (b) is obtained by multiplying this expression out.
125. $2^{2x} - 2^x - 12$ 127. $5^{2y} - 2(5^y) + 1$

Section 4.3 Dividing Polynomials; Synthetic Division   1. $3p^3 - 4p^2 + p$ 2. $4a^2 - \frac{2}{a} + \frac{1}{5a^3}$ 3. $\frac{xy^3}{4} + \frac{2y}{x} - \frac{1}{x^2}$ 4. $0; (3x - 1)(x + 1);$

factors   5. dividend; divisor; remainder   6. Quotient; Divisor; Remainder; Dividend   7. $x^2 + 7x - 3 + \frac{9}{x - 4}$ 8. $x^2 + 5x + 4$

9. $x^3 - 5x^2 + 2 + \frac{6}{x^2 - 2}$ 10. False   11. False   12. $2x^2 + 5x + 3 - \frac{7}{x - 2}$ 13. $x^3 + 5x^2 - 2$ 14. (a) $3x^2 - 4x + 3 + \frac{2x + 1}{x^2 - 2}$

(b) 19   15. (a) 42   (b) 0   16. (a) $f(-2) = -35; x + 2$ is not a factor   (b) $f(5) = 0; f(x) = (x - 5)(2x^2 + x - 1)$ 17. $2x + 3$

19. $\frac{2}{5}a^2 - 3a + 2$ 21. $\frac{y}{2} + \frac{3}{2y}$ 23. $1 + \frac{3}{2n} - \frac{9}{2m}$ 25. $x + 3$ 27. $2x + 5 + \frac{6}{x - 2}$ 29. $w + 6 - \frac{7}{2w - 7}$ 31. $x^2 + 5x - 14$

33. $w^2 - 4w - 5$ 35. $3x^2 - 14x - 5$ 37. $x - 7$ 39. $z + 7 + \frac{4z - 5}{3z^2 + 1}$ 41. $2x^2 - 15x + 28 + \frac{-3x + 4}{x^2 + 2x + 5}$ 43. $x + 2$

45. $2x + 3$ 47. $x + 3 + \frac{4}{x - 6}$ 49. $x^2 + 5x + 6 + \frac{15}{x - 5}$ 51. $3x^3 + 4x^2 - 9x - 10 - \frac{5}{x - 3}$ 53. $x^3 - 6x^2 - 4x + 24 - \frac{35}{x + 6}$

55. $2x^2 + 8x + 6$ 57. (a) $\left(\frac{f}{g}\right)(x) = x^2 - 2x + 3$ (b) 3   59. (a) $\left(\frac{f}{g}\right)(x) = x + 3$ (b) 5   61. (a) $\left(\frac{f}{g}\right)(x) = 2x - 1 + \frac{2}{x + 3}$

(b) $\frac{17}{5}$ 63. (a) $\left(\frac{f}{g}\right)(x) = x^2 + 3x - 4$ (b) 6   65. (a) $\left(\frac{f}{g}\right)(x) = x - \frac{4x + 12}{x^2 - 9}$ (b) 6   67. -5 69. -119 71. 231   73. 2

75. $x - 2$ is a factor; $f(x) = (x - 2)(x - 1)$ 77. $x + 2$ is a factor; $f(x) = (x + 2)(2x + 1)$ 79. $x - 3$ is not a factor   81. $x + 1$ is a factor;

$f(x) = (x + 1)(4x^2 - 11x + 6)$ 83. $a^2b - 3a + 6$ 85. $y + 3$ 87. $x + 6 + \frac{3x + 2}{x^2 + 5}$ 89. $\frac{2}{3}x + \frac{1}{2x}$ 91. $x^2 + 3x - 10 - \frac{6}{x + 4}$

93. $x^2 - 8$ 95. $4x^2 + 6x + 9$ 97. $f(x) = 3x^2 - 10x - 25$ 99. $f(x) = x^2 + 5x - 20$ 101. $(5x + 2)$ ft   103. $(2x + 5)$ cm

105. (a) $\overline{C}(x) = 0.01x^2 - 0.4x + 13 + \frac{400}{x}$ (b) \$26   107. $a = 2, b = -7, c = -12,$ and $d = -13,$ thus, $a + b + c + d = -30$

109. The dividend is the polynomial f and has degree n. Remember, (Divisor)(Quotient) + Remainder = Dividend. Since the remainder must be 0 or a polynomial that has lower degree than f, the degree n must be obtained from the product of the divisor and the quotient. The divisor is $x + 4$, which is of degree 1, so the quotient must be of degree $n - 1$.   111. Yes; $(3x + 4)(2x^2 - 3x + 1) = 6x^3 - x^2 - 9x + 4$.

Putting the Concepts Together (Sections 4.1–4.3)   1. $5m^4 - 2m^3 + 3m + 8$ Degree: 4   2. $-4a^3 + 9a^2 + a - 8$ 3. $-\frac{19}{5}y^2 + 3y - 8$

4. 29   5. -25 6. $x^2 + 4x + 10$ 7. $2m^3n^4 - 8m^2n^4 + 12mn^3$ 8. $9a^2 - 30ab + 25b^2$ 9. $49n^4 - 9$ 10. $18a^3 + 6a^2b - ab^2 + 2b^3$

11. $x^3 - 2x^2 + 3x + 22$ 12. $5z^2 + 3z - 7$ 13. $2x^2 + 7x - 1 + \frac{3}{x + 9}$ 14. $x^2 + 3x - 1 + \frac{4}{x - 1}$ 15. yes: $f(x) = (x + 5)(3x^2 - 7x + 12)$

Section 4.4 Greatest Common Factor; Factoring by Grouping   1. factors   2. prime   3. greatest common factor   4. True   5. False
6. 5   7. $2z$ 8. $3xy^3$ 9. $7z(z - 2)$ 10. $2y(3y^2 - 7y + 5)$ 11. $2m^2n^2(m^2 + 4mn^2 - 3n^3)$ 12. $-5y(y - 2)$ 13. $-3a(a^2 - 2a + 4)$
14. $(a - 3)(4a + 3)$ 15. $3(w - 5)(w + 1)$ 16. $(x + y)(5 + b)$ 17. $(w^2 + 4)(w - 3)$ 18. $(2x + 1)(x - 5)$ 19. $5(a + 7)$
21. $-3(y - 7)$ 23. $7x(2x - 3)$ 25. $3z(z^2 - 2z + 6)$ 27. $-5p^2(p^2 - 2p + 5)$ 29. $7mn(7m^2 + 12n^2 - 5m^3n)$ 31. $-2z(9z^2 - 7z - 2)$
33. $(3c - 2)(5c - 3)$ 35. $2(a - 3)(3a - 2)$ 37. $(x + y)(5 + a)$ 39. $(z + 5)(2z^2 - 5)$ 41. $(w - 5)(w + 3)$ 43. $2(x - 4)(x - 2)$
45. $3x(x + 5)(x - 4)$ 47. $(x - y)(2a - b)$ 49. $5(w - 3)$ 51. $(2y + 5)(y - 2)$ 53. $3x^2y(2xy^2 - 7xy + 3)$ 55. $(x + 1)(x^2 + 3)$
57. $2(x - 2)(2x - 3)$ 59. $x^2(4x + 1)(20x + 3)$ 61. $(x + 9)^2(8x + 33)$ 63. $(x - 5)^2(2x - 1)(10x - 23)$ 65. $4(x^2 + 1)(4x - 3)^2(7x^2 - 3x + 3)$
67. $x^2(4 - \pi)$ square units   69. $2\pi r(r + 4)$ square inches   71. (a) $1.4x$ (b) $1.4x - 0.4(1.4x)$ (c) $0.84x$ (d) No

73. (a) $x + 0.15x = 1.15x$ (b) $1.15x + 0.1(1.15x)$ (c) $1.265x$ (d) \$25.30   75. $\frac{1}{4}(x - 7)$ 77. $\frac{1}{25}b(5b^2 + 8)$ 79. $x^n(1 + 3x + 6x^n)$
81. $2y^{n+2}(2y - 4 + 3y^3)$

Section 4.5 Factoring Trinomials **1.** $m \cdot n$; $m + n$ **2.** True **3.** $(y + 6)(y + 3)$ **4.** $(p + 2)(p + 12)$ **5.** $(q - 4)(q - 2)$
6. $(x - 2)(x - 6)$ **7.** $(w - 7)(w + 3)$ **8.** $(q - 12)(q + 3)$ **9.**

Integers Whose Product Is 8	1, 8	2, 4	−1, −8	−2, −4
Sum	9	6	−9	−6

There are no factors of 8 whose sum is −5.

10. $2x(x - 9)(x + 3)$
11. $-3(z + 2)(z + 5)$
12. $(x + 3y)(x + 5y)$

13. $(m + 5n)(m - 4n)$ **14.** $(2b - 3)(b + 5)$ **15.** $(2x + 3)(5x + 6)$ **16.** $(2x + 1)(4x + 5)$ **17.** $(6y - 5)(2y + 7)$ **18.** $(6x - y)(5x + 2y)$
19. $2(4x + 7y)(x - 3y)$ **20.** $-1(6y + 1)(y - 4)$ **21.** $-1(3x + 2y)(3x + 5y)$ **22.** $2x - 3$ **23.** $(y^2 + 4)(y^2 - 6)$ **24.** $(x - 1)(4x - 15)$
25. $(x + 3)(x + 5)$ **27.** $(p + 6)(p - 3)$ **29.** $(r + 5)^2$ **31.** $(s + 12)(s - 5)$ **33.** $(x - 7)(x - 8)$ **35.** $-(w + 6)(w - 4)$
37. $(x + 3y)(x + 4y)$ **39.** $(p - 4q)(p + 6q)$ **41.** $(2p + 1)(p - 8)$ **43.** $(y - 2)(4y - 3)$ **45.** $(2s - 1)(4s + 3)$ **47.** $(4z - 3)(4z + 5)$
49. $(2y + 1)(9y + 4)$ **51.** $(x + 7y)(2x - 3y)$ **53.** $(r - 5s)(4r - 3s)$ **55.** $(3r + 4s)(8r - 3s)$ **57.** $(x^2 + 1)(x^2 + 2)$
59. $(mn + 7)(mn - 2)$ **61.** $(x - 7)(x + 3)$ **63.** $3(r - 2)(3r - 5)$ **65.** $(y + 2)(2y - 3)$ **67.** $(5w + 3)(2w + 7)$ **69.** $2y(8y + 5)$
71. $(3x + 2y)(4x + 5y)$ **73.** prime **75.** $(x^2 + 4)(x^2 + 2)$ **77.** $(z^3 + 5)(z^3 + 4)$ **79.** $(r - 4s)(r - 8s)$ **81.** $(2z + 3)(4z + 3)$
83. prime **85.** $2(x - 3)(x + 9)$ **87.** $-3(r - 5)(r - 8)$ **89.** $-2(2m - 5)(4m + 7)$ **91.** $4(4z + 1)(3z + 7)$ **93.** $3x(x - 10)(x + 8)$
95. $4xy^2(x - 7)(2x - 5)$ **97.** $2r^2s(5r - 4)(7r + 2)$ **99. (a)** $V(3) = 1296$; when 3-inch square corners are cut from the piece of cardboard, the resulting box will have a volume of 1296 cubic inches. **(b)** $V(x) = 4x(x - 15)(x - 12)$ **(c)** $V(3) = 4(3)(3 - 15)(3 - 12) = 1296$

(d) Answers may vary. **101.** $2x - 5$ **103.** $\frac{1}{2}(x + 4)(x + 2)$ **105.** $\frac{1}{3}(p - 3)(p + 1)$ **107.** $\frac{4}{3}(a - 6)(a + 4)$ **109.** $(2^n - 5)(2^n + 1)$
111. $(4^x - 8)(4^x - 4)$ **113.** The trial and error method would be better when ac gets large and there are quite a few factors of the product whose sum must be determined. **115.** There is a common factor of 3 in the factor $3p + 6$ that should have been factored out.

Section 4.6 Factoring Special Products **1.** perfect square trinomial **2.** False **3.** $(x - 9)^2$ **4.** $(2x + 5y)^2$ **5.** $2(3p^2 - 7)^2$
6. $(z - 4)(z + 4)$ **7.** $(4m - 9n)(4m + 9n)$ **8.** $(2a - 3b^2)(2a + 3b^2)$ **9.** $3(b + 2)(b - 2)(b^2 + 4)$ **10.** $(p - 4 - q)(p - 4 + q)$
11. $(A + B)(A^2 - AB + B^2)$ **12.** $(A - B)(A^2 + AB + B^2)$ **13.** $(z + 4)(z^2 - 4z + 16)$ **14.** $(5p - 6q^2)(25p^2 + 30pq^2 + 36q^4)$
15. $4(2m + 5n^2)(4m^2 - 10mn^2 + 25n^4)$ **16.** $(-2x + 1)(13x^2 + 5x + 1)$ **17.** $(x + 2)^2$ **19.** $(w + 6)^2$ **21.** $(2x + 1)^2$ **23.** $(3p - 5)^2$
25. $(5a + 9)^2$ **27.** $(3x + 4y)^2$ **29.** $3(w - 5)^2$ **31.** $-5(t + 7)^2$ **33.** $2(4a - 5b)^2$ **35.** $(z^2 - 3)^2$
37. $(x - 3)(x + 3)$ **39.** $(2 - y)(2 + y)$ **41.** $(2z - 3)(2z + 3)$ **43.** $(10m - 9n)(10m + 9n)$ **45.** $(m^2 - 6n)(m^2 + 6n)$
47. $2(2p - 3q)(2p + 3q)$ **49.** $5r(4p - 7b)(4p + 7b)$ **51.** $(x + y - 3)(x + y + 3)$ **53.** $(x - 2)(x^2 + 2x + 4)$ **55.** $(m + 5)(m^2 - 5m + 25)$
57. $(x^2 - 4y)(x^4 + 4x^2y + 16y^2)$ **59.** $3(2x - 5y)(4x^2 + 10xy + 25y^2)$ **61.** $(p - 2)(p^2 + 5p + 13)$ **63.** $(5y + 1)(7y^2 + 4y + 1)$
65. $18(x^2 + 3)$ **67.** $(y^2 + z^3)(y^4 - y^2z^3 + z^6)$ **69.** $(y - 1)(y^2 + y + 1)(y^6 + y^3 + 1)$ **71.** $(5x - y)(5x + y)$ **73.** $(2x + 3)(4x^2 - 6x + 9)$
75. $(z - 4)^2$ **77.** $5x(x - 2y)(x^2 + 2xy + 4y^2)$ **79.** $(7m - 3n)^2$ **81.** $4(x^2 + 4)$ **83.** $(y - 2)^2(y + 2)^2$ **85.** $(2ab + 3)^2$ **87.** prime
89. $(x - y - 2)(x + y - 2)$ **91.** $2(n - m + 10)(n + m - 10)$ **93.** $3(y - 2)(y^2 + 2y + 4)$ **95.** $(4x + 3y - 10)(4x + 3y + 10)$
97. $(x - 3)(x + 3)$ square units **99.** $(x - 4)(x + 4)$ square units **101.** $\pi(R - r)(R + r)$ square units **103.** $10a(a - b)(a + b)$ cubic units
105. $A = a \cdot a + a \cdot b + a \cdot b + b \cdot b = a^2 + 2ab + b^2 = (a + b)^2$ **107.** $b = \pm 36$; the middle term must equal $\pm$ twice the product of the quantities that are squared to get the first and last terms. **109.** We need to add 81 to make a perfect square trinomial.

111. $(b - 0.2)^2$ **113.** $\left(3b - \frac{1}{5}\right)\left(3b + \frac{1}{5}\right)$ **115.** $\left(\frac{x}{3} - \frac{y}{5}\right)\left(\frac{x}{3} + \frac{y}{5}\right)$ **117.** $\left(\frac{x}{2} - \frac{y}{3}\right)\left(\frac{x^2}{4} + \frac{xy}{6} + \frac{y^2}{9}\right)$

Section 4.7 Factoring: A General Strategy **1.** $2q(p + 5q)(p - 9q)$ **2.** $-3y(3x + 1)(5x - 9)$ **3.** $(9x - 10y)(9x + 10y)$
4. $-3n(m - 7)(m + 7)$ **5.** $(p - 8q)^2$ **6.** $5(2x + 3)^2$ **7.** $(4y - 5)(16y^2 + 20y + 25)$ **8.** $-2(2m + n)(4m^2 - 2mn + n^2)$
9. $5(2z^2 - 3z + 7)$ **10.** $3x(2y^2 + 27x^2)$ **11.** $(x^2 + 2)(2x + 5)$ **12.** $3(3x + 1)(x - 1)(x + 1)$ **13.** $(2x + y - 9)(2x + y + 9)$
14. $(4 - m - 4n)(4 + m + 4n)$ **15.** $G(x) = (2x + 7)(x - 2)$ **16.** $F(p) = 3(3p + 2)(3p - 2)$ **17.** $2(x - 12)(x + 6)$ **19.** $-3(y - 3)(y + 3)$
21. $(2b + 5)^2$ **23.** $2(2w + y^2)(4w^2 - 2wy^2 + y^4)$ **25.** $-3(z^2 - 4z + 6)$ **27.** $(4y + 3)(5y - 6)$ **29.** $(x - 4)(x^2 + 5)$ **31.** $2(100x^2 + 9y^2)$
33. $(x - 3)(x + 3)(x^2 + 9)$ **35.** prime **37.** $4q(3q + 1)^2$ **39.** $3mn(4m + 3)(2m - 7)$ **41.** $3r^2(r - 2s)(r^2 + 2rs + 4s^2)$
43. $2(x + 4)(x - 3)(x + 3)$ **45.** $(3x^2 - 1)(3x^2 + 1)$ **47.** $(w^2 + 3)(3w^2 - 5)$ **49.** $2y(2y + 1)$ **51.** $(p - 6q - 5)(p + 6q - 5)$
53. $(y + 2)(y^2 - 2y + 4)(y^3 - 2)$ **55.** $(p - 1)(p + 1)(p^2 + p + 1)(p^2 - p + 1)$ **57.** $-3(x + 5)(x - 3)(x + 3)$ **59.** $3a(1 - 3a)(1 + 3a)$
61. $2t(t^2 + 4)(2t - 3)(2t + 3)$ **63.** $2xy(x + 5)(x - 3)(x + 3)$ **65.** $f(x) = (x - 9)(x + 7)$ **67.** $P(m) = (7m + 3)(m + 4)$
69. $G(x) = -3(2x + 7)(2x - 7)$ **71.** $s(t) = -16(t + 2)(t - 8)$ **73.** $H(a) = (2a + 5)(a - 4)(a + 4)$ **75.** $(x + 3)(3x + 7)$ square units
77. $(x + y)(x - y)$ square units **79.** $(3x - 4)(9x^2 + 12x + 16)$ cubic units **81.** The factors of 9 are: 1, 9; 3, 3; −1, −9; −3, −3. None of these factors sum to 0. Therefore, $x^2 + 9$ is prime. **83.** $x^{\frac{1}{2}}(x - 3)(x + 3)$ **85.** $x^{-2}(x + 4)(x + 2)$ **87.** See pages 377–378.

Section 4.8 Polynomial Equations **1.** polynomial equation **2.** $a = 0$; $b = 0$ **3.** $\{-7, 0\}$ **4.** $\left\{-\frac{3}{4}, 3\right\}$ **5.** quadratic equation

6. $\{2, 3\}$ **7.** $\left\{-\frac{1}{3}, 5\right\}$ **8.** $\left\{-2, -\frac{2}{3}\right\}$ **9.** $\{-2, -1\}$ **10.** $\{-6, 4\}$ **11.** $\{-3, 1, 3\}$ **12. (a)** −1 and 9; $(-1, 12)$ and $(9, 12)$ are points

on the graph of g. **(b)** 1 and 7; $(1, -4)$ and $(7, -4)$ are points on the graph of g. **13.** Zeros: −4 and $\frac{5}{2}$; x-intercepts: −4 and $\frac{5}{2}$

14. 9 miles by 15 miles **15.** 60 boxes **16. (a)** After 4 seconds and after 6 seconds **(b)** After 10 seconds **17.** $\{-1, 3\}$ **19.** $\left\{-\frac{4}{3}, 0\right\}$

21. $\{-3, 0, 5\}$ **23.** $\{0, 4\}$ **25.** $\{0, 8\}$ **27.** $\{-5, 3\}$ **29.** $\{4, 9\}$ **31.** $\{3\}$ **33.** $\left\{-\frac{3}{5}, 1\right\}$ **35.** $\left\{\frac{5}{6}, 3\right\}$ **37.** $\{-8, 5\}$

39. $\left\{-6, \frac{5}{2}\right\}$ **41.** $\{-6, 2\}$ **43.** $\left\{-\frac{7}{2}, 2\right\}$ **45.** $\{-11, 3\}$ **47.** $\{-5, -1, 2\}$ **49.** $\left\{-\frac{1}{2}, 0, 3\right\}$ **51.** $\left\{-\frac{5}{2}, -2, 2\right\}$ **53.** $\left\{-\frac{3}{5}, -\frac{2}{3}, 0\right\}$

55. $\left\{\frac{4}{3}, 1\right\}$ **57. (a)** $x = -5$ or $x = -2$ **(b)** $x = -8$ or $x = 1$ $(-5, 2)$, $(-2, 2)$, $(-8, 20)$, and $(1, 20)$ are on the graph of f. **59. (a)** $x = 4$

or $x = -1$ **(b)** $x = 5$ or $x = -2$ $(-1, 3)$, $(4, 3)$, $(-2, 15)$, and $(5, 15)$ are on the graph of g. **61. (a)** $x = 0$ or $x = 4$ **(b)** $x = 5$ or $x = -1$

$(0, 5)$, $(4, 5)$, $(-1, -10)$, and $(5, -10)$ are on the graph of F. **63.** zeros: −7 and −2; x-intercepts: −7 and −2 **65.** zeros: $-\frac{1}{3}$ and $\frac{9}{2}$; x-intercepts: $-\frac{1}{3}$, $\frac{9}{2}$

67. zeros: −5, 0, and 4; x-intercepts: −5, 0, and 4 **69.** $\{-4, 6\}$ **71.** $\left\{-\frac{7}{2}, 2\right\}$ **73.** $\{0, 7\}$ **75.** $\left\{-\frac{6}{7}\right\}$

77. $\{-5, -2, 2\}$ **79.** $\varnothing$ or $\{\ \}$ **81.** $\left\{-2, -\dfrac{1}{2}, \dfrac{1}{2}, 2\right\}$ **83.** $\{-1, 0\}$ **85.** $\{x \mid x \ne -2, 2\}$ **87.** $\left\{x \mid x \ne \dfrac{1}{2}, 1\right\}$ **89.** The width is 16 cm and the length is 8 cm.   **91.** The base is 10 ft and the height is 22 ft.   **93.** 8 sides   **95.** 40 meters by 20 meters (along the river) or 10 meters by 80 meters (along the river).   **97.** 3 ft   **99.** The width is 11 in. and the length is 16 in.   **101. (a)** \$300   **(b)** 20 bicycles   **(c)** 15 bicycles   **103. (a)** after 2.5 seconds (on the way up), and again after 5 seconds (on the way down)   **(b)** after 7.5 seconds   **105.** $\{-0.61, 4.11\}$ **107.** $\{0.60, 24.90\}$ **109.** $\{-1.15, 1.75\}$

Chapter 4 Review   **1.** Coefficient: -7; Degree: 4   **2.** Coefficient: $\dfrac{1}{9}$; Degree: 3   **3.** $7x^3 - 2x^2 + x - 8$; Degree: 3   **4.** $y^4 - 3y^2 + 2y + 3$;

Degree: 4   **5.** $4x^2 + x - 11$ **6.** $-x^4 + 4x^3 - 5x^2 + 8x - 6$ **7.** $\dfrac{1}{4}x^2 - \dfrac{9}{2}x + \dfrac{1}{6}$ **8.** $\dfrac{5}{6}x^2 - x + \dfrac{13}{20}$ **9.** $10x^2y^2$ **10.** $-a^2b - 6ab^2 - 4$
11. (a) -24 **(b)** -8 **(c)** -29 **12. (a)** -82 **(b)** -1 **(c)** -7 **13. (a)** $x^2 + 7x - 1$ **(b)** 29   **14. (a)** $2x^3 - 2x^2 + x - 12$ **(b)** -2
15. (a) $P(x) = -2.5x^2 + 280x - 3290$ **(b)** \$2147.50   **16. (a)** 6 square units **(b)** 4 square units   **17.** $-12x^4y^3$ **18.** $6m^4n^7$
19. $-10a^3b^2 + 5a^2b^3 - 15a^2b^2$ **20.** $0.85c^3 + 2.15c^2 + 4.45c$ **21.** $x^2 - 7x - 18$ **22.** $-6x^2 + 26x - 8$ **23.** $2m^2 - 7mn - 4n^2$
24. $-2a^2 - 9a + 45$ **25.** $3x^3 + x^2 - 9x + 2$ **26.** $w^3 - 3w^2 - 12w + 32$ **27.** $2m^4 + m^3 - 11m^2 + 29m - 21$
28. $2p^3 + 11p^2q - 29pq^2 + 12q^3$ **29.** $9w^2 - 1$ **30.** $4x^2 - 25y^2$ **31.** $36k^2 - 60k + 25$ **32.** $9a^2 + 12ab + 4b^2$ **33.** $x^3 + 8$
34. $8x^3 - 27$ **35. (a)** $18x^2 - 27x - 35$ **(b)** 91   **36. (a)** $3x^3 + 5x^2 - x + 2$ **(b)** 270   **37.** $5x^2 - 30x + 53$ **38.** $-2xh + 3h - h^2$
39. $4x^2 - 2x$ **40.** $3w^4 - w^2 + 5w + 2$ **41.** $\dfrac{7}{2}y^2 + 6y - 3$ **42.** $\dfrac{m}{2n} + \dfrac{2}{n} - \dfrac{7}{2m}$ **43.** $3x + 4$ **44.** $-2x + 7 + \dfrac{5}{x + 5}$ **45.** $3z^2 + 2 - \dfrac{12}{2z + 3}$
46. $4k^2 + k - 2$ **47.** $8x^3 + 12x^2 + 18x + 27$ **48.** $2x^2 - 5x + 12 + \dfrac{2x + 7}{x^2 - 3x + 4}$ **49.** $5x + 1 + \dfrac{6}{x + 2}$ **50.** $9a + 4$ **51.** $3m^2 + 2m - 11$
52. $n^2 + 6n - 15 + \dfrac{7}{n - 4}$ **53.** $x^3 - x^2 + 7x - 7$ **54.** $2x^2 - 4x + 13 - \dfrac{34}{x + 2}$ **55. (a)** $x^2 + 5x - 3$ **(b)** 11   **56. (a)** $3x + 20 + \dfrac{9}{3x - 2}$
(b) $\dfrac{112}{11}$ **57. (a)** $2x^2 + 4x - 7$ **(b)** -7 **58. (a)** $3x^2 - 11x + 5 + \dfrac{2x - 3}{x^2 - x + 5}$ **(b)** $\dfrac{158}{17}$ **59.** 59   **60.** -45 **61.** $x - 2$ is a factor;
$f(x) = (x - 2)(3x + 7)$ **62.** $x + 4$ is not a factor   **63.** $(5x + 1)$ m   **64.** $(2x^2 + 5x + 3)$ square centimeters   **65.** $4(z + 6)$
66. $-7y(y - 13)$ **67.** $2xy(7x^2y - 4x + y)$ **68.** $5a^2b(6a^2b^2 + 3a - 5b)$ **69.** $(x + 5)(3x - 4)$ **70.** $(2c + 9)(3 - 4c)$
71. $(x - 5y)(6x + 5)$ **72.** $(a + 7)(2a - b - 1)$ **73.** $(x + 6)(x - 3)$ **74.** $(c + 2)(c - 5)$ **75.** $(7z + 8)(2z - 3)$ **76.** $(3w - 4)(7w + 2)$
77. $2x(x + 1)(x - 9)$ **78.** $5a^2(2a + 3)(a + 7)$ **79. (a)** $\dfrac{1}{2}n(n + 1)$ **(b)** 528   **80.** $R(x) = 2x(2600 - x^2)$ **81.** $(w + 2)(w - 13)$
82. prime   **83.** $-1(t - 12)(t + 6)$ **84.** $(m + 3)(m + 7)$ **85.** $(x + 20y)(x - 16y)$ **86.** $(r - 2s)(r - 3s)$ **87.** $(x + 3)(5x - 2)$
88. $(2m + 11)(3m + 4)$ **89.** prime   **90.** $2(t + 3)(4t - 1)$ **91.** $(2x - 1)(3x - 5)$ **92.** $(7r + 2s)(3r - s)$ **93.** $(5x - 3y)(4x - 9y)$
94. $-2(s - 7)(s + 1)$ **95.** $(x^2 + 1)(x^2 - 11)$ **96.** $(xy + 4)(10xy + 1)$ **97.** $(a + 7)(a - 8)$ **98.** $w(2w + 7)$ **99.** $(x + 11)^2$
100. $(w - 17)^2$ **101.** $(12 - c)^2$ **102.** $(x - 4)^2$ **103.** $(8y + 5)^2$ **104.** $12(z + 2)^2$ **105.** $(x - 14)(x + 14)$ **106.** $(7 - y)(7 + y)$
107. $(t - 15)(t + 15)$ **108.** $(2w - 9)(2w + 9)$ **109.** $(6x^2 - 5y)(6x^2 + 5y)$ **110.** $20m(2n - 1)(2n + 1)$ **111.** $(x - 7)(x^2 + 7x + 49)$
112. $(9 - y)(y^2 + 9y + 81)$ **113.** $(3x - 5y)(9x^2 + 15xy + 25y^2)$ **114.** $(2m^2 + 3n)(4m^4 - 6m^2n + 9n^2)$
115. $2(a - b)(a + b)(a^2 + ab + b^2)(a^2 - ab + b^2)$ **116.** $(y + 3)(y^2 - 6y + 21)$ **117.** $(x + 1)(x + 6)$ **118.** $-4xy^3(2x - 3)$
119. $7x(x - 1)(x - 4)$ **120.** $3(x - 3)(x + 2)$ **121.** $(2z - 15)^2$ **122.** $(3x + 7)(4x - 7)$ **123.** $(2n - 7)(5n + 1)$
124. $-(y - 2)(y + 4)$ **125.** $2(x - 5)(x^2 + 3)$ **126.** $9(h + 2)(3h^2 + 4)$ **127.** $5p(pq - 4)(pq + 4)$ **128.** $(m - 1)(m + 1)(m - 2)(m + 2)$
129. $-2(2m^2 - 7)(4m^4 + 14m^2 + 49)$ **130.** $(h - 1)(h + 1)(h + 2)$ **131.** $4(3x + y)(9x^2 - 3xy + y^2)$ **132.** $F(c) = (c - 12)^2$
133. $f(x) = -3(x - 5)(x + 3)$ **134.** $g(x) = 4(2x + 5)(2x - 5)$ **135.** $G(y) = 2(2y + 5)(4y^2 - 10y + 25)$ **136.** $f(x) = -4(x^2 + 4)$
137. $(x - 5)(x + 5)$ square units   **138.** $(4 - \pi)x^2$ square units   **139.** $\{-5, 13\}$ **140.** $\left\{0, -\dfrac{1}{2}, \dfrac{5}{3}\right\}$ **141.** $\{0, -4\}$ **142.** $\{-5, 3\}$
143. $\{-18, -3\}$ **144.** $\left\{\dfrac{2}{5}, -\dfrac{7}{3}\right\}$ **145.** $\{-11, 10\}$ **146.** $\{-6, -4\}$ **147.** $\{4, -2\}$ **148.** $\{-5, -2\}$ **149. (a)** $x = -8$ or $x = 3$
(b) $x = -7$ or $x = 2$; $(-8, 6), (3, 6), (-7, -4)$, and $(2, -4)$ are on the graph.   **150. (a)** $x = 0$ or $x = \dfrac{4}{5}$ **(b)** $x = -\dfrac{1}{5}$ or $x = 1$; $(0, 3)$,
$\left(\dfrac{4}{5}, 3\right), \left(-\dfrac{1}{5}, 4\right)$, and $(1, 4)$ are on the graph.   **151.** zeros: $-4, -2$, and 0; x-intercepts: $-4, -2$, and 0 **152.** zeros: $-\dfrac{3}{2}$ and 7; x-intercepts: $-\dfrac{3}{2}$ and 7
153. after 7 seconds   **154. (a)** 0.80   **(b)** 0.90

Chapter 4 Test   **1.** $-5x^7 + x^4 + 7x^2 - x + 1$; Degree: 7   **2.** $-\dfrac{5}{3}a^3b^2 + 9a^2b - 5ab - 4$ **3.** 7   **4.** $7x^3 - 4x^2 - 3x + 1$

5. $2a^3b^3 - 3a^3b^2 + 4a^2b$ **6.** $12x^2 + 47x - 17$ **7.** $4m^2 - 4mn + n^2$ **8.** $3z - 7 + \dfrac{-2z + 11}{2z^2 + 1}$ **9.** $5x + 3$ **10.** 2   **11.** 22

12. $4ab^2(3a^2 + 2a - 4b)$ **13.** $(2c + 7)(3c - 2)$ **14.** $(x - 16)(x + 3)$ **15.** $-(2p + 3)(7p - 2)$ **16.** $(z + 3)(5z - 8)$

17. $-2(7x - 4)^2$ **18.** $4(2x - 7)(2x + 7)$ **19.** $\left\{\dfrac{7}{3}, 1\right\}$ **20.** 9 meters by 12 meters

Getting Ready for Chapter 5: A Review of Operations on Rational Numbers

1. lowest terms   **2.** $\dfrac{5}{6}$ **3.** $\dfrac{20}{3}$ **4.** $\dfrac{3}{2}$ **5.** $\dfrac{1}{2}$ **6.** $\dfrac{5}{3}$ **7.** $-\dfrac{3}{5}$ **8.** $\dfrac{4}{3}$ **9.** $-\dfrac{5}{9}$ **10.** LCD $= 75$; $\dfrac{3}{25} = \dfrac{9}{75}, \dfrac{2}{15} = \dfrac{10}{75}$

11. LCD $= 126$; $\dfrac{5}{18} = \dfrac{35}{126}, -\dfrac{1}{63} = -\dfrac{2}{126}$ **12.** $\dfrac{19}{20}$ **13.** $\dfrac{17}{60}$ **14.** $-\dfrac{1}{6}$ **15.** $\dfrac{1}{3}$ **17.** $-\dfrac{3}{7}$ **19.** 5   **21.** $\dfrac{5}{3}$ **23.** -3 **25.** $\dfrac{1}{12}$ **27.** $\dfrac{2}{5}$
29. $-\dfrac{9}{4}$ **31.** 6   **33.** 2   **35.** $\dfrac{5}{3}$ **37.** $\dfrac{19}{20}$ **39.** $\dfrac{13}{12}$ **41.** $-\dfrac{23}{30}$ **43.** $\dfrac{41}{90}$ **45.** $-\dfrac{23}{40}$ **47.** $\dfrac{17}{120}$ **49.** $\dfrac{41}{45}$ **51.** $-\dfrac{59}{150}$

53. To find the least common denominator (LCD) between two rational numbers, factor each denominator as the product of prime numbers. First copy the common factors and then the uncommon factors. The product of these factors is the LCD.

Chapter 5 Rational Expressions and Rational Functions

Section 5.1 Multiplying and Dividing Rational Expressions

1. rational expression **2.** numerator; denominator **3.** False

4. $\{x | x \neq -6\}$ **5.** $\{z | z \neq 4, z \neq -7\}$ **6.** False **7.** $\dfrac{x-4}{x+7}$ **8.** $\dfrac{z^2+4z+16}{2z+5}$ **9.** $-(w+5)$ **10.** $\dfrac{(3p+2)(p-1)}{2(p+2)}$ **11.** -1

12. $-(m+n)$ **13.** $9a^2b^3$ **14.** $\dfrac{(m-5)(m+1)}{2}$ **15.** $\{x | x \neq -6, x \neq 5\}$ **16. (a)** $R(x)=x+1; \left\{x \middle| x \neq -3, x \neq \dfrac{5}{3}, x \neq 5\right\}$

(b) $H(x)=\dfrac{3x(x-5)}{4x+3}; \left\{x \middle| x \neq -1, x \neq -\dfrac{3}{4}, x \neq 0, x \neq \dfrac{5}{3}\right\}$ **17.** $\{x | x \neq -5\}$ **19.** $\{x | x \neq -2, x \neq 8\}$ **21.** $\left\{p \middle| p \neq -\dfrac{5}{2}, p \neq 2\right\}$

23. $\{x | x$ is any real number$\}$ or $(-\infty, \infty)$ **25.** $\{x | x \neq 1\}$ **27.** $\dfrac{2}{x-4}$ **29.** $p+3$ **31.** $\dfrac{5}{x^2}$ **33.** $\dfrac{q+3}{q-2}$ **35.** $\dfrac{y-4}{y+5}$ **37.** $-\dfrac{x+3}{x+5}$

39. $\dfrac{x-2}{2x(x-4)}$ **41.** $\dfrac{x-3y}{x-2y}$ **43.** $\dfrac{x^2+3}{x-5}$ **45.** $\dfrac{x^2-2x+4}{x-7}$ **47.** $\dfrac{1}{4x(x+3)}$ **49.** $\dfrac{x-2}{x-1}$ **51.** $\dfrac{(x+3)^2}{(x+5)(x+7)}$

53. $-\dfrac{(2q+1)(q+2)}{q+6}$ **55.** $x-3$ **57.** 1 **59.** $\dfrac{9(x+3)}{8x(x-4)}$ **61.** $\dfrac{2}{ab}$ **63.** $\dfrac{(p-5)(p+3)}{p(2p+1)}$ **65.** $\dfrac{x^2+3x+1}{3(x+1)}$ **67.** $\{x | x \neq 1\}$

69. $\left\{x \middle| x \neq -\dfrac{1}{2}, x \neq 4\right\}$ **71.** $\{x | x \neq -5, x \neq -1\}$ **73.** $\left\{x \middle| x \neq 2, x \neq \dfrac{5}{2}\right\}$ **75.** $\{x | x$ is any real number$\}$

77. (a) $\dfrac{(x+3)(x-1)}{2x+3}; \left\{x \middle| x \neq -6, x \neq -\dfrac{3}{2}, x \neq 5\right\}$ **(b)** $(x-5)(3x-1); \left\{x \middle| x \neq -6, x \neq -3, x \neq \dfrac{1}{3}\right\}$

79. (a) $\dfrac{(3x+5)(x+6)}{(x^2+x+1)(2x+7)}; \left\{x \middle| x \neq -\dfrac{7}{2}, x \neq 1, x \neq 2\right\}$ **(b)** $\dfrac{x-2}{x^2+x+1}; \left\{x \middle| x \neq -\dfrac{5}{3}, x \neq -1, x \neq 1\right\}$ **81.** $\dfrac{z+3}{2}$ **83.** $\dfrac{m-2n}{2(m-n)}$

85. $\dfrac{4}{w}$ **87.** $\dfrac{2(x+2)}{(x+1)(x-1)}$ **89.** Answers will vary. One possible rational expression is $\dfrac{x}{x-3}$.

91. Answers will vary. One possible rational expression is $\dfrac{7}{(x+4)(x-5)} - \dfrac{7}{x^2-x-20}$. **93.** $R(x)=\dfrac{4}{x^2+x-2}$

95. (a) approximately 9.8208 m/sec^2 **(b)** approximately 9.8159 m/sec^2 **(c)** approximately 9.7936 m/sec^2 **97. (a)** $\{x | x \neq 2\}$

(b)

x	3	2.5	2.1	2.01	2.001	2.0001
$f(x)$	1	2	10	100	1000	10,000

f gets larger in the positive direction

(c)

x	1	1.5	1.9	1.99	1.999	1.9999
$f(x)$	-1	-2	-10	-100	-1000	$-10,000$

f gets larger in the negative direction

(d) f gets larger in the positive direction; f gets larger in the negative direction; these results are the same as those in parts (b) and (c).

99. $\dfrac{1}{x(x+1)}$ **101.** A rational expression is simplified provided there are no common factors between the numerator and denominator.

103. It is not a rational expression because $\sqrt{x} = x^{\frac{1}{2}}$. A rational expression is the ratio of two polynomials and polynomials must have non-negative integer exponents (1/2 is not a non-negative integer).

105.   **107.**   **109.**   **111.** Answers will vary. Ideally, the linear functions would be graphed using the properties of a linear function (i.e. slope and intercepts). The functions in problems 109 and 110 are likely graphed using point-plotting, which is less efficient than using properties.

Section 5.2 Adding and Subtracting Rational Expressions

1. $2x-1$ **2.** $\dfrac{3(x+3)}{x+5}$ **3.** $\dfrac{4x-3}{x-5}$ **4.** least common denominator

5. $24x^2y^3$ **6.** $(x+2)^2(x-7)$ **7.** $\dfrac{9a+8}{30a^2}$ **8.** $-\dfrac{1}{6y}$ **9.** $\dfrac{4x^2+10x-5}{(x-1)(x+2)}$ **10.** $\dfrac{(x-1)(3x+7)}{(x+2)(x+4)(2x+3)}$ **11.** $\dfrac{x^2+15x+5}{(2x-3)(x+2)^2}$

12. $\dfrac{-4}{x-2}$ **13.** $\dfrac{3x+5}{x+1}$ **15.** $\dfrac{2x-1}{2x+5}$ **17.** $\dfrac{1}{x-5}$ **19.** $\dfrac{x-3}{x+3}$ **21.** $\dfrac{3x-1}{x-5}$ **23.** $3x-1$ **25.** LCD $= 8x^3$

27. LCD $= 90x^3y^2$ **29.** LCD $= (x-4)(x+2)$ **31.** LCD $= (x-4)(x+3)(x-5)$ **33.** LCD $= p^2(p+2)(2p-1)$ **35.** $\dfrac{5x+6}{8x^2}$

37. $\dfrac{25b-16a}{60a^2b^2}$ **39.** $\dfrac{14(y-1)}{(y-5)(y+3)}$ **41.** $\dfrac{a+4}{a+2}$ **43.** $\dfrac{-2(x-11)}{(x+3)(x-2)(x+4)}$ **45.** $\dfrac{2x^2-5x+5}{(x+2)(x+1)(x-2)}$

47. $\dfrac{-11w+9}{(2w+1)(w+1)(w-3)}$ **49.** $\dfrac{2x^2+xy-5y^2}{(x-3y)^2(x+y)}$ **51.** $\dfrac{1}{(x+1)(x-1)}$ **53.** 0 **55.** $\dfrac{6}{w(w-2)}$ **57.** $\dfrac{(2p+1)(p-8)}{(p+3)^2(2p-5)}$

59. $\dfrac{x+2}{x(x-1)^2}$ **61.** $\dfrac{3}{x^2+3x+9}$ **63.** $x-1$ **65.** $\dfrac{7x+15}{x+3}$ **67.** $\dfrac{-1}{(b-2)(b+4)}$ **69.** $\dfrac{y-3}{y+3}$ **71.** $\dfrac{7x+9}{(x-2)(x-3)(x+1)}$

73. (a) $\dfrac{5x-1}{(x-2)(x+1)}$ **(b)** $\{x | x \neq -1, x \neq 2\}$ **75. (a)** $\dfrac{2x+7}{(x-4)(x+3)}$ **(b)** $\{x | x \neq -3, x \neq -1, x \neq 4\}$ **(c)** $\dfrac{-1}{(x-4)(x+3)}$

(d) $\{x | x \neq -3, x \neq -1, x \neq 4\}$ **77. (a)** $S(x) = \dfrac{2x^3+8000}{x}$ **(b)** $S(10) = 1000$; if the length of the base is 10 inches, then the surface area of the box will be 1000 square inches.

79. (a) $\dfrac{200s + 500}{s(s + 10)}$ **(b)** $T(50) = 3.5$; if the average speed for the first 50 miles of the trip is 50 miles per hour, then it will take a total time of 3.5 hours to get to the neighboring university.

81. $\dfrac{x + y}{xy}$ **83.** Completely factor each expression in the denominator of the rational expressions. Copy all common factors that are numerical. Then, copy all common variables and use the largest exponent for the LCD. Finally, copy all uncommon factors. The product of these factors represents the LCD. **85.** $4a^2 - 12a$ **87.** $p^2 - 9$ **89.** $w^3 - 8$ **91.** $x^2 + 2x + 4$

Section 5.3 Complex Rational Expressions

1. complex rational expression **2.** $\dfrac{7}{5}$ **3.** $\dfrac{4(z - 4)}{z}$ **4.** $\dfrac{1}{4}$ **5.** $\dfrac{7}{5}$ **6.** $\dfrac{4(z - 4)}{z}$

7. $\dfrac{-4(x + 2)}{x(x + 5)}$ **8.** $\dfrac{ab}{3b - a}$ **9.** $\dfrac{4}{9}$ **11.** $\dfrac{x + 1}{x - 1}$ **13.** $\dfrac{-2a}{(a - 2)^2}$ **15.** $\dfrac{1}{(x - 1)(x + 3)}$ **17.** $-\dfrac{23}{12}$ **19.** $\dfrac{(w - 1)(w + 1)}{w^2 + 1}$

21. $\dfrac{x + 2}{(x - 2)(x - 7)}$ **23.** $\dfrac{z^2 + 4}{4z}$ **25.** $\dfrac{1}{y + 3}$ **27.** $2(n - m)$ **29.** $\dfrac{x + 3}{x(x - 3)}$ **31.** $-x$ **33.** $\dfrac{1}{(x - 1)(x - 3)}$ **35.** $\dfrac{2(x + 1)}{x + 4}$

37. $-b$ **39.** $\dfrac{3xy}{y - x}$ **41.** $\dfrac{mn}{(m + n)^2}$ **43.** $\dfrac{1}{4(b + a)}$ **45. (a)** $\dfrac{R_1 R_2}{R_1 + R_2}$ **(b)** approximately 2.857 ohms **47. (a)** $\dfrac{R_1 R_2}{(n - 1)(R_1 + R_2)}$

(b) 0.375 meter **49. (a)** $\dfrac{2x + 1}{x + 1}$ **(b)** $\dfrac{3x + 2}{2x + 1}$ **(c)** $\dfrac{5x + 3}{3x + 2}$ **(d)** $\dfrac{8x + 5}{5x + 3}$ **(e)** from part (a): 2, 1, 1; from part (b): 3, 2, 1; from part (c): 5, 3, 2; from part (d): 8, 5, 3; Each number is the sum of the previous two. The sequence begins 1, 1, 2, 3, 5, 8.

51. $-\dfrac{2x + h}{x^2(x + h)^2}$ **53.** $-\dfrac{1}{(x - 1)(x + h - 1)}$ **55.** Answers will vary. **57.** $\{-4\}$ **59.** $\left\{-\dfrac{109}{4}\right\}$

Putting the Concepts Together (Sections 5.1–5.3)

1. $\left\{x \middle| x \neq -\dfrac{1}{3}, x \neq 6\right\}$ **2.** $\dfrac{-4n}{2n + 3}$ **3.** $\dfrac{2p - 5q}{3p - 4q}$ **4.** $\dfrac{a(a - 5)}{2(a + 6)}$ **5.** $\dfrac{(x + 2)(x - 7)}{(3x + 1)^2}$

6. $\dfrac{x - 5}{x - 2}$ **7.** $\dfrac{n}{(n - 2)(n - 3)}$ **8.** $\dfrac{3y^2 - 3y - 29}{(y - 3)(y - 4)(y + 8)}$ **9.** $\dfrac{3}{(x - 7)(2x + 1)}$ **10.** $\dfrac{3x^2 - 14x - 1}{(x - 4)(x - 7)}$ **11.** $\dfrac{n + m}{mn}$ **12.** $\dfrac{z + 3}{z - 5}$

Section 5.4 Rational Equations

1. rational equation **2.** $\{-2\}$ **3.** $\left\{\dfrac{2}{3}\right\}$ **4.** $\{-2\}$ **5.** $\left\{-\dfrac{5}{3}\right\}$ **6.** $\{8\}$ **7.** Extraneous solutions

8. True **9.** $\{\ \}$ or $\varnothing$ **10.** $\{0\}$ **11.** $\left\{-\dfrac{3}{2}, 4\right\}$ **12.** $\{-5\}$ **13.** $\left\{-1, \dfrac{3}{2}\right\}$; $(-1, 1)$ and $\left(\dfrac{3}{2}, 1\right)$ **14.** After $\dfrac{1}{2}$ hour and 12 hours

15. $\{-4\}$ **17.** $\{-16\}$ **19.** $\varnothing$ or $\{\ \}$ **21.** $\{-1, 5\}$ **23.** $\left\{-\dfrac{1}{3}, \dfrac{3}{2}\right\}$ **25.** $\{1\}$ **27.** $\{4\}$ **29.** $\{-5, 6\}$ **31.** $\{4\}$ **33.** $\varnothing$ or $\{\ \}$

35. $\{-8\}$ **37.** $\left\{\dfrac{1}{4}\right\}$ **39.** $\{-1\}$ **41.** $x = -9$ or $x = 1$; $(1, 10)$ and $(9, 10)$ **43.** $x = -\dfrac{1}{2}$ or $x = -4$; $\left(-\dfrac{1}{2}, -9\right)$ and $(-4, -9)$

45. $x = 6$; $\left(6, \dfrac{9}{2}\right)$ **47.** $x = -5$ or $x = 3$; $(-5, 3)$ and $\left(3, \dfrac{1}{3}\right)$ **49.** $\left\{\dfrac{1}{4}\right\}$ **51.** $\{3\}$ **53.** $\{-19\}$ **55.** $\{2\}$ **57.** $\left\{0, -\dfrac{3}{5}\right\}$ **59.** $-\dfrac{1}{3}$; x-int: $-\dfrac{1}{3}$

61. $-4, \dfrac{3}{2}$; x-int: $-4, \dfrac{3}{2}$ **63.** $-2, 2$; x-int: $-2, 2$ **65.** either 50 or 100 bicycles **67. (a)** 80% **(b)** 90% **69.** 650 walks

71. Answers will vary. One possibility follows: $\dfrac{2}{x - 1} = \dfrac{3}{x + 1}$ **73.** $\left\{-\dfrac{5}{3}, -1\right\}$ **75.** We find the domain of the rational equation so that we can identify extraneous solutions.

77. $\left\{-\dfrac{1}{2}, 3\right\}$ **79.** $\dfrac{-2x^2 + 6x + 5}{(x - 2)(x + 1)}$ **81.** $\{-1, 10\}$ **83.** $\{12\}$ **85.** $\{-13\}$ **87.** $\{\ \}$ or $\varnothing$

Section 5.5 Rational Inequalities

1. rational **2.** $\{x | x < -3$ or $x \geq 7\}$; $(-\infty, -3) \cup [7, \infty)$

3. $\{x | -5 < x < 1\}$; $(-5, 1)$

4. $\{x | -2 < x < 1\}$; $(-2, 1)$

5. $\{x | x < -1$ or $x > 4\}$ or $(-\infty, -1) \cup (4, \infty)$

7. $\{x | -9 < x < 3\}$ or $(-9, 3)$

9. $\{x | x \leq -10$ or $x > 4\}$ or $(-\infty, -10] \cup (4, \infty)$

11. $\left\{x | x \leq -8$ or $-\dfrac{5}{3} \leq x < 2\right\}$ or $(-\infty, -8] \cup \left[-\dfrac{5}{3}, 2\right)$

13. $\{x | x > -1\}$ or $(-1, \infty)$

15. $\left\{x \middle| \dfrac{3}{2} < x < 3\right\}$ or $\left(\dfrac{3}{2}, 3\right)$

17. $\{x | 0 < x \leq 1$ or $x > 4\}$ or $(0, 1] \cup (4, \infty)$

19. $\{x | -5 < x < 2$ or $x \geq 23\}$ or $(-5, 2) \cup [23, \infty)$

21. $\left\{x \middle| -3 < x < \dfrac{1}{2}$ or $x > 5\right\}$ or $\left(-3, \dfrac{1}{2}\right) \cup (5, \infty)$

23. $\{x | x > -3\}$; $(-3, \infty)$

25. $\{x | -7 \leq x < 8\}$ or $[-7, 8)$

27. $\{x|x \geq 4\}; [4, \infty)$ **29.** $\{x|x < -4 \text{ or } x \geq 9\}$ or $(-\infty, -4) \cup [9, \infty)$

31. $\{x|-1 < x \leq 6\}$ or $(-1, 6]$ **33.** $\left\{x|-2 < x < \dfrac{5}{2}\right\}$ or $\left(-2, \dfrac{5}{2}\right)$ **35.** 100 or more bicycles

37. Answers will vary. One possibility: $\dfrac{1}{x-2} > 0$ **39.** Because -1 is not in the domain of the variable x, the solution set is $\{x|-1 < x \leq 4\}$.

41. 2   **43.** $-\dfrac{7}{2}, 2$ **45.** $\dfrac{2}{3}$ **47.** $\{x|x \leq -4 \text{ or } x > -1\}$ or $(-\infty, -4] \cup (-1, \infty)$ **49.** $\{x|7 < x < 26\}$ or $(7, 26)$

Section 5.6 Models Involving Rational Expressions

1. (a) $b = \dfrac{Y-G}{Y}$ **(b)** 0.9   **2.** proportion; similar   **3.** 120 feet

4. $AB = 12; DF = 4$ **5.** approximately 312.4 million people   **6.** $\dfrac{40}{3}$ hours or 13 hours, 20 minutes   **7.** 33.33 minutes or 33 minutes,

20 seconds   **8.** 4 miles per hour   **9.** $P_1 = \dfrac{V_2 P_2}{V_1}$ **11.** $t = \dfrac{R-r}{R}$ **13.** $x = \dfrac{y - y_1 + mx_1}{m}$ **15.** $v = \dfrac{\omega(I + mr^2)}{rm}$ **17.** $m = \dfrac{MV}{v-V}$

19. $AB = 16; DF = 5$ **21.** 283,941,177 people   **23.** approximately \$6.40   **25.** 12.5 pounds   **27.** approximately 34.3 minutes   **29.** 6 hours

31. 10 hours   **33.** 35 miles per hour   **35.** 1.8 feet per second   **37.** Shockey will be on his own 35-yard line when Urlacher catches up to him.

39. 8 miles per hour   **41.** 45 miles per hour   **43.** Approximately 2.00 m   **45.** a^{15} **47.** $\dfrac{a^4}{b^6}$ **49.** $\dfrac{n^{12}}{9m^4}$

Chapter 5 Review

1. $\left\{x|x \neq \dfrac{2}{3}\right\}$ **2.** $\{a|a \neq -4, a \neq 7\}$ **3.** $\{m|m \text{ is any real number}\}$ or $(-\infty, \infty)$ **4.** $\{n|n \neq -2, n \neq 4\}$

5. $\dfrac{6}{x-5}$ **6.** $\dfrac{2}{y^3}$ **7.** $\dfrac{w-7}{w+4}$ **8.** $\dfrac{3a+b}{5a+2b}$ **9.** $\dfrac{-1}{3m+1}$ **10.** $\dfrac{n^2+3}{n-4}$ **11.** $\dfrac{p}{2(p-6)}$ **12.** $\dfrac{2q}{3(q-5)}$ **13.** $\dfrac{(x-4)(x+6)}{(x+2)^2}$

14. $\dfrac{2(y+5)}{y(y-5)}$ **15.** $\dfrac{3a+b}{2a-b}$ **16.** $\dfrac{3}{m-2}$ **17.** $\dfrac{9c}{2d^3}$ **18.** $\dfrac{6(z-3)}{7}$ **19.** $\dfrac{x+7}{x-3}$ **20.** $\dfrac{m+4n}{m+5n}$ **21.** $\dfrac{2(p-q)}{p+3q}$ **22.** $\dfrac{2a+5}{9a^2+6a+4}$

23. $(x+2)^2; \left\{x|x \neq \dfrac{1}{2}, x \neq 5\right\}$ **24.** $\dfrac{x-5}{x+7}; \left\{x|x \neq -7, x \neq -2, x \neq \dfrac{1}{2}\right\}$ **25.** $\dfrac{(x-5)^2}{(2x-1)^2}; \left\{x|x \neq -2, x \neq \dfrac{1}{2}, x \neq 5\right\}$

26. $\dfrac{(x+2)^2(x+7)}{x-5}; \left\{x|x \neq -7, x \neq -2, x \neq \dfrac{1}{2}, x \neq 5\right\}$ **27.** $\dfrac{4x+3}{x-5}$ **28.** 4   **29.** $\dfrac{a+6}{a-2}$ **30.** $\dfrac{b+5}{2b+3}$ **31.** $3c$ **32.** $\dfrac{d+3}{d+1}$

33. LCD $= 36x^4$ **34.** LCD $= (y+2)(y-9)$ **35.** LCD $= p^2(2p+5)(p-4)$ **36.** LCD $= (q+5)(q-1)(q-3)$

37. $\dfrac{m^2+4n^2}{m^3n^4}$ **38.** $\dfrac{9x-7y^2}{6x^2y^3}$ **39.** $\dfrac{p^2+q^2}{(p-q)(p+q)}$ **40.** $\dfrac{20x+17}{(x-7)(x-3)(x+4)}$ **41.** $\dfrac{y+8}{(y-1)^2(y+2)}$ **42.** $\dfrac{11a+7b}{(2a-3b)(2a+3b)}$

43. $\dfrac{6x}{x+3}$ **44.** $\dfrac{5}{n^2-5n+25}$ **45.** $\dfrac{2n}{m-7n}$ **46.** $\dfrac{1}{z-3}$ **47.** $\dfrac{3}{y+2}$ **48.** $\dfrac{a-3}{(a+4)(a-2)}$ **49. (a)** $\dfrac{x^2+x+10}{(x-4)(x+2)}$

(b) $\{x|x \neq -2, x \neq 4\}$ **50. (a)** $\dfrac{x+8}{(2x-5)(2x+1)}$ **(b)** $\left\{x|x \neq -3, x \neq -\dfrac{1}{2}, x \neq \dfrac{5}{2}\right\}$ **51.** $x+1$ **52.** $\dfrac{xy}{x+y}$ **53.** $\dfrac{a-b}{a+b}$

54. $\dfrac{-a}{a+3}$ **55.** $\dfrac{3t+4}{5t^2+1}$ **56.** $\dfrac{1}{a+b}$ **57.** $\dfrac{z+1}{z-1}$ **58.** $\dfrac{x-1}{x+1}$ **59.** $\dfrac{x+y}{x-y}$ **60.** 1   **61.** $\dfrac{2}{x(x-2)}$ **62.** $\dfrac{z-5}{z+5}$ **63.** $\dfrac{n}{m}$

64. $\dfrac{2}{(x+1)^2(x-2)}$ **65.** $\dfrac{3y^2-3x^2}{xy}$ **66.** $\dfrac{12d-2c}{c}$ **67.** $\{10\}$ **68.** $\left\{\dfrac{4}{3}\right\}$ **69.** $\{-2, 7\}$ **70.** $\{9\}$ **71.** $\{2\}$ **72.** $\{3\}$

73. $\varnothing$ or $\{\ \}$ **74.** $\{-3\}$ **75.** $\{6\}$ **76.** $\left\{-\dfrac{4}{3}\right\}$ **77.** $\{5\}$ **78.** $\varnothing$ or $\{\ \}$ **79.** $x = 5; (5, 2)$

80. $x = -3$ or $x = 7; (-3, 4)$ and $(7, 4)$ **81.** $\{x|x < -2 \text{ or } x \geq 4\}$ or $(-\infty, -2) \cup [4, \infty)$

82. $\{y|-4 < y < 5\}$ or $(-4, 5)$ **83.** $\{z|-3 < z < 3\}$ or $(-3, 3)$

84. $\{w|w < -7 \text{ or } 2 < w < 4\}$ or $(-\infty, -7) \cup (2, 4)$

85. $\{m|-5 < m < 2 \text{ or } m \geq 5\}$ or $(-5, 2) \cup [5, \infty)$

86. $\{n|0 \leq n < 2\}$ or $[0, 2)$ **87.** $\left\{a|2 < a < \dfrac{7}{2}\right\}$ or $\left(2, \dfrac{7}{2}\right)$

88. $\{c|c < -6 \text{ or } 0 < c < 2\}$ or $(-\infty, -6) \cup (0, 2)$ **89.** $\left\{x|-\dfrac{3}{2} < x < 4\right\}$ or $\left(-\dfrac{3}{2}, 4\right)$

90. $\{x|x \leq -5 \text{ or } x > -1\}$ or $(-\infty, -5] \cup (-1, \infty)$ **91.** $C = \dfrac{C_1 C_2}{C_2 + C_1}$ **92.** $T_2 = \dfrac{T_1 P_2 V_2}{P_1 V_1}$ **93.** $G = \dfrac{4\pi^2 a^2}{MT}$ **94.** $x = z \cdot \sigma + \mu$

95. $AB = 24$ and $DF = 10$ **96.** 18.75 feet   **97.** 104 grams   **98.** \$78.00   **99.** 28.8 minutes (or 28 minutes and 48 seconds)

100. 2.8 hours (or 2 hours and 48 minutes)   **101.** 21 hours; 28 hours   **102.** 3 minutes   **103.** 60 miles per hour   **104.** 15 miles per hour

105. Todd's average walking speed is 3 miles per hour and his average running speed is 12 miles per hour.   **106.** 60 miles per hour

Chapter 5 Test

1. $\left\{x|x \neq -\dfrac{1}{2}, x \neq 7\right\}$ **2.** $\dfrac{2m-3}{3m-1}$ **3.** $-\dfrac{1}{a+4b}$ **4.** $\dfrac{2x+5}{2x(x-4)}$ **5.** $\dfrac{y+4}{3y+1}$

6. $\dfrac{2q}{p-q}$ **7.** $\dfrac{3c-4}{(c-2)(c-1)}$ **8.** $\dfrac{x-4}{3(x-2)(x-5)}; \{x|x \neq -2, x \neq 0, x \neq 2, x \neq 4, x \neq 5\}$

9. $\dfrac{3(x^2 + 2x - 4)}{x(x + 2)(x - 2)}$; $\{x \mid x \neq -2, x \neq 0, x \neq 2\}$ **10.** $\dfrac{a}{a + 1}$ **11.** $\dfrac{4(d - 3)}{-3(d + 6)}$ **12.** $\{-1\}$ **13.** $\varnothing$ or $\{\ \}$

14. $\left\{x \mid 2 < x \leq \dfrac{11}{2}\right\}$ or $\left(2, \dfrac{11}{2}\right]$    **15.** $k = \dfrac{FD^2}{q_1 q_2}$ **16.** 120 seconds (or 2 minutes)

17. 2.4 hours (or 2 hours and 24 minutes)   **18.** 3 miles per hour

Cumulative Review Chapters R–5

1. 12   **2.** $2x^2 - 2x + 7$ **3.** -3 **4.** $\{-8\}$ **5.** $\left\{x \mid -5 \leq x \leq \dfrac{1}{3}\right\}$; $\left[-5, \dfrac{1}{3}\right]$ **6.** $\left\{x \mid x \neq -\dfrac{3}{2}, x \neq 5\right\}$ **7.** **(a)** 24 **(b)** $-\dfrac{19}{16}$ **(c)** $x^2 - x - 6$

8.   **9.** $y = -\dfrac{3}{5}x - 2$; $3x + 5y = -10$ **10.** $y = 4x - 7$; $4x - y = 7$ **11.** 2160 mg   **12.** $\begin{cases} 2x - 3y = 7 \\ 5x + 2y = 8 \end{cases}$

13. (a) $\begin{bmatrix} 1 & 1 & 0 & | & -3 \\ 0 & 2 & -1 & | & -1 \\ 0 & -5 & 1 & | & 16 \end{bmatrix}$ **(b)** $\begin{bmatrix} 1 & 1 & 0 & | & -3 \\ 0 & 1 & -\frac{1}{2} & | & -\frac{1}{2} \\ 0 & -5 & 1 & | & 16 \end{bmatrix}$ **14.** $\left(-3, \dfrac{1}{4}\right)$ **15.** -14

16.   **17.** $8x^2 - 13xy + 9y^2$ **18.** $3x^2 + x + 27$ **19.** $2x^3 - 11x^2 + 24x - 18$ **20.** $2x^2 - 5x + 9$

21. $(x + 5)(x - 2)(x^2 + 2x + 4)$ **22.** $(2x - 3)(3x + 5)$ **23.** $\dfrac{x - 7}{x + 2}$ **24.** $\dfrac{x + 1}{(x - 2)(x - 1)(x + 3)}$ **25.** 48 minutes

Getting Ready for Chapter 6: Square Roots

1. radical sign   **2.** principal square root   **3.** $-4, 4$ **4.** 9   **5.** 30   **6.** $\dfrac{1}{2}$ **7.** 0.4   **8.** 13   **9.** 15   **10.** 10   **11.** 14   **12.** 7

13. True   **14.** rational; 20   **15.** irrational; ≈ 6.32 **16.** not a real number   **17.** rational; -14 **18.** $|a|$ **19.** 14   **20.** $|z|$ **21.** $|2x + 3|$

22. $|p - 6|$ **23.** 1   **25.** -10 **27.** $\dfrac{1}{2}$ **29.** 0.6   **31.** 1.6   **33.** not a real number   **35.** rational; 8   **37.** rational; $\dfrac{1}{4}$ **39.** irrational; 6.63

41. irrational; 7.07   **43.** not a real number   **45.** 8   **47.** 19   **49.** $|r|$ **51.** $|x + 4|$ **53.** $|4x - 3|$ **55.** $|2y + 3|$ **57.** 13   **59.** 17

61. not a real number   **63.** 15   **65.** -8 **67.** 6   **69.** not a real number   **71.** -4 **73.** 13   **75.** The square roots of 36 are -6 and 6;

$\sqrt{36} = 6$ **77.** $\dfrac{4\sqrt{13}}{3}$; 4.81   **79.** Answers will vary. One reasonable explanation follows. Because $a^2 \geq 0$, the radicand of $\sqrt{a^2}$ is greater than or equal to 0 (nonnegative). The principal square root of a nonnegative number is nonnegative. The absolute value ensures this result.

Chapter 6 Radicals and Rational Exponents

Section 6.1 nth Roots and Rational Exponents   **1.** index   **2.** 4   **3.** 3   **4.** -6 **5.** not a real number   **6.** $\dfrac{1}{2}$ **7.** 3.68   **8.** 2.99

9. 5   **10.** $|z|$ **11.** $3x - 2$ **12.** 2   **13.** $-\dfrac{2}{3}$ **14.** $\sqrt[n]{a}$ **15.** 5   **16.** -3 **17.** -8 **18.** not a real number   **19.** $\sqrt{b}$ **20.** $(8b)^{\frac{1}{5}}$

21. $\left(\dfrac{mn^5}{3}\right)^{\frac{1}{8}}$ **22.** $\sqrt[n]{a^m}$; $\left(\sqrt[n]{a}\right)^m$ **23.** 64   **24.** 9   **25.** -8 **26.** 16   **27.** not a real number   **28.** 13.57   **29.** 1.74   **30.** $a^{\frac{3}{8}}$

31. $(12ab^3)^{\frac{9}{4}}$ **32.** $\dfrac{1}{9}$ **33.** 4   **34.** $\dfrac{1}{(13x)^{3/2}}$ **35.** 5   **37.** -3 **39.** -5 **41.** $-\dfrac{1}{2}$ **43.** 3   **45.** 2.92   **47.** 1.86   **49.** 5   **51.** $|m|$

53. $x - 3$ **55.** $-|3p + 1|$ **57.** 2   **59.** -6 **61.** 2   **63.** -2 **65.** $\dfrac{2}{5}$ **67.** -5 **69.** not a real number   **71.** $(3x)^{\frac{1}{3}}$ **73.** $\left(\dfrac{x}{3}\right)^{\frac{1}{4}}$

75. 32   **77.** -64 **79.** 16   **81.** 16   **83.** 8   **85.** $\dfrac{1}{12}$ **87.** 125   **89.** 32   **91.** $x^{\frac{3}{4}}$ **93.** $(3x)^{\frac{2}{5}}$ **95.** $\left(\dfrac{5x}{y}\right)^{\frac{3}{2}}$ **97.** $(9ab)^{\frac{4}{3}}$ **99.** 4.47

101. 10.08   **103.** 1.26   **105.** $5x$ **107.** -10 **109.** 8   **111.** 243   **113.** not a real number   **115.** $\dfrac{3}{4}$ **117.** 0.2   **119.** 127

121. not a real number   **123.** $3p - 5$ **125.** -18 **127.** 2   **129.** 8   **131.** 16   **133.** 10; 10   **135. (a)** about 21.25°F **(b)** about 17.36°F

(c) about -15.93°F   **137. (a)** $\sqrt{\dfrac{8r\rho_w g}{3C\rho}}$ m/s **(b)** about 7.38 m/s   **139.** $(-9)^{\frac{1}{2}} = \sqrt{-9}$, but there is no real number whose square is -9. However,

$-9^{\frac{1}{2}} = -1 \cdot 9^{\frac{1}{2}} = -1\sqrt{9} = -3$.   **141.** If $\dfrac{m}{n}$, in lowest terms, is positive, then $a^{\frac{m}{n}}$ is a real number provided $\sqrt[n]{a}$ exists. If $\dfrac{m}{n}$, in lowest terms, is negative,

then $a^{\frac{m}{n}}$ is a real number provided $a \neq 0$ and $\sqrt[n]{a}$ exists.   **143.** $(x + 2)(x - 1)^3$ **145.** $\dfrac{z - 6}{z - 1}$

Section 6.2 Simplify Expressions Using the Laws of Exponents

1. $a^r b^r$ **2.** a^{r+s} **3.** $5^{\frac{11}{12}}$ **4.** 8   **5.** 10   **6.** $ab^{\frac{5}{6}}$ **7.** $x^{\frac{2}{3}}$ **8.** $\dfrac{4x^{\frac{1}{2}}}{y^{\frac{2}{3}}}$

9. $\dfrac{5x^{\frac{5}{8}}}{y^{8}}$ **10.** $\dfrac{200a^{\frac{1}{2}}}{b^{\frac{2}{3}}}$ **11.** 6   **12.** $2a^2b^3$ **13.** $\sqrt[12]{x^5}$ **14.** $\sqrt[6]{a}$ **15.** $x^{\frac{1}{2}}(20x+9)$ **16.** $\dfrac{12x+1}{x^{\frac{2}{3}}}$ **17.** 25   **19.** 8   **21.** $\dfrac{1}{2^6}$ **23.** $\dfrac{1}{x^{\frac{7}{12}}}$

25. 2   **27.** $\dfrac{125}{8}$ **29.** $x^{\frac{1}{2}}y^{\frac{2}{9}}$ **31.** $\dfrac{x^{\frac{1}{6}}}{y^{\frac{1}{3}}}$ **33.** $\dfrac{2a}{b^{\frac{3}{4}}}$ **35.** $\dfrac{x^{\frac{1}{18}}}{2y^{\frac{4}{9}}}$ **37.** $8x^{\frac{1}{8}}y^{\frac{1}{2}}$ **39.** x^4 **41.** 2   **43.** $2ab^4$ **45.** $\sqrt[4]{x}$ **47.** $\sqrt[6]{x^5}$ **49.** $\sqrt[8]{x^3}$

51. $\sqrt[6]{3^7}$ **53.** 1   **55.** $5x^{\frac{1}{2}}(x+3)$ **57.** $8(x+2)^{\frac{2}{3}}(3x+1)$ **59.** $\dfrac{6x+5}{x^{\frac{1}{2}}}$ **61.** $\dfrac{2(10x-27)}{(x-4)^{\frac{1}{3}}}$ **63.** $5(x^2+4)^{\frac{1}{2}}(x^2+3x+4)$ **65.** 2

67. 4   **69.** 10   **71.** 5   **73.** 0   **75.** $\dfrac{1}{48}$ **77.** $x^2-2x^{\frac{1}{2}}$ **79.** $\dfrac{2}{y^{\frac{1}{3}}}+6y^{\frac{2}{3}}$ **81.** $4z^3-32=4(z-2)(z^2+2z+4)$ **83.** 5   **85.** 3   **87.** $\sqrt[24]{x}$

89. 36   **91.** $\{x \mid x>-1\}$ or $(-1,\infty)$ **93.** $2(2a^2-4a-3)$ **95.** -6

Section 6.3 Simplifying Radical Expressions Using Properties of Radicals

1. $\sqrt[n]{ab}$ **2.** $\sqrt{77}$ **3.** $\sqrt[4]{42}$ **4.** $\sqrt{x^2-25}$ **5.** $\sqrt[n]{20p^4}$

6. $1,4,9,16,25,36$ **7.** $1,8,27,64,125,216$ **8.** $4\sqrt{3}$ **9.** $12\sqrt[3]{2}$ **10.** $10|a|\sqrt{2}$ **11.** Fully simplified   **12.** $2+\sqrt{5}$

13. $\dfrac{-1+2\sqrt{2}}{2}$ or $-\dfrac{1}{2}+\sqrt{2}$ **14.** $5a^3\sqrt{3}$ **15.** $3a^2\sqrt{2a}$ **16.** $4x^2y^3\sqrt[3]{2y}$ **17.** $2ab^2\sqrt[4]{ab^3}$ **18.** $4\sqrt{3}$ **19.** $2a^2\sqrt[3]{15}$ **20.** $8ab^3\sqrt[3]{6a}$

21. $\dfrac{\sqrt{13}}{7}$ **22.** $\dfrac{3p}{2}$ **23.** $\dfrac{q\sqrt[4]{3}}{2}$ **24.** $2a^2$ **25.** $-2x$ **26.** $\dfrac{5a\sqrt[3]{a}}{b}$ **27.** $\sqrt[12]{10,125}$ **28.** $2\sqrt[6]{2250}$ **29.** $\sqrt[3]{60}$ **31.** $\sqrt{15ab}$ if $a,b \geq 0$

33. $\sqrt{x^2-49}$ if $|x| \geq 7$ **35.** $\sqrt{5}$ if $x>0$ **37.** $5\sqrt{2}$ **39.** $3\sqrt[3]{2}$ **41.** $4|x|\sqrt{3}$ **43.** $-3x$ **45.** $2|m|\sqrt[4]{2}$ **47.** $2|p|\sqrt{3q}$

49. $9m^2\sqrt{2}$ **51.** $y^6\sqrt{y}$ **53.** $c^2\sqrt[3]{c^2}$ **55.** $5pq^2\sqrt{5p}$ **57.** $-2x^3\sqrt[3]{2}$ **59.** $-m\sqrt[5]{16m^3n^2}$ **61.** $(x-y)\sqrt[4]{x-y}$ **63.** $2\sqrt[3]{x^3-y^3}$

65. 5   **67.** $3+\sqrt{2}$ **69.** $\dfrac{1-\sqrt{2}}{2}$ **71.** 5   **73.** 4   **75.** 2   **77.** $5x\sqrt{3}$ **79.** $2b\sqrt[3]{3b}$ **81.** $18ab^2\sqrt{10}$ **83.** $3pq\sqrt[4]{4p}$

85. $-2ab\sqrt[5]{3a}$ **87.** $2(x-y)\sqrt[4]{3(x-y)}$ **89.** $\dfrac{\sqrt{3}}{4}$ **91.** $\dfrac{x\sqrt[4]{5}}{2}$ **93.** $\dfrac{3y}{5x}$ **95.** $-\dfrac{3x^3}{4y^4}$ **97.** 2   **99.** 4   **101.** $2a\sqrt{2}$

103. $\dfrac{2a^2\sqrt{2}}{b}$ **105.** $\dfrac{16a^3}{3b}$ **107.** $a^2\sqrt[3]{26}$ **109.** $\dfrac{3x^3\sqrt{5}}{y}$ **111.** $\sqrt[6]{432}$ **113.** $\sqrt[6]{12}$ **115.** $3\sqrt[6]{12}$ **117.** $\sqrt[3]{18}$ **119.** $\dfrac{\sqrt[3]{5x}}{2}$

121. $\sqrt[3]{45a^2}$ **123.** $6a^2\sqrt{2}$ **125.** $3a\sqrt[3]{2b^2}$ **127.** $\dfrac{-2\sqrt[3]{2}}{a}$ **129.** $-10m\sqrt[3]{4}$ **131.** $3ab^2\sqrt[3]{3ab}$ **133.** 6

135. (a) 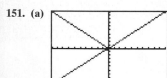   **(b)** $3\sqrt{5}$ units   **137. (a)** roughly \$1,587,000   **(b)** roughly \$2,381,000   **139. (a)** $4x^2$ **(b)** 36

141. $x=-3-\sqrt{6}$ or $x=-3+\sqrt{6}$ **143.** $x=\dfrac{-2-\sqrt{7}}{3}$ or $x=\dfrac{-2+\sqrt{7}}{3}$

145. The index of each radical must be the same. We can use the Laws of Exponents to rewrite radicals so that they have common indices.   **147.** $\left\{-\dfrac{5}{7},1\right\}$ **149.** $\{x \mid -5 \leq x \leq 3\}$; $[-5,3]$

151. (a)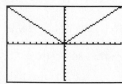

The graphs of $y=\sqrt{x^2}$ and $y=x$ are not the same so the expressions cannot be equal.

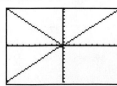

The graphs of $y=\sqrt{x^2}$ and $y=|x|$ appear to be the same. $\sqrt{x^2}=|x|$

(b)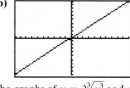

The graphs of $y=\sqrt[3]{x^3}$ and $y=x$ appear to be the same. $\sqrt[3]{x^3}=x$

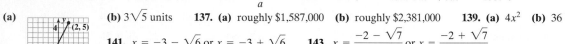

The graphs of $y=\sqrt[3]{x^3}$ and $y=|x|$ are not the same so the expressions cannot be equal.

(c)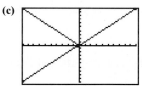

The graphs of $y=\sqrt[4]{x^4}$ and $y=x$ are not the same so the expressions cannot be equal.

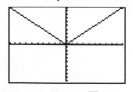

The graphs of $y=\sqrt[4]{x^4}$ and $y=|x|$ appear to be the same. $\sqrt[4]{x^4}=|x|$

(d) Answers will vary.

Section 6.4 Adding, Subtracting, and Multiplying Radical Expressions

1. like radicals   **2.** $13\sqrt{13y}$ **3.** $7\sqrt[4]{5}$ **4.** $6\sqrt{2}$

5. $-8x\sqrt[3]{2x}$ **6.** Fully simplified   **7.** $(8z+5)\sqrt[3]{z}$ **8.** $2\sqrt{m}$ **9.** $3(\sqrt{6}-10)$ **10.** $3\sqrt[3]{12}-2\sqrt[3]{3}$ **11.** $-74-27\sqrt{3}$

12. conjugates   **13.** False   **14.** $53+10\sqrt{6}$ **15.** $25-6\sqrt{14}$ **16.** 1   **17.** $10\sqrt{2}$ **19.** $2\sqrt[3]{x}$ **21.** $14\sqrt{5x}$ **23.** $11\sqrt[3]{5}-11\sqrt{5}$

25. $8\sqrt{2}$ **27.** $-2\sqrt[3]{3}$ **29.** $-25\sqrt[3]{2}$ **31.** $9\sqrt{6x}$ **33.** $4\sqrt{2}+3\sqrt{10}$ **35.** $32x\sqrt{3x}$ **37.** $2x\sqrt{3}-11x\sqrt{2}$ **39.** $(3x-8)\sqrt[3]{2}$

41. $5\sqrt{x-1}$ **43.** $3\sqrt{x}$ **45.** $5\sqrt[6]{x}$ **47.** $2\sqrt{3}-3\sqrt{6}$ **49.** $\sqrt{6}+3\sqrt{2}$ **51.** $\sqrt[3]{12}-2\sqrt[3]{3}$ **53.** $3\sqrt{2x}-2x\sqrt{5}$

55. $12+3\sqrt{3}+4\sqrt{2}+\sqrt{6}$ **57.** $12-6\sqrt{7}+2\sqrt{3}-\sqrt{21}$ **59.** $6\sqrt{7}-30$ **61.** $\sqrt{6}-12\sqrt{3}+9\sqrt{2}-4$ **63.** $31-2\sqrt{15}$

65. $4+2\sqrt{3}$ **67.** $7-2\sqrt{10}$ **69.** $x-2\sqrt{2x}+2$ **71.** 1   **73.** -11 **75.** $2x-3y$ **77.** $\sqrt[3]{x^2}+\sqrt[3]{x}-12$ **79.** $\sqrt[3]{4a^2}-25$

81. $\sqrt{15}+5\sqrt{2}$ **83.** $26x^2\sqrt{7x}$ **85.** -13 **87.** $2\sqrt[3]{7}+\sqrt[3]{28}$ **89.** $-4+12\sqrt{2}$ **91.** $20\sqrt{2}$ **93.** $8-2\sqrt{15}$

95. $(3x + 2)\sqrt[3]{5y}$ **97.** $2x - 7y$ **99.** $\dfrac{11\sqrt{5}}{25}$ **101. (a)** $3\sqrt{3x}$ **(b)** $6\sqrt{3}$ **(c)** $6x$

103. Check $x = -2 + \sqrt{5}$:

$0 \overset{?}{=} x^2 + 4x - 1$

$0 \overset{?}{=} \left(-2 + \sqrt{5}\right)^2 + 4\left(-2 + \sqrt{5}\right) - 1$

$0 \overset{?}{=} (-2)^2 + 2(-2)\left(\sqrt{5}\right) + \left(\sqrt{5}\right)^2 - 8 + 4\sqrt{5} - 1$

$0 \overset{?}{=} 4 - 4\sqrt{5} + \sqrt{25} - 8 + 4\sqrt{5} - 1$

$0 \overset{?}{=} 9 - 9$

$0 = 0$ true

The value is a solution.

Check $x = -2 - \sqrt{5}$:

$0 \overset{?}{=} x^2 + 4x - 1$

$0 \overset{?}{=} \left(-2 - \sqrt{5}\right)^2 + 4\left(-2 - \sqrt{5}\right) - 1$

$0 \overset{?}{=} (-2)^2 - 2(-2)\left(\sqrt{5}\right) + \left(\sqrt{5}\right)^2 - 8 - 4\sqrt{5} - 1$

$0 \overset{?}{=} 4 + 4\sqrt{5} + \sqrt{25} - 8 - 4\sqrt{5} - 1$

$0 \overset{?}{=} 9 - 9$

$0 = 0$ true

The value is a solution.

105. The area is 108 square units. The perimeter is $30\sqrt{2}$ units. **107.** $12\sqrt{6}$ square units **109.** To add or subtract radicals, the indices and radicands must be the same. Then use the Distributive Property "in reverse" to add the "coefficients" of the radicals. **111.** $12a^5b^5$ **113.** $6y^2 + y - 2$ **115.** $25w^2 - 4$

Section 6.5 Rationalizing Radical Expressions

1. rationalizing the denominator **2.** $\sqrt{11}$ **3.** $\dfrac{\sqrt{3}}{3}$ **4.** $\dfrac{\sqrt{10}}{4}$ **5.** $\dfrac{\sqrt{10x}}{2x}$

6. $\dfrac{4\sqrt[3]{9}}{3}$ **7.** $\dfrac{\sqrt[3]{150}}{10}$ **8.** $\dfrac{3\sqrt[4]{p^3}}{p}$ **9.** $-2 - \sqrt{7}$ **10.** $2(\sqrt{3} - 1)$ **11.** $\dfrac{\sqrt{3} + 1}{2}$ **12.** $\dfrac{5 + \sqrt{10} + 4\sqrt{5} + 4\sqrt{2}}{3}$

13. $\dfrac{\sqrt{2}}{2}$ **15.** $-\dfrac{2\sqrt{3}}{5}$ **17.** $\dfrac{\sqrt{3}}{2}$ **19.** $\dfrac{\sqrt{3}}{3}$ **21.** $\dfrac{\sqrt{2p}}{p}$ **23.** $\dfrac{2\sqrt{2y}}{y^2}$ **25.** $\sqrt[3]{4}$ **27.** $\dfrac{\sqrt[3]{7q^2}}{q}$ **29.** $-\dfrac{\sqrt[3]{60}}{10}$ **31.** $\dfrac{\sqrt[3]{50y^2}}{5y}$

33. $-\dfrac{4\sqrt[4]{27x}}{3x}$ **35.** $\dfrac{12\sqrt[5]{m^2n^3}}{mn}$ **37.** $2\left(\sqrt{6} + 2\right)$ **39.** $5\left(\sqrt{5} - 2\right)$ **41.** $2\left(\sqrt{7} + \sqrt{3}\right)$ **43.** $\dfrac{\sqrt{5} + \sqrt{3}}{2}$ **45.** $\dfrac{p - \sqrt{pq}}{p - q}$

47. $-3\left(2\sqrt{3} - 3\sqrt{2}\right)$ or $3\left(3\sqrt{2} - 2\sqrt{3}\right)$ **49.** $-8 - 3\sqrt{7}$ or $-\left(8 + 3\sqrt{7}\right)$ **51.** $\dfrac{13\sqrt{6} - 46}{38}$ **53.** $\dfrac{p + 4\sqrt{p} + 4}{p - 4}$

55. $\dfrac{2 - 3\sqrt{2}}{2}$ **57.** $\dfrac{4\sqrt{3}}{3}$ **59.** $\dfrac{\sqrt{10} - \sqrt{2}}{2}$ **61.** $\dfrac{22\sqrt{3}}{3}$ **63.** 0 **65.** $\dfrac{1}{2}$ **67.** $\dfrac{\sqrt{2}}{4}$ **69.** $\dfrac{2\sqrt{3}}{3}$ **71.** $\sqrt{3} - 2$

73. $2\left(\sqrt{5} - 2\right)$ **75.** 2 **77.** $\dfrac{\sqrt{3}}{3}$ **79.** $\dfrac{\sqrt[3]{18}}{6}$ **81.** $\dfrac{5 - \sqrt{3}}{22}$ **83.** $\dfrac{\sqrt{6} - \sqrt{2}}{4}$ **85.** $\dfrac{1}{3\left(\sqrt{2} - 1\right)}$ **87.** $\dfrac{x - h}{x + \sqrt{xh}}$

89. $\dfrac{\left(\sqrt{6}\right)^2 + 2 \cdot \sqrt{6} \cdot \sqrt{2} + \left(\sqrt{2}\right)^2}{4^2} \overset{?}{=} \left(\dfrac{\sqrt{2} + \sqrt{3}}{2}\right)^2$

$\dfrac{6 + 2\sqrt{12} + 2}{16} \overset{?}{=} \dfrac{2 + \sqrt{3}}{4}$

$\dfrac{8 + 2 \cdot 2\sqrt{3}}{16} \overset{?}{=} \dfrac{2 + \sqrt{3}}{4}$

$\dfrac{8 + 4\sqrt{3}}{16} \overset{?}{=} \dfrac{2 + \sqrt{3}}{4}$

$\dfrac{2 + \sqrt{3}}{4} = \dfrac{2 + \sqrt{3}}{4}$

91. (a) $\dfrac{1}{\sqrt{x + h} + \sqrt{x}}$ **(b)** $\dfrac{1}{2\sqrt{x}}$ **(c)** $\dfrac{1}{4}$ **(d)** $2; (4, 2)$ **(e)** $y = \dfrac{1}{4}x + 1$

(f)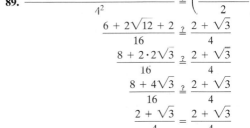

93. It is called rationalization because we are rewriting the expression so that the denominator is a rational number.

95. 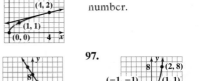 **97.**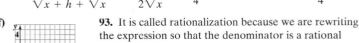

Putting the Concepts Together (Sections 6.1–6.5)

1. -5 **2.** $\dfrac{1}{16}$ **3.** $(3x^3)^{1/4}$ **4.** $7\sqrt[5]{z^4}$ **5.** $2x^{1/2}$ or $2\sqrt{x}$ **6.** $c^2 + c^3$ **7.** $\dfrac{a^2}{b^2}$

8. $x^{5/8}$ or $\sqrt[8]{x^5}$ **9.** $\dfrac{x^6}{y}$ **10.** $\sqrt{30ab}$ **11.** $10m^2n\sqrt{2n}$ **12.** $-2xy$ **13.** $\sqrt{3}$ **14.** $11b\sqrt{2b}$ **15.** $y\sqrt[3]{2y}$ **16.** $12x$ **17.** $7\sqrt{x}$

18. $14 - 28\sqrt{2} = 14(1 - 2\sqrt{2})$ **19.** $41 - 24\sqrt{2}$ **20.** $\dfrac{3\sqrt{2}}{16}$ **21.** $-\dfrac{4\left(\sqrt{3} + 8\right)}{61}$

Section 6.6 Functions Involving Radicals

1. (a) 4 **(b)** $2\sqrt{7}$ **2. (a)** -1 **(b)** 3 **3.** even; odd **4.** $\{x \mid x \geq -6\}$ or $[-6, \infty)$

5. $\{t \mid t$ is any real number$\}$ or $(-\infty, \infty)$ **6.** $\{m \mid m \leq 2\}$ or $(-\infty, 2]$

7. (a) $\{x \mid x \geq -3\}$ or $[-3, \infty)$ **8. (a)** $\{x \mid x$ is any real number$\}$ or $(-\infty, \infty)$

(b) **(b)**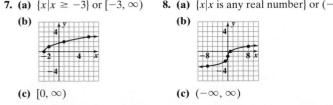

(c) $[0, \infty)$ **(c)** $(-\infty, \infty)$

9. (a) 3 **(b)** $\sqrt{14}$ **(c)** 2 **11. (a)** -5 **(b)** -1 **(c)** $-\dfrac{\sqrt{13}}{2}$

13. (a) 4 **(b)** $4\sqrt{6}$ **(c)** $\sqrt{6}$ **15. (a)** 2 **(b)** -2 **(c)** $-2\sqrt[3]{2}$

17. (a) $\dfrac{\sqrt{5}}{3}$ **(b)** $\dfrac{\sqrt{2}}{2}$ **(c)** $\dfrac{\sqrt{6}}{3}$ **19. (a)** 1 **(b)** $\sqrt[3]{4}$ **(c)** $\sqrt[3]{3}$

21. $\{x \mid x \geq 7\}$ or $[7, \infty)$ **23.** $\left\{x \mid x \geq -\dfrac{7}{2}\right\}$ or $\left[-\dfrac{7}{2}, \infty\right)$

25. $\left\{x \mid x \leq \dfrac{4}{3}\right\}$ or $\left(-\infty, \dfrac{4}{3}\right]$ **27.** $\{z \mid z$ is any real number$\}$ or $(-\infty, \infty)$ **29.** $\left\{p \mid p \geq \dfrac{2}{7}\right\}$ or $\left[\dfrac{2}{7}, \infty\right)$ **31.** $\{x \mid x$ is any real number$\}$ or

$(-\infty, \infty)$ **33.** $\{x \mid x > -5\}$ or $(-5, \infty)$ **35.** $\{x \mid x \leq -3$ or $x > 3\}$ or $(-\infty, -3] \cup (3, \infty)$

37. (a) $\{x \mid x \geq 4\}$ or $[4, \infty)$
(b)

(c) $[0, \infty)$

39. (a) $\{x \mid x \geq -2\}$ or $[-2, \infty)$
(b)

(c) $[0, \infty)$

41. (a) $\{x \mid x \leq 2\}$ or $(-\infty, 2]$
(b)

(c) $[0, \infty)$

43. (a) $\{x \mid x \geq 0\}$ or $[0, \infty)$
(b)

(c) $[3, \infty)$

45. (a) $\{x \mid x \geq 0\}$ or $[0, \infty)$
(b)

(c) $[-4, \infty)$

47. (a) $\{x \mid x \geq 0\}$ or $[0, \infty)$
(b)

(c) $[0, \infty)$

49. (a) $\{x \mid x \geq 0\}$ or $[0, \infty)$
(b)

(c) $[0, \infty)$

51. (a) $\{x \mid x \geq 0\}$ or $[0, \infty)$
(b)
(c) $(-\infty, 0]$

53. (a) $\{x \mid x \text{ is any real number}\}$ or $(-\infty, \infty)$
(b)
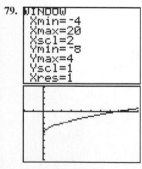
(c) $(-\infty, \infty)$

55. (a) $\{x \mid x \text{ is any real number}\}$ or $(-\infty, \infty)$
(b)
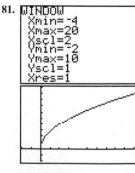
(c) $(-\infty, \infty)$

57. (a) $\{x \mid x \text{ is any real number}\}$ or $(-\infty, \infty)$
(b)
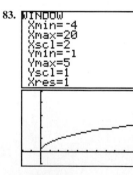
(c) $(-\infty, \infty)$

59. (a) 5 units
(b) $\sqrt{17} \approx 4.123$ units
(c) $5\sqrt{17} \approx 20.616$ units

61. (a) $4\sqrt{2} \approx 5.657$ square units
(b) $4\sqrt{5} \approx 8.944$ square units
(c) $2\sqrt{14} \approx 7.483$ square units

63. Shift the graph of $f(x)$ $|c|$ units to the right (if $c < 0$) or c units to the left (if $c > 0$).
65. $\dfrac{5}{6}$
67. $\dfrac{4x + 1}{x(x + 1)}$
69. $\dfrac{7x + 1}{(x - 1)(x + 1)}$ or $\dfrac{7x + 1}{x^2 - 1}$

71.
```
WINDOW
Xmin=0
Xmax=24
Xscl=2
Ymin=-2
Ymax=10
Yscl=1
Xres=1
```

73.
```
WINDOW
Xmin=-4
Xmax=20
Xscl=2
Ymin=-2
Ymax=10
Yscl=1
Xres=1
```

75.
```
WINDOW
Xmin=-16
Xmax=8
Xscl=2
Ymin=-2
Ymax=10
Yscl=1
Xres=1
```

77.
```
WINDOW
Xmin=-4
Xmax=20
Xscl=2
Ymin=-2
Ymax=10
Yscl=1
Xres=1
```

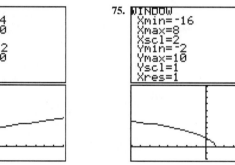

79.
```
WINDOW
Xmin=-4
Xmax=20
Xscl=2
Ymin=-8
Ymax=4
Yscl=1
Xres=1
```

81.
```
WINDOW
Xmin=-4
Xmax=20
Xscl=2
Ymin=-2
Ymax=10
Yscl=1
Xres=1
```

83.
```
WINDOW
Xmin=-4
Xmax=20
Xscl=2
Ymin=-1
Ymax=5
Yscl=1
Xres=1
```

85.
```
WINDOW
Xmin=-4
Xmax=20
Xscl=2
Ymin=-6
Ymax=6
Yscl=1
Xres=1
```

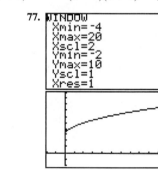
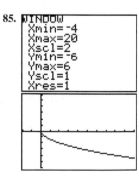

87.
```
WINDOW
Xmin=-12
Xmax=12
Xscl=2
Ymin=-6
Ymax=6
Yscl=1
Xres=1
```

89.
```
WINDOW
Xmin=-12
Xmax=12
Xscl=2
Ymin=-6
Ymax=6
Yscl=1
Xres=1
```

91.
```
WINDOW
Xmin=-12
Xmax=12
Xscl=2
Ymin=-6
Ymax=6
Yscl=1
Xres=1
```

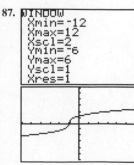
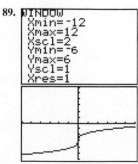
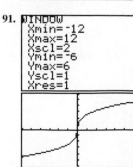

Section 6.7 Radical Equations and Their Applications   **1.** radical equation   **2.** extraneous   **3.** False   **4.** {5}   **5.** {−5}

6. ∅ or { }   **7.** {4}   **8.** {−3}   **9.** {15}   **10.** {−3, 1}   **11.** {12}   **12.** (a) $L = \dfrac{8T^2}{\pi^2}$ (b) 32 feet   **13.** {16}   **15.** {7}

17. {11}   **19.** ∅ or { }   **21.** {2}   **23.** {12}   **25.** {25}   **27.** {11}   **29.** {−4}   **31.** {1}   **33.** {−5}

35. $\left\{0, \dfrac{1}{4}\right\}$ **37.** {3}   **39.** {4}   **41.** {4}   **43.** {6}   **45.** {4}   **47.** {−3}   **49.** {−1, 10}   **51.** {0, 4}   **53.** {3}

55. {5}   **57.** {2, 10}   **59.** {3}   **61.** {4}   **63.** {6}   **65.** $r = \dfrac{A^2 - P^2}{P^2}$ **67.** $V = \dfrac{4}{3}\pi r^3$ **69.** $F = \dfrac{q_1 q_2 r^2}{4\pi\varepsilon_0}$

71. ∅ or { }   **73.** {4}   **75.** {2}   **77.** {9}   **79.** {−3}   **81.** {−6}   **83.** {9}   **85.** {5}   **87.** {−2}

89. (a) {2}; (2, 0)   (b) {3}; (3, 1)   (c) {6}; (6, 2)

91. (a) $y = 5$ or $y = -1$

93. (a) after 2 years   (b) after 16 years

95. (a) in the year 2053   (b) in the year 2021

(d) 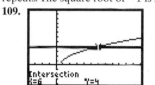   (e) The equation $f(x) = -1$ has no solution because the graph of the function does not go below the x-axis.

(b)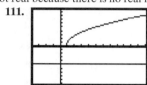

97. $\left\{-\dfrac{3}{4}, 0\right\}$

99. If the index is even, it is important so that you can identify extraneous solutions. Regardless of the index, it is important to make sure that your answer is correct.   **101.** In radical expressions with an even index, the radicand must be greater than or equal to zero. After raising both sides of the equation to an even index, it is possible that we obtain solutions which result in a negative radicand. We do not have any restrictions on the value of the radicand when the index is odd, so we don't need to be worried about extraneous solutions.   **103.** $0, -4, 12$ **105.** $\sqrt{2^3}$, π, and $\sqrt[3]{-4}$ **107.** A rational number is a number that can be written as the quotient of two integers, where the denominator is not zero; a rational number is also a number where the decimal either terminates, or does not terminate, but repeats. An irrational number has a decimal form that neither terminates, nor repeats. The square root of -1 is not real because there is no real number whose square is -1.

109.

111.

The two graphs do not intersect. Therefore, the equation has no real solution.

Section 6.8 The Complex Number System   **1.** imaginary unit   **2.** pure imaginary number   **3.** $\sqrt{N}i$ **4.** True   **5.** $6i$ **6.** $\sqrt{5}i$

7. $2\sqrt{3}i$ **8.** $4 + 10i$ **9.** $-2 - 2\sqrt{2}i$ **10.** $2 - 2\sqrt{2}i$ **11.** $1 + 11i$ **12.** $6 - 9i$ **13.** $-3 + i$ **14.** $12 + 15i$ **15.** $2 + 24i$

16. -18 **17.** $38 + 14i$ **18.** $-3 - 5i$ **19.** 73 **20.** 29 **21.** $\dfrac{1}{3} + \dfrac{4}{3}i$ **22.** $-\dfrac{1}{2} + \dfrac{3}{2}i$ **23.** $-i$ **24.** -1 **25.** $2i$ **27.** $-9i$

29. $3\sqrt{5}i$ **31.** $10\sqrt{3}i$ **33.** $\sqrt{7}i$ **35.** $5 + 7i$ **37.** $-2 - 2\sqrt{7}i$ **39.** $2 + i$ **41.** $\dfrac{1}{3} + \dfrac{\sqrt{2}}{6}i$ **43.** $6 - 2i$ **45.** $-4 + 6i$

47. $2 - 5i$ **49.** $3 - 2\sqrt{2}i$ **51.** $24 + 12i$ **53.** $-5 - 2i$ **55.** $5 + 10i$ **57.** $14 - 22i$ **59.** 26 **61.** $-4 + 5\sqrt{2}i$ **63.** $\dfrac{25}{48} + \dfrac{5}{24}i$

65. $5 + 12i$ **67.** $-9 + 40i$ **69.** -6 **71.** $-4\sqrt{5}$ **73.** $84 - 47i$ **75.** (a) $3 - 5i$ (b) 34 **77.** (a) $2 + 7i$ (b) 53 **79.** (a) $-7 - 2i$

(b) 53 **81.** $\dfrac{1}{3} - \dfrac{1}{3}i$ **83.** $\dfrac{2}{5} + i$ **85.** $\dfrac{6}{5} - \dfrac{3}{5}i$ **87.** $\dfrac{3}{29} - \dfrac{7}{29}i$ **89.** i **91.** $1 + 3i$ **93.** $-\dfrac{1}{5} - \dfrac{7}{5}i$ **95.** i **97.** $-i$ **99.** i

101. $-i$ **103.** $-15 - 8i$ **105.** $5 + 12i$ **107.** $\dfrac{2}{3} + i$ **109.** $\dfrac{1}{2} - \dfrac{1}{2}i$ **111.** 12 **113.** $-15 - 20i$ **115.** $-5\sqrt{6}$ **117.** $-\dfrac{1}{5}i$

119. $\dfrac{2}{5} + \dfrac{1}{5}i$ **121.** $-\dfrac{4}{41} - \dfrac{5}{41}i$ **123.** (a) -1 (b) $2i$ **125.** (a) $-7 + 6i$ (b) $4 - 4i$ **127.** (a) $10 - i$ ohms (b) 10 ohms (c) -1 ohm

129. (a) 0 (b) 0 **131.** (a) 0 (b) 0 (c) 0 **133.** For a polynomial with real coefficients, the zeros will be real numbers or will occur in conjugate pairs. If the complex number $a + bi$ is a complex zero of the polynomial, then its conjugate $a - bi$ is also a complex zero.

135. The set of natural numbers are a subset of the set of whole numbers, which is a subset of the set of integers, which is a subset of the set of rational numbers, which is a subset of the set of real numbers, which is a subset of the set of complex numbers. So, all real numbers are, more generally, complex numbers.   **137.** Both methods can rely on the "FOIL" method or the Distributive Property.   **139.** $x^3 + 6x^2 + 12x + 8$ **141.** $18 + 26i$

143. Both methods rely on special product formulas to obtain the results.   **145.** $-9.9 + 7.2i$ **147.** $-30.86 + 3.59i$ **149.** $-\dfrac{11}{17} + \dfrac{27}{17}i$ **151.** $6 - 25i$

Chapter 6 Review   **1.** 7 **2.** -5 **3.** $\dfrac{2}{3}$ **4.** 3 **5.** 3 **6.** 10 **7.** z **8.** $|5p - 3|$ **9.** 9 **10.** not a real number   **11.** -2

12. 9 **13.** 128 **14.** -9 **15.** -1331 **16.** 6 **17.** -4.02 **18.** 2.30 **19.** 4.64 **20.** 1.78 **21.** $(5a)^{1/3}$ **22.** $p^{7/5}$ **23.** $(10z)^{3/4}$

24. $(2ab)^{5/6}$ **25.** 64 **26.** $\dfrac{1}{k^{1/4}}$ **27.** $p^2 \cdot q^6$ or $(p \cdot q^3)^2$ **28.** $\dfrac{2b^{1/20}}{a^{3/10}}$ or $2\left(\dfrac{b}{a^6}\right)^{1/20}$ **29.** $10m^{1/3} + \dfrac{5}{m}$ **30.** $\dfrac{1}{2x^{1/3}}$ **31.** $\sqrt[4]{x^3}$ **32.** $11x^2 y^5$

33. $m^2 \sqrt[6]{m}$ **34.** $\dfrac{1}{\sqrt[3]{c}}$ **35.** $(3m - 1)^{1/4}(3m^2 - 22m + 9)$ **36.** $\dfrac{(3x + 5)(x - 3)}{(x^2 - 5)^{2/3}}$ **37.** $\sqrt{105}$ **38.** $\sqrt[4]{12a^3 b^3}$ **39.** $4\sqrt{5}$ **40.** $-5\sqrt[3]{4}$

41. $3m^2 n \sqrt[3]{6n}$ **42.** $p^2 |q| \sqrt[4]{50}$ **43.** $8|x^3|\sqrt{y}$ as long as $y \geq 0$ **44.** $(2x + 1)\sqrt{2x + 1}$ as long as $2x + 1 \geq 0$ **45.** $wz\sqrt{w}$ **46.** $3x^2 z\sqrt{5yz}$

47. $2a^4 b\sqrt[3]{2b^2}$ **48.** $2(x + 1)$ **49.** $3\sqrt{30}$ **50.** $2\sqrt[3]{75}$ **51.** $-2x^2 y^3 \sqrt[3]{9x}$ **52.** $30xy\sqrt{3xy}$ **53.** $\dfrac{11}{5}$ **54.** $\dfrac{a^2\sqrt{5}}{8b}$ **55.** $\dfrac{\sqrt[3]{6}}{k}$

56. $\dfrac{-2w^5 \sqrt[3]{20}}{7}$ **57.** $2h$ **58.** $\dfrac{5b^3}{2a}$ **59.** $\dfrac{-2x^2}{3y}$ **60.** $\dfrac{2n\sqrt{n}}{m}$ **61.** $\sqrt[6]{500}$ **62.** $2\sqrt[12]{2}$ **63.** $8\sqrt[4]{x}$ **64.** $6\sqrt[3]{4y}$ **65.** $5\sqrt{2} - 4\sqrt{3}$

66. $13\sqrt{2}$ **67.** $\sqrt[3]{2z}$ **68.** $17\sqrt[3]{x^2}$ **69.** $7\sqrt{a}$ **70.** $9x\sqrt{3}$ **71.** $4m\sqrt[3]{4m^2 y^2}$ **72.** $(y - 1)\sqrt{y - 4}$ **73.** $\sqrt{15} - 3\sqrt{5}$

74. $3\sqrt[3]{5} + \sqrt[3]{20}$ **75.** $7 + \sqrt{5}$ **76.** $42 + 7\sqrt{2} + 6\sqrt{3} + \sqrt{6}$ **77.** -44 **78.** $9\sqrt[3]{x^2} + 5\sqrt[3]{x} - 4$ **79.** $x - 2\sqrt{5x} + 5$

80. $247 + 22\sqrt{10}$ **81.** $2a - b^2$ **82.** $\sqrt[3]{36s^2} - 5\sqrt[3]{6s} - 14$ **83.** $\dfrac{\sqrt{6}}{3}$ **84.** $2\sqrt{3}$ **85.** $\dfrac{4\sqrt{3p}}{p^2}$ **86.** $\dfrac{5\sqrt{2a}}{2a}$ **87.** $-\dfrac{\sqrt{6y}}{3y^2}$

88. $\dfrac{3\sqrt[3]{25}}{5}$ **89.** $-\dfrac{\sqrt[3]{300}}{15}$ **90.** $\dfrac{27\sqrt[5]{4p^2q}}{2pq}$ **91.** $\dfrac{42 + 6\sqrt{6}}{43}$ **92.** $-\dfrac{\sqrt{3} + 9}{26}$ **93.** $\dfrac{\sqrt{3}(3 - \sqrt{2})}{7}$ or $\dfrac{3\sqrt{3} - \sqrt{6}}{7}$ **94.** $\dfrac{k + \sqrt{km}}{k - m}$

95. $\dfrac{7 + 2\sqrt{10}}{3}$ **96.** $\dfrac{9 - 6\sqrt{y} + y}{9 - y}$ or $\dfrac{y - 6\sqrt{y} + 9}{9 - y}$ **97.** $\dfrac{10\sqrt{2} - 4\sqrt{3}}{19}$ **98.** $\dfrac{8\sqrt{2} - 3\sqrt{15}}{7}$ **99.** $\dfrac{25\sqrt{7}}{21}$ **100.** $\dfrac{4 + \sqrt{7}}{9}$

101. (a) 1 **(b)** 2 **(c)** 3   **102. (a)** 0 **(b)** 2 **(c)** 4   **103. (a)** 1 **(b)** -1 **(c)** 2   **104. (a)** 0 **(b)** 2 **(c)** $\dfrac{1}{2}$ **105.** $\left\{x \middle| x \geq \dfrac{5}{3}\right\}$ or $\left[\dfrac{5}{3}, \infty\right)$

106. $\{x | x \text{ is any real number}\}$ or $(-\infty, \infty)$ **107.** $\left\{x \middle| x \geq -\dfrac{1}{6}\right\}$ or $\left[-\dfrac{1}{6}, \infty\right)$ **108.** $\{x | x \text{ is any real number}\}$ or $(-\infty, \infty)$

109. $\{x | x > 2\}$ or $(2, \infty)$ **110.** $\{x | x < 0 \text{ or } x \geq 3\}$ or $(-\infty, 0) \cup [3, \infty)$

111. (a) $\{x | x \leq 1\}$ or $(-\infty, 1]$ **112. (a)** $\{x | x \geq -1\}$ or $[-1, \infty)$ **113. (a)** $\{x | x \geq -3\}$ or $[-3, \infty)$ **114. (a)** $\{x | x \text{ is any real number}\}$ or $(-\infty, \infty)$

(b)

(b)

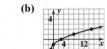

(b)

(b)

(c) $[0, \infty)$ **(c)** $[-2, \infty)$ **(c)** $(-\infty, 0]$ **(c)** $(-\infty, \infty)$

115. $\{169\}$ **116.** $\{-3\}$ **117.** $\left\{\dfrac{89}{3}\right\}$ **118.** $\varnothing$ or $\{\ \}$ **119.** $\{-5\}$ **120.** $\{25\}$ **121.** $\{-512\}$ **122.** $\{2\}$ **123.** $\{5\}$ **124.** $\{2\}$

125. $\{11\}$ **126.** $\{6\}$ **127.** $\{9\}$ **128.** $\varnothing$ or $\{\ \}$ **129.** $\left\{\dfrac{15}{2}\right\}$ **130.** $\{-5, 5\}$ **131.** $h = \dfrac{3V}{\pi r^2}$ **132.** $v = \dfrac{30}{f_s^3}$ **133.** $\sqrt{29}i$

134. $3\sqrt{6}i$ **135.** $14 - 9\sqrt{2}i$ **136.** $2 + \sqrt{5}i$ **137.** $1 - 2i$ **138.** $-5 + 10i$ **139.** $5 - 7\sqrt{5}i$ **140.** $-5 + 7i$ **141.** $47 + 13i$

142. $8 - \dfrac{11}{6}i$ **143.** -9 **144.** $67 - 42i$ **145.** 145 **146.** $27 + 38i$ **147.** $\dfrac{6}{17} - \dfrac{10}{17}i$ **148.** $-\dfrac{21}{53} - \dfrac{6}{53}i$ **149.** $\dfrac{4}{29} - \dfrac{19}{29}i$

150. $\dfrac{1}{2} + \dfrac{7}{2}i$ **151.** $-i$ **152.** i

Chapter 6 Test **1.** $\dfrac{1}{7}$ **2.** $6y\sqrt[12]{x^8y^3}$ **3.** $2a^5b^4\sqrt[5]{4a^3b}$ **4.** $\sqrt{39mn}$ **5.** $4x^3y^2\sqrt{2x}$ **6.** $\dfrac{3a}{2b^2}$ **7.** $(x + 6)\sqrt{5x}$ **8.** $a\sqrt{b}$

9. $33 - 5\sqrt{x} - 2x$ **10.** $-\dfrac{\sqrt{2}}{18}$ **11.** $5 - 2\sqrt{5}$ **12. (a)** 1 **(b)** 3   **13.** $\left\{x \middle| x \leq \dfrac{5}{3}\right\}$ or $\left(-\infty, \dfrac{5}{3}\right]$ **14. (a)** $\{x | x \geq 0\}$ or $[0, \infty)$

(b)

(c) $[-3, \infty)$ **15.** $\{13\}$ **16.** $\{3\}$ **17.** $\{2\}$ **18.** $17 - 13i$ **19.** $29 - 2i$ **20.** $\dfrac{73}{265} - \dfrac{89}{265}i$

Chapter 7 Quadratic Equations and Functions

Section 7.1 Solving Quadratic Equations by Completing the Square   **1.** $\sqrt{p}; -\sqrt{p}$ **2.** $\{-4\sqrt{3}, 4\sqrt{3}\}$ **3.** $\{-5, 5\}$ **4.** $\{-9, 9\}$

5. $\{-6\sqrt{2}i, 6\sqrt{2}i\}$ **6.** $\{-3i, 3i\}$ **7.** $\{-13, 7\}$ **8.** $\{5 - 4i, 5 + 4i\}$ **9.** $49; (p + 7)^2$ **10.** $\dfrac{9}{4}; \left(w + \dfrac{3}{2}\right)^2$ **11.** $\{-4, 2\}$

12. $\{4 - \sqrt{7}, 4 + \sqrt{7}\}$ **13.** $\left\{\dfrac{-3 - \sqrt{11}}{2}, \dfrac{-3 + \sqrt{11}}{2}\right\}$ **14.** $\left\{-\dfrac{1}{3} - \dfrac{2\sqrt{5}}{3}i, -\dfrac{1}{3} + \dfrac{2\sqrt{5}}{3}i\right\}$ **15.** hypotenuse; legs   **16.** False   **17.** $c = 5$

18. Approximately 17.32 miles   **19.** $\{-10, 10\}$ **21.** $\{-5\sqrt{2}, 5\sqrt{2}\}$ **23.** $\{-5i, 5i\}$ **25.** $\left\{-\dfrac{\sqrt{5}}{2}, \dfrac{\sqrt{5}}{2}\right\}$ **27.** $\{-2\sqrt{2}, 2\sqrt{2}\}$

29. $\{-4, 4\}$ **31.** $\left\{-\dfrac{2\sqrt{6}}{3}, \dfrac{2\sqrt{6}}{3}\right\}$ **33.** $\{-2i, 2i\}$ **35.** $\{1 - 3\sqrt{2}i, 1 + 3\sqrt{2}i\}$ **37.** $\{-5 - \sqrt{3}, -5 + \sqrt{3}\}$ **39.** $\left\{-\dfrac{4}{3}, \dfrac{2}{3}\right\}$

41. $\left\{\dfrac{2}{3} - \dfrac{\sqrt{5}}{3}, \dfrac{2}{3} + \dfrac{\sqrt{5}}{3}\right\}$ **43.** $\{-13, 5\}$ **45.** $x^2 + 10x + 25; (x + 5)^2$ **47.** $z^2 - 18z + 81; (z - 9)^2$ **49.** $y^2 + 7y + \dfrac{49}{4}; \left(y + \dfrac{7}{2}\right)^2$

51. $w^2 + \dfrac{1}{2}w + \dfrac{1}{16}; \left(w + \dfrac{1}{4}\right)^2$ **53.** $\{-6, 2\}$ **55.** $\{2 - \sqrt{3}, 2 + \sqrt{3}\}$ **57.** $\{2 - i, 2 + i\}$ **59.** $\left\{-\dfrac{5}{2} - \dfrac{\sqrt{33}}{2}, -\dfrac{5}{2} + \dfrac{\sqrt{33}}{2}\right\}$

61. $\{4 - \sqrt{19}, 4 + \sqrt{19}\}$ **63.** $\left\{\dfrac{1}{2} - \dfrac{\sqrt{11}}{2}i, \dfrac{1}{2} + \dfrac{\sqrt{11}}{2}i\right\}$ **65.** $\left\{-\dfrac{3}{2}, 4\right\}$ **67.** $\left\{1 - \dfrac{\sqrt{3}}{3}, 1 + \dfrac{\sqrt{3}}{3}\right\}$ **69.** $\left\{\dfrac{5}{4} - \dfrac{\sqrt{17}}{4}, \dfrac{5}{4} + \dfrac{\sqrt{17}}{4}\right\}$

71. $\left\{-1 - \dfrac{\sqrt{6}}{2}i, -1 + \dfrac{\sqrt{6}}{2}i\right\}$　　**73.** 10　　**75.** 20　　**77.** $5\sqrt{2}$; 7.07　　**79.** 2　　**81.** $2\sqrt{34}$; 11.66　　**83.** $b = 4\sqrt{3} \approx 6.93$　　**85.** $a = 4\sqrt{5} \approx 8.94$

87. $\{-3, 9\}$; $(-3, 36), (9, 36)$　　**89.** $\{-2 - 3\sqrt{2}, -2 + 3\sqrt{2}\}$; $(-2 - 3\sqrt{2}, 18), (-2 + 3\sqrt{2}, 18)$　　**91.** $16\sqrt{5}$ units　　**93.** approximately 104.403 yards　　**95.** approximately 31.623 feet　　**97. (a)** approximately 22.913 feet　**(b)** 15 feet　　**99. (a)** 1 second　**(b)** approximately 1.732 seconds **(c)** 2 seconds　　**101.** approximately 9.54%　　**103.** The triangle is a right triangle; the hypotenuse is 17.　　**105.** The triangle is not a right triangle.

107. $c^2 = (m^2 + n^2)^2 = m^4 + 2m^2n^2 + n^4$　　**109.** $\{-4, 9\}$　　**111.** $\left\{-1, \dfrac{1}{2}\right\}$　　**113.** In both cases, the simpler equations are linear.
$a^2 + b^2 = (m^2 - n^2)^2 + (2mn)^2$
$ = m^4 - 2m^2n^2 + n^4 + 4m^2n^2$
$ = m^4 + 2m^2n^2 + n^4$

Because c^2 and $a^2 + b^2$ result in the same expression, $a, b,$ and c are the lengths of the sides of a right triangle.

Section 7.2 Solving Quadratic Equations by the Quadratic Formula
1. $\dfrac{-b \pm \sqrt{b^2 - 4ac}}{2a}$　　**2.** $\left\{-\dfrac{3}{2}, 3\right\}$　　**3.** $\left\{-4, \dfrac{1}{2}\right\}$

4. $\left\{1 - \dfrac{\sqrt{3}}{2}, 1 + \dfrac{\sqrt{3}}{2}\right\}$　　**5.** $\left\{\dfrac{5}{2}\right\}$　　**6.** $\left\{2 - \dfrac{\sqrt{10}}{2}, 2 + \dfrac{\sqrt{10}}{2}\right\}$　　**7.** $\{-1 - 5i, -1 + 5i\}$　　**8.** discriminant　　**9.** negative　　**10.** False

11. True　　**12.** Two complex solutions that are not real　　**13.** One repeated real solution　　**14.** Two irrational solutions　　**15.** True

16. $\{-3, 3\}$　　**17.** $\left\{\dfrac{5}{4} - \dfrac{\sqrt{23}}{4}i, \dfrac{5}{4} + \dfrac{\sqrt{23}}{4}i\right\}$　　**18.** $\left\{-\dfrac{5}{3}, 1\right\}$　　**19. (a)** 200 or 600 DVDs　**(b)** 400 DVDs　　**20.** 16 meters by 30 meters

21. $\{-2, 6\}$　　**23.** $\left\{-\dfrac{3}{2}, \dfrac{5}{3}\right\}$　　**25.** $\left\{1 - \dfrac{\sqrt{3}}{2}, 1 + \dfrac{\sqrt{3}}{2}\right\}$　　**27.** $\left\{1 - \dfrac{2\sqrt{3}}{3}, 1 + \dfrac{2\sqrt{3}}{3}\right\}$　　**29.** $\left\{-\dfrac{1}{3} - \dfrac{\sqrt{13}}{3}, -\dfrac{1}{3} + \dfrac{\sqrt{13}}{3}\right\}$

31. $\{1 - \sqrt{6}i, 1 + \sqrt{6}i\}$　　**33.** $\left\{\dfrac{1}{2} - \dfrac{\sqrt{13}}{2}i, \dfrac{1}{2} + \dfrac{\sqrt{13}}{2}i\right\}$　　**35.** $\left\{\dfrac{1}{4} - \dfrac{\sqrt{5}}{4}, \dfrac{1}{4} + \dfrac{\sqrt{5}}{4}\right\}$　　**37.** $\left\{-\dfrac{2}{3} - \dfrac{\sqrt{7}}{3}, -\dfrac{2}{3} + \dfrac{\sqrt{7}}{3}\right\}$　　**39.** 21; two irrational solutions　　**41.** -56; two complex solutions that are not real　　**43.** 0; one repeated real solution　　**45.** -8; two complex solutions that are not real　　**47.** 44; two irrational solutions　　**49.** $\left\{\dfrac{5}{2} - \dfrac{\sqrt{5}}{2}, \dfrac{5}{2} + \dfrac{\sqrt{5}}{2}\right\}$　　**51.** $\left\{-\dfrac{8}{3}, 1\right\}$　　**53.** $\left\{-\dfrac{7}{2}, 5\right\}$　　**55.** $\{-1 - \sqrt{7}i, -1 + \sqrt{7}i\}$

57. $\left\{-\dfrac{3}{2}\right\}$　　**59.** $\left\{\dfrac{1}{7} - \dfrac{\sqrt{29}}{7}, \dfrac{1}{7} + \dfrac{\sqrt{29}}{7}\right\}$　　**61.** $\{-4, 4\}$　　**63.** $\left\{\dfrac{1}{4} - \dfrac{1}{4}i, \dfrac{1}{4} + \dfrac{1}{4}i\right\}$　　**65.** $\left\{-\dfrac{2}{3}\right\}$　　**67.** $\left\{-\dfrac{1}{3} - \dfrac{2\sqrt{7}}{3}, -\dfrac{1}{3} + \dfrac{2\sqrt{7}}{3}\right\}$

69. $\{2 - \sqrt{13}, 2 + \sqrt{13}\}$　　**71.** $\{1 - \sqrt{5}, 1 + \sqrt{5}\}$　　**73.** $\left\{\dfrac{1}{4} - \dfrac{3\sqrt{7}}{4}i, \dfrac{1}{4} + \dfrac{3\sqrt{7}}{4}i\right\}$　　**75. (a)** $\{-7, 3\}$　**(b)** $\{-4, 0\}$; $(-4, -21), (0, -21)$

77. (a) $\left\{-1 - \dfrac{\sqrt{6}}{2}, -1 + \dfrac{\sqrt{6}}{2}\right\}$　**(b)** $\left\{-1 - \dfrac{\sqrt{2}}{2}, -1 + \dfrac{\sqrt{2}}{2}\right\}$　　**79.** $\dfrac{-1 - \sqrt{7}}{3}, \dfrac{-1 + \sqrt{7}}{3}$　　**81.** $x = 3$; the three sides measure 3, 4, and 5 units

83. Either $x = 1$ and the three sides measure 3, 4, and 5 units, or $x = 5$ and the three sides measure 7, 24, and 25 units.　　**85.** $-2 + 2\sqrt{11}$ inches by $2 + 2\sqrt{11}$ inches, which is approximately 4.633 inches by 8.633 inches.　　**87.** The base is $\dfrac{3}{2} + \dfrac{\sqrt{209}}{2}$ inches, which is approximately 8.728 inches; the height is $-\dfrac{3}{2} + \dfrac{\sqrt{209}}{2}$ inches, which is approximately 5.728 inches.　　**89. (a)** $R(17) = 1161.1$; if 17 pairs of sunglasses are sold per week, then the company's revenue will be \$1161.10. $R(25) = 1687.5$; if 25 pairs of sunglasses are sold per week, then the company's revenue will be \$1687.50. **(b)** either 200 or 500 pairs of sunglasses　**(c)** 350 pairs of sunglasses　　**91. (a)** after approximately 0.6 second and after approximately 3.8 seconds **(b)** after approximately 1.3 seconds and after approximately 3.0 seconds　**(c)** No; the solutions to the equation are complex solutions that are not real. **93.** 12 inches　　**95. (a)** ages 25 and 68　**(b)** ages 30 and 63　　**97.** approximately 4.3 miles per hour　　**99.** approximately 4.6 hours

101. By the quadratic formula, the solutions of the equation $ax^2 + bx + c = 0$ are $x = \dfrac{-b - \sqrt{b^2 - 4ac}}{2a}$ and $x = \dfrac{-b + \sqrt{b^2 - 4ac}}{2a}$. The sum of these two solutions is
$\dfrac{-b - \sqrt{b^2 - 4ac}}{2a} + \dfrac{-b + \sqrt{b^2 - 4ac}}{2a} = \dfrac{-2b}{2a} = -\dfrac{b}{a}$.

103. The solutions of $ax^2 + bx + c = 0$ are $x = \dfrac{-b \pm \sqrt{b^2 - 4ac}}{2a}$. The solutions of $ax^2 - bx + c = 0$ are $x = \dfrac{-(-b) \pm \sqrt{(-b)^2 - 4ac}}{2a} = \dfrac{b \pm \sqrt{b^2 - 4ac}}{2a}$.
Now, the negatives of the solutions to $ax^2 - bx + c = 0$ are $-\left(\dfrac{b \pm \sqrt{b^2 - 4ac}}{2a}\right) = \dfrac{-b \mp \sqrt{b^2 - 4ac}}{2a} = \dfrac{-b \pm \sqrt{b^2 - 4ac}}{2a}$ which are the solutions to $ax^2 + bx + c = 0$.

105. Use factoring if the discriminant is a perfect square.
107. (a)　　　　**(b)** $x = -1$ or $x = -2$

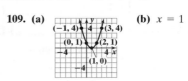

(c) The x-intercepts of the function $f(x) = x^2 + 3x + 2$ are -2 and -1, which are the same as the solutions of the equation $x^2 + 3x + 2 = 0$.

109. (a)　　　　**(b)** $x = 1$

(c) The x-intercept of the function $g(x) = x^2 - 2x + 1$ is 1, which is the same as the solution of the equation $x^2 - 2x + 1 = 0$.

111. The discriminant is 37; the equation has two irrational solutions. This conclusion based on the discriminant is apparent in the graph because the graph has two x-intercepts.　　**113.** The discriminant is -7; the equation has two complex solutions that are not real. This conclusion based on the discriminant is apparent in the graph because the graph has no x-intercept.

115. (a) $x = -3$ or $x = 8$
(b) The x-intercepts are -3 and 8.

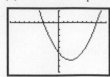

The x-intercepts of $y = x^2 - 5x - 24$ are the same as the solutions of $x^2 - 5x - 24 = 0$.

117. (a) $x = 3$
(b) The x-intercept is 3.

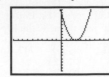

The x-intercept of $y = x^2 - 6x + 9$ is the same as the solution of $x^2 - 6x + 9 = 0$.

119. (a) $x = -\dfrac{5}{2} \pm \dfrac{\sqrt{7}}{2}i$
(b) The graph has no x-intercepts.

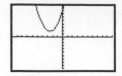

$y = x^2 + 5x + 8$ has no x-intercepts, and the solutions of $x^2 + 5x + 8 = 0$ are not real.

Section 7.3 Solving Equations Quadratic in Form

1. quadratic in form
2. $3x + 1$
3. True
4. $u = \dfrac{1}{x}$
5. $\{-3, -2, 2, 3\}$

6. $\{-3, 3, \sqrt{2}i, -\sqrt{2}i\}$
7. $\{-3, -2, 2, 3\}$
8. $\left\{-\dfrac{\sqrt{3}}{2}, \dfrac{\sqrt{3}}{2}, -i, i\right\}$
9. $\left\{\dfrac{4}{9}, 16\right\}$
10. $\{25\}$
11. $\left\{-\dfrac{5}{2}, -\dfrac{1}{2}\right\}$
12. $\{-1, 125\}$

13. $\{-2, -1, 1, 2\}$
15. $\{-3i, -2i, 2i, 3i\}$
17. $\left\{-\dfrac{1}{2}, -2, \dfrac{1}{2}, 2\right\}$
19. $\{-\sqrt{2}, -\sqrt{3}, \sqrt{2}, \sqrt{3}\}$
21. $\{10, 2\}$
23. $\{-2, -3, 2, 3\}$

25. $\{-2i, -\sqrt{7}i, 2i, \sqrt{7}i\}$
27. $\{16\}$
29. $\varnothing$ or $\{\ \}$
31. $\left\{\dfrac{1}{4}\right\}$
33. $\left\{-\dfrac{1}{7}, \dfrac{1}{4}\right\}$
35. $\left\{-\dfrac{2}{3}, \dfrac{5}{2}\right\}$
37. $\{-64, 1\}$

39. $\{-1, 8\}$
41. $\{25\}$
43. $\left\{\dfrac{1}{3}, \dfrac{1}{2}\right\}$
45. $\left\{-\dfrac{11}{5}, -1\right\}$
47. $\left\{1, 3, -\dfrac{1}{2} - \dfrac{\sqrt{3}}{2}i, -\dfrac{3}{2} - \dfrac{3\sqrt{3}}{2}i, -\dfrac{1}{2} + \dfrac{\sqrt{3}}{2}i, -\dfrac{3}{2} + \dfrac{3\sqrt{3}}{2}i\right\}$
49. $\{-2, 4\}$

51. $\{-2i, -2\sqrt{2}, 2i, 2\sqrt{2}\}$
53. $\{16\}$
55. $\{-3, -2i, 3, 2i\}$
57. $\left\{-\dfrac{10}{3}, -2\right\}$
59. $\{9, 16\}$
61. $\left\{\dfrac{1}{2}, 5\right\}$
63. (a) $0, -\sqrt{7}i, \sqrt{7}i$

(b) $-\sqrt{6}i, \sqrt{6}i, -i, i$
65. (a) $0, -\sqrt{3}, \sqrt{3}$ **(b)** $-\sqrt{2}i, \sqrt{2}i, -\sqrt{5}, \sqrt{5}$
67. (a) $-1, \dfrac{1}{6}$ **(b)** $-\dfrac{1}{2}, \dfrac{1}{7}$
69. $-\sqrt{7}i, \sqrt{7}i, -\sqrt{2}i$ and $\sqrt{2}i$

71. $\dfrac{81}{4}$
73. $-\dfrac{8}{3}, -2$
75. (a) $x = 2$ or $x = 3$ **(b)** $x = 5$ or $x = 6$; comparing these solutions to those in part (a), we note that $5 = 2 + 3$ and $6 = 3 + 3$. **(c)** $x = 0$ or $x = 1$; comparing these solutions to those in part (a), we note that $0 = 2 - 2$ and $1 = 3 - 2$. **(d)** $x = 7$ or $x = 8$; comparing these solutions to those in part (a), we note that $7 = 2 + 5$ and $8 = 3 + 5$. **(e)** The solution set of the equation $(x - a)^2 - 5(x - a) + 6 = 0$ is $\{2 + a, 3 + a\}$. **77. (a)** $x = \dfrac{1}{2}$ or $x = 1$ **(b)** $x = \dfrac{5}{2}$ or $x = 3$; comparing these solutions to those in part (a), we note that $\dfrac{5}{2} = \dfrac{1}{2} + 2$ and $3 = 1 + 2$. **(c)** $x = \dfrac{11}{2}$ or $x = 6$; comparing these solutions to those in part (a), we note that $\dfrac{11}{2} = \dfrac{1}{2} + 5$ and $6 = 1 + 5$. **(d)** For $f(x) = 2x^2 - 3x + 1$, the zeros of $f(x - a)$ are $\dfrac{1}{2} + a$ and $1 + a$ **79. (a)** $R(1990) = 3000$; the revenue in 1990 was $\$3,000$ thousand (or $\$3,000,000$) **(b)** $x = 2000$; in the year 2000, revenue was $\$3,065$ thousand (or $\$3,065,000$) **(c)** 2015

81. $x = +\dfrac{\sqrt{10 + 2\sqrt{17}}}{2}i$ or $x = \pm\dfrac{\sqrt{10 - 2\sqrt{17}}}{2}i$
83. $x = \pm\dfrac{3\sqrt{2}}{2}$
85. $\{36\}$; Answers will vary.

87. Extraneous solutions may result after squaring both sides of the equation.
89. $p^2 + 4p^{-1} + 9$
91. $5\sqrt[3]{2a} - 4a\sqrt[3]{2a} = (5 - 4a)\sqrt[3]{2a}$

93. Let $Y_1 = x^4 + 5x^2 - 14$.

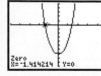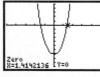

The solution set is approximately $\{-1.41, 1.41\}$.

95. Let $Y_1 = 2(x - 2)^2$ and $Y_2 = 5(x - 2) + 1$.

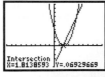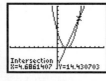

The solution set is approximately $\{1.81, 4.69\}$.

97. Let $Y_1 = x - 5\sqrt{x}$ and $Y_2 = -3$.

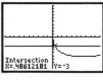

The solution set is approximately $\{0.49\}$.

99. (a) $Y_1 = x^2 - 5x - 6$

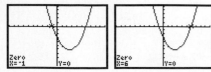

The x-intercepts are -1 and 6.

(b) $Y_1 = (x + 2)^2 - 5(x + 2) - 6$

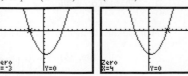

The x-intercepts are -3 and 4.

(c) $Y_1 = (x + 5)^2 - 5(x + 5) - 6$

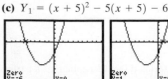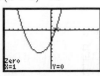

The x-intercepts are -6 and 1.

(d) The x-intercepts of the graph of $y = f(x) = x^2 - 5x - 6$ are -1 and 6. The x-intercepts of the graph of $y = f(x + a) = (x + a)^2 - 5(x + a) - 6$ are $-1 - a$ and $6 - a$.

Putting the Concepts Together (Sections 7.1–7.3)

1. $z^2 + 10z + 25 = (z + 5)^2$
2. $x^2 + 7x + \dfrac{49}{4} = \left(x + \dfrac{7}{2}\right)^2$

3. $n^2 - \dfrac{1}{4}n + \dfrac{1}{64} = \left(n - \dfrac{1}{8}\right)^2$
4. $\left\{\dfrac{1}{2}, \dfrac{5}{2}\right\}$
5. $\{-4 - 2\sqrt{3}, -4 + 2\sqrt{3}\}$
6. $\{3 - \sqrt{2}, 3 + \sqrt{2}\}$
7. $\left\{-\dfrac{4\sqrt{5}}{7}, \dfrac{4\sqrt{5}}{7}\right\}$

8. $\{4 - \sqrt{10}, 4 + \sqrt{10}\}$
9. $\left\{-1 - \dfrac{\sqrt{3}}{3}i, -1 + \dfrac{\sqrt{3}}{3}i\right\}$

10. $\left\{-2 - \dfrac{\sqrt{42}}{3}, -2 + \dfrac{\sqrt{42}}{3}\right\}$ **11.** $b^2 - 4ac = 0$; the quadratic equation will have one repeated real solution.   **12.** $b^2 - 4ac = 60$; the quadratic equation will have two irrational solutions.   **13.** $b^2 - 4ac = -4$; the quadratic equation will have two complex solutions that are not real.

14. $c = \sqrt{116} = 2\sqrt{29}$ **15.** $\left\{\dfrac{9}{4}\right\}$ **16.** $\left\{\dfrac{1}{6}, -\dfrac{1}{3}\right\}$ **17.** Revenue will be \$12,000 when either 150 microwaves or 200 microwaves are sold.

18. The speed of the wind was approximately 52.9 miles per hour.

Section 7.4 Graphing Quadratic Functions Using Transformations   **1.** quadratic function   **2.** up; down

3.   **4.**   **5.** False   **6.**   **7.**   **8.**

9. 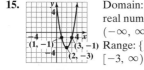   **10.** y; a; vertically stretched; vertically compressed   **11.** 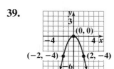   **12.** 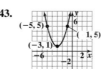   **13.** True   **14.** Domain: $\{x \mid x$ is any real number$\}$ or $(-\infty, \infty)$; Range: $\{y \mid y \le 1\}$ or $(-\infty, 1]$

15. Domain: $\{x \mid x$ is any real number$\}$ or $(-\infty, \infty)$ Range: $\{y \mid y \ge -3\}$ or $[-3, \infty)$ **16.** $f(x) = -(x + 1)^2 + 2$ **17.** (I) (D) (II) (A) (III) (C) (IV) (B)   **19.** shift 10 units to the left   **21.** shift 12 units up   **23.** vertically stretch by a factor of 2 (multiply the y-coordinates by 2) and shift 5 units to the right   **25.** multiply the y-coordinates by -3 (which means it opens down and is stretched vertically by a factor of 3), shift 5 units to the left, and shift up 8 units

27.   **29.**   **31.**   **33.** 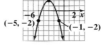   **35.**   **37.**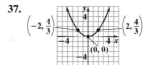

39.   **41.** 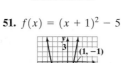   **43.**   **45.**    **47.**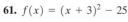

49. 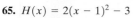   **51.** $f(x) = (x + 1)^2 - 5$ **53.** $g(x) = (x - 2)^2 + 4$ 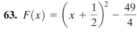   **55.** $f(x) = (x + 1)^2 - 3$ **57.** $f(x) = -2(x - 3)^2 + 7$ **59.** $f(x) = (x + 4)^2$

61. $f(x) = (x + 3)^2 - 25$ vertex is $(-3, -25)$; axis of symmetry is $x = -3$; domain is the set of all real numbers $(-\infty, \infty)$; range is $\{y \mid y \ge -25\}$, or $[-25, \infty)$

63. $F(x) = \left(x + \dfrac{1}{2}\right)^2 - \dfrac{49}{4}$ 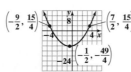 vertex is $\left(-\dfrac{1}{2}, -\dfrac{49}{4}\right)$; axis of symmetry is $x = -\dfrac{1}{2}$ domain is the set of all real numbers, or $(-\infty, \infty)$; range is $\left\{y \mid y \ge -\dfrac{49}{4}\right\}$, or $\left[-\dfrac{49}{4}, \infty\right)$

65. $H(x) = 2(x - 1)^2 - 3$ vertex is $(1, -3)$; axis of symmetry is $x = 1$; domain is the set of all real numbers, $(-\infty, \infty)$; range is $\{y \mid y \ge -3\}$, or $[-3, \infty)$

67. $P(x) = 3(x + 2)^2 + 1$ vertex is $(-2, 1)$; axis of symmetry is $x = -2$; domain is the set of all real numbers, or $(-\infty, \infty)$; range is $\{y \mid y \ge 1\}$, or $[1, \infty)$

69. $F(x) = -(x + 5)^2 + 4$ vertex is $(-5, 4)$; axis of symmetry is $x = -5$; domain is the set of all real numbers, or $(-\infty, \infty)$; range is $\{y \mid y \le 4\}$, or $(-\infty, 4]$

71. $g(x) = -(x - 3)^2 + 8$ vertex is $(3, 8)$; axis of symmetry is $x = 3$; domain is the set of all real numbers, or $(-\infty, \infty)$; range is $\{y \mid y \le 8\}$, or $(-\infty, 8]$

73. $H(x) = -2(x - 2)^2 + 4$

vertex is $(2, 4)$; axis of symmetry is $x = 2$; domain is the set of all real numbers, or $(-\infty, \infty)$; range is $\{y \mid y \le 4\}$, or $(-\infty, 4]$

75. $f(x) = \dfrac{1}{3}(x - 3)^2 + 1$

vertex is $(3, 1)$; axis of symmetry is $x = 3$; domain is the set of all real numbers, or $(-\infty, \infty)$; range is $\{y \mid y \ge 1\}$, or $[1, \infty)$

77. $G(x) = -12\left(x + \dfrac{1}{2}\right)^2 + 4$

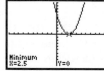

vertex is $\left(-\dfrac{1}{2}, 4\right)$; axis of symmetry is $x = -\dfrac{1}{2}$; domain is the set of all real numbers, or $(-\infty, \infty)$; range is $\{y \mid y \le 4\}$, or $(-\infty, 4]$

79. Answers may vary. One possibility: $f(x) = (x - 3)^2$ **81.** Answers may vary. One possibility: $f(x) = (x + 3)^2 + 1$ **83.** Answers may vary. One possibility: $f(x) = -(x - 5)^2 - 1$ **85.** Answers may vary. One possibility: $f(x) = 4(x - 9)^2 - 6$ **87.** Answers may vary. One possibility: $f(x) = -\dfrac{1}{3}x^2 + 6$ **89.** The highest or lowest point on a parabola is called the vertex. If $a < 0$, the vertex is the highest point; if $a > 0$, the vertex is the lowest point. **91.** No. Explanations may vary. **93.** $29 + \dfrac{1}{12}$ **95.** $x^3 - 5x^2 + 4x - 2 + \dfrac{-2}{2x - 1}$

97.

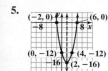

Vertex: $(0, 1.3)$
Axis of symmetry: $x = 0$
Range: $\{y \mid y \ge 1.3\} = [1.3, \infty)$

99.

Vertex: $(2.5, 0)$
Axis of symmetry: $x = 2.5$
Range: $\{y \mid y \ge 0\} = [0, \infty)$

101.

Vertex: $(1.4, 0.5)$
Axis of symmetry: $x = 1.4$
Range: $\{y \mid y \ge 0.5\} = [0.5, \infty)$

103.

Vertex: $(2.8, 5.9)$
Axis of symmetry: $x = 2.8$
Range: $\{y \mid y \le 5.9\} = (-\infty, 5.9]$

Section 7.5 Graphing Quadratic Functions Using Properties

1. $-\dfrac{b}{2a}$ **2.** $>$ **3.** 2 **4.** $(-2, -7)$

5.

6.

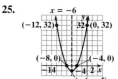

7.

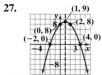

8.

9. True **10.** minimum; -7 **11.** maximum; 33
12. (a) The revenue will be maximized at a price of $75. **(b)** The maximum revenue is $2812.50.
13. The maximum area that can be enclosed is 62,500 feet. The dimensions are 250 feet by 250 feet.

14. The number of boxes that should be sold to maximize revenue is 65 and the maximum revenue is $4225. **15. (a)** $(3, -25)$ **(b)** the discriminant is positive; there are two distinct x-intercepts: -2 and 8 **17. (a)** $(1, -3)$ **(b)** the discriminant is negative; there are no x-intercepts

19. (a) $\left(-\dfrac{1}{2}, 0\right)$ **(b)** the discriminant is zero; there is one x-intercept: $-\dfrac{1}{2}$ **21. (a)** $\left(\dfrac{1}{8}, -\dfrac{17}{16}\right)$ **(b)** the discriminant is positive; there are two distinct x-intercepts; 0.39 and 0.64

23.

Domain: $\{x \mid x$ is any real number$\}$ or $(-\infty, \infty)$
Range: $\{y \mid y \ge -9\}$ or $[-9, \infty)$

25.

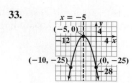

Domain: $\{x \mid x$ is any real number$\}$ or $(-\infty, \infty)$
Range: $\{y \mid y \ge -4\}$ or $[-4, \infty)$

27.

Domain: $\{x \mid x$ is any real number$\}$ or $(-\infty, \infty)$
Range: $\{y \mid y \le 9\}$ or $(-\infty, 9]$

29.

Domain: $\{x \mid x$ is any real number$\}$ or $(-\infty, \infty)$
Range: $\{y \mid y \ge 0\}$ or $[0, \infty)$

31.

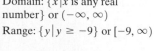

Domain: $\{x \mid x$ is any real number$\}$ or $(-\infty, \infty)$
Range: $\{y \mid y \ge 4\}$ or $[4, \infty)$

33.

Domain: $\{x \mid x$ is any real number$\}$ or $(-\infty, \infty)$
Range: $\{y \mid y \le 0\}$ or $(-\infty, 0]$

35.

Domain: $\{x \mid x$ is any real number$\}$ or $(-\infty, \infty)$
Range: $\{y \mid y \le -4\}$ or $(-\infty, -4]$

37.

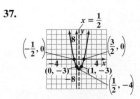

Domain: $\{x \mid x$ is any real number$\}$ or $(-\infty, \infty)$
Range: $\{y \mid y \ge -4\}$ or $[-4, \infty)$

39.

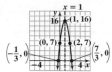

Domain: $\{x \mid x$ is any real number$\}$ or $(-\infty, \infty)$
Range: $\{y \mid y \leq 16\}$ or $(-\infty, 16]$

41.

Domain: $\{x \mid x$ is any real number$\}$ or $(-\infty, \infty)$
Range: $\{y \mid y \geq 0\}$ or $[0, \infty)$

43.

Domain: $\{x \mid x$ is any real number$\}$ or $(-\infty, \infty)$
Range: $\{y \mid y \leq 0\}$ or $(-\infty, 0]$

45.

Domain: $\{x \mid x$ is any real number$\}$ or $(-\infty, \infty)$
Range: $\{y \mid y \geq 3\}$ or $[3, \infty)$

47.

Domain: $\{x \mid x$ is any real number$\}$ or $(-\infty, \infty)$
Range: $\left\{y \mid y \leq -\dfrac{3}{4}\right\}$ or $\left(-\infty, -\dfrac{3}{4}\right]$

49.

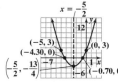

Domain: $\{x \mid x$ is any real number$\}$ or $(-\infty, \infty)$
Range: $\left\{y \mid y \geq -\dfrac{13}{4}\right\}$ or $\left[-\dfrac{13}{4}, \infty\right)$

51.

Domain: $\{x \mid x$ is any real number$\}$ or $(-\infty, \infty)$
Range: $\left\{y \mid y \leq \dfrac{22}{3}\right\}$ or $\left(-\infty, \dfrac{22}{3}\right]$

53.

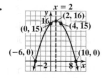

Domain: $\{x \mid x$ is any real number$\}$ or $(-\infty, \infty)$
Range: $\left\{y \mid y \geq \dfrac{3}{4}\right\}$ or $\left[\dfrac{3}{4}, \infty\right)$

55.

Domain: $\{x \mid x$ is any real number$\}$ or $(-\infty, \infty)$
Range: $\{y \mid y \leq 3\}$ or $(-\infty, 3]$

57.

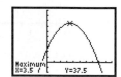

Domain: $\{x \mid x$ is any real number$\}$ or $(-\infty, \infty)$
Range: $\left\{y \mid y \geq -\dfrac{49}{16}\right\}$ or $\left[-\dfrac{49}{16}, \infty\right)$

59.

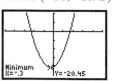

Domain: $\{x \mid x$ is any real number$\}$ or $(-\infty, \infty)$
Range: $\{y \mid y \geq -8\}$ or $[-8, \infty)$

61.

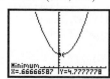

Domain: $\{x \mid x$ is any real number$\}$ or $(-\infty, \infty)$; Range: $\{y \mid y \leq 16\}$ or $(-\infty, 16]$

63. minimum; -3 **65.** maximum; 28 **67.** maximum; 23 **69.** minimum; -19 **71.** minimum; $-\dfrac{17}{8}$
73. maximum; $\dfrac{7}{3}$ **75. (a)** $120 **(b)** $36,000 **77.** 60; $35 **79. (a)** after 7.5 seconds **(b)** 910 feet
(c) about 15.042 seconds **81. (a)** about 1753.52 feet from the cannon **(b)** about 886.76 feet **(c)** about
3517 feet from the cannon **(d)** The two answers are close. Explanations may vary. **83. (a)** about 46.5 years
(b) $64,661.75 **85.** 18 and 18 **87.** -9 and 9 **89.** 15,625 square yards; 125 yards $\times$ 125 yards
91. 500,000 square meters; 500 m $\times$ 1000 m and the long side is parallel to the river **93.** 5 inches
95. (a) $R = -p^2 + 110p$ **(b)** $55; $3025 **(c)** 55 pairs **97. (a)** $f(x) = x^2 - 8x + 12$;
$f(x) = 2x^2 - 16x + 24$; $f(x) = -2x^2 + 16x - 24$ **(b)** The value of a has no effect on the x-intercepts.

(c) The value of a has no effect on the axis of symmetry. **(d)** The x-coordinate of the vertex is 4, which does not depend on a. However, the
y-coordinate is $-4a$, which does depend on a. **99.** If the discriminant is positive, the equation $ax^2 + bx + c = 0$ will have two distinct real solutions,
which means the graph of $f(x) = ax^2 + bx + c$ will have two x-intercepts. If the discriminant is zero, the equation $ax^2 + bx + c = 0$ will have one real
solution, which means the graph of $f(x) = ax^2 + bx + c$ will have one x-intercept. If the discriminant is negative, the equation $ax^2 + bx + c = 0$ will
have no real solutions, which means the graph of $f(x) = ax^2 + bx + c$ will have no x-intercepts. **101.** If the price is too high, the quantity demanded
will be 0.

103.

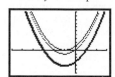

105.

107. Vertex: $(3.5, -9.25)$

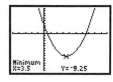

109. Vertex: $(3.5, 37.5)$

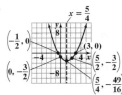

111. Vertex: $(-0.3, -20.45)$

113. Vertex: $(0.67, 4.78)$

115. c is the y-intercept

Section 7.6 Quadratic Inequalities   **1.** $\{x\,|\,x \le -5 \text{ or } x \ge 2\}$; $(-\infty, -5] \cup [2, \infty)$

2. $\{x\,|\,x \le -5 \text{ or } x \ge 2\}$; $(-\infty, -5] \cup [2, \infty)$ **3.** $\{x\,|\,-6 < x < 4\}$; $(-6, 4)$

4. $\left\{x\,\middle|\,x < \dfrac{-1 - \sqrt{61}}{6} \text{ or } x > \dfrac{-1 + \sqrt{61}}{6}\right\}$; $\left(-\infty, \dfrac{-1 - \sqrt{61}}{6}\right) \cup \left(\dfrac{-1 + \sqrt{61}}{6}, \infty\right)$

5. (a) $\{x\,|\,x < -6 \text{ or } x > 5\}$ or $(-\infty, -6) \cup (5, \infty)$ **(b)** $\{x\,|\,-6 \le x \le 5\}$ or $[-6, 5]$

7. (a) $\left\{x\,\middle|\,-6 \le x \le \dfrac{5}{2}\right\}$ or $\left[-6, \dfrac{5}{2}\right]$ **(b)** $\left\{x\,\middle|\,x < -6 \text{ or } x > \dfrac{5}{2}\right\}$ or $(-\infty, -6) \cup \left(\dfrac{5}{2}, \infty\right)$

9. $\{x\,|\,x \le -2 \text{ or } x \ge 5\}$ or $(-\infty, -2] \cup [5, \infty)$

11. $\{x\,|\,-7 < x < -3\}$ or $(-7, -3)$

13. $\{x\,|\,x < -5 \text{ or } x > 7\}$ or $(-\infty, -5) \cup (7, \infty)$

15. $\left\{n\,\middle|\,3 - \sqrt{17} \le n \le 3 + \sqrt{17}\right\}$ or $\left[3 - \sqrt{17}, 3 + \sqrt{17}\right]$

17. $\{m\,|\,m \le -7 \text{ or } m \ge 2\}$ or $(-\infty, -7] \cup [2, \infty)$

19. $\left\{q\,\middle|\,q \le -\dfrac{5}{2} \text{ or } q \ge 3\right\}$ or $\left(-\infty, -\dfrac{5}{2}\right] \cup [3, \infty)$

21. $\{x\,|\,-1 \le x \le 4\}$ or $[-1, 4]$

23. $\{x\,|\,x < -2 \text{ or } x > 5\}$ or $(-\infty, -2) \cup (5, \infty)$

25. $\left\{x\,\middle|\,x \le -\dfrac{2}{3} \text{ or } x \ge 4\right\}$ or $\left(-\infty, -\dfrac{2}{3}\right] \cup [4, \infty)$

27. $\left\{x\,\middle|\,-2 - \sqrt{3} < x < -2 + \sqrt{3}\right\}$ or $\left(-2 - \sqrt{3}, -2 + \sqrt{3}\right)$

29. $\left\{a\,\middle|\,-\dfrac{1}{2} \le a \le 4\right\}$ or $\left[-\dfrac{1}{2}, 4\right]$

31. $\{z\,|\,z \text{ is any real number}\}$ or $(-\infty, \infty)$

33. $\varnothing$ or $\{\ \}$

35. $\{x\,|\,x \ne 3\}$ or $(-\infty, 3) \cup (3, \infty)$

37. $\{x\,|\,0 < x < 5\}$ or $(0, 5)$ **39.** $\{x\,|\,x \le -4 \text{ or } x \ge 7\}$ or $(-\infty, -4] \cup [7, \infty)$ **41.** $\left\{x\,\middle|\,x < -\dfrac{5}{2} \text{ or } x > 2\right\}$ or $\left(-\infty, -\dfrac{5}{2}\right) \cup (2, \infty)$

43. $\{x\,|\,x \le -8 \text{ or } x \ge 0\}$ or $(-\infty, -8] \cup [0, \infty)$ **45.** $\{x\,|\,x \le -5 \text{ or } x \ge 6\}$ or $(-\infty, -5] \cup [6, \infty)$ **47.** between 2 and 3 seconds after the ball is thrown   **49.** between $110 and $130   **51.** $x = -3$; a perfect square cannot be negative. Therefore, the only solution will be where the perfect square expression equals zero, which is -3.   **53.** all real numbers; a perfect square must always be zero or greater. Therefore, it must always be larger than -2. Thus, all values of x will make the inequality true.   **55.** Answers may vary. One possibility follows: $x^2 + x - 6 \le 0$ **57.** Answer will vary. One possibility follows: The inequalities have the same solution set because they are equivalent.   **59.** $\{x\,|\,x < -3 \text{ or } 1 < x < 3\}$ or

$(-\infty, -3) \cup (1, 3)$ **61.** $\left\{x\,\middle|\,-\dfrac{4}{3} \le x \le 2 \text{ or } x \ge 6\right\}$ or $\left[-\dfrac{4}{3}, 2\right] \cup [6, \infty)$ **63.** $\{x\,|\,x < -2 \text{ or } -1 < x < 5\}$ or $(-\infty, -2) \cup (-1, 5)$

65. The square of a real number is greater than or equal to zero. Therefore, $x^2 - 1$ is greater than or equal to -1 for all real numbers.

67. No. The inequality $x^2 + 1 > 1$ is true for all real numbers except $x = 0$.   **69.** $\dfrac{-8m^5}{n^2}$ **71.** $\dfrac{b^{\frac{1}{4}}}{9a^{\frac{7}{9}}}$

73.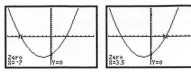

$\{x | x < -7 \text{ or } x > 3.5\}$ or $(-\infty, -7)$ or $(3.5, \infty)$

75.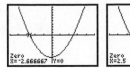

$\{x | -2.67 \le x \le 2.5\}$ or $[-2.67, 2.5]$

Chapter 7 Review **1.** $\{-13, 13\}$ **2.** $\{-5\sqrt{3}, 5\sqrt{3}\}$ **3.** $\{-4i, 4i\}$ **4.** $\left\{-\dfrac{2\sqrt{2}}{3}, \dfrac{2\sqrt{2}}{3}\right\}$ **5.** $\{-1, 17\}$ **6.** $\{2 - 5\sqrt{6}, 2 + 5\sqrt{6}\}$

7. $\left\{-5, \dfrac{5}{3}\right\}$ **8.** $\left\{-\dfrac{3\sqrt{14}}{7}, \dfrac{3\sqrt{14}}{7}\right\}$ **9.** $\{-4\sqrt{5}i, 4\sqrt{5}i\}$ **10.** $\left\{-\dfrac{3}{4} - \dfrac{\sqrt{13}}{4}, -\dfrac{3}{4} + \dfrac{\sqrt{13}}{4}\right\}$ **11.** $a^2 + 30a + 225; (a + 15)^2$

12. $b^2 - 14b + 49; (b - 7)^2$ **13.** $c^2 - 11c + \dfrac{121}{4}; \left(c - \dfrac{11}{2}\right)^2$ **14.** $d^2 + 9d + \dfrac{81}{4}; \left(d + \dfrac{9}{2}\right)^2$ **15.** $m^2 - \dfrac{1}{4}m + \dfrac{1}{64}; \left(m - \dfrac{1}{8}\right)^2$

16. $n^2 + \dfrac{6}{7}n + \dfrac{9}{49}; \left(n + \dfrac{3}{7}\right)^2$ **17.** $\{2, 8\}$ **18.** $\{-4, 7\}$ **19.** $\{3 - 2\sqrt{3}, 3 + 2\sqrt{3}\}$ **20.** $\left\{\dfrac{5}{2} - \dfrac{\sqrt{53}}{2}, \dfrac{5}{2} + \dfrac{\sqrt{53}}{2}\right\}$

21. $\left\{-\dfrac{1}{2} - \dfrac{3\sqrt{3}}{2}i, -\dfrac{1}{2} + \dfrac{3\sqrt{3}}{2}i\right\}$ **22.** $\{3 - 2\sqrt{2}i, 3 + 2\sqrt{2}i\}$ **23.** $\left\{\dfrac{1}{2}, 3\right\}$ **24.** $\left\{-\dfrac{1}{2} - \dfrac{3}{2}i, -\dfrac{1}{2} + \dfrac{3}{2}i\right\}$ **25.** $\left\{\dfrac{3}{2} - \dfrac{\sqrt{15}}{6}i, \dfrac{3}{2} + \dfrac{\sqrt{15}}{6}i\right\}$

26. $\left\{-\dfrac{2}{3} - \dfrac{\sqrt{10}}{3}, -\dfrac{2}{3} + \dfrac{\sqrt{10}}{3}\right\}$ **27.** $c = 15$ **28.** $c = 8\sqrt{2}$ **29.** $c = 3\sqrt{5}$ **30.** $c = 26$ **31.** $c = 6$ **32.** $c = 7$ **33.** $b = 3\sqrt{7}$

34. $a = 5\sqrt{3}$ **35.** $a = \sqrt{253}$ **36.** approximately 127.3 feet **37.** $\{-4, 5\}$ **38.** $\left\{-\dfrac{3}{2}, \dfrac{7}{2}\right\}$ **39.** $\left\{-\dfrac{4}{3} - \dfrac{\sqrt{7}}{3}, -\dfrac{4}{3} + \dfrac{\sqrt{7}}{3}\right\}$

40. $\left\{1 - \dfrac{\sqrt{10}}{2}, 1 + \dfrac{\sqrt{10}}{2}\right\}$ **41.** $\left\{-\dfrac{1}{6} - \dfrac{\sqrt{35}}{6}i, -\dfrac{1}{6} + \dfrac{\sqrt{35}}{6}i\right\}$ **42.** $\left\{\dfrac{4}{3}\right\}$ **43.** $\{2 - \sqrt{2}, 2 + \sqrt{2}\}$ **44.** $\left\{-\dfrac{2}{5} - \dfrac{1}{5}i, -\dfrac{2}{5} + \dfrac{1}{5}i\right\}$

45. $\left\{-\dfrac{5}{2} - \dfrac{3\sqrt{3}}{2}i, -\dfrac{5}{2} + \dfrac{3\sqrt{3}}{2}i\right\}$ **46.** $\left\{-\dfrac{3}{2} - \dfrac{\sqrt{5}}{2}i, -\dfrac{3}{2} + \dfrac{\sqrt{5}}{2}i\right\}$ **47.** 57; two irrational solutions **48.** 0; one repeated real solution

49. -47; two complex solutions that are not real **50.** -20; two complex solutions that are not real **51.** 0; one repeated real solution

52. 25; two rational solutions **53.** $\{-9, 1\}$ **54.** $\left\{-\dfrac{5}{2}, \dfrac{1}{3}\right\}$ **55.** $\{-2 - 3i, -2 + 3i\}$ **56.** $\{-2\sqrt{3}, 2\sqrt{3}\}$ **57.** $\left\{1 - \dfrac{\sqrt{10}}{2}, 1 + \dfrac{\sqrt{10}}{2}\right\}$

58. $\{-4 - 2i, -4 + 2i\}$ **59.** $\{-3, 5\}$ **60.** $\{1 - \sqrt{2}, 1 + \sqrt{2}\}$ **61.** $\left\{-\dfrac{4}{3}, \dfrac{4}{3}\right\}$ **62.** $\{-1 - \sqrt{3}i, -1 + \sqrt{3}i\}$ **63.** $x = 10$; the three sides

measure 5, 12, and 13 **64.** 12 centimeters by 9 centimeters **65.** (a) either 300 or 600 cellular phones (b) 450 cellular phones **66.** (a) after approximately 0.5 second and after approximately 2.7 seconds (b) after approximately 4.3 seconds (c) No; the solutions to the equation are complex solutions that are not real **67.** approximately 10.8 miles per hour **68.** approximately 67.8 minutes **69.** $\{-4i, 4i, -3, 3\}$

70. $\left\{-\dfrac{\sqrt{3}}{2}, \dfrac{\sqrt{3}}{2}, -\sqrt{2}i, \sqrt{2}i\right\}$ **71.** $\left\{-\dfrac{10}{3}, -1\right\}$ **72.** $\{-4, 4, -2\sqrt{2}, 2\sqrt{2}\}$ **73.** $\{16, 81\}$ **74.** $\left\{\dfrac{9}{25}\right\}$ **75.** $\left\{-\dfrac{1}{3}, \dfrac{1}{7}\right\}$ **76.** $\left\{-343, \dfrac{1}{8}\right\}$

77. $\{16\}$ **78.** $\left\{-\dfrac{36}{7}, -\dfrac{19}{4}\right\}$ **79.** $\left\{\dfrac{9}{4}, \dfrac{49}{4}\right\}$ **80.** $\{-2\sqrt{3}, -\sqrt{5}, \sqrt{5}, 2\sqrt{3}\}$

81. 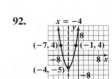 **82.** **83.** 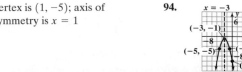 **84.** 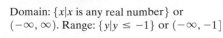 **85.** 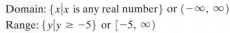 **86.**

87. **88.** **89.** 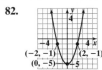 **90.** **91.** 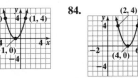 vertex is $(3, 1)$; axis of symmetry is $x = 3$; Domain: $\{x | x$ is any real number$\}$ or $(-\infty, \infty)$; Range: $\{y | y \ge 1\}$ or $[1, \infty)$

92. 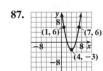 vertex is $(-4, -5)$; axis of symmetry is $x = -4$

93. vertex is $(1, -5)$; axis of symmetry is $x = 1$

94. vertex is $(-3, -1)$; axis of symmetry is $x = -3$

Domain: $\{x | x$ is any real number$\}$ or $(-\infty, \infty)$. Range: $\{y | y \ge -5\}$ or $[-5, \infty)$

Domain: $\{x | x$ is any real number$\}$ or $(-\infty, \infty)$ Range: $\{y | y \ge -5\}$ or $[-5, \infty)$

Domain: $\{x | x$ is any real number$\}$ or $(-\infty, \infty)$. Range: $\{y | y \le -1\}$ or $(-\infty, -1]$

95. vertex is $(2, 4)$; axis of symmetry is $x = 2$
Domain: $\{x | x \text{ is any real number}\}$ or $(-\infty, \infty)$
Range: $\{y | y \leq 4\}$ or $(-\infty, 4]$

96. vertex is $(2, 3)$; axis of symmetry is $x = 2$
Domain: $\{x | x \text{ is any real number}\}$ or $(-\infty, \infty)$
Range: $\{y | y \geq 3\}$ or $[3, \infty)$

97. $f(x) = 2(x - 2)^2 - 4$ or $f(x) = 2x^2 - 8x + 4$ **98.** $f(x) = -(x - 4)^2 + 3$ or $f(x) = -x^2 + 8x - 13$

99. $f(x) = -\dfrac{1}{2}(x + 2)^2 - 1$ or $f(x) = -\dfrac{1}{2}x^2 - 2x - 3$ **100.** $f(x) = 3(x + 2)^2$ or $f(x) = 3x^2 + 12x + 12$

101.
Domain: $\{x | x \text{ is any real number}\}$ or $(-\infty, \infty)$
Range: $\{y | y \geq -9\}$ or $[-9, \infty)$

102.
Domain: $\{x | x \text{ is any real number}\}$ or $(-\infty, \infty)$
Range: $\left\{y | y \geq -\dfrac{1}{8}\right\}$ or $\left[-\dfrac{1}{8}, \infty\right)$

103.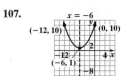
Domain: $\{x | x \text{ is any real number}\}$ or $(-\infty, \infty)$
Range: $\{y | y \leq 2\}$ or $(-\infty, 2]$

104.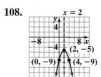
Domain: $\{x | x \text{ is any real number}\}$ or $(-\infty, \infty)$
Range: $\{y | y \leq 5\}$ or $(-\infty, 5]$

105.
Domain: $\{x | x \text{ is any real number}\}$ or $(-\infty, \infty)$
Range: $\{y | y \geq 0\}$ or $[0, \infty)$

106.
Domain: $\{x | x \text{ is any real number}\}$ or $(-\infty, \infty)$
Range: $\{y | y \geq 0\}$ or $[0, \infty)$

107.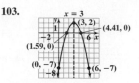
Domain: $\{x | x \text{ is any real number}\}$ or $(-\infty, \infty)$
Range: $\{y | y \geq 1\}$ or $[1, \infty)$

108.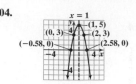
Domain: $\{x | x \text{ is any real number}\}$ or $(-\infty, \infty)$
Range: $\{y | y \leq -5\}$ or $(-\infty, -5]$

109. maximum; 22   **110.** minimum; $-\dfrac{11}{8}$ **111.** maximum; 7   **112.** maximum; 5   **113.** (a) $225 (b) $16,875   **114.** (a) 3.75 amperes
(b) 225 watts   **115.** both numbers are 12   **116.** (a) 3.75 yards by 7.5 yards   (b) 28.125 square yards   **117.** (a) 100 feet   (b) 50 feet
(c) 200 feet   **118.** (a) $R = -0.002p^2 + 60p$ (b) $15,000; $450,000   (c) 30 automobiles per month   **119.** (a) $\{x | x < -2 \text{ or } x > 3\}$ or

$(-\infty, -2) \cup (3, \infty)$ (b) $\{x | -2 < x < 3\}$ or $(-2, 3)$ **120.** (a) $\left\{x \left| -\dfrac{7}{2} \leq x \leq 1\right.\right\}$ or $\left[-\dfrac{7}{2}, 1\right]$ (b) $\left\{x \left| x \leq -\dfrac{7}{2} \text{ or } x \geq 1\right.\right\}$ or $\left(-\infty, -\dfrac{7}{2}\right] \cup [1, \infty)$

121. $\{x | -4 \leq x \leq 6\}$ or $[-4, 6]$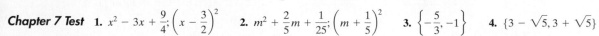

122. $\{y | y \leq -8 \text{ or } y \geq 1\}$ or, $(-\infty, -8] \cup [1, \infty)$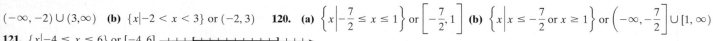

123. $\left\{z \left| z < \dfrac{4}{3} \text{ or } z > 5\right.\right\}$ or $\left(-\infty, \dfrac{4}{3}\right) \cup (5, \infty)$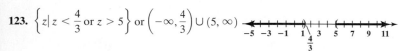

124. $\{p | -2 - \sqrt{6} < p < -2 + \sqrt{6}\}$ or $\left(-2 - \sqrt{6}, -2 + \sqrt{6}\right)$

125. $\{m | m \text{ is any real number}\}$ or $(-\infty, \infty)$

126. $\left\{w \left| -\dfrac{1}{3} \leq w \leq \dfrac{7}{2}\right.\right\}$ or $\left[-\dfrac{1}{3}, \dfrac{7}{2}\right]$

Chapter 7 Test **1.** $x^2 - 3x + \dfrac{9}{4}; \left(x - \dfrac{3}{2}\right)^2$ **2.** $m^2 + \dfrac{2}{5}m + \dfrac{1}{25}; \left(m + \dfrac{1}{5}\right)^2$ **3.** $\left\{-\dfrac{5}{3}, -1\right\}$ **4.** $\{3 - \sqrt{5}, 3 + \sqrt{5}\}$

5. $\left\{1 - \dfrac{\sqrt{2}}{2}i, 1 + \dfrac{\sqrt{2}}{2}i\right\}$ **6.** $\left\{\dfrac{3}{2} - \dfrac{\sqrt{3}}{6}i, \dfrac{3}{2} + \dfrac{\sqrt{3}}{6}i\right\}$ **7.** 57; two irrational solutions   **8.** $a = 6\sqrt{2}$ **9.** $\{-3, 3, -2i, 2i\}$ **10.** $\left\{\dfrac{1}{81}\right\}$

11. 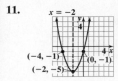 vertex is $(-2, -5)$; axis of symmetry is $x = -2$
Domain: $\{x | x \text{ is any real number}\}$ or $(-\infty, \infty)$
Range: $\{y | y \geq -5\}$ or $[-5, \infty)$

12. 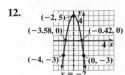 vertex is $(-2, 5)$; axis of symmetry is $x = -2$
Domain: $\{x | x \text{ is any real number}\}$ or $(-\infty, \infty)$
Range: $\{y | y \leq 5\}$ or $(-\infty, 5]$

13. $f(x) = \frac{1}{3}(x + 3)^2 - 5$ or $f(x) = \frac{1}{3}x^2 + 2x - 2$ **14.** maximum; 6

15. $\left\{m \mid m < -3 \text{ or } m > \frac{5}{2}\right\}$ or $(-\infty, -3) \cup \left(\frac{5}{2}, \infty\right)$

16. $\left\{z \mid -3 - \sqrt{10} \le z \le -3 + \sqrt{10}\right\}$ or $\left[-3 - \sqrt{10}, -3 + \sqrt{10}\right]$

17. 0.4 second and 4.6 seconds **18.** 34.1 hours **19. (a)** \$340 **(b)** \$28,900 **20. (a)** 12.5 in. by 12.5 in. by 12 in. **(b)** 1875 cubic inches

Cumulative Review Chapters R–7 **1.** 2 **2.** $3c + 11$ **3.** $\{5\}$ **4.** $(-\infty, -3) \cup (1, \infty)$ **5.** $\{x \mid x \ne -4, x \ne 3\}$

6. [graph] **7.** $y = -\frac{2}{5}x + 1$; $2x + 5y = 5$ **8.** $(-2, 5)$ **9.** -4 **10.** [graph] **11.** $a^3 - 2a^2 - 5a + 3$

12. $4x^2 + 2x - 3 + \dfrac{4x - 3}{2x^2 - x + 5}$ **13.** $(2m + 3n)(4m^2 - 6mn + 9n^2)$ **14.** $(7y - 5)(y + 4)$ **15.** $\dfrac{w + 5}{w - 2}$ **16.** $\dfrac{k + 23}{(k - 4)(k - 1)(k + 5)}$

17. $\left\{-\dfrac{3}{2}\right\}$ **18.** $(-\infty, -5) \cup [4, \infty)$ or $\{x \mid x < -5 \text{ or } x \ge 4\}$ [number line]

19. One plane is traveling 126 miles per hour and the other plane is traveling 142 miles per hour. **20.** $7\sqrt{3}$ **21.** $\dfrac{5\sqrt[3]{4}}{4}$ **22.** $\{16\}$ **23.** $x = 11$
24. $\{-2, 10\}$ **25.** [graph]

Chapter 8 Exponential and Logarithmic Functions

Section 8.1 Composite Functions and Inverse Functions
1. composite function **2. (a)** 17 **(b)** 26 **(c)** -63 **3.** False
4. $g(x) = 4x - 3$ **5. (a)** $9x^2 + 3x - 1$ **(b)** $3x^2 - 9x + 5$ **(c)** 29 **6.** one-to-one **7.** not one-to-one **8.** one-to-one
9. (a) not one-to-one **(b)** one-to-one
10.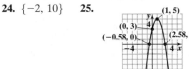

The domain of the inverse function is $\{36.05, 35.57, 34.58, 34.20, 34.73\}$. The range of the inverse function is $\{24.80, 24.59, 24.29, 23.81, 24.87\}$.

11. $\{(3, -3), (2, -2), (1, -1), (0, 0), (-1, 1)\}$. The domain of the inverse function is $\{3, 2, 1, 0, -1\}$. The range of the inverse function is $\{-3, -2, -1, 0, 1\}$.

12. [graph] **13.** True **14.** False **15.** $g^{-1}(x) = \dfrac{x + 1}{5}$ **16.** $f^{-1}(x) = \sqrt[5]{x - 3}$ **17. (a)** 3 **(b)** -3 **(c)** 19 **(d)** -12

19. (a) 85 **(b)** 19 **(c)** 29 **(d)** -7 **21. (a)** -4394 **(b)** -507 **(c)** 16 **(d)** -1453 **23. (a)** 8 **(b)** $\dfrac{4}{5}$ **(c)** 1 **(d)** $-\dfrac{4}{3}$

25. (a) $(f \circ g)(x) = 2x + 1$ **(b)** $(g \circ f)(x) = 2x + 2$ **(c)** $(f \circ f)(x) = x + 2$ **(d)** $(g \circ g)(x) = 4x$

27. (a) $(f \circ g)(x) = -8x + 17$ **(b)** $(g \circ f)(x) = -8x - 23$ **(c)** $(f \circ f)(x) = 4x + 21$ **(d)** $(g \circ g)(x) = 16x - 15$

29. (a) $(f \circ g)(x) = x^2 - 6x + 9$ **(b)** $(g \circ f)(x) = x^2 - 3$ **(c)** $(f \circ f)(x) = x^4$ **(d)** $(g \circ g)(x) = x - 6$

31. (a) $(f \circ g)(x) = \sqrt{x + 4}$ **(b)** $(g \circ f)(x) = \sqrt{x} + 4$ **(c)** $(f \circ f)(x) = \sqrt[4]{x}$ **(d)** $(g \circ g)(x) = x + 8$ **33. (a)** $(f \circ g)(x) = x^2$

(b) $(g \circ f)(x) = x^2 + 8x + 12$ **(c)** $(f \circ f)(x) = \|x + 4\| + 4\|$ **(d)** $(g \circ g)(x) = x^4 - 8x^2 + 12$ **35. (a)** $(f \circ g)(x) = \dfrac{2x}{x + 1}$, where $x \ne -1, 0$

(b) $(g \circ f)(x) = \dfrac{x + 1}{2}$, where $x \ne -1$ **(c)** $(f \circ f)(x) = \dfrac{2(x + 1)}{x + 3}$, where $x \ne -1, -3$ **(d)** $(g \circ g)(x) = x$, where $x \ne 0$ **37.** one-to-one

39. not one-to-one **41.** one-to-one **43.** not one-to-one **45.** one-to-one **47.** one-to-one **49.** not one-to-one **51.** one-to-one

53. [table] **55.** $\{(3, 0), (4, 1), (5, 2), (6, 3)\}$ **57.** $\{(3, -2), (1, -1), (-3, 0), (9, 1)\}$

59. [graph] **61.** [graph] **63.** [graph] **65.** $f(g(x)) = (x - 5) + 5 = x$
$g(f(x)) = (x + 5) - 5 = x$

67. $f(g(x)) = 5\left(\dfrac{x - 7}{5}\right) + 7 = x - 7 + 7 = x$ **69.** $f(g(x)) = \dfrac{3}{\left(\dfrac{3}{x} + 1\right) - 1} = \dfrac{3}{\dfrac{3}{x}} = 3 \cdot \dfrac{x}{3} = x$

$g(f(x)) = \dfrac{(5x + 7) - 7}{5} = \dfrac{5x}{5} = x$

$g(f(x)) = \dfrac{3}{\dfrac{3}{x - 1}} + 1 = 3 \cdot \dfrac{x - 1}{3} + 1 = x - 1 + 1 = x$

71. $f(g(x)) = \sqrt[3]{(x^3 - 4) + 4} = \sqrt[3]{x^3} = x$ **73.** $f^{-1}(x) = \dfrac{x}{6}$ **75.** $f^{-1}(x) = x - 4$ **77.** $h^{-1}(x) = \dfrac{x + 7}{2}$ **79.** $G^{-1}(x) = \dfrac{2 - x}{5}$
$g(f(x)) = \left(\sqrt[3]{x + 4}\right)^3 - 4 = x + 4 - 4 = x$

81. $g^{-1}(x) = \sqrt[3]{x - 3}$ **83.** $p^{-1}(x) = \dfrac{1}{x} - 3$ **85.** $F^{-1}(x) = 2 - \dfrac{5}{x}$ **87.** $f^{-1}(x) = x^3 + 2$ **89.** $R^{-1}(x) = \dfrac{2x}{1 - x}$

91. $f^{-1}(x) = (x - 4)^3 + 1$ **93.** $A(t) = 400\pi t^2; 3600\pi \approx 11{,}309.73$ sq ft **95. (a)** $C(x) = 2x$ **(b)** \$630 **97.** $f^{-1}(12) = 4$

99. Domain of f^{-1}: $[-5, \infty)$ Range of f^{-1}: $[0, \infty)$ **101.** Domain of g^{-1}: $(-6, 12)$ Range of g^{-1}: $[-4, 10]$ **103.** $x(T) = \dfrac{T + 300}{0.15}$ for $600 \le T \le 3960$

105. $\left\{-\dfrac{5}{2}, 3\right\}$ **107.** A function is one-to-one provided no two different inputs correspond to the same output. A function must be one-to-one in order for the inverse to be a function because we interchange the inputs and outputs to obtain the inverse. So, if a function is not one-to-one, the inverse will have a single input corresponding to two different outputs. **109.** The domain of f equals the range of f^{-1} because we interchange the roles of the inputs and outputs to obtain the inverse of a function. The same logic explains why the range of f equals the domain of f^{-1}. **111. (a)** 3 **(b)** -3
(c) 19 **(d)** -12 **113. (a)** 85 **(b)** 19 **(c)** 29 **(d)** -7 **115. (a)** -4394 **(b)** -507 **(c)** 16 **(d)** -1453 **117. (a)** 8 **(b)** $\dfrac{4}{5}$ **(c)** 1 **(d)** $-\dfrac{4}{3}$
119. $f(x) = x + 5; g(x) = x - 5$ **121.** $f(x) = 5x + 7; g(x) = \dfrac{x - 7}{5}$

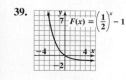

Section 8.2 Exponential Functions

1. $>;\ \ne$ **2. (a)** 3.249009585 **(b)** 3.317278183 **(c)** 3.321880096 **(d)** 3.32211036 **(e)** 3.321997085

3. The domain of f is all real numbers or, using interval notation, $(-\infty, \infty)$. The range of f is $\{y \mid y > 0\}$ or, using interval notation, $(0, \infty)$. **4.** $\left(-1, \dfrac{1}{a}\right); (0, 1); (1, a)$ **5.** True **6.** False **7.** The domain of f is all real numbers or, using interval notation, $(-\infty, \infty)$. The range of f is $\{y \mid y > 0\}$ or, using interval notation, $(0, \infty)$.

8. The domain of f is all real numbers or, using interval notation, $(-\infty, \infty)$. The range of f is $\{y \mid y > 0\}$ or, using interval notation, $(0, \infty)$.

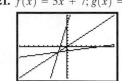

9. The domain of f is all real numbers or, using interval notation, $(-\infty, \infty)$. The range of f is $\{y \mid y > 1\}$ or, using interval notation, $(1, \infty)$.

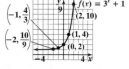

10. 2.71828 **11. (a)** 54.598 **(b)** 0.018 **12.** $\{3\}$ **13.** $\{2\}$ **14.** $\{0, 5\}$ **15.** $\{-1, 3\}$
16. (a) 0.918 or 91.8% **(b)** 0.998 or 99.8% **17. (a)** approximately 6.91 grams **(b)** 5 grams
(c) 0.625 gram **(d)** approximately 0.247 gram **18. (a)** \$2253.65 **(b)** \$11,991.60 **(c)** \$71,899.28
19. (a) 11.212 **(b)** 11.587 **(c)** 11.664 **(d)** 11.665 **(e)** 11.665 **21. (a)** 73.517 **(b)** 77.708
(c) 77.924 **(d)** 77.881 **(e)** 77.880 **23.** g **25.** e **27.** f **29.** h

31. Domain: all real numbers or $(-\infty, \infty)$
Range: $\{y \mid y > 0\}$ or $(0, \infty)$

33. 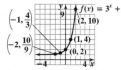 Domain: all real numbers or $(-\infty, \infty)$
Range: $\{y \mid y > 0\}$ or $(0, \infty)$

35. Domain: all real numbers or $(-\infty, \infty)$
Range: $\{y \mid y > 0\}$ or $(0, \infty)$

37. Domain: all real numbers or $(-\infty, \infty)$
Range: $\{y \mid y > 3\}$ or $(3, \infty)$

39. Domain: all real numbers or $(-\infty, \infty)$
Range: $\{y \mid y > -1\}$ or $(-1, \infty)$

41. Domain: all real numbers or $(-\infty, \infty)$
Range: $\{y \mid y > 0\}$ or $(0, \infty)$

43. (a) 21.217 **(b)** 22.472 **(c)** 22.460 **(d)** 22.460
(e) 22.459 **45.** 7.389 **47.** 0.135 **49.** 9.974
51. 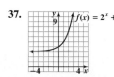 Domain: all real numbers or $(-\infty, \infty)$
Range: $\{y \mid y > 0\}$ or $(0, \infty)$

53. 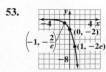 Domain: all real numbers or $(-\infty, \infty)$
Range: $\{y \mid y < 0\}$ or $(-\infty, 0)$

55. $\{5\}$ **57.** $\{-4\}$ **59.** $\{5\}$ **61.** $\{5\}$ **63.** $\left\{\dfrac{3}{2}\right\}$ **65.** $\{1\}$ **67.** $\{-1, 4\}$ **69.** $\{-4, 2\}$
71. $\{9\}$ **73.** $\{-2\}$ **75.** $\{-2, 2\}$ **77.** $\{-2\}$ **79.** $\{2\}$ **81. (a)** $f(3) = 8; (3, 8)$
(b) $x = -3; \left(-3, \dfrac{1}{8}\right)$ **83. (a)** $g(-1) = -\dfrac{3}{4}; \left(-1, -\dfrac{3}{4}\right)$ **(b)** $x = 2; (2, 15)$

85. (a) $H(-3) = 24; (-3, 24)$ **(b)** $x = 2; \left(2, \dfrac{3}{4}\right)$ **87. (a)** approximately 310.7 million people **(b)** approximately 441.0 million people
(c) Answers may vary. One possibility is that the population is not growing exponentially. **89. (a)** \$5308.39 **(b)** \$5983.40 **(c)** \$6744.25

91. (a) $2318.55 **(b)** $2322.37 **(c)** $2323.23 **(d)** $2323.65 **(e)** The future value is higher with more compounding periods. **93. (a)** $14,512
(b) $9757.87 **(c)** $5380.18 **95. (a)** approximately 95.105 grams **(b)** 50 grams **(c)** 25 grams **(d)** approximately 0.661 gram
97. (a) approximately 300.233°F **(b)** approximately 230.628°F **(c)** yes **99. (a)** approximately 29 words **(b)** approximately 38 words
101. (a) approximately 0.238 ampere **(b)** approximately 0.475 ampere **103.** $y = 3^x$ **105.** As x increases the graph increases very rapidly. As x
decreases, the graph approaches the x-axis. **107.** Answers may vary. The big difference is that exponential functions are of the form $f(x) = a^x$ (the
variable is in the exponent), while polynomial functions are of the form $f(x) = a_n x^n + a_{n-1} x^{n-1} + \cdots + a_1 x + a_0$ (the variable is a base).
109. (a) 15 **(b)** −5 **111. (a)** undefined **(b)** $\dfrac{4}{5}$ **113. (a)** 3 **(b)** $3\sqrt{3}$

115. $f(x) = 1.5^x$

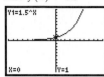

Domain: all real
numbers or
$(-\infty, \infty)$
Range: $\{y|y > 0\}$
or $(0, \infty)$

117. $H(x) = 0.9^x$

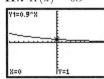

Domain: all real
numbers or
$(-\infty, \infty)$
Range: $\{y|y > 0\}$
or $(0,\infty)$

119. $g(x) = 2.5^x + 3$

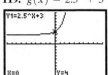

Domain: all real
numbers or
$(-\infty, \infty)$
Range: $\{y|y > 3\}$
or $(3, \infty)$

121. $F(x) = 1.6^{x-3}$

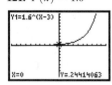

Domain: all real numbers or $(-\infty,\infty)$
Range: $\{y|y > 0\}$ or $(0,\infty)$

Section 8.3 Logarithmic Functions

1. $x = a^y$; >; ≠ **2.** $3 = \log_4 w$ **3.** $-2 = \log_p 8$ **4.** $2^y = 16$ **5.** $a^5 = 20$ **6.** $5^{-3} = z$ **7.** 2
8. −3 **9.** 2 **10.** −1 **11.** $\{x|x > -3\}$ or $(-3, \infty)$ **12.** $\left\{x \middle| x < \dfrac{5}{2}\right\}$ or $\left(-\infty, \dfrac{5}{2}\right)$
13. The domain of f is $\{x|x > 0\}$ or, using interval notation, $(0, \infty)$.
The range of f is all real numbers or, using interval notation, $(-\infty, \infty)$.
14. The domain of f is $\{x|x > 0\}$ or, using interval notation, $(0,\infty)$.
The range of f is all real numbers or, using interval notation, $(-\infty, \infty)$.

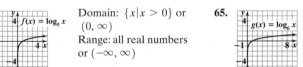

15. 3.146 **16.** 1.569 **17.** −0.523 **18.** $\{16\}$ **19.** $\{4\}$ **20.** $\{e^{-2}\}$ **21.** $\{10,020\}$ **22.** 100 decibels **23.** $3 = \log_4 64$
25. $-3 = \log_2\left(\dfrac{1}{8}\right)$ **27.** $\log_a 19 = 3$ **29.** $\log_5 c = -6$ **31.** $2^4 = 16$ **33.** $3^{-2} = \dfrac{1}{9}$ **35.** $5^{-3} = a$ **37.** $a^2 = 4$ **39.** $\left(\dfrac{1}{2}\right)^y = 12$
41. 0 **43.** 3 **45.** −2 **47.** 4 **49.** 4 **51.** $\dfrac{1}{2}$ **53.** $\{x|x > 4\}$ or $(4, \infty)$ **55.** $\{x|x > 0\}$ or $(0, \infty)$ **57.** $\left\{x \middle| x > \dfrac{2}{3}\right\}$ or $\left(\dfrac{2}{3}, \infty\right)$
59. $\left\{x \middle| x > -\dfrac{1}{2}\right\}$ or $\left(-\dfrac{1}{2}, \infty\right)$ **61.** $\left\{x \middle| x < \dfrac{1}{4}\right\}$ or $\left(-\infty, \dfrac{1}{4}\right)$

63. 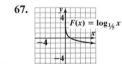 Domain: $\{x|x > 0\}$ or $(0, \infty)$
Range: all real numbers or $(-\infty, \infty)$

65. Domain: $\{x|x > 0\}$ or $(0, \infty)$
Range: all real numbers or $(-\infty, \infty)$

67. Domain: $\{x|x > 0\}$ or $(0, \infty)$
Range: all real numbers or $(-\infty, \infty)$

69. $\ln 12 = x$ **71.** $e^4 = x$ **73.** −1 **75.** 3 **77.** 1.826 **79.** 1.686 **81.** −0.456 **83.** −1.609 **85.** 0.097 **87.** −0.981 **89.** $\{4\}$
91. $\left\{\dfrac{13}{2}\right\}$ **93.** $\{6\}$ **95.** $\{3\sqrt{2}\}$ **97.** $\{10\}$ **99.** $\{e^5\}$ **101.** $\left\{\dfrac{11}{20}\right\}$ **103.** $\{-3\}$ **105.** $\{4\}$ **107.** $\{-3, 3\}$ **109. (a)** $f(16) = 4$;
$(16, 4)$ **(b)** $x = \dfrac{1}{8}; \left(\dfrac{1}{8}, -3\right)$ **111. (a)** $G(7) = \dfrac{3}{2}; \left(7, \dfrac{3}{2}\right)$ **(b)** $x = 15; (15, 2)$ **113.** $a = 4$ **115.** 20 decibels **117.** 130 decibels
119. approximately 7.8 on the Richter scale **121.** approximately 630,957 millimeters **123. (a)** 12; basic **(b)** 5; acidic **(c)** 2; acidic
(d) $10^{-7.4}$ moles per liter **125.** $\{x|x < -2 \text{ or } x > 5\}$ or $(-\infty, -2) \cup (5, \infty)$ **127.** $\{x|x < -1 \text{ or } x > 3\}$ or $(-\infty, -1) \cup (3, \infty)$
129. The base of $f(x) = \log_a x$ cannot equal 1 because $y = \log_a x$ is equivalent to $x = a^y$ and a does not equal 1 in the exponential function. In addition,
the graph of $y = \log_a x$ is a vertical line ($x = 1$), which is not a function. **131.** The domain of $f(x) = \log_a(x^2 + 1)$ is the set of all real numbers
because $x^2 + 1 > 0$ for all x. **133.** $-3x^2 - 7x + 10$ **135.** $\dfrac{4x^2 + 2x + 3}{(x + 1)(x - 1)(x + 2)}$ **137.** $5x\sqrt{2x}$

139. $f(x) = \log(x + 1)$

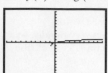

Domain: $\{x \mid x > -1\}$ or $(-1, \infty)$
Range: all real number or $(-\infty, \infty)$

141. $G(x) = \ln(x) + 1$

Domain: $\{x \mid x > 0\}$ or $(0, \infty)$
Range: all real number or $(-\infty, \infty)$

143. $f(x) = 2\log(x - 3) + 1$

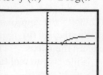

Domain: $\{x \mid x > 3\}$ or $(3, \infty)$
Range: all real number or $(-\infty, \infty)$

Putting the Concepts Together (Sections 8.1–8.3)

1. (a) $(f \circ g)(x) = 4x^2 - 8x + 3$ **(b)** $(g \circ f)(x) = 8x^2 + 16x + 6$ **(c)** $(f \circ g)(3) = 15$
(d) $(g \circ f)(-2) = 6$ **(e)** $(f \circ f)(1) = 13$ **2. (a)** $f^{-1}(x) = \dfrac{x - 4}{3}$ **(b)** $g^{-1}(x) = \sqrt[3]{x + 4}$

3.

4. (a) 14.611   **(b)** 15.206   **(c)** 15.146   **(d)** 15.155   **(e)** 15.154   **5. (a)** $\log_a 6.4 = 4$ **(b)** $\log 278 = x$
6. (a) $2^7 = x$ **(b)** $e^M = 16$ **7. (a)** 4   **(b)** -2 **8.** $\{x \mid x > -6\}$ or $(-6, \infty)$

9.

Domain: all real numbers or $(-\infty, \infty)$
Range: $\{y \mid y > 0\}$ or $(0, \infty)$

10.

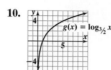

Domain: $\{x \mid x > 0\}$ or $(0, \infty)$
Range: all real numbers or $(-\infty, \infty)$

11. $\{-1\}$ **12.** $\{-5\}$ **13.** $\left\{\dfrac{11}{2}\right\}$
14. $\{e^7\}$ **15.** approximately 56 terms

Section 8.4 Properties of Logarithms

1. 0   **2.** 0   **3.** 1   **4.** 1   **5.** $\sqrt{2}$ **6.** 0.2   **7.** 1.2   **8.** -4 **9.** False   **10.** $\log_4 9 + \log_4 5$
11. $\log 5 + \log w$ **12.** $\log_7 9 - \log_7 5$ **13.** $\ln p - \ln 3$ **14.** $\log_2 3 + \log_2 m - \log_2 n$ **15.** $\ln q - \ln 3 - \ln p$ **16.** $1.6 \log_2 5$ **17.** $5 \log b$
18. $2\log_4 a + \log_4 b$ **19.** $2 + 4\log_3 m - \dfrac{1}{3}\log_3 n$ **20.** 2   **21.** $\log_3\left(\dfrac{x + 4}{x - 1}\right)$ **22.** $\log_5 \dfrac{x}{8}$ **23.** $\log_2 \dfrac{x^2 + 3x + 2}{x^2}$ **24.** 10;3;10;3

25. 3.155   **26.** 2.807   **27.** 3   **29.** -7 **31.** 5   **33.** 2   **35.** 1   **37.** 0   **39.** $a + b$ **41.** $2b$ **43.** $2a + b$ **45.** $\dfrac{1}{2}a$

47. $\log a + \log b$ **49.** $4\log_5 x$ **51.** $\log_2 x + 2\log_2 y$ **53.** $2 + \log_5 x$ **55.** $2 - \log_7 y$ **57.** $2 + \ln x$ **59.** $3 + \dfrac{1}{2}\log_3 x$
61. $2\log_5 x + \dfrac{1}{2}\log_5(x^2 + 1)$ **63.** $4\log x - \dfrac{1}{3}\log(x - 1)$ **65.** $\dfrac{1}{2}\log_7(x + 1) - \dfrac{1}{2}\log_7 x$ **67.** $\log_2 x + 2\log_2(x - 1) - \dfrac{1}{2}\log_2(x + 1)$

69. 2   **71.** $\log(3x)$ **73.** 2   **75.** 4   **77.** $\log_3 x^3$ **79.** $\log_4\left(\dfrac{x + 1}{x}\right)$ **81.** $\ln(x^2 y^3)$ **83.** $\log_3\left[\sqrt{x}(x - 1)^3\right]$ **85.** $\log(x^2)$
87. $\log\left(x\sqrt{xy}\right)$ **89.** $\log_8(x - 1)$ **91.** $\log\left(\dfrac{x^{12}}{10}\right)$ **93.** 3.322   **95.** 0.528   **97.** -2.680 **99.** 4.644   **101.** 3   **103.** 1

105. $\log_a\left(x + \sqrt{x^2 - 1}\right) + \log_a\left(x - \sqrt{x^2 - 1}\right)$
$\quad = \log_a\left[\left(x + \sqrt{x^2 - 1}\right)\left(x - \sqrt{x^2 - 1}\right)\right]$
$\quad = \log_a\left[x^2 - x\sqrt{x^2 - 1} + x\sqrt{x^2 - 1} - (x^2 - 1)\right]$
$\quad = \log_a(x^2 - x^2 + 1)$
$\quad = \log_a 1$
$\quad = 0$

107. If $f(x) = \log_a x$, then
$\quad f(AB) = \log_a(AB)$
$\quad\quad = \log_a A + \log_a B$
$\quad\quad = f(A) + f(B)$

109. Answers will vary. One possibility: The logarithm of the product of two expressions equals the sum of the logarithms of each expression.
111. Answers will vary. One possibility:
$\log_2(2 + 4) \neq \log_2 2 + \log_2 4$
113. $\left\{\dfrac{5}{2}\right\}$ **115.** $\left\{-2 - \sqrt{2}, -2 + \sqrt{2}\right\}$
117. $\{47\}$

119. $f(x) = \log_3 x = \dfrac{\log x}{\log 3}$

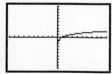

Domain: $\{x \mid x > 0\}$ or $(0, \infty)$
Range: all real numbers or $(-\infty, \infty)$

121. $F(x) = \log_{1/2} x = \dfrac{\log x}{\log\left(\frac{1}{2}\right)}$

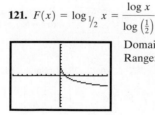

Domain: $\{x \mid x > 0\}$ or $(0, \infty)$
Range: all real numbers or $(-\infty, \infty)$

Section 8.5 Exponential and Logarithmic Equations

1. $M = N$ **2.** $\{3\}$ **3.** $\{8\}$ **4.** $\{-2\}$ **5.** $\left\{\dfrac{\ln 11}{\ln 2}\right\}$ or $\left\{\dfrac{\log 11}{\log 2}\right\}$; $\approx \{3.459\}$

6. $\left\{\dfrac{\ln 3}{2\ln 5}\right\}$ or $\left\{\dfrac{\log 3}{2\log 5}\right\}$; $\approx \{0.341\}$ **7.** $\left\{\dfrac{\ln 5}{2}\right\}$; $\approx \{0.805\}$ **8.** $\left\{-\dfrac{\ln\left(\frac{20}{3}\right)}{4}\right\}$; $\approx \{-0.474\}$ **9. (a)** approximately 2.85 days   **(b)** approximately
32.52 days   **10. (a)** approximately 6.77 years   **(b)** approximately 11.58 years   **11.** $\{7\}$ **13.** $\{9\}$ **15.** $\{3\}$ **17.** $\{81\}$ **19.** $\{1\}$

21. $\{-1\}$ **23.** $\left\{\dfrac{1}{3}\right\}$ **25.** $\left\{\dfrac{7}{5}\right\}$ **27.** $\{-5\}$ **29.** $\left\{\dfrac{1}{\log 2}\right\} \approx \{3.322\}$ or $\left\{\dfrac{\ln 10}{\ln 2}\right\} \approx \{3.322\}$ **31.** $\left\{\dfrac{\log 20}{\log 5}\right\} \approx \{1.861\}$ or $\left\{\dfrac{\ln 20}{\ln 5}\right\} \approx \{1.861\}$

33. $\left\{\dfrac{\log 7}{\log\left(\frac{1}{2}\right)}\right\} \approx \{-2.807\}$ or $\left\{\dfrac{\ln 7}{\ln\left(\frac{1}{2}\right)}\right\} \approx \{-2.807\}$ **35.** $\{\ln 5\} \approx \{1.609\}$ **37.** $\{\log 5\} \approx \{0.699\}$

39. $\left\{\dfrac{\log 13}{2\log 3}\right\} \approx \{1.167\}$ or $\left\{\dfrac{\ln 13}{2\ln 3}\right\} \approx \{1.167\}$ **41.** $\left\{\dfrac{\log 3}{4\log\left(\frac{1}{2}\right)}\right\} \approx \{-0.396\}$ or $\left\{\dfrac{\ln 3}{4\ln\left(\frac{1}{2}\right)}\right\} \approx \{-0.396\}$

43. $\left\{\dfrac{\log\left(\frac{5}{4}\right)}{\log 2}\right\} \approx \{0.322\}$ or $\left\{\dfrac{\ln\left(\frac{5}{4}\right)}{\ln 2}\right\} \approx \{0.322\}$ **45.** $\{\ln 6\} \approx \{1.792\}$ **47.** $\left\{\dfrac{\log 0.2}{\log 3 - \log 0.2}\right\} \approx \{-0.594\}$ or $\left\{\dfrac{\ln 0.2}{\ln 3 - \ln 0.2}\right\} \approx \{-0.594\}$

49. $\{8\}$ **51.** $\left\{\dfrac{\log 7}{3\log 5}\right\} \approx \{0.403\}$ or $\left\{\dfrac{\ln 7}{3\ln 5}\right\} \approx \{0.403\}$ **53.** $\{2\}$ **55.** $\{\ln 15\} \approx \{2.708\}$ **57.** $\left\{-\dfrac{2}{5}\right\}$ **59.** $\{-4, 4\}$ **61.** $\{-2\}$

63. $\{2 + \sqrt{7}\}$ **65. (a)** 2013 **(b)** 2048 **67. (a)** approximately 5.6 years **(b)** approximately 11.6 years **69. (a)** approximately 1.876 years
(b) approximately 5.369 years **(c)** approximately 13.479 years **71. (a)** approximately 2.099 seconds **(b)** 27.62 seconds **(c)** approximately
45.876 seconds **73. (a)** approximately 5 minutes **(b)** approximately 11 minutes **75. (a)** approximately 82 minutes **(b)** approximately

396 minutes (or 6.6 hours) **77. (a)** approximately 9 years **(b)** $t = \dfrac{\log 2}{n\log\left(1 + \dfrac{r}{n}\right)}$ **(c)** approximately 8.693 years, which is about the same as the

result from the Rule of 72 **79.** 29 minutes **81. (a)** 1 **(b)** 11 **(c)** 7 **83. (a)** $-\dfrac{3}{2}$ **(b)** $\dfrac{2}{7}$ **(c)** 0 **85. (a)** 8 **(b)** $\dfrac{1}{4}$ **(c)** 1

87. approximately $\{1.06\}$ **89.** approximately $\{-0.70\}$ **91.** approximately $\{0.05, 1.48\}$ **93.** approximately $\{0.45, 1\}$

Chapter 8 Review **1. (a)** 32 **(b)** -9 **(c)** 2 **(d)** 13 **2. (a)** 24 **(b)** -28 **(c)** -8 **(d)** 112 **3. (a)** 201 **(b)** 24 **(c)** 163 **(d)** 14
4. (a) 23 **(b)** 37 **(c)** -8 **(d)** 290 **5. (a)** $(f \circ g)(x) - 5x + 1$ **(b)** $(g \circ f)(x) = 5x + 5$ **(c)** $(f \circ f)(x) = x + 2$ **(d)** $(g \circ g)(x) = 25x$
6. (a) $(f \circ g)(x) = 2x + 9$ **(b)** $(g \circ f)(x) = 2x + 3$ **(c)** $(f \circ f)(x) = 4x - 9$ **(d)** $(g \circ g)(x) = x + 12$ **7. (a)** $(f \circ g)(x) = 4x^2 + 4x + 2$
(b) $(g \circ f)(x) = 2x^2 + 3$ **(c)** $(f \circ f)(x) = x^4 + 2x^2 + 2$ **(d)** $(g \circ g)(x) = 4x + 3$

8. (a) $(f \circ g)(x) = \dfrac{2x}{x + 1}$, where $x \neq -1, 0$ **(b)** $(g \circ f)(x) - \dfrac{x + 1}{2}$, where $x \neq -1$ **(c)** $(f \circ f)(x) = \dfrac{2(x + 1)}{x + 3}$, where $x \neq -1, -3$

(d) $(g \circ g)(x) = x$, where $x \neq 0$ **9.** not one-to-one **10.** one-to-one **11.** one-to-one **12.** not one-to-one

13.

Height (inches)	Age
69	24
71	59
72	29
73	81
74	37

14.

Quantity Demanded	Price ($)
112	300
129	200
144	170
161	150
176	130

15. $\{(3, -5), (1, -3), (-3, 1), (9, 2)\}$ **16.** $\{(1, -20), (4, -15), (3, 5), (2, 25)\}$

17.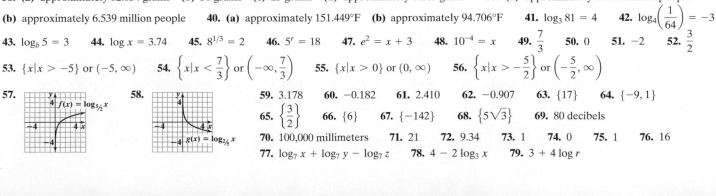
18.

19. $f^{-1}(x) = \dfrac{x}{5}$ **20.** $H^{-1}(x) = \dfrac{x - 7}{2}$ **21.** $P^{-1}(x) = \dfrac{4}{x} - 2$ **22.** $g^{-1}(x) = \sqrt[3]{\dfrac{x + 1}{2}}$

23. (a) 27.332 **(b)** 28.975 **(c)** 29.088 **(d)** 29.093 **(e)** 29.091 **24. (a)** 1258.925
(b) 1380.384 **(c)** 1386.756 **(d)** 1385.479 **(e)** 1385.456 **25. (a)** 1.649 **(b)** 0.368
(c) 4.482 **(d)** 0.449 **(e)** 5.885

26. 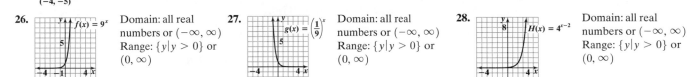 Domain: all real numbers or $(-\infty, \infty)$ Range: $\{y \mid y > 0\}$ or $(0, \infty)$

27. Domain: all real numbers or $(-\infty, \infty)$ Range: $\{y \mid y > 0\}$ or $(0, \infty)$

28. Domain: all real numbers or $(-\infty, \infty)$ Range: $\{y \mid y > 0\}$ or $(0, \infty)$

29. 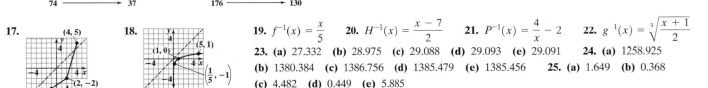 Domain: all real numbers or $(-\infty, \infty)$ Range: $\{y \mid y > -2\}$ or $(-2, \infty)$

30. The number e is defined as the number that the expression $\left(1 + \dfrac{1}{n}\right)^n$ approaches as n becomes unbounded in the positive direction. **31.** $\{6\}$ **32.** $\left\{\dfrac{7}{2}\right\}$ **33.** $\{-4, 1\}$ **34.** $\{-2\}$
35. $\{9\}$ **36.** $\{-3, 3\}$ **37. (a)** $7513.59 **(b)** $7652.33 **(c)** $7684.36 **(d)** $7700.01

38. (a) approximately 82.034 grams **(b)** 50 grams **(c)** 25 grams **(d)** approximately 0.263 gram **39. (a)** approximately 3.057 million people
(b) approximately 6.539 million people **40. (a)** approximately 151.449°F **(b)** approximately 94.706°F **41.** $\log_3 81 = 4$ **42.** $\log_4\left(\dfrac{1}{64}\right) = -3$

43. $\log_b 5 = 3$ **44.** $\log x = 3.74$ **45.** $8^{1/3} = 2$ **46.** $5^r = 18$ **47.** $e^2 = x + 3$ **48.** $10^{-4} = x$ **49.** $\dfrac{7}{3}$ **50.** 0 **51.** -2 **52.** $\dfrac{3}{2}$

53. $\{x \mid x > -5\}$ or $(-5, \infty)$ **54.** $\left\{x \mid x < \dfrac{7}{3}\right\}$ or $\left(-\infty, \dfrac{7}{3}\right)$ **55.** $\{x \mid x > 0\}$ or $(0, \infty)$ **56.** $\left\{x \mid x > -\dfrac{5}{2}\right\}$ or $\left(-\dfrac{5}{2}, \infty\right)$

57. **58.** **59.** 3.178 **60.** -0.182 **61.** 2.410 **62.** -0.907 **63.** $\{17\}$ **64.** $\{-9, 1\}$
65. $\left\{\dfrac{3}{2}\right\}$ **66.** $\{6\}$ **67.** $\{-142\}$ **68.** $\{5\sqrt{3}\}$ **69.** 80 decibels
70. 100,000 millimeters **71.** 21 **72.** 9.34 **73.** 1 **74.** 0 **75.** 1 **76.** 16
77. $\log_7 x + \log_7 y - \log_7 z$ **78.** $4 - 2\log_3 x$ **79.** $3 + 4\log r$

80. $\frac{1}{2}\ln(x-1) - \frac{1}{2}\ln x$ **81.** $\log_3(x^4 y^2)$ **82.** $\ln\left(\frac{7\sqrt[4]{x}}{9}\right)$ **83.** -1 **84.** $\log_6(x-4)$ **85.** 2.183   **86.** 0.606   **87.** -4.419 **88.** 3.723

89. $\{10\}$ **90.** $\{-5\}$ **91.** $\{\sqrt{2}\} \approx \{1.414\}$ **92.** $\{64\}$ **93.** $\left\{\frac{\log 15}{\log 2}\right\} \approx \{3.907\}$ or $\left\{\frac{\ln 15}{\ln 2}\right\} \approx \{3.907\}$ **94.** $\left\{\frac{\log 27}{3}\right\} \approx \{0.477\}$

95. $\left\{\frac{\ln 39}{7}\right\} \approx \{0.523\}$ **96.** $\left\{\frac{\log 2}{\log 3 - \log 2}\right\} \approx \{1.710\}$ or $\left\{\frac{\ln 2}{\ln 3 - \ln 2}\right\} \approx \{1.710\}$ **97. (a)** approximately 1.453 days   **(b)** approximately 23.253 days   **98. (a)** about 2015   **(b)** about 2030

Chapter 8 Test   **1.** not one-to-one   **2.** $f^{-1}(x) = \dfrac{x+3}{4}$ **3. (a)** 33.360   **(b)** 36.338   **(c)** 36.494   **(d)** 36.463   **(e)** 36.462   **4.** $\log_4 19 = x$

5. $b^y = x$ **6. (a)** -3 **(b)** 4   **7.** $\left\{x \mid x < \dfrac{7}{4}\right\}$ or $\left(-\infty, \dfrac{7}{4}\right)$

8. 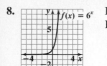   Domain: all real numbers or $(-\infty, \infty)$
Range: $\{y \mid y > 0\}$ or $(0, \infty)$

9.   Domain: $\{x \mid x > 0\}$ or $(0, \infty)$
Range: all real numbers or $(-\infty, \infty)$

10. (a) 10   **(b)** 15   **11.** $\frac{1}{2}\log_4 x - 3\log_4 y$ **12.** $\log(M^4 N^3)$ **13.** -8.004 **14.** $\{1\}$ **15.** $\{1, 3\}$ **16.** $\{4\}$ **17.** $\{-17, 17\}$ **18.** $\{9\}$

19. $\left\{\dfrac{\log 17 + \log 3}{\log 3}\right\} \approx \{3.579\}$ or $\left\{\dfrac{\ln 17 + \ln 3}{\ln 3}\right\} \approx \{3.579\}$ **20.** $\{2\sqrt{26}\} \approx \{10.198\}$ **21. (a)** approximately 34 million people   **(b)** about 2058   **22.** 10 decibels

Chapter 9 Conics

Section 9.1 Distance and Midpoint Formulas

1. $d = \sqrt{(x_2 - x_1)^2 + (y_2 - y_1)^2}$ **2.** False   **3.** 5   **4.** $6\sqrt{5} \approx 13.42$

5. (a) 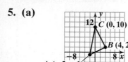   **(b)** $d(A, B) = 3\sqrt{5}$; $d(A, C) = 5\sqrt{5}$; $d(B, C) = 4\sqrt{5}$ **(c)** $[d(A, C)]^2 = [d(A, B)]^2 + [d(B, C)]^2$
(d) 30 square units   **6.** $M = \left(\dfrac{x_1 + x_2}{2}, \dfrac{y_1 + y_2}{2}\right)$ **7.** $\left(\dfrac{3}{2}, 6\right)$ **8.** $\left(1, \dfrac{5}{2}\right)$ **9.** 5

11. $4\sqrt{5} \approx 8.94$ **13.** 5   **15.** 13   **17.** 6   **19.** $3\sqrt{5} \approx 6.71$ **21.** $3\sqrt{7} \approx 7.94$ **23.** $\sqrt{12.56} \approx 3.54$

25. $(4, 3)$ **27.** $(3, -1)$ **29.** $\left(-1, \dfrac{7}{2}\right)$ **31.** $\left(-\dfrac{3}{2}, 0\right)$ **33.** $\left(\dfrac{7\sqrt{2}}{2}, \dfrac{5\sqrt{5}}{2}\right)$ **35.** $(0.8, -1.6)$

37. (a)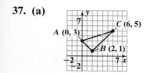
(b) $d(A, B) = 2\sqrt{2} \approx 2.83$; $d(B, C) = 4\sqrt{2} \approx 5.66$; $d(A, C) = 2\sqrt{10} \approx 6.32$
(c) $[d(A, B)]^2 + [d(B, C)]^2 \overset{?}{=} [d(A, C)]^2$
$(2\sqrt{2})^2 + (4\sqrt{2})^2 \overset{?}{=} (2\sqrt{10})^2$
$4 \cdot 2 + 16 \cdot 2 \overset{?}{=} 4 \cdot 10$
$8 + 32 \overset{?}{=} 40$
$40 = 40 \leftarrow$ True
Therefore, triangle ABC is a right triangle.
(d) 8 square units

39. (a)
(b) $d(A, B) = 5\sqrt{2} \approx 7.07$; $d(B, C) = 12\sqrt{2} \approx 16.97$; $d(A, C) = 13\sqrt{2} \approx 18.38$
(c) $[d(A, B)]^2 + [d(B, C)]^2 \overset{?}{=} [d(A, C)]^2$
$(5\sqrt{2})^2 + (12\sqrt{2})^2 \overset{?}{=} (13\sqrt{2})^2$
$25 \cdot 2 + 144 \cdot 2 \overset{?}{=} 169 \cdot 2$
$50 + 288 \overset{?}{=} 338$
$338 = 338 \leftarrow$ True
Therefore, triangle ABC is a right triangle.
(d) 60 square units

41. $(2, -3), (2, 5)$ **43.** $(-6, -3), (10, -3)$ **45. (a)** approximately 37.36 blocks   **(b)** approximately 35.13 blocks   **(c)** approximately 71.34 blocks
47. (a) approximately 1.85 seconds   **(b)** No. The ball will reach second base (2.65 seconds) before the runner (3.33 seconds).   **49.** Answers will vary. Essentially, the Pythagorean Theorem is a theorem that relates the hypotenuse to the lengths of the legs in a right triangle. The hypotenuse in the right triangle is the distance between the two points in the Cartesian Plane.   **51.** 9; 3   **53.** 81; 3   **55.** If n is a positive integer and $a^n = b$, then
$\sqrt[n]{b} = \begin{cases} |a| & \text{if } n \text{ is even} \\ a & \text{if } n \text{ is odd} \end{cases}$

Section 9.2 Circles

1. circle   **2.** radius   **3.** $(x-2)^2 + (y-4)^2 = 25$ **4.** $(x+2)^2 + y^2 = 2$ **5.** False   **6.** True

7.

$(x - 3)^2 + (y - 1)^2 = 4$

8.

$(x + 5)^2 + y^2 = 16$

9.

$x^2 + y^2 - 6x - 4y + 4 = 0$

10.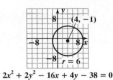

$2x^2 + 2y^2 - 16x + 4y - 38 = 0$

11. $(x - 1)^2 + (y - 2)^2 = 4$
13. $(x - 2)^2 + (y + 1)^2 = 16$
15. $x^2 + y^2 = 9$
17. $(x - 1)^2 + (y - 4)^2 = 4$

19. $(x + 2)^2 + (y - 4)^2 = 36$ **21.** $x^2 + (y - 3)^2 = 16$ **23.** $(x - 5)^2 + (y + 5)^2 = 25$ **25.** $(x - 1)^2 + (y - 2)^2 = 5$

27. $C = (0, 0), r = 6$

29. $C = (4, 1), r = 5$

31. $C = (-3, 2), r = 9$

33. $C = (0, 3), r = 8$

35. $C = (1, -1), r = \dfrac{1}{2}$

37. $C = (3, -1), r = 3$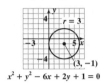

$x^2 + y^2 - 6x + 2y + 1 = 0$

39. $C = (-5, -2), r = 5$

$x^2 + y^2 + 10x + 4y + 4 = 0$

41. $C = (3, -6), r = 9$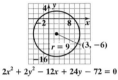

$2x^2 + 2y^2 - 12x + 24y - 72 = 0$

43. $x^2 + y^2 = 20$ **45.** $(x + 3)^2 + (y - 2)^2 = 9$ **47.** $(x + 1)^2 + (y + 1)^2 = 25$ **49.** $A = 64\pi$ square units; $C = 16\pi$ units

51. 32 square units   **53.** (a), (e)   **55.** The distance formula is used along with the definition of a circle to obtain the equation of the circle.

57. Yes, since it can be written as $x^2 + y^2 = 36$. Center: $(0, 0)$; radius $= 6$.

59. $f(x) = 4x - 3$

61. $g(x) = x^2 - 4x - 5$

63. $G(x) = -2(x + 3)^2 - 5$

65.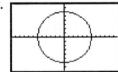

The graph here agrees with that in Problem 27.

67.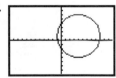

The graph here agrees with that in Problem 29.

69.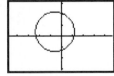

The graph here agrees with that in Problem 31.

71.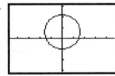

The graph here agrees with that in Problem 33.

73.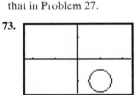

The graph here agrees with that in Problem 35.

Section 9.3 Parabolas   **1.** parabola   **2.** vertex   **3.** axis of symmetry

4. $D: x = -2$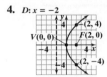

5.

6.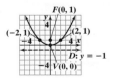

7.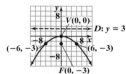

8. $x^2 = -32y$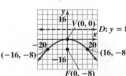

9. $y^2 = \dfrac{4}{3}x$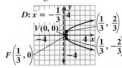

10. $(-3, 2)$

11. $D: x = -6$

12. The receiver should be located 2 feet from the base of the dish along its axis of symmetry.

13. c   **15.** a   **17.** b   **19.** e

21. vertex $(0,0)$, focus $(0,6)$, directrix $y = -6$

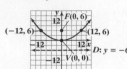

23. vertex $(0,0)$, focus $\left(-\frac{3}{2}, 0\right)$, directrix $x = \frac{3}{2}$

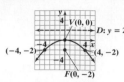

25. vertex $(0,0)$, focus $(0,-2)$, directrix $y = 2$

27. $y^2 = 20x$

29. $x^2 = -24y$

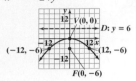

31. $x^2 = 6y$

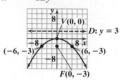

33. $x^2 = -12y$

35. $y^2 = -12x$

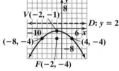

37. $y^2 = x$

39. vertex $(2,4)$, focus $(2,5)$, directrix $y = 3$

41. vertex $(-2,-3)$, focus $(-4,-3)$, directrix $x = 0$

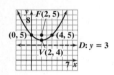

43. vertex $(-5,1)$, focus $(-5,-4)$, directrix $y = 6$

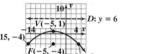

45. vertex $(-2,-1)$, focus $(-2,-4)$, directrix $y = 2$

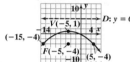

47. vertex $(1,4)$, focus $(2,4)$, directrix $x = 0$

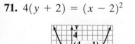
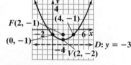

49. vertex $(-5,2)$, focus $\left(-5, \frac{1}{2}\right)$, directrix $y = \frac{7}{2}$

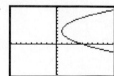

51. 1 inch from the vertex along the axis of symmetry   **53.** 21.6 feet

55. The height of the bridge is 28.8 feet at a distance of 10 feet from the center, 19.2 feet at a distance of 30 feet from the center, and 0 feet (i.e., ground level) at a distance of 50 feet from the center.

57. $(x-3)^2 = 4(y+2)$ **59.** $(y-3)^2 = -4(x-2)$

61. (a) Let $x = 4$ and $y = 2$:
$4^2 \stackrel{?}{=} 8 \cdot 2$

$16 = 16 \leftarrow$ True
Thus, $(4,2)$ is on the parabola.

(b) The focus of the parabola is $F(0,2)$, and the directrix is $D: y = -2$.
$d(F,P) = \sqrt{(0-4)^2 + (2-2)^2} = \sqrt{16} = 4$,
$d(P,D) = 2 - (-2) = 4$.
Thus, $d(F,P) = d(P,D) = 4$.

63. 8 units   **65.** See Figure 12.

67. $y = (x+3)^2$

69. $y = (x+3)^2$

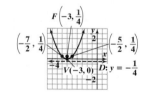

71. $4(y+2) = (x-2)^2$

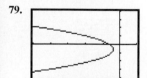

73.

75.

77.

79.

81.

83.

Section 9.4 Ellipses   **1.** ellipse; foci   **2.** major axis   **3.** vertices   **4.** False

5.

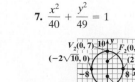

6.

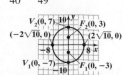

7. $\frac{x^2}{40} + \frac{y^2}{49} = 1$

8. $(3,-1)$ **9.**

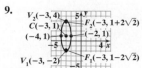

10. $\dfrac{x^2}{2500} + \dfrac{y^2}{1600} = 1$; 40 feet **15.** Foci: $(-3, 0)$ and $(3, 0)$; Vertices: $(-5, 0)$ and $(5, 0)$

11. c   **13.** d

17. Foci: $(0, -8)$ and $(0, 8)$; Vertices: $(0, -10)$ and $(0, 10)$

19. Foci: $\left(-3\sqrt{5}, 0\right)$ and $\left(3\sqrt{5}, 0\right)$; Vertices: $(-7, 0)$ and $(7, 0)$

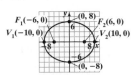

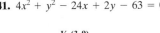

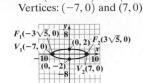

21. Foci: $\left(0, -4\sqrt{3}\right)$ and $\left(0, 4\sqrt{3}\right)$; Vertices: $(0, -7)$ and $(0, 7)$

23. Foci: $\left(0, -2\sqrt{3}\right)$ and $\left(0, 2\sqrt{3}\right)$; Vertices: $(0, -4)$ and $(0, 4)$

25. $\dfrac{x^2}{36} + \dfrac{y^2}{20} = 1$

27. $\dfrac{x^2}{33} + \dfrac{y^2}{49} = 1$

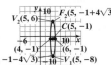

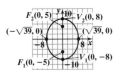

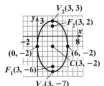

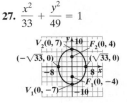

29. $\dfrac{x^2}{100} + \dfrac{y^2}{64} = 1$

31. $\dfrac{x^2}{39} + \dfrac{y^2}{64} = 1$

33. $\dfrac{(x - 3)^2}{9} + \dfrac{(y + 2)^2}{25} = 1$

35. $\dfrac{(x + 2)^2}{16} + \dfrac{(y - 5)^2}{4} = 1$

37. $(x - 5)^2 + \dfrac{(y + 1)^2}{49} = 1$

39. $4(x + 2)^2 + 16(y - 1)^2 = 64$

41. $4x^2 + y^2 - 24x + 2y - 63 = 0$

43. (a) $\dfrac{x^2}{225} + \dfrac{y^2}{100} = 1$ (b) Yes

(c) No

45. Perihelion = 91.5 million miles; $\dfrac{x^2}{8649} + \dfrac{y^2}{8646.75} = 1$

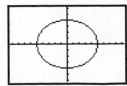

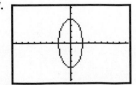

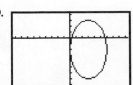

47. Perihelion = 460.6 million miles; Mean distance = 483.8 million miles; $\dfrac{x^2}{234{,}062.44} + \dfrac{y^2}{233{,}524.2} = 1$

49. $\dfrac{(x - 1)^2}{16} + \dfrac{(y - 2)^2}{9} = 1$

51. $\dfrac{(x - 2)^2}{4} + \dfrac{y^2}{16} = 1$

53. Let $a = b$, then

$$\dfrac{x^2}{a^2} + \dfrac{y^2}{b^2} = 1$$

$$\dfrac{x^2}{a^2} + \dfrac{y^2}{a^2} = 1$$

$$a^2\left(\dfrac{x^2}{a^2} + \dfrac{y^2}{a^2}\right) = a^2(1)$$

$$x^2 + y^2 = a^2$$

which is the equation of a circle with center $(0, 0)$ and radius a. $c = 0$; The foci are located at the center point.

55.

57.

x	5	10	100	1000
$f(x)$	0.71429	0.41667	0.04902	0.00499

59.

x	5	10	100	1000
$f(x)$	5.5	3	2.07216	2.00702

61.

x	5	10	100	1000
$f(x)$	6.83333	11.90909	101.99010	1001.99900
$g(x)$	7	12	102	1002

63. In Problems 57 and 58, the degree of the numerator is less than the degree of the denominator. In Problems 59 and 60, the degree of the numerator and denominator are the same.

Conjecture 1: If the degree of the numerator of a rational function is less than the degree of the denominator, then as x increases, the value of the function will approach zero (0).

Conjecture 2: If the degree of the numerator of a rational function equals the degree of the denominator, then as x increases, the value of the function will approach the ratio of the leading coefficients of the numerator and denominator.

65.

67.

69.

71.

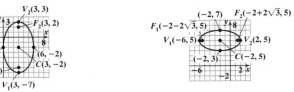

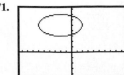

Section 9.5 Hyperbolas   **1.** hyperbola   **2.** transverse axis   **3.** conjugate axis

4.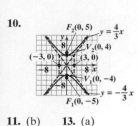

5.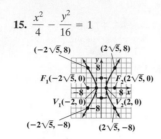

6. False

7. $\dfrac{x^2}{16} - \dfrac{y^2}{20} = 1$

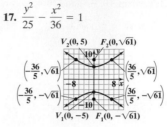

8. $y = -\dfrac{b}{a}x;\ y = \dfrac{b}{a}x$

9.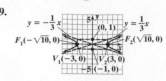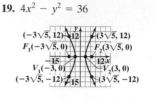

10.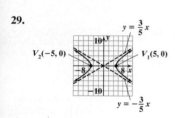

11. (b)   **13.** (a)

15. $\dfrac{x^2}{4} - \dfrac{y^2}{16} = 1$

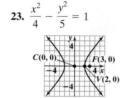

17. $\dfrac{y^2}{25} - \dfrac{x^2}{36} = 1$

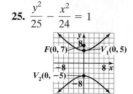

19. $4x^2 - y^2 = 36$

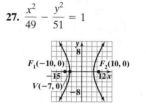

21. $25y^2 - x^2 = 100$

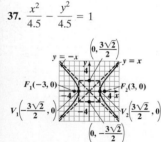

23. $\dfrac{x^2}{4} - \dfrac{y^2}{5} = 1$

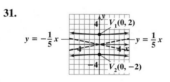

25. $\dfrac{y^2}{25} - \dfrac{x^2}{24} = 1$

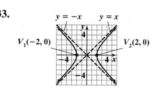

27. $\dfrac{x^2}{49} - \dfrac{y^2}{51} = 1$

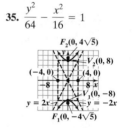

29.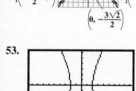

31.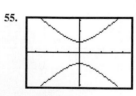

33.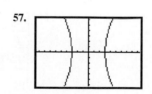

35. $\dfrac{y^2}{64} - \dfrac{x^2}{16} = 1$

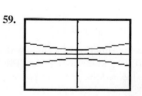

37. $\dfrac{x^2}{4.5} - \dfrac{y^2}{4.5} = 1$

39. $x^2 - y^2 = 1$

41. $\dfrac{y^2}{36} - \dfrac{x^2}{9} = 1$

43. The asymptotes of both hyperbolas are $y = -\dfrac{1}{2}x$ and $y = \dfrac{1}{2}x$. Thus, they are conjugates.

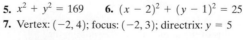

45. Answers will vary.   **47.** $(-3, 1)$

49. $\{(x, y)\,|\,2x - 3y = 6\}$

51. $\{(x, y)\,|\,6x + 3y = 4\}$

53.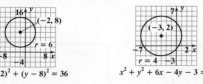

55.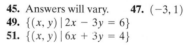

57.

59.

Putting the Concepts Together (Sections 9.1–9.5)

1. $3\sqrt{13}$ **2.** $(1, -3)$

3. $C = (-2, 8),\ r = 6$

4. $C = (-3, 2),\ r = 4$

5. $x^2 + y^2 = 169$ **6.** $(x - 2)^2 + (y - 1)^2 = 25$

7. Vertex: $(-2, 4)$; focus: $(-2, 3)$; directrix: $y = 5$

8. Vertex: $(3, -1)$; focus: $(5, -1)$; directrix: $x = 1$

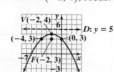

9. $(x + 1)^2 = -12(y + 2)$ **10.** $(y - 3)^2 = 8(x + 3)$

11. Center: $(0,0)$; Foci: $\left(-6\sqrt{2},0\right)$ and $\left(6\sqrt{2},0\right)$; vertices: $(-9,0)$ and $(9,0)$

12. Center: $(-1,2)$; vertices: $(-1,-5)$ and $(-1,9)$; foci: $\left(-1,2-\sqrt{13}\right)$ and $\left(-1,2+\sqrt{13}\right)$

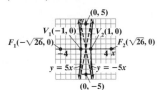

13. $\dfrac{x^2}{45}+\dfrac{y^2}{81}=1$

14. $\dfrac{(x-3)^2}{16}+\dfrac{(y+4)^2}{7}=1$

15. Vertices: $(0,-9)$ and $(0,9)$; foci: $\left(0,-3\sqrt{10}\right)$ and $\left(0,3\sqrt{10}\right)$; asymptotes: $y=3x$ and $y=-3x$

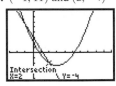

16. Vertices: $(-1,0)$ and $(1,0)$; foci: $\left(-\sqrt{26},0\right)$ and $\left(\sqrt{26},0\right)$; asymptotes: $y=-5x$ and $y=5x$

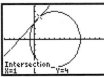

17. $\dfrac{y^2}{4}-\dfrac{x^2}{21}=1$

18. 6.75 inches from the vertex along its axis of symmetry

Section 9.6 Systems of Nonlinear Equations

1. $(-3,5)$ and $(1,-3)$ **2.** $\left(\dfrac{11}{5},-\dfrac{22}{5}\right)$ and $(1,-2)$ **3.** $(0,-4),\ (-2\sqrt{3},2),\ (2\sqrt{3},2)$

4. $\varnothing$ or $\{\ \}$ **5.** $(0,4)$ and $(1,5)$ **7.** $(3,4)$ and $(4,3)$ **9.** $(0,-2),\left(-\sqrt{3},1\right)$, and $\left(\sqrt{3},1\right)$ **11.** $(-2,-2)$ and $(2,2)$

13. $(0,-2),(0,2),\left(-1,-\sqrt{3}\right)$, and $\left(-1,\sqrt{3}\right)$ **15.** $\varnothing$ **17.** $(0,0),(-3,3)$, and $(3,3)$ **19.** $(-3,7)$ and $(2,-8)$ **21.** $(-1,11)$ and $(2,-4)$

23. $(-4,0)$ and $(4,0)$ **25.** $(0,3)$ and $(1,4)$ **27.** $\left(0,-2-\sqrt{3}\right),\left(0,-2+\sqrt{3}\right),(1,-4)$, and $(1,0)$

29. $\varnothing$ **31.** $(5,2)$ **33.** $\left(-\dfrac{8}{3},-\dfrac{2\sqrt{10}}{3}\right),\left(\dfrac{8}{3},\dfrac{2\sqrt{10}}{3}\right),\left(\dfrac{8}{3},-\dfrac{2\sqrt{10}}{3}\right)$, and $\left(\dfrac{8}{3},\dfrac{2\sqrt{10}}{3}\right)$ **35.** $(0,-5),(3,4),(4,3)$, and $(5,0)$

37. Either -5 and -3, or 3 and 5 **39.** 14 feet by 10 feet **41.** 19 cm by 10 cm **43.** $(0,-2),(0,1)$, and $(2,-1)$ **45.** $(81,3)$

47. If $r_1=\dfrac{-b+\sqrt{b^2-4ac}}{2a}$, then $r_2=\dfrac{-b-\sqrt{b^2-4ac}}{2a}$; if $r_1=\dfrac{-b-\sqrt{b^2-4ac}}{2a}$, then $r_2=\dfrac{-b+\sqrt{b^2-4ac}}{2a}$.

49. (a) $f(1)=7$ **(b)** $g(1)=2$ **51. (a)** $f(3)=13$ **(b)** $g(3)=8$ **53. (a)** $f(5)=19$ **(b)** $g(5)=32$

55. $(-1,11)$ and $(2,-4)$ **57.** $(4,0)$ and $(4,0)$ **59.** $(0,3)$ and $(1,4)$ **61.** $(0.056,-0.237)$ and $(2.981,-1.727)$ **63.** $\varnothing$

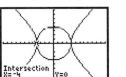

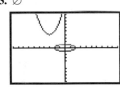

Chapter 9 Review

1. 5 **2.** 10 **3.** $2\sqrt{10}\approx 6.32$ **4.** 6 **5.** $3\sqrt{19}\approx 13.08$ **6.** 2.5 **7.** $(-2,5)$ **8.** $(6,-2)$ **9.** $\left(-4\sqrt{3},-3\sqrt{6}\right)$ **10.** $\left(\dfrac{5}{2},\dfrac{1}{2}\right)$ **11.** $\left(\dfrac{3}{4},\dfrac{1}{2}\right)$

12. (a)

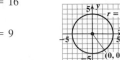

(b) $d(A,B)=3\sqrt{2}\approx 4.24$; $d(B,C)=2\sqrt{2}\approx 2.83$; $d(A,C)=\sqrt{26}\approx 5.10$

(c) $[d(A,B)]^2+[d(B,C)]^2\overset{?}{=}[d(A,C)]^2$
$\left(3\sqrt{2}\right)^2+\left(2\sqrt{2}\right)^2\overset{?}{=}\left(\sqrt{26}\right)^2$
$9\cdot 2+4\cdot 2\overset{?}{=}26$
$18+8\overset{?}{=}26$
$26=26\leftarrow$ True

Therefore, triangle ABC is a right triangle.

(d) 6 square units

13. $C=(-2,1);\ r=4$; $(x+2)^2+(y-1)^2=16$

14. $C=(5,3);\ r=3$; $(x-5)^2+(y-3)^2=9$

15. $x^2+y^2=16$ **16.** $(x+3)^2+(y-1)^2=9$ **17.** $(x-5)^2+(y+2)^2=1$ **18.** $(x-4)^2+y^2=7$

19. $(x-2)^2+(y+1)^2=25$ **21.** $C=(0,0),r=5$ **22.** $C=(1,2),r=2$ **23.** $C=(0,4),r=4$ **24.** $C=(-1,-6),r=7$

20. $(x+1)^2+(y-3)^2=20$

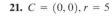

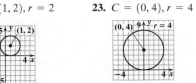

25. $C = \left(-2, \dfrac{3}{2}\right), r = \dfrac{1}{2}$ **26.** $C = (-3, -3), r = 2$ **27.** $C = (-3, -5), r = 6$ **28.** $C = (4, -2), r = 2$ **29.** $C = (-1, 2), r = 3$

30. $C = (5, 1), r = 3$ **31.** $x^2 = -12y$ **32.** $y^2 = -16x$ **33.** $y^2 = \dfrac{1}{2}x$ **34.** $x^2 = 8y$

 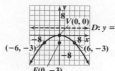 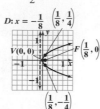

35. Vertex $(0, 0)$; focus $\left(0, \dfrac{1}{2}\right)$; directrix $y = -\dfrac{1}{2}$

36. Vertex $(0, 0)$; focus $(4, 0)$; directrix $x = -4$

37. Vertex $(-1, 3)$; focus $(-1, 5)$; directrix $y = 1$

38. Vertex $(-3, 4)$; focus $\left(-\dfrac{7}{2}, 4\right)$; directrix $x = -\dfrac{5}{2}$

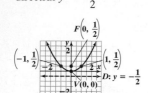 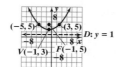 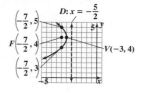

39. Vertex $(5, 2)$; focus $\left(5, \dfrac{5}{4}\right)$; directrix $y = \dfrac{11}{4}$

40. approximately 127.84 feet from the center of the dish along its axis of symmetry

41. Foci: $\left(-2\sqrt{2}, 0\right)$ and $\left(2\sqrt{2}, 0\right)$; vertices: $(-3, 0)$ and $(3, 0)$

42. Foci: $\left(0, -\sqrt{5}\right)$ and $\left(0, \sqrt{5}\right)$; vertices: $(0, -3)$, and $(0, 3)$

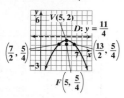 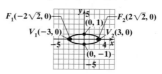 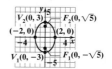

43. $\dfrac{x^2}{16} + \dfrac{y^2}{25} = 1$

44. $\dfrac{x^2}{36} + \dfrac{y^2}{32} = 1$

45. $\dfrac{x^2}{100} + \dfrac{y^2}{36} = 1$

46. Center: $(1, -2)$; vertices: $(-6, -2)$ and $(8, -2)$; foci: $\left(1 - 2\sqrt{6}, -2\right)$ and $\left(1 + 2\sqrt{6}, -2\right)$

 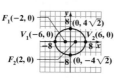 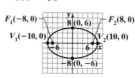 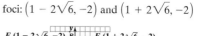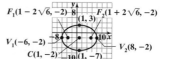

47. Center: $(-3, 4)$; vertices: $(-3, -1)$ and $(-3, 9)$; foci: $(-3, 0)$ and $(-3, 8)$

48. (a) $\dfrac{x^2}{900} + \dfrac{y}{256} = 1$ **(b)** Yes

49. Vertices: $(-2, 0)$ and $(2, 0)$; foci: $\left(-\sqrt{13}, 0\right)$ and $\left(\sqrt{13}, 0\right)$

50. Vertices: $(0, -5)$ and $(0, 5)$; foci: $\left(0, -\sqrt{74}\right)$ and $\left(0, \sqrt{74}\right)$

 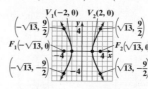 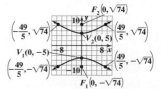

51. Vertices: $(0, -5)$ and $(0, 5)$; foci: $\left(0, -\sqrt{41}\right)$ and $\left(0, \sqrt{41}\right)$

52. Asymptotes: $y = x$ and $y = -x$

53. Asymptotes: $y = \dfrac{5}{2}x$ and $y = -\dfrac{5}{2}x$

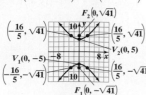 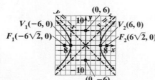 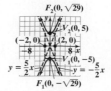

54. $\dfrac{x^2}{9} - \dfrac{y^2}{7} = 1$

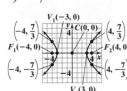

55. $\dfrac{y^2}{9} - \dfrac{x^2}{16} = 1$

56. $\dfrac{y^2}{16} - \dfrac{x^2}{9} = 1$

57. $\left(\sqrt{2}, \sqrt{2}\right)$ and $\left(-\sqrt{2}, -\sqrt{2}\right)$

58. $\left(-\dfrac{1}{2}, \dfrac{3}{2}\right)$ and $(1, 3)$

59. $\left(-\dfrac{1}{6}, -6\right)$ and $(1, 1)$

60. $(-5, -1), (-5, 1), (5, -1),$ and $(5, 1)$

61. $\left(2, -2\sqrt{2}\right)$ and $\left(2, 2\sqrt{2}\right)$

62. $(-1, 3)$ and $(1, 3)$

63. $\left(-\sqrt{3}, -\sqrt{5}\right), \left(-\sqrt{3}, \sqrt{5}\right), \left(\sqrt{3}, -\sqrt{5}\right),$ and $\left(\sqrt{3}, \sqrt{5}\right)$ **64.** $(0, 0), \left(5, -\sqrt{15}\right),$ and $\left(5, \sqrt{15}\right)$ **65.** $(2, 4)$ and $(-1, 1)$

66. $(-7, -20)$ and $\left(2, \dfrac{5}{2}\right)$ **67.** $(0, 6)$ and $(-6, 0)$ **68.** $(4, 4)$ and $(1, -2)$ **69.** $\varnothing$ **70.** $(-1, -2), (-1, 2), (1, -2),$ and $(1, 2)$

71. $(-4, 0), (4, 0),$ and $(0, 4)$ **72.** $(4, 0)$ and $(0, -2)$ **73.** 7 and 5 **74.** 12 cm by 5 cm **75.** 72 inches by 30 inches **76.** 12 feet and 9 feet

Chapter 9 Test **1.** $4\sqrt{5}$ **2.** $(-1, 2)$

3. $C = (4, -1), r = 3$

4. $C = (-5, 2), r = 4$

5. $(x + 3)^2 + (y - 7)^2 = 36$

6. $(x + 5)^2 + (y - 8)^2 = 100$

7. Vertex $(1, -2)$; focus $(2, -2)$; directrix $x = 0$

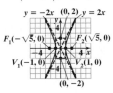

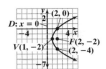

8. Vertex $(2, 4)$; focus $\left(2, \dfrac{13}{4}\right)$; directrix $y = \dfrac{19}{4}$

9. $x^2 = 16y$

10. $(y - 4)^2 = 8(x - 1)$

11. Foci: $(-4, 0)$ and $(4, 0)$; vertices: $(-5, 0)$ and $(5, 0)$

12. Vertices: $(2, -8)$ and $(2, 0)$; foci: $\left(2, -4 - \sqrt{7}\right)$ and $\left(2, -4 + \sqrt{7}\right)$

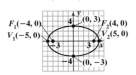

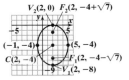

13. $\dfrac{x^2}{9} + \dfrac{y^2}{25} = 1$

14. $\dfrac{(x + 1)^2}{16} + \dfrac{(y - 2)^2}{25} = 1$

15. Vertices: $(-1, 0)$ and $(1, 0)$; foci: $\left(-\sqrt{5}, 0\right)$ and $\left(\sqrt{5}, 0\right)$; asymptotes: $y = 2x$ and $y = -2x$

16. Vertices: $(0, -10)$ and $(0, 10)$; foci: $\left(0, -2\sqrt{41}\right)$ and $\left(0, 2\sqrt{41}\right)$; asymptotes: $y = \dfrac{5}{4}x$ and $y = -\dfrac{5}{4}x$

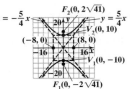

17. $\dfrac{x^2}{9} - \dfrac{y^2}{55} = 1$ **18.** $(-4, 1)$ and $(1, -4)$ **19.** $\left(-\sqrt{5}, -2\right), \left(-\sqrt{5}, 2\right), \left(\sqrt{5}, -2\right),$ and $\left(\sqrt{5}, 2\right)$ **20. (a)** $\dfrac{x^2}{225} + \dfrac{y^2}{100} = 1$ **(b)** 6 feet

Cumulative Review Chapters R–9 **1.** $\{x \mid x \neq 7\}$

2.

3. $y = \dfrac{4}{3}x + 2$ or $4x - 3y = -6$ **4.** $(3, -8)$ **5.** -35 **6.** $(2m + n)(4m^2 - 2mn + n^2)$ **7.** $(3p - 4)(3p - 2)$

8. $\dfrac{2a + 1}{a - 7}$ **9.** $\dfrac{1}{(t - 2)(t - 1)}$ **10.** $\{2\}$ **11.** $\{x \mid x < -4 \text{ or } x \geq 5\}$ or $(-\infty, -4) \cup [5, \infty)$ **12.** $9\sqrt{3}$

13. $-3(2 - \sqrt{7})$ **14.** $\{5\}$ **15.** $31 + 5i$ **16.** $\left\{\dfrac{2 - \sqrt{10}}{2}, \dfrac{2 + \sqrt{10}}{2}\right\}$

17.

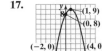

18. $\{x \mid -1 \leq x \leq 4\}$ or $[-1, 4]$

19. Domain: all real numbers or $(-\infty, \infty)$; Range: $\{y \mid y > 0\}$ or $(0, \infty)$

20. Domain: $\{x \mid x > 0\}$ or $(0, \infty)$; Range: all real numbers or $(-\infty, \infty)$

21. $\dfrac{5}{2}$ **22.** $\{2\}$ **23.** $\{-5, 5\}$

24. $(x + 3)^2 + (y - 1)^2 = 10$

25. Vertex: $(-3, 3)$; Focus: $(-1, 3)$; Directrix: $x = -5$

Chapter 10 Sequences, Series, and the Binomial Theorem

Section 10.1 Sequences **1.** sequence **2.** infinite; finite **3.** True **4.** $-1, 1, 3, 5, 7$ **5.** $-4, 8, -12, 16, -20$ **6.** $a_n = 2n + 3$

7. $b_n = \dfrac{(-1)^{n+1}}{n+1}$ **8.** partial sum **9.** $3 + 7 + 11 = 21$ **10.** $2 + 9 + 28 + 65 + 126 = 230$ **11.** $\displaystyle\sum_{k=1}^{12} k^2$ **12.** $\displaystyle\sum_{n=1}^{6} 2^{n-1}$ **13.** $8, 11, 14, 17, 20$

15. $\dfrac{1}{3}, \dfrac{1}{2}, \dfrac{3}{5}, \dfrac{2}{3},$ and $\dfrac{5}{7}$ **17.** $-1, 2, -3, 4,$ and -5 **19.** $3, 5, 9, 17,$ and 33 **21.** $1, 1, \dfrac{3}{4}, \dfrac{1}{2},$ and $\dfrac{5}{16}$ **23.** $\dfrac{1}{e}, \dfrac{2}{e^2}, \dfrac{3}{e^3}, \dfrac{4}{e^4},$ and $\dfrac{5}{e^5}$ **25.** $a_n = 2n$

27. $a_n = \dfrac{n}{n+1}$ **29.** $a_n = n^2 + 2$ **31.** $a_n = (-1)^n n^2$ **33.** 54 **35.** $\dfrac{55}{2}$ **37.** 14 **39.** 6 **41.** 50 **43.** 45 **45.** $\displaystyle\sum_{k=1}^{15} k$ **47.** $\displaystyle\sum_{i=1}^{12} \dfrac{1}{i}$

49. $\displaystyle\sum_{i=1}^{9} (-1)^{i+1}\left(\dfrac{1}{3^{i-1}}\right)$ **51.** $\displaystyle\sum_{k=1}^{11} (2k + 3)$ **53. (a)** $\$12,180$ **(b)** $\$12,736.36$ **(c)** $\$21,768.22$ **55. (a)** 318 million **(b)** 481 million

57. $1, 1, 2, 3, 5, 8, 13, 21, 34, 55$ **59.** $10, 10.5, 11.025, 11.57625,$ and 12.1550625 **61.** $8, 10, 13, 17,$ and 22

63. (a) $1; 2; 1.5; 1.\overline{6}; 1.6; 1.625; \dfrac{21}{13} \approx 1.615385; \dfrac{34}{21} \approx 1.619048; \dfrac{55}{34} \approx 1.617647; \dfrac{89}{55} \approx 1.618182$ **(b)** around 1.618 **(c)** $1; 0.5; \dfrac{2}{3} = 0.\overline{6}; 0.6; 0.625;$

$\dfrac{8}{13} \approx 0.615385; \dfrac{13}{21} \approx 0.619048; \dfrac{21}{34} \approx 0.617647; \dfrac{34}{55} \approx 0.618182; \dfrac{55}{89} \approx 0.617978$ **(d)** around 0.618 **65.** The main difference between a function and a sequence is that the domain of a function is based on the real number system, whereas the domain of a sequence is the positive integers.

67. The symbol $\sum$ means to add up the terms of a sequence. **69. (a)** $m = 4$ **(b)** $f(1) = -2; f(2) = 2; f(3) = 6; f(4) = 10$ **71. (a)** $m = -5$

(b) $f(1) = 3; f(2) = -2; f(3) = -7; f(4) = -12$ **73.** $8, 11, 14, 17,$ and 20 **75.** $\dfrac{1}{3}, \dfrac{1}{2}, \dfrac{3}{5}, \dfrac{2}{3},$ and $\dfrac{5}{7}$ **77.** $-1, 2, -3, 4,$ and -5

79. $3, 5, 9, 17,$ and 33 **81.** 54 **83.** $\dfrac{55}{2}$ **85.** 14 **87.** 6

Section 10.2 Arithmetic Sequences **1.** arithmetic **2.** Arithmetic; $a = -3; d = 2$ **3.** Not arithmetic **4.** Arithmetic; $a = -5; d = 3$
5. Not arithmetic **6.** Arithmetic; $a = 3; d = -2$ **7.** $a_n = a + (n - 1)d$ **8. (a)** $a_n = 6n - 5$ **(b)** 79 **9. (a)** $a = -5; d = 3$
(b) $a_n = 3n - 8$ **10.** $10,400$ **11.** 9730 **12.** 7550 **13.** -1050 **14.** 1470 seats **15.** $a_n - a_{n-1} = d = 1; a = 6$
17. $a_n - a_{n-1} = d = 7; a = 9$ **19.** $a_n - a_{n-1} = d = -3; a = 4$ **21.** $a_n - a_{n-1} = d = \dfrac{1}{2}; a = \dfrac{11}{2}$ **23.** $a_n = 3n + 1; a_5 = 16$
25. $a_n = -5n + 15; a_5 = -10$ **27.** $a_n = \dfrac{1}{3}n + \dfrac{5}{3}; a_5 = \dfrac{10}{3}$ **29.** $a_n = -\dfrac{1}{5}n + \dfrac{26}{5}; a_5 = \dfrac{21}{5}$ **31.** $a_n = 5n - 3; a_{20} = 97$
33. $a_n = -3n + 15; a_{20} = -45$ **35.** $a_n = \dfrac{1}{4}n + \dfrac{3}{4}; a_{20} = \dfrac{23}{4}$ **37.** $a = 7; d = 5; a_n = 5n + 2$ **39.** $a = -23; d = 7; a_n = 7n - 30$
41. $a = 11; d = -3; a_n = -3n + 14$ **43.** $a = 4; d = -\dfrac{1}{2}; a_n = -\dfrac{1}{2}n + \dfrac{9}{2}$ **45.** $S_{30} = 2670$ **47.** $S_{25} = 700$ **49.** $S_{40} = -5060$ **51.** $S_{40} = 3160$
53. $S_{75} = -9000$ **55.** $S_{30} = 460$ **57.** $x = -\dfrac{3}{2}$ **59.** There are 630 cans in the stack. **61.** There are 1600 seats in the auditorium.
63. There are 84 terms in the sequence. **65.** There are 63 terms in the sequence. **67.** It will take about 15.22 years. **69.** A sequence is arithmetic if the difference in consecutive terms is a constant. So, if the actual terms are given, compute the difference between each pair of consecutive terms and determine if the differences are constant. If a formula is given for the sequence, compute $a_n - a_{n-1}$ and determine if the result is a constant—if it is, then the sequence is arithmetic. **71. (a)** 3 **(b)** $3; 9; 27; 81$ **73. (a)** $\dfrac{1}{2}$ **(b)** $5; \dfrac{5}{2}; \dfrac{5}{4}; \dfrac{5}{8}$ **75.** 806.9 **77.** 1427.5

Section 10.3 Geometric Sequences and Series **1.** geometric **2.** Geometric; $a = 4, r = 2$ **3.** Not geometric **4.** Geometric; $a = 9, r = \dfrac{1}{3}$
5. Geometric; $r = 5$ **6.** Not geometric **7.** Geometric; $r = \dfrac{2}{3}$ **8.** $a_n - 5 \cdot 2^{n-1}; a_9 - 1280$ **9.** $a_n = 50 \cdot \left(\dfrac{1}{2}\right)^{n-1}; a_9 = 0.1953125$ or $a_9 = \dfrac{25}{128}$
10. $S_n = a \cdot \dfrac{1 - r^n}{1 - r}$ **11.** $24,573$ **12.** 7.9921875 **13.** $\dfrac{a}{1 - r}$ **14.** $\dfrac{40}{3}$ **15.** $\dfrac{1}{2}$ **16.** $\dfrac{2}{9}$ **17.** The U.S. economy will grow by $\$10,000$.
18. $\$244,129.08$ **19.** $\dfrac{a_n}{a_{n-1}} = r = 4; a = 4$ **21.** $\dfrac{a_n}{a_{n-1}} = r = \dfrac{2}{3}; a = \dfrac{2}{3}$ **23.** $\dfrac{a_n}{a_{n-1}} = r = \dfrac{1}{2}; a = \dfrac{3}{2}$ **25.** $\dfrac{a_n}{a_{n-1}} = r = \dfrac{5}{2}; a = \dfrac{1}{2}$

27. (a) $a_n = 10 \cdot 2^{n-1}$ **(b)** $a_8 = 1280$ **29. (a)** $a_n = 100 \cdot \left(\dfrac{1}{2}\right)^{n-1}$ **(b)** $a_8 = \dfrac{25}{32}$ **31. (a)** $a_n = (-3)^{n-1}$ **(b)** $a_8 = -2187$

33. (a) $a_n = 100 \cdot (1.05)^{n-1}$ **(b)** $a_8 = 100 \cdot (1.05)^7$ **35.** $a_{10} = 1536$ **37.** $a_{15} = \dfrac{1}{4096}$ **39.** $a_9 = 0.000000005$ **41.** 8190 **43.** 83.3245952

45. 6138 **47.** 7.96875 **49.** 2 **51.** 15 **53.** $\dfrac{9}{2}$ **55.** $\dfrac{5}{4}$ **57.** 9 **59.** $\dfrac{5}{9}$ **61.** $\dfrac{89}{99}$ **63.** arithmetic; $d = 5$ **65.** Neither

67. geometric; $r = \dfrac{1}{2}$ **69.** geometric; $r = \dfrac{2}{3}$ **71.** arithmetic; $d = 4$ **73.** Neither **75.** $x = -4$ **77. (a)** $\$42,000$ **(b)** $\$62,053$
(c) $\$503,116$ **79.** $\$13,182$ **81. (a)** About 1.891 feet **(b)** On the 23rd swing **(c)** About 24.08 feet **(d)** The pendulum will swing a total of
60 feet. **83.** Option A will yield the larger annual salary in the final year of the contract and option B will yield the larger cumulative salary over the life of the contract. **85.** The multiplier is 50. **87.** $\$31.14$ per share **89.** $\$149,035.94$ **91.** $\$114,401.52$ **93.** $\$395.09$, or about $\$395$

95. $0.4\overline{9} = \dfrac{1}{2}$ **97.** $2,147,483,646$ **99.** A geometric sequence with $r > 1$ yields faster growth due to the effect of compounding. Answers will vary. However, a reasonable answer is that because geometric growth is faster than arithmetic growth, the population will grow beyond the ability of food supplies to sustain the population and hunger will ensue. **101.** A geometric series has a sum provided the common ratio r is between -1 and 1.
103. 1 **105.** approximately 288.1404315 **107.** approximately 41.66310217

Putting the Concepts Together (Sections 10.1–10.3) **1.** Geometric with $a = \dfrac{3}{4}$ and common ratio $r = \dfrac{1}{4}$ **2.** Arithmetic with $a = 8$

and $d = 2$ **3.** Arithmetic with $a = 1$ and $d = \dfrac{7}{9}$ **4.** Neither arithmetic nor geometric **5.** Geometric with $a = 12$ and $r = 2$

6. Neither arithmetic nor geometric   **7.** 87   **8.** $\displaystyle\sum_{i=1}^{12} \frac{1}{2(6+i)}$ **9.** $a_n = 27 - 2n$; 25, 23, 21, 19, and 17   **10.** $a_n = 11n - 35$; $-24, -13, -2, 9,$

and 20   **11.** $a_n = 45 \cdot \left(\dfrac{1}{5}\right)^{n-1}$; $45, 9, \dfrac{9}{5}, \dfrac{9}{25}$, and $\dfrac{9}{125}$ **12.** $a_n = 150 \cdot (1.04)^{n-1}$; 150, 156, 162.24, 168.7296, and 175.478784   **13.** $S_{11} = 177{,}146$

14. $S_{20} = 990$ **15.** $\dfrac{10{,}000}{9}$ **16.** A party of 24 people would require 11 tables.

Section 10.4 The Binomial Theorem   **1.** $n(n-1)(n-2) \cdot \cdots \cdot 3 \cdot 2 \cdot 1$ **2.** $1; 1$ **3.** 120   **4.** 840   **5.** False   **6.** True   **7.** 7   **8.** 20
9. $x^4 + 8x^3 + 24x^2 + 32x + 16$ **10.** $32p^5 - 80p^4 + 80p^3 - 40p^2 + 10p - 1$ **11.** 6   **13.** 40,320   **15.** 90   **17.** 336   **19.** 21   **21.** 210
23. $x^5 + 5x^4 + 10x^3 + 10x^2 + 5x + 1$ **25.** $x^4 - 16x^3 + 96x^2 - 256x + 256$ **27.** $81p^4 + 216p^3 + 216p^2 + 96p + 16$
29. $32z^5 - 240z^4 + 720z^3 - 1080z^2 + 810z - 243$ **31.** $x^8 + 8x^6 + 24x^4 + 32x^2 + 16$ **33.** $32p^{15} + 80p^{12} + 80p^9 + 40p^6 + 10p^3 + 1$
35. $x^6 + 12x^5 + 60x^4 + 160x^3 + 240x^2 + 192x + 64$ **37.** $16p^8 - 32p^6q^2 + 24p^4q^4 - 8p^2q^6 + q^8$ **39.** 1.00401   **41.** 0.99004   **43.** $84x^5$
45. $-108{,}864p^3$ **47.** $\dbinom{n}{n-1} = \dfrac{n!}{(n-1)!(n-(n-1))!} = \dfrac{n!}{(n-1)!1!} = \dfrac{n \cdot (n-1)!}{(n-1)!} = n$; $\dbinom{n}{n} = \dfrac{n!}{n!(n-n)!} = \dfrac{n!}{n!0!} = \dfrac{n!}{n!} = 1$

49.
```
        1
      1   1
    1   2   1
  1   3   3   1
```
    51. The degree of each monomial equals n.   **53.** $a^4 - 8a^3 + 24a^2 - 32a + 16$
55. $p^5 + p^4 - 6p^3 - 14p^2 - 11p - 3$

Chapter 10 Review   **1.** $-1, -4, -7, -10,$ and -13 **2.** $-\dfrac{1}{5}, 0, \dfrac{1}{7}, \dfrac{1}{4},$ and $\dfrac{1}{3}$ **3.** 6, 26, 126, 626, and 3126   **4.** $3, -6, 9, -12,$ and 15

5. $\dfrac{1}{2}, \dfrac{4}{3}, \dfrac{9}{4}, \dfrac{16}{5},$ and $\dfrac{25}{6}$ **6.** $\pi, \dfrac{\pi^2}{2}, \dfrac{\pi^3}{3}, \dfrac{\pi^4}{4},$ and $\dfrac{\pi^5}{5}$ **7.** $a_n = -3n$ **8.** $a_n = \dfrac{n}{3}$ **9.** $a_n = 5 \cdot 2^{n-1}$ **10.** $a_n = (-1)^n \cdot \dfrac{n}{2}$ **11.** $a_n = n^2 + 5$

12. $a_n = \dfrac{n-1}{n+1}$ **13.** 65   **14.** $\dfrac{33}{2}$ **15.** -30 **16.** $\dfrac{26}{3}$ **17.** $\displaystyle\sum_{i=1}^{15}(4 + 3i)$ **18.** $\displaystyle\sum_{i=1}^{8}\dfrac{1}{3^i}$ **19.** $\displaystyle\sum_{i=1}^{10}\dfrac{i^3 + 1}{i + 1}$ **20.** $\displaystyle\sum_{i=1}^{7}[(-1)^{i-1} \cdot i^2]$

21. arithmetic with $d = 6$ **22.** arithmetic with $d = \dfrac{3}{2}$ **23.** not arithmetic   **24.** not arithmetic   **25.** arithmetic with $d = 4$

26. not arithmetic   **27.** $a_n = 8n - 5$; $a_{25} = 195$ **28.** $a_n = -3n - 1$; $a_{25} = -76$ **29.** $a_n = -\dfrac{1}{3}n + \dfrac{22}{3}$; $a_{25} = -1$

30. $a_n = 6n + 5$; $a_{25} = 155$ **31.** $a_n = \dfrac{18}{5}n - \dfrac{19}{5}$; $a_{25} = \dfrac{431}{5}$ **32.** $a_n = -4n - 4$; $a_{25} = -104$ **33.** 4320   **34.** -2140 **35.** -4080

36. $\dfrac{1875}{4}$ or 468.75   **37.** 2106   **38.** 300 yards   **39.** geometric with $r = 6$ **40.** geometric with $r = -3$

41. not geometric   **42.** geometric with $r = \dfrac{2}{3}$ **43.** geometric with $r = -2$ **44.** not geometric   **45.** $a_n = 4 \cdot 3^{n-1}$; $a_{10} = 78{,}732$

46. $a_n = 8 \cdot \left(\dfrac{1}{4}\right)^{n-1}$; $a_{10} = \dfrac{1}{32{,}768}$ **47.** $a_n = 5 \cdot (-2)^{n-1}$; $a_{10} = -2560$ **48.** $a_n = 1000 \cdot (1.08)^{n-1}$; $a_{10} \approx 1999.005$ **49.** 65,534

50. ≈ 45.71428571 **51.** $\dfrac{12{,}285}{4}$ or 3071.25   **52.** $-258{,}280{,}320$ **53.** $\dfrac{20}{3}$ **54.** $\dfrac{100}{3}$ **55.** $\dfrac{5}{4}$ **56.** $\dfrac{8}{9}$

57. After 72 years, there will be 3.125 grams of the Tritium remaining.   **58.** After 15 minutes about 38.15 billion e-mails will have been sent.
59. After 25 years, Scott's 403(b) will be worth $360,114.89.   **60.** The lump sum option would yield more money after 26 years.   **61.** Sheri would need
to contribute $534.04, or about $534, each month to reach her goal.   **62.** When Samantha turns 18, the plan will be worth $62,950.79 and will cover about
185 credit hours.   **63.** 120   **64.** 7920   **65.** 5040   **66.** 1716   **67.** 35   **68.** 252   **69.** 1   **70.** 1   **71.** $z^4 + 4z^3 + 6z^2 + 4z + 1$
72. $y^5 - 15y^4 + 90y^3 - 270y^2 + 405y - 243$ **73.** $729y^6 + 5832y^5 + 19{,}440y^4 + 34{,}560y^3 + 34{,}560y^2 + 18{,}432y + 4096$
74. $16x^8 - 96x^6 + 216x^4 - 216x^2 + 81$ **75.** $81p^4 - 216p^3q + 216p^2q^2 - 96pq^3 + 16q^4$ **76.** $a^{15} + 15a^{12}b + 90a^9b^2 + 270a^6b^3 + 405a^3b^4 + 243b^5$
77. $-448x^5$ **78.** $14{,}784x^5$

Chapter 10 Test   **1.** arithmetic with $a = -15$ and $d = 8$ **2.** geometric with $a = -4$ and $r = -4$ **3.** neither arithmetic nor geometric
4. arithmetic with $a = -\dfrac{1}{5}$ and $d = \dfrac{2}{5}$ **5.** neither arithmetic nor geometric   **6.** geometric with $a = 21$ and $r = 3$ **7.** $\dfrac{17{,}269}{1200}$ **8.** $\displaystyle\sum_{i=1}^{8}\dfrac{i + 2}{i + 4}$
9. $a_n = 10n - 4$; 6, 16, 26, 36, and 46   **10.** $a_n = 4 - 4n$; $0, -4, -8, -12,$ and -16 **11.** $a_n = 10 \cdot 2^{n-1}$; 10, 20, 40, 80, and 160
12. $a_n = (-3)^{n-1}$; $1, -3, 9, -27,$ and 81   **13.** 720   **14.** $-\dfrac{132{,}860}{9}$ **15.** 324   **16.** 6435   **17.** 792
18. $625m^4 - 1000m^3 + 600m^2 - 160m + 16$ **19.** about $64,512   **20.** 2012, 2117, and 2125

Applications Index

Subject Index

Photo Credits

Formulas for Lines and Slope (Chapter 1)

Standard form of a line	$Ax + By = C$
Equation of a vertical line	$x = a$ where a is the x-intercept
Equation of a horizontal line	$y = b$ where b is the y-intercept
Slope of a line	$m = \dfrac{y_2 - y_1}{x_2 - x_1}, \ x_1 \neq x_2$ Slope undefined if $x_1 = x_2$
Point-slope form of a line	$y - y_1 = m(x - x_1)$
Slope-intercept form of a line	$y = mx + b$

Functions (Chapter 2)

- A **function** is a special type of relation where any given input, x, corresponds to only one output y. Functions can be represented through maps, sets of ordered pairs, equations, or graphs.
- **Vertical Line Test:** A set of points in the xy-plane is the graph of a function if and only if every vertical line intersects the graph in at most one point.
- The graph of a function, f, is the set of all ordered pairs $(x, f(x))$.
- When only an equation of a function is given, the **domain** of the function is the largest set of real numbers for which $f(x)$ is a real number.
- The **range** of a function is the set of all outputs of the function.

Steps for Factoring (Chapter 4)

Step 1: Factor out the Greatest Common Factor (GCF), if any exists.

Step 2: Count the number of terms.

Step 3: (a) 2 terms
- Is it the difference of two squares? If so, $A^2 - B^2 = (A - B)(A + B)$
- Is it the difference of two cubes? If so, $A^3 - B^3 = (A - B)(A^2 + AB + B^2)$
- Is it the sum of two cubes? If so, $A^3 + B^3 = (A + B)(A^2 - AB + B^2)$

(b) 3 terms
- Is it a perfect square trinomial? If so, $A^2 + 2AB + B^2 = (A + B)^2$ or $A^2 - 2AB + B^2 = (A - B)^2$
- Is the coefficient of the square term 1? If so, $x^2 + bx + c = (x + m)(x + n)$ where $mn = c$ and $m + n = b$
- Is the coefficient of the square term different from 1? If so,
  a. Use factoring by grouping
  b. Use trial and error

(c) 4 terms
- Use factoring by grouping

Step 4: Check your work by multiplying out the factored form.

The Rules of Exponents (Getting Ready for Chapter 4, Chapter 6)

If a and b are real numbers and if r and s are rational numbers, then assuming the expression is defined,

Zero Exponent Rule:	$a^0 = 1$	if $a \neq 0$
Negative Exponent Rule:	$a^{-r} = \dfrac{1}{a^r}$	if $a \neq 0$
Product Rule:	$a^r \cdot a^s = a^{r+s}$	
Quotient Rule:	$\dfrac{a^r}{a^s} = a^{r-s} = \dfrac{1}{a^{s-r}}$	if $a \neq 0$
Power Rule:	$(a^r)^s = a^{r \cdot s}$	
Product to Power Rule:	$(a \cdot b)^r = a^r \cdot b^r$	
Quotient to Power Rule:	$\left(\dfrac{a}{b}\right)^r = \dfrac{a^r}{b^r}$	if $b \neq 0$
Quotient to a Negative Power Rule:	$\left(\dfrac{a}{b}\right)^{-r} = \left(\dfrac{b}{a}\right)^r$	if $a \neq 0, b \neq 0$

Working with Rational Expressions (Chapter 5)

Multiplying Rational Expressions	$\dfrac{a}{b} \cdot \dfrac{c}{d} = \dfrac{ac}{bd}$	$b \neq 0, d \neq 0$
Adding Rational Expressions	$\dfrac{a}{c} + \dfrac{b}{c} = \dfrac{a + b}{c}$	$c \neq 0$
Subtracting Rational Expressions	$\dfrac{a}{c} - \dfrac{b}{c} = \dfrac{a - b}{c}$	$c \neq 0$
Dividing Rational Expressions	$\dfrac{a}{b} \div \dfrac{c}{d} = \dfrac{\frac{a}{b}}{\frac{c}{d}} = \dfrac{a}{b} \cdot \dfrac{d}{c} = \dfrac{ad}{bc}$	$b \neq 0, c \neq 0,$ $d \neq 0$

Working with Radicals (Getting Ready for Chapter 6, Chapter 6)

Simplifying $\sqrt[n]{a^n}$

- If $n \geq 2$ is a positive integer and a is a real number, then

  $\sqrt[n]{a^n} = a$ if $n \geq 3$ is odd

  $\sqrt[n]{a^n} = |a|$ if $n \geq 2$ is even

- If a is a real number and $n \geq 2$ is an integer, then $a^{\frac{1}{n}} = \sqrt[n]{a}$ provided that $\sqrt[n]{a}$ exists.

- If a is a real number, m/n is a rational number in lowest terms with $n \geq 2$, then $a^{\frac{m}{n}} = \sqrt[n]{a^m} = \left(\sqrt[n]{a}\right)^m$ provided that $\sqrt[n]{a}$ exists.

- If m/n is a rational number and if a is a nonzero real number, then $a^{-\frac{m}{n}} = \dfrac{1}{a^{\frac{m}{n}}}$ or $\dfrac{1}{a^{-\frac{m}{n}}} = a^{\frac{m}{n}}$

Product Property of Radicals

If $\sqrt[n]{a}$ and $\sqrt[n]{b}$ are real numbers and $n \geq 2$ is an integer, then $\sqrt[n]{a} \cdot \sqrt[n]{b} = \sqrt[n]{ab}$

Quotient Property of Radicals

If $\sqrt[n]{a}$ and $\sqrt[n]{b}$ are real numbers, $b \neq 0$ and $n \geq 2$ is an integer, then $\dfrac{\sqrt[n]{a}}{\sqrt[n]{b}} = \sqrt[n]{\dfrac{a}{b}}$

Quadratic Equations and Quadratic Functions (Chapter 7)

- **Square Root Property**

  If $x^2 = p$, then $x = \sqrt{p}$ or $x = -\sqrt{p}$

- **Pythagorean Theorem**

  In a right triangle, the square of the length of the hypotenuse is equal to the sum of the squares of the lengths of the legs. That is, $\text{leg}^2 + \text{leg}^2 = \text{hypotenuse}^2$.

- **The Quadratic Formula**

  The solutions to the equation $ax^2 + bx + c = 0$, $a \neq 0$, are given by $x = \dfrac{-b \pm \sqrt{b^2 - 4ac}}{2a}$

- **Discriminant**

  For the quadratic equation $ax^2 + bx + c = 0$, $a \neq 0$:

  - If $b^2 - 4ac > 0$, the equation has two unequal real solutions.
    - If $b^2 - 4ac$ is a perfect square, the equation has two rational solutions.
    - If $b^2 - 4ac$ is not a perfect square, the equation has two irrational solutions.
  - If $b^2 - 4ac = 0$, the equation has a repeated real solution.
  - If $b^2 - 4ac < 0$, the equation has two complex solutions that are not real.

- **Vertex of a Parabola**

  Any quadratic function of the form $f(x) = ax^2 + bx + c$, $a \neq 0$, will have vertex $\left(-\dfrac{b}{2a}, f\left(-\dfrac{b}{2a}\right)\right)$

- **The x-Intercepts of the Graph of a Quadratic Function**

  1. If $b^2 - 4ac > 0$, the graph of $f(x) = ax^2 + bx + c$ has two different x-intercepts.
  2. If $b^2 - 4ac = 0$, the graph of $f(x) = ax^2 + bx + c$ has one x-intercept.
  3. If $b^2 - 4ac < 0$, the graph of $f(x) = ax^2 + bx + c$ has no x-intercepts.